HEALTH CARE STATE RANKINGS
2004

Health Care in the 50 United States

Kathleen O'Leary Morgan and Scott Morgan, Editors

Morgan Quitno Press
© Copyright 2004, All Rights Reserved

512 East 9th Street, P.O. Box 1656
Lawrence, KS 66044-8656
USA
800-457-0742 or 785-841-3534
www.statestats.com
Twelfth Edition

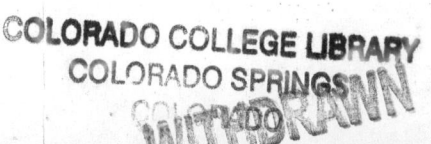

ISBN: 0-7401-0911-1
ISSN: 1065-1403

Health Care State Rankings 2004 sells for $54.95 ($6.00 shipping) and is only available in paper binding. For those who prefer ranking information tailored to a particular state, we also offer Health Care State Perspectives, state-specific reports for each of the 50 states. These individual guides provide information on a state's data and rank for each of the categories featured in the national Health Care State Rankings volume. Perspectives sell for $19.00 or $9.50 if ordered with Health Care State Rankings. If crime statistics are your interest, please ask about our annual Crime State Rankings ($54.95 paper). If you are interested in city and metropolitan crime data, we offer City Crime Rankings ($42.95 paper). For a general view of the states, please ask about our annual State Rankings reference book ($54.95 paper) or our monthly State Statistical Trends ($299 a year). Also available is the first edition of our Education State Rankings. This view of K-12 education at the state level is $49.95. All of our data sets are also available on CD in pdf format as well as various database formats. These sell for $100 each. Shipping and handling is $6.00 per order. For information, please visit our website at www.statestats.com.

Twelfth Edition
Printed in the United States of America
March 2004

PREFACE

Health care continues to be a "hot button" issue for all Americans. With health insurance premiums, prescription drug prices and other health care costs continuing to rise, access to reliable health care information is more important than ever. Now in its 12th edition, *Health Care State Rankings* provides a solid collection of state health care data. Births and reproductive health, deaths, disease, insurance and finance, health care providers, facilities and physical fitness are compared state-by-state. In all, more than 500 tables of state comparisons are provided, covering virtually every aspect of health care in the 50 United States.

Important Notes About *Health Care State Rankings 2004*

Health Care State Rankings 2004 presents information from government and private sector sources in one user-friendly volume. Our goal is to translate complicated and often convoluted health care data into easy-to-understand, meaningful state comparisons. As we revise this volume each year, we reexamine each table, update most, delete others and add new tables of interest to our readers. In this 2004 edition, our regular readers will once again note that a number of tables in the Finance Chapter are repeated. The Centers For Medicare and Medicaid Services plans to update its state health care expenditures numbers later this year.

We make every effort to present the data in *Health Care State Rankings 2004* as simply and straightforwardly as possible. Source information and other pertinent footnotes are clearly shown at the bottom of each page. National totals, rates and percentages are prominently displayed at the top of each table. Every other line is shaded in gray for easier reading. In addition, numerous information-finding tools are provided: a thorough table of contents, table listings at the beginning of each chapter, a roster of sources with addresses and phone numbers, a detailed index and a chapter thumb index.

For the ease of our readers, the numbers shown in *Health Care State Rankings* require no additional calculations to convert them from millions, thousands, etc. All states are ranked on a high to low basis, with any ties among the states listed alphabetically for a given ranking. Negative numbers are shown in parentheses "( )." For tables with national totals (as opposed to rates, per capitas, etc.) a separate column is included showing what percent of the national total each individual state's total represents. This column is headed by "% of USA." This percentage figure is particularly interesting when compared with a state's share of the nation's population for a particular year (provided in an appendix).

Those researchers who need information for just one state should check out our *Health Care State Perspective* series of publications. These 21-page comb bound reports feature data and ranking information for an individual state, as reported in *Health Care State Rankings 2004*. (For example *California Health Care in Perspective* features information about the state of California only.) These serve as handy, quick reference guides for those who do not want to page through the entire *Health Care State Rankings* volume searching for information for their particular state. *Health Care State Perspectives* sell for $19. When purchased with a copy of *Health Care State Rankings 2004*, these handy quick reference guides are just $9.50. For additional information, please call us toll-free at 1-800-457-0742.

Other Books From Morgan Quitno Press

In addition to *Health Care State Rankings 2004*, our company offers four other rankings reference books. The first of these, *State Rankings 2004*, is our original rankings reference book, providing a general view of the states. Statistics for categories ranging from agriculture to transportation, government finance to social welfare are featured. *Education State Rankings* is our newest state reference book and now is in its second edition. This volume compares states in teachers' salaries, class sizes, graduation rates and more than 400 other categories relating to K-12 education. Our *Crime State Rankings* book provides a huge collection of user-friendly state statistics on law enforcement personnel and expenditures, corrections, juvenile crime and delinquency, arrests and offenses. For crime information in communities, *City Crime Rankings* compares crime in all metropolitan areas and cities of 75,000 or more population (approx. 300 cities). Numbers of crimes, crime rates and changes in crime rates over one and five years are presented for all major crime categories reported by the FBI. Final 2002 crime data are featured in the most recent 10th edition. For true data aficionados, the information in all our books also is available CD-ROM. These electronic editions provide a searchable PDF version of each book as well as the raw data in .dbf, Excel and ASCII formats.

State Statistical Trends is our popular monthly journal that examines changes in life and government for the 50 United States. Each 100-page monthly issue focuses on a different subject and provides a collection of tables, graphics and commentary showing state multi-year trends. For further information about *Trends* or any of our other publications, please call us toll-free at 1-800-457-0742 or check out our web site at www.statestats.com.

Finally, many thanks to the librarians, government and health care industry officials who help us each year. Thanks also to you, our readers. We always welcome your thoughts and suggestions, so please give us a call, send us an e-mail or drop us a note with your ideas.

- THE EDITORS

WHICH STATE IS HEALTHIEST?

It was close, but New Hampshire has reclaimed its bragging rights as the winner of Morgan Quitno's 12th annual Healthiest State Award. The Granite State edged past three-time winner Vermont to earn the title.

Following New Hampshire and Vermont were Hawaii in third, Iowa in fourth and Minnesota in fifth.

Mississippi unfortunately remains at the bottom of the list, bringing up the least healthy end of the rankings for the fifth year in a row. It is preceded by New Mexico in 49th, Louisiana in 48th and Alabama in 47th.

Each year we take a step back from our objective reporting of health statistics, feed some basic figures into our computer and determine which is the nation's Healthiest State. While we never claim our findings are indisputable, we do believe they provide an interesting statistical match-up of how states are doing with regard to health care.

Methodology

The Healthiest State designation is awarded based on 21 factors chosen from the year 2004 edition of our annual reference book, *Health Care State Rankings*.

2004 HEALTHIEST STATE AWARD

RANK	STATE	SUM	03	RANK	STATE	SUM	03
1	New Hampshire	19.86	2	26	Pennsylvania	1.84	24
2	Vermont	19.66	1	27	Colorado	1.54	25
3	Hawaii	15.33	8	28	Indiana	1.41	27
4	Iowa	15.03	4	29	Kentucky	0.45	31
5	Minnesota	14.28	5	30	North Carolina	(0.17)	29
6	Utah	14.01	9	31	Illinois	(0.20)	32
7	Nebraska	13.83	3	32	Maryland	(0.97)	35
8	Massachusetts	13.67	6	33	New York	(2.00)	33
9	Maine	12.05	7	34	West Virginia	(2.73)	30
10	Connecticut	9.73	11	35	Alaska	(4.01)	36
11	New Jersey	9.67	16	36	Tennessee	(4.26)	37
12	North Dakota	8.86	10	37	Missouri	(4.94)	34
13	Washington	8.76	12	38	Arkansas	(6.71)	43
14	California	8.45	14	39	Oklahoma	(6.77)	40
15	Oregon	7.95	19	40	Arizona	(7.40)	41
16	Wyoming	7.07	20	41	Florida	(7.55)	44
17	Kansas	6.97	15	42	Georgia	(8.51)	42
18	Rhode Island	6.78	17	42	Texas	(8.51)	39
19	South Dakota	5.86	13	44	Delaware	(9.58)	38
20	Idaho	5.46	21	45	Nevada	(10.51)	45
21	Wisconsin	5.09	23	46	South Carolina	(12.95)	48
22	Virginia	3.90	22	47	Alabama	(13.42)	47
23	Montana	3.68	18	48	Louisiana	(13.84)	49
24	Ohio	3.00	26	49	New Mexico	(14.34)	46
25	Michigan	2.48	28	50	Mississippi	(19.21)	50

These factors reflect access to health care providers, affordability of health care and a generally healthy population (see box below.) No factors were changed for this year's award. The 21 factors were divided into two groups: those that are "negative" for which a high ranking would be considered bad for a state, and those that are "positive" for which a high ranking would be considered good for a state. Rates for each of the 21 factors were processed through a formula that measures how a state compares to the national average for a given category. The positive and negative nature of each factor was taken into account as part of the formula. Once these computations were made, the factors then were weighted equally. These weighted scores then were added together to get a state's final score ("SUM" on the table above.) This way, states are assessed based on how they stack up against the national average. The end result is that the farther below the national average a state's health ranking is, the lower (and less healthy) it ranks. The farther above the national average, the higher (and healthier) a state ranks. This same methodology was used for our Dangerous State and Safest/Dangerous City Awards.

The table above shows how each state fared in the 2004 Healthiest State Award as well as its placement in 2003. Congratulations to the very healthy citizens of New Hampshire.

THE EDITORS

POSITIVE (+) AND NEGATIVE (-) FACTORS CONSIDERED:
1. Births of Low Birthweight as a Percent of All Births (Table 12) -
2. Teenage Birth Rate (Table 30) -
3. Percent of Mothers Receiving Late or No Prenatal Care (Table 56) -
4. Age-Adjusted Death Rate (Table 80) -
5. Infant Mortality Rate (Table 84) -
6. Age-Adjusted Death Rate by Malignant Neoplasms (Table 148) -
7. Age-Adjusted Death Rate by Suicide (Table 169) -
8. Percent of Population Not Covered by Health Insurance (Table 226) -
9. Health Care Expenditures as a Percent of Gross State Product (Table 282) -
10. Per Capita Personal Health Expenditures (Table 283) -
11. Estimated Rate of New Cancer Cases (Table 328) -
12. AIDS Rate (Table 357) -
13. Sexually Transmitted Disease Rate (Table 394) -
14. Percent of Population Lacking Access to Primary Care (Table 426) -
15. Percent of Adults Who Are Binge Drinkers (Table 494) -
16. Percent of Adults Who Smoke (Table 495) -
17. Percent of Adults Obese (Table 500) -
18. Number of Days in Past Month When Physical Health was "Not Good" (Table 509) -
19. Beds in Community Hospitals per 100,000 Population (Table 193) +
20. Percent of Children Aged 19-35 Months Immunized (Table 390) +
21. Safety Belt Usage Rate (Table 512) +

TABLE OF CONTENTS

I. Births and Reproductive Health

TABLE OF CONTENTS (continued)

Abortions

II. Deaths

TABLE OF CONTENTS (continued)

TABLE OF CONTENTS (continued)

III. Facilities

IV. Finance

TABLE OF CONTENTS (continued)

TABLE OF CONTENTS (continued)

V. Incidence of Disease

TABLE OF CONTENTS (continued)

VI. Providers

TABLE OF CONTENTS (continued)

TABLE OF CONTENTS (continued)

VII. Physical Fitness

VIII. Appendix

IX. Sources

X. Index

I. BIRTHS AND REPRODUCTIVE HEALTH

I. BIRTHS AND REPRODUCTIVE HEALTH
(CONTINUED)

Abortions

Births in 2002

National Total = 4,021,726 Live Births*

ALPHA ORDER

RANK	STATE	BIRTHS	% of USA
24	Alabama	58,967	1.5%
47	Alaska	9,938	0.2%
13	Arizona	87,837	2.2%
34	Arkansas	37,437	0.9%
1	California	529,357	13.2%
21	Colorado	68,418	1.7%
30	Connecticut	42,001	1.0%
44	Delaware	11,090	0.3%
4	Florida	205,579	5.1%
8	Georgia	133,300	3.3%
40	Hawaii	17,477	0.4%
38	Idaho	20,970	0.5%
5	Illinois	180,622	4.5%
14	Indiana	85,081	2.1%
33	Iowa	37,559	0.9%
32	Kansas	39,412	1.0%
26	Kentucky	54,233	1.3%
23	Louisiana	64,872	1.6%
42	Maine	13,559	0.3%
19	Maryland	73,323	1.8%
15	Massachusetts	80,645	2.0%
9	Michigan	129,967	3.2%
22	Minnesota	68,025	1.7%
31	Mississippi	41,518	1.0%
18	Missouri	75,251	1.9%
45	Montana	11,049	0.3%
37	Nebraska	25,383	0.6%
35	Nevada	32,571	0.8%
41	New Hampshire	14,442	0.4%
11	New Jersey	114,751	2.9%
36	New Mexico	27,753	0.7%
3	New York	251,415	6.3%
10	North Carolina	117,335	2.9%
48	North Dakota	7,757	0.2%
6	Ohio	148,720	3.7%
27	Oklahoma	50,387	1.3%
29	Oregon	45,192	1.1%
7	Pennsylvania	142,850	3.6%
43	Rhode Island	12,894	0.3%
25	South Carolina	54,570	1.4%
46	South Dakota	10,698	0.3%
17	Tennessee	77,482	1.9%
2	Texas	372,450	9.3%
28	Utah	49,182	1.2%
50	Vermont	6,387	0.2%
12	Virginia	99,672	2.5%
16	Washington	79,028	2.0%
39	West Virginia	20,712	0.5%
20	Wisconsin	68,560	1.7%
49	Wyoming	6,550	0.2%

RANK ORDER

RANK	STATE	BIRTHS	% of USA
1	California	529,357	13.2%
2	Texas	372,450	9.3%
3	New York	251,415	6.3%
4	Florida	205,579	5.1%
5	Illinois	180,622	4.5%
6	Ohio	148,720	3.7%
7	Pennsylvania	142,850	3.6%
8	Georgia	133,300	3.3%
9	Michigan	129,967	3.2%
10	North Carolina	117,335	2.9%
11	New Jersey	114,751	2.9%
12	Virginia	99,672	2.5%
13	Arizona	87,837	2.2%
14	Indiana	85,081	2.1%
15	Massachusetts	80,645	2.0%
16	Washington	79,028	2.0%
17	Tennessee	77,482	1.9%
18	Missouri	75,251	1.9%
19	Maryland	73,323	1.8%
20	Wisconsin	68,560	1.7%
21	Colorado	68,418	1.7%
22	Minnesota	68,025	1.7%
23	Louisiana	64,872	1.6%
24	Alabama	58,967	1.5%
25	South Carolina	54,570	1.4%
26	Kentucky	54,233	1.3%
27	Oklahoma	50,387	1.3%
28	Utah	49,182	1.2%
29	Oregon	45,192	1.1%
30	Connecticut	42,001	1.0%
31	Mississippi	41,518	1.0%
32	Kansas	39,412	1.0%
33	Iowa	37,559	0.9%
34	Arkansas	37,437	0.9%
35	Nevada	32,571	0.8%
36	New Mexico	27,753	0.7%
37	Nebraska	25,383	0.6%
38	Idaho	20,970	0.5%
39	West Virginia	20,712	0.5%
40	Hawaii	17,477	0.4%
41	New Hampshire	14,442	0.4%
42	Maine	13,559	0.3%
43	Rhode Island	12,894	0.3%
44	Delaware	11,090	0.3%
45	Montana	11,049	0.3%
46	South Dakota	10,698	0.3%
47	Alaska	9,938	0.2%
48	North Dakota	7,757	0.2%
49	Wyoming	6,550	0.2%
50	Vermont	6,387	0.2%
	District of Columbia	7,498	0.2%

Source: U.S. Department of Health and Human Services, National Center for Health Statistics
"National Vital Statistics Reports" (Vol. 52, No. 10, December 17, 2003)
*Final data by state of residence.

Birth Rate in 2002

National Rate = 13.9 Live Births per 1,000 Population*

RANK	STATE	RATE
31	Alabama	13.1
6	Alaska	15.4
3	Arizona	16.1
20	Arkansas	13.8
8	California	15.1
7	Colorado	15.2
43	Connecticut	12.1
22	Delaware	13.7
41	Florida	12.3
4	Georgia	15.6
19	Hawaii	14.0
4	Idaho	15.6
16	Illinois	14.3
20	Indiana	13.8
37	Iowa	12.8
12	Kansas	14.5
28	Kentucky	13.3
12	Louisiana	14.5
49	Maine	10.5
25	Maryland	13.4
40	Massachusetts	12.5
36	Michigan	12.9
24	Minnesota	13.6
12	Mississippi	14.5
28	Missouri	13.3
43	Montana	12.1
11	Nebraska	14.7
9	Nevada	15.0
48	New Hampshire	11.3
25	New Jersey	13.4
9	New Mexico	15.0
31	New York	13.1
17	North Carolina	14.1
42	North Dakota	12.2
34	Ohio	13.0
15	Oklahoma	14.4
37	Oregon	12.8
46	Pennsylvania	11.6
43	Rhode Island	12.1
28	South Carolina	13.3
17	South Dakota	14.1
25	Tennessee	13.4
2	Texas	17.1
1	Utah	21.2
50	Vermont	10.4
22	Virginia	13.7
34	Washington	13.0
47	West Virginia	11.5
39	Wisconsin	12.6
31	Wyoming	13.1

RANK	STATE	RATE
1	Utah	21.2
2	Texas	17.1
3	Arizona	16.1
4	Georgia	15.6
4	Idaho	15.6
6	Alaska	15.4
7	Colorado	15.2
8	California	15.1
9	Nevada	15.0
9	New Mexico	15.0
11	Nebraska	14.7
12	Kansas	14.5
12	Louisiana	14.5
12	Mississippi	14.5
15	Oklahoma	14.4
16	Illinois	14.3
17	North Carolina	14.1
17	South Dakota	14.1
19	Hawaii	14.0
20	Arkansas	13.8
20	Indiana	13.8
22	Delaware	13.7
22	Virginia	13.7
24	Minnesota	13.6
25	Maryland	13.4
25	New Jersey	13.4
25	Tennessee	13.4
28	Kentucky	13.3
28	Missouri	13.3
28	South Carolina	13.3
31	Alabama	13.1
31	New York	13.1
31	Wyoming	13.1
34	Ohio	13.0
34	Washington	13.0
36	Michigan	12.9
37	Iowa	12.8
37	Oregon	12.8
39	Wisconsin	12.6
40	Massachusetts	12.5
41	Florida	12.3
42	North Dakota	12.2
43	Connecticut	12.1
43	Montana	12.1
43	Rhode Island	12.1
46	Pennsylvania	11.6
47	West Virginia	11.5
48	New Hampshire	11.3
49	Maine	10.5
50	Vermont	10.4
	District of Columbia	13.1

Source: U.S. Department of Health and Human Services, National Center for Health Statistics
"National Vital Statistics Reports" (Vol. 52, No. 10, December 17, 2003)
*Final data by state of residence.

Percent Change in Birth Rate: 1990 to 2002

National Percent Change = 16.8% Decrease*

<table>
<tr><td colspan="3">ALPHA ORDER</td><td colspan="3">RANK ORDER</td></tr>
<tr><td>RANK</td><td>STATE</td><td>PERCENT CHANGE</td><td>RANK</td><td>STATE</td><td>PERCENT CHANGE</td></tr>
<tr><td>30</td><td>Alabama</td><td>(16.6)</td><td>1</td><td>Utah</td><td>0.5</td></tr>
<tr><td>49</td><td>Alaska</td><td>(28.7)</td><td>2</td><td>Idaho</td><td>(4.3)</td></tr>
<tr><td>20</td><td>Arizona</td><td>(14.4)</td><td>3</td><td>Nebraska</td><td>(4.5)</td></tr>
<tr><td>14</td><td>Arkansas</td><td>(11.0)</td><td>4</td><td>Oklahoma</td><td>(4.6)</td></tr>
<tr><td>47</td><td>California</td><td>(26.7)</td><td>5</td><td>Colorado</td><td>(6.2)</td></tr>
<tr><td>5</td><td>Colorado</td><td>(6.2)</td><td>6</td><td>Kansas</td><td>(7.6)</td></tr>
<tr><td>41</td><td>Connecticut</td><td>(20.4)</td><td>7</td><td>Texas</td><td>(8.1)</td></tr>
<tr><td>34</td><td>Delaware</td><td>(18.0)</td><td>8</td><td>West Virginia</td><td>(8.7)</td></tr>
<tr><td>38</td><td>Florida</td><td>(20.1)</td><td>9</td><td>Iowa</td><td>(9.9)</td></tr>
<tr><td>11</td><td>Georgia</td><td>(10.3)</td><td>10</td><td>Kentucky</td><td>(10.1)</td></tr>
<tr><td>45</td><td>Hawaii</td><td>(24.3)</td><td>11</td><td>Georgia</td><td>(10.3)</td></tr>
<tr><td>2</td><td>Idaho</td><td>(4.3)</td><td>12</td><td>North Carolina</td><td>(10.8)</td></tr>
<tr><td>29</td><td>Illinois</td><td>(16.4)</td><td>12</td><td>South Dakota</td><td>(10.8)</td></tr>
<tr><td>15</td><td>Indiana</td><td>(11.5)</td><td>14</td><td>Arkansas</td><td>(11.0)</td></tr>
<tr><td>9</td><td>Iowa</td><td>(9.9)</td><td>15</td><td>Indiana</td><td>(11.5)</td></tr>
<tr><td>6</td><td>Kansas</td><td>(7.6)</td><td>16</td><td>Minnesota</td><td>(12.3)</td></tr>
<tr><td>10</td><td>Kentucky</td><td>(10.1)</td><td>17</td><td>Tennessee</td><td>(13.0)</td></tr>
<tr><td>23</td><td>Louisiana</td><td>(15.2)</td><td>18</td><td>Mississippi</td><td>(14.2)</td></tr>
<tr><td>46</td><td>Maine</td><td>(25.5)</td><td>18</td><td>Missouri</td><td>(14.2)</td></tr>
<tr><td>39</td><td>Maryland</td><td>(20.2)</td><td>20</td><td>Arizona</td><td>(14.4)</td></tr>
<tr><td>35</td><td>Massachusetts</td><td>(18.8)</td><td>21</td><td>Virginia</td><td>(14.9)</td></tr>
<tr><td>44</td><td>Michigan</td><td>(21.8)</td><td>21</td><td>Wyoming</td><td>(14.9)</td></tr>
<tr><td>16</td><td>Minnesota</td><td>(12.3)</td><td>23</td><td>Louisiana</td><td>(15.2)</td></tr>
<tr><td>18</td><td>Mississippi</td><td>(14.2)</td><td>23</td><td>New Jersey</td><td>(15.2)</td></tr>
<tr><td>18</td><td>Missouri</td><td>(14.2)</td><td>23</td><td>Oregon</td><td>(15.2)</td></tr>
<tr><td>30</td><td>Montana</td><td>(16.6)</td><td>26</td><td>Wisconsin</td><td>(15.4)</td></tr>
<tr><td>3</td><td>Nebraska</td><td>(4.5)</td><td>27</td><td>Ohio</td><td>(15.6)</td></tr>
<tr><td>32</td><td>Nevada</td><td>(16.7)</td><td>28</td><td>North Dakota</td><td>(15.9)</td></tr>
<tr><td>48</td><td>New Hampshire</td><td>(28.5)</td><td>29</td><td>Illinois</td><td>(16.4)</td></tr>
<tr><td>23</td><td>New Jersey</td><td>(15.2)</td><td>30</td><td>Alabama</td><td>(16.6)</td></tr>
<tr><td>33</td><td>New Mexico</td><td>(17.1)</td><td>30</td><td>Montana</td><td>(16.6)</td></tr>
<tr><td>42</td><td>New York</td><td>(20.6)</td><td>32</td><td>Nevada</td><td>(16.7)</td></tr>
<tr><td>12</td><td>North Carolina</td><td>(10.8)</td><td>33</td><td>New Mexico</td><td>(17.1)</td></tr>
<tr><td>28</td><td>North Dakota</td><td>(15.9)</td><td>34</td><td>Delaware</td><td>(18.0)</td></tr>
<tr><td>27</td><td>Ohio</td><td>(15.6)</td><td>35</td><td>Massachusetts</td><td>(18.8)</td></tr>
<tr><td>4</td><td>Oklahoma</td><td>(4.6)</td><td>36</td><td>Rhode Island</td><td>(19.9)</td></tr>
<tr><td>23</td><td>Oregon</td><td>(15.2)</td><td>37</td><td>Pennsylvania</td><td>(20.0)</td></tr>
<tr><td>37</td><td>Pennsylvania</td><td>(20.0)</td><td>38</td><td>Florida</td><td>(20.1)</td></tr>
<tr><td>36</td><td>Rhode Island</td><td>(19.9)</td><td>39</td><td>Maryland</td><td>(20.2)</td></tr>
<tr><td>43</td><td>South Carolina</td><td>(20.8)</td><td>39</td><td>Washington</td><td>(20.2)</td></tr>
<tr><td>12</td><td>South Dakota</td><td>(10.8)</td><td>41</td><td>Connecticut</td><td>(20.4)</td></tr>
<tr><td>17</td><td>Tennessee</td><td>(13.0)</td><td>42</td><td>New York</td><td>(20.6)</td></tr>
<tr><td>7</td><td>Texas</td><td>(8.1)</td><td>43</td><td>South Carolina</td><td>(20.8)</td></tr>
<tr><td>1</td><td>Utah</td><td>0.5</td><td>44</td><td>Michigan</td><td>(21.8)</td></tr>
<tr><td>50</td><td>Vermont</td><td>(29.3)</td><td>45</td><td>Hawaii</td><td>(24.3)</td></tr>
<tr><td>21</td><td>Virginia</td><td>(14.9)</td><td>46</td><td>Maine</td><td>(25.5)</td></tr>
<tr><td>39</td><td>Washington</td><td>(20.2)</td><td>47</td><td>California</td><td>(26.7)</td></tr>
<tr><td>8</td><td>West Virginia</td><td>(8.7)</td><td>48</td><td>New Hampshire</td><td>(28.5)</td></tr>
<tr><td>26</td><td>Wisconsin</td><td>(15.4)</td><td>49</td><td>Alaska</td><td>(28.7)</td></tr>
<tr><td>21</td><td>Wyoming</td><td>(14.9)</td><td>50</td><td>Vermont</td><td>(29.3)</td></tr>
<tr><td></td><td></td><td></td><td></td><td>District of Columbia</td><td>(32.8)</td></tr>
</table>

Source: Morgan Quitno Press using data from U.S. Department of Health and Human Services
"National Vital Statistics Reports" (Vol. 52, No. 10, December 17, 2003) and
"Monthly Vital Statistics Report" (Vol. 41, No. 9, Supplement, February 25, 1993)
*Final data by state of residence.

Fertility Rate in 2002

National Rate = 64.8 Live Births per 1,000 Women 15 to 44 Years Old*

ALPHA ORDER

RANK	STATE	RATE
33	Alabama	61.2
5	Alaska	73.5
2	Arizona	77.8
16	Arkansas	66.6
14	California	68.3
9	Colorado	69.3
42	Connecticut	58.8
25	Delaware	62.2
24	Florida	62.5
13	Georgia	68.4
12	Hawaii	68.6
4	Idaho	73.8
17	Illinois	66.1
21	Indiana	64.8
31	Iowa	61.7
11	Kansas	68.7
37	Kentucky	60.5
19	Louisiana	65.4
49	Maine	49.8
36	Maryland	60.6
45	Massachusetts	56.7
34	Michigan	60.7
28	Minnesota	62.0
18	Mississippi	65.7
27	Missouri	62.1
38	Montana	60.3
8	Nebraska	69.5
6	Nevada	72.5
48	New Hampshire	52.4
23	New Jersey	63.5
7	New Mexico	70.7
40	New York	59.8
19	North Carolina	65.4
43	North Dakota	58.7
31	Ohio	61.7
10	Oklahoma	68.8
29	Oregon	61.9
46	Pennsylvania	56.4
47	Rhode Island	54.6
34	South Carolina	60.7
14	South Dakota	68.3
25	Tennessee	62.2
3	Texas	77.1
1	Utah	90.6
50	Vermont	48.9
29	Virginia	61.9
39	Washington	60.2
44	West Virginia	57.0
41	Wisconsin	59.0
22	Wyoming	63.6

RANK ORDER

RANK	STATE	RATE
1	Utah	90.6
2	Arizona	77.8
3	Texas	77.1
4	Idaho	73.8
5	Alaska	73.5
6	Nevada	72.5
7	New Mexico	70.7
8	Nebraska	69.5
9	Colorado	69.3
10	Oklahoma	68.8
11	Kansas	68.7
12	Hawaii	68.6
13	Georgia	68.4
14	California	68.3
14	South Dakota	68.3
16	Arkansas	66.6
17	Illinois	66.1
18	Mississippi	65.7
19	Louisiana	65.4
19	North Carolina	65.4
21	Indiana	64.8
22	Wyoming	63.6
23	New Jersey	63.5
24	Florida	62.5
25	Delaware	62.2
25	Tennessee	62.2
27	Missouri	62.1
28	Minnesota	62.0
29	Oregon	61.9
29	Virginia	61.9
31	Iowa	61.7
31	Ohio	61.7
33	Alabama	61.2
34	Michigan	60.7
34	South Carolina	60.7
36	Maryland	60.6
37	Kentucky	60.5
38	Montana	60.3
39	Washington	60.2
40	New York	59.8
41	Wisconsin	59.0
42	Connecticut	58.8
43	North Dakota	58.7
44	West Virginia	57.0
45	Massachusetts	56.7
46	Pennsylvania	56.4
47	Rhode Island	54.6
48	New Hampshire	52.4
49	Maine	49.8
50	Vermont	48.9

District of Columbia	52.9

Source: U.S. Department of Health and Human Services, National Center for Health Statistics
   "National Vital Statistics Reports" (Vol. 52, No. 10, December 17, 2003)
*Final data by state of residence.

Births to White Women in 2002

National Total = 3,174,760 Live Births to White Women*

RANK	STATE	BIRTHS	% of USA
26	Alabama	39,978	1.3%
47	Alaska	6,377	0.2%
12	Arizona	77,043	2.4%
33	Arkansas	29,209	0.9%
1	California	428,549	13.5%
17	Colorado	62,425	2.0%
32	Connecticut	34,654	1.1%
45	Delaware	7,925	0.2%
4	Florida	152,855	4.8%
9	Georgia	85,809	2.7%
50	Hawaii	3,953	0.1%
38	Idaho	20,151	0.6%
5	Illinois	140,163	4.4%
13	Indiana	74,309	2.3%
30	Iowa	35,112	1.1%
31	Kansas	34,904	1.1%
22	Kentucky	48,399	1.5%
28	Louisiana	36,757	1.2%
41	Maine	13,049	0.4%
24	Maryland	45,198	1.4%
15	Massachusetts	66,689	2.1%
8	Michigan	102,590	3.2%
21	Minnesota	58,023	1.8%
37	Mississippi	22,618	0.7%
18	Missouri	62,374	2.0%
43	Montana	9,512	0.3%
36	Nebraska	22,980	0.7%
34	Nevada	26,979	0.8%
40	New Hampshire	13,691	0.4%
11	New Jersey	84,493	2.7%
35	New Mexico	23,281	0.7%
3	New York	181,212	5.7%
10	North Carolina	85,210	2.7%
46	North Dakota	6,762	0.2%
6	Ohio	122,887	3.9%
27	Oklahoma	39,508	1.2%
25	Oregon	41,047	1.3%
7	Pennsylvania	117,817	3.7%
42	Rhode Island	11,036	0.3%
29	South Carolina	35,373	1.1%
44	South Dakota	8,657	0.3%
19	Tennessee	59,627	1.9%
2	Texas	317,150	10.0%
23	Utah	46,572	1.5%
48	Vermont	6,239	0.2%
14	Virginia	71,415	2.2%
16	Washington	66,519	2.1%
39	West Virginia	19,877	0.6%
20	Wisconsin	58,979	1.9%
49	Wyoming	6,147	0.2%

RANK	STATE	BIRTHS	% of USA
1	California	428,549	13.5%
2	Texas	317,150	10.0%
3	New York	181,212	5.7%
4	Florida	152,855	4.8%
5	Illinois	140,163	4.4%
6	Ohio	122,887	3.9%
7	Pennsylvania	117,817	3.7%
8	Michigan	102,590	3.2%
9	Georgia	85,809	2.7%
10	North Carolina	85,210	2.7%
11	New Jersey	84,493	2.7%
12	Arizona	77,043	2.4%
13	Indiana	74,309	2.3%
14	Virginia	71,415	2.2%
15	Massachusetts	66,689	2.1%
16	Washington	66,519	2.1%
17	Colorado	62,425	2.0%
18	Missouri	62,374	2.0%
19	Tennessee	59,627	1.9%
20	Wisconsin	58,979	1.9%
21	Minnesota	58,023	1.8%
22	Kentucky	48,399	1.5%
23	Utah	46,572	1.5%
24	Maryland	45,198	1.4%
25	Oregon	41,047	1.3%
26	Alabama	39,978	1.3%
27	Oklahoma	39,508	1.2%
28	Louisiana	36,757	1.2%
29	South Carolina	35,373	1.1%
30	Iowa	35,112	1.1%
31	Kansas	34,904	1.1%
32	Connecticut	34,654	1.1%
33	Arkansas	29,209	0.9%
34	Nevada	26,979	0.8%
35	New Mexico	23,281	0.7%
36	Nebraska	22,980	0.7%
37	Mississippi	22,618	0.7%
38	Idaho	20,151	0.6%
39	West Virginia	19,877	0.6%
40	New Hampshire	13,691	0.4%
41	Maine	13,049	0.4%
42	Rhode Island	11,036	0.3%
43	Montana	9,512	0.3%
44	South Dakota	8,657	0.3%
45	Delaware	7,925	0.2%
46	North Dakota	6,762	0.2%
47	Alaska	6,377	0.2%
48	Vermont	6,239	0.2%
49	Wyoming	6,147	0.2%
50	Hawaii	3,953	0.1%
	District of Columbia	2,677	0.1%

Source: U.S. Department of Health and Human Services, National Center for Health Statistics
   "National Vital Statistics Reports" (Vol. 52, No. 10, December 17, 2003)
Final data by state of residence. By race of mother.

White Births as a Percent of All Births in 2002

National Percent = 78.9% of Live Births*

ALPHA ORDER

RANK	STATE	PERCENT
43	Alabama	67.8
46	Alaska	64.2
14	Arizona	87.7
34	Arkansas	78.0
30	California	81.0
9	Colorado	91.2
28	Connecticut	82.5
42	Delaware	71.5
37	Florida	74.4
45	Georgia	64.4
50	Hawaii	22.6
3	Idaho	96.1
35	Illinois	77.6
15	Indiana	87.3
8	Iowa	93.5
13	Kansas	88.6
12	Kentucky	89.2
48	Louisiana	56.7
2	Maine	96.2
47	Maryland	61.6
26	Massachusetts	82.7
32	Michigan	78.9
20	Minnesota	85.3
49	Mississippi	54.5
24	Missouri	82.9
17	Montana	86.1
11	Nebraska	90.5
25	Nevada	82.8
5	New Hampshire	94.8
38	New Jersey	73.6
23	New Mexico	83.9
40	New York	72.1
39	North Carolina	72.6
16	North Dakota	87.2
27	Ohio	82.6
33	Oklahoma	78.4
10	Oregon	90.8
28	Pennsylvania	82.5
19	Rhode Island	85.6
44	South Carolina	64.8
31	South Dakota	80.9
36	Tennessee	77.0
21	Texas	85.2
6	Utah	94.7
1	Vermont	97.7
41	Virginia	71.7
22	Washington	84.2
4	West Virginia	96.0
18	Wisconsin	86.0
7	Wyoming	93.8

RANK ORDER

RANK	STATE	PERCENT
1	Vermont	97.7
2	Maine	96.2
3	Idaho	96.1
4	West Virginia	96.0
5	New Hampshire	94.8
6	Utah	94.7
7	Wyoming	93.8
8	Iowa	93.5
9	Colorado	91.2
10	Oregon	90.8
11	Nebraska	90.5
12	Kentucky	89.2
13	Kansas	88.6
14	Arizona	87.7
15	Indiana	87.3
16	North Dakota	87.2
17	Montana	86.1
18	Wisconsin	86.0
19	Rhode Island	85.6
20	Minnesota	85.3
21	Texas	85.2
22	Washington	84.2
23	New Mexico	83.9
24	Missouri	82.9
25	Nevada	82.8
26	Massachusetts	82.7
27	Ohio	82.6
28	Connecticut	82.5
28	Pennsylvania	82.5
30	California	81.0
31	South Dakota	80.9
32	Michigan	78.9
33	Oklahoma	78.4
34	Arkansas	78.0
35	Illinois	77.6
36	Tennessee	77.0
37	Florida	74.4
38	New Jersey	73.6
39	North Carolina	72.6
40	New York	72.1
41	Virginia	71.7
42	Delaware	71.5
43	Alabama	67.8
44	South Carolina	64.8
45	Georgia	64.4
46	Alaska	64.2
47	Maryland	61.6
48	Louisiana	56.7
49	Mississippi	54.5
50	Hawaii	22.6

District of Columbia 35.7

Source: Morgan Quitno Press using data from U.S. Dept. of Health and Human Services, Nat'l Center for Health Statistics
   "National Vital Statistics Reports" (Vol. 52, No. 10, December 17, 2003)
*Final data by state of residence. By race of mother.

Births to Black Women in 2002

National Total = 593,691 Live Births to Black Women*

ALPHA ORDER

RANK	STATE	BIRTHS	% of USA
15	Alabama	18,292	3.1%
41	Alaska	432	0.1%
31	Arizona	2,779	0.5%
22	Arkansas	7,427	1.3%
5	California	32,653	5.5%
29	Colorado	2,934	0.5%
24	Connecticut	5,195	0.9%
32	Delaware	2,708	0.5%
2	Florida	46,238	7.8%
3	Georgia	42,777	7.2%
40	Hawaii	475	0.1%
45	Idaho	103	0.0%
6	Illinois	31,833	5.4%
20	Indiana	9,332	1.6%
35	Iowa	1,263	0.2%
30	Kansas	2,890	0.5%
25	Kentucky	4,943	0.8%
8	Louisiana	26,659	4.5%
44	Maine	174	0.0%
9	Maryland	24,214	4.1%
21	Massachusetts	8,344	1.4%
11	Michigan	22,440	3.8%
26	Minnesota	4,862	0.8%
16	Mississippi	18,202	3.1%
19	Missouri	11,028	1.9%
50	Montana	37	0.0%
34	Nebraska	1,442	0.2%
33	Nevada	2,611	0.4%
43	New Hampshire	225	0.0%
14	New Jersey	19,952	3.4%
39	New Mexico	511	0.1%
1	New York	49,590	8.4%
7	North Carolina	27,571	4.6%
47	North Dakota	90	0.0%
10	Ohio	22,547	3.8%
27	Oklahoma	4,704	0.8%
37	Oregon	941	0.2%
13	Pennsylvania	20,265	3.4%
36	Rhode Island	1,145	0.2%
17	South Carolina	18,183	3.1%
45	South Dakota	103	0.0%
18	Tennessee	16,304	2.7%
4	Texas	41,642	7.0%
42	Utah	339	0.1%
49	Vermont	44	0.0%
12	Virginia	22,084	3.7%
28	Washington	3,393	0.6%
38	West Virginia	679	0.1%
23	Wisconsin	6,418	1.1%
48	Wyoming	54	0.0%

RANK ORDER

RANK	STATE	BIRTHS	% of USA
1	New York	49,590	8.4%
2	Florida	46,238	7.8%
3	Georgia	42,777	7.2%
4	Texas	41,642	7.0%
5	California	32,653	5.5%
6	Illinois	31,833	5.4%
7	North Carolina	27,571	4.6%
8	Louisiana	26,659	4.5%
9	Maryland	24,214	4.1%
10	Ohio	22,547	3.8%
11	Michigan	22,440	3.8%
12	Virginia	22,084	3.7%
13	Pennsylvania	20,265	3.4%
14	New Jersey	19,952	3.4%
15	Alabama	18,292	3.1%
16	Mississippi	18,202	3.1%
17	South Carolina	18,183	3.1%
18	Tennessee	16,304	2.7%
19	Missouri	11,028	1.9%
20	Indiana	9,332	1.6%
21	Massachusetts	8,344	1.4%
22	Arkansas	7,427	1.3%
23	Wisconsin	6,418	1.1%
24	Connecticut	5,195	0.9%
25	Kentucky	4,943	0.8%
26	Minnesota	4,862	0.8%
27	Oklahoma	4,704	0.8%
28	Washington	3,393	0.6%
29	Colorado	2,934	0.5%
30	Kansas	2,890	0.5%
31	Arizona	2,779	0.5%
32	Delaware	2,708	0.5%
33	Nevada	2,611	0.4%
34	Nebraska	1,442	0.2%
35	Iowa	1,263	0.2%
36	Rhode Island	1,145	0.2%
37	Oregon	941	0.2%
38	West Virginia	679	0.1%
39	New Mexico	511	0.1%
40	Hawaii	475	0.1%
41	Alaska	432	0.1%
42	Utah	339	0.1%
43	New Hampshire	225	0.0%
44	Maine	174	0.0%
45	Idaho	103	0.0%
45	South Dakota	103	0.0%
47	North Dakota	90	0.0%
48	Wyoming	54	0.0%
49	Vermont	44	0.0%
50	Montana	37	0.0%
	District of Columbia	4,620	0.8%

Source: U.S. Department of Health and Human Services, National Center for Health Statistics
   "National Vital Statistics Reports" (Vol. 52, No. 10, December 17, 2003)
*Final data by state of residence. By race of mother.

Black Births as a Percent of All Births in 2002

National Percent = 14.8% of Live Births*

ALPHA ORDER

RANK	STATE	PERCENT
6	Alabama	31.0
33	Alaska	4.3
38	Arizona	3.2
12	Arkansas	19.8
31	California	6.2
33	Colorado	4.3
20	Connecticut	12.4
7	Delaware	24.4
9	Florida	22.5
5	Georgia	32.1
39	Hawaii	2.7
49	Idaho	0.5
14	Illinois	17.6
22	Indiana	11.0
36	Iowa	3.4
29	Kansas	7.3
26	Kentucky	9.1
2	Louisiana	41.1
43	Maine	1.3
4	Maryland	33.0
23	Massachusetts	10.3
16	Michigan	17.3
30	Minnesota	7.1
1	Mississippi	43.8
18	Missouri	14.7
50	Montana	0.3
32	Nebraska	5.7
28	Nevada	8.0
42	New Hampshire	1.6
15	New Jersey	17.4
41	New Mexico	1.8
13	New York	19.7
8	North Carolina	23.5
44	North Dakota	1.2
17	Ohio	15.2
25	Oklahoma	9.3
40	Oregon	2.1
19	Pennsylvania	14.2
27	Rhode Island	8.9
3	South Carolina	33.3
45	South Dakota	1.0
11	Tennessee	21.0
21	Texas	11.2
47	Utah	0.7
47	Vermont	0.7
10	Virginia	22.2
33	Washington	4.3
37	West Virginia	3.3
24	Wisconsin	9.4
46	Wyoming	0.8

RANK ORDER

RANK	STATE	PERCENT
1	Mississippi	43.8
2	Louisiana	41.1
3	South Carolina	33.3
4	Maryland	33.0
5	Georgia	32.1
6	Alabama	31.0
7	Delaware	24.4
8	North Carolina	23.5
9	Florida	22.5
10	Virginia	22.2
11	Tennessee	21.0
12	Arkansas	19.8
13	New York	19.7
14	Illinois	17.6
15	New Jersey	17.4
16	Michigan	17.3
17	Ohio	15.2
18	Missouri	14.7
19	Pennsylvania	14.2
20	Connecticut	12.4
21	Texas	11.2
22	Indiana	11.0
23	Massachusetts	10.3
24	Wisconsin	9.4
25	Oklahoma	9.3
26	Kentucky	9.1
27	Rhode Island	8.9
28	Nevada	8.0
29	Kansas	7.3
30	Minnesota	7.1
31	California	6.2
32	Nebraska	5.7
33	Alaska	4.3
33	Colorado	4.3
33	Washington	4.3
36	Iowa	3.4
37	West Virginia	3.3
38	Arizona	3.2
39	Hawaii	2.7
40	Oregon	2.1
41	New Mexico	1.8
42	New Hampshire	1.6
43	Maine	1.3
44	North Dakota	1.2
45	South Dakota	1.0
46	Wyoming	0.8
47	Utah	0.7
47	Vermont	0.7
49	Idaho	0.5
50	Montana	0.3

District of Columbia   61.6

Source: Morgan Quitno Press using data from U.S. Dept. of Health and Human Services, Nat'l Center for Health Statistics
"National Vital Statistics Reports" (Vol. 52, No. 10, December 17, 2003)
*Final data by state of residence. By race of mother.

Births to Hispanic Women in 2002

National Total = 876,642 Live Births to Hispanic Women*

ALPHA ORDER

RANK	STATE	BIRTHS	% of USA
34	Alabama	2,569	0.3%
42	Alaska	799	0.1%
6	Arizona	37,938	4.3%
32	Arkansas	3,050	0.3%
1	California	263,061	30.0%
8	Colorado	21,029	2.4%
19	Connecticut	6,982	0.8%
40	Delaware	1,316	0.2%
4	Florida	51,619	5.9%
9	Georgia	16,819	1.9%
35	Hawaii	2,422	0.3%
33	Idaho	2,788	0.3%
5	Illinois	41,022	4.7%
21	Indiana	6,169	0.7%
36	Iowa	2,390	0.3%
25	Kansas	5,023	0.6%
38	Kentucky	1,630	0.2%
39	Louisiana	1,383	0.2%
47	Maine	167	0.0%
22	Maryland	6,062	0.7%
15	Massachusetts	9,592	1.1%
18	Michigan	7,265	0.8%
27	Minnesota	4,646	0.5%
41	Mississippi	823	0.1%
30	Missouri	3,267	0.4%
45	Montana	382	0.0%
29	Nebraska	3,313	0.4%
13	Nevada	11,386	1.3%
44	New Hampshire	503	0.1%
7	New Jersey	24,664	2.8%
11	New Mexico	14,623	1.7%
3	New York	54,700	6.2%
10	North Carolina	15,064	1.7%
48	North Dakota	149	0.0%
26	Ohio	4,817	0.5%
24	Oklahoma	5,259	0.6%
17	Oregon	8,040	0.9%
16	Pennsylvania	8,696	1.0%
37	Rhode Island	2,328	0.3%
31	South Carolina	3,175	0.4%
46	South Dakota	318	0.0%
28	Tennessee	4,348	0.5%
2	Texas	178,968	20.4%
20	Utah	6,952	0.8%
50	Vermont	32	0.0%
14	Virginia	9,790	1.1%
12	Washington	12,349	1.4%
49	West Virginia	84	0.0%
23	Wisconsin	5,295	0.6%
43	Wyoming	622	0.1%

RANK ORDER

RANK	STATE	BIRTHS	% of USA
1	California	263,061	30.0%
2	Texas	178,968	20.4%
3	New York	54,700	6.2%
4	Florida	51,619	5.9%
5	Illinois	41,022	4.7%
6	Arizona	37,938	4.3%
7	New Jersey	24,664	2.8%
8	Colorado	21,029	2.4%
9	Georgia	16,819	1.9%
10	North Carolina	15,064	1.7%
11	New Mexico	14,623	1.7%
12	Washington	12,349	1.4%
13	Nevada	11,386	1.3%
14	Virginia	9,790	1.1%
15	Massachusetts	9,592	1.1%
16	Pennsylvania	8,696	1.0%
17	Oregon	8,040	0.9%
18	Michigan	7,265	0.8%
19	Connecticut	6,982	0.8%
20	Utah	6,952	0.8%
21	Indiana	6,169	0.7%
22	Maryland	6,062	0.7%
23	Wisconsin	5,295	0.6%
24	Oklahoma	5,259	0.6%
25	Kansas	5,023	0.6%
26	Ohio	4,817	0.5%
27	Minnesota	4,646	0.5%
28	Tennessee	4,348	0.5%
29	Nebraska	3,313	0.4%
30	Missouri	3,267	0.4%
31	South Carolina	3,175	0.4%
32	Arkansas	3,050	0.3%
33	Idaho	2,788	0.3%
34	Alabama	2,569	0.3%
35	Hawaii	2,422	0.3%
36	Iowa	2,390	0.3%
37	Rhode Island	2,328	0.3%
38	Kentucky	1,630	0.2%
39	Louisiana	1,383	0.2%
40	Delaware	1,316	0.2%
41	Mississippi	823	0.1%
42	Alaska	799	0.1%
43	Wyoming	622	0.1%
44	New Hampshire	503	0.1%
45	Montana	382	0.0%
46	South Dakota	318	0.0%
47	Maine	167	0.0%
48	North Dakota	149	0.0%
49	West Virginia	84	0.0%
50	Vermont	32	0.0%
	District of Columbia	954	0.1%

Source: U.S. Department of Health and Human Services, National Center for Health Statistics
"National Vital Statistics Reports" (Vol. 52, No. 10, December 17, 2003)
*Final data by state of residence. By race of mother. Persons of Hispanic origin may be of any race.

Hispanic Births as a Percent of All Births in 2002

National Percent = 21.8% of Live Births*

RANK	STATE	PERCENT
38	Alabama	4.4
29	Alaska	8.0
4	Arizona	43.2
28	Arkansas	8.1
2	California	49.7
6	Colorado	30.7
13	Connecticut	16.6
22	Delaware	11.9
7	Florida	25.1
21	Georgia	12.6
16	Hawaii	13.9
17	Idaho	13.3
8	Illinois	22.7
31	Indiana	7.3
33	Iowa	6.4
20	Kansas	12.7
43	Kentucky	3.0
45	Louisiana	2.1
48	Maine	1.2
27	Maryland	8.3
22	Massachusetts	11.9
36	Michigan	5.6
32	Minnesota	6.8
46	Mississippi	2.0
39	Missouri	4.3
40	Montana	3.5
18	Nebraska	13.1
5	Nevada	35.0
40	New Hampshire	3.5
10	New Jersey	21.5
1	New Mexico	52.7
9	New York	21.8
19	North Carolina	12.8
47	North Dakota	1.9
42	Ohio	3.2
24	Oklahoma	10.4
12	Oregon	17.8
34	Pennsylvania	6.1
11	Rhode Island	18.1
35	South Carolina	5.8
43	South Dakota	3.0
36	Tennessee	5.6
3	Texas	48.1
15	Utah	14.1
49	Vermont	0.5
25	Virginia	9.8
14	Washington	15.6
50	West Virginia	0.4
30	Wisconsin	7.7
26	Wyoming	9.5

RANK	STATE	PERCENT
1	New Mexico	52.7
2	California	49.7
3	Texas	48.1
4	Arizona	43.2
5	Nevada	35.0
6	Colorado	30.7
7	Florida	25.1
8	Illinois	22.7
9	New York	21.8
10	New Jersey	21.5
11	Rhode Island	18.1
12	Oregon	17.8
13	Connecticut	16.6
14	Washington	15.6
15	Utah	14.1
16	Hawaii	13.9
17	Idaho	13.3
18	Nebraska	13.1
19	North Carolina	12.8
20	Kansas	12.7
21	Georgia	12.6
22	Delaware	11.9
22	Massachusetts	11.9
24	Oklahoma	10.4
25	Virginia	9.8
26	Wyoming	9.5
27	Maryland	8.3
28	Arkansas	8.1
29	Alaska	8.0
30	Wisconsin	7.7
31	Indiana	7.3
32	Minnesota	6.8
33	Iowa	6.4
34	Pennsylvania	6.1
35	South Carolina	5.8
36	Michigan	5.6
36	Tennessee	5.6
38	Alabama	4.4
39	Missouri	4.3
40	Montana	3.5
40	New Hampshire	3.5
42	Ohio	3.2
43	Kentucky	3.0
43	South Dakota	3.0
45	Louisiana	2.1
46	Mississippi	2.0
47	North Dakota	1.9
48	Maine	1.2
49	Vermont	0.5
50	West Virginia	0.4

	District of Columbia	12.7

Source: Morgan Quitno Press using data from U.S. Dept. of Health and Human Services, Nat'l Center for Health Statistics "National Vital Statistics Reports" (Vol. 52, No. 10, December 17, 2003)

*Final data by state of residence. By race of mother. Persons of Hispanic origin may be of any race.

Births of Low Birthweight in 2002

National Total = 314,077 Live Births*

ALPHA ORDER

RANK	STATE	BIRTHS	% of USA
21	Alabama	5,825	1.9%
47	Alaska	579	0.2%
20	Arizona	5,938	1.9%
30	Arkansas	3,204	1.0%
1	California	33,824	10.8%
17	Colorado	6,067	1.9%
29	Connecticut	3,258	1.0%
41	Delaware	1,102	0.4%
4	Florida	17,320	5.5%
7	Georgia	11,915	3.8%
39	Hawaii	1,450	0.5%
40	Idaho	1,284	0.4%
5	Illinois	14,725	4.7%
16	Indiana	6,463	2.1%
34	Iowa	2,489	0.8%
32	Kansas	2,757	0.9%
23	Kentucky	4,657	1.5%
14	Louisiana	6,774	2.2%
44	Maine	853	0.3%
15	Maryland	6,607	2.1%
18	Massachusetts	6,046	1.9%
10	Michigan	10,363	3.3%
27	Minnesota	4,251	1.4%
24	Mississippi	4,635	1.5%
19	Missouri	6,034	1.9%
46	Montana	755	0.2%
38	Nebraska	1,817	0.6%
35	Nevada	2,445	0.8%
43	New Hampshire	914	0.3%
11	New Jersey	9,185	2.9%
36	New Mexico	2,225	0.7%
3	New York	19,802	6.3%
9	North Carolina	10,514	3.3%
49	North Dakota	486	0.2%
6	Ohio	12,334	3.9%
28	Oklahoma	4,019	1.3%
33	Oregon	2,608	0.8%
8	Pennsylvania	11,685	3.7%
42	Rhode Island	1,019	0.3%
22	South Carolina	5,455	1.7%
45	South Dakota	765	0.2%
13	Tennessee	7,106	2.3%
2	Texas	28,646	9.1%
31	Utah	3,164	1.0%
50	Vermont	409	0.1%
12	Virginia	7,888	2.5%
25	Washington	4,604	1.5%
37	West Virginia	1,855	0.6%
26	Wisconsin	4,538	1.4%
48	Wyoming	553	0.2%

RANK ORDER

RANK	STATE	BIRTHS	% of USA
1	California	33,824	10.8%
2	Texas	28,646	9.1%
3	New York	19,802	6.3%
4	Florida	17,320	5.5%
5	Illinois	14,725	4.7%
6	Ohio	12,334	3.9%
7	Georgia	11,915	3.8%
8	Pennsylvania	11,685	3.7%
9	North Carolina	10,514	3.3%
10	Michigan	10,363	3.3%
11	New Jersey	9,185	2.9%
12	Virginia	7,888	2.5%
13	Tennessee	7,106	2.3%
14	Louisiana	6,774	2.2%
15	Maryland	6,607	2.1%
16	Indiana	6,463	2.1%
17	Colorado	6,067	1.9%
18	Massachusetts	6,046	1.9%
19	Missouri	6,034	1.9%
20	Arizona	5,938	1.9%
21	Alabama	5,825	1.9%
22	South Carolina	5,455	1.7%
23	Kentucky	4,657	1.5%
24	Mississippi	4,635	1.5%
25	Washington	4,604	1.5%
26	Wisconsin	4,538	1.4%
27	Minnesota	4,251	1.4%
28	Oklahoma	4,019	1.3%
29	Connecticut	3,258	1.0%
30	Arkansas	3,204	1.0%
31	Utah	3,164	1.0%
32	Kansas	2,757	0.9%
33	Oregon	2,608	0.8%
34	Iowa	2,489	0.8%
35	Nevada	2,445	0.8%
36	New Mexico	2,225	0.7%
37	West Virginia	1,855	0.6%
38	Nebraska	1,817	0.6%
39	Hawaii	1,450	0.5%
40	Idaho	1,284	0.4%
41	Delaware	1,102	0.4%
42	Rhode Island	1,019	0.3%
43	New Hampshire	914	0.3%
44	Maine	853	0.3%
45	South Dakota	765	0.2%
46	Montana	755	0.2%
47	Alaska	579	0.2%
48	Wyoming	553	0.2%
49	North Dakota	486	0.2%
50	Vermont	409	0.1%
	District of Columbia	866	0.3%

Source: U.S. Department of Health and Human Services, National Center for Health Statistics
"National Vital Statistics Reports" (Vol. 52, No. 10, December 17, 2003)
Final data by state of residence. Births of less than 2,500 grams (5 pounds 8 ounces).

Births of Low Birthweight as a Percent of All Births in 2002

National Percent = 7.8% of Live Births*

ALPHA ORDER

RANK	STATE	PERCENT
4	Alabama	9.9
49	Alaska	5.8
36	Arizona	6.8
12	Arkansas	8.6
40	California	6.4
10	Colorado	8.9
28	Connecticut	7.8
4	Delaware	9.9
14	Florida	8.4
10	Georgia	8.9
16	Hawaii	8.3
47	Idaho	6.1
18	Illinois	8.2
30	Indiana	7.6
38	Iowa	6.6
35	Kansas	7.0
12	Kentucky	8.6
2	Louisiana	10.4
43	Maine	6.3
7	Maryland	9.0
31	Massachusetts	7.5
20	Michigan	8.0
43	Minnesota	6.3
1	Mississippi	11.2
20	Missouri	8.0
36	Montana	6.8
33	Nebraska	7.2
31	Nevada	7.5
43	New Hampshire	6.3
20	New Jersey	8.0
20	New Mexico	8.0
25	New York	7.9
7	North Carolina	9.0
43	North Dakota	6.3
16	Ohio	8.3
20	Oklahoma	8.0
49	Oregon	5.8
18	Pennsylvania	8.2
25	Rhode Island	7.9
3	South Carolina	10.0
33	South Dakota	7.2
6	Tennessee	9.2
29	Texas	7.7
40	Utah	6.4
40	Vermont	6.4
25	Virginia	7.9
48	Washington	5.9
7	West Virginia	9.0
38	Wisconsin	6.6
14	Wyoming	8.4

RANK ORDER

RANK	STATE	PERCENT
1	Mississippi	11.2
2	Louisiana	10.4
3	South Carolina	10.0
4	Alabama	9.9
4	Delaware	9.9
6	Tennessee	9.2
7	Maryland	9.0
7	North Carolina	9.0
7	West Virginia	9.0
10	Colorado	8.9
10	Georgia	8.9
12	Arkansas	8.6
12	Kentucky	8.6
14	Florida	8.4
14	Wyoming	8.4
16	Hawaii	8.3
16	Ohio	8.3
18	Illinois	8.2
18	Pennsylvania	8.2
20	Michigan	8.0
20	Missouri	8.0
20	New Jersey	8.0
20	New Mexico	8.0
20	Oklahoma	8.0
25	New York	7.9
25	Rhode Island	7.9
25	Virginia	7.9
28	Connecticut	7.8
29	Texas	7.7
30	Indiana	7.6
31	Massachusetts	7.5
31	Nevada	7.5
33	Nebraska	7.2
33	South Dakota	7.2
35	Kansas	7.0
36	Arizona	6.8
36	Montana	6.8
38	Iowa	6.6
38	Wisconsin	6.6
40	California	6.4
40	Utah	6.4
40	Vermont	6.4
43	Maine	6.3
43	Minnesota	6.3
43	New Hampshire	6.3
43	North Dakota	6.3
47	Idaho	6.1
48	Washington	5.9
49	Alaska	5.8
49	Oregon	5.8

	District of Columbia	11.6

Source: U.S. Department of Health and Human Services, National Center for Health Statistics
"National Vital Statistics Reports" (Vol. 52, No. 10, December 17, 2003)
*Final data by state of residence. Births of less than 2,500 grams (5 pounds 8 ounces).

Births of Low Birthweight to White Women in 2002

National Total = 215,799 Live Births*

ALPHA ORDER

RANK	STATE	BIRTHS	% of USA
24	Alabama	3,140	1.5%
49	Alaska	331	0.2%
14	Arizona	5,039	2.3%
33	Arkansas	2,136	1.0%
1	California	25,064	11.6%
12	Colorado	5,338	2.5%
29	Connecticut	2,406	1.1%
43	Delaware	651	0.3%
4	Florida	10,902	5.1%
11	Georgia	5,840	2.7%
50	Hawaii	278	0.1%
39	Idaho	1,228	0.6%
5	Illinois	9,451	4.4%
13	Indiana	5,140	2.4%
32	Iowa	2,277	1.1%
30	Kansas	2,312	1.1%
19	Kentucky	3,875	1.8%
27	Louisiana	2,749	1.3%
42	Maine	822	0.4%
23	Maryland	3,145	1.5%
15	Massachusetts	4,663	2.2%
8	Michigan	6,869	3.2%
22	Minnesota	3,343	1.5%
36	Mississippi	1,824	0.8%
18	Missouri	4,365	2.0%
44	Montana	634	0.3%
38	Nebraska	1,538	0.7%
35	Nevada	1,843	0.9%
40	New Hampshire	866	0.4%
10	New Jersey	5,846	2.7%
34	New Mexico	1,871	0.9%
3	New York	12,276	5.7%
9	North Carolina	6,238	2.9%
47	North Dakota	412	0.2%
6	Ohio	8,927	4.1%
25	Oklahoma	2,946	1.4%
31	Oregon	2,290	1.1%
7	Pennsylvania	8,463	3.9%
41	Rhode Island	823	0.4%
28	South Carolina	2,672	1.2%
45	South Dakota	604	0.3%
17	Tennessee	4,593	2.1%
2	Texas	22,264	10.3%
26	Utah	2,938	1.4%
48	Vermont	406	0.2%
16	Virginia	4,615	2.1%
20	Washington	3,646	1.7%
37	West Virginia	1,741	0.8%
21	Wisconsin	3,462	1.6%
46	Wyoming	511	0.2%

RANK ORDER

RANK	STATE	BIRTHS	% of USA
1	California	25,064	11.6%
2	Texas	22,264	10.3%
3	New York	12,276	5.7%
4	Florida	10,902	5.1%
5	Illinois	9,451	4.4%
6	Ohio	8,927	4.1%
7	Pennsylvania	8,463	3.9%
8	Michigan	6,869	3.2%
9	North Carolina	6,238	2.9%
10	New Jersey	5,846	2.7%
11	Georgia	5,840	2.7%
12	Colorado	5,338	2.5%
13	Indiana	5,140	2.4%
14	Arizona	5,039	2.3%
15	Massachusetts	4,663	2.2%
16	Virginia	4,615	2.1%
17	Tennessee	4,593	2.1%
18	Missouri	4,365	2.0%
19	Kentucky	3,875	1.8%
20	Washington	3,646	1.7%
21	Wisconsin	3,462	1.6%
22	Minnesota	3,343	1.5%
23	Maryland	3,145	1.5%
24	Alabama	3,140	1.5%
25	Oklahoma	2,946	1.4%
26	Utah	2,938	1.4%
27	Louisiana	2,749	1.3%
28	South Carolina	2,672	1.2%
29	Connecticut	2,406	1.1%
30	Kansas	2,312	1.1%
31	Oregon	2,290	1.1%
32	Iowa	2,277	1.1%
33	Arkansas	2,136	1.0%
34	New Mexico	1,871	0.9%
35	Nevada	1,843	0.9%
36	Mississippi	1,824	0.8%
37	West Virginia	1,741	0.8%
38	Nebraska	1,538	0.7%
39	Idaho	1,228	0.6%
40	New Hampshire	866	0.4%
41	Rhode Island	823	0.4%
42	Maine	822	0.4%
43	Delaware	651	0.3%
44	Montana	634	0.3%
45	South Dakota	604	0.3%
46	Wyoming	511	0.2%
47	North Dakota	412	0.2%
48	Vermont	406	0.2%
49	Alaska	331	0.2%
50	Hawaii	278	0.1%
	District of Columbia	186	0.1%

Source: U.S. Department of Health and Human Services, National Center for Health Statistics
    "National Vital Statistics Reports" (Vol. 52, No. 10, December 17, 2003)
*Final data by state of residence. Births of less than 2,500 grams (5 pounds 8 ounces).

Births of Low Birthweight to White Women
As a Percent of All Births to White Women in 2002
National Percent = 6.8% of Live Births to White Women*

ALPHA ORDER

RANK ORDER

RANK	STATE	PERCENT	RANK	STATE	PERCENT
8	Alabama	7.9	1	West Virginia	8.8
50	Alaska	5.2	2	Colorado	8.6
36	Arizona	6.5	3	Wyoming	8.3
14	Arkansas	7.3	4	Delaware	8.2
46	California	5.8	5	Mississippi	8.1
2	Colorado	8.6	6	Kentucky	8.0
25	Connecticut	6.9	6	New Mexico	8.0
4	Delaware	8.2	8	Alabama	7.9
18	Florida	7.1	9	Tennessee	7.7
28	Georgia	6.8	10	South Carolina	7.6
19	Hawaii	7.0	11	Louisiana	7.5
43	Idaho	6.1	11	Oklahoma	7.5
31	Illinois	6.7	11	Rhode Island	7.5
25	Indiana	6.9	14	Arkansas	7.3
36	Iowa	6.5	14	North Carolina	7.3
35	Kansas	6.6	14	Ohio	7.3
6	Kentucky	8.0	17	Pennsylvania	7.2
11	Louisiana	7.5	18	Florida	7.1
40	Maine	6.3	19	Hawaii	7.0
19	Maryland	7.0	19	Maryland	7.0
19	Massachusetts	7.0	19	Massachusetts	7.0
31	Michigan	6.7	19	Missouri	7.0
46	Minnesota	5.8	19	South Dakota	7.0
5	Mississippi	8.1	19	Texas	7.0
19	Missouri	7.0	25	Connecticut	6.9
31	Montana	6.7	25	Indiana	6.9
31	Nebraska	6.7	25	New Jersey	6.9
28	Nevada	6.8	28	Georgia	6.8
40	New Hampshire	6.3	28	Nevada	6.8
25	New Jersey	6.9	28	New York	6.8
6	New Mexico	8.0	31	Illinois	6.7
28	New York	6.8	31	Michigan	6.7
14	North Carolina	7.3	31	Montana	6.7
43	North Dakota	6.1	31	Nebraska	6.7
14	Ohio	7.3	35	Kansas	6.6
11	Oklahoma	7.5	36	Arizona	6.5
48	Oregon	5.6	36	Iowa	6.5
17	Pennsylvania	7.2	36	Vermont	6.5
11	Rhode Island	7.5	36	Virginia	6.5
10	South Carolina	7.6	40	Maine	6.3
19	South Dakota	7.0	40	New Hampshire	6.3
9	Tennessee	7.7	40	Utah	6.3
19	Texas	7.0	43	Idaho	6.1
40	Utah	6.3	43	North Dakota	6.1
36	Vermont	6.5	45	Wisconsin	5.9
36	Virginia	6.5	46	California	5.8
49	Washington	5.5	46	Minnesota	5.8
1	West Virginia	8.8	48	Oregon	5.6
45	Wisconsin	5.9	49	Washington	5.5
3	Wyoming	8.3	50	Alaska	5.2

District of Columbia   7.0

*Source: U.S. Department of Health and Human Services, National Center for Health Statistics
"National Vital Statistics Reports" (Vol. 52, No. 10, December 17, 2003)*
Final data by state of residence. Births of less than 2,500 grams (5 pounds 8 ounces).

Births of Low Birthweight to Black Women in 2002

National Total = 78,813 Live Births*

ALPHA ORDER

RANK	STATE	BIRTHS	% of USA
16	Alabama	2,626	3.3%
42	Alaska	48	0.1%
33	Arizona	326	0.4%
21	Arkansas	1,008	1.3%
8	California	3,765	4.8%
28	Colorado	422	0.5%
25	Connecticut	652	0.8%
29	Delaware	403	0.5%
2	Florida	5,889	7.5%
3	Georgia	5,672	7.2%
40	Hawaii	49	0.1%
45	Idaho	12	0.0%
5	Illinois	4,545	5.8%
20	Indiana	1,205	1.5%
35	Iowa	130	0.2%
31	Kansas	354	0.4%
24	Kentucky	711	0.9%
6	Louisiana	3,905	5.0%
44	Maine	16	0.0%
9	Maryland	3,178	4.0%
22	Massachusetts	933	1.2%
10	Michigan	3,120	4.0%
27	Minnesota	520	0.7%
14	Mississippi	2,767	3.5%
19	Missouri	1,527	1.9%
49	Montana	6	0.0%
34	Nebraska	196	0.2%
30	Nevada	379	0.5%
43	New Hampshire	18	0.0%
17	New Jersey	2,546	3.2%
39	New Mexico	71	0.1%
1	New York	5,945	7.5%
7	North Carolina	3,875	4.9%
45	North Dakota	12	0.0%
11	Ohio	3,118	4.0%
25	Oklahoma	652	0.8%
38	Oregon	90	0.1%
12	Pennsylvania	2,839	3.6%
36	Rhode Island	123	0.2%
15	South Carolina	2,679	3.4%
45	South Dakota	12	0.0%
18	Tennessee	2,370	3.0%
4	Texas	5,301	6.7%
40	Utah	49	0.1%
50	Vermont	0	0.0%
13	Virginia	2,781	3.5%
32	Washington	344	0.4%
37	West Virginia	96	0.1%
23	Wisconsin	848	1.1%
48	Wyoming	7	0.0%

RANK ORDER

RANK	STATE	BIRTHS	% of USA
1	New York	5,945	7.5%
2	Florida	5,889	7.5%
3	Georgia	5,672	7.2%
4	Texas	5,301	6.7%
5	Illinois	4,545	5.8%
6	Louisiana	3,905	5.0%
7	North Carolina	3,875	4.9%
8	California	3,765	4.8%
9	Maryland	3,178	4.0%
10	Michigan	3,120	4.0%
11	Ohio	3,118	4.0%
12	Pennsylvania	2,839	3.6%
13	Virginia	2,781	3.5%
14	Mississippi	2,767	3.5%
15	South Carolina	2,679	3.4%
16	Alabama	2,626	3.3%
17	New Jersey	2,546	3.2%
18	Tennessee	2,370	3.0%
19	Missouri	1,527	1.9%
20	Indiana	1,205	1.5%
21	Arkansas	1,008	1.3%
22	Massachusetts	933	1.2%
23	Wisconsin	848	1.1%
24	Kentucky	711	0.9%
25	Connecticut	652	0.8%
25	Oklahoma	652	0.8%
27	Minnesota	520	0.7%
28	Colorado	422	0.5%
29	Delaware	403	0.5%
30	Nevada	379	0.5%
31	Kansas	354	0.4%
32	Washington	344	0.4%
33	Arizona	326	0.4%
34	Nebraska	196	0.2%
35	Iowa	130	0.2%
36	Rhode Island	123	0.2%
37	West Virginia	96	0.1%
38	Oregon	90	0.1%
39	New Mexico	71	0.1%
40	Hawaii	49	0.1%
40	Utah	49	0.1%
42	Alaska	48	0.1%
43	New Hampshire	18	0.0%
44	Maine	16	0.0%
45	Idaho	12	0.0%
45	North Dakota	12	0.0%
45	South Dakota	12	0.0%
48	Wyoming	7	0.0%
49	Montana	6	0.0%
50	Vermont	0	0.0%
	District of Columbia	673	0.9%

Source: U.S. Department of Health and Human Services, National Center for Health Statistics
   "National Vital Statistics Reports" (Vol. 52, No. 10, December 17, 2003)
*Final data by state of residence. Births of less than 2,500 grams (5 pounds 8 ounces).

Births of Low Birthweight to Black Women
As a Percent of All Births to Black Women in 2002
National Percent = 13.3% of Live Births to Black Women*

ALPHA ORDER				RANK ORDER		
RANK	STATE	PERCENT		RANK	STATE	PERCENT
8	Alabama	14.4		1	Mississippi	15.2
36	Alaska	11.1		2	Delaware	14.9
33	Arizona	11.7		3	Louisiana	14.7
20	Arkansas	13.6		3	South Carolina	14.7
34	California	11.5		5	Tennessee	14.6
8	Colorado	14.4		6	Nevada	14.5
29	Connecticut	12.6		6	Utah	14.5
2	Delaware	14.9		8	Alabama	14.4
27	Florida	12.7		8	Colorado	14.4
22	Georgia	13.3		8	Kentucky	14.4
39	Hawaii	10.3		11	Illinois	14.3
NA	Idaho**	NA		12	West Virginia	14.2
11	Illinois	14.3		13	North Carolina	14.1
25	Indiana	13.0		14	Pennsylvania	14.0
39	Iowa	10.3		15	Michigan	13.9
31	Kansas	12.3		15	Missouri	13.9
8	Kentucky	14.4		15	New Mexico	13.9
3	Louisiana	14.7		15	Oklahoma	13.9
NA	Maine**	NA		19	Ohio	13.8
24	Maryland	13.1		20	Arkansas	13.6
35	Massachusetts	11.2		20	Nebraska	13.6
15	Michigan	13.9		22	Georgia	13.3
38	Minnesota	10.7		23	Wisconsin	13.2
1	Mississippi	15.2		24	Maryland	13.1
15	Missouri	13.9		25	Indiana	13.0
NA	Montana**	NA		26	New Jersey	12.8
20	Nebraska	13.6		27	Florida	12.7
6	Nevada	14.5		27	Texas	12.7
NA	New Hampshire**	NA		29	Connecticut	12.6
26	New Jersey	12.8		29	Virginia	12.6
15	New Mexico	13.9		31	Kansas	12.3
32	New York	12.0		32	New York	12.0
13	North Carolina	14.1		33	Arizona	11.7
NA	North Dakota**	NA		34	California	11.5
19	Ohio	13.8		35	Massachusetts	11.2
15	Oklahoma	13.9		36	Alaska	11.1
42	Oregon	9.6		37	Rhode Island	10.8
14	Pennsylvania	14.0		38	Minnesota	10.7
37	Rhode Island	10.8		39	Hawaii	10.3
3	South Carolina	14.7		39	Iowa	10.3
NA	South Dakota**	NA		41	Washington	10.2
5	Tennessee	14.6		42	Oregon	9.6
27	Texas	12.7		NA	Idaho**	NA
6	Utah	14.5		NA	Maine**	NA
NA	Vermont**	NA		NA	Montana**	NA
29	Virginia	12.6		NA	New Hampshire**	NA
41	Washington	10.2		NA	North Dakota**	NA
12	West Virginia	14.2		NA	South Dakota**	NA
23	Wisconsin	13.2		NA	Vermont**	NA
NA	Wyoming**	NA		NA	Wyoming**	NA
					District of Columbia	14.6

Source: U.S. Department of Health and Human Services, National Center for Health Statistics
   "National Vital Statistics Reports" (Vol. 52, No. 10, December 17, 2003)
*Final data by state of residence. Births of less than 2,500 grams (5 pounds 8 ounces).
**Not available. Fewer than 20 births of low birthweight to black women.

Births of Low Birthweight to Hispanic Women in 2002

National Total = 57,383 Live Births*

<table>
<tr><td colspan="4">ALPHA ORDER</td><td colspan="4">RANK ORDER</td></tr>
<tr><th>RANK</th><th>STATE</th><th>BIRTHS</th><th>% of USA</th><th>RANK</th><th>STATE</th><th>BIRTHS</th><th>% of USA</th></tr>
<tr><td>33</td><td>Alabama</td><td>189</td><td>0.3%</td><td>1</td><td>California</td><td>15,134</td><td>26.4%</td></tr>
<tr><td>42</td><td>Alaska</td><td>51</td><td>0.1%</td><td>2</td><td>Texas</td><td>12,534</td><td>21.8%</td></tr>
<tr><td>6</td><td>Arizona</td><td>2,415</td><td>4.2%</td><td>3</td><td>New York</td><td>4,077</td><td>7.1%</td></tr>
<tr><td>36</td><td>Arkansas</td><td>169</td><td>0.3%</td><td>4</td><td>Florida</td><td>3,503</td><td>6.1%</td></tr>
<tr><td>1</td><td>California</td><td>15,134</td><td>26.4%</td><td>5</td><td>Illinois</td><td>2,530</td><td>4.4%</td></tr>
<tr><td>7</td><td>Colorado</td><td>1,777</td><td>3.1%</td><td>6</td><td>Arizona</td><td>2,415</td><td>4.2%</td></tr>
<tr><td>17</td><td>Connecticut</td><td>560</td><td>1.0%</td><td>7</td><td>Colorado</td><td>1,777</td><td>3.1%</td></tr>
<tr><td>39</td><td>Delaware</td><td>97</td><td>0.2%</td><td>8</td><td>New Jersey</td><td>1,753</td><td>3.1%</td></tr>
<tr><td>4</td><td>Florida</td><td>3,503</td><td>6.1%</td><td>9</td><td>New Mexico</td><td>1,200</td><td>2.1%</td></tr>
<tr><td>10</td><td>Georgia</td><td>1,015</td><td>1.8%</td><td>10</td><td>Georgia</td><td>1,015</td><td>1.8%</td></tr>
<tr><td>29</td><td>Hawaii</td><td>218</td><td>0.4%</td><td>11</td><td>North Carolina</td><td>923</td><td>1.6%</td></tr>
<tr><td>34</td><td>Idaho</td><td>184</td><td>0.3%</td><td>12</td><td>Massachusetts</td><td>813</td><td>1.4%</td></tr>
<tr><td>5</td><td>Illinois</td><td>2,530</td><td>4.4%</td><td>13</td><td>Pennsylvania</td><td>798</td><td>1.4%</td></tr>
<tr><td>22</td><td>Indiana</td><td>388</td><td>0.7%</td><td>14</td><td>Nevada</td><td>738</td><td>1.3%</td></tr>
<tr><td>37</td><td>Iowa</td><td>149</td><td>0.3%</td><td>15</td><td>Washington</td><td>651</td><td>1.1%</td></tr>
<tr><td>26</td><td>Kansas</td><td>299</td><td>0.5%</td><td>16</td><td>Virginia</td><td>605</td><td>1.1%</td></tr>
<tr><td>38</td><td>Kentucky</td><td>132</td><td>0.2%</td><td>17</td><td>Connecticut</td><td>560</td><td>1.0%</td></tr>
<tr><td>40</td><td>Louisiana</td><td>79</td><td>0.1%</td><td>18</td><td>Michigan</td><td>458</td><td>0.8%</td></tr>
<tr><td>47</td><td>Maine</td><td>11</td><td>0.0%</td><td>19</td><td>Utah</td><td>451</td><td>0.8%</td></tr>
<tr><td>21</td><td>Maryland</td><td>418</td><td>0.7%</td><td>20</td><td>Oregon</td><td>428</td><td>0.7%</td></tr>
<tr><td>12</td><td>Massachusetts</td><td>813</td><td>1.4%</td><td>21</td><td>Maryland</td><td>418</td><td>0.7%</td></tr>
<tr><td>18</td><td>Michigan</td><td>458</td><td>0.8%</td><td>22</td><td>Indiana</td><td>388</td><td>0.7%</td></tr>
<tr><td>27</td><td>Minnesota</td><td>284</td><td>0.5%</td><td>23</td><td>Oklahoma</td><td>367</td><td>0.6%</td></tr>
<tr><td>43</td><td>Mississippi</td><td>47</td><td>0.1%</td><td>24</td><td>Ohio</td><td>351</td><td>0.6%</td></tr>
<tr><td>31</td><td>Missouri</td><td>210</td><td>0.4%</td><td>25</td><td>Wisconsin</td><td>302</td><td>0.5%</td></tr>
<tr><td>44</td><td>Montana</td><td>25</td><td>0.0%</td><td>26</td><td>Kansas</td><td>299</td><td>0.5%</td></tr>
<tr><td>32</td><td>Nebraska</td><td>202</td><td>0.4%</td><td>27</td><td>Minnesota</td><td>284</td><td>0.5%</td></tr>
<tr><td>14</td><td>Nevada</td><td>738</td><td>1.3%</td><td>28</td><td>Tennessee</td><td>253</td><td>0.4%</td></tr>
<tr><td>46</td><td>New Hampshire</td><td>20</td><td>0.0%</td><td>29</td><td>Hawaii</td><td>218</td><td>0.4%</td></tr>
<tr><td>8</td><td>New Jersey</td><td>1,753</td><td>3.1%</td><td>30</td><td>South Carolina</td><td>216</td><td>0.4%</td></tr>
<tr><td>9</td><td>New Mexico</td><td>1,200</td><td>2.1%</td><td>31</td><td>Missouri</td><td>210</td><td>0.4%</td></tr>
<tr><td>3</td><td>New York</td><td>4,077</td><td>7.1%</td><td>32</td><td>Nebraska</td><td>202</td><td>0.4%</td></tr>
<tr><td>11</td><td>North Carolina</td><td>923</td><td>1.6%</td><td>33</td><td>Alabama</td><td>189</td><td>0.3%</td></tr>
<tr><td>47</td><td>North Dakota</td><td>11</td><td>0.0%</td><td>34</td><td>Idaho</td><td>184</td><td>0.3%</td></tr>
<tr><td>24</td><td>Ohio</td><td>351</td><td>0.6%</td><td>35</td><td>Rhode Island</td><td>173</td><td>0.3%</td></tr>
<tr><td>23</td><td>Oklahoma</td><td>367</td><td>0.6%</td><td>36</td><td>Arkansas</td><td>169</td><td>0.3%</td></tr>
<tr><td>20</td><td>Oregon</td><td>428</td><td>0.7%</td><td>37</td><td>Iowa</td><td>149</td><td>0.3%</td></tr>
<tr><td>13</td><td>Pennsylvania</td><td>798</td><td>1.4%</td><td>38</td><td>Kentucky</td><td>132</td><td>0.2%</td></tr>
<tr><td>35</td><td>Rhode Island</td><td>173</td><td>0.3%</td><td>39</td><td>Delaware</td><td>97</td><td>0.2%</td></tr>
<tr><td>30</td><td>South Carolina</td><td>216</td><td>0.4%</td><td>40</td><td>Louisiana</td><td>79</td><td>0.1%</td></tr>
<tr><td>45</td><td>South Dakota</td><td>24</td><td>0.0%</td><td>41</td><td>Wyoming</td><td>54</td><td>0.1%</td></tr>
<tr><td>28</td><td>Tennessee</td><td>253</td><td>0.4%</td><td>42</td><td>Alaska</td><td>51</td><td>0.1%</td></tr>
<tr><td>2</td><td>Texas</td><td>12,534</td><td>21.8%</td><td>43</td><td>Mississippi</td><td>47</td><td>0.1%</td></tr>
<tr><td>19</td><td>Utah</td><td>451</td><td>0.8%</td><td>44</td><td>Montana</td><td>25</td><td>0.0%</td></tr>
<tr><td>50</td><td>Vermont</td><td>2</td><td>0.0%</td><td>45</td><td>South Dakota</td><td>24</td><td>0.0%</td></tr>
<tr><td>16</td><td>Virginia</td><td>605</td><td>1.1%</td><td>46</td><td>New Hampshire</td><td>20</td><td>0.0%</td></tr>
<tr><td>15</td><td>Washington</td><td>651</td><td>1.1%</td><td>47</td><td>Maine</td><td>11</td><td>0.0%</td></tr>
<tr><td>49</td><td>West Virginia</td><td>7</td><td>0.0%</td><td>47</td><td>North Dakota</td><td>11</td><td>0.0%</td></tr>
<tr><td>25</td><td>Wisconsin</td><td>302</td><td>0.5%</td><td>49</td><td>West Virginia</td><td>7</td><td>0.0%</td></tr>
<tr><td>41</td><td>Wyoming</td><td>54</td><td>0.1%</td><td>50</td><td>Vermont</td><td>2</td><td>0.0%</td></tr>
<tr><td></td><td></td><td></td><td></td><td></td><td>District of Columbia</td><td>88</td><td>0.2%</td></tr>
</table>

Source: U.S. Department of Health and Human Services, National Center for Health Statistics
   "National Vital Statistics Reports" (Vol. 52, No. 10, December 17, 2003)
*Final data by state of residence. Births of less than 2,500 grams (5 pounds 8 ounces). Hispanic can be of any race.

Births of Low Birthweight to Hispanic Women
As a Percent of All Births to Hispanic Women in 2002
National Percent = 6.5% of Live Births to Hispanic Women*

ALPHA ORDER

RANK ORDER

RANK	STATE	PERCENT		RANK	STATE	PERCENT
12	Alabama	7.4		1	Pennsylvania	9.2
25	Alaska	6.4		2	Hawaii	9.0
25	Arizona	6.4		3	Wyoming	8.7
43	Arkansas	5.5		4	Colorado	8.5
38	California	5.8		4	Massachusetts	8.5
4	Colorado	8.5		6	New Mexico	8.2
8	Connecticut	8.0		7	Kentucky	8.1
12	Delaware	7.4		8	Connecticut	8.0
19	Florida	6.8		9	New York	7.5
36	Georgia	6.0		9	Rhode Island	7.5
2	Hawaii	9.0		9	South Dakota	7.5
21	Idaho	6.6		12	Alabama	7.4
30	Illinois	6.2		12	Delaware	7.4
28	Indiana	6.3		14	Ohio	7.3
30	Iowa	6.2		15	New Jersey	7.1
36	Kansas	6.0		16	Oklahoma	7.0
7	Kentucky	8.1		16	Texas	7.0
40	Louisiana	5.7		18	Maryland	6.9
NA	Maine**	NA		19	Florida	6.8
18	Maryland	6.9		19	South Carolina	6.8
4	Massachusetts	8.5		21	Idaho	6.6
28	Michigan	6.3		22	Montana	6.5
33	Minnesota	6.1		22	Nevada	6.5
40	Mississippi	5.7		22	Utah	6.5
25	Missouri	6.4		25	Alaska	6.4
22	Montana	6.5		25	Arizona	6.4
33	Nebraska	6.1		25	Missouri	6.4
22	Nevada	6.5		28	Indiana	6.3
46	New Hampshire	4.0		28	Michigan	6.3
15	New Jersey	7.1		30	Illinois	6.2
6	New Mexico	8.2		30	Iowa	6.2
9	New York	7.5		30	Virginia	6.2
33	North Carolina	6.1		33	Minnesota	6.1
NA	North Dakota**	NA		33	Nebraska	6.1
14	Ohio	7.3		33	North Carolina	6.1
16	Oklahoma	7.0		36	Georgia	6.0
44	Oregon	5.3		36	Kansas	6.0
1	Pennsylvania	9.2		38	California	5.8
9	Rhode Island	7.5		38	Tennessee	5.8
19	South Carolina	6.8		40	Louisiana	5.7
9	South Dakota	7.5		40	Mississippi	5.7
38	Tennessee	5.8		40	Wisconsin	5.7
16	Texas	7.0		43	Arkansas	5.5
22	Utah	6.5		44	Oregon	5.3
NA	Vermont**	NA		44	Washington	5.3
30	Virginia	6.2		46	New Hampshire	4.0
44	Washington	5.3		NA	Maine**	NA
NA	West Virginia**	NA		NA	North Dakota**	NA
40	Wisconsin	5.7		NA	Vermont**	NA
3	Wyoming	8.7		NA	West Virginia**	NA

District of Columbia   9.2

Source: U.S. Department of Health and Human Services, National Center for Health Statistics
   "National Vital Statistics Reports" (Vol. 52, No. 10, December 17, 2003)
Final data by state of residence. Births of less than 2,500 grams (5 pounds 8 ounces). Hispanic can be of any race.
**Not available. Fewer than 20 births of low birthweight to Hispanic women.*

Births to Unmarried Women in 2002

National Total = 1,365,966 Live Births*

ALPHA ORDER

RANK	STATE	BIRTHS	% of USA
23	Alabama	20,515	1.5%
47	Alaska	3,379	0.2%
11	Arizona	35,494	2.6%
30	Arkansas	13,891	1.0%
1	California	174,681	12.8%
27	Colorado	18,320	1.3%
33	Connecticut	12,213	0.9%
42	Delaware	4,505	0.3%
4	Florida	80,843	5.9%
7	Georgia	50,401	3.7%
39	Hawaii	5,870	0.4%
41	Idaho	4,595	0.3%
5	Illinois	62,890	4.6%
13	Indiana	30,929	2.3%
35	Iowa	11,022	0.8%
32	Kansas	12,249	0.9%
28	Kentucky	18,011	1.3%
14	Louisiana	30,498	2.2%
43	Maine	4,419	0.3%
18	Maryland	25,530	1.9%
21	Massachusetts	21,620	1.6%
9	Michigan	44,366	3.2%
25	Minnesota	18,668	1.4%
24	Mississippi	19,553	1.4%
17	Missouri	26,511	1.9%
45	Montana	3,627	0.3%
37	Nebraska	7,259	0.5%
34	Nevada	12,183	0.9%
46	New Hampshire	3,546	0.3%
12	New Jersey	33,625	2.5%
31	New Mexico	13,020	1.0%
3	New York	89,840	6.6%
10	North Carolina	40,669	3.0%
48	North Dakota	2,250	0.2%
6	Ohio	52,677	3.9%
26	Oklahoma	18,357	1.3%
29	Oregon	13,976	1.0%
8	Pennsylvania	47,748	3.5%
40	Rhode Island	4,604	0.3%
20	South Carolina	22,026	1.6%
44	South Dakota	3,744	0.3%
16	Tennessee	28,039	2.1%
2	Texas	120,704	8.8%
36	Utah	8,465	0.6%
49	Vermont	2,036	0.1%
15	Virginia	30,233	2.2%
19	Washington	22,780	1.7%
38	West Virginia	6,811	0.5%
22	Wisconsin	20,551	1.5%
50	Wyoming	1,987	0.1%

RANK ORDER

RANK	STATE	BIRTHS	% of USA
1	California	174,681	12.8%
2	Texas	120,704	8.8%
3	New York	89,840	6.6%
4	Florida	80,843	5.9%
5	Illinois	62,890	4.6%
6	Ohio	52,677	3.9%
7	Georgia	50,401	3.7%
8	Pennsylvania	47,748	3.5%
9	Michigan	44,366	3.2%
10	North Carolina	40,669	3.0%
11	Arizona	35,494	2.6%
12	New Jersey	33,625	2.5%
13	Indiana	30,929	2.3%
14	Louisiana	30,498	2.2%
15	Virginia	30,233	2.2%
16	Tennessee	28,039	2.1%
17	Missouri	26,511	1.9%
18	Maryland	25,530	1.9%
19	Washington	22,780	1.7%
20	South Carolina	22,026	1.6%
21	Massachusetts	21,620	1.6%
22	Wisconsin	20,551	1.5%
23	Alabama	20,515	1.5%
24	Mississippi	19,553	1.4%
25	Minnesota	18,668	1.4%
26	Oklahoma	18,357	1.3%
27	Colorado	18,320	1.3%
28	Kentucky	18,011	1.3%
29	Oregon	13,976	1.0%
30	Arkansas	13,891	1.0%
31	New Mexico	13,020	1.0%
32	Kansas	12,249	0.9%
33	Connecticut	12,213	0.9%
34	Nevada	12,183	0.9%
35	Iowa	11,022	0.8%
36	Utah	8,465	0.6%
37	Nebraska	7,259	0.5%
38	West Virginia	6,811	0.5%
39	Hawaii	5,870	0.4%
40	Rhode Island	4,604	0.3%
41	Idaho	4,595	0.3%
42	Delaware	4,505	0.3%
43	Maine	4,419	0.3%
44	South Dakota	3,744	0.3%
45	Montana	3,627	0.3%
46	New Hampshire	3,546	0.3%
47	Alaska	3,379	0.2%
48	North Dakota	2,250	0.2%
49	Vermont	2,036	0.1%
50	Wyoming	1,987	0.1%
	District of Columbia	4,236	0.3%

Source: U.S. Department of Health and Human Services, National Center for Health Statistics
"National Vital Statistics Reports" (Vol. 52, No. 10, December 17, 2003)
*Final data by state of residence.

Births to Unmarried Women as a Percent of All Births in 2002

National Percent = 34.0% of Live Births*

<table>
<tr><td colspan="3">ALPHA ORDER</td><td colspan="3">RANK ORDER</td></tr>
<tr><td>RANK</td><td>STATE</td><td>PERCENT</td><td>RANK</td><td>STATE</td><td>PERCENT</td></tr>
<tr><td>19</td><td>Alabama</td><td>34.8</td><td>1</td><td>Mississippi</td><td>47.1</td></tr>
<tr><td>24</td><td>Alaska</td><td>34.0</td><td>2</td><td>Louisiana</td><td>47.0</td></tr>
<tr><td>5</td><td>Arizona</td><td>40.4</td><td>3</td><td>New Mexico</td><td>46.9</td></tr>
<tr><td>10</td><td>Arkansas</td><td>37.1</td><td>4</td><td>Delaware</td><td>40.6</td></tr>
<tr><td>28</td><td>California</td><td>33.0</td><td>5</td><td>Arizona</td><td>40.4</td></tr>
<tr><td>46</td><td>Colorado</td><td>26.8</td><td>5</td><td>South Carolina</td><td>40.4</td></tr>
<tr><td>41</td><td>Connecticut</td><td>29.1</td><td>7</td><td>Florida</td><td>39.3</td></tr>
<tr><td>4</td><td>Delaware</td><td>40.6</td><td>8</td><td>Georgia</td><td>37.8</td></tr>
<tr><td>7</td><td>Florida</td><td>39.3</td><td>9</td><td>Nevada</td><td>37.4</td></tr>
<tr><td>8</td><td>Georgia</td><td>37.8</td><td>10</td><td>Arkansas</td><td>37.1</td></tr>
<tr><td>25</td><td>Hawaii</td><td>33.6</td><td>11</td><td>Indiana</td><td>36.4</td></tr>
<tr><td>49</td><td>Idaho</td><td>21.9</td><td>11</td><td>Oklahoma</td><td>36.4</td></tr>
<tr><td>19</td><td>Illinois</td><td>34.8</td><td>13</td><td>Tennessee</td><td>36.2</td></tr>
<tr><td>11</td><td>Indiana</td><td>36.4</td><td>14</td><td>New York</td><td>35.7</td></tr>
<tr><td>39</td><td>Iowa</td><td>29.3</td><td>14</td><td>Rhode Island</td><td>35.7</td></tr>
<tr><td>34</td><td>Kansas</td><td>31.1</td><td>16</td><td>Ohio</td><td>35.4</td></tr>
<tr><td>27</td><td>Kentucky</td><td>33.2</td><td>17</td><td>Missouri</td><td>35.2</td></tr>
<tr><td>2</td><td>Louisiana</td><td>47.0</td><td>18</td><td>South Dakota</td><td>35.0</td></tr>
<tr><td>31</td><td>Maine</td><td>32.6</td><td>19</td><td>Alabama</td><td>34.8</td></tr>
<tr><td>19</td><td>Maryland</td><td>34.8</td><td>19</td><td>Illinois</td><td>34.8</td></tr>
<tr><td>46</td><td>Massachusetts</td><td>26.8</td><td>19</td><td>Maryland</td><td>34.8</td></tr>
<tr><td>23</td><td>Michigan</td><td>34.1</td><td>22</td><td>North Carolina</td><td>34.7</td></tr>
<tr><td>45</td><td>Minnesota</td><td>27.4</td><td>23</td><td>Michigan</td><td>34.1</td></tr>
<tr><td>1</td><td>Mississippi</td><td>47.1</td><td>24</td><td>Alaska</td><td>34.0</td></tr>
<tr><td>17</td><td>Missouri</td><td>35.2</td><td>25</td><td>Hawaii</td><td>33.6</td></tr>
<tr><td>30</td><td>Montana</td><td>32.8</td><td>26</td><td>Pennsylvania</td><td>33.4</td></tr>
<tr><td>44</td><td>Nebraska</td><td>28.6</td><td>27</td><td>Kentucky</td><td>33.2</td></tr>
<tr><td>9</td><td>Nevada</td><td>37.4</td><td>28</td><td>California</td><td>33.0</td></tr>
<tr><td>48</td><td>New Hampshire</td><td>24.6</td><td>29</td><td>West Virginia</td><td>32.9</td></tr>
<tr><td>39</td><td>New Jersey</td><td>29.3</td><td>30</td><td>Montana</td><td>32.8</td></tr>
<tr><td>3</td><td>New Mexico</td><td>46.9</td><td>31</td><td>Maine</td><td>32.6</td></tr>
<tr><td>14</td><td>New York</td><td>35.7</td><td>32</td><td>Texas</td><td>32.4</td></tr>
<tr><td>22</td><td>North Carolina</td><td>34.7</td><td>33</td><td>Vermont</td><td>31.9</td></tr>
<tr><td>42</td><td>North Dakota</td><td>29.0</td><td>34</td><td>Kansas</td><td>31.1</td></tr>
<tr><td>16</td><td>Ohio</td><td>35.4</td><td>35</td><td>Oregon</td><td>30.9</td></tr>
<tr><td>11</td><td>Oklahoma</td><td>36.4</td><td>36</td><td>Virginia</td><td>30.3</td></tr>
<tr><td>35</td><td>Oregon</td><td>30.9</td><td>36</td><td>Wyoming</td><td>30.3</td></tr>
<tr><td>26</td><td>Pennsylvania</td><td>33.4</td><td>38</td><td>Wisconsin</td><td>30.0</td></tr>
<tr><td>14</td><td>Rhode Island</td><td>35.7</td><td>39</td><td>Iowa</td><td>29.3</td></tr>
<tr><td>5</td><td>South Carolina</td><td>40.4</td><td>39</td><td>New Jersey</td><td>29.3</td></tr>
<tr><td>18</td><td>South Dakota</td><td>35.0</td><td>41</td><td>Connecticut</td><td>29.1</td></tr>
<tr><td>13</td><td>Tennessee</td><td>36.2</td><td>42</td><td>North Dakota</td><td>29.0</td></tr>
<tr><td>32</td><td>Texas</td><td>32.4</td><td>43</td><td>Washington</td><td>28.8</td></tr>
<tr><td>50</td><td>Utah</td><td>17.2</td><td>44</td><td>Nebraska</td><td>28.6</td></tr>
<tr><td>33</td><td>Vermont</td><td>31.9</td><td>45</td><td>Minnesota</td><td>27.4</td></tr>
<tr><td>36</td><td>Virginia</td><td>30.3</td><td>46</td><td>Colorado</td><td>26.8</td></tr>
<tr><td>43</td><td>Washington</td><td>28.8</td><td>46</td><td>Massachusetts</td><td>26.8</td></tr>
<tr><td>29</td><td>West Virginia</td><td>32.9</td><td>48</td><td>New Hampshire</td><td>24.6</td></tr>
<tr><td>38</td><td>Wisconsin</td><td>30.0</td><td>49</td><td>Idaho</td><td>21.9</td></tr>
<tr><td>36</td><td>Wyoming</td><td>30.3</td><td>50</td><td>Utah</td><td>17.2</td></tr>
<tr><td></td><td></td><td></td><td></td><td>District of Columbia</td><td>56.5</td></tr>
</table>

Source: U.S. Department of Health and Human Services, National Center for Health Statistics
"National Vital Statistics Reports" (Vol. 52, No. 10, December 17, 2003)
Final data by state of residence.

Births to Unmarried White Women in 2002

National Total = 904,461 Live Births*

ALPHA ORDER

RANK	STATE	BIRTHS	% of USA
34	Alabama	7,879	0.9%
49	Alaska	1,530	0.2%
8	Arizona	29,419	3.3%
33	Arkansas	8,054	0.9%
1	California	143,842	15.9%
16	Colorado	16,092	1.8%
32	Connecticut	8,532	0.9%
44	Delaware	2,549	0.3%
4	Florida	48,647	5.4%
11	Georgia	21,583	2.4%
50	Hawaii	686	0.1%
39	Idaho	4,312	0.5%
5	Illinois	37,769	4.2%
10	Indiana	23,578	2.6%
29	Iowa	9,758	1.1%
28	Kansas	9,875	1.1%
21	Kentucky	14,228	1.6%
27	Louisiana	10,041	1.1%
40	Maine	4,248	0.5%
25	Maryland	10,806	1.2%
18	Massachusetts	15,883	1.8%
9	Michigan	27,056	3.0%
22	Minnesota	13,763	1.5%
38	Mississippi	5,458	0.6%
15	Missouri	17,752	2.0%
43	Montana	2,623	0.3%
37	Nebraska	5,946	0.7%
30	Nevada	9,451	1.0%
42	New Hampshire	3,388	0.4%
13	New Jersey	20,170	2.2%
26	New Mexico	10,129	1.1%
3	New York	53,571	5.9%
12	North Carolina	21,232	2.3%
48	North Dakota	1,624	0.2%
6	Ohio	35,336	3.9%
24	Oklahoma	12,238	1.4%
23	Oregon	12,545	1.4%
7	Pennsylvania	31,830	3.5%
41	Rhode Island	3,576	0.4%
31	South Carolina	8,784	1.0%
45	South Dakota	2,265	0.3%
19	Tennessee	15,859	1.8%
2	Texas	93,441	10.3%
35	Utah	7,660	0.8%
46	Vermont	1,991	0.2%
17	Virginia	15,976	1.8%
14	Washington	18,428	2.0%
36	West Virginia	6,299	0.7%
20	Wisconsin	14,306	1.6%
47	Wyoming	1,768	0.2%

RANK ORDER

RANK	STATE	BIRTHS	% of USA
1	California	143,842	15.9%
2	Texas	93,441	10.3%
3	New York	53,571	5.9%
4	Florida	48,647	5.4%
5	Illinois	37,769	4.2%
6	Ohio	35,336	3.9%
7	Pennsylvania	31,830	3.5%
8	Arizona	29,419	3.3%
9	Michigan	27,056	3.0%
10	Indiana	23,578	2.6%
11	Georgia	21,583	2.4%
12	North Carolina	21,232	2.3%
13	New Jersey	20,170	2.2%
14	Washington	18,428	2.0%
15	Missouri	17,752	2.0%
16	Colorado	16,092	1.8%
17	Virginia	15,976	1.8%
18	Massachusetts	15,883	1.8%
19	Tennessee	15,859	1.8%
20	Wisconsin	14,306	1.6%
21	Kentucky	14,228	1.6%
22	Minnesota	13,763	1.5%
23	Oregon	12,545	1.4%
24	Oklahoma	12,238	1.4%
25	Maryland	10,806	1.2%
26	New Mexico	10,129	1.1%
27	Louisiana	10,041	1.1%
28	Kansas	9,875	1.1%
29	Iowa	9,758	1.1%
30	Nevada	9,451	1.0%
31	South Carolina	8,784	1.0%
32	Connecticut	8,532	0.9%
33	Arkansas	8,054	0.9%
34	Alabama	7,879	0.9%
35	Utah	7,660	0.8%
36	West Virginia	6,299	0.7%
37	Nebraska	5,946	0.7%
38	Mississippi	5,458	0.6%
39	Idaho	4,312	0.5%
40	Maine	4,248	0.5%
41	Rhode Island	3,576	0.4%
42	New Hampshire	3,388	0.4%
43	Montana	2,623	0.3%
44	Delaware	2,549	0.3%
45	South Dakota	2,265	0.3%
46	Vermont	1,991	0.2%
47	Wyoming	1,768	0.2%
48	North Dakota	1,624	0.2%
49	Alaska	1,530	0.2%
50	Hawaii	686	0.1%
	District of Columbia	685	0.1%

Source: U.S. Department of Health and Human Services, National Center for Health Statistics
"National Vital Statistics Reports" (Vol. 52, No. 10, December 17, 2003)
*Final data by state of residence. By race of mother.

Births to Unmarried White Women
As a Percent of All Births to White Women in 2002
National Percent = 28.5% of Live Births*

ALPHA ORDER

RANK	STATE	PERCENT
48	Alabama	19.7
40	Alaska	24.0
2	Arizona	38.2
23	Arkansas	27.6
4	California	33.6
32	Colorado	25.8
37	Connecticut	24.6
7	Delaware	32.2
9	Florida	31.8
33	Georgia	25.2
49	Hawaii	17.4
47	Idaho	21.4
27	Illinois	26.9
10	Indiana	31.7
21	Iowa	27.8
20	Kansas	28.3
16	Kentucky	29.4
25	Louisiana	27.3
5	Maine	32.6
42	Maryland	23.9
44	Massachusetts	23.8
29	Michigan	26.4
45	Minnesota	23.7
39	Mississippi	24.1
19	Missouri	28.5
23	Montana	27.6
31	Nebraska	25.9
3	Nevada	35.0
36	New Hampshire	24.7
42	New Jersey	23.9
1	New Mexico	43.5
14	New York	29.6
34	North Carolina	24.9
40	North Dakota	24.0
17	Ohio	28.8
12	Oklahoma	31.0
13	Oregon	30.6
26	Pennsylvania	27.0
6	Rhode Island	32.4
35	South Carolina	24.8
30	South Dakota	26.2
28	Tennessee	26.6
15	Texas	29.5
50	Utah	16.4
8	Vermont	31.9
46	Virginia	22.4
22	Washington	27.7
10	West Virginia	31.7
38	Wisconsin	24.3
17	Wyoming	28.8

RANK ORDER

RANK	STATE	PERCENT
1	New Mexico	43.5
2	Arizona	38.2
3	Nevada	35.0
4	California	33.6
5	Maine	32.6
6	Rhode Island	32.4
7	Delaware	32.2
8	Vermont	31.9
9	Florida	31.8
10	Indiana	31.7
10	West Virginia	31.7
12	Oklahoma	31.0
13	Oregon	30.6
14	New York	29.6
15	Texas	29.5
16	Kentucky	29.4
17	Ohio	28.8
17	Wyoming	28.8
19	Missouri	28.5
20	Kansas	28.3
21	Iowa	27.8
22	Washington	27.7
23	Arkansas	27.6
23	Montana	27.6
25	Louisiana	27.3
26	Pennsylvania	27.0
27	Illinois	26.9
28	Tennessee	26.6
29	Michigan	26.4
30	South Dakota	26.2
31	Nebraska	25.9
32	Colorado	25.8
33	Georgia	25.2
34	North Carolina	24.9
35	South Carolina	24.8
36	New Hampshire	24.7
37	Connecticut	24.6
38	Wisconsin	24.3
39	Mississippi	24.1
40	Alaska	24.0
40	North Dakota	24.0
42	Maryland	23.9
42	New Jersey	23.9
44	Massachusetts	23.8
45	Minnesota	23.7
46	Virginia	22.4
47	Idaho	21.4
48	Alabama	19.7
49	Hawaii	17.4
50	Utah	16.4

District of Columbia	25.6

Source: U.S. Department of Health and Human Services, National Center for Health Statistics
"National Vital Statistics Reports" (Vol. 52, No. 10, December 17, 2003)
Final data by state of residence. By race of mother.

Births to Unmarried Black Women in 2002

National Total = 404,864 Live Births*

ALPHA ORDER				RANK ORDER			
RANK	STATE	BIRTHS	% of USA	RANK	STATE	BIRTHS	% of USA
17	Alabama	12,511	3.1%	1	New York	32,589	8.0%
40	Alaska	187	0.0%	2	Florida	30,918	7.6%
32	Arizona	1,712	0.4%	3	Georgia	28,149	7.0%
21	Arkansas	5,633	1.4%	4	Texas	25,828	6.4%
6	California	20,394	5.0%	5	Illinois	24,448	6.0%
33	Colorado	1,592	0.4%	6	California	20,394	5.0%
25	Connecticut	3,450	0.9%	7	Louisiana	20,013	4.9%
29	Delaware	1,907	0.5%	8	North Carolina	18,140	4.5%
2	Florida	30,918	7.6%	9	Ohio	16,879	4.2%
3	Georgia	28,149	7.0%	10	Michigan	16,546	4.1%
43	Hawaii	88	0.0%	11	Pennsylvania	15,240	3.8%
46	Idaho	34	0.0%	12	Maryland	14,359	3.5%
5	Illinois	24,448	6.0%	13	Mississippi	13,841	3.4%
20	Indiana	7,127	1.8%	14	Virginia	13,733	3.4%
35	Iowa	935	0.2%	15	South Carolina	13,032	3.2%
28	Kansas	1,961	0.5%	16	New Jersey	12,824	3.2%
24	Kentucky	3,619	0.9%	17	Alabama	12,511	3.1%
7	Louisiana	20,013	4.9%	18	Tennessee	11,890	2.9%
44	Maine	59	0.0%	19	Missouri	8,346	2.1%
12	Maryland	14,359	3.5%	20	Indiana	7,127	1.8%
23	Massachusetts	4,883	1.2%	21	Arkansas	5,633	1.4%
10	Michigan	16,546	4.1%	22	Wisconsin	5,256	1.3%
27	Minnesota	2,840	0.7%	23	Massachusetts	4,883	1.2%
13	Mississippi	13,841	3.4%	24	Kentucky	3,619	0.9%
19	Missouri	8,346	2.1%	25	Connecticut	3,450	0.9%
50	Montana	16	0.0%	26	Oklahoma	3,308	0.8%
34	Nebraska	956	0.2%	27	Minnesota	2,840	0.7%
30	Nevada	1,826	0.5%	28	Kansas	1,961	0.5%
42	New Hampshire	96	0.0%	29	Delaware	1,907	0.5%
16	New Jersey	12,824	3.2%	30	Nevada	1,826	0.5%
39	New Mexico	289	0.1%	31	Washington	1,806	0.4%
1	New York	32,589	8.0%	32	Arizona	1,712	0.4%
8	North Carolina	18,140	4.5%	33	Colorado	1,592	0.4%
47	North Dakota	32	0.0%	34	Nebraska	956	0.2%
9	Ohio	16,879	4.2%	35	Iowa	935	0.2%
26	Oklahoma	3,308	0.8%	36	Rhode Island	721	0.2%
37	Oregon	577	0.1%	37	Oregon	577	0.1%
11	Pennsylvania	15,240	3.8%	38	West Virginia	489	0.1%
36	Rhode Island	721	0.2%	39	New Mexico	289	0.1%
15	South Carolina	13,032	3.2%	40	Alaska	187	0.0%
45	South Dakota	39	0.0%	41	Utah	159	0.0%
18	Tennessee	11,890	2.9%	42	New Hampshire	96	0.0%
4	Texas	25,828	6.4%	43	Hawaii	88	0.0%
41	Utah	159	0.0%	44	Maine	59	0.0%
49	Vermont	26	0.0%	45	South Dakota	39	0.0%
14	Virginia	13,733	3.4%	46	Idaho	34	0.0%
31	Washington	1,806	0.4%	47	North Dakota	32	0.0%
38	West Virginia	489	0.1%	48	Wyoming	28	0.0%
22	Wisconsin	5,256	1.3%	49	Vermont	26	0.0%
48	Wyoming	28	0.0%	50	Montana	16	0.0%
					District of Columbia	3,533	0.9%

Source: U.S. Department of Health and Human Services, National Center for Health Statistics
"National Vital Statistics Reports" (Vol. 52, No. 10, December 17, 2003)
*Final data by state of residence. By race of mother.

Births to Unmarried Black Women
As a Percent of All Births to Black Women in 2002
National Percent = 68.2% of Live Births*

ALPHA ORDER

RANK	STATE	PERCENT
19	Alabama	68.4
43	Alaska	43.3
32	Arizona	61.6
5	Arkansas	75.8
29	California	62.5
39	Colorado	54.3
22	Connecticut	66.4
16	Delaware	70.4
21	Florida	66.9
24	Georgia	65.8
49	Hawaii	18.5
48	Idaho	33.0
2	Illinois	76.8
3	Indiana	76.4
10	Iowa	74.0
20	Kansas	67.9
12	Kentucky	73.2
8	Louisiana	75.1
47	Maine	33.9
34	Maryland	59.3
36	Massachusetts	58.5
11	Michigan	73.7
37	Minnesota	58.4
4	Mississippi	76.0
6	Missouri	75.7
NA	Montana**	NA
23	Nebraska	66.3
18	Nevada	69.9
44	New Hampshire	42.7
27	New Jersey	64.3
38	New Mexico	56.6
26	New York	65.7
24	North Carolina	65.8
46	North Dakota	35.6
9	Ohio	74.9
17	Oklahoma	70.3
33	Oregon	61.3
7	Pennsylvania	75.2
28	Rhode Island	63.0
15	South Carolina	71.7
45	South Dakota	37.9
13	Tennessee	72.9
31	Texas	62.0
42	Utah	46.9
35	Vermont	59.1
30	Virginia	62.2
40	Washington	53.2
14	West Virginia	72.0
1	Wisconsin	81.9
41	Wyoming	51.9

RANK ORDER

RANK	STATE	PERCENT
1	Wisconsin	81.9
2	Illinois	76.8
3	Indiana	76.4
4	Mississippi	76.0
5	Arkansas	75.8
6	Missouri	75.7
7	Pennsylvania	75.2
8	Louisiana	75.1
9	Ohio	74.9
10	Iowa	74.0
11	Michigan	73.7
12	Kentucky	73.2
13	Tennessee	72.9
14	West Virginia	72.0
15	South Carolina	71.7
16	Delaware	70.4
17	Oklahoma	70.3
18	Nevada	69.9
19	Alabama	68.4
20	Kansas	67.9
21	Florida	66.9
22	Connecticut	66.4
23	Nebraska	66.3
24	Georgia	65.8
24	North Carolina	65.8
26	New York	65.7
27	New Jersey	64.3
28	Rhode Island	63.0
29	California	62.5
30	Virginia	62.2
31	Texas	62.0
32	Arizona	61.6
33	Oregon	61.3
34	Maryland	59.3
35	Vermont	59.1
36	Massachusetts	58.5
37	Minnesota	58.4
38	New Mexico	56.6
39	Colorado	54.3
40	Washington	53.2
41	Wyoming	51.9
42	Utah	46.9
43	Alaska	43.3
44	New Hampshire	42.7
45	South Dakota	37.9
46	North Dakota	35.6
47	Maine	33.9
48	Idaho	33.0
49	Hawaii	18.5
NA	Montana**	NA
	District of Columbia	76.5

Source: U.S. Department of Health and Human Services, National Center for Health Statistics
   "National Vital Statistics Reports" (Vol. 52, No. 10, December 17, 2003)
Final data by state of residence. By race of mother.
**Insufficient data.*

Births to Unmarried Hispanic Women in 2002

National Total = 381,466 Live Births*

ALPHA ORDER

RANK	STATE	BIRTHS	% of USA
39	Alabama	629	0.2%
42	Alaska	331	0.1%
5	Arizona	19,705	5.2%
33	Arkansas	1,138	0.3%
1	California	111,099	29.1%
8	Colorado	8,714	2.3%
16	Connecticut	4,247	1.1%
37	Delaware	740	0.2%
4	Florida	20,446	5.4%
10	Georgia	7,243	1.9%
34	Hawaii	1,061	0.3%
35	Idaho	1,004	0.3%
6	Illinois	17,550	4.6%
19	Indiana	3,064	0.8%
36	Iowa	986	0.3%
27	Kansas	2,133	0.6%
38	Kentucky	717	0.2%
40	Louisiana	449	0.1%
47	Maine	60	0.0%
21	Maryland	2,753	0.7%
12	Massachusetts	5,903	1.5%
20	Michigan	3,053	0.8%
25	Minnesota	2,357	0.6%
41	Mississippi	345	0.1%
29	Missouri	1,466	0.4%
45	Montana	158	0.0%
30	Nebraska	1,379	0.4%
15	Nevada	5,054	1.3%
44	New Hampshire	182	0.0%
7	New Jersey	12,960	3.4%
9	New Mexico	7,821	2.1%
3	New York	32,571	8.5%
11	North Carolina	7,189	1.9%
48	North Dakota	59	0.0%
24	Ohio	2,383	0.6%
26	Oklahoma	2,229	0.6%
18	Oregon	3,350	0.9%
13	Pennsylvania	5,294	1.4%
30	Rhode Island	1,379	0.4%
32	South Carolina	1,374	0.4%
46	South Dakota	155	0.0%
28	Tennessee	1,999	0.5%
2	Texas	63,723	16.7%
22	Utah	2,670	0.7%
50	Vermont	11	0.0%
17	Virginia	3,928	1.0%
14	Washington	5,122	1.3%
49	West Virginia	29	0.0%
23	Wisconsin	2,431	0.6%
43	Wyoming	270	0.1%

RANK ORDER

RANK	STATE	BIRTHS	% of USA
1	California	111,099	29.1%
2	Texas	63,723	16.7%
3	New York	32,571	8.5%
4	Florida	20,446	5.4%
5	Arizona	19,705	5.2%
6	Illinois	17,550	4.6%
7	New Jersey	12,960	3.4%
8	Colorado	8,714	2.3%
9	New Mexico	7,821	2.1%
10	Georgia	7,243	1.9%
11	North Carolina	7,189	1.9%
12	Massachusetts	5,903	1.5%
13	Pennsylvania	5,294	1.4%
14	Washington	5,122	1.3%
15	Nevada	5,054	1.3%
16	Connecticut	4,247	1.1%
17	Virginia	3,928	1.0%
18	Oregon	3,350	0.9%
19	Indiana	3,064	0.8%
20	Michigan	3,053	0.8%
21	Maryland	2,753	0.7%
22	Utah	2,670	0.7%
23	Wisconsin	2,431	0.6%
24	Ohio	2,383	0.6%
25	Minnesota	2,357	0.6%
26	Oklahoma	2,229	0.6%
27	Kansas	2,133	0.6%
28	Tennessee	1,999	0.5%
29	Missouri	1,466	0.4%
30	Nebraska	1,379	0.4%
30	Rhode Island	1,379	0.4%
32	South Carolina	1,374	0.4%
33	Arkansas	1,138	0.3%
34	Hawaii	1,061	0.3%
35	Idaho	1,004	0.3%
36	Iowa	986	0.3%
37	Delaware	740	0.2%
38	Kentucky	717	0.2%
39	Alabama	629	0.2%
40	Louisiana	449	0.1%
41	Mississippi	345	0.1%
42	Alaska	331	0.1%
43	Wyoming	270	0.1%
44	New Hampshire	182	0.0%
45	Montana	158	0.0%
46	South Dakota	155	0.0%
47	Maine	60	0.0%
48	North Dakota	59	0.0%
49	West Virginia	29	0.0%
50	Vermont	11	0.0%
	District of Columbia	553	0.1%

Source: U.S. Department of Health and Human Services, National Center for Health Statistics
"National Vital Statistics Reports" (Vol. 52, No. 10, December 17, 2003)
*Final data by state of residence. By race of mother. Persons of Hispanic origin may be of any race.

Births to Unmarried Hispanic Women
As a Percent of All Births to Hispanic Women in 2002
National Percent = 43.5% of Live Births*

ALPHA ORDER

RANK	STATE	PERCENT
49	Alabama	24.5
34	Alaska	41.4
9	Arizona	51.9
42	Arkansas	37.3
28	California	42.2
34	Colorado	41.4
3	Connecticut	60.8
6	Delaware	56.2
39	Florida	39.6
24	Georgia	43.1
21	Hawaii	43.8
44	Idaho	36.0
25	Illinois	42.8
11	Indiana	49.7
37	Iowa	41.3
26	Kansas	42.5
20	Kentucky	44.0
48	Louisiana	32.5
45	Maine	35.9
17	Maryland	45.4
1	Massachusetts	61.5
29	Michigan	42.0
10	Minnesota	50.7
30	Mississippi	41.9
18	Missouri	44.9
34	Montana	41.4
32	Nebraska	41.6
19	Nevada	44.4
43	New Hampshire	36.2
8	New Jersey	52.5
7	New Mexico	53.5
4	New York	59.5
14	North Carolina	47.7
39	North Dakota	39.6
12	Ohio	49.5
27	Oklahoma	42.4
31	Oregon	41.7
2	Pennsylvania	60.9
5	Rhode Island	59.2
23	South Carolina	43.3
13	South Dakota	48.7
15	Tennessee	46.0
46	Texas	35.6
41	Utah	38.4
NA	Vermont**	NA
38	Virginia	40.1
33	Washington	41.5
47	West Virginia	34.5
16	Wisconsin	45.9
22	Wyoming	43.4

RANK ORDER

RANK	STATE	PERCENT
1	Massachusetts	61.5
2	Pennsylvania	60.9
3	Connecticut	60.8
4	New York	59.5
5	Rhode Island	59.2
6	Delaware	56.2
7	New Mexico	53.5
8	New Jersey	52.5
9	Arizona	51.9
10	Minnesota	50.7
11	Indiana	49.7
12	Ohio	49.5
13	South Dakota	48.7
14	North Carolina	47.7
15	Tennessee	46.0
16	Wisconsin	45.9
17	Maryland	45.4
18	Missouri	44.9
19	Nevada	44.4
20	Kentucky	44.0
21	Hawaii	43.8
22	Wyoming	43.4
23	South Carolina	43.3
24	Georgia	43.1
25	Illinois	42.8
26	Kansas	42.5
27	Oklahoma	42.4
28	California	42.2
29	Michigan	42.0
30	Mississippi	41.9
31	Oregon	41.7
32	Nebraska	41.6
33	Washington	41.5
34	Alaska	41.4
34	Colorado	41.4
34	Montana	41.4
37	Iowa	41.3
38	Virginia	40.1
39	Florida	39.6
39	North Dakota	39.6
41	Utah	38.4
42	Arkansas	37.3
43	New Hampshire	36.2
44	Idaho	36.0
45	Maine	35.9
46	Texas	35.6
47	West Virginia	34.5
48	Louisiana	32.5
49	Alabama	24.5
NA	Vermont**	NA
	District of Columbia	58.0

Source: U.S. Department of Health and Human Services, National Center for Health Statistics
    "National Vital Statistics Reports" (Vol. 52, No. 10, December 17, 2003)
*Final data by state of residence. By race of mother. Persons of Hispanic origin may be of any race.
**Insufficient data.

Pregnancy Rate for 15 to 19 Year Old Women in 2000

National Rate = 64.8 Births and Abortions per 1,000 Women 15-19 Years Old*

ALPHA ORDER

RANK	STATE	RATE
8	Alabama	76.8
NA	Alaska**	NA
5	Arizona	79.0
7	Arkansas	77.6
NA	California**	NA
26	Colorado	57.4
27	Connecticut	55.9
10	Delaware	75.4
NA	Florida**	NA
3	Georgia	80.9
15	Hawaii	70.0
37	Idaho	45.8
16	Illinois	69.8
24	Indiana	59.0
39	Iowa	45.3
17	Kansas	69.6
22	Kentucky	60.8
12	Louisiana	73.3
43	Maine	42.2
33	Maryland	52.6
36	Massachusetts	48.1
31	Michigan	54.4
42	Minnesota	43.1
9	Mississippi	76.7
29	Missouri	55.0
32	Montana	52.8
34	Nebraska	50.9
4	Nevada	79.6
NA	New Hampshire**	NA
28	New Jersey	55.7
2	New Mexico	82.9
14	New York	70.1
6	North Carolina	77.7
45	North Dakota	41.6
21	Ohio	63.2
13	Oklahoma	71.1
19	Oregon	65.9
35	Pennsylvania	49.6
24	Rhode Island	59.0
18	South Carolina	68.6
40	South Dakota	44.2
10	Tennessee	75.4
1	Texas	83.8
41	Utah	44.1
46	Vermont	40.1
23	Virginia	59.7
20	Washington	63.8
30	West Virginia	54.9
38	Wisconsin	45.5
44	Wyoming	41.8

RANK ORDER

RANK	STATE	RATE
1	Texas	83.8
2	New Mexico	82.9
3	Georgia	80.9
4	Nevada	79.6
5	Arizona	79.0
6	North Carolina	77.7
7	Arkansas	77.6
8	Alabama	76.8
9	Mississippi	76.7
10	Delaware	75.4
10	Tennessee	75.4
12	Louisiana	73.3
13	Oklahoma	71.1
14	New York	70.1
15	Hawaii	70.0
16	Illinois	69.8
17	Kansas	69.6
18	South Carolina	68.6
19	Oregon	65.9
20	Washington	63.8
21	Ohio	63.2
22	Kentucky	60.8
23	Virginia	59.7
24	Indiana	59.0
24	Rhode Island	59.0
26	Colorado	57.4
27	Connecticut	55.9
28	New Jersey	55.7
29	Missouri	55.0
30	West Virginia	54.9
31	Michigan	54.4
32	Montana	52.8
33	Maryland	52.6
34	Nebraska	50.9
35	Pennsylvania	49.6
36	Massachusetts	48.1
37	Idaho	45.8
38	Wisconsin	45.5
39	Iowa	45.3
40	South Dakota	44.2
41	Utah	44.1
42	Minnesota	43.1
43	Maine	42.2
44	Wyoming	41.8
45	North Dakota	41.6
46	Vermont	40.1
NA	Alaska**	NA
NA	California**	NA
NA	Florida**	NA
NA	New Hampshire**	NA

District of Columbia 114.0

Source: Morgan Quitno Press using data from US Dept of Health & Human Serv's, Centers for Disease Control-Prevention "Abortion Surveillance-United States, 2000" (Morbidity Mortality Weekly Report, Vol. 52, No. SS-12, 11/28/03)
*The sum of live births and legal induced abortions per 1,000 women aged 15-19 years old. Births by state of residence, abortions by state of occurrence. Miscarriages are not included in these rates. National rate includes only states reporting abortions and births.
**Not available.

Percent Change in Pregnancy Rate for 15 to 19 Year Old Women: 1997 to 2000

National Percent Change = 9.1% Decrease*

<table>
<tr><td colspan="3">ALPHA ORDER</td><td colspan="3">RANK ORDER</td></tr>
<tr><td>RANK</td><td>STATE</td><td>PERCENT CHANGE</td><td>RANK</td><td>STATE</td><td>PERCENT CHANGE</td></tr>
<tr><td>17</td><td>Alabama</td><td>(7.6)</td><td>1</td><td>North Dakota</td><td>2.5</td></tr>
<tr><td>NA</td><td>Alaska**</td><td>NA</td><td>2</td><td>New Jersey</td><td>0.7</td></tr>
<tr><td>9</td><td>Arizona</td><td>(5.6)</td><td>3</td><td>Hawaii</td><td>0.4</td></tr>
<tr><td>31</td><td>Arkansas</td><td>(9.5)</td><td>4</td><td>New Mexico</td><td>(2.4)</td></tr>
<tr><td>NA</td><td>California**</td><td>NA</td><td>5</td><td>Idaho</td><td>(3.0)</td></tr>
<tr><td>28</td><td>Colorado</td><td>(9.3)</td><td>6</td><td>Maryland</td><td>(4.4)</td></tr>
<tr><td>38</td><td>Connecticut</td><td>(15.4)</td><td>7</td><td>Nebraska</td><td>(4.5)</td></tr>
<tr><td>43</td><td>Delaware</td><td>(30.1)</td><td>8</td><td>Mississippi</td><td>(5.4)</td></tr>
<tr><td>NA</td><td>Florida**</td><td>NA</td><td>9</td><td>Arizona</td><td>(5.6)</td></tr>
<tr><td>36</td><td>Georgia</td><td>(12.1)</td><td>10</td><td>Kansas</td><td>(5.7)</td></tr>
<tr><td>3</td><td>Hawaii</td><td>0.4</td><td>11</td><td>Wyoming</td><td>(6.1)</td></tr>
<tr><td>5</td><td>Idaho</td><td>(3.0)</td><td>12</td><td>Louisiana</td><td>(6.4)</td></tr>
<tr><td>NA</td><td>Illinois**</td><td>NA</td><td>12</td><td>Wisconsin</td><td>(6.4)</td></tr>
<tr><td>33</td><td>Indiana</td><td>(10.7)</td><td>14</td><td>West Virginia</td><td>(6.5)</td></tr>
<tr><td>NA</td><td>Iowa**</td><td>NA</td><td>15</td><td>Montana</td><td>(6.9)</td></tr>
<tr><td>10</td><td>Kansas</td><td>(5.7)</td><td>16</td><td>South Dakota</td><td>(7.1)</td></tr>
<tr><td>37</td><td>Kentucky</td><td>(12.4)</td><td>17</td><td>Alabama</td><td>(7.6)</td></tr>
<tr><td>12</td><td>Louisiana</td><td>(6.4)</td><td>18</td><td>Ohio</td><td>(8.0)</td></tr>
<tr><td>22</td><td>Maine</td><td>(8.7)</td><td>19</td><td>Minnesota</td><td>(8.5)</td></tr>
<tr><td>6</td><td>Maryland</td><td>(4.4)</td><td>19</td><td>South Carolina</td><td>(8.5)</td></tr>
<tr><td>40</td><td>Massachusetts</td><td>(15.5)</td><td>19</td><td>Texas</td><td>(8.5)</td></tr>
<tr><td>24</td><td>Michigan</td><td>(9.0)</td><td>22</td><td>Maine</td><td>(8.7)</td></tr>
<tr><td>19</td><td>Minnesota</td><td>(8.5)</td><td>23</td><td>Pennsylvania</td><td>(8.8)</td></tr>
<tr><td>8</td><td>Mississippi</td><td>(5.4)</td><td>24</td><td>Michigan</td><td>(9.0)</td></tr>
<tr><td>30</td><td>Missouri</td><td>(9.4)</td><td>24</td><td>Washington</td><td>(9.0)</td></tr>
<tr><td>15</td><td>Montana</td><td>(6.9)</td><td>26</td><td>Virginia</td><td>(9.1)</td></tr>
<tr><td>7</td><td>Nebraska</td><td>(4.5)</td><td>27</td><td>North Carolina</td><td>(9.2)</td></tr>
<tr><td>35</td><td>Nevada</td><td>(12.0)</td><td>28</td><td>Colorado</td><td>(9.3)</td></tr>
<tr><td>NA</td><td>New Hampshire**</td><td>NA</td><td>28</td><td>Tennessee</td><td>(9.3)</td></tr>
<tr><td>2</td><td>New Jersey</td><td>0.7</td><td>30</td><td>Missouri</td><td>(9.4)</td></tr>
<tr><td>4</td><td>New Mexico</td><td>(2.4)</td><td>31</td><td>Arkansas</td><td>(9.5)</td></tr>
<tr><td>38</td><td>New York</td><td>(15.4)</td><td>32</td><td>Utah</td><td>(9.6)</td></tr>
<tr><td>27</td><td>North Carolina</td><td>(9.2)</td><td>33</td><td>Indiana</td><td>(10.7)</td></tr>
<tr><td>1</td><td>North Dakota</td><td>2.5</td><td>34</td><td>Oregon</td><td>(11.8)</td></tr>
<tr><td>18</td><td>Ohio</td><td>(8.0)</td><td>35</td><td>Nevada</td><td>(12.0)</td></tr>
<tr><td>NA</td><td>Oklahoma**</td><td>NA</td><td>36</td><td>Georgia</td><td>(12.1)</td></tr>
<tr><td>34</td><td>Oregon</td><td>(11.8)</td><td>37</td><td>Kentucky</td><td>(12.4)</td></tr>
<tr><td>23</td><td>Pennsylvania</td><td>(8.8)</td><td>38</td><td>Connecticut</td><td>(15.4)</td></tr>
<tr><td>42</td><td>Rhode Island</td><td>(23.3)</td><td>38</td><td>New York</td><td>(15.4)</td></tr>
<tr><td>19</td><td>South Carolina</td><td>(8.5)</td><td>40</td><td>Massachusetts</td><td>(15.5)</td></tr>
<tr><td>16</td><td>South Dakota</td><td>(7.1)</td><td>41</td><td>Vermont</td><td>(17.8)</td></tr>
<tr><td>28</td><td>Tennessee</td><td>(9.3)</td><td>42</td><td>Rhode Island</td><td>(23.3)</td></tr>
<tr><td>19</td><td>Texas</td><td>(8.5)</td><td>43</td><td>Delaware</td><td>(30.1)</td></tr>
<tr><td>32</td><td>Utah</td><td>(9.6)</td><td>NA</td><td>Alaska**</td><td>NA</td></tr>
<tr><td>41</td><td>Vermont</td><td>(17.8)</td><td>NA</td><td>California**</td><td>NA</td></tr>
<tr><td>26</td><td>Virginia</td><td>(9.1)</td><td>NA</td><td>Florida**</td><td>NA</td></tr>
<tr><td>24</td><td>Washington</td><td>(9.0)</td><td>NA</td><td>Illinois**</td><td>NA</td></tr>
<tr><td>14</td><td>West Virginia</td><td>(6.5)</td><td>NA</td><td>Iowa**</td><td>NA</td></tr>
<tr><td>12</td><td>Wisconsin</td><td>(6.4)</td><td>NA</td><td>New Hampshire**</td><td>NA</td></tr>
<tr><td>11</td><td>Wyoming</td><td>(6.1)</td><td>NA</td><td>Oklahoma**</td><td>NA</td></tr>
</table>

District of Columbia   (46.2)

Source: Morgan Quitno Press using data from US Dept of Health & Human Serv's, Centers for Disease Control-Prevention "Abortion Surveillance-United States, 2000" (Morbidity Mortality Weekly Report, Vol. 52, No. SS-12, 11/28/03)
The sum of live births and legal induced abortions per 1,000 women aged 15-19 years old. Births by state of residence, abortions by state of occurrence. Miscarriages are not included in these rates. National rate includes only states reporting abortions and births.
**Not available.*

Births to Teenage Mothers in 2002

National Total = 425,493 Live Births*

ALPHA ORDER

RANK	STATE	BIRTHS	% of USA
17	Alabama	8,427	2.0%
46	Alaska	1,068	0.3%
11	Arizona	11,363	2.7%
27	Arkansas	5,681	1.3%
2	California	50,222	11.8%
21	Colorado	7,238	1.7%
36	Connecticut	2,901	0.7%
42	Delaware	1,209	0.3%
3	Florida	23,181	5.4%
6	Georgia	16,258	3.8%
40	Hawaii	1,538	0.4%
39	Idaho	2,080	0.5%
5	Illinois	18,217	4.3%
14	Indiana	9,594	2.3%
35	Iowa	3,392	0.8%
32	Kansas	4,321	1.0%
24	Kentucky	6,899	1.6%
13	Louisiana	10,056	2.4%
44	Maine	1,139	0.3%
25	Maryland	6,547	1.5%
29	Massachusetts	4,643	1.1%
10	Michigan	12,261	2.9%
28	Minnesota	5,079	1.2%
23	Mississippi	6,961	1.6%
16	Missouri	8,835	2.1%
41	Montana	1,266	0.3%
38	Nebraska	2,394	0.6%
33	Nevada	3,663	0.9%
47	New Hampshire	881	0.2%
19	New Jersey	7,352	1.7%
30	New Mexico	4,513	1.1%
4	New York	18,394	4.3%
8	North Carolina	13,756	3.2%
49	North Dakota	653	0.2%
7	Ohio	15,698	3.7%
18	Oklahoma	7,358	1.7%
31	Oregon	4,411	1.0%
9	Pennsylvania	12,961	3.0%
43	Rhode Island	1,197	0.3%
20	South Carolina	7,327	1.7%
45	South Dakota	1,138	0.3%
12	Tennessee	10,300	2.4%
1	Texas	52,142	12.3%
34	Utah	3,574	0.8%
50	Vermont	533	0.1%
15	Virginia	9,030	2.1%
22	Washington	7,035	1.7%
37	West Virginia	2,630	0.6%
26	Wisconsin	6,436	1.5%
48	Wyoming	804	0.2%

RANK ORDER

RANK	STATE	BIRTHS	% of USA
1	Texas	52,142	12.3%
2	California	50,222	11.8%
3	Florida	23,181	5.4%
4	New York	18,394	4.3%
5	Illinois	18,217	4.3%
6	Georgia	16,258	3.8%
7	Ohio	15,698	3.7%
8	North Carolina	13,756	3.2%
9	Pennsylvania	12,961	3.0%
10	Michigan	12,261	2.9%
11	Arizona	11,363	2.7%
12	Tennessee	10,300	2.4%
13	Louisiana	10,056	2.4%
14	Indiana	9,594	2.3%
15	Virginia	9,030	2.1%
16	Missouri	8,835	2.1%
17	Alabama	8,427	2.0%
18	Oklahoma	7,358	1.7%
19	New Jersey	7,352	1.7%
20	South Carolina	7,327	1.7%
21	Colorado	7,238	1.7%
22	Washington	7,035	1.7%
23	Mississippi	6,961	1.6%
24	Kentucky	6,899	1.6%
25	Maryland	6,547	1.5%
26	Wisconsin	6,436	1.5%
27	Arkansas	5,681	1.3%
28	Minnesota	5,079	1.2%
29	Massachusetts	4,643	1.1%
30	New Mexico	4,513	1.1%
31	Oregon	4,411	1.0%
32	Kansas	4,321	1.0%
33	Nevada	3,663	0.9%
34	Utah	3,574	0.8%
35	Iowa	3,392	0.8%
36	Connecticut	2,901	0.7%
37	West Virginia	2,630	0.6%
38	Nebraska	2,394	0.6%
39	Idaho	2,080	0.5%
40	Hawaii	1,538	0.4%
41	Montana	1,266	0.3%
42	Delaware	1,209	0.3%
43	Rhode Island	1,197	0.3%
44	Maine	1,139	0.3%
45	South Dakota	1,138	0.3%
46	Alaska	1,068	0.3%
47	New Hampshire	881	0.2%
48	Wyoming	804	0.2%
49	North Dakota	653	0.2%
50	Vermont	533	0.1%
	District of Columbia	937	0.2%

Source: Morgan Quitno Press using data from U.S. Dept. of Health and Human Services, Nat'l Center for Health Statistics (unpublished data)

Live births to women 15 to 19 years old by state of residence.

Teenage Birth Rate in 2002

National Rate = 43.0 Live Births per 1,000 Women 15 to 19 Years Old*

ALPHA ORDER

RANK	STATE	RATE
9	Alabama	54.5
25	Alaska	39.5
4	Arizona	61.2
5	Arkansas	59.9
23	California	41.1
15	Colorado	47.0
46	Connecticut	25.8
16	Delaware	46.3
19	Florida	44.5
8	Georgia	55.7
28	Hawaii	38.2
27	Idaho	39.1
22	Illinois	42.2
18	Indiana	44.6
39	Iowa	32.5
21	Kansas	43.0
14	Kentucky	51.0
6	Louisiana	58.1
47	Maine	25.4
36	Maryland	35.4
49	Massachusetts	23.3
37	Michigan	34.8
43	Minnesota	27.5
1	Mississippi	64.7
20	Missouri	44.1
34	Montana	36.4
31	Nebraska	37.0
11	Nevada	53.9
50	New Hampshire	20.0
45	New Jersey	26.8
3	New Mexico	62.4
42	New York	29.5
13	North Carolina	52.2
44	North Dakota	27.2
25	Ohio	39.5
7	Oklahoma	58.0
32	Oregon	36.8
41	Pennsylvania	31.6
35	Rhode Island	35.6
12	South Carolina	53.0
29	South Dakota	38.0
10	Tennessee	54.3
2	Texas	64.4
32	Utah	36.8
48	Vermont	24.2
30	Virginia	37.6
38	Washington	33.0
17	West Virginia	45.5
40	Wisconsin	32.3
24	Wyoming	39.9

RANK ORDER

RANK	STATE	RATE
1	Mississippi	64.7
2	Texas	64.4
3	New Mexico	62.4
4	Arizona	61.2
5	Arkansas	59.9
6	Louisiana	58.1
7	Oklahoma	58.0
8	Georgia	55.7
9	Alabama	54.5
10	Tennessee	54.3
11	Nevada	53.9
12	South Carolina	53.0
13	North Carolina	52.2
14	Kentucky	51.0
15	Colorado	47.0
16	Delaware	46.3
17	West Virginia	45.5
18	Indiana	44.6
19	Florida	44.5
20	Missouri	44.1
21	Kansas	43.0
22	Illinois	42.2
23	California	41.1
24	Wyoming	39.9
25	Alaska	39.5
25	Ohio	39.5
27	Idaho	39.1
28	Hawaii	38.2
29	South Dakota	38.0
30	Virginia	37.6
31	Nebraska	37.0
32	Oregon	36.8
32	Utah	36.8
34	Montana	36.4
35	Rhode Island	35.6
36	Maryland	35.4
37	Michigan	34.8
38	Washington	33.0
39	Iowa	32.5
40	Wisconsin	32.3
41	Pennsylvania	31.6
42	New York	29.5
43	Minnesota	27.5
44	North Dakota	27.2
45	New Jersey	26.8
46	Connecticut	25.8
47	Maine	25.4
48	Vermont	24.2
49	Massachusetts	23.3
50	New Hampshire	20.0
	District of Columbia	69.1

Source: U.S. Department of Health and Human Services, National Center for Health Statistics
"National Vital Statistics Reports" (Vol. 52, No. 10, December 17, 2003)
*Final data by state of residence.

Births to Teenage Mothers as a Percent of Births in 2002

National Percent = 10.6% of Live Births*

ALPHA ORDER

RANK	STATE	PERCENT
6	Alabama	14.3
23	Alaska	10.7
10	Arizona	12.9
4	Arkansas	15.2
30	California	9.5
24	Colorado	10.6
47	Connecticut	6.9
22	Delaware	10.9
18	Florida	11.3
14	Georgia	12.2
40	Hawaii	8.8
28	Idaho	9.9
27	Illinois	10.1
18	Indiana	11.3
37	Iowa	9.0
21	Kansas	11.0
11	Kentucky	12.7
3	Louisiana	15.5
41	Maine	8.4
38	Maryland	8.9
50	Massachusetts	5.8
31	Michigan	9.4
44	Minnesota	7.5
1	Mississippi	16.8
15	Missouri	11.7
17	Montana	11.5
31	Nebraska	9.4
20	Nevada	11.2
49	New Hampshire	6.1
48	New Jersey	6.4
2	New Mexico	16.3
45	New York	7.3
15	North Carolina	11.7
41	North Dakota	8.4
24	Ohio	10.6
5	Oklahoma	14.6
29	Oregon	9.8
35	Pennsylvania	9.1
34	Rhode Island	9.3
8	South Carolina	13.4
24	South Dakota	10.6
9	Tennessee	13.3
7	Texas	14.0
45	Utah	7.3
43	Vermont	8.3
35	Virginia	9.1
38	Washington	8.9
11	West Virginia	12.7
31	Wisconsin	9.4
13	Wyoming	12.3

RANK ORDER

RANK	STATE	PERCENT
1	Mississippi	16.8
2	New Mexico	16.3
3	Louisiana	15.5
4	Arkansas	15.2
5	Oklahoma	14.6
6	Alabama	14.3
7	Texas	14.0
8	South Carolina	13.4
9	Tennessee	13.3
10	Arizona	12.9
11	Kentucky	12.7
11	West Virginia	12.7
13	Wyoming	12.3
14	Georgia	12.2
15	Missouri	11.7
15	North Carolina	11.7
17	Montana	11.5
18	Florida	11.3
18	Indiana	11.3
20	Nevada	11.2
21	Kansas	11.0
22	Delaware	10.9
23	Alaska	10.7
24	Colorado	10.6
24	Ohio	10.6
24	South Dakota	10.6
27	Illinois	10.1
28	Idaho	9.9
29	Oregon	9.8
30	California	9.5
31	Michigan	9.4
31	Nebraska	9.4
31	Wisconsin	9.4
34	Rhode Island	9.3
35	Pennsylvania	9.1
35	Virginia	9.1
37	Iowa	9.0
38	Maryland	8.9
38	Washington	8.9
40	Hawaii	8.8
41	Maine	8.4
41	North Dakota	8.4
43	Vermont	8.3
44	Minnesota	7.5
45	New York	7.3
45	Utah	7.3
47	Connecticut	6.9
48	New Jersey	6.4
49	New Hampshire	6.1
50	Massachusetts	5.8

District of Columbia   12.5

Source: Morgan Quitno Press using data from U.S. Dept. of Health and Human Services, Nat'l Center for Health Statistics (unpublished data)

*Live births to women age 15 to 19 years old by state of residence.

Percent Change in Teenage Birth Rate: 1990 to 2002

National Percent Change = 28.2% Decrease*

ALPHA ORDER

RANK	STATE	PERCENT CHANGE
16	Alabama	(23.2)
47	Alaska	(39.5)
7	Arizona	(18.9)
26	Arkansas	(25.2)
50	California	(41.8)
3	Colorado	(13.8)
39	Connecticut	(33.5)
5	Delaware	(15.0)
43	Florida	(35.6)
28	Georgia	(26.2)
44	Hawaii	(37.6)
14	Idaho	(22.7)
38	Illinois	(32.9)
19	Indiana	(23.9)
9	Iowa	(19.8)
18	Kansas	(23.4)
23	Kentucky	(24.6)
13	Louisiana	(21.7)
48	Maine	(40.9)
39	Maryland	(33.5)
41	Massachusetts	(33.6)
49	Michigan	(41.0)
21	Minnesota	(24.2)
10	Mississippi	(20.1)
34	Missouri	(29.8)
24	Montana	(24.8)
1	Nebraska	(12.5)
29	Nevada	(26.5)
46	New Hampshire	(39.4)
42	New Jersey	(33.8)
11	New Mexico	(20.2)
36	New York	(32.3)
15	North Carolina	(22.8)
16	North Dakota	(23.2)
35	Ohio	(31.8)
2	Oklahoma	(13.2)
37	Oregon	(32.6)
33	Pennsylvania	(29.6)
7	Rhode Island	(18.9)
27	South Carolina	(25.7)
6	South Dakota	(18.8)
25	Tennessee	(24.9)
4	Texas	(14.5)
20	Utah	(24.1)
30	Vermont	(28.8)
31	Virginia	(28.9)
45	Washington	(37.9)
12	West Virginia	(20.6)
21	Wisconsin	(24.2)
32	Wyoming	(29.1)

RANK ORDER

RANK	STATE	PERCENT CHANGE
1	Nebraska	(12.5)
2	Oklahoma	(13.2)
3	Colorado	(13.8)
4	Texas	(14.5)
5	Delaware	(15.0)
6	South Dakota	(18.8)
7	Arizona	(18.9)
7	Rhode Island	(18.9)
9	Iowa	(19.8)
10	Mississippi	(20.1)
11	New Mexico	(20.2)
12	West Virginia	(20.6)
13	Louisiana	(21.7)
14	Idaho	(22.7)
15	North Carolina	(22.8)
16	Alabama	(23.2)
16	North Dakota	(23.2)
18	Kansas	(23.4)
19	Indiana	(23.9)
20	Utah	(24.1)
21	Minnesota	(24.2)
21	Wisconsin	(24.2)
23	Kentucky	(24.6)
24	Montana	(24.8)
25	Tennessee	(24.9)
26	Arkansas	(25.2)
27	South Carolina	(25.7)
28	Georgia	(26.2)
29	Nevada	(26.5)
30	Vermont	(28.8)
31	Virginia	(28.9)
32	Wyoming	(29.1)
33	Pennsylvania	(29.6)
34	Missouri	(29.8)
35	Ohio	(31.8)
36	New York	(32.3)
37	Oregon	(32.6)
38	Illinois	(32.9)
39	Connecticut	(33.5)
39	Maryland	(33.5)
41	Massachusetts	(33.6)
42	New Jersey	(33.8)
43	Florida	(35.6)
44	Hawaii	(37.6)
45	Washington	(37.9)
46	New Hampshire	(39.4)
47	Alaska	(39.5)
48	Maine	(40.9)
49	Michigan	(41.0)
50	California	(41.8)

| | District of Columbia | (25.8) |

Source: Morgan Quitno Press using data from U.S. Department of Health and Human Services
   "National Vital Statistics Reports" (Vol. 52, No. 10, December 17, 2003)
      "Surveillance for Pregnancy and Birth Rates Among Teenagers" (MMWR, Vol. 42, No. SS-6, 12/17/93)
*Women aged 15 to 19 years old.

Births to White Teenage Mothers in 2002

National Total = 305,988 Live Births*

ALPHA ORDER

RANK	STATE	BIRTHS	% of USA
20	Alabama	4,739	1.5%
47	Alaska	523	0.2%
7	Arizona	9,763	3.2%
25	Arkansas	3,946	1.3%
2	California	43,092	14.1%
14	Colorado	6,544	2.1%
37	Connecticut	2,137	0.7%
46	Delaware	673	0.2%
3	Florida	14,784	4.8%
8	Georgia	8,883	2.9%
50	Hawaii	172	0.1%
38	Idaho	1,963	0.6%
5	Illinois	11,522	3.8%
12	Indiana	7,729	2.5%
32	Iowa	3,029	1.0%
28	Kansas	3,643	1.2%
16	Kentucky	5,976	2.0%
23	Louisiana	4,141	1.4%
40	Maine	1,091	0.4%
33	Maryland	2,933	1.0%
30	Massachusetts	3,509	1.1%
11	Michigan	8,126	2.7%
29	Minnesota	3,606	1.2%
35	Mississippi	2,871	0.9%
15	Missouri	6,441	2.1%
42	Montana	924	0.3%
39	Nebraska	1,960	0.6%
34	Nevada	2,924	1.0%
43	New Hampshire	836	0.3%
21	New Jersey	4,372	1.4%
26	New Mexico	3,782	1.2%
4	New York	11,909	3.9%
10	North Carolina	8,338	2.7%
49	North Dakota	464	0.2%
6	Ohio	11,164	3.6%
18	Oklahoma	5,332	1.7%
24	Oregon	4,021	1.3%
9	Pennsylvania	8,874	2.9%
41	Rhode Island	930	0.3%
27	South Carolina	3,750	1.2%
45	South Dakota	704	0.2%
13	Tennessee	7,043	2.3%
1	Texas	44,049	14.4%
31	Utah	3,320	1.1%
48	Vermont	519	0.2%
19	Virginia	5,254	1.7%
17	Washington	5,945	1.9%
36	West Virginia	2,504	0.8%
22	Wisconsin	4,363	1.4%
44	Wyoming	731	0.2%

RANK ORDER

RANK	STATE	BIRTHS	% of USA
1	Texas	44,049	14.4%
2	California	43,092	14.1%
3	Florida	14,784	4.8%
4	New York	11,909	3.9%
5	Illinois	11,522	3.8%
6	Ohio	11,164	3.6%
7	Arizona	9,763	3.2%
8	Georgia	8,883	2.9%
9	Pennsylvania	8,874	2.9%
10	North Carolina	8,338	2.7%
11	Michigan	8,126	2.7%
12	Indiana	7,729	2.5%
13	Tennessee	7,043	2.3%
14	Colorado	6,544	2.1%
15	Missouri	6,441	2.1%
16	Kentucky	5,976	2.0%
17	Washington	5,945	1.9%
18	Oklahoma	5,332	1.7%
19	Virginia	5,254	1.7%
20	Alabama	4,739	1.5%
21	New Jersey	4,372	1.4%
22	Wisconsin	4,363	1.4%
23	Louisiana	4,141	1.4%
24	Oregon	4,021	1.3%
25	Arkansas	3,946	1.3%
26	New Mexico	3,782	1.2%
27	South Carolina	3,750	1.2%
28	Kansas	3,643	1.2%
29	Minnesota	3,606	1.2%
30	Massachusetts	3,509	1.1%
31	Utah	3,320	1.1%
32	Iowa	3,029	1.0%
33	Maryland	2,933	1.0%
34	Nevada	2,924	1.0%
35	Mississippi	2,871	0.9%
36	West Virginia	2,504	0.8%
37	Connecticut	2,137	0.7%
38	Idaho	1,963	0.6%
39	Nebraska	1,960	0.6%
40	Maine	1,091	0.4%
41	Rhode Island	930	0.3%
42	Montana	924	0.3%
43	New Hampshire	836	0.3%
44	Wyoming	731	0.2%
45	South Dakota	704	0.2%
46	Delaware	673	0.2%
47	Alaska	523	0.2%
48	Vermont	519	0.2%
49	North Dakota	464	0.2%
50	Hawaii	172	0.1%
	District of Columbia	140	0.0%

Source: Morgan Quitno Press using data from U.S. Dept. of Health and Human Services, Nat'l Center for Health Statistics
(unpublished data)
*Live births to women 15 to 19 years old by state of residence.

White Teenage Birth Rate in 2002

National Rate = 39.0 Births per 1,000 White Teenage Women*

ALPHA ORDER

RANK	STATE	RATE
11	Alabama	47.3
36	Alaska	27.3
3	Arizona	61.4
4	Arkansas	54.2
15	California	44.9
12	Colorado	46.9
44	Connecticut	22.7
26	Delaware	35.1
21	Florida	38.1
9	Georgia	48.8
50	Hawaii	9.9
20	Idaho	38.2
27	Illinois	34.4
18	Indiana	40.6
33	Iowa	30.5
19	Kansas	40.3
8	Kentucky	49.3
17	Louisiana	41.4
41	Maine	25.1
40	Maryland	25.2
48	Massachusetts	20.5
35	Michigan	28.5
45	Minnesota	21.8
7	Mississippi	50.0
21	Missouri	38.1
34	Montana	29.6
29	Nebraska	33.0
6	Nevada	51.0
49	New Hampshire	19.6
46	New Jersey	21.2
2	New Mexico	62.8
38	New York	26.5
13	North Carolina	45.8
47	North Dakota	21.1
28	Ohio	33.2
5	Oklahoma	54.1
24	Oregon	36.5
39	Pennsylvania	25.4
31	Rhode Island	31.9
16	South Carolina	44.5
37	South Dakota	27.1
10	Tennessee	48.0
1	Texas	65.4
25	Utah	36.2
43	Vermont	24.2
32	Virginia	30.7
30	Washington	32.1
14	West Virginia	45.6
42	Wisconsin	24.7
23	Wyoming	38.0

RANK ORDER

RANK	STATE	RATE
1	Texas	65.4
2	New Mexico	62.8
3	Arizona	61.4
4	Arkansas	54.2
5	Oklahoma	54.1
6	Nevada	51.0
7	Mississippi	50.0
8	Kentucky	49.3
9	Georgia	48.8
10	Tennessee	48.0
11	Alabama	47.3
12	Colorado	46.9
13	North Carolina	45.8
14	West Virginia	45.6
15	California	44.9
16	South Carolina	44.5
17	Louisiana	41.4
18	Indiana	40.6
19	Kansas	40.3
20	Idaho	38.2
21	Florida	38.1
21	Missouri	38.1
23	Wyoming	38.0
24	Oregon	36.5
25	Utah	36.2
26	Delaware	35.1
27	Illinois	34.4
28	Ohio	33.2
29	Nebraska	33.0
30	Washington	32.1
31	Rhode Island	31.9
32	Virginia	30.7
33	Iowa	30.5
34	Montana	29.6
35	Michigan	28.5
36	Alaska	27.3
37	South Dakota	27.1
38	New York	26.5
39	Pennsylvania	25.4
40	Maryland	25.2
41	Maine	25.1
42	Wisconsin	24.7
43	Vermont	24.2
44	Connecticut	22.7
45	Minnesota	21.8
46	New Jersey	21.2
47	North Dakota	21.1
48	Massachusetts	20.5
49	New Hampshire	19.6
50	Hawaii	9.9

District of Columbia   25.5

Source: Morgan Quitno Press using data from U.S. Dept. of Health and Human Services, Nat'l Center for Health Statistics
(unpublished data)

*Live births to women age 15 to 19 years old by state of residence. Rates calculated using Census 2002 estimates
for white females ages 15 to 19 years old.

Births to White Teenage Mothers as a Percent of White Births in 2002

National Percent = 9.6% of White Live Births*

ALPHA ORDER

RANK	STATE	PERCENT
9	Alabama	11.9
34	Alaska	8.2
5	Arizona	12.7
3	Arkansas	13.5
20	California	10.1
15	Colorado	10.5
45	Connecticut	6.2
29	Delaware	8.5
23	Florida	9.7
16	Georgia	10.4
50	Hawaii	4.4
23	Idaho	9.7
34	Illinois	8.2
16	Indiana	10.4
28	Iowa	8.6
16	Kansas	10.4
8	Kentucky	12.3
12	Louisiana	11.3
31	Maine	8.4
44	Maryland	6.5
48	Massachusetts	5.3
37	Michigan	7.9
45	Minnesota	6.2
5	Mississippi	12.7
19	Missouri	10.3
23	Montana	9.7
29	Nebraska	8.5
13	Nevada	10.8
47	New Hampshire	6.1
49	New Jersey	5.2
1	New Mexico	16.2
43	New York	6.6
21	North Carolina	9.8
42	North Dakota	6.9
26	Ohio	9.1
3	Oklahoma	13.5
21	Oregon	9.8
38	Pennsylvania	7.5
31	Rhode Island	8.4
14	South Carolina	10.6
36	South Dakota	8.1
11	Tennessee	11.8
2	Texas	13.9
41	Utah	7.1
33	Vermont	8.3
39	Virginia	7.4
27	Washington	8.9
7	West Virginia	12.6
39	Wisconsin	7.4
9	Wyoming	11.9

RANK ORDER

RANK	STATE	PERCENT
1	New Mexico	16.2
2	Texas	13.9
3	Arkansas	13.5
3	Oklahoma	13.5
5	Arizona	12.7
5	Mississippi	12.7
7	West Virginia	12.6
8	Kentucky	12.3
9	Alabama	11.9
9	Wyoming	11.9
11	Tennessee	11.8
12	Louisiana	11.3
13	Nevada	10.8
14	South Carolina	10.6
15	Colorado	10.5
16	Georgia	10.4
16	Indiana	10.4
16	Kansas	10.4
19	Missouri	10.3
20	California	10.1
21	North Carolina	9.8
21	Oregon	9.8
23	Florida	9.7
23	Idaho	9.7
23	Montana	9.7
26	Ohio	9.1
27	Washington	8.9
28	Iowa	8.6
29	Delaware	8.5
29	Nebraska	8.5
31	Maine	8.4
31	Rhode Island	8.4
33	Vermont	8.3
34	Alaska	8.2
34	Illinois	8.2
36	South Dakota	8.1
37	Michigan	7.9
38	Pennsylvania	7.5
39	Virginia	7.4
39	Wisconsin	7.4
41	Utah	7.1
42	North Dakota	6.9
43	New York	6.6
44	Maryland	6.5
45	Connecticut	6.2
45	Minnesota	6.2
47	New Hampshire	6.1
48	Massachusetts	5.3
49	New Jersey	5.2
50	Hawaii	4.4
	District of Columbia	5.2

Source: Morgan Quitno Press using data from U.S. Dept. of Health and Human Services, Nat'l Center for Health Statistics (unpublished data)
Live births to women age 15 to 19 years old by state of residence.

Births to Black Teenage Mothers in 2002

National Total = 103,795 Live Births*

ALPHA ORDER

RANK	STATE	BIRTHS	% of USA
14	Alabama	3,643	3.5%
40	Alaska	59	0.1%
32	Arizona	459	0.4%
21	Arkansas	1,658	1.6%
8	California	4,411	4.2%
31	Colorado	485	0.5%
27	Connecticut	721	0.7%
29	Delaware	526	0.5%
1	Florida	8,106	7.8%
3	Georgia	7,197	6.9%
41	Hawaii	44	0.0%
48	Idaho	11	0.0%
4	Illinois	6,554	6.3%
20	Indiana	1,809	1.7%
35	Iowa	265	0.3%
28	Kansas	550	0.5%
25	Kentucky	880	0.8%
6	Louisiana	5,764	5.6%
44	Maine	18	0.0%
15	Maryland	3,524	3.4%
24	Massachusetts	902	0.9%
12	Michigan	3,898	3.8%
26	Minnesota	742	0.7%
10	Mississippi	4,008	3.9%
19	Missouri	2,281	2.2%
50	Montana	5	0.0%
34	Nebraska	333	0.3%
30	Nevada	494	0.5%
43	New Hampshire	23	0.0%
18	New Jersey	2,854	2.7%
39	New Mexico	81	0.1%
5	New York	6,036	5.8%
7	North Carolina	4,927	4.7%
45	North Dakota	17	0.0%
9	Ohio	4,400	4.2%
23	Oklahoma	928	0.9%
37	Oregon	151	0.1%
11	Pennsylvania	3,918	3.8%
36	Rhode Island	162	0.2%
16	South Carolina	3,503	3.4%
46	South Dakota	15	0.0%
17	Tennessee	3,181	3.1%
2	Texas	7,635	7.4%
42	Utah	42	0.0%
48	Vermont	11	0.0%
13	Virginia	3,644	3.5%
33	Washington	422	0.4%
38	West Virginia	122	0.1%
22	Wisconsin	1,573	1.5%
47	Wyoming	12	0.0%

RANK ORDER

RANK	STATE	BIRTHS	% of USA
1	Florida	8,106	7.8%
2	Texas	7,635	7.4%
3	Georgia	7,197	6.9%
4	Illinois	6,554	6.3%
5	New York	6,036	5.8%
6	Louisiana	5,764	5.6%
7	North Carolina	4,927	4.7%
8	California	4,411	4.2%
9	Ohio	4,400	4.2%
10	Mississippi	4,008	3.9%
11	Pennsylvania	3,918	3.8%
12	Michigan	3,898	3.8%
13	Virginia	3,644	3.5%
14	Alabama	3,643	3.5%
15	Maryland	3,524	3.4%
16	South Carolina	3,503	3.4%
17	Tennessee	3,181	3.1%
18	New Jersey	2,854	2.7%
19	Missouri	2,281	2.2%
20	Indiana	1,809	1.7%
21	Arkansas	1,658	1.6%
22	Wisconsin	1,573	1.5%
23	Oklahoma	928	0.9%
24	Massachusetts	902	0.9%
25	Kentucky	880	0.8%
26	Minnesota	742	0.7%
27	Connecticut	721	0.7%
28	Kansas	550	0.5%
29	Delaware	526	0.5%
30	Nevada	494	0.5%
31	Colorado	485	0.5%
32	Arizona	459	0.4%
33	Washington	422	0.4%
34	Nebraska	333	0.3%
35	Iowa	265	0.3%
36	Rhode Island	162	0.2%
37	Oregon	151	0.1%
38	West Virginia	122	0.1%
39	New Mexico	81	0.1%
40	Alaska	59	0.1%
41	Hawaii	44	0.0%
42	Utah	42	0.0%
43	New Hampshire	23	0.0%
44	Maine	18	0.0%
45	North Dakota	17	0.0%
46	South Dakota	15	0.0%
47	Wyoming	12	0.0%
48	Idaho	11	0.0%
48	Vermont	11	0.0%
50	Montana	5	0.0%
	District of Columbia	791	0.8%

Source: Morgan Quitno Press using data from U.S. Dept. of Health and Human Services, Nat'l Center for Health Statistics (unpublished data)

*Live births to women 15 to 19 years old by state of residence.

Black Teenage Birth Rate in 2002

National Rate = 65.4 Births per 1,000 Black Teenage Women*

ALPHA ORDER				RANK ORDER		
RANK	STATE	RATE		RANK	STATE	RATE
18	Alabama	69.3		1	Wisconsin	99.4
39	Alaska	41.8		2	Nebraska	90.8
32	Arizona	52.3		3	Louisiana	81.9
7	Arkansas	80.2		4	Mississippi	81.8
41	California	40.4		5	Delaware	81.4
29	Colorado	55.8		6	Indiana	80.4
34	Connecticut	47.3		7	Arkansas	80.2
5	Delaware	81.4		8	Illinois	80.1
24	Florida	66.4		9	Iowa	79.2
17	Georgia	69.6		10	Missouri	78.7
47	Hawaii	30.6		11	Tennessee	78.3
49	Idaho	24.2		12	Ohio	77.0
8	Illinois	80.1		13	Nevada	76.1
6	Indiana	80.4		14	Minnesota	74.7
9	Iowa	79.2		15	Pennsylvania	73.8
16	Kansas	71.3		16	Kansas	71.3
21	Kentucky	67.6		17	Georgia	69.6
3	Louisiana	81.9		18	Alabama	69.3
46	Maine	32.2		19	Oklahoma	68.9
28	Maryland	57.7		20	Texas	68.8
33	Massachusetts	48.2		21	Kentucky	67.6
25	Michigan	65.7		22	North Carolina	67.0
14	Minnesota	74.7		23	South Carolina	66.6
4	Mississippi	81.8		24	Florida	66.4
10	Missouri	78.7		25	Michigan	65.7
50	Montana	19.6		26	Virginia	60.6
2	Nebraska	90.8		27	North Dakota	57.8
13	Nevada	76.1		28	Maryland	57.7
45	New Hampshire	33.4		29	Colorado	55.8
30	New Jersey	55.2		30	New Jersey	55.2
43	New Mexico	37.2		31	Rhode Island	53.8
37	New York	43.7		32	Arizona	52.3
22	North Carolina	67.0		33	Massachusetts	48.2
27	North Dakota	57.8		34	Connecticut	47.3
12	Ohio	77.0		35	West Virginia	47.0
19	Oklahoma	68.9		36	Wyoming	46.2
38	Oregon	43.6		37	New York	43.7
15	Pennsylvania	73.8		38	Oregon	43.6
31	Rhode Island	53.8		39	Alaska	41.8
23	South Carolina	66.6		40	South Dakota	41.1
40	South Dakota	41.1		41	California	40.4
11	Tennessee	78.3		42	Washington	37.6
20	Texas	68.8		43	New Mexico	37.2
48	Utah	27.3		44	Vermont	36.4
44	Vermont	36.4		45	New Hampshire	33.4
26	Virginia	60.6		46	Maine	32.2
42	Washington	37.6		47	Hawaii	30.6
35	West Virginia	47.0		48	Utah	27.3
1	Wisconsin	99.4		49	Idaho	24.2
36	Wyoming	46.2		50	Montana	19.6
					District of Columbia	103.6

Source: Morgan Quitno Press using data from U.S. Dept. of Health and Human Services, Nat'l Center for Health Statistics
   (unpublished data)
*Live births to women age 15 to 19 years old by state of residence. Rates calculated using Census 2002 estimates
for white females ages 15 to 19 years old.

Births to Black Teenage Mothers as a Percent of Black Births in 2002

National Percent = 17.5% of Black Live Births*

RANK	STATE	PERCENT
11	Alabama	19.9
40	Alaska	13.7
29	Arizona	16.5
4	Arkansas	22.3
41	California	13.5
29	Colorado	16.5
39	Connecticut	13.9
15	Delaware	19.4
26	Florida	17.5
28	Georgia	16.8
50	Hawaii	9.3
47	Idaho	10.7
10	Illinois	20.6
15	Indiana	19.4
8	Iowa	21.0
19	Kansas	19.0
25	Kentucky	17.8
7	Louisiana	21.6
48	Maine	10.3
35	Maryland	14.6
46	Massachusetts	10.8
27	Michigan	17.4
34	Minnesota	15.3
6	Mississippi	22.0
9	Missouri	20.7
41	Montana	13.5
3	Nebraska	23.1
20	Nevada	18.9
49	New Hampshire	10.2
37	New Jersey	14.3
33	New Mexico	15.9
45	New York	12.2
24	North Carolina	17.9
20	North Dakota	18.9
13	Ohio	19.5
12	Oklahoma	19.7
32	Oregon	16.0
17	Pennsylvania	19.3
38	Rhode Island	14.1
17	South Carolina	19.3
35	South Dakota	14.6
13	Tennessee	19.5
22	Texas	18.3
43	Utah	12.4
1	Vermont	25.0
29	Virginia	16.5
43	Washington	12.4
23	West Virginia	18.0
2	Wisconsin	24.5
5	Wyoming	22.2

RANK	STATE	PERCENT
1	Vermont	25.0
2	Wisconsin	24.5
3	Nebraska	23.1
4	Arkansas	22.3
5	Wyoming	22.2
6	Mississippi	22.0
7	Louisiana	21.6
8	Iowa	21.0
9	Missouri	20.7
10	Illinois	20.6
11	Alabama	19.9
12	Oklahoma	19.7
13	Ohio	19.5
13	Tennessee	19.5
15	Delaware	19.4
15	Indiana	19.4
17	Pennsylvania	19.3
17	South Carolina	19.3
19	Kansas	19.0
20	Nevada	18.9
20	North Dakota	18.9
22	Texas	18.3
23	West Virginia	18.0
24	North Carolina	17.9
25	Kentucky	17.8
26	Florida	17.5
27	Michigan	17.4
28	Georgia	16.8
29	Arizona	16.5
29	Colorado	16.5
29	Virginia	16.5
32	Oregon	16.0
33	New Mexico	15.9
34	Minnesota	15.3
35	Maryland	14.6
35	South Dakota	14.6
37	New Jersey	14.3
38	Rhode Island	14.1
39	Connecticut	13.9
40	Alaska	13.7
41	California	13.5
41	Montana	13.5
43	Utah	12.4
43	Washington	12.4
45	New York	12.2
46	Massachusetts	10.8
47	Idaho	10.7
48	Maine	10.3
49	New Hampshire	10.2
50	Hawaii	9.3

District of Columbia — 17.1

Source: Morgan Quitno Press using data from U.S. Dept. of Health and Human Services, Nat'l Center for Health Statistics (unpublished data)

*Live births to women 15 to 19 years old by state of residence.

Births to Women 35 to 54 Years Old in 2002

National Total = 555,202 Live Births*

ALPHA ORDER

RANK	STATE	BIRTHS	% of USA
27	Alabama	5,052	0.9%
45	Alaska	1,352	0.2%
18	Arizona	9,673	1.7%
38	Arkansas	2,744	0.5%
1	California	87,615	15.8%
17	Colorado	9,709	1.7%
20	Connecticut	9,169	1.7%
44	Delaware	1,499	0.3%
4	Florida	29,372	5.3%
12	Georgia	15,735	2.8%
36	Hawaii	2,880	0.5%
41	Idaho	2,034	0.4%
5	Illinois	26,258	4.7%
21	Indiana	8,712	1.6%
31	Iowa	4,073	0.7%
30	Kansas	4,293	0.8%
28	Kentucky	4,841	0.9%
24	Louisiana	5,775	1.0%
42	Maine	1,887	0.3%
13	Maryland	13,539	2.4%
8	Massachusetts	18,383	3.3%
10	Michigan	16,755	3.0%
16	Minnesota	10,281	1.9%
34	Mississippi	3,024	0.5%
22	Missouri	8,289	1.5%
46	Montana	1,264	0.2%
35	Nebraska	2,949	0.5%
32	Nevada	4,058	0.7%
39	New Hampshire	2,675	0.5%
6	New Jersey	24,261	4.4%
37	New Mexico	2,858	0.5%
2	New York	48,802	8.8%
14	North Carolina	13,311	2.4%
49	North Dakota	878	0.2%
9	Ohio	17,784	3.2%
33	Oklahoma	4,034	0.7%
25	Oregon	5,774	1.0%
7	Pennsylvania	22,143	4.0%
40	Rhode Island	2,264	0.4%
26	South Carolina	5,750	1.0%
48	South Dakota	1,107	0.2%
23	Tennessee	7,411	1.3%
3	Texas	39,097	7.0%
29	Utah	4,304	0.8%
47	Vermont	1,109	0.2%
11	Virginia	15,747	2.8%
15	Washington	11,650	2.1%
43	West Virginia	1,712	0.3%
19	Wisconsin	9,297	1.7%
50	Wyoming	600	0.1%

RANK ORDER

RANK	STATE	BIRTHS	% of USA
1	California	87,615	15.8%
2	New York	48,802	8.8%
3	Texas	39,097	7.0%
4	Florida	29,372	5.3%
5	Illinois	26,258	4.7%
6	New Jersey	24,261	4.4%
7	Pennsylvania	22,143	4.0%
8	Massachusetts	18,383	3.3%
9	Ohio	17,784	3.2%
10	Michigan	16,755	3.0%
11	Virginia	15,747	2.8%
12	Georgia	15,735	2.8%
13	Maryland	13,539	2.4%
14	North Carolina	13,311	2.4%
15	Washington	11,650	2.1%
16	Minnesota	10,281	1.9%
17	Colorado	9,709	1.7%
18	Arizona	9,673	1.7%
19	Wisconsin	9,297	1.7%
20	Connecticut	9,169	1.7%
21	Indiana	8,712	1.6%
22	Missouri	8,289	1.5%
23	Tennessee	7,411	1.3%
24	Louisiana	5,775	1.0%
25	Oregon	5,774	1.0%
26	South Carolina	5,750	1.0%
27	Alabama	5,052	0.9%
28	Kentucky	4,841	0.9%
29	Utah	4,304	0.8%
30	Kansas	4,293	0.8%
31	Iowa	4,073	0.7%
32	Nevada	4,058	0.7%
33	Oklahoma	4,034	0.7%
34	Mississippi	3,024	0.5%
35	Nebraska	2,949	0.5%
36	Hawaii	2,880	0.5%
37	New Mexico	2,858	0.5%
38	Arkansas	2,744	0.5%
39	New Hampshire	2,675	0.5%
40	Rhode Island	2,264	0.4%
41	Idaho	2,034	0.4%
42	Maine	1,887	0.3%
43	West Virginia	1,712	0.3%
44	Delaware	1,499	0.3%
45	Alaska	1,352	0.2%
46	Montana	1,264	0.2%
47	Vermont	1,109	0.2%
48	South Dakota	1,107	0.2%
49	North Dakota	878	0.2%
50	Wyoming	600	0.1%
	District of Columbia	1,419	0.3%

Source: Morgan Quitno Press using data from U.S. Dept of Health & Human Services, National Center for Health Statistics
(unpublished data)
*By state of residence.

Births to Women 35 to 54 Years Old as a Percent of All Births in 2002

National Percent = 13.8% of Live Births*

ALPHA ORDER			RANK ORDER		
RANK	STATE	PERCENT	RANK	STATE	PERCENT
46	Alabama	8.6	1	Massachusetts	22.8
19	Alaska	13.6	2	Connecticut	21.8
31	Arizona	11.0	3	New Jersey	21.1
49	Arkansas	7.3	4	New York	19.4
9	California	16.6	5	Maryland	18.5
17	Colorado	14.2	5	New Hampshire	18.5
2	Connecticut	21.8	7	Rhode Island	17.6
21	Delaware	13.5	8	Vermont	17.4
16	Florida	14.3	9	California	16.6
26	Georgia	11.8	10	Hawaii	16.5
10	Hawaii	16.5	11	Virginia	15.8
40	Idaho	9.7	12	Pennsylvania	15.5
15	Illinois	14.5	13	Minnesota	15.1
39	Indiana	10.2	14	Washington	14.7
34	Iowa	10.8	15	Illinois	14.5
33	Kansas	10.9	16	Florida	14.3
43	Kentucky	8.9	17	Colorado	14.2
43	Louisiana	8.9	18	Maine	13.9
18	Maine	13.9	19	Alaska	13.6
5	Maryland	18.5	19	Wisconsin	13.6
1	Massachusetts	22.8	21	Delaware	13.5
22	Michigan	12.9	22	Michigan	12.9
13	Minnesota	15.1	23	Oregon	12.8
49	Mississippi	7.3	24	Nevada	12.5
31	Missouri	11.0	25	Ohio	12.0
28	Montana	11.4	26	Georgia	11.8
27	Nebraska	11.6	27	Nebraska	11.6
24	Nevada	12.5	28	Montana	11.4
5	New Hampshire	18.5	29	North Carolina	11.3
3	New Jersey	21.1	29	North Dakota	11.3
37	New Mexico	10.3	31	Arizona	11.0
4	New York	19.4	31	Missouri	11.0
29	North Carolina	11.3	33	Kansas	10.9
29	North Dakota	11.3	34	Iowa	10.8
25	Ohio	12.0	35	South Carolina	10.5
48	Oklahoma	8.0	35	Texas	10.5
23	Oregon	12.8	37	New Mexico	10.3
12	Pennsylvania	15.5	37	South Dakota	10.3
7	Rhode Island	17.6	39	Indiana	10.2
35	South Carolina	10.5	40	Idaho	9.7
37	South Dakota	10.3	41	Tennessee	9.6
41	Tennessee	9.6	42	Wyoming	9.2
35	Texas	10.5	43	Kentucky	8.9
45	Utah	8.8	43	Louisiana	8.9
8	Vermont	17.4	45	Utah	8.8
11	Virginia	15.8	46	Alabama	8.6
14	Washington	14.7	47	West Virginia	8.3
47	West Virginia	8.3	48	Oklahoma	8.0
19	Wisconsin	13.6	49	Arkansas	7.3
42	Wyoming	9.2	49	Mississippi	7.3
				District of Columbia	18.9

Source: Morgan Quitno Press using data from U.S. Dept of Health & Human Services, National Center for Health Statistics (unpublished data)
*By state of residence.

40

Births by Vaginal Delivery in 2002

National Total = 2,972,056 Live Births*

RANK	STATE	BIRTHS	% of USA
24	Alabama	42,043	1.4%
47	Alaska	8,000	0.3%
13	Arizona	69,128	2.3%
34	Arkansas	26,543	0.9%
1	California	387,489	13.0%
20	Colorado	53,982	1.8%
30	Connecticut	31,039	1.0%
46	Delaware	8,062	0.3%
4	Florida	146,989	4.9%
8	Georgia	98,775	3.3%
40	Hawaii	13,737	0.5%
38	Idaho	16,839	0.6%
5	Illinois	137,453	4.6%
14	Indiana	63,981	2.2%
33	Iowa	28,244	1.0%
31	Kansas	29,638	1.0%
26	Kentucky	39,048	1.3%
23	Louisiana	45,151	1.5%
42	Maine	10,074	0.3%
21	Maryland	53,159	1.8%
16	Massachusetts	58,064	2.0%
9	Michigan	97,605	3.3%
22	Minnesota	52,923	1.8%
32	Mississippi	28,606	1.0%
18	Missouri	55,911	1.9%
44	Montana	8,519	0.3%
37	Nebraska	18,606	0.6%
35	Nevada	24,200	0.8%
41	New Hampshire	10,947	0.4%
11	New Jersey	79,293	2.7%
36	New Mexico	22,452	0.8%
3	New York	183,282	6.2%
10	North Carolina	86,359	2.9%
48	North Dakota	5,965	0.2%
6	Ohio	113,622	3.8%
28	Oklahoma	36,228	1.2%
29	Oregon	34,617	1.2%
7	Pennsylvania	107,423	3.6%
43	Rhode Island	9,516	0.3%
27	South Carolina	38,963	1.3%
45	South Dakota	8,066	0.3%
17	Tennessee	56,174	1.9%
2	Texas	268,536	9.0%
25	Utah	39,788	1.3%
50	Vermont	5,052	0.2%
12	Virginia	72,960	2.5%
15	Washington	60,061	2.0%
39	West Virginia	14,643	0.5%
19	Wisconsin	54,437	1.8%
49	Wyoming	5,168	0.2%

RANK	STATE	BIRTHS	% of USA
1	California	387,489	13.0%
2	Texas	268,536	9.0%
3	New York	183,282	6.2%
4	Florida	146,989	4.9%
5	Illinois	137,453	4.6%
6	Ohio	113,622	3.8%
7	Pennsylvania	107,423	3.6%
8	Georgia	98,775	3.3%
9	Michigan	97,605	3.3%
10	North Carolina	86,359	2.9%
11	New Jersey	79,293	2.7%
12	Virginia	72,960	2.5%
13	Arizona	69,128	2.3%
14	Indiana	63,981	2.2%
15	Washington	60,061	2.0%
16	Massachusetts	58,064	2.0%
17	Tennessee	56,174	1.9%
18	Missouri	55,911	1.9%
19	Wisconsin	54,437	1.8%
20	Colorado	53,982	1.8%
21	Maryland	53,159	1.8%
22	Minnesota	52,923	1.8%
23	Louisiana	45,151	1.5%
24	Alabama	42,043	1.4%
25	Utah	39,788	1.3%
26	Kentucky	39,048	1.3%
27	South Carolina	38,963	1.3%
28	Oklahoma	36,228	1.2%
29	Oregon	34,617	1.2%
30	Connecticut	31,039	1.0%
31	Kansas	29,638	1.0%
32	Mississippi	28,606	1.0%
33	Iowa	28,244	1.0%
34	Arkansas	26,543	0.9%
35	Nevada	24,200	0.8%
36	New Mexico	22,452	0.8%
37	Nebraska	18,606	0.6%
38	Idaho	16,839	0.6%
39	West Virginia	14,643	0.5%
40	Hawaii	13,737	0.5%
41	New Hampshire	10,947	0.4%
42	Maine	10,074	0.3%
43	Rhode Island	9,516	0.3%
44	Montana	8,519	0.3%
45	South Dakota	8,066	0.3%
46	Delaware	8,062	0.3%
47	Alaska	8,000	0.3%
48	North Dakota	5,965	0.2%
49	Wyoming	5,168	0.2%
50	Vermont	5,052	0.2%
	District of Columbia	5,511	0.2%

Source: Morgan Quitno Press using data from U.S. Dept of Health & Human Services, National Center for Health Statistics
"National Vital Statistics Reports" (Vol. 52, No. 10, December 17, 2003)
*By state of residence.

Percent of Births by Vaginal Delivery in 2002

National Percent = 73.9% of Live Births*

ALPHA ORDER

RANK	STATE	PERCENT
45	Alabama	71.3
3	Alaska	80.5
9	Arizona	78.7
46	Arkansas	70.9
33	California	73.2
7	Colorado	78.9
29	Connecticut	73.9
36	Delaware	72.7
43	Florida	71.5
28	Georgia	74.1
10	Hawaii	78.6
4	Idaho	80.3
16	Illinois	76.1
20	Indiana	75.2
20	Iowa	75.2
20	Kansas	75.2
40	Kentucky	72.0
48	Louisiana	69.6
25	Maine	74.3
37	Maryland	72.5
40	Massachusetts	72.0
24	Michigan	75.1
11	Minnesota	77.8
50	Mississippi	68.9
25	Missouri	74.3
12	Montana	77.1
32	Nebraska	73.3
25	Nevada	74.3
18	New Hampshire	75.8
49	New Jersey	69.1
1	New Mexico	80.9
35	New York	72.9
31	North Carolina	73.6
13	North Dakota	76.9
15	Ohio	76.4
42	Oklahoma	71.9
14	Oregon	76.6
20	Pennsylvania	75.2
30	Rhode Island	73.8
44	South Carolina	71.4
19	South Dakota	75.4
37	Tennessee	72.5
39	Texas	72.1
1	Utah	80.9
6	Vermont	79.1
33	Virginia	73.2
17	Washington	76.0
47	West Virginia	70.7
5	Wisconsin	79.4
7	Wyoming	78.9

RANK ORDER

RANK	STATE	PERCENT
1	New Mexico	80.9
1	Utah	80.9
3	Alaska	80.5
4	Idaho	80.3
5	Wisconsin	79.4
6	Vermont	79.1
7	Colorado	78.9
7	Wyoming	78.9
9	Arizona	78.7
10	Hawaii	78.6
11	Minnesota	77.8
12	Montana	77.1
13	North Dakota	76.9
14	Oregon	76.6
15	Ohio	76.4
16	Illinois	76.1
17	Washington	76.0
18	New Hampshire	75.8
19	South Dakota	75.4
20	Indiana	75.2
20	Iowa	75.2
20	Kansas	75.2
20	Pennsylvania	75.2
24	Michigan	75.1
25	Maine	74.3
25	Missouri	74.3
25	Nevada	74.3
28	Georgia	74.1
29	Connecticut	73.9
30	Rhode Island	73.8
31	North Carolina	73.6
32	Nebraska	73.3
33	California	73.2
33	Virginia	73.2
35	New York	72.9
36	Delaware	72.7
37	Maryland	72.5
37	Tennessee	72.5
39	Texas	72.1
40	Kentucky	72.0
40	Massachusetts	72.0
42	Oklahoma	71.9
43	Florida	71.5
44	South Carolina	71.4
45	Alabama	71.3
46	Arkansas	70.9
47	West Virginia	70.7
48	Louisiana	69.6
49	New Jersey	69.1
50	Mississippi	68.9

District of Columbia 73.5

Source: Morgan Quitno Press using data from U.S. Dept of Health & Human Services, National Center for Health Statistics "National Vital Statistics Reports" (Vol. 52, No. 10, December 17, 2003)

By state of residence.

Births by Cesarean Delivery in 2002

National Total = 1,049,670 Live Cesarean Births*

ALPHA ORDER

RANK	STATE	BIRTHS	% of USA
21	Alabama	16,924	1.6%
47	Alaska	1,938	0.2%
20	Arizona	18,709	1.8%
30	Arkansas	10,894	1.0%
1	California	141,868	13.5%
25	Colorado	14,436	1.4%
29	Connecticut	10,962	1.0%
44	Delaware	3,028	0.3%
4	Florida	58,590	5.6%
9	Georgia	34,525	3.3%
40	Hawaii	3,740	0.4%
39	Idaho	4,131	0.4%
5	Illinois	43,169	4.1%
15	Indiana	21,100	2.0%
34	Iowa	9,315	0.9%
32	Kansas	9,774	0.9%
23	Kentucky	15,185	1.4%
17	Louisiana	19,721	1.9%
42	Maine	3,485	0.3%
16	Maryland	20,164	1.9%
13	Massachusetts	22,581	2.2%
10	Michigan	32,362	3.1%
24	Minnesota	15,102	1.4%
28	Mississippi	12,912	1.2%
18	Missouri	19,340	1.8%
46	Montana	2,530	0.2%
36	Nebraska	6,777	0.6%
35	Nevada	8,371	0.8%
41	New Hampshire	3,495	0.3%
6	New Jersey	35,458	3.4%
38	New Mexico	5,301	0.5%
3	New York	68,133	6.5%
11	North Carolina	30,976	3.0%
48	North Dakota	1,792	0.2%
8	Ohio	35,098	3.3%
26	Oklahoma	14,159	1.3%
31	Oregon	10,575	1.0%
7	Pennsylvania	35,427	3.4%
43	Rhode Island	3,378	0.3%
22	South Carolina	15,607	1.5%
45	South Dakota	2,632	0.3%
14	Tennessee	21,308	2.0%
2	Texas	103,914	9.9%
33	Utah	9,394	0.9%
50	Vermont	1,335	0.1%
12	Virginia	26,712	2.5%
19	Washington	18,967	1.8%
37	West Virginia	6,069	0.6%
27	Wisconsin	14,123	1.3%
49	Wyoming	1,382	0.1%

RANK ORDER

RANK	STATE	BIRTHS	% of USA
1	California	141,868	13.5%
2	Texas	103,914	9.9%
3	New York	68,133	6.5%
4	Florida	58,590	5.6%
5	Illinois	43,169	4.1%
6	New Jersey	35,458	3.4%
7	Pennsylvania	35,427	3.4%
8	Ohio	35,098	3.3%
9	Georgia	34,525	3.3%
10	Michigan	32,362	3.1%
11	North Carolina	30,976	3.0%
12	Virginia	26,712	2.5%
13	Massachusetts	22,581	2.2%
14	Tennessee	21,308	2.0%
15	Indiana	21,100	2.0%
16	Maryland	20,164	1.9%
17	Louisiana	19,721	1.9%
18	Missouri	19,340	1.8%
19	Washington	18,967	1.8%
20	Arizona	18,709	1.8%
21	Alabama	16,924	1.6%
22	South Carolina	15,607	1.5%
23	Kentucky	15,185	1.4%
24	Minnesota	15,102	1.4%
25	Colorado	14,436	1.4%
26	Oklahoma	14,159	1.3%
27	Wisconsin	14,123	1.3%
28	Mississippi	12,912	1.2%
29	Connecticut	10,962	1.0%
30	Arkansas	10,894	1.0%
31	Oregon	10,575	1.0%
32	Kansas	9,774	0.9%
33	Utah	9,394	0.9%
34	Iowa	9,315	0.9%
35	Nevada	8,371	0.8%
36	Nebraska	6,777	0.6%
37	West Virginia	6,069	0.6%
38	New Mexico	5,301	0.5%
39	Idaho	4,131	0.4%
40	Hawaii	3,740	0.4%
41	New Hampshire	3,495	0.3%
42	Maine	3,485	0.3%
43	Rhode Island	3,378	0.3%
44	Delaware	3,028	0.3%
45	South Dakota	2,632	0.3%
46	Montana	2,530	0.2%
47	Alaska	1,938	0.2%
48	North Dakota	1,792	0.2%
49	Wyoming	1,382	0.1%
50	Vermont	1,335	0.1%
	District of Columbia	1,987	0.2%

Source: Morgan Quitno Press using data from U.S. Dept of Health & Human Services, National Center for Health Statistics
"National Vital Statistics Reports" (Vol. 52, No. 10, December 17, 2003)
*By state of residence.

43

Percent of Births by Cesarean Delivery in 2002

National Percent = 26.1% of Live Births*

ALPHA ORDER			RANK ORDER		
RANK	STATE	PERCENT	RANK	STATE	PERCENT
6	Alabama	28.7	1	Mississippi	31.1
48	Alaska	19.5	2	New Jersey	30.9
42	Arizona	21.3	3	Louisiana	30.4
5	Arkansas	29.1	4	West Virginia	29.3
17	California	26.8	5	Arkansas	29.1
43	Colorado	21.1	6	Alabama	28.7
22	Connecticut	26.1	7	South Carolina	28.6
15	Delaware	27.3	8	Florida	28.5
8	Florida	28.5	9	Oklahoma	28.1
23	Georgia	25.9	10	Kentucky	28.0
41	Hawaii	21.4	10	Massachusetts	28.0
47	Idaho	19.7	12	Texas	27.9
35	Illinois	23.9	13	Maryland	27.5
28	Indiana	24.8	13	Tennessee	27.5
28	Iowa	24.8	15	Delaware	27.3
28	Kansas	24.8	16	New York	27.1
10	Kentucky	28.0	17	California	26.8
3	Louisiana	30.4	17	Virginia	26.8
24	Maine	25.7	19	Nebraska	26.7
13	Maryland	27.5	20	North Carolina	26.4
10	Massachusetts	28.0	21	Rhode Island	26.2
27	Michigan	24.9	22	Connecticut	26.1
40	Minnesota	22.2	23	Georgia	25.9
1	Mississippi	31.1	24	Maine	25.7
24	Missouri	25.7	24	Missouri	25.7
39	Montana	22.9	24	Nevada	25.7
19	Nebraska	26.7	27	Michigan	24.9
24	Nevada	25.7	28	Indiana	24.8
33	New Hampshire	24.2	28	Iowa	24.8
2	New Jersey	30.9	28	Kansas	24.8
49	New Mexico	19.1	28	Pennsylvania	24.8
16	New York	27.1	32	South Dakota	24.6
20	North Carolina	26.4	33	New Hampshire	24.2
38	North Dakota	23.1	34	Washington	24.0
36	Ohio	23.6	35	Illinois	23.9
9	Oklahoma	28.1	36	Ohio	23.6
37	Oregon	23.4	37	Oregon	23.4
28	Pennsylvania	24.8	38	North Dakota	23.1
21	Rhode Island	26.2	39	Montana	22.9
7	South Carolina	28.6	40	Minnesota	22.2
32	South Dakota	24.6	41	Hawaii	21.4
13	Tennessee	27.5	42	Arizona	21.3
12	Texas	27.9	43	Colorado	21.1
49	Utah	19.1	43	Wyoming	21.1
45	Vermont	20.9	45	Vermont	20.9
17	Virginia	26.8	46	Wisconsin	20.6
34	Washington	24.0	47	Idaho	19.7
4	West Virginia	29.3	48	Alaska	19.5
46	Wisconsin	20.6	49	New Mexico	19.1
43	Wyoming	21.1	49	Utah	19.1
				District of Columbia	26.5

Source: U.S. Department of Health and Human Services, National Center for Health Statistics
    "National Vital Statistics Reports" (Vol. 52, No. 10, December 17, 2003)
*Final data by state of residence.

Percent Change in Rate of Cesarean Births: 1998 to 2002

National Percent Change = 23.1% Increase*

ALPHA ORDER

RANK	STATE	PERCENT CHANGE
39	Alabama	19.6
6	Alaska	32.7
21	Arizona	25.3
45	Arkansas	16.9
26	California	23.5
14	Colorado	28.7
10	Connecticut	29.9
44	Delaware	17.7
15	Florida	27.2
24	Georgia	24.5
1	Hawaii	37.2
20	Idaho	25.5
28	Illinois	23.2
25	Indiana	24.0
17	Iowa	26.5
5	Kansas	33.3
30	Kentucky	22.8
45	Louisiana	16.9
9	Maine	30.5
12	Maryland	29.1
4	Massachusetts	34.0
37	Michigan	20.9
27	Minnesota	23.3
48	Mississippi	15.2
23	Missouri	24.8
36	Montana	21.2
11	Nebraska	29.6
38	Nevada	20.1
8	New Hampshire	30.8
33	New Jersey	21.7
47	New Mexico	16.5
43	New York	18.3
30	North Carolina	22.8
41	North Dakota	19.1
22	Ohio	24.9
28	Oklahoma	23.2
7	Oregon	31.5
17	Pennsylvania	26.5
2	Rhode Island	34.4
32	South Carolina	22.2
49	South Dakota	14.4
33	Tennessee	21.7
42	Texas	18.7
40	Utah	19.4
16	Vermont	26.7
19	Virginia	26.4
3	Washington	34.1
35	West Virginia	21.6
13	Wisconsin	28.8
50	Wyoming	13.4

RANK ORDER

RANK	STATE	PERCENT CHANGE
1	Hawaii	37.2
2	Rhode Island	34.4
3	Washington	34.1
4	Massachusetts	34.0
5	Kansas	33.3
6	Alaska	32.7
7	Oregon	31.5
8	New Hampshire	30.8
9	Maine	30.5
10	Connecticut	29.9
11	Nebraska	29.6
12	Maryland	29.1
13	Wisconsin	28.8
14	Colorado	28.7
15	Florida	27.2
16	Vermont	26.7
17	Iowa	26.5
17	Pennsylvania	26.5
19	Virginia	26.4
20	Idaho	25.5
21	Arizona	25.3
22	Ohio	24.9
23	Missouri	24.8
24	Georgia	24.5
25	Indiana	24.0
26	California	23.5
27	Minnesota	23.3
28	Illinois	23.2
28	Oklahoma	23.2
30	Kentucky	22.8
30	North Carolina	22.8
32	South Carolina	22.2
33	New Jersey	21.7
33	Tennessee	21.7
35	West Virginia	21.6
36	Montana	21.2
37	Michigan	20.9
38	Nevada	20.1
39	Alabama	19.6
40	Utah	19.4
41	North Dakota	19.1
42	Texas	18.7
43	New York	18.3
44	Delaware	17.7
45	Arkansas	16.9
45	Louisiana	16.9
47	New Mexico	16.5
48	Mississippi	15.2
49	South Dakota	14.4
50	Wyoming	13.4

District of Columbia   27.4

Source: Morgan Quitno Press using data from U.S. Dept of Health & Human Services, National Center for Health Statistics
"National Vital Statistics Reports" (Vol. 52, No. 10, December 17, 2003 and Vol. 48, No. 3, March 28, 2000)
*By state of residence.

Percent of Vaginal Births After a Cesarean (VBAC) in 2002

National Percent = 12.6% of Live Births to Women Who Have Had a Cesarean*

ALPHA ORDER

RANK	STATE	PERCENT
42	Alabama	9.4
4	Alaska	20.8
36	Arizona	11.4
33	Arkansas	11.9
47	California	8.0
6	Colorado	18.6
25	Connecticut	13.3
29	Delaware	12.8
46	Florida	8.3
38	Georgia	11.1
15	Hawaii	16.7
11	Idaho	17.4
12	Illinois	17.1
31	Indiana	12.2
32	Iowa	12.0
34	Kansas	11.7
42	Kentucky	9.4
50	Louisiana	6.4
39	Maine	10.4
13	Maryland	17.0
22	Massachusetts	14.9
27	Michigan	13.0
18	Minnesota	16.4
49	Mississippi	6.9
24	Missouri	14.1
20	Montana	16.1
40	Nebraska	9.8
37	Nevada	11.3
21	New Hampshire	15.7
14	New Jersey	16.8
3	New Mexico	21.5
9	New York	18.2
26	North Carolina	13.2
15	North Dakota	16.7
5	Ohio	18.9
45	Oklahoma	8.4
19	Oregon	16.3
7	Pennsylvania	18.4
27	Rhode Island	13.0
41	South Carolina	9.5
15	South Dakota	16.7
35	Tennessee	11.6
47	Texas	8.0
2	Utah	24.1
1	Vermont	25.6
30	Virginia	12.6
23	Washington	14.6
44	West Virginia	9.3
8	Wisconsin	18.3
10	Wyoming	18.0

RANK ORDER

RANK	STATE	PERCENT
1	Vermont	25.6
2	Utah	24.1
3	New Mexico	21.5
4	Alaska	20.8
5	Ohio	18.9
6	Colorado	18.6
7	Pennsylvania	18.4
8	Wisconsin	18.3
9	New York	18.2
10	Wyoming	18.0
11	Idaho	17.4
12	Illinois	17.1
13	Maryland	17.0
14	New Jersey	16.8
15	Hawaii	16.7
15	North Dakota	16.7
15	South Dakota	16.7
18	Minnesota	16.4
19	Oregon	16.3
20	Montana	16.1
21	New Hampshire	15.7
22	Massachusetts	14.9
23	Washington	14.6
24	Missouri	14.1
25	Connecticut	13.3
26	North Carolina	13.2
27	Michigan	13.0
27	Rhode Island	13.0
29	Delaware	12.8
30	Virginia	12.6
31	Indiana	12.2
32	Iowa	12.0
33	Arkansas	11.9
34	Kansas	11.7
35	Tennessee	11.6
36	Arizona	11.4
37	Nevada	11.3
38	Georgia	11.1
39	Maine	10.4
40	Nebraska	9.8
41	South Carolina	9.5
42	Alabama	9.4
42	Kentucky	9.4
44	West Virginia	9.3
45	Oklahoma	8.4
46	Florida	8.3
47	California	8.0
47	Texas	8.0
49	Mississippi	6.9
50	Louisiana	6.4
	District of Columbia	8.4

*Source: U.S. Department of Health and Human Services, National Center for Health Statistics
"National Vital Statistics Reports" (Vol. 52, No. 10, December 17, 2003)*
Vaginal births after a cesarean delivery as a percent of all births to women with a previous cesarean delivery giving birth in 2002.

Assisted Reproductive Technology Procedures in 2000

National Total = 98,207 Procedures*

ALPHA ORDER

RANK	STATE	PROCEDURES	% of USA
32	Alabama	578	0.6%
49	Alaska	73	0.1%
21	Arizona	1,111	1.1%
39	Arkansas	371	0.4%
1	California	13,194	13.4%
18	Colorado	1,588	1.6%
14	Connecticut	1,947	2.0%
37	Delaware	438	0.4%
7	Florida	4,168	4.2%
13	Georgia	2,308	2.4%
35	Hawaii	457	0.5%
40	Idaho	293	0.3%
4	Illinois	7,323	7.5%
16	Indiana	1,940	2.0%
23	Iowa	800	0.8%
29	Kansas	707	0.7%
26	Kentucky	722	0.7%
26	Louisiana	722	0.7%
48	Maine	90	0.1%
10	Maryland	3,202	3.3%
3	Massachusetts	8,041	8.2%
9	Michigan	3,420	3.5%
15	Minnesota	1,943	2.0%
41	Mississippi	268	0.3%
20	Missouri	1,271	1.3%
47	Montana	94	0.1%
34	Nebraska	468	0.5%
25	Nevada	735	0.7%
38	New Hampshire	428	0.4%
5	New Jersey	5,506	5.6%
42	New Mexico	228	0.2%
2	New York	11,239	11.4%
19	North Carolina	1,551	1.6%
44	North Dakota	174	0.2%
12	Ohio	2,349	2.4%
33	Oklahoma	527	0.5%
24	Oregon	748	0.8%
8	Pennsylvania	3,511	3.6%
28	Rhode Island	720	0.7%
30	South Carolina	657	0.7%
46	South Dakota	105	0.1%
31	Tennessee	603	0.6%
6	Texas	5,249	5.3%
36	Utah	446	0.5%
45	Vermont	127	0.1%
11	Virginia	2,406	2.4%
17	Washington	1,846	1.9%
43	West Virginia	210	0.2%
22	Wisconsin	879	0.9%
50	Wyoming	46	0.0%

RANK ORDER

RANK	STATE	PROCEDURES	% of USA
1	California	13,194	13.4%
2	New York	11,239	11.4%
3	Massachusetts	8,041	8.2%
4	Illinois	7,323	7.5%
5	New Jersey	5,506	5.6%
6	Texas	5,249	5.3%
7	Florida	4,168	4.2%
8	Pennsylvania	3,511	3.6%
9	Michigan	3,420	3.5%
10	Maryland	3,202	3.3%
11	Virginia	2,406	2.4%
12	Ohio	2,349	2.4%
13	Georgia	2,308	2.4%
14	Connecticut	1,947	2.0%
15	Minnesota	1,943	2.0%
16	Indiana	1,940	2.0%
17	Washington	1,846	1.9%
18	Colorado	1,588	1.6%
19	North Carolina	1,551	1.6%
20	Missouri	1,271	1.3%
21	Arizona	1,111	1.1%
22	Wisconsin	879	0.9%
23	Iowa	800	0.8%
24	Oregon	748	0.8%
25	Nevada	735	0.7%
26	Kentucky	722	0.7%
26	Louisiana	722	0.7%
28	Rhode Island	720	0.7%
29	Kansas	707	0.7%
30	South Carolina	657	0.7%
31	Tennessee	603	0.6%
32	Alabama	578	0.6%
33	Oklahoma	527	0.5%
34	Nebraska	468	0.5%
35	Hawaii	457	0.5%
36	Utah	446	0.5%
37	Delaware	438	0.4%
38	New Hampshire	428	0.4%
39	Arkansas	371	0.4%
40	Idaho	293	0.3%
41	Mississippi	268	0.3%
42	New Mexico	228	0.2%
43	West Virginia	210	0.2%
44	North Dakota	174	0.2%
45	Vermont	127	0.1%
46	South Dakota	105	0.1%
47	Montana	94	0.1%
48	Maine	90	0.1%
49	Alaska	73	0.1%
50	Wyoming	46	0.0%
	District of Columbia	380	0.4%

*Source: U.S. Department of Health and Human Services, Centers for Disease Control and Prevention "Assisted Reproductive Technology, 2000" (Morbidity Mortality Weekly Report, Vol. 52, No. SS-09, 08/29/03) *By patient's residence. Does not include 1,422 procedures for patients with residences outside the U.S. Assisted reproductive technology (ART) includes treatments in which both eggs and sperm are handled in the laboratory. In 2000, 76% of ART treatments were freshly fertilized embryos using the patient's eggs, 3% were thawed embryos using the patient's eggs, 8% were freshly fertilized embryos from donor eggs and 3% were thawed embryos from donor eggs.*

Infants Born from Assisted Reproductive Technology Procedures in 2000

National Total = 34,464 Live Births*

ALPHA ORDER

RANK	STATE	BIRTHS	% of USA
31	Alabama	216	0.6%
45	Alaska	44	0.1%
21	Arizona	444	1.3%
37	Arkansas	142	0.4%
1	California	4,453	12.9%
13	Colorado	863	2.5%
16	Connecticut	679	2.0%
40	Delaware	117	0.3%
7	Florida	1,534	4.5%
15	Georgia	774	2.2%
39	Hawaii	128	0.4%
35	Idaho	162	0.5%
5	Illinois	2,137	6.2%
19	Indiana	597	1.7%
27	Iowa	275	0.8%
28	Kansas	255	0.7%
29	Kentucky	247	0.7%
32	Louisiana	189	0.5%
48	Maine	37	0.1%
8	Maryland	1,153	3.3%
3	Massachusetts	2,609	7.6%
9	Michigan	1,122	3.3%
12	Minnesota	908	2.6%
42	Mississippi	84	0.2%
20	Missouri	491	1.4%
47	Montana	39	0.1%
38	Nebraska	138	0.4%
23	Nevada	313	0.9%
36	New Hampshire	145	0.4%
4	New Jersey	2,139	6.2%
41	New Mexico	107	0.3%
2	New York	3,771	10.9%
18	North Carolina	638	1.9%
44	North Dakota	51	0.1%
14	Ohio	843	2.4%
30	Oklahoma	220	0.6%
22	Oregon	321	0.9%
10	Pennsylvania	997	2.9%
33	Rhode Island	174	0.5%
26	South Carolina	283	0.8%
49	South Dakota	32	0.1%
25	Tennessee	287	0.8%
6	Texas	1,978	5.7%
34	Utah	171	0.5%
46	Vermont	40	0.1%
11	Virginia	922	2.7%
17	Washington	639	1.9%
43	West Virginia	68	0.2%
24	Wisconsin	305	0.9%
50	Wyoming	26	0.1%

RANK ORDER

RANK	STATE	BIRTHS	% of USA
1	California	4,453	12.9%
2	New York	3,771	10.9%
3	Massachusetts	2,609	7.6%
4	New Jersey	2,139	6.2%
5	Illinois	2,137	6.2%
6	Texas	1,978	5.7%
7	Florida	1,534	4.5%
8	Maryland	1,153	3.3%
9	Michigan	1,122	3.3%
10	Pennsylvania	997	2.9%
11	Virginia	922	2.7%
12	Minnesota	908	2.6%
13	Colorado	863	2.5%
14	Ohio	843	2.4%
15	Georgia	774	2.2%
16	Connecticut	679	2.0%
17	Washington	639	1.9%
18	North Carolina	638	1.9%
19	Indiana	597	1.7%
20	Missouri	491	1.4%
21	Arizona	444	1.3%
22	Oregon	321	0.9%
23	Nevada	313	0.9%
24	Wisconsin	305	0.9%
25	Tennessee	287	0.8%
26	South Carolina	283	0.8%
27	Iowa	275	0.8%
28	Kansas	255	0.7%
29	Kentucky	247	0.7%
30	Oklahoma	220	0.6%
31	Alabama	216	0.6%
32	Louisiana	189	0.5%
33	Rhode Island	174	0.5%
34	Utah	171	0.5%
35	Idaho	162	0.5%
36	New Hampshire	145	0.4%
37	Arkansas	142	0.4%
38	Nebraska	138	0.4%
39	Hawaii	128	0.4%
40	Delaware	117	0.3%
41	New Mexico	107	0.3%
42	Mississippi	84	0.2%
43	West Virginia	68	0.2%
44	North Dakota	51	0.1%
45	Alaska	44	0.1%
46	Vermont	40	0.1%
47	Montana	39	0.1%
48	Maine	37	0.1%
49	South Dakota	32	0.1%
50	Wyoming	26	0.1%
	District of Columbia	157	0.5%

Source: U.S. Department of Health and Human Services, Centers for Disease Control and Prevention
"Assisted Reproductive Technology, 2000" (Morbidity Mortality Weekly Report, Vol. 52, No. SS-09, 08/29/03)
*By patient's residence. Does not include 561 births to patients with residences outside the U.S. Assisted reproductive technology (ART) includes treatments in which both eggs and sperm are handled in the laboratory. In 2000, 76% of ART treatments were freshly fertilized embryos using the patient's eggs, 3% were thawed embryos using the patient's eggs, 8% were freshly fertilized embryos from donor eggs and 3% were thawed embryos from donor eggs.

Percent of Assisted Reproductive Technology Procedures that Resulted in Live Births in 2000
National Percent = 25.3%*

ALPHA ORDER

RANK	STATE	PERCENT
30	Alabama	24.9
1	Alaska	42.5
20	Arizona	26.9
14	Arkansas	28.3
33	California	24.6
2	Colorado	37.7
29	Connecticut	25.0
48	Delaware	19.6
22	Florida	26.4
32	Georgia	24.7
47	Hawaii	20.4
4	Idaho	36.5
45	Illinois	21.2
44	Indiana	22.0
26	Iowa	25.3
22	Kansas	26.4
27	Kentucky	25.2
49	Louisiana	18.3
8	Maine	32.2
24	Maryland	25.8
36	Massachusetts	24.3
38	Michigan	23.4
6	Minnesota	34.4
42	Mississippi	22.8
19	Missouri	27.1
10	Montana	29.8
43	Nebraska	22.2
13	Nevada	28.7
37	New Hampshire	24.1
18	New Jersey	27.4
7	New Mexico	33.3
34	New York	24.5
16	North Carolina	27.7
40	North Dakota	23.0
27	Ohio	25.2
9	Oklahoma	30.0
12	Oregon	29.3
46	Pennsylvania	21.1
50	Rhode Island	17.1
10	South Carolina	29.8
41	South Dakota	22.9
5	Tennessee	35.0
20	Texas	26.9
14	Utah	28.3
35	Vermont	24.4
17	Virginia	27.6
30	Washington	24.9
39	West Virginia	23.3
25	Wisconsin	25.5
3	Wyoming	37.0

RANK ORDER

RANK	STATE	PERCENT
1	Alaska	42.5
2	Colorado	37.7
3	Wyoming	37.0
4	Idaho	36.5
5	Tennessee	35.0
6	Minnesota	34.4
7	New Mexico	33.3
8	Maine	32.2
9	Oklahoma	30.0
10	Montana	29.8
10	South Carolina	29.8
12	Oregon	29.3
13	Nevada	28.7
14	Arkansas	28.3
14	Utah	28.3
16	North Carolina	27.7
17	Virginia	27.6
18	New Jersey	27.4
19	Missouri	27.1
20	Arizona	26.9
20	Texas	26.9
22	Florida	26.4
22	Kansas	26.4
24	Maryland	25.8
25	Wisconsin	25.5
26	Iowa	25.3
27	Kentucky	25.2
27	Ohio	25.2
29	Connecticut	25.0
30	Alabama	24.9
30	Washington	24.9
32	Georgia	24.7
33	California	24.6
34	New York	24.5
35	Vermont	24.4
36	Massachusetts	24.3
37	New Hampshire	24.1
38	Michigan	23.4
39	West Virginia	23.3
40	North Dakota	23.0
41	South Dakota	22.9
42	Mississippi	22.8
43	Nebraska	22.2
44	Indiana	22.0
45	Illinois	21.2
46	Pennsylvania	21.1
47	Hawaii	20.4
48	Delaware	19.6
49	Louisiana	18.3
50	Rhode Island	17.1
	District of Columbia	28.7

Source: U.S. Department of Health and Human Services, Centers for Disease Control and Prevention
"Assisted Reproductive Technology, 2000" (Morbidity Mortality Weekly Report, Vol. 52, No. SS-09, 08/29/03)
*Assisted reproductive technology (ART) includes fertility treatments in which both eggs and sperm are handled in the laboratory (i.e. in vitro fertilization and related procedures). In 2000, 76% of ART treatments were freshly fertilized embryos using the patient's eggs, 3% were thawed embryos using the patient's eggs, 8% were freshly fertilized embryos from donor eggs and 3% were thawed embryos from donor eggs.

Percent of Total Live Births Resulting from Assisted Reproductive Technology Procedures in 2000
National Percent = 0.8% of Live Births*

ALPHA ORDER

RANK	STATE	PERCENT
45	Alabama	0.3
35	Alaska	0.4
30	Arizona	0.5
35	Arkansas	0.4
14	California	0.8
7	Colorado	1.3
3	Connecticut	1.6
10	Delaware	1.1
14	Florida	0.8
25	Georgia	0.6
19	Hawaii	0.7
14	Idaho	0.8
9	Illinois	1.2
19	Indiana	0.7
19	Iowa	0.7
25	Kansas	0.6
35	Kentucky	0.4
45	Louisiana	0.3
45	Maine	0.3
3	Maryland	1.6
1	Massachusetts	3.2
14	Michigan	0.8
7	Minnesota	1.3
50	Mississippi	0.2
25	Missouri	0.6
35	Montana	0.4
25	Nebraska	0.6
11	Nevada	1.0
11	New Hampshire	1.0
2	New Jersey	1.8
35	New Mexico	0.4
5	New York	1.5
30	North Carolina	0.5
19	North Dakota	0.7
30	Ohio	0.5
35	Oklahoma	0.4
19	Oregon	0.7
19	Pennsylvania	0.7
6	Rhode Island	1.4
30	South Carolina	0.5
45	South Dakota	0.3
35	Tennessee	0.4
30	Texas	0.5
35	Utah	0.4
25	Vermont	0.6
13	Virginia	0.9
14	Washington	0.8
45	West Virginia	0.3
35	Wisconsin	0.4
35	Wyoming	0.4

RANK ORDER

RANK	STATE	PERCENT
1	Massachusetts	3.2
2	New Jersey	1.8
3	Connecticut	1.6
3	Maryland	1.6
5	New York	1.5
6	Rhode Island	1.4
7	Colorado	1.3
7	Minnesota	1.3
9	Illinois	1.2
10	Delaware	1.1
11	Nevada	1.0
11	New Hampshire	1.0
13	Virginia	0.9
14	California	0.8
14	Florida	0.8
14	Idaho	0.8
14	Michigan	0.8
14	Washington	0.8
19	Hawaii	0.7
19	Indiana	0.7
19	Iowa	0.7
19	North Dakota	0.7
19	Oregon	0.7
19	Pennsylvania	0.7
25	Georgia	0.6
25	Kansas	0.6
25	Missouri	0.6
25	Nebraska	0.6
25	Vermont	0.6
30	Arizona	0.5
30	North Carolina	0.5
30	Ohio	0.5
30	South Carolina	0.5
30	Texas	0.5
35	Alaska	0.4
35	Arkansas	0.4
35	Kentucky	0.4
35	Montana	0.4
35	New Mexico	0.4
35	Oklahoma	0.4
35	Tennessee	0.4
35	Utah	0.4
35	Wisconsin	0.4
35	Wyoming	0.4
45	Alabama	0.3
45	Louisiana	0.3
45	Maine	0.3
45	South Dakota	0.3
45	West Virginia	0.3
50	Mississippi	0.2

District of Columbia   2.0

Source: Morgan Quitno Press using data from US Dept of Health & Human Serv's, Centers for Disease Control-Prevention "Assisted Reproductive Technology, 2000" (Morbidity Mortality Weekly Report, Vol. 52, No. SS-09, 08/29/03) and "National Vital Statistics Reports" (Vol. 50, No. 5, February 12, 2002)
*By patient's residence. Does not include births or procedures to patients with residences outside the U.S. Assisted reproductive technology (ART) includes treatments in which both eggs and sperm are handled in the laboratory (i.e. in vitro fertilization and related procedures).

Percent of Assisted Reproductive Technology Procedures
Resulting in Multiple-Birth Deliveries in 2000
National Percent = 53.1% of Procedures*

ALPHA ORDER				RANK ORDER		
RANK	STATE	PERCENT		RANK	STATE	PERCENT
7	Alabama	59.3		1	Wyoming	69.2
10	Alaska	56.8		2	Nevada	62.3
6	Arizona	59.5		3	North Carolina	61.1
43	Arkansas	49.3		4	Idaho	60.5
29	California	52.0		5	Oregon	60.1
9	Colorado	58.1		6	Arizona	59.5
23	Connecticut	53.6		7	Alabama	59.3
38	Delaware	50.4		8	Louisiana	58.2
23	Florida	53.6		9	Colorado	58.1
41	Georgia	49.7		10	Alaska	56.8
20	Hawaii	53.9		11	New Hampshire	56.6
4	Idaho	60.5		12	New Jersey	56.3
32	Illinois	51.4		13	South Carolina	56.2
28	Indiana	52.8		14	Missouri	55.4
34	Iowa	51.3		15	New Mexico	55.1
37	Kansas	50.6		16	Ohio	55.0
32	Kentucky	51.4		16	Texas	55.0
8	Louisiana	58.2		18	Maryland	54.6
49	Maine	43.2		19	Rhode Island	54.0
18	Maryland	54.6		20	Hawaii	53.9
45	Massachusetts	48.6		21	Virginia	53.8
22	Michigan	53.7		22	Michigan	53.7
42	Minnesota	49.4		23	Connecticut	53.6
44	Mississippi	48.8		23	Florida	53.6
14	Missouri	55.4		25	Oklahoma	53.2
34	Montana	51.3		25	Washington	53.2
48	Nebraska	44.9		27	West Virginia	52.9
2	Nevada	62.3		28	Indiana	52.8
11	New Hampshire	56.6		29	California	52.0
12	New Jersey	56.3		30	New York	51.6
15	New Mexico	55.1		31	Wisconsin	51.5
30	New York	51.6		32	Illinois	51.4
3	North Carolina	61.1		32	Kentucky	51.4
50	North Dakota	43.1		34	Iowa	51.3
16	Ohio	55.0		34	Montana	51.3
25	Oklahoma	53.2		36	Utah	50.9
5	Oregon	60.1		37	Kansas	50.6
46	Pennsylvania	48.4		38	Delaware	50.4
19	Rhode Island	54.0		39	Tennessee	50.2
13	South Carolina	56.2		40	South Dakota	50.0
40	South Dakota	50.0		41	Georgia	49.7
39	Tennessee	50.2		42	Minnesota	49.4
16	Texas	55.0		43	Arkansas	49.3
36	Utah	50.9		44	Mississippi	48.8
47	Vermont	45.0		45	Massachusetts	48.6
21	Virginia	53.8		46	Pennsylvania	48.4
25	Washington	53.2		47	Vermont	45.0
27	West Virginia	52.9		48	Nebraska	44.9
31	Wisconsin	51.5		49	Maine	43.2
1	Wyoming	69.2		50	North Dakota	43.1

District of Columbia 59.9

Source: U.S. Department of Health and Human Services, Centers for Disease Control and Prevention
"Assisted Reproductive Technology, 2000" (Morbidity Mortality Weekly Report, Vol. 52, No. SS-09, 08/29/03)
*By patient's residence. Does not include births or procedures to patients with residences outside the U.S. Assisted reproductive technology (ART) includes treatments in which both eggs and sperm are handled in the laboratory (i.e. in vitro fertilization and related procedures).

Percent of Mothers Beginning Prenatal Care in First Trimester in 2002

National Percent = 83.7% of Mothers*

ALPHA ORDER				RANK ORDER		
RANK	STATE	PERCENT		RANK	STATE	PERCENT
33	Alabama	83.3		1	New Hampshire	91.5
40	Alaska	80.3		2	Massachusetts	89.9
48	Arizona	76.5		3	Rhode Island	89.6
42	Arkansas	79.6		4	Vermont	88.9
13	California	86.4		5	Iowa	88.8
44	Colorado	79.1		6	Connecticut	88.3
6	Connecticut	88.3		7	Maine	87.9
10	Delaware	87.1		8	Missouri	87.8
18	Florida	85.4		8	Ohio	87.8
22	Georgia	84.7		10	Delaware	87.1
27	Hawaii	83.9		11	Kansas	86.8
35	Idaho	82.1		11	Kentucky	86.8
20	Illinois	84.9		13	California	86.4
38	Indiana	81.4		14	North Dakota	86.1
5	Iowa	88.8		15	West Virginia	85.9
11	Kansas	86.8		16	Michigan	85.6
11	Kentucky	86.8		17	Minnesota	85.5
28	Louisiana	83.8		18	Florida	85.4
7	Maine	87.9		19	Virginia	85.2
26	Maryland	84.1		20	Illinois	84.9
2	Massachusetts	89.9		20	Wyoming	84.9
16	Michigan	85.6		22	Georgia	84.7
17	Minnesota	85.5		23	Pennsylvania	84.6
28	Mississippi	83.8		24	North Carolina	84.3
8	Missouri	87.8		24	Wisconsin	84.3
30	Montana	83.7		26	Maryland	84.1
31	Nebraska	83.4		27	Hawaii	83.9
49	Nevada	75.9		28	Louisiana	83.8
1	New Hampshire	91.5		28	Mississippi	83.8
40	New Jersey	80.3		30	Montana	83.7
50	New Mexico	69.0		31	Nebraska	83.4
36	New York	81.6		31	Washington	83.4
24	North Carolina	84.3		33	Alabama	83.3
14	North Dakota	86.1		34	Tennessee	82.8
8	Ohio	87.8		35	Idaho	82.1
47	Oklahoma	76.8		36	New York	81.6
36	Oregon	81.6		36	Oregon	81.6
23	Pennsylvania	84.6		38	Indiana	81.4
3	Rhode Island	89.6		39	Texas	80.5
45	South Carolina	78.4		40	Alaska	80.3
46	South Dakota	77.7		40	New Jersey	80.3
34	Tennessee	82.8		42	Arkansas	79.6
39	Texas	80.5		43	Utah	79.5
43	Utah	79.5		44	Colorado	79.1
4	Vermont	88.9		45	South Carolina	78.4
19	Virginia	85.2		46	South Dakota	77.7
31	Washington	83.4		47	Oklahoma	76.8
15	West Virginia	85.9		48	Arizona	76.5
24	Wisconsin	84.3		49	Nevada	75.9
20	Wyoming	84.9		50	New Mexico	69.0

District of Columbia   76.4

Source: U.S. Department of Health and Human Services, National Center for Health Statistics
    "National Vital Statistics Reports" (Vol. 52, No. 10, December 17, 2003)
*Final data by state of residence.

Percent of White Mothers Beginning Prenatal Care in First Trimester in 2002

National Percent = 85.4% of White Mothers*

ALPHA ORDER

RANK	STATE	PERCENT
20	Alabama	87.7
35	Alaska	84.2
48	Arizona	77.1
41	Arkansas	82.1
27	California	86.6
46	Colorado	79.5
6	Connecticut	89.3
13	Delaware	88.5
19	Florida	87.8
23	Georgia	87.3
14	Hawaii	88.4
40	Idaho	82.3
25	Illinois	87.2
38	Indiana	82.9
6	Iowa	89.3
21	Kansas	87.5
21	Kentucky	87.5
4	Louisiana	90.4
15	Maine	88.2
16	Maryland	88.1
2	Massachusetts	91.4
11	Michigan	88.6
17	Minnesota	88.0
5	Mississippi	90.1
6	Missouri	89.3
30	Montana	86.1
33	Nebraska	84.5
49	Nevada	76.2
1	New Hampshire	91.8
37	New Jersey	83.6
50	New Mexico	70.4
33	New York	84.5
23	North Carolina	87.3
11	North Dakota	88.6
6	Ohio	89.3
47	Oklahoma	78.6
42	Oregon	81.9
26	Pennsylvania	86.9
3	Rhode Island	91.0
39	South Carolina	82.5
43	South Dakota	81.8
31	Tennessee	85.7
44	Texas	80.6
45	Utah	80.5
10	Vermont	89.0
18	Virginia	87.9
36	Washington	83.9
29	West Virginia	86.3
27	Wisconsin	86.6
32	Wyoming	85.4

RANK ORDER

RANK	STATE	PERCENT
1	New Hampshire	91.8
2	Massachusetts	91.4
3	Rhode Island	91.0
4	Louisiana	90.4
5	Mississippi	90.1
6	Connecticut	89.3
6	Iowa	89.3
6	Missouri	89.3
6	Ohio	89.3
10	Vermont	89.0
11	Michigan	88.6
11	North Dakota	88.6
13	Delaware	88.5
14	Hawaii	88.4
15	Maine	88.2
16	Maryland	88.1
17	Minnesota	88.0
18	Virginia	87.9
19	Florida	87.8
20	Alabama	87.7
21	Kansas	87.5
21	Kentucky	87.5
23	Georgia	87.3
23	North Carolina	87.3
25	Illinois	87.2
26	Pennsylvania	86.9
27	California	86.6
27	Wisconsin	86.6
29	West Virginia	86.3
30	Montana	86.1
31	Tennessee	85.7
32	Wyoming	85.4
33	Nebraska	84.5
33	New York	84.5
35	Alaska	84.2
36	Washington	83.9
37	New Jersey	83.6
38	Indiana	82.9
39	South Carolina	82.5
40	Idaho	82.3
41	Arkansas	82.1
42	Oregon	81.9
43	South Dakota	81.8
44	Texas	80.6
45	Utah	80.5
46	Colorado	79.5
47	Oklahoma	78.6
48	Arizona	77.1
49	Nevada	76.2
50	New Mexico	70.4

District of Columbia   85.1

Source: U.S. Department of Health and Human Services, National Center for Health Statistics
    "National Vital Statistics Reports" (Vol. 52, No. 10, December 17, 2003)
*Final data by state of residence.

Percent of Black Mothers Beginning Prenatal Care in First Trimester in 2002

National Percent = 75.2% of Black Mothers*

ALPHA ORDER

RANK	STATE	PERCENT
30	Alabama	73.6
2	Alaska	83.9
23	Arizona	76.4
40	Arkansas	70.5
3	California	83.0
43	Colorado	70.2
7	Connecticut	81.7
4	Delaware	82.3
19	Florida	77.1
15	Georgia	79.1
1	Hawaii	94.2
6	Idaho	81.8
29	Illinois	74.3
45	Indiana	69.6
17	Iowa	78.1
13	Kansas	79.6
8	Kentucky	80.8
28	Louisiana	74.7
31	Maine	73.0
22	Maryland	76.5
9	Massachusetts	80.7
36	Michigan	71.3
44	Minnesota	70.1
24	Mississippi	76.1
12	Missouri	79.7
41	Montana	70.3
38	Nebraska	70.6
38	Nevada	70.6
10	New Hampshire	80.4
48	New Jersey	64.0
47	New Mexico	68.5
33	New York	72.1
27	North Carolina	75.5
5	North Dakota	82.2
16	Ohio	78.9
46	Oklahoma	69.4
25	Oregon	76.0
37	Pennsylvania	71.0
11	Rhode Island	79.9
41	South Carolina	70.3
49	South Dakota	61.2
32	Tennessee	72.3
20	Texas	76.7
50	Utah	59.7
34	Vermont	71.8
21	Virginia	76.6
17	Washington	78.1
26	West Virginia	75.6
35	Wisconsin	71.4
14	Wyoming	79.2

RANK ORDER

RANK	STATE	PERCENT
1	Hawaii	94.2
2	Alaska	83.9
3	California	83.0
4	Delaware	82.3
5	North Dakota	82.2
6	Idaho	81.8
7	Connecticut	81.7
8	Kentucky	80.8
9	Massachusetts	80.7
10	New Hampshire	80.4
11	Rhode Island	79.9
12	Missouri	79.7
13	Kansas	79.6
14	Wyoming	79.2
15	Georgia	79.1
16	Ohio	78.9
17	Iowa	78.1
17	Washington	78.1
19	Florida	77.1
20	Texas	76.7
21	Virginia	76.6
22	Maryland	76.5
23	Arizona	76.4
24	Mississippi	76.1
25	Oregon	76.0
26	West Virginia	75.6
27	North Carolina	75.5
28	Louisiana	74.7
29	Illinois	74.3
30	Alabama	73.6
31	Maine	73.0
32	Tennessee	72.3
33	New York	72.1
34	Vermont	71.8
35	Wisconsin	71.4
36	Michigan	71.3
37	Pennsylvania	71.0
38	Nebraska	70.6
38	Nevada	70.6
40	Arkansas	70.5
41	Montana	70.3
41	South Carolina	70.3
43	Colorado	70.2
44	Minnesota	70.1
45	Indiana	69.6
46	Oklahoma	69.4
47	New Mexico	68.5
48	New Jersey	64.0
49	South Dakota	61.2
50	Utah	59.7
	District of Columbia	70.5

Source: U.S. Department of Health and Human Services, National Center for Health Statistics
   "National Vital Statistics Reports" (Vol. 52, No. 10, December 17, 2003)
*Final data by state of residence.

Percent of Hispanic Mothers Beginning Prenatal Care in First Trimester in 2002

National Percent = 76.7% of Hispanic Mothers*

ALPHA ORDER

RANK ORDER

RANK	STATE	PERCENT	RANK	STATE	PERCENT
50	Alabama	53.9	1	Rhode Island	86.1
18	Alaska	76.8	2	New Hampshire	84.8
40	Arizona	66.7	3	California	84.1
38	Arkansas	68.4	4	Florida	83.7
3	California	84.1	5	North Dakota	83.6
42	Colorado	65.9	6	Louisiana	83.3
17	Connecticut	77.0	7	Maine	83.2
19	Delaware	75.2	8	Massachusetts	82.9
4	Florida	83.7	9	Hawaii	82.5
26	Georgia	73.6	10	Vermont	81.3
9	Hawaii	82.5	11	Montana	79.4
32	Idaho	70.2	11	Wyoming	79.4
13	Illinois	78.4	13	Illinois	78.4
43	Indiana	65.1	14	Missouri	78.1
23	Iowa	74.7	15	Ohio	78.0
29	Kansas	72.3	16	Michigan	77.4
27	Kentucky	72.6	17	Connecticut	77.0
6	Louisiana	83.3	18	Alaska	76.8
7	Maine	83.2	19	Delaware	75.2
31	Maryland	70.6	20	Texas	75.1
8	Massachusetts	82.9	21	New York	75.0
16	Michigan	77.4	21	West Virginia	75.0
39	Minnesota	68.0	23	Iowa	74.7
23	Mississippi	74.7	23	Mississippi	74.7
14	Missouri	78.1	25	Washington	74.2
11	Montana	79.4	26	Georgia	73.6
36	Nebraska	69.2	27	Kentucky	72.6
46	Nevada	63.4	28	Pennsylvania	72.4
2	New Hampshire	84.8	29	Kansas	72.3
37	New Jersey	68.7	30	Oregon	71.4
41	New Mexico	66.4	31	Maryland	70.6
21	New York	75.0	32	Idaho	70.2
32	North Carolina	70.2	32	North Carolina	70.2
5	North Dakota	83.6	34	Virginia	70.1
15	Ohio	78.0	35	Wisconsin	69.4
45	Oklahoma	63.6	36	Nebraska	69.2
30	Oregon	71.4	37	New Jersey	68.7
28	Pennsylvania	72.4	38	Arkansas	68.4
1	Rhode Island	86.1	39	Minnesota	68.0
48	South Carolina	60.4	40	Arizona	66.7
44	South Dakota	64.8	41	New Mexico	66.4
49	Tennessee	58.7	42	Colorado	65.9
20	Texas	75.1	43	Indiana	65.1
47	Utah	62.4	44	South Dakota	64.8
10	Vermont	81.3	45	Oklahoma	63.6
34	Virginia	70.1	46	Nevada	63.4
25	Washington	74.2	47	Utah	62.4
21	West Virginia	75.0	48	South Carolina	60.4
35	Wisconsin	69.4	49	Tennessee	58.7
11	Wyoming	79.4	50	Alabama	53.9
				District of Columbia	73.5

Source: U.S. Department of Health and Human Services, National Center for Health Statistics
"National Vital Statistics Reports" (Vol. 52, No. 10, December 17, 2003)
*Final data by state of residence. Persons of Hispanic origin may be of any race.

Percent of Mothers Receiving Late or No Prenatal Care in 2002

National Percent = 3.6% of Mothers*

ALPHA ORDER

RANK	STATE	PERCENT
15	Alabama	3.8
11	Alaska	4.6
3	Arizona	6.6
6	Arkansas	4.9
40	California	2.6
12	Colorado	4.5
45	Connecticut	2.0
19	Delaware	3.5
31	Florida	2.9
25	Georgia	3.4
19	Hawaii	3.5
25	Idaho	3.4
31	Illinois	2.9
19	Indiana	3.5
43	Iowa	2.2
36	Kansas	2.8
41	Kentucky	2.5
17	Louisiana	3.6
48	Maine	1.6
17	Maryland	3.6
45	Massachusetts	2.0
19	Michigan	3.5
42	Minnesota	2.3
28	Mississippi	3.1
38	Missouri	2.7
36	Montana	2.8
28	Nebraska	3.1
2	Nevada	7.1
50	New Hampshire	1.4
6	New Jersey	4.9
1	New Mexico	7.9
9	New York	4.7
31	North Carolina	2.9
38	North Dakota	2.7
31	Ohio	2.9
4	Oklahoma	5.4
15	Oregon	3.8
19	Pennsylvania	3.5
49	Rhode Island	1.5
9	South Carolina	4.7
13	South Dakota	4.4
14	Tennessee	3.9
5	Texas	5.0
6	Utah	4.9
47	Vermont	1.7
19	Virginia	3.5
28	Washington	3.1
43	West Virginia	2.2
27	Wisconsin	3.2
31	Wyoming	2.9

RANK ORDER

RANK	STATE	PERCENT
1	New Mexico	7.9
2	Nevada	7.1
3	Arizona	6.6
4	Oklahoma	5.4
5	Texas	5.0
6	Arkansas	4.9
6	New Jersey	4.9
6	Utah	4.9
9	New York	4.7
9	South Carolina	4.7
11	Alaska	4.6
12	Colorado	4.5
13	South Dakota	4.4
14	Tennessee	3.9
15	Alabama	3.8
15	Oregon	3.8
17	Louisiana	3.6
17	Maryland	3.6
19	Delaware	3.5
19	Hawaii	3.5
19	Indiana	3.5
19	Michigan	3.5
19	Pennsylvania	3.5
19	Virginia	3.5
25	Georgia	3.4
25	Idaho	3.4
27	Wisconsin	3.2
28	Mississippi	3.1
28	Nebraska	3.1
28	Washington	3.1
31	Florida	2.9
31	Illinois	2.9
31	North Carolina	2.9
31	Ohio	2.9
31	Wyoming	2.9
36	Kansas	2.8
36	Montana	2.8
38	Missouri	2.7
38	North Dakota	2.7
40	California	2.6
41	Kentucky	2.5
42	Minnesota	2.3
43	Iowa	2.2
43	West Virginia	2.2
45	Connecticut	2.0
45	Massachusetts	2.0
47	Vermont	1.7
48	Maine	1.6
49	Rhode Island	1.5
50	New Hampshire	1.4

| | District of Columbia | 7.4 |

Source: U.S. Department of Health and Human Services, National Center for Health Statistics
   "National Vital Statistics Reports" (Vol. 52, No. 10, December 17, 2003)
*Final data by state of residence. "Late" means care begun in third trimester.

Percent of White Mothers Receiving Late or No Prenatal Care in 2002

National Percent = 3.1% of White Mothers*

ALPHA ORDER

RANK	STATE	PERCENT
16	Alabama	2.9
9	Alaska	3.8
3	Arizona	6.5
8	Arkansas	4.2
25	California	2.6
7	Colorado	4.4
42	Connecticut	1.8
16	Delaware	2.9
31	Florida	2.3
16	Georgia	2.9
28	Hawaii	2.5
14	Idaho	3.3
36	Illinois	2.1
15	Indiana	3.0
39	Iowa	2.0
28	Kansas	2.5
31	Kentucky	2.3
44	Louisiana	1.7
46	Maine	1.6
31	Maryland	2.3
48	Massachusetts	1.5
28	Michigan	2.5
44	Minnesota	1.7
42	Mississippi	1.8
36	Missouri	2.1
40	Montana	1.9
21	Nebraska	2.8
2	Nevada	7.0
49	New Hampshire	1.4
10	New Jersey	3.7
1	New Mexico	7.4
10	New York	3.7
35	North Carolina	2.2
40	North Dakota	1.9
31	Ohio	2.3
5	Oklahoma	4.9
10	Oregon	3.7
21	Pennsylvania	2.8
50	Rhode Island	1.2
13	South Carolina	3.4
23	South Dakota	2.7
16	Tennessee	2.9
4	Texas	5.0
6	Utah	4.5
46	Vermont	1.6
23	Virginia	2.7
16	Washington	2.9
36	West Virginia	2.1
25	Wisconsin	2.6
25	Wyoming	2.6

RANK ORDER

RANK	STATE	PERCENT
1	New Mexico	7.4
2	Nevada	7.0
3	Arizona	6.5
4	Texas	5.0
5	Oklahoma	4.9
6	Utah	4.5
7	Colorado	4.4
8	Arkansas	4.2
9	Alaska	3.8
10	New Jersey	3.7
10	New York	3.7
10	Oregon	3.7
13	South Carolina	3.4
14	Idaho	3.3
15	Indiana	3.0
16	Alabama	2.9
16	Delaware	2.9
16	Georgia	2.9
16	Tennessee	2.9
16	Washington	2.9
21	Nebraska	2.8
21	Pennsylvania	2.8
23	South Dakota	2.7
23	Virginia	2.7
25	California	2.6
25	Wisconsin	2.6
25	Wyoming	2.6
28	Hawaii	2.5
28	Kansas	2.5
28	Michigan	2.5
31	Florida	2.3
31	Kentucky	2.3
31	Maryland	2.3
31	Ohio	2.3
35	North Carolina	2.2
36	Illinois	2.1
36	Missouri	2.1
36	West Virginia	2.1
39	Iowa	2.0
40	Montana	1.9
40	North Dakota	1.9
42	Connecticut	1.8
42	Mississippi	1.8
44	Louisiana	1.7
44	Minnesota	1.7
46	Maine	1.6
46	Vermont	1.6
48	Massachusetts	1.5
49	New Hampshire	1.4
50	Rhode Island	1.2

District of Columbia	3.7

Source: U.S. Department of Health and Human Services, National Center for Health Statistics
   "National Vital Statistics Reports" (Vol. 52, No. 10, December 17, 2003)
*Final data by state of residence. "Late" means care begun in third trimester.

Percent of Black Mothers Receiving Late or No Prenatal Care in 2002

National Percent = 6.2% of Black Mothers*

ALPHA ORDER				RANK ORDER		
RANK	STATE	PERCENT		RANK	STATE	PERCENT
23	Alabama	5.7		1	Utah	14.2
NA	Alaska**	NA		2	New Jersey	11.0
26	Arizona	5.5		3	Nevada	8.6
8	Arkansas	7.5		4	New York	8.4
39	California	3.4		5	Michigan	7.9
11	Colorado	7.3		5	New Mexico	7.9
38	Connecticut	3.5		7	Pennsylvania	7.8
23	Delaware	5.7		8	Arkansas	7.5
31	Florida	4.9		8	Oklahoma	7.5
34	Georgia	4.5		8	Tennessee	7.5
NA	Hawaii**	NA		11	Colorado	7.3
NA	Idaho**	NA		11	Wisconsin	7.3
15	Illinois	6.7		13	Indiana	7.1
13	Indiana	7.1		13	South Carolina	7.1
26	Iowa	5.5		15	Illinois	6.7
30	Kansas	5.0		16	Maryland	6.2
36	Kentucky	4.4		16	Minnesota	6.2
19	Louisiana	6.1		16	Ohio	6.2
NA	Maine**	NA		19	Louisiana	6.1
16	Maryland	6.2		20	Nebraska	6.0
28	Massachusetts	5.1		21	Virginia	5.9
5	Michigan	7.9		22	Texas	5.8
16	Minnesota	6.2		23	Alabama	5.7
32	Mississippi	4.6		23	Delaware	5.7
25	Missouri	5.6		25	Missouri	5.6
NA	Montana**	NA		26	Arizona	5.5
20	Nebraska	6.0		26	Iowa	5.5
3	Nevada	8.6		28	Massachusetts	5.1
NA	New Hampshire**	NA		28	North Carolina	5.1
2	New Jersey	11.0		30	Kansas	5.0
5	New Mexico	7.9		31	Florida	4.9
4	New York	8.4		32	Mississippi	4.6
28	North Carolina	5.1		32	Washington	4.6
NA	North Dakota**	NA		34	Georgia	4.5
16	Ohio	6.2		34	Oregon	4.5
8	Oklahoma	7.5		36	Kentucky	4.4
34	Oregon	4.5		36	West Virginia	4.4
7	Pennsylvania	7.8		38	Connecticut	3.5
39	Rhode Island	3.4		39	California	3.4
13	South Carolina	7.1		39	Rhode Island	3.4
NA	South Dakota**	NA		NA	Alaska**	NA
8	Tennessee	7.5		NA	Hawaii**	NA
22	Texas	5.8		NA	Idaho**	NA
1	Utah	14.2		NA	Maine**	NA
NA	Vermont**	NA		NA	Montana**	NA
21	Virginia	5.9		NA	New Hampshire**	NA
32	Washington	4.6		NA	North Dakota**	NA
36	West Virginia	4.4		NA	South Dakota**	NA
11	Wisconsin	7.3		NA	Vermont**	NA
NA	Wyoming**	NA		NA	Wyoming**	NA

District of Columbia   10.0

Source: U.S. Department of Health and Human Services, National Center for Health Statistics
"National Vital Statistics Reports" (Vol. 52, No. 10, December 17, 2003)
*Final data by state of residence. "Late" means care begun in third trimester.
**Insufficient data.

Percent of Hispanic Mothers Receiving Late or No Prenatal Care in 2002

National Percent = 5.5% of Hispanic Mothers*

ALPHA ORDER

RANK	STATE	PERCENT
1	Alabama	19.0
24	Alaska	5.9
5	Arizona	10.4
8	Arkansas	9.4
42	California	3.1
11	Colorado	7.9
36	Connecticut	3.8
24	Delaware	5.9
40	Florida	3.3
14	Georgia	7.1
41	Hawaii	3.2
21	Idaho	6.4
37	Illinois	3.5
11	Indiana	7.9
30	Iowa	5.6
17	Kansas	6.6
17	Kentucky	6.6
39	Louisiana	3.4
NA	Maine**	NA
24	Maryland	5.9
43	Massachusetts	3.0
35	Michigan	4.7
28	Minnesota	5.8
17	Mississippi	6.6
34	Missouri	4.8
NA	Montana**	NA
16	Nebraska	6.8
3	Nevada	11.1
NA	New Hampshire**	NA
14	New Jersey	7.1
9	New Mexico	8.8
24	New York	5.9
23	North Carolina	6.1
NA	North Dakota**	NA
33	Ohio	5.1
10	Oklahoma	8.3
31	Oregon	5.5
29	Pennsylvania	5.7
44	Rhode Island	2.1
5	South Carolina	10.4
4	South Dakota	10.8
2	Tennessee	12.2
17	Texas	6.6
7	Utah	9.5
NA	Vermont**	NA
13	Virginia	7.5
32	Washington	5.2
NA	West Virginia**	NA
22	Wisconsin	6.3
37	Wyoming	3.5

RANK ORDER

RANK	STATE	PERCENT
1	Alabama	19.0
2	Tennessee	12.2
3	Nevada	11.1
4	South Dakota	10.8
5	Arizona	10.4
5	South Carolina	10.4
7	Utah	9.5
8	Arkansas	9.4
9	New Mexico	8.8
10	Oklahoma	8.3
11	Colorado	7.9
11	Indiana	7.9
13	Virginia	7.5
14	Georgia	7.1
14	New Jersey	7.1
16	Nebraska	6.8
17	Kansas	6.6
17	Kentucky	6.6
17	Mississippi	6.6
17	Texas	6.6
21	Idaho	6.4
22	Wisconsin	6.3
23	North Carolina	6.1
24	Alaska	5.9
24	Delaware	5.9
24	Maryland	5.9
24	New York	5.9
28	Minnesota	5.8
29	Pennsylvania	5.7
30	Iowa	5.6
31	Oregon	5.5
32	Washington	5.2
33	Ohio	5.1
34	Missouri	4.8
35	Michigan	4.7
36	Connecticut	3.8
37	Illinois	3.5
37	Wyoming	3.5
39	Louisiana	3.4
40	Florida	3.3
41	Hawaii	3.2
42	California	3.1
43	Massachusetts	3.0
44	Rhode Island	2.1
NA	Maine**	NA
NA	Montana**	NA
NA	New Hampshire**	NA
NA	North Dakota**	NA
NA	Vermont**	NA
NA	West Virginia**	NA

District of Columbia   7.9

Source: U.S. Department of Health and Human Services, National Center for Health Statistics
    "National Vital Statistics Reports" (Vol. 52, No. 10, December 17, 2003)
*Final data by state of residence. "Late" means care begun in third trimester.
**Insufficient data.

Reported Legal Abortions in 2000

Reporting States' Total = 857,475 Abortions*

ALPHA ORDER

RANK	STATE	ABORTIONS	% of USA
17	Alabama	13,553	1.6%
NA	Alaska**	NA	NA
24	Arizona	10,064	1.2%
30	Arkansas	5,501	0.6%
NA	California**	NA	NA
35	Colorado	4,215	0.5%
18	Connecticut	12,908	1.5%
33	Delaware	5,082	0.6%
2	Florida	88,563	10.3%
8	Georgia	31,678	3.7%
37	Hawaii	3,941	0.5%
46	Idaho	801	0.1%
4	Illinois	45,884	5.4%
20	Indiana	12,272	1.4%
29	Iowa	5,747	0.7%
21	Kansas	12,225	1.4%
34	Kentucky	4,630	0.5%
22	Louisiana	11,384	1.3%
41	Maine	2,536	0.3%
19	Maryland	12,337	1.4%
11	Massachusetts	27,180	3.2%
12	Michigan	26,807	3.1%
15	Minnesota	14,468	1.7%
38	Mississippi	3,758	0.4%
25	Missouri	7,884	0.9%
42	Montana	2,441	0.3%
36	Nebraska	4,178	0.5%
28	Nevada	5,972	0.7%
NA	New Hampshire**	NA	NA
7	New Jersey	33,026	3.9%
31	New Mexico	5,465	0.6%
1	New York	129,678	15.1%
9	North Carolina	30,157	3.5%
44	North Dakota	1,341	0.2%
5	Ohio	38,140	4.4%
27	Oklahoma	7,182	0.8%
16	Oregon	14,194	1.7%
6	Pennsylvania	35,630	4.2%
32	Rhode Island	5,413	0.6%
26	South Carolina	7,527	0.9%
45	South Dakota	878	0.1%
14	Tennessee	17,479	2.0%
3	Texas	76,121	8.9%
39	Utah	3,509	0.4%
43	Vermont	1,781	0.2%
10	Virginia	27,999	3.3%
13	Washington	25,692	3.0%
40	West Virginia	2,549	0.3%
23	Wisconsin	11,040	1.3%
47	Wyoming	6	0.0%

RANK ORDER

RANK	STATE	ABORTIONS	% of USA
1	New York	129,678	15.1%
2	Florida	88,563	10.3%
3	Texas	76,121	8.9%
4	Illinois	45,884	5.4%
5	Ohio	38,140	4.4%
6	Pennsylvania	35,630	4.2%
7	New Jersey	33,026	3.9%
8	Georgia	31,678	3.7%
9	North Carolina	30,157	3.5%
10	Virginia	27,999	3.3%
11	Massachusetts	27,180	3.2%
12	Michigan	26,807	3.1%
13	Washington	25,692	3.0%
14	Tennessee	17,479	2.0%
15	Minnesota	14,468	1.7%
16	Oregon	14,194	1.7%
17	Alabama	13,553	1.6%
18	Connecticut	12,908	1.5%
19	Maryland	12,337	1.4%
20	Indiana	12,272	1.4%
21	Kansas	12,225	1.4%
22	Louisiana	11,384	1.3%
23	Wisconsin	11,040	1.3%
24	Arizona	10,064	1.2%
25	Missouri	7,884	0.9%
26	South Carolina	7,527	0.9%
27	Oklahoma	7,182	0.8%
28	Nevada	5,972	0.7%
29	Iowa	5,747	0.7%
30	Arkansas	5,501	0.6%
31	New Mexico	5,465	0.6%
32	Rhode Island	5,413	0.6%
33	Delaware	5,082	0.6%
34	Kentucky	4,630	0.5%
35	Colorado	4,215	0.5%
36	Nebraska	4,178	0.5%
37	Hawaii	3,941	0.5%
38	Mississippi	3,758	0.4%
39	Utah	3,509	0.4%
40	West Virginia	2,549	0.3%
41	Maine	2,536	0.3%
42	Montana	2,441	0.3%
43	Vermont	1,781	0.2%
44	North Dakota	1,341	0.2%
45	South Dakota	878	0.1%
46	Idaho	801	0.1%
47	Wyoming	6	0.0%
NA	Alaska**	NA	NA
NA	California**	NA	NA
NA	New Hampshire**	NA	NA
	District of Columbia	6,659	0.8%

Source: U.S. Department of Health and Human Services, Centers for Disease Control and Prevention
"Abortion Surveillance-United States, 2000" (Morbidity Mortality Weekly Report, Vol. 52, No. SS-12, 11/28/03)
*By state of occurrence. Total is for reporting states only.
**Not reported.

Percent Change in Reported Legal Abortions: 1996 to 2000

National Percent Change = 8.5% Decrease*

ALPHA ORDER

ALPHA ORDER

RANK	STATE	PERCENT CHANGE
16	Alabama	(2.0)
NA	Alaska**	NA
27	Arizona	(8.6)
23	Arkansas	(6.5)
NA	California**	NA
46	Colorado	(56.6)
26	Connecticut	(8.4)
2	Delaware	13.4
3	Florida	10.6
31	Georgia	(11.5)
40	Hawaii	(19.8)
42	Idaho	(21.6)
34	Illinois	(14.4)
25	Indiana	(8.0)
43	Iowa	(24.4)
1	Kansas	14.4
45	Kentucky	(33.9)
21	Louisiana	(4.1)
19	Maine	(3.0)
13	Maryland	(0.2)
24	Massachusetts	(7.2)
30	Michigan	(11.3)
12	Minnesota	1.9
29	Mississippi	(10.7)
44	Missouri	(32.2)
32	Montana	(11.7)
41	Nebraska	(19.9)
33	Nevada	(14.3)
NA	New Hampshire**	NA
9	New Jersey	3.7
4	New Mexico	8.6
35	New York	(15.2)
28	North Carolina	(10.1)
8	North Dakota	3.9
7	Ohio	4.4
6	Oklahoma	6.1
11	Oregon	3.1
22	Pennsylvania	(6.2)
14	Rhode Island	(0.4)
38	South Carolina	(19.3)
17	South Dakota	(2.6)
18	Tennessee	(2.8)
37	Texas	(16.8)
20	Utah	(3.6)
36	Vermont	(16.7)
4	Virginia	8.6
15	Washington	(1.7)
10	West Virginia	3.2
38	Wisconsin	(19.3)
47	Wyoming	(97.1)

RANK ORDER

RANK	STATE	PERCENT CHANGE
1	Kansas	14.4
2	Delaware	13.4
3	Florida	10.6
4	New Mexico	8.6
4	Virginia	8.6
6	Oklahoma	6.1
7	Ohio	4.4
8	North Dakota	3.9
9	New Jersey	3.7
10	West Virginia	3.2
11	Oregon	3.1
12	Minnesota	1.9
13	Maryland	(0.2)
14	Rhode Island	(0.4)
15	Washington	(1.7)
16	Alabama	(2.0)
17	South Dakota	(2.6)
18	Tennessee	(2.8)
19	Maine	(3.0)
20	Utah	(3.6)
21	Louisiana	(4.1)
22	Pennsylvania	(6.2)
23	Arkansas	(6.5)
24	Massachusetts	(7.2)
25	Indiana	(8.0)
26	Connecticut	(8.4)
27	Arizona	(8.6)
28	North Carolina	(10.1)
29	Mississippi	(10.7)
30	Michigan	(11.3)
31	Georgia	(11.5)
32	Montana	(11.7)
33	Nevada	(14.3)
34	Illinois	(14.4)
35	New York	(15.2)
36	Vermont	(16.7)
37	Texas	(16.8)
38	South Carolina	(19.3)
38	Wisconsin	(19.3)
40	Hawaii	(19.8)
41	Nebraska	(19.9)
42	Idaho	(21.6)
43	Iowa	(24.4)
44	Missouri	(32.2)
45	Kentucky	(33.9)
46	Colorado	(56.6)
47	Wyoming	(97.1)
NA	Alaska**	NA
NA	California**	NA
NA	New Hampshire**	NA

District of Columbia (51.3)

Source: Morgan Quitno Press using data from US Dept of Health & Human Serv's, Centers for Disease Control-Prevention "Abortion Surveillance-United States, 2000" (Morbidity Mortality Weekly Report, Vol. 52, No. SS-12, 11/28/03) "Abortion Surveillance-United States, 1996" (Morbidity Mortality Weekly Report, Vol. 48, No. SS-4, 07/30/99)

*By state of occurrence. Total is for reporting states only.

**Not reported.

Reported Legal Abortions per 1,000 Live Births in 2000

Reporting States' Ratio = 245 Abortions per 1,000 Live Births*

<u>ALPHA ORDER</u>

RANK	STATE	RATIO
21	Alabama	214
NA	Alaska**	NA
39	Arizona	118
34	Arkansas	146
NA	California**	NA
45	Colorado	64
9	Connecticut	300
2	Delaware	460
3	Florida	434
17	Georgia	239
18	Hawaii	225
46	Idaho	39
14	Illinois	248
36	Indiana	140
33	Iowa	150
8	Kansas	308
43	Kentucky	83
30	Louisiana	168
27	Maine	186
31	Maryland	166
5	Massachusetts	333
25	Michigan	197
21	Minnesota	214
41	Mississippi	85
40	Missouri	103
19	Montana	223
29	Nebraska	170
26	Nevada	194
NA	New Hampshire**	NA
10	New Jersey	286
24	New Mexico	201
1	New York	501
13	North Carolina	251
28	North Dakota	175
15	Ohio	245
35	Oklahoma	144
7	Oregon	310
16	Pennsylvania	244
4	Rhode Island	433
37	South Carolina	134
41	South Dakota	85
20	Tennessee	220
23	Texas	209
44	Utah	74
12	Vermont	274
11	Virginia	283
6	Washington	317
38	West Virginia	122
32	Wisconsin	159
NA	Wyoming**	NA

<u>RANK ORDER</u>

RANK	STATE	RATIO
1	New York	501
2	Delaware	460
3	Florida	434
4	Rhode Island	433
5	Massachusetts	333
6	Washington	317
7	Oregon	310
8	Kansas	308
9	Connecticut	300
10	New Jersey	286
11	Virginia	283
12	Vermont	274
13	North Carolina	251
14	Illinois	248
15	Ohio	245
16	Pennsylvania	244
17	Georgia	239
18	Hawaii	225
19	Montana	223
20	Tennessee	220
21	Alabama	214
21	Minnesota	214
23	Texas	209
24	New Mexico	201
25	Michigan	197
26	Nevada	194
27	Maine	186
28	North Dakota	175
29	Nebraska	170
30	Louisiana	168
31	Maryland	166
32	Wisconsin	159
33	Iowa	150
34	Arkansas	146
35	Oklahoma	144
36	Indiana	140
37	South Carolina	134
38	West Virginia	122
39	Arizona	118
40	Missouri	103
41	Mississippi	85
41	South Dakota	85
43	Kentucky	83
44	Utah	74
45	Colorado	64
46	Idaho	39
NA	Alaska**	NA
NA	California**	NA
NA	New Hampshire**	NA
NA	Wyoming**	NA

District of Columbia   869

Source: U.S. Department of Health and Human Services, Centers for Disease Control and Prevention
"Abortion Surveillance-United States, 2000" (Morbidity Mortality Weekly Report, Vol. 52, No. SS-12, 11/28/03)
*By state of occurrence. National figure is for reporting states only.
**Not reported.

Reported Legal Abortions per 1,000 Women Ages 15 to 44 in 2000

Reporting States' Rate = 16 Abortions per 1,000 Women Ages 15 to 44*

ALPHA ORDER			RANK ORDER		
RANK	STATE	RATE	RANK	STATE	RATE
18	Alabama	14	1	New York	31
NA	Alaska**	NA	2	Delaware	29
34	Arizona	9	3	Florida	27
29	Arkansas	10	4	Rhode Island	23
NA	California**	NA	5	Kansas	21
45	Colorado	4	6	Oregon	20
9	Connecticut	18	6	Washington	20
2	Delaware	29	8	Massachusetts	19
3	Florida	27	9	Connecticut	18
12	Georgia	17	9	New Jersey	18
15	Hawaii	16	9	Virginia	18
46	Idaho	3	12	Georgia	17
12	Illinois	17	12	Illinois	17
34	Indiana	9	12	North Carolina	17
34	Iowa	9	15	Hawaii	16
5	Kansas	21	15	Ohio	16
44	Kentucky	5	15	Texas	16
27	Louisiana	11	18	Alabama	14
34	Maine	9	18	Nevada	14
29	Maryland	10	18	New Mexico	14
8	Massachusetts	19	18	Pennsylvania	14
26	Michigan	12	18	Tennessee	14
24	Minnesota	13	18	Vermont	14
42	Mississippi	6	24	Minnesota	13
39	Missouri	7	24	Montana	13
24	Montana	13	26	Michigan	12
27	Nebraska	11	27	Louisiana	11
18	Nevada	14	27	Nebraska	11
NA	New Hampshire**	NA	29	Arkansas	10
9	New Jersey	18	29	Maryland	10
18	New Mexico	14	29	North Dakota	10
1	New York	31	29	Oklahoma	10
12	North Carolina	17	29	Wisconsin	10
29	North Dakota	10	34	Arizona	9
15	Ohio	16	34	Indiana	9
29	Oklahoma	10	34	Iowa	9
6	Oregon	20	34	Maine	9
18	Pennsylvania	14	34	South Carolina	9
4	Rhode Island	23	39	Missouri	7
34	South Carolina	9	39	Utah	7
42	South Dakota	6	39	West Virginia	7
18	Tennessee	14	42	Mississippi	6
15	Texas	16	42	South Dakota	6
39	Utah	7	44	Kentucky	5
18	Vermont	14	45	Colorado	4
9	Virginia	18	46	Idaho	3
6	Washington	20	NA	Alaska**	NA
39	West Virginia	7	NA	California**	NA
29	Wisconsin	10	NA	New Hampshire**	NA
NA	Wyoming**	NA	NA	Wyoming**	NA
				District of Columbia	46

Source: U.S. Department of Health and Human Services, Centers for Disease Control and Prevention
"Abortion Surveillance-United States, 2000" (Morbidity Mortality Weekly Report, Vol. 52, No. SS-12, 11/28/03)
*By state of occurrence. National figure is for reporting states only.
**Not reported.

Percent of Legal Abortions Obtained by Out-Of-State Residents in 2000

Reporting States' Percent = 8.7% of Abortions*

ALPHA ORDER			RANK ORDER		
RANK	**STATE**	**PERCENT**	**RANK**	**STATE**	**PERCENT**
6	Alabama	18.5	1	Kansas	48.8
NA	Alaska**	NA	2	North Dakota	35.6
41	Arizona	2.6	3	Delaware	32.3
9	Arkansas	17.3	4	Rhode Island	21.9
NA	California**	NA	5	South Dakota	19.4
8	Colorado	18.2	6	Alabama	18.5
36	Connecticut	3.4	6	Tennessee	18.5
3	Delaware	32.3	8	Colorado	18.2
NA	Florida**	NA	9	Arkansas	17.3
19	Georgia	8.8	10	Vermont	17.2
42	Hawaii	0.4	11	Kentucky	16.2
40	Idaho	2.7	12	Nebraska	16.1
17	Illinois	10.6	13	Montana	13.2
32	Indiana	4.1	14	North Carolina	13.1
NA	Iowa**	NA	15	West Virginia	12.5
1	Kansas	48.8	16	Oregon	12.3
11	Kentucky	16.2	17	Illinois	10.6
NA	Louisiana**	NA	18	Missouri	9.7
37	Maine	3.3	19	Georgia	8.8
25	Maryland	6.7	19	Nevada	8.8
22	Massachusetts	7.8	21	Minnesota	8.7
38	Michigan	2.9	22	Massachusetts	7.8
21	Minnesota	8.7	23	Ohio	7.7
28	Mississippi	4.8	24	Utah	6.8
18	Missouri	9.7	25	Maryland	6.7
13	Montana	13.2	26	Virginia	6.2
12	Nebraska	16.1	27	Pennsylvania	4.9
19	Nevada	8.8	28	Mississippi	4.8
NA	New Hampshire**	NA	29	Washington	4.7
34	New Jersey	3.9	30	Oklahoma	4.4
33	New Mexico	4.0	31	South Carolina	4.2
NA	New York**	NA	32	Indiana	4.1
14	North Carolina	13.1	33	New Mexico	4.0
2	North Dakota	35.6	34	New Jersey	3.9
23	Ohio	7.7	35	Texas	3.7
30	Oklahoma	4.4	36	Connecticut	3.4
16	Oregon	12.3	37	Maine	3.3
27	Pennsylvania	4.9	38	Michigan	2.9
4	Rhode Island	21.9	39	Wisconsin	2.8
31	South Carolina	4.2	40	Idaho	2.7
5	South Dakota	19.4	41	Arizona	2.6
6	Tennessee	18.5	42	Hawaii	0.4
35	Texas	3.7	NA	Alaska**	NA
24	Utah	6.8	NA	California**	NA
10	Vermont	17.2	NA	Florida**	NA
26	Virginia	6.2	NA	Iowa**	NA
29	Washington	4.7	NA	Louisiana**	NA
15	West Virginia	12.5	NA	New Hampshire**	NA
39	Wisconsin	2.8	NA	New York**	NA
NA	Wyoming**	NA	NA	Wyoming**	NA

District of Columbia   55.9

Source: U.S. Department of Health and Human Services, Centers for Disease Control and Prevention
   "Abortion Surveillance-United States, 2000" (Morbidity Mortality Weekly Report, Vol. 52, No. SS-12, 11/28/03)
*By state of occurrence. National figure is for reporting states only.
**Not reported.

Percent of Reported Legal Abortions Obtained by White Women in 2000

Reporting States' Percent = 54.8% of Abortions*

ALPHA ORDER

RANK	STATE	PERCENT
32	Alabama	47.3
NA	Alaska**	NA
13	Arizona	79.2
24	Arkansas	58.2
NA	California**	NA
14	Colorado	78.8
NA	Connecticut**	NA
27	Delaware	54.2
NA	Florida**	NA
35	Georgia	41.6
40	Hawaii	24.5
3	Idaho	93.8
NA	Illinois**	NA
22	Indiana	61.0
11	Iowa	81.1
16	Kansas	72.7
17	Kentucky	70.8
36	Louisiana	39.7
4	Maine	92.2
38	Maryland	32.8
26	Massachusetts	57.1
NA	Michigan**	NA
21	Minnesota	65.7
39	Mississippi	27.6
25	Missouri	57.5
7	Montana	87.9
NA	Nebraska**	NA
NA	Nevada**	NA
NA	New Hampshire**	NA
37	New Jersey	33.4
9	New Mexico	83.2
34	New York**	42.1
33	North Carolina	45.1
6	North Dakota	88.3
23	Ohio	59.2
20	Oklahoma	68.5
8	Oregon	84.1
29	Pennsylvania	52.9
15	Rhode Island	77.6
28	South Carolina	54.0
10	South Dakota	82.5
30	Tennessee	52.8
18	Texas	70.5
12	Utah	80.8
2	Vermont	95.5
31	Virginia	49.2
NA	Washington**	NA
5	West Virginia	88.7
19	Wisconsin	68.7
1	Wyoming	100.0

RANK ORDER

RANK	STATE	PERCENT
1	Wyoming	100.0
2	Vermont	95.5
3	Idaho	93.8
4	Maine	92.2
5	West Virginia	88.7
6	North Dakota	88.3
7	Montana	87.9
8	Oregon	84.1
9	New Mexico	83.2
10	South Dakota	82.5
11	Iowa	81.1
12	Utah	80.8
13	Arizona	79.2
14	Colorado	78.8
15	Rhode Island	77.6
16	Kansas	72.7
17	Kentucky	70.8
18	Texas	70.5
19	Wisconsin	68.7
20	Oklahoma	68.5
21	Minnesota	65.7
22	Indiana	61.0
23	Ohio	59.2
24	Arkansas	58.2
25	Missouri	57.5
26	Massachusetts	57.1
27	Delaware	54.2
28	South Carolina	54.0
29	Pennsylvania	52.9
30	Tennessee	52.8
31	Virginia	49.2
32	Alabama	47.3
33	North Carolina	45.1
34	New York**	42.1
35	Georgia	41.6
36	Louisiana	39.7
37	New Jersey	33.4
38	Maryland	32.8
39	Mississippi	27.6
40	Hawaii	24.5
NA	Alaska**	NA
NA	California**	NA
NA	Connecticut**	NA
NA	Florida**	NA
NA	Illinois**	NA
NA	Michigan**	NA
NA	Nebraska**	NA
NA	Nevada**	NA
NA	New Hampshire**	NA
NA	Washington**	NA
	District of Columbia	9.2

Source: U.S. Department of Health and Human Services, Centers for Disease Control and Prevention
"Abortion Surveillance-United States, 2000" (Morbidity Mortality Weekly Report, Vol. 52, No. SS-12, 11/28/03)
*By state of occurrence. Includes those of Hispanic ethnicity. National percent is for reporting states only.
**Not reported. New York's number is for New York City only.

Percent of Reported Legal Abortions Obtained by Black Women in 2000

Reporting States' Percent = 35.1% of Abortions*

ALPHA ORDER				RANK ORDER		
RANK	STATE	PERCENT		RANK	STATE	PERCENT
5	Alabama	50.8		1	Mississippi	71.2
NA	Alaska**	NA		2	Maryland	57.4
29	Arizona	5.4		3	Georgia	54.4
14	Arkansas	38.3		4	Louisiana	52.1
NA	California**	NA		5	Alabama	50.8
30	Colorado	4.2		6	New York**	49.3
NA	Connecticut**	NA		7	New Jersey	44.4
12	Delaware	42.8		8	South Carolina	43.5
NA	Florida**	NA		9	Pennsylvania	43.4
3	Georgia	54.4		10	Tennessee	43.3
31	Hawaii	3.3		11	North Carolina	43.1
38	Idaho	1.0		12	Delaware	42.8
NA	Illinois**	NA		13	Virginia	39.2
17	Indiana	25.9		14	Arkansas	38.3
27	Iowa	6.8		15	Missouri	37.8
19	Kansas	22.4		16	Ohio	35.3
20	Kentucky	21.3		17	Indiana	25.9
4	Louisiana	52.1		18	Wisconsin	24.9
36	Maine	1.5		19	Kansas	22.4
2	Maryland	57.4		20	Kentucky	21.3
23	Massachusetts	18.2		21	Texas	21.1
NA	Michigan**	NA		22	Minnesota	18.4
22	Minnesota	18.4		23	Massachusetts	18.2
1	Mississippi	71.2		24	Oklahoma	16.9
15	Missouri	37.8		25	Rhode Island	14.7
39	Montana	0.2		26	West Virginia	9.5
NA	Nebraska**	NA		27	Iowa	6.8
NA	Nevada**	NA		28	Oregon	6.4
NA	New Hampshire**	NA		29	Arizona	5.4
7	New Jersey	44.4		30	Colorado	4.2
31	New Mexico	3.3		31	Hawaii	3.3
6	New York**	49.3		31	New Mexico	3.3
11	North Carolina	43.1		31	South Dakota	3.3
37	North Dakota	1.4		34	Utah	2.2
16	Ohio	35.3		35	Vermont	1.6
24	Oklahoma	16.9		36	Maine	1.5
28	Oregon	6.4		37	North Dakota	1.4
9	Pennsylvania	43.4		38	Idaho	1.0
25	Rhode Island	14.7		39	Montana	0.2
8	South Carolina	43.5		40	Wyoming	0.0
31	South Dakota	3.3		NA	Alaska**	NA
10	Tennessee	43.3		NA	California**	NA
21	Texas	21.1		NA	Connecticut**	NA
34	Utah	2.2		NA	Florida**	NA
35	Vermont	1.6		NA	Illinois**	NA
13	Virginia	39.2		NA	Michigan**	NA
NA	Washington**	NA		NA	Nebraska**	NA
26	West Virginia	9.5		NA	Nevada**	NA
18	Wisconsin	24.9		NA	New Hampshire**	NA
40	Wyoming	0.0		NA	Washington**	NA
					District of Columbia	78.7

Source: U.S. Department of Health and Human Services, Centers for Disease Control and Prevention
"Abortion Surveillance-United States, 2000" (Morbidity Mortality Weekly Report, Vol. 52, No. SS-12, 11/28/03)

By state of occurrence. National percent is for reporting states only.
**Not reported. New York's number is for New York City only.*

Percent of Reported Legal Abortions Obtained by Hispanic Women in 2000

Reporting States' Percent = 16.6%*

ALPHA ORDER

RANK	STATE	PERCENT
26	Alabama	1.4
NA	Alaska**	NA
4	Arizona	30.5
21	Arkansas	3.3
NA	California**	NA
7	Colorado	15.4
NA	Connecticut**	NA
14	Delaware	6.5
NA	Florida**	NA
19	Georgia	4.4
NA	Hawaii**	NA
9	Idaho	10.9
NA	Illinois**	NA
16	Indiana	5.3
NA	Iowa**	NA
12	Kansas	7.8
30	Kentucky	0.0
NA	Louisiana**	NA
28	Maine	1.1
NA	Maryland**	NA
10	Massachusetts	9.8
NA	Michigan**	NA
17	Minnesota	5.2
29	Mississippi	0.4
25	Missouri	1.9
NA	Montana**	NA
NA	Nebraska**	NA
NA	Nevada**	NA
NA	New Hampshire**	NA
5	New Jersey	19.1
1	New Mexico	45.9
3	New York**	32.9
NA	North Carolina**	NA
NA	North Dakota**	NA
23	Ohio	2.5
15	Oklahoma	5.4
11	Oregon	9.4
19	Pennsylvania	4.4
NA	Rhode Island**	NA
22	South Carolina	2.6
18	South Dakota	4.6
24	Tennessee	2.4
2	Texas	34.9
7	Utah	15.4
27	Vermont	1.2
NA	Virginia**	NA
NA	Washington**	NA
NA	West Virginia**	NA
13	Wisconsin	6.7
6	Wyoming	16.7

RANK ORDER

RANK	STATE	PERCENT
1	New Mexico	45.9
2	Texas	34.9
3	New York**	32.9
4	Arizona	30.5
5	New Jersey	19.1
6	Wyoming	16.7
7	Colorado	15.4
7	Utah	15.4
9	Idaho	10.9
10	Massachusetts	9.8
11	Oregon	9.4
12	Kansas	7.8
13	Wisconsin	6.7
14	Delaware	6.5
15	Oklahoma	5.4
16	Indiana	5.3
17	Minnesota	5.2
18	South Dakota	4.6
19	Georgia	4.4
19	Pennsylvania	4.4
21	Arkansas	3.3
22	South Carolina	2.6
23	Ohio	2.5
24	Tennessee	2.4
25	Missouri	1.9
26	Alabama	1.4
27	Vermont	1.2
28	Maine	1.1
29	Mississippi	0.4
30	Kentucky	0.0
NA	Alaska**	NA
NA	California**	NA
NA	Connecticut**	NA
NA	Florida**	NA
NA	Hawaii**	NA
NA	Illinois**	NA
NA	Iowa**	NA
NA	Louisiana**	NA
NA	Maryland**	NA
NA	Michigan**	NA
NA	Montana**	NA
NA	Nebraska**	NA
NA	Nevada**	NA
NA	New Hampshire**	NA
NA	North Carolina**	NA
NA	North Dakota**	NA
NA	Rhode Island**	NA
NA	Virginia**	NA
NA	Washington**	NA
NA	West Virginia**	NA

	District of Columbia	10.7

Source: U.S. Department of Health and Human Services, Centers for Disease Control and Prevention
  "Abortion Surveillance-United States, 2000" (Morbidity Mortality Weekly Report, Vol. 52, No. SS-12, 11/28/03)
*By state of occurrence. National percent is for reporting states only. Hispanic can be of any race.
**Not reported. New York's number is for New York City only.

Percent of Reported Legal Abortions Obtained by Married Women in 2000

Reporting States' Percent = 18.1% of Abortions*

<table>
<tr><td colspan="3">ALPHA ORDER</td><td colspan="3">RANK ORDER</td></tr>
<tr><td>RANK</td><td>STATE</td><td>PERCENT</td><td>RANK</td><td>STATE</td><td>PERCENT</td></tr>
<tr><td>36</td><td>Alabama</td><td>14.3</td><td>1</td><td>Massachusetts</td><td>24.8</td></tr>
<tr><td>NA</td><td>Alaska**</td><td>NA</td><td>2</td><td>Utah</td><td>24.7</td></tr>
<tr><td>NA</td><td>Arizona**</td><td>NA</td><td>3</td><td>Oregon</td><td>22.4</td></tr>
<tr><td>26</td><td>Arkansas</td><td>16.7</td><td>4</td><td>Colorado</td><td>22.1</td></tr>
<tr><td>NA</td><td>California**</td><td>NA</td><td>5</td><td>North Carolina</td><td>21.6</td></tr>
<tr><td>4</td><td>Colorado</td><td>22.1</td><td>6</td><td>Iowa</td><td>21.4</td></tr>
<tr><td>NA</td><td>Connecticut**</td><td>NA</td><td>7</td><td>Texas</td><td>21.1</td></tr>
<tr><td>32</td><td>Delaware</td><td>16.0</td><td>8</td><td>Hawaii</td><td>21.0</td></tr>
<tr><td>20</td><td>Florida</td><td>17.6</td><td>9</td><td>Missouri</td><td>20.5</td></tr>
<tr><td>19</td><td>Georgia</td><td>17.8</td><td>10</td><td>Nevada</td><td>20.4</td></tr>
<tr><td>8</td><td>Hawaii</td><td>21.0</td><td>11</td><td>Vermont</td><td>20.3</td></tr>
<tr><td>NA</td><td>Idaho**</td><td>NA</td><td>12</td><td>Minnesota</td><td>20.2</td></tr>
<tr><td>33</td><td>Illinois</td><td>15.3</td><td>13</td><td>Kansas</td><td>19.8</td></tr>
<tr><td>37</td><td>Indiana</td><td>13.2</td><td>14</td><td>South Dakota</td><td>19.5</td></tr>
<tr><td>6</td><td>Iowa</td><td>21.4</td><td>15</td><td>Oklahoma</td><td>19.0</td></tr>
<tr><td>13</td><td>Kansas</td><td>19.8</td><td>16</td><td>Tennessee</td><td>18.9</td></tr>
<tr><td>29</td><td>Kentucky</td><td>16.3</td><td>17</td><td>West Virginia</td><td>18.6</td></tr>
<tr><td>NA</td><td>Louisiana**</td><td>NA</td><td>18</td><td>Wisconsin</td><td>17.9</td></tr>
<tr><td>NA</td><td>Maine**</td><td>NA</td><td>19</td><td>Georgia</td><td>17.8</td></tr>
<tr><td>29</td><td>Maryland</td><td>16.3</td><td>20</td><td>Florida</td><td>17.6</td></tr>
<tr><td>1</td><td>Massachusetts</td><td>24.8</td><td>21</td><td>Ohio</td><td>17.4</td></tr>
<tr><td>34</td><td>Michigan</td><td>15.1</td><td>22</td><td>New Mexico</td><td>17.2</td></tr>
<tr><td>12</td><td>Minnesota</td><td>20.2</td><td>22</td><td>North Dakota</td><td>17.2</td></tr>
<tr><td>38</td><td>Mississippi</td><td>12.7</td><td>24</td><td>Virginia</td><td>17.0</td></tr>
<tr><td>9</td><td>Missouri</td><td>20.5</td><td>25</td><td>New Jersey</td><td>16.8</td></tr>
<tr><td>35</td><td>Montana</td><td>15.0</td><td>26</td><td>Arkansas</td><td>16.7</td></tr>
<tr><td>NA</td><td>Nebraska**</td><td>NA</td><td>27</td><td>South Carolina</td><td>16.6</td></tr>
<tr><td>10</td><td>Nevada</td><td>20.4</td><td>28</td><td>New York**</td><td>16.4</td></tr>
<tr><td>NA</td><td>New Hampshire**</td><td>NA</td><td>29</td><td>Kentucky</td><td>16.3</td></tr>
<tr><td>25</td><td>New Jersey</td><td>16.8</td><td>29</td><td>Maryland</td><td>16.3</td></tr>
<tr><td>22</td><td>New Mexico</td><td>17.2</td><td>29</td><td>Pennsylvania</td><td>16.3</td></tr>
<tr><td>28</td><td>New York**</td><td>16.4</td><td>32</td><td>Delaware</td><td>16.0</td></tr>
<tr><td>5</td><td>North Carolina</td><td>21.6</td><td>33</td><td>Illinois</td><td>15.3</td></tr>
<tr><td>22</td><td>North Dakota</td><td>17.2</td><td>34</td><td>Michigan</td><td>15.1</td></tr>
<tr><td>21</td><td>Ohio</td><td>17.4</td><td>35</td><td>Montana</td><td>15.0</td></tr>
<tr><td>15</td><td>Oklahoma</td><td>19.0</td><td>36</td><td>Alabama</td><td>14.3</td></tr>
<tr><td>3</td><td>Oregon</td><td>22.4</td><td>37</td><td>Indiana</td><td>13.2</td></tr>
<tr><td>29</td><td>Pennsylvania</td><td>16.3</td><td>38</td><td>Mississippi</td><td>12.7</td></tr>
<tr><td>NA</td><td>Rhode Island**</td><td>NA</td><td>39</td><td>Wyoming</td><td>0.0</td></tr>
<tr><td>27</td><td>South Carolina</td><td>16.6</td><td>NA</td><td>Alaska**</td><td>NA</td></tr>
<tr><td>14</td><td>South Dakota</td><td>19.5</td><td>NA</td><td>Arizona**</td><td>NA</td></tr>
<tr><td>16</td><td>Tennessee</td><td>18.9</td><td>NA</td><td>California**</td><td>NA</td></tr>
<tr><td>7</td><td>Texas</td><td>21.1</td><td>NA</td><td>Connecticut**</td><td>NA</td></tr>
<tr><td>2</td><td>Utah</td><td>24.7</td><td>NA</td><td>Idaho**</td><td>NA</td></tr>
<tr><td>11</td><td>Vermont</td><td>20.3</td><td>NA</td><td>Louisiana**</td><td>NA</td></tr>
<tr><td>24</td><td>Virginia</td><td>17.0</td><td>NA</td><td>Maine**</td><td>NA</td></tr>
<tr><td>NA</td><td>Washington**</td><td>NA</td><td>NA</td><td>Nebraska**</td><td>NA</td></tr>
<tr><td>17</td><td>West Virginia</td><td>18.6</td><td>NA</td><td>New Hampshire**</td><td>NA</td></tr>
<tr><td>18</td><td>Wisconsin</td><td>17.9</td><td>NA</td><td>Rhode Island**</td><td>NA</td></tr>
<tr><td>39</td><td>Wyoming</td><td>0.0</td><td>NA</td><td>Washington**</td><td>NA</td></tr>
<tr><td></td><td></td><td></td><td></td><td>District of Columbia**</td><td>NA</td></tr>
</table>

Source: U.S. Department of Health and Human Services, Centers for Disease Control and Prevention
   "Abortion Surveillance-United States, 2000" (Morbidity Mortality Weekly Report, Vol. 52, No. SS-12, 11/28/03)
*By state of occurrence. National percent is for reporting states only.
**Not reported. New York's number is for New York City only.

Percent of Reported Legal Abortions Obtained by Unmarried Women in 2000

Reporting States' Percent = 78.5% of Abortions*

ALPHA ORDER			RANK ORDER		
RANK	STATE	PERCENT	RANK	STATE	PERCENT
21	Alabama	79.6	1	Wyoming	100.0
NA	Alaska**	NA	2	Mississippi	85.9
NA	Arizona**	NA	3	Delaware	84.0
22	Arkansas	79.0	4	Kentucky	83.7
NA	California**	NA	4	Michigan	83.7
27	Colorado	76.8	4	Pennsylvania	83.7
NA	Connecticut**	NA	7	South Carolina	83.4
3	Delaware	84.0	8	North Dakota	82.6
18	Florida	80.7	9	New Jersey	82.2
11	Georgia	81.6	10	Wisconsin	81.9
23	Hawaii	78.9	11	Georgia	81.6
NA	Idaho**	NA	12	New Mexico	81.4
13	Illinois	81.1	13	Illinois	81.1
35	Indiana	72.7	13	Tennessee	81.1
26	Iowa	77.8	13	West Virginia	81.1
20	Kansas	80.1	16	New York**	81.0
4	Kentucky	83.7	16	Ohio	81.0
NA	Louisiana**	NA	18	Florida	80.7
NA	Maine**	NA	19	South Dakota	80.5
28	Maryland	76.7	20	Kansas	80.1
39	Massachusetts	67.7	21	Alabama	79.6
4	Michigan	83.7	22	Arkansas	79.0
34	Minnesota	74.7	23	Hawaii	78.9
2	Mississippi	85.9	24	Missouri	78.2
24	Missouri	78.2	24	Oklahoma	78.2
33	Montana	74.8	26	Iowa	77.8
NA	Nebraska**	NA	27	Colorado	76.8
38	Nevada	68.8	28	Maryland	76.7
NA	New Hampshire**	NA	29	Vermont	76.2
9	New Jersey	82.2	30	Oregon	75.4
12	New Mexico	81.4	31	Utah	75.0
16	New York**	81.0	32	Texas	74.9
36	North Carolina	72.6	33	Montana	74.8
8	North Dakota	82.6	34	Minnesota	74.7
16	Ohio	81.0	35	Indiana	72.7
24	Oklahoma	78.2	36	North Carolina	72.6
30	Oregon	75.4	37	Virginia	70.8
4	Pennsylvania	83.7	38	Nevada	68.8
NA	Rhode Island**	NA	39	Massachusetts	67.7
7	South Carolina	83.4	NA	Alaska**	NA
19	South Dakota	80.5	NA	Arizona**	NA
13	Tennessee	81.1	NA	California**	NA
32	Texas	74.9	NA	Connecticut**	NA
31	Utah	75.0	NA	Idaho**	NA
29	Vermont	76.2	NA	Louisiana**	NA
37	Virginia	70.8	NA	Maine**	NA
NA	Washington**	NA	NA	Nebraska**	NA
13	West Virginia	81.1	NA	New Hampshire**	NA
10	Wisconsin	81.9	NA	Rhode Island**	NA
1	Wyoming	100.0	NA	Washington**	NA
				District of Columbia**	NA

Source: U.S. Department of Health and Human Services, Centers for Disease Control and Prevention
"Abortion Surveillance-United States, 2000" (Morbidity Mortality Weekly Report, Vol. 52, No. SS-12, 11/28/03)
*By state of occurrence. National percent is for reporting states only.
**Not reported. New York's number is for New York City only.

Reported Legal Abortions Obtained by Teenagers in 2000

Reporting States' Total = 143,286 Abortions Obtained by Teenagers*

ALPHA ORDER

RANK	STATE	ABORTIONS	% of USA
15	Alabama	2,703	1.9%
NA	Alaska**	NA	NA
23	Arizona	2,036	1.4%
29	Arkansas	1,158	0.8%
NA	California**	NA	NA
33	Colorado	933	0.7%
16	Connecticut	2,680	1.9%
37	Delaware	794	0.6%
NA	Florida**	NA	NA
7	Georgia	5,444	3.8%
32	Hawaii	946	0.7%
45	Idaho	166	0.1%
3	Illinois	9,736	6.8%
19	Indiana	2,273	1.6%
28	Iowa	1,267	0.9%
17	Kansas	2,500	1.7%
35	Kentucky	838	0.6%
20	Louisiana	2,160	1.5%
39	Maine	582	0.4%
22	Maryland	2,066	1.4%
11	Massachusetts	4,663	3.3%
10	Michigan	5,113	3.6%
18	Minnesota	2,455	1.7%
36	Mississippi	805	0.6%
26	Missouri	1,340	0.9%
40	Montana	570	0.4%
34	Nebraska	890	0.6%
30	Nevada	1,042	0.7%
NA	New Hampshire**	NA	NA
6	New Jersey	6,274	4.4%
27	New Mexico	1,269	0.9%
1	New York	23,916	16.7%
8	North Carolina	5,237	3.7%
43	North Dakota	297	0.2%
4	Ohio	7,174	5.0%
25	Oklahoma	1,525	1.1%
14	Oregon	2,822	2.0%
5	Pennsylvania	6,809	4.8%
31	Rhode Island	969	0.7%
24	South Carolina	1,588	1.1%
44	South Dakota	189	0.1%
13	Tennessee	3,181	2.2%
2	Texas	12,095	8.4%
38	Utah	652	0.5%
42	Vermont	373	0.3%
12	Virginia	4,588	3.2%
9	Washington	5,231	3.7%
41	West Virginia	532	0.4%
21	Wisconsin	2,130	1.5%
46	Wyoming	1	0.0%

RANK ORDER

RANK	STATE	ABORTIONS	% of USA
1	New York	23,916	16.7%
2	Texas	12,095	8.4%
3	Illinois	9,736	6.8%
4	Ohio	7,174	5.0%
5	Pennsylvania	6,809	4.8%
6	New Jersey	6,274	4.4%
7	Georgia	5,444	3.8%
8	North Carolina	5,237	3.7%
9	Washington	5,231	3.7%
10	Michigan	5,113	3.6%
11	Massachusetts	4,663	3.3%
12	Virginia	4,588	3.2%
13	Tennessee	3,181	2.2%
14	Oregon	2,822	2.0%
15	Alabama	2,703	1.9%
16	Connecticut	2,680	1.9%
17	Kansas	2,500	1.7%
18	Minnesota	2,455	1.7%
19	Indiana	2,273	1.6%
20	Louisiana	2,160	1.5%
21	Wisconsin	2,130	1.5%
22	Maryland	2,066	1.4%
23	Arizona	2,036	1.4%
24	South Carolina	1,588	1.1%
25	Oklahoma	1,525	1.1%
26	Missouri	1,340	0.9%
27	New Mexico	1,269	0.9%
28	Iowa	1,267	0.9%
29	Arkansas	1,158	0.8%
30	Nevada	1,042	0.7%
31	Rhode Island	969	0.7%
32	Hawaii	946	0.7%
33	Colorado	933	0.7%
34	Nebraska	890	0.6%
35	Kentucky	838	0.6%
36	Mississippi	805	0.6%
37	Delaware	794	0.6%
38	Utah	652	0.5%
39	Maine	582	0.4%
40	Montana	570	0.4%
41	West Virginia	532	0.4%
42	Vermont	373	0.3%
43	North Dakota	297	0.2%
44	South Dakota	189	0.1%
45	Idaho	166	0.1%
46	Wyoming	1	0.0%
NA	Alaska**	NA	NA
NA	California**	NA	NA
NA	Florida**	NA	NA
NA	New Hampshire**	NA	NA

District of Columbia — 1,274 — 0.9%

Source: U.S. Department of Health and Human Services, Centers for Disease Control and Prevention
"Abortion Surveillance-United States, 2000" (Morbidity Mortality Weekly Report, Vol. 52, No. SS-12, 11/28/03)
Nineteen years old and younger by state of occurrence. National total is for reporting states only.
**Not reported.*

Percent of Reported Legal Abortions Obtained by Teenagers in 2000

Reporting States' Percent = 18.7% of Abortions*

ALPHA ORDER

RANK	STATE	PERCENT
23	Alabama	19.9
NA	Alaska**	NA
22	Arizona	20.2
15	Arkansas	21.0
NA	California**	NA
6	Colorado	22.1
19	Connecticut	20.7
4	Delaware	23.1
NA	Florida**	NA
41	Georgia	17.1
1	Hawaii	24.0
17	Idaho	20.8
11	Illinois	21.3
32	Indiana	18.5
6	Iowa	22.1
20	Kansas	20.4
35	Kentucky	18.1
27	Louisiana	19.0
5	Maine	22.9
36	Maryland	18.0
40	Massachusetts	17.2
27	Michigan	19.0
42	Minnesota	17.0
10	Mississippi	21.4
42	Missouri	17.0
2	Montana	23.4
11	Nebraska	21.3
38	Nevada	17.4
NA	New Hampshire**	NA
27	New Jersey	19.0
3	New Mexico	23.2
33	New York	18.4
39	North Carolina	17.3
6	North Dakota	22.1
30	Ohio	18.8
13	Oklahoma	21.2
23	Oregon	19.9
26	Pennsylvania	19.2
37	Rhode Island	17.9
14	South Carolina	21.1
9	South Dakota	21.6
34	Tennessee	18.2
46	Texas	15.9
31	Utah	18.6
16	Vermont	20.9
45	Virginia	16.3
20	Washington	20.4
17	West Virginia	20.8
23	Wisconsin	19.9
44	Wyoming	16.7

RANK ORDER

RANK	STATE	PERCENT
1	Hawaii	24.0
2	Montana	23.4
3	New Mexico	23.2
4	Delaware	23.1
5	Maine	22.9
6	Colorado	22.1
6	Iowa	22.1
6	North Dakota	22.1
9	South Dakota	21.6
10	Mississippi	21.4
11	Illinois	21.3
11	Nebraska	21.3
13	Oklahoma	21.2
14	South Carolina	21.1
15	Arkansas	21.0
16	Vermont	20.9
17	Idaho	20.8
17	West Virginia	20.8
19	Connecticut	20.7
20	Kansas	20.4
20	Washington	20.4
22	Arizona	20.2
23	Alabama	19.9
23	Oregon	19.9
23	Wisconsin	19.9
26	Pennsylvania	19.2
27	Louisiana	19.0
27	Michigan	19.0
27	New Jersey	19.0
30	Ohio	18.8
31	Utah	18.6
32	Indiana	18.5
33	New York	18.4
34	Tennessee	18.2
35	Kentucky	18.1
36	Maryland	18.0
37	Rhode Island	17.9
38	Nevada	17.4
39	North Carolina	17.3
40	Massachusetts	17.2
41	Georgia	17.1
42	Minnesota	17.0
42	Missouri	17.0
44	Wyoming	16.7
45	Virginia	16.3
46	Texas	15.9
NA	Alaska**	NA
NA	California**	NA
NA	Florida**	NA
NA	New Hampshire**	NA

District of Columbia   19.1

Source: U.S. Department of Health and Human Services, Centers for Disease Control and Prevention
   "Abortion Surveillance-United States, 2000" (Morbidity Mortality Weekly Report, Vol. 52, No. SS-12, 11/28/03)
*Nineteen years old and younger by state of occurrence. National total is for reporting states only.
**Not reported.

Reported Legal Abortions Obtained by Teenagers 17 Years and Younger in 2000

Reporting States' Total = 50,239 Abortions*

RANK	STATE	ABORTIONS	% of USA
15	Alabama	1,029	2.0%
NA	Alaska**	NA	NA
21	Arizona	761	1.5%
26	Arkansas	470	0.9%
NA	California**	NA	NA
29	Colorado	385	0.8%
12	Connecticut	1,198	2.4%
31	Delaware	353	0.7%
NA	Florida**	NA	NA
6	Georgia	2,114	4.2%
30	Hawaii	363	0.7%
42	Idaho	60	0.1%
NA	Illinois**	NA	NA
19	Indiana	820	1.6%
25	Iowa	475	0.9%
16	Kansas	985	2.0%
33	Kentucky	311	0.6%
18	Louisiana	822	1.6%
38	Maine	225	0.4%
NA	Maryland**	NA	NA
11	Massachusetts	1,531	3.0%
8	Michigan	1,905	3.8%
17	Minnesota	826	1.6%
34	Mississippi	300	0.6%
28	Missouri	413	0.8%
37	Montana	236	0.5%
31	Nebraska	353	0.7%
27	Nevada	418	0.8%
NA	New Hampshire**	NA	NA
4	New Jersey	2,549	5.1%
24	New Mexico	553	1.1%
1	New York	10,215	20.3%
9	North Carolina	1,888	3.8%
41	North Dakota	110	0.2%
3	Ohio	2,749	5.5%
23	Oklahoma	591	1.2%
14	Oregon	1,061	2.1%
5	Pennsylvania	2,428	4.8%
35	Rhode Island	287	0.6%
22	South Carolina	703	1.4%
43	South Dakota	57	0.1%
13	Tennessee	1,113	2.2%
2	Texas	3,979	7.9%
36	Utah	239	0.5%
40	Vermont	143	0.3%
10	Virginia	1,590	3.2%
7	Washington	2,062	4.1%
39	West Virginia	202	0.4%
20	Wisconsin	789	1.6%
44	Wyoming	1	0.0%

RANK	STATE	ABORTIONS	% of USA
1	New York	10,215	20.3%
2	Texas	3,979	7.9%
3	Ohio	2,749	5.5%
4	New Jersey	2,549	5.1%
5	Pennsylvania	2,428	4.8%
6	Georgia	2,114	4.2%
7	Washington	2,062	4.1%
8	Michigan	1,905	3.8%
9	North Carolina	1,888	3.8%
10	Virginia	1,590	3.2%
11	Massachusetts	1,531	3.0%
12	Connecticut	1,198	2.4%
13	Tennessee	1,113	2.2%
14	Oregon	1,061	2.1%
15	Alabama	1,029	2.0%
16	Kansas	985	2.0%
17	Minnesota	826	1.6%
18	Louisiana	822	1.6%
19	Indiana	820	1.6%
20	Wisconsin	789	1.6%
21	Arizona	761	1.5%
22	South Carolina	703	1.4%
23	Oklahoma	591	1.2%
24	New Mexico	553	1.1%
25	Iowa	475	0.9%
26	Arkansas	470	0.9%
27	Nevada	418	0.8%
28	Missouri	413	0.8%
29	Colorado	385	0.8%
30	Hawaii	363	0.7%
31	Delaware	353	0.7%
31	Nebraska	353	0.7%
33	Kentucky	311	0.6%
34	Mississippi	300	0.6%
35	Rhode Island	287	0.6%
36	Utah	239	0.5%
37	Montana	236	0.5%
38	Maine	225	0.4%
39	West Virginia	202	0.4%
40	Vermont	143	0.3%
41	North Dakota	110	0.2%
42	Idaho	60	0.1%
43	South Dakota	57	0.1%
44	Wyoming	1	0.0%
NA	Alaska**	NA	NA
NA	California**	NA	NA
NA	Florida**	NA	NA
NA	Illinois**	NA	NA
NA	Maryland**	NA	NA
NA	New Hampshire**	NA	NA
	District of Columbia	577	1.1%

Source: U.S. Department of Health and Human Services, Centers for Disease Control and Prevention "Abortion Surveillance-United States, 2000" (Morbidity Mortality Weekly Report, Vol. 52, No. SS-12, 11/28/03)
*By state of occurrence. National total is for reporting states only.
**Not reported.

Percent of Reported Legal Abortions Obtained
By Teenagers 17 Years and Younger in 2000
Reporting States' Percent = 7.1% of Abortions*

ALPHA ORDER

RANK	STATE	PERCENT
21	Alabama	7.6
NA	Alaska**	NA
21	Arizona	7.6
9	Arkansas	8.5
NA	California**	NA
7	Colorado	9.1
4	Connecticut	9.3
30	Delaware	6.9
NA	Florida**	NA
33	Georgia	6.7
6	Hawaii	9.2
23	Idaho	7.5
NA	Illinois**	NA
33	Indiana	6.7
11	Iowa	8.3
14	Kansas	8.1
33	Kentucky	6.7
25	Louisiana	7.2
8	Maine	8.9
NA	Maryland**	NA
41	Massachusetts	5.6
27	Michigan	7.1
39	Minnesota	5.7
15	Mississippi	8.0
43	Missouri	5.2
3	Montana	9.7
10	Nebraska	8.4
29	Nevada	7.0
NA	New Hampshire**	NA
20	New Jersey	7.7
2	New Mexico	10.1
18	New York	7.9
38	North Carolina	6.3
12	North Dakota	8.2
25	Ohio	7.2
12	Oklahoma	8.2
23	Oregon	7.5
31	Pennsylvania	6.8
42	Rhode Island	5.3
4	South Carolina	9.3
36	South Dakota	6.5
37	Tennessee	6.4
43	Texas	5.2
31	Utah	6.8
15	Vermont	8.0
39	Virginia	5.7
15	Washington	8.0
18	West Virginia	7.9
27	Wisconsin	7.1
1	Wyoming	16.7

RANK ORDER

RANK	STATE	PERCENT
1	Wyoming	16.7
2	New Mexico	10.1
3	Montana	9.7
4	Connecticut	9.3
4	South Carolina	9.3
6	Hawaii	9.2
7	Colorado	9.1
8	Maine	8.9
9	Arkansas	8.5
10	Nebraska	8.4
11	Iowa	8.3
12	North Dakota	8.2
12	Oklahoma	8.2
14	Kansas	8.1
15	Mississippi	8.0
15	Vermont	8.0
15	Washington	8.0
18	New York	7.9
18	West Virginia	7.9
20	New Jersey	7.7
21	Alabama	7.6
21	Arizona	7.6
23	Idaho	7.5
23	Oregon	7.5
25	Louisiana	7.2
25	Ohio	7.2
27	Michigan	7.1
27	Wisconsin	7.1
29	Nevada	7.0
30	Delaware	6.9
31	Pennsylvania	6.8
31	Utah	6.8
33	Georgia	6.7
33	Indiana	6.7
33	Kentucky	6.7
36	South Dakota	6.5
37	Tennessee	6.4
38	North Carolina	6.3
39	Minnesota	5.7
39	Virginia	5.7
41	Massachusetts	5.6
42	Rhode Island	5.3
43	Missouri	5.2
43	Texas	5.2
NA	Alaska**	NA
NA	California**	NA
NA	Florida**	NA
NA	Illinois**	NA
NA	Maryland**	NA
NA	New Hampshire**	NA

District of Columbia   8.7

Source: Morgan Quitno Press using data from US Dept of Health & Human Serv's, Centers for Disease Control-Prevention
    "Abortion Surveillance-United States, 2000" (Morbidity Mortality Weekly Report, Vol. 52, No. SS-12, 11/28/03)
*By state of occurrence. National percent is for reporting states only.
**Not reported.

Percent of Teenage Abortions Obtained
By Teenagers 17 Years and Younger in 2000
Reporting States' Percent = 38.3% of Teenage Abortions*

<table>
<tr><td colspan="3">ALPHA ORDER</td><td colspan="3">RANK ORDER</td></tr>
<tr><td>RANK</td><td>STATE</td><td>PERCENT</td><td>RANK</td><td>STATE</td><td>PERCENT</td></tr>
<tr><td>21</td><td>Alabama</td><td>38.0</td><td>1</td><td>Wyoming</td><td>100.0</td></tr>
<tr><td>NA</td><td>Alaska**</td><td>NA</td><td>2</td><td>Connecticut</td><td>44.6</td></tr>
<tr><td>26</td><td>Arizona</td><td>37.4</td><td>3</td><td>Delaware</td><td>44.4</td></tr>
<tr><td>9</td><td>Arkansas</td><td>40.6</td><td>4</td><td>South Carolina</td><td>44.3</td></tr>
<tr><td>NA</td><td>California**</td><td>NA</td><td>5</td><td>New Mexico</td><td>43.5</td></tr>
<tr><td>8</td><td>Colorado</td><td>41.3</td><td>6</td><td>New York</td><td>42.7</td></tr>
<tr><td>2</td><td>Connecticut</td><td>44.6</td><td>7</td><td>Montana</td><td>41.4</td></tr>
<tr><td>3</td><td>Delaware</td><td>44.4</td><td>8</td><td>Colorado</td><td>41.3</td></tr>
<tr><td>NA</td><td>Florida**</td><td>NA</td><td>9</td><td>Arkansas</td><td>40.6</td></tr>
<tr><td>15</td><td>Georgia</td><td>38.8</td><td>9</td><td>New Jersey</td><td>40.6</td></tr>
<tr><td>18</td><td>Hawaii</td><td>38.4</td><td>11</td><td>Nevada</td><td>40.2</td></tr>
<tr><td>33</td><td>Idaho</td><td>36.1</td><td>12</td><td>Nebraska</td><td>39.6</td></tr>
<tr><td>NA</td><td>Illinois**</td><td>NA</td><td>13</td><td>Washington</td><td>39.4</td></tr>
<tr><td>33</td><td>Indiana</td><td>36.1</td><td>14</td><td>Kansas</td><td>39.3</td></tr>
<tr><td>25</td><td>Iowa</td><td>37.5</td><td>15</td><td>Georgia</td><td>38.8</td></tr>
<tr><td>14</td><td>Kansas</td><td>39.3</td><td>15</td><td>Oklahoma</td><td>38.8</td></tr>
<tr><td>29</td><td>Kentucky</td><td>37.1</td><td>17</td><td>Maine</td><td>38.7</td></tr>
<tr><td>21</td><td>Louisiana</td><td>38.0</td><td>18</td><td>Hawaii</td><td>38.4</td></tr>
<tr><td>17</td><td>Maine</td><td>38.7</td><td>18</td><td>Ohio</td><td>38.4</td></tr>
<tr><td>NA</td><td>Maryland**</td><td>NA</td><td>18</td><td>Vermont</td><td>38.4</td></tr>
<tr><td>41</td><td>Massachusetts</td><td>32.8</td><td>21</td><td>Alabama</td><td>38.0</td></tr>
<tr><td>27</td><td>Michigan</td><td>37.3</td><td>21</td><td>Louisiana</td><td>38.0</td></tr>
<tr><td>39</td><td>Minnesota</td><td>33.6</td><td>23</td><td>West Virginia</td><td>37.8</td></tr>
<tr><td>27</td><td>Mississippi</td><td>37.3</td><td>24</td><td>Oregon</td><td>37.6</td></tr>
<tr><td>42</td><td>Missouri</td><td>30.8</td><td>25</td><td>Iowa</td><td>37.5</td></tr>
<tr><td>7</td><td>Montana</td><td>41.4</td><td>26</td><td>Arizona</td><td>37.4</td></tr>
<tr><td>12</td><td>Nebraska</td><td>39.6</td><td>27</td><td>Michigan</td><td>37.3</td></tr>
<tr><td>11</td><td>Nevada</td><td>40.2</td><td>27</td><td>Mississippi</td><td>37.3</td></tr>
<tr><td>NA</td><td>New Hampshire**</td><td>NA</td><td>29</td><td>Kentucky</td><td>37.1</td></tr>
<tr><td>9</td><td>New Jersey</td><td>40.6</td><td>29</td><td>North Dakota</td><td>37.1</td></tr>
<tr><td>5</td><td>New Mexico</td><td>43.5</td><td>29</td><td>Wisconsin</td><td>37.1</td></tr>
<tr><td>6</td><td>New York</td><td>42.7</td><td>32</td><td>Utah</td><td>36.7</td></tr>
<tr><td>33</td><td>North Carolina</td><td>36.1</td><td>33</td><td>Idaho</td><td>36.1</td></tr>
<tr><td>29</td><td>North Dakota</td><td>37.1</td><td>33</td><td>Indiana</td><td>36.1</td></tr>
<tr><td>18</td><td>Ohio</td><td>38.4</td><td>33</td><td>North Carolina</td><td>36.1</td></tr>
<tr><td>15</td><td>Oklahoma</td><td>38.8</td><td>36</td><td>Pennsylvania</td><td>35.7</td></tr>
<tr><td>24</td><td>Oregon</td><td>37.6</td><td>37</td><td>Tennessee</td><td>35.0</td></tr>
<tr><td>36</td><td>Pennsylvania</td><td>35.7</td><td>38</td><td>Virginia</td><td>34.7</td></tr>
<tr><td>44</td><td>Rhode Island</td><td>29.6</td><td>39</td><td>Minnesota</td><td>33.6</td></tr>
<tr><td>4</td><td>South Carolina</td><td>44.3</td><td>40</td><td>Texas</td><td>32.9</td></tr>
<tr><td>43</td><td>South Dakota</td><td>30.1</td><td>41</td><td>Massachusetts</td><td>32.8</td></tr>
<tr><td>37</td><td>Tennessee</td><td>35.0</td><td>42</td><td>Missouri</td><td>30.8</td></tr>
<tr><td>40</td><td>Texas</td><td>32.9</td><td>43</td><td>South Dakota</td><td>30.1</td></tr>
<tr><td>32</td><td>Utah</td><td>36.7</td><td>44</td><td>Rhode Island</td><td>29.6</td></tr>
<tr><td>18</td><td>Vermont</td><td>38.4</td><td>NA</td><td>Alaska**</td><td>NA</td></tr>
<tr><td>38</td><td>Virginia</td><td>34.7</td><td>NA</td><td>California**</td><td>NA</td></tr>
<tr><td>13</td><td>Washington</td><td>39.4</td><td>NA</td><td>Florida**</td><td>NA</td></tr>
<tr><td>23</td><td>West Virginia</td><td>37.8</td><td>NA</td><td>Illinois**</td><td>NA</td></tr>
<tr><td>29</td><td>Wisconsin</td><td>37.1</td><td>NA</td><td>Maryland**</td><td>NA</td></tr>
<tr><td>1</td><td>Wyoming</td><td>100.0</td><td>NA</td><td>New Hampshire**</td><td>NA</td></tr>
<tr><td></td><td></td><td></td><td></td><td>District of Columbia</td><td>45.2</td></tr>
</table>

Source: U.S. Department of Health and Human Services, Centers for Disease Control and Prevention
   "Abortion Surveillance-United States, 2000" (Morbidity Mortality Weekly Report, Vol. 52, No. SS-12, 11/28/03)
*By state of occurrence. National percent is for reporting states only.
**Not reported.

Reported Legal Abortions Performed at 12 Weeks or Less of Gestation in 2000

Reporting States' Total = 558,443 Abortions*

ALPHA ORDER

RANK	STATE	ABORTIONS	% of USA
14	Alabama	11,947	2.1%
NA	Alaska**	NA	NA
20	Arizona	7,934	1.4%
28	Arkansas	4,370	0.8%
NA	California**	NA	NA
30	Colorado	3,596	0.6%
16	Connecticut	11,329	2.0%
34	Delaware	3,051	0.5%
NA	Florida**	NA	NA
5	Georgia	27,126	4.9%
31	Hawaii	3,408	0.6%
41	Idaho	767	0.1%
15	Illinois	11,751	2.1%
NA	Indiana**	NA	NA
24	Iowa	5,284	0.9%
17	Kansas	10,219	1.8%
29	Kentucky	3,856	0.7%
18	Louisiana	9,177	1.6%
35	Maine	2,498	0.4%
NA	Maryland**	NA	NA
NA	Massachusetts**	NA	NA
9	Michigan	23,003	4.1%
12	Minnesota	12,899	2.3%
32	Mississippi	3,321	0.6%
22	Missouri	7,212	1.3%
37	Montana	2,008	0.4%
NA	Nebraska**	NA	NA
25	Nevada	5,193	0.9%
NA	New Hampshire**	NA	NA
8	New Jersey	26,186	4.7%
27	New Mexico	4,705	0.8%
1	New York**	81,344	14.6%
7	North Carolina	26,242	4.7%
39	North Dakota	1,203	0.2%
3	Ohio	32,454	5.8%
23	Oklahoma	6,497	1.2%
13	Oregon	12,292	2.2%
4	Pennsylvania	30,849	5.5%
26	Rhode Island	4,924	0.9%
21	South Carolina	7,222	1.3%
40	South Dakota	840	0.2%
11	Tennessee	16,649	3.0%
2	Texas	66,069	11.8%
33	Utah	3,210	0.6%
38	Vermont	1,704	0.3%
6	Virginia	26,936	4.8%
10	Washington	22,231	4.0%
36	West Virginia	2,184	0.4%
19	Wisconsin	9,160	1.6%
42	Wyoming	6	0.0%

RANK ORDER

RANK	STATE	ABORTIONS	% of USA
1	New York**	81,344	14.6%
2	Texas	66,069	11.8%
3	Ohio	32,454	5.8%
4	Pennsylvania	30,849	5.5%
5	Georgia	27,126	4.9%
6	Virginia	26,936	4.8%
7	North Carolina	26,242	4.7%
8	New Jersey	26,186	4.7%
9	Michigan	23,003	4.1%
10	Washington	22,231	4.0%
11	Tennessee	16,649	3.0%
12	Minnesota	12,899	2.3%
13	Oregon	12,292	2.2%
14	Alabama	11,947	2.1%
15	Illinois	11,751	2.1%
16	Connecticut	11,329	2.0%
17	Kansas	10,219	1.8%
18	Louisiana	9,177	1.6%
19	Wisconsin	9,160	1.6%
20	Arizona	7,934	1.4%
21	South Carolina	7,222	1.3%
22	Missouri	7,212	1.3%
23	Oklahoma	6,497	1.2%
24	Iowa	5,284	0.9%
25	Nevada	5,193	0.9%
26	Rhode Island	4,924	0.9%
27	New Mexico	4,705	0.8%
28	Arkansas	4,370	0.8%
29	Kentucky	3,856	0.7%
30	Colorado	3,596	0.6%
31	Hawaii	3,408	0.6%
32	Mississippi	3,321	0.6%
33	Utah	3,210	0.6%
34	Delaware	3,051	0.5%
35	Maine	2,498	0.4%
36	West Virginia	2,184	0.4%
37	Montana	2,008	0.4%
38	Vermont	1,704	0.3%
39	North Dakota	1,203	0.2%
40	South Dakota	840	0.2%
41	Idaho	767	0.1%
42	Wyoming	6	0.0%
NA	Alaska**	NA	NA
NA	California**	NA	NA
NA	Florida**	NA	NA
NA	Indiana**	NA	NA
NA	Maryland**	NA	NA
NA	Massachusetts**	NA	NA
NA	Nebraska**	NA	NA
NA	New Hampshire**	NA	NA
	District of Columbia	5,587	1.0%

Source: Morgan Quitno Press using data from US Dept of Health & Human Serv's, Centers for Disease Control-Prevention "Abortion Surveillance-United States, 2000" (Morbidity Mortality Weekly Report, Vol. 52, No. SS-12, 11/28/03)
*By state of occurrence. National total is for reporting states only.
**Not reported. New York's number is for New York City only.

Percent of Reported Legal Abortions Performed
At 12 Weeks or Less of Gestation in 2000
Reporting States' Percent = 86.9% of Abortions*

ALPHA ORDER

RANK	STATE	PERCENT
19	Alabama	88.2
NA	Alaska**	NA
42	Arizona	78.9
40	Arkansas	79.4
NA	California**	NA
34	Colorado	85.3
20	Connecticut	87.7
17	Delaware	88.7
NA	Florida**	NA
31	Georgia	85.6
27	Hawaii	86.4
5	Idaho	95.7
5	Illinois	95.7
NA	Indiana**	NA
10	Iowa	92.0
36	Kansas	83.6
37	Kentucky	83.4
39	Louisiana	80.7
2	Maine	98.5
NA	Maryland**	NA
NA	Massachusetts**	NA
30	Michigan	85.8
16	Minnesota	89.1
18	Mississippi	88.4
11	Missouri	91.5
38	Montana	82.3
NA	Nebraska**	NA
21	Nevada	87.0
NA	New Hampshire**	NA
41	New Jersey	79.3
28	New Mexico	86.1
28	New York**	86.1
21	North Carolina	87.0
15	North Dakota	89.7
35	Ohio	85.2
14	Oklahoma	90.5
24	Oregon	86.6
24	Pennsylvania	86.6
13	Rhode Island	91.0
4	South Carolina	95.9
5	South Dakota	95.7
9	Tennessee	95.3
23	Texas	86.7
12	Utah	91.4
8	Vermont	95.6
3	Virginia	96.3
26	Washington	86.5
31	West Virginia	85.6
33	Wisconsin	85.4
1	Wyoming	100.0

RANK ORDER

RANK	STATE	PERCENT
1	Wyoming	100.0
2	Maine	98.5
3	Virginia	96.3
4	South Carolina	95.9
5	Idaho	95.7
5	Illinois	95.7
5	South Dakota	95.7
8	Vermont	95.6
9	Tennessee	95.3
10	Iowa	92.0
11	Missouri	91.5
12	Utah	91.4
13	Rhode Island	91.0
14	Oklahoma	90.5
15	North Dakota	89.7
16	Minnesota	89.1
17	Delaware	88.7
18	Mississippi	88.4
19	Alabama	88.2
20	Connecticut	87.7
21	Nevada	87.0
21	North Carolina	87.0
23	Texas	86.7
24	Oregon	86.6
24	Pennsylvania	86.6
26	Washington	86.5
27	Hawaii	86.4
28	New Mexico	86.1
28	New York**	86.1
30	Michigan	85.8
31	Georgia	85.6
31	West Virginia	85.6
33	Wisconsin	85.4
34	Colorado	85.3
35	Ohio	85.2
36	Kansas	83.6
37	Kentucky	83.4
38	Montana	82.3
39	Louisiana	80.7
40	Arkansas	79.4
41	New Jersey	79.3
42	Arizona	78.9
NA	Alaska**	NA
NA	California**	NA
NA	Florida**	NA
NA	Indiana**	NA
NA	Maryland**	NA
NA	Massachusetts**	NA
NA	Nebraska**	NA
NA	New Hampshire**	NA

District of Columbia   83.9

Source: Morgan Quitno Press using data from US Dept of Health & Human Serv's, Centers for Disease Control-Prevention "Abortion Surveillance-United States, 2000" (Morbidity Mortality Weekly Report, Vol. 52, No. SS-12, 11/28/03)
By state of occurrence. National percent is for reporting states only.
***Not reported. New York's number is for New York City only.*

Reported Legal Abortions Performed At or After 21 Weeks of Gestation in 2000

Reporting States' Total = 9,108 Abortions*

ALPHA ORDER

RANK	STATE	ABORTIONS	% of USA
15	Alabama	81	0.9%
NA	Alaska**	NA	NA
33	Arizona	6	0.1%
24	Arkansas	28	0.3%
NA	California**	NA	NA
13	Colorado	144	1.6%
26	Connecticut	24	0.3%
29	Delaware	15	0.2%
NA	Florida**	NA	NA
3	Georgia	812	8.9%
22	Hawaii	40	0.4%
34	Idaho	5	0.1%
38	Illinois	0	0.0%
NA	Indiana**	NA	NA
35	Iowa	2	0.0%
4	Kansas	706	7.8%
16	Kentucky	74	0.8%
9	Louisiana	311	3.4%
35	Maine	2	0.0%
NA	Maryland**	NA	NA
NA	Massachusetts**	NA	NA
11	Michigan	275	3.0%
14	Minnesota	114	1.3%
32	Mississippi	7	0.1%
24	Missouri	28	0.3%
20	Montana	46	0.5%
NA	Nebraska**	NA	NA
18	Nevada	63	0.7%
NA	New Hampshire**	NA	NA
6	New Jersey	647	7.1%
21	New Mexico	41	0.5%
1	New York**	2,303	25.3%
19	North Carolina	59	0.6%
38	North Dakota	0	0.0%
5	Ohio	670	7.4%
23	Oklahoma	30	0.3%
10	Oregon	281	3.1%
7	Pennsylvania	595	6.5%
31	Rhode Island	8	0.1%
28	South Carolina	20	0.2%
38	South Dakota	0	0.0%
26	Tennessee	24	0.3%
2	Texas	889	9.8%
38	Utah	0	0.0%
37	Vermont	1	0.0%
17	Virginia	64	0.7%
8	Washington	491	5.4%
30	West Virginia	11	0.1%
12	Wisconsin	191	2.1%
38	Wyoming	0	0.0%

RANK ORDER

RANK	STATE	ABORTIONS	% of USA
1	New York**	2,303	25.3%
2	Texas	889	9.8%
3	Georgia	812	8.9%
4	Kansas	706	7.8%
5	Ohio	670	7.4%
6	New Jersey	647	7.1%
7	Pennsylvania	595	6.5%
8	Washington	491	5.4%
9	Louisiana	311	3.4%
10	Oregon	281	3.1%
11	Michigan	275	3.0%
12	Wisconsin	191	2.1%
13	Colorado	144	1.6%
14	Minnesota	114	1.3%
15	Alabama	81	0.9%
16	Kentucky	74	0.8%
17	Virginia	64	0.7%
18	Nevada	63	0.7%
19	North Carolina	59	0.6%
20	Montana	46	0.5%
21	New Mexico	41	0.5%
22	Hawaii	40	0.4%
23	Oklahoma	30	0.3%
24	Arkansas	28	0.3%
24	Missouri	28	0.3%
26	Connecticut	24	0.3%
26	Tennessee	24	0.3%
28	South Carolina	20	0.2%
29	Delaware	15	0.2%
30	West Virginia	11	0.1%
31	Rhode Island	8	0.1%
32	Mississippi	7	0.1%
33	Arizona	6	0.1%
34	Idaho	5	0.1%
35	Iowa	2	0.0%
35	Maine	2	0.0%
37	Vermont	1	0.0%
38	Illinois	0	0.0%
38	North Dakota	0	0.0%
38	South Dakota	0	0.0%
38	Utah	0	0.0%
38	Wyoming	0	0.0%
NA	Alaska**	NA	NA
NA	California**	NA	NA
NA	Florida**	NA	NA
NA	Indiana**	NA	NA
NA	Maryland**	NA	NA
NA	Massachusetts**	NA	NA
NA	Nebraska**	NA	NA
NA	New Hampshire**	NA	NA

District of Columbia   0   0.0%

Source: Morgan Quitno Press using data from US Dept of Health & Human Serv's, Centers for Disease Control-Prevention
   "Abortion Surveillance-United States, 2000" (Morbidity Mortality Weekly Report, Vol. 52, No. SS-12, 11/28/03)
*By state of occurrence. National total is for reporting states only.
**Not reported. New York's number is for New York City only.

Percent of Reported Legal Abortions Performed At or After
21 Weeks of Gestation in 2000
Reporting States' Percent = 1.4% of Abortions*

ALPHA ORDER

RANK	STATE	PERCENT
20	Alabama	0.6
NA	Alaska**	NA
32	Arizona	0.1
22	Arkansas	0.5
NA	California**	NA
2	Colorado	3.4
28	Connecticut	0.2
23	Delaware	0.4
NA	Florida**	NA
4	Georgia	2.6
16	Hawaii	1.0
20	Idaho	0.6
37	Illinois	0.0
NA	Indiana**	NA
37	Iowa	0.0
1	Kansas	5.8
13	Kentucky	1.6
3	Louisiana	2.7
32	Maine	0.1
NA	Maryland**	NA
NA	Massachusetts**	NA
16	Michigan	1.0
18	Minnesota	0.8
28	Mississippi	0.2
23	Missouri	0.4
8	Montana	1.9
NA	Nebraska**	NA
15	Nevada	1.1
NA	New Hampshire**	NA
6	New Jersey	2.0
18	New Mexico	0.8
5	New York**	2.4
28	North Carolina	0.2
37	North Dakota	0.0
10	Ohio	1.8
23	Oklahoma	0.4
6	Oregon	2.0
12	Pennsylvania	1.7
32	Rhode Island	0.1
27	South Carolina	0.3
37	South Dakota	0.0
32	Tennessee	0.1
14	Texas	1.2
37	Utah	0.0
32	Vermont	0.1
28	Virginia	0.2
8	Washington	1.9
23	West Virginia	0.4
10	Wisconsin	1.8
37	Wyoming	0.0

RANK ORDER

RANK	STATE	PERCENT
1	Kansas	5.8
2	Colorado	3.4
3	Louisiana	2.7
4	Georgia	2.6
5	New York**	2.4
6	New Jersey	2.0
6	Oregon	2.0
8	Montana	1.9
8	Washington	1.9
10	Ohio	1.8
10	Wisconsin	1.8
12	Pennsylvania	1.7
13	Kentucky	1.6
14	Texas	1.2
15	Nevada	1.1
16	Hawaii	1.0
16	Michigan	1.0
18	Minnesota	0.8
18	New Mexico	0.8
20	Alabama	0.6
20	Idaho	0.6
22	Arkansas	0.5
23	Delaware	0.4
23	Missouri	0.4
23	Oklahoma	0.4
23	West Virginia	0.4
27	South Carolina	0.3
28	Connecticut	0.2
28	Mississippi	0.2
28	North Carolina	0.2
28	Virginia	0.2
32	Arizona	0.1
32	Maine	0.1
32	Rhode Island	0.1
32	Tennessee	0.1
32	Vermont	0.1
37	Illinois	0.0
37	Iowa	0.0
37	North Dakota	0.0
37	South Dakota	0.0
37	Utah	0.0
37	Wyoming	0.0
NA	Alaska**	NA
NA	California**	NA
NA	Florida**	NA
NA	Indiana**	NA
NA	Maryland**	NA
NA	Massachusetts**	NA
NA	Nebraska**	NA
NA	New Hampshire**	NA

District of Columbia   0.0

Source: Morgan Quitno Press using data from US Dept of Health & Human Serv's, Centers for Disease Control-Prevention "Abortion Surveillance-United States, 2000" (Morbidity Mortality Weekly Report, Vol. 52, No. SS-12, 11/28/03)
By state of occurrence. National percent is for reporting states only.
**Not reported. New York's number is for New York City only.*

II. DEATHS

II. DEATHS (Continued)

Deaths in 2001

National Total = 2,416,425 Deaths*

ALPHA ORDER

RANK	STATE	DEATHS	% of USA
18	Alabama	45,316	1.9%
50	Alaska	2,974	0.1%
22	Arizona	41,058	1.7%
32	Arkansas	27,759	1.1%
1	California	234,044	9.7%
29	Colorado	28,294	1.2%
28	Connecticut	29,827	1.2%
45	Delaware	7,112	0.3%
2	Florida	167,269	6.9%
11	Georgia	64,485	2.7%
43	Hawaii	8,394	0.3%
42	Idaho	9,753	0.4%
7	Illinois	105,430	4.4%
14	Indiana	55,198	2.3%
31	Iowa	27,791	1.2%
33	Kansas	24,647	1.0%
23	Kentucky	39,861	1.6%
21	Louisiana	41,757	1.7%
39	Maine	12,421	0.5%
20	Maryland	43,839	1.8%
12	Massachusetts	56,754	2.3%
8	Michigan	86,424	3.6%
24	Minnesota	37,735	1.6%
30	Mississippi	28,259	1.2%
16	Missouri	54,982	2.3%
44	Montana	8,265	0.3%
36	Nebraska	15,174	0.6%
35	Nevada	16,285	0.7%
41	New Hampshire	9,815	0.4%
9	New Jersey	74,710	3.1%
37	New Mexico	14,129	0.6%
3	New York	159,240	6.6%
10	North Carolina	70,934	2.9%
47	North Dakota	6,048	0.3%
6	Ohio	108,027	4.5%
26	Oklahoma	34,682	1.4%
27	Oregon	30,158	1.2%
5	Pennsylvania	129,729	5.4%
40	Rhode Island	10,021	0.4%
25	South Carolina	36,612	1.5%
46	South Dakota	6,923	0.3%
15	Tennessee	55,151	2.3%
4	Texas	152,779	6.3%
38	Utah	12,662	0.5%
48	Vermont	5,201	0.2%
13	Virginia	56,280	2.3%
19	Washington	44,642	1.8%
34	West Virginia	20,967	0.9%
17	Wisconsin	46,628	1.9%
49	Wyoming	4,029	0.2%

RANK ORDER

RANK	STATE	DEATHS	% of USA
1	California	234,044	9.7%
2	Florida	167,269	6.9%
3	New York	159,240	6.6%
4	Texas	152,779	6.3%
5	Pennsylvania	129,729	5.4%
6	Ohio	108,027	4.5%
7	Illinois	105,430	4.4%
8	Michigan	86,424	3.6%
9	New Jersey	74,710	3.1%
10	North Carolina	70,934	2.9%
11	Georgia	64,485	2.7%
12	Massachusetts	56,754	2.3%
13	Virginia	56,280	2.3%
14	Indiana	55,198	2.3%
15	Tennessee	55,151	2.3%
16	Missouri	54,982	2.3%
17	Wisconsin	46,628	1.9%
18	Alabama	45,316	1.9%
19	Washington	44,642	1.8%
20	Maryland	43,839	1.8%
21	Louisiana	41,757	1.7%
22	Arizona	41,058	1.7%
23	Kentucky	39,861	1.6%
24	Minnesota	37,735	1.6%
25	South Carolina	36,612	1.5%
26	Oklahoma	34,682	1.4%
27	Oregon	30,158	1.2%
28	Connecticut	29,827	1.2%
29	Colorado	28,294	1.2%
30	Mississippi	28,259	1.2%
31	Iowa	27,791	1.2%
32	Arkansas	27,759	1.1%
33	Kansas	24,647	1.0%
34	West Virginia	20,967	0.9%
35	Nevada	16,285	0.7%
36	Nebraska	15,174	0.6%
37	New Mexico	14,129	0.6%
38	Utah	12,662	0.5%
39	Maine	12,421	0.5%
40	Rhode Island	10,021	0.4%
41	New Hampshire	9,815	0.4%
42	Idaho	9,753	0.4%
43	Hawaii	8,394	0.3%
44	Montana	8,265	0.3%
45	Delaware	7,112	0.3%
46	South Dakota	6,923	0.3%
47	North Dakota	6,048	0.3%
48	Vermont	5,201	0.2%
49	Wyoming	4,029	0.2%
50	Alaska	2,974	0.1%
	District of Columbia	5,951	0.2%

Source: U.S. Department of Health and Human Services, National Center for Health Statistics
"National Vital Statistics Reports" (Vol. 52, No. 3, September 18, 2003)
*Final data by state of residence.

Age-Adjusted Death Rate in 2001

National Rate = 854.5 Deaths per 100,000 Population*

ALPHA ORDER

RANK	STATE	RATE
4	Alabama	992.9
28	Alaska	825.8
42	Arizona	787.4
9	Arkansas	948.1
47	California	775.1
41	Colorado	787.8
48	Connecticut	767.8
16	Delaware	891.9
36	Florida	799.7
8	Georgia	956.5
50	Hawaii	652.6
38	Idaho	798.0
22	Illinois	857.3
14	Indiana	908.3
44	Iowa	777.4
26	Kansas	839.8
5	Kentucky	987.7
2	Louisiana	1,005.9
24	Maine	843.2
17	Maryland	881.4
34	Massachusetts	801.4
19	Michigan	877.6
49	Minnesota	744.9
1	Mississippi	1,023.2
13	Missouri	909.5
25	Montana	840.3
39	Nebraska	793.5
11	Nevada	922.6
37	New Hampshire	798.5
27	New Jersey	831.9
30	New Mexico	825.4
35	New York	800.9
12	North Carolina	911.0
46	North Dakota	775.9
15	Ohio	905.7
7	Oklahoma	959.7
29	Oregon	825.6
20	Pennsylvania	869.9
33	Rhode Island	806.4
10	South Carolina	939.1
43	South Dakota	784.8
6	Tennessee	972.9
18	Texas	877.8
45	Utah	776.8
31	Vermont	811.2
21	Virginia	862.2
40	Washington	792.9
3	West Virginia	994.9
32	Wisconsin	806.5
23	Wyoming	851.7

RANK ORDER

RANK	STATE	RATE
1	Mississippi	1,023.2
2	Louisiana	1,005.9
3	West Virginia	994.9
4	Alabama	992.9
5	Kentucky	987.7
6	Tennessee	972.9
7	Oklahoma	959.7
8	Georgia	956.5
9	Arkansas	948.1
10	South Carolina	939.1
11	Nevada	922.6
12	North Carolina	911.0
13	Missouri	909.5
14	Indiana	908.3
15	Ohio	905.7
16	Delaware	891.9
17	Maryland	881.4
18	Texas	877.8
19	Michigan	877.6
20	Pennsylvania	869.9
21	Virginia	862.2
22	Illinois	857.3
23	Wyoming	851.7
24	Maine	843.2
25	Montana	840.3
26	Kansas	839.8
27	New Jersey	831.9
28	Alaska	825.8
29	Oregon	825.6
30	New Mexico	825.4
31	Vermont	811.2
32	Wisconsin	806.5
33	Rhode Island	806.4
34	Massachusetts	801.4
35	New York	800.9
36	Florida	799.7
37	New Hampshire	798.5
38	Idaho	798.0
39	Nebraska	793.5
40	Washington	792.9
41	Colorado	787.8
42	Arizona	787.4
43	South Dakota	784.8
44	Iowa	777.4
45	Utah	776.8
46	North Dakota	775.9
47	California	775.1
48	Connecticut	767.8
49	Minnesota	744.9
50	Hawaii	652.6

	District of Columbia	1,038.2

Source: U.S. Department of Health and Human Services, National Center for Health Statistics
"National Vital Statistics Reports" (Vol. 52, No. 3, September 18, 2003)
Final data by state of residence. Age-adjusted rates eliminate the distorting effects of the aging of the population.
Rates based on the year 2000 standard population.

Death Rate in 2001

National Rate = 848.5 Deaths per 100,000 Population*

ALPHA ORDER

RANK	STATE	RATE
5	Alabama	1,014.0
50	Alaska	469.4
39	Arizona	773.7
3	Arkansas	1,030.1
47	California	676.4
48	Colorado	638.5
26	Connecticut	868.4
22	Delaware	892.8
4	Florida	1,021.6
41	Georgia	767.2
46	Hawaii	684.1
44	Idaho	738.5
32	Illinois	842.1
21	Indiana	900.9
14	Iowa	947.9
19	Kansas	912.1
8	Kentucky	979.7
16	Louisiana	934.1
10	Maine	967.0
35	Maryland	813.9
23	Massachusetts	886.6
29	Michigan	863.7
42	Minnesota	757.0
7	Mississippi	988.2
9	Missouri	975.3
17	Montana	912.9
24	Nebraska	882.2
38	Nevada	776.3
37	New Hampshire	779.4
25	New Jersey	877.8
40	New Mexico	771.7
33	New York	834.4
28	North Carolina	864.4
12	North Dakota	950.1
13	Ohio	948.5
6	Oklahoma	999.6
27	Oregon	868.2
2	Pennsylvania	1,054.4
15	Rhode Island	945.7
20	South Carolina	901.3
17	South Dakota	912.9
11	Tennessee	959.2
45	Texas	714.9
49	Utah	555.7
31	Vermont	848.5
36	Virginia	782.0
43	Washington	744.9
1	West Virginia	1,164.2
30	Wisconsin	862.5
34	Wyoming	816.0

RANK ORDER

RANK	STATE	RATE
1	West Virginia	1,164.2
2	Pennsylvania	1,054.4
3	Arkansas	1,030.1
4	Florida	1,021.6
5	Alabama	1,014.0
6	Oklahoma	999.6
7	Mississippi	988.2
8	Kentucky	979.7
9	Missouri	975.3
10	Maine	967.0
11	Tennessee	959.2
12	North Dakota	950.1
13	Ohio	948.5
14	Iowa	947.9
15	Rhode Island	945.7
16	Louisiana	934.1
17	Montana	912.9
17	South Dakota	912.9
19	Kansas	912.1
20	South Carolina	901.3
21	Indiana	900.9
22	Delaware	892.8
23	Massachusetts	886.6
24	Nebraska	882.2
25	New Jersey	877.8
26	Connecticut	868.4
27	Oregon	868.2
28	North Carolina	864.4
29	Michigan	863.7
30	Wisconsin	862.5
31	Vermont	848.5
32	Illinois	842.1
33	New York	834.4
34	Wyoming	816.0
35	Maryland	813.9
36	Virginia	782.0
37	New Hampshire	779.4
38	Nevada	776.3
39	Arizona	773.7
40	New Mexico	771.7
41	Georgia	767.2
42	Minnesota	757.0
43	Washington	744.9
44	Idaho	738.5
45	Texas	714.9
46	Hawaii	684.1
47	California	676.4
48	Colorado	638.5
49	Utah	555.7
50	Alaska	469.4

District of Columbia   1,037.1

Source: U.S. Department of Health and Human Services, National Center for Health Statistics
    "National Vital Statistics Reports" (Vol. 52, No. 3, September 18, 2003)
*Final data by state of residence. Not age-adjusted.

Percent Change in Death Rate: 1990 to 2001

National Percent Change = 1.7% Decrease*

ALPHA ORDER

RANK	STATE	PERCENT CHANGE
12	Alabama	4.1
1	Alaska	17.9
35	Arizona	(1.3)
38	Arkansas	(1.7)
48	California	(5.9)
42	Colorado	(2.5)
16	Connecticut	3.4
17	Delaware	3.3
37	Florida	(1.6)
45	Georgia	(4.0)
3	Hawaii	12.0
32	Idaho	(0.2)
49	Illinois	(6.4)
27	Indiana	0.8
40	Iowa	(2.1)
22	Kansas	1.5
18	Kentucky	3.0
10	Louisiana	5.0
6	Maine	6.9
23	Maryland	1.4
29	Massachusetts	0.3
20	Michigan	2.0
46	Minnesota	(4.8)
24	Mississippi	1.3
33	Missouri	(0.9)
8	Montana	6.3
47	Nebraska	(5.7)
30	Nevada	0.2
21	New Hampshire	1.9
44	New Jersey	(3.5)
4	New Mexico	10.1
50	New York	(11.0)
31	North Carolina	0.0
7	North Dakota	6.8
12	Ohio	4.1
15	Oklahoma	3.5
39	Oregon	(1.8)
19	Pennsylvania	2.8
33	Rhode Island	(0.9)
9	South Carolina	5.8
28	South Dakota	0.4
25	Tennessee	1.1
43	Texas	(3.1)
11	Utah	4.3
14	Vermont	3.9
26	Virginia	0.9
41	Washington	(2.2)
5	West Virginia	7.8
35	Wisconsin	(1.3)
2	Wyoming	15.6

RANK ORDER

RANK	STATE	PERCENT CHANGE
1	Alaska	17.9
2	Wyoming	15.6
3	Hawaii	12.0
4	New Mexico	10.1
5	West Virginia	7.8
6	Maine	6.9
7	North Dakota	6.8
8	Montana	6.3
9	South Carolina	5.8
10	Louisiana	5.0
11	Utah	4.3
12	Alabama	4.1
12	Ohio	4.1
14	Vermont	3.9
15	Oklahoma	3.5
16	Connecticut	3.4
17	Delaware	3.3
18	Kentucky	3.0
19	Pennsylvania	2.8
20	Michigan	2.0
21	New Hampshire	1.9
22	Kansas	1.5
23	Maryland	1.4
24	Mississippi	1.3
25	Tennessee	1.1
26	Virginia	0.9
27	Indiana	0.8
28	South Dakota	0.4
29	Massachusetts	0.3
30	Nevada	0.2
31	North Carolina	0.0
32	Idaho	(0.2)
33	Missouri	(0.9)
33	Rhode Island	(0.9)
35	Arizona	(1.3)
35	Wisconsin	(1.3)
37	Florida	(1.6)
38	Arkansas	(1.7)
39	Oregon	(1.8)
40	Iowa	(2.1)
41	Washington	(2.2)
42	Colorado	(2.5)
43	Texas	(3.1)
44	New Jersey	(3.5)
45	Georgia	(4.0)
46	Minnesota	(4.8)
47	Nebraska	(5.7)
48	California	(5.9)
49	Illinois	(6.4)
50	New York	(11.0)

| | District of Columbia | (13.6) |

*Source: Morgan Quitno Press using data from U.S. Department of Health and Human Services
"National Vital Statistics Reports" (Vol. 52, No. 3, September 18, 2003) and
"Monthly Vital Statistics Report" (Vol. 41, No. 7(S), January 7, 1993)*
*Final data by state of residence. Not age-adjusted.

Infant Deaths in 2001

National Total = 27,568 Infant Deaths*

ALPHA ORDER

RANK	STATE	DEATHS	% of USA
18	Alabama	567	2.1%
44	Alaska	81	0.3%
17	Arizona	592	2.1%
29	Arkansas	309	1.1%
1	California	2,830	10.3%
25	Colorado	388	1.4%
31	Connecticut	260	0.9%
40	Delaware	115	0.4%
3	Florida	1,495	5.4%
7	Georgia	1,146	4.2%
41	Hawaii	106	0.4%
39	Idaho	129	0.5%
5	Illinois	1,413	5.1%
14	Indiana	650	2.4%
34	Iowa	212	0.8%
30	Kansas	287	1.0%
28	Kentucky	325	1.2%
15	Louisiana	643	2.3%
43	Maine	84	0.3%
16	Maryland	594	2.2%
24	Massachusetts	405	1.5%
8	Michigan	1,069	3.9%
27	Minnesota	361	1.3%
23	Mississippi	445	1.6%
19	Missouri	558	2.0%
46	Montana	74	0.3%
37	Nebraska	168	0.6%
35	Nevada	180	0.7%
48	New Hampshire	56	0.2%
11	New Jersey	747	2.7%
36	New Mexico	174	0.6%
4	New York	1,482	5.4%
10	North Carolina	1,009	3.7%
47	North Dakota	67	0.2%
6	Ohio	1,161	4.2%
26	Oklahoma	366	1.3%
32	Oregon	246	0.9%
9	Pennsylvania	1,033	3.7%
42	Rhode Island	86	0.3%
20	South Carolina	496	1.8%
45	South Dakota	78	0.3%
13	Tennessee	681	2.5%
2	Texas	2,171	7.9%
33	Utah	232	0.8%
50	Vermont	35	0.1%
11	Virginia	747	2.7%
22	Washington	459	1.7%
38	West Virginia	148	0.5%
21	Wisconsin	491	1.8%
49	Wyoming	36	0.1%

RANK ORDER

RANK	STATE	DEATHS	% of USA
1	California	2,830	10.3%
2	Texas	2,171	7.9%
3	Florida	1,495	5.4%
4	New York	1,482	5.4%
5	Illinois	1,413	5.1%
6	Ohio	1,161	4.2%
7	Georgia	1,146	4.2%
8	Michigan	1,069	3.9%
9	Pennsylvania	1,033	3.7%
10	North Carolina	1,009	3.7%
11	New Jersey	747	2.7%
11	Virginia	747	2.7%
13	Tennessee	681	2.5%
14	Indiana	650	2.4%
15	Louisiana	643	2.3%
16	Maryland	594	2.2%
17	Arizona	592	2.1%
18	Alabama	567	2.1%
19	Missouri	558	2.0%
20	South Carolina	496	1.8%
21	Wisconsin	491	1.8%
22	Washington	459	1.7%
23	Mississippi	445	1.6%
24	Massachusetts	405	1.5%
25	Colorado	388	1.4%
26	Oklahoma	366	1.3%
27	Minnesota	361	1.3%
28	Kentucky	325	1.2%
29	Arkansas	309	1.1%
30	Kansas	287	1.0%
31	Connecticut	260	0.9%
32	Oregon	246	0.9%
33	Utah	232	0.8%
34	Iowa	212	0.8%
35	Nevada	180	0.7%
36	New Mexico	174	0.6%
37	Nebraska	168	0.6%
38	West Virginia	148	0.5%
39	Idaho	129	0.5%
40	Delaware	115	0.4%
41	Hawaii	106	0.4%
42	Rhode Island	86	0.3%
43	Maine	84	0.3%
44	Alaska	81	0.3%
45	South Dakota	78	0.3%
46	Montana	74	0.3%
47	North Dakota	67	0.2%
48	New Hampshire	56	0.2%
49	Wyoming	36	0.1%
50	Vermont	35	0.1%
	District of Columbia	81	0.3%

Source: U.S. Department of Health and Human Services, National Center for Health Statistics
   "National Vital Statistics Reports" (Vol. 52, No. 3, September 18, 2003)
*Final data. Deaths under 1 year old by state of residence.

Infant Mortality Rate in 2001

National Rate = 6.8 Infant Deaths per 1,000 Live Births*

ALPHA ORDER

RANK	STATE	RATE
4	Alabama	9.4
11	Alaska	8.1
26	Arizona	6.9
10	Arkansas	8.3
45	California	5.4
39	Colorado	5.8
34	Connecticut	6.1
1	Delaware	10.7
21	Florida	7.3
8	Georgia	8.6
32	Hawaii	6.2
32	Idaho	6.2
14	Illinois	7.7
17	Indiana	7.5
43	Iowa	5.6
18	Kansas	7.4
36	Kentucky	5.9
3	Louisiana	9.8
34	Maine	6.1
11	Maryland	8.1
48	Massachusetts	5.0
13	Michigan	8.0
47	Minnesota	5.3
2	Mississippi	10.5
18	Missouri	7.4
29	Montana	6.7
27	Nebraska	6.8
42	Nevada	5.7
50	New Hampshire	3.8
30	New Jersey	6.5
31	New Mexico	6.4
39	New York	5.8
9	North Carolina	8.5
6	North Dakota	8.8
14	Ohio	7.7
21	Oklahoma	7.3
45	Oregon	5.4
23	Pennsylvania	7.2
27	Rhode Island	6.8
5	South Carolina	8.9
18	South Dakota	7.4
7	Tennessee	8.7
36	Texas	5.9
49	Utah	4.8
44	Vermont	5.5
16	Virginia	7.6
39	Washington	5.8
23	West Virginia	7.2
25	Wisconsin	7.1
36	Wyoming	5.9

RANK ORDER

RANK	STATE	RATE
1	Delaware	10.7
2	Mississippi	10.5
3	Louisiana	9.8
4	Alabama	9.4
5	South Carolina	8.9
6	North Dakota	8.8
7	Tennessee	8.7
8	Georgia	8.6
9	North Carolina	8.5
10	Arkansas	8.3
11	Alaska	8.1
11	Maryland	8.1
13	Michigan	8.0
14	Illinois	7.7
14	Ohio	7.7
16	Virginia	7.6
17	Indiana	7.5
18	Kansas	7.4
18	Missouri	7.4
18	South Dakota	7.4
21	Florida	7.3
21	Oklahoma	7.3
23	Pennsylvania	7.2
23	West Virginia	7.2
25	Wisconsin	7.1
26	Arizona	6.9
27	Nebraska	6.8
27	Rhode Island	6.8
29	Montana	6.7
30	New Jersey	6.5
31	New Mexico	6.4
32	Hawaii	6.2
32	Idaho	6.2
34	Connecticut	6.1
34	Maine	6.1
36	Kentucky	5.9
36	Texas	5.9
36	Wyoming	5.9
39	Colorado	5.8
39	New York	5.8
39	Washington	5.8
42	Nevada	5.7
43	Iowa	5.6
44	Vermont	5.5
45	California	5.4
45	Oregon	5.4
47	Minnesota	5.3
48	Massachusetts	5.0
49	Utah	4.8
50	New Hampshire	3.8

District of Columbia — 10.6

Source: U.S. Department of Health and Human Services, National Center for Health Statistics
   "National Vital Statistics Reports" (Vol. 52, No. 3, September 18, 2003)
*Final data. Deaths under 1 year old by state of residence.

Percent Change in Infant Mortality Rate: 1990 to 2001

National Percent Change = 26.1% Decrease*

ALPHA ORDER

RANK	STATE	PERCENT CHANGE
8	Alabama	(13.0)
23	Alaska	(22.9)
20	Arizona	(21.6)
5	Arkansas	(9.8)
44	California	(31.6)
46	Colorado	(34.1)
22	Connecticut	(22.8)
2	Delaware	5.9
25	Florida	(24.0)
40	Georgia	(30.6)
4	Hawaii	(7.5)
37	Idaho	(28.7)
37	Illinois	(28.7)
21	Indiana	(21.9)
42	Iowa	(30.9)
7	Kansas	(11.9)
40	Kentucky	(30.6)
6	Louisiana	(11.7)
3	Maine	(1.6)
13	Maryland	(15.6)
36	Massachusetts	(28.6)
27	Michigan	(25.2)
34	Minnesota	(27.4)
9	Mississippi	(13.2)
18	Missouri	(21.3)
29	Montana	(25.6)
15	Nebraska	(18.1)
45	Nevada	(32.1)
50	New Hampshire	(46.5)
35	New Jersey	(27.8)
39	New Mexico	(28.9)
49	New York	(39.6)
16	North Carolina	(19.8)
1	North Dakota	10.0
19	Ohio	(21.4)
17	Oklahoma	(20.7)
47	Oregon	(34.9)
26	Pennsylvania	(25.0)
14	Rhode Island	(16.0)
24	South Carolina	(23.9)
31	South Dakota	(26.7)
12	Tennessee	(15.5)
32	Texas	(27.2)
48	Utah	(36.0)
11	Vermont	(14.1)
28	Virginia	(25.5)
29	Washington	(25.6)
33	West Virginia	(27.3)
10	Wisconsin	(13.4)
43	Wyoming	(31.4)

RANK ORDER

RANK	STATE	PERCENT CHANGE
1	North Dakota	10.0
2	Delaware	5.9
3	Maine	(1.6)
4	Hawaii	(7.5)
5	Arkansas	(9.8)
6	Louisiana	(11.7)
7	Kansas	(11.9)
8	Alabama	(13.0)
9	Mississippi	(13.2)
10	Wisconsin	(13.4)
11	Vermont	(14.1)
12	Tennessee	(15.5)
13	Maryland	(15.6)
14	Rhode Island	(16.0)
15	Nebraska	(18.1)
16	North Carolina	(19.8)
17	Oklahoma	(20.7)
18	Missouri	(21.3)
19	Ohio	(21.4)
20	Arizona	(21.6)
21	Indiana	(21.9)
22	Connecticut	(22.8)
23	Alaska	(22.9)
24	South Carolina	(23.9)
25	Florida	(24.0)
26	Pennsylvania	(25.0)
27	Michigan	(25.2)
28	Virginia	(25.5)
29	Montana	(25.6)
29	Washington	(25.6)
31	South Dakota	(26.7)
32	Texas	(27.2)
33	West Virginia	(27.3)
34	Minnesota	(27.4)
35	New Jersey	(27.8)
36	Massachusetts	(28.6)
37	Idaho	(28.7)
37	Illinois	(28.7)
39	New Mexico	(28.9)
40	Georgia	(30.6)
40	Kentucky	(30.6)
42	Iowa	(30.9)
43	Wyoming	(31.4)
44	California	(31.6)
45	Nevada	(32.1)
46	Colorado	(34.1)
47	Oregon	(34.9)
48	Utah	(36.0)
49	New York	(39.6)
50	New Hampshire	(46.5)

District of Columbia   (48.8)

Source: Morgan Quitno Press using data from US Dept of Health & Human Services, National Center for Health Statistics
"National Vital Statistics Reports" (Vol. 52, No. 3, September 18, 2003) and
"Monthly Vital Statistics Report" (Vol. 41, No. 7(S), January 7, 1993)
*Final data by state of residence. Infant deaths are those occurring under 1 year, exclusive of fetal deaths.

White Infant Deaths in 2001

National Total = 17,955 Deaths*

ALPHA ORDER

RANK	STATE	DEATHS	% of USA
22	Alabama	276	1.5%
47	Alaska	37	0.2%
12	Arizona	458	2.6%
31	Arkansas	196	1.1%
1	California	2,131	11.9%
19	Colorado	336	1.9%
33	Connecticut	167	0.9%
43	Delaware	61	0.3%
5	Florida	844	4.7%
9	Georgia	535	3.0%
50	Hawaii	23	0.1%
39	Idaho	125	0.7%
4	Illinois	854	4.8%
11	Indiana	515	2.9%
32	Iowa	195	1.1%
28	Kansas	225	1.3%
23	Kentucky	275	1.5%
26	Louisiana	239	1.3%
40	Maine	76	0.4%
25	Maryland	248	1.4%
20	Massachusetts	312	1.7%
8	Michigan	646	3.6%
21	Minnesota	281	1.6%
34	Mississippi	160	0.9%
17	Missouri	371	2.1%
42	Montana	63	0.4%
35	Nebraska	144	0.8%
38	Nevada	133	0.7%
44	New Hampshire	53	0.3%
13	New Jersey	430	2.4%
36	New Mexico	143	0.8%
3	New York	926	5.2%
10	North Carolina	522	2.9%
44	North Dakota	53	0.3%
6	Ohio	773	4.3%
24	Oklahoma	254	1.4%
27	Oregon	228	1.3%
7	Pennsylvania	725	4.0%
41	Rhode Island	67	0.4%
30	South Carolina	210	1.2%
46	South Dakota	52	0.3%
14	Tennessee	403	2.2%
2	Texas	1,637	9.1%
29	Utah	222	1.2%
48	Vermont	35	0.2%
16	Virginia	380	2.1%
15	Washington	383	2.1%
37	West Virginia	140	0.8%
18	Wisconsin	352	2.0%
49	Wyoming	34	0.2%

RANK ORDER

RANK	STATE	DEATHS	% of USA
1	California	2,131	11.9%
2	Texas	1,637	9.1%
3	New York	926	5.2%
4	Illinois	854	4.8%
5	Florida	844	4.7%
6	Ohio	773	4.3%
7	Pennsylvania	725	4.0%
8	Michigan	646	3.6%
9	Georgia	535	3.0%
10	North Carolina	522	2.9%
11	Indiana	515	2.9%
12	Arizona	458	2.6%
13	New Jersey	430	2.4%
14	Tennessee	403	2.2%
15	Washington	383	2.1%
16	Virginia	380	2.1%
17	Missouri	371	2.1%
18	Wisconsin	352	2.0%
19	Colorado	336	1.9%
20	Massachusetts	312	1.7%
21	Minnesota	281	1.6%
22	Alabama	276	1.5%
23	Kentucky	275	1.5%
24	Oklahoma	254	1.4%
25	Maryland	248	1.4%
26	Louisiana	239	1.3%
27	Oregon	228	1.3%
28	Kansas	225	1.3%
29	Utah	222	1.2%
30	South Carolina	210	1.2%
31	Arkansas	196	1.1%
32	Iowa	195	1.1%
33	Connecticut	167	0.9%
34	Mississippi	160	0.9%
35	Nebraska	144	0.8%
36	New Mexico	143	0.8%
37	West Virginia	140	0.8%
38	Nevada	133	0.7%
39	Idaho	125	0.7%
40	Maine	76	0.4%
41	Rhode Island	67	0.4%
42	Montana	63	0.4%
43	Delaware	61	0.3%
44	New Hampshire	53	0.3%
44	North Dakota	53	0.3%
46	South Dakota	52	0.3%
47	Alaska	37	0.2%
48	Vermont	35	0.2%
49	Wyoming	34	0.2%
50	Hawaii	23	0.1%
	District of Columbia	7	0.0%

Source: U.S. Department of Health and Human Services, National Center for Health Statistics
    "National Vital Statistics Reports" (Vol. 52, No. 3, September 18, 2003)
Final data. Deaths of infants under 1 year old, exclusive of fetal deaths. Based on race of the mother.

White Infant Mortality Rate in 2001

National Rate = 5.7 White Infant Deaths per 1,000 White Live Births*

ALPHA ORDER

RANK	STATE	RATE
5	Alabama	6.8
30	Alaska	5.8
18	Arizona	6.1
5	Arkansas	6.8
45	California	5.0
35	Colorado	5.5
48	Connecticut	4.7
1	Delaware	8.0
35	Florida	5.5
16	Georgia	6.2
24	Hawaii	6.0
14	Idaho	6.3
24	Illinois	6.0
5	Indiana	6.8
35	Iowa	5.5
10	Kansas	6.5
33	Kentucky	5.6
10	Louisiana	6.5
31	Maine	5.7
35	Maryland	5.5
49	Massachusetts	4.6
18	Michigan	6.1
47	Minnesota	4.8
4	Mississippi	7.0
26	Missouri	5.9
8	Montana	6.7
13	Nebraska	6.4
42	Nevada	5.1
50	New Hampshire	3.8
42	New Jersey	5.1
14	New Mexico	6.3
42	New York	5.1
18	North Carolina	6.1
1	North Dakota	8.0
16	Ohio	6.2
10	Oklahoma	6.5
35	Oregon	5.5
18	Pennsylvania	6.1
18	Rhode Island	6.1
26	South Carolina	5.9
18	South Dakota	6.1
8	Tennessee	6.7
41	Texas	5.2
46	Utah	4.9
33	Vermont	5.6
40	Virginia	5.4
31	Washington	5.7
3	West Virginia	7.2
26	Wisconsin	5.9
26	Wyoming	5.9

RANK ORDER

RANK	STATE	RATE
1	Delaware	8.0
1	North Dakota	8.0
3	West Virginia	7.2
4	Mississippi	7.0
5	Alabama	6.8
5	Arkansas	6.8
5	Indiana	6.8
8	Montana	6.7
8	Tennessee	6.7
10	Kansas	6.5
10	Louisiana	6.5
10	Oklahoma	6.5
13	Nebraska	6.4
14	Idaho	6.3
14	New Mexico	6.3
16	Georgia	6.2
16	Ohio	6.2
18	Arizona	6.1
18	Michigan	6.1
18	North Carolina	6.1
18	Pennsylvania	6.1
18	Rhode Island	6.1
18	South Dakota	6.1
24	Hawaii	6.0
24	Illinois	6.0
26	Missouri	5.9
26	South Carolina	5.9
26	Wisconsin	5.9
26	Wyoming	5.9
30	Alaska	5.8
31	Maine	5.7
31	Washington	5.7
33	Kentucky	5.6
33	Vermont	5.6
35	Colorado	5.5
35	Florida	5.5
35	Iowa	5.5
35	Maryland	5.5
35	Oregon	5.5
40	Virginia	5.4
41	Texas	5.2
42	Nevada	5.1
42	New Jersey	5.1
42	New York	5.1
45	California	5.0
46	Utah	4.9
47	Minnesota	4.8
48	Connecticut	4.7
49	Massachusetts	4.6
50	New Hampshire	3.8

District of Columbia**	NA

Source: U.S. Department of Health and Human Services, National Center for Health Statistics
   "National Vital Statistics Reports" (Vol. 52, No. 3, September 18, 2003)
*Final data. Deaths of infants under 1 year old, exclusive of fetal deaths. Based on race of the mother.
**Not available, fewer than 20 white infant deaths.

Percent Change in White Infant Mortality Rate: 1990 to 2001

National Percent Change = 26.0% Decrease*

ALPHA ORDER

RANK	STATE	PERCENT CHANGE
13	Alabama	(18.1)
40	Alaska	(31.8)
25	Arizona	(25.6)
8	Arkansas	(15.0)
47	California	(34.2)
48	Colorado	(34.5)
33	Connecticut	(28.8)
2	Delaware	9.6
29	Florida	(27.6)
41	Georgia	(31.9)
1	Hawaii	17.6
29	Idaho	(27.6)
16	Illinois	(22.1)
19	Indiana	(23.6)
36	Iowa	(29.5)
10	Kansas	(15.6)
37	Kentucky	(30.0)
5	Louisiana	(11.0)
4	Maine	(8.1)
9	Maryland	(15.4)
39	Massachusetts	(31.3)
18	Michigan	(22.8)
32	Minnesota	(28.4)
12	Mississippi	(17.6)
20	Missouri	(24.4)
16	Montana	(22.1)
6	Nebraska	(11.1)
49	Nevada	(37.0)
50	New Hampshire	(47.2)
22	New Jersey	(25.0)
43	New Mexico	(32.3)
45	New York	(33.8)
26	North Carolina	(26.5)
3	North Dakota	1.3
20	Ohio	(24.4)
38	Oklahoma	(30.9)
42	Oregon	(32.1)
15	Pennsylvania	(21.8)
26	Rhode Island	(26.5)
34	South Carolina	(28.9)
35	South Dakota	(29.1)
11	Tennessee	(16.3)
28	Texas	(26.8)
45	Utah	(33.8)
7	Vermont	(13.8)
31	Virginia	(28.0)
22	Washington	(25.0)
22	West Virginia	(25.0)
13	Wisconsin	(18.1)
44	Wyoming	(33.0)

RANK ORDER

RANK	STATE	PERCENT CHANGE
1	Hawaii	17.6
2	Delaware	9.6
3	North Dakota	1.3
4	Maine	(8.1)
5	Louisiana	(11.0)
6	Nebraska	(11.1)
7	Vermont	(13.8)
8	Arkansas	(15.0)
9	Maryland	(15.4)
10	Kansas	(15.6)
11	Tennessee	(16.3)
12	Mississippi	(17.6)
13	Alabama	(18.1)
13	Wisconsin	(18.1)
15	Pennsylvania	(21.8)
16	Illinois	(22.1)
16	Montana	(22.1)
18	Michigan	(22.8)
19	Indiana	(23.6)
20	Missouri	(24.4)
20	Ohio	(24.4)
22	New Jersey	(25.0)
22	Washington	(25.0)
22	West Virginia	(25.0)
25	Arizona	(25.6)
26	North Carolina	(26.5)
26	Rhode Island	(26.5)
28	Texas	(26.8)
29	Florida	(27.6)
29	Idaho	(27.6)
31	Virginia	(28.0)
32	Minnesota	(28.4)
33	Connecticut	(28.8)
34	South Carolina	(28.9)
35	South Dakota	(29.1)
36	Iowa	(29.5)
37	Kentucky	(30.0)
38	Oklahoma	(30.9)
39	Massachusetts	(31.3)
40	Alaska	(31.8)
41	Georgia	(31.9)
42	Oregon	(32.1)
43	New Mexico	(32.3)
44	Wyoming	(33.0)
45	New York	(33.8)
45	Utah	(33.8)
47	California	(34.2)
48	Colorado	(34.5)
49	Nevada	(37.0)
50	New Hampshire	(47.2)

District of Columbia** NA

Source: Morgan Quitno Press using data from US Dept of Health & Human Services, National Center for Health Statistics
"National Vital Statistics Reports" (Vol. 52, No. 3, September 18, 2003) and "Vital Statistics of the United States"
*Final data. Deaths of infants under 1 year old, exclusive of fetal deaths. Based on race of the mother.
**Not available, fewer than 20 white infant deaths.

Black Infant Deaths in 2001

National Total = 8,498 Deaths*

ALPHA ORDER

RANK ORDER

RANK	STATE	DEATHS	% of USA
15	Alabama	290	3.4%
41	Alaska	4	0.0%
26	Arizona	63	0.7%
22	Arkansas	108	1.3%
7	California	435	5.1%
33	Colorado	38	0.4%
23	Connecticut	87	1.0%
28	Delaware	54	0.6%
1	Florida	635	7.5%
2	Georgia	583	6.9%
41	Hawaii	4	0.0%
44	Idaho	1	0.0%
3	Illinois	515	6.1%
20	Indiana	132	1.6%
34	Iowa	14	0.2%
27	Kansas	57	0.7%
29	Kentucky	48	0.6%
9	Louisiana	390	4.6%
40	Maine	6	0.1%
12	Maryland	333	3.9%
24	Massachusetts	79	0.9%
8	Michigan	401	4.7%
30	Minnesota	46	0.5%
17	Mississippi	280	3.3%
19	Missouri	184	2.2%
47	Montana	0	0.0%
34	Nebraska	14	0.2%
31	Nevada	43	0.5%
47	New Hampshire	0	0.0%
13	New Jersey	293	3.4%
39	New Mexico	7	0.1%
4	New York	507	6.0%
6	North Carolina	449	5.3%
44	North Dakota	1	0.0%
10	Ohio	377	4.4%
25	Oklahoma	69	0.8%
37	Oregon	8	0.1%
14	Pennsylvania	291	3.4%
36	Rhode Island	12	0.1%
16	South Carolina	284	3.3%
44	South Dakota	1	0.0%
18	Tennessee	269	3.2%
5	Texas	491	5.8%
43	Utah	3	0.0%
47	Vermont	0	0.0%
11	Virginia	351	4.1%
31	Washington	43	0.5%
37	West Virginia	8	0.1%
21	Wisconsin	117	1.4%
47	Wyoming	0	0.0%

RANK	STATE	DEATHS	% of USA
1	Florida	635	7.5%
2	Georgia	583	6.9%
3	Illinois	515	6.1%
4	New York	507	6.0%
5	Texas	491	5.8%
6	North Carolina	449	5.3%
7	California	435	5.1%
8	Michigan	401	4.7%
9	Louisiana	390	4.6%
10	Ohio	377	4.4%
11	Virginia	351	4.1%
12	Maryland	333	3.9%
13	New Jersey	293	3.4%
14	Pennsylvania	291	3.4%
15	Alabama	290	3.4%
16	South Carolina	284	3.3%
17	Mississippi	280	3.3%
18	Tennessee	269	3.2%
19	Missouri	184	2.2%
20	Indiana	132	1.6%
21	Wisconsin	117	1.4%
22	Arkansas	108	1.3%
23	Connecticut	87	1.0%
24	Massachusetts	79	0.9%
25	Oklahoma	69	0.8%
26	Arizona	63	0.7%
27	Kansas	57	0.7%
28	Delaware	54	0.6%
29	Kentucky	48	0.6%
30	Minnesota	46	0.5%
31	Nevada	43	0.5%
31	Washington	43	0.5%
33	Colorado	38	0.4%
34	Iowa	14	0.2%
34	Nebraska	14	0.2%
36	Rhode Island	12	0.1%
37	Oregon	8	0.1%
37	West Virginia	8	0.1%
39	New Mexico	7	0.1%
40	Maine	6	0.1%
41	Alaska	4	0.0%
41	Hawaii	4	0.0%
43	Utah	3	0.0%
44	Idaho	1	0.0%
44	North Dakota	1	0.0%
44	South Dakota	1	0.0%
47	Montana	0	0.0%
47	New Hampshire	0	0.0%
47	Vermont	0	0.0%
47	Wyoming	0	0.0%

| | District of Columbia | 73 | 0.9% |

Source: Morgan Quitno Press using data from US Dept of Health & Human Services, National Center for Health Statistics
"National Vital Statistics Reports" (Vol. 52, No. 3, September 18, 2003) and
"Vital Statistics of the United States, 1980" (Vol. I-Natality, issued 1984) and unpublished data
*Final data by state of residence. Infant deaths are those occurring under 1 year, exclusive of fetal deaths.

Black Infant Mortality Rate in 2001

National Rate = 14.0 Black Infant Deaths per 1,000 Black Live Births*

ALPHA ORDER

RANK	STATE	RATE
14	Alabama	15.1
NA	Alaska**	NA
1	Arizona	22.8
18	Arkansas	14.5
26	California	12.9
28	Colorado	12.8
7	Connecticut	16.9
3	Delaware	19.9
24	Florida	13.5
25	Georgia	13.3
NA	Hawaii**	NA
NA	Idaho**	NA
13	Illinois	15.5
22	Indiana	13.7
NA	Iowa**	NA
2	Kansas	20.5
30	Kentucky	9.7
19	Louisiana	14.4
NA	Maine**	NA
22	Maryland	13.7
32	Massachusetts	9.6
6	Michigan	17.0
32	Minnesota	9.6
17	Mississippi	14.9
8	Missouri	16.5
NA	Montana**	NA
NA	Nebraska**	NA
5	Nevada	17.1
NA	New Hampshire**	NA
21	New Jersey	14.2
NA	New Mexico**	NA
30	New York	9.7
11	North Carolina	15.8
NA	North Dakota**	NA
9	Ohio	16.4
15	Oklahoma	15.0
NA	Oregon**	NA
19	Pennsylvania	14.4
NA	Rhode Island**	NA
15	South Carolina	15.0
NA	South Dakota**	NA
10	Tennessee	16.2
29	Texas	12.0
NA	Utah**	NA
NA	Vermont**	NA
11	Virginia	15.8
26	Washington	12.9
NA	West Virginia**	NA
4	Wisconsin	17.8
NA	Wyoming**	NA

RANK ORDER

RANK	STATE	RATE
1	Arizona	22.8
2	Kansas	20.5
3	Delaware	19.9
4	Wisconsin	17.8
5	Nevada	17.1
6	Michigan	17.0
7	Connecticut	16.9
8	Missouri	16.5
9	Ohio	16.4
10	Tennessee	16.2
11	North Carolina	15.8
11	Virginia	15.8
13	Illinois	15.5
14	Alabama	15.1
15	Oklahoma	15.0
15	South Carolina	15.0
17	Mississippi	14.9
18	Arkansas	14.5
19	Louisiana	14.4
19	Pennsylvania	14.4
21	New Jersey	14.2
22	Indiana	13.7
22	Maryland	13.7
24	Florida	13.5
25	Georgia	13.3
26	California	12.9
26	Washington	12.9
28	Colorado	12.8
29	Texas	12.0
30	Kentucky	9.7
30	New York	9.7
32	Massachusetts	9.6
32	Minnesota	9.6
NA	Alaska**	NA
NA	Hawaii**	NA
NA	Idaho**	NA
NA	Iowa**	NA
NA	Maine**	NA
NA	Montana**	NA
NA	Nebraska**	NA
NA	New Hampshire**	NA
NA	New Mexico**	NA
NA	North Dakota**	NA
NA	Oregon**	NA
NA	Rhode Island**	NA
NA	South Dakota**	NA
NA	Utah**	NA
NA	Vermont**	NA
NA	West Virginia**	NA
NA	Wyoming**	NA

District of Columbia 15.0

*Source: U.S. Department of Health and Human Services, National Center for Health Statistics
"National Vital Statistics Reports" (Vol. 52, No. 3, September 18, 2003)*
Final data. Deaths of infants under 1 year old, exclusive of fetal deaths. Based on race of the mother.
***Not available, fewer than 20 black infant deaths.*

Percent Change in Black Infant Mortality Rate: 1990 to 2001

National Percent Change = 17.6% Decrease*

ALPHA ORDER				RANK ORDER		
RANK	STATE	PERCENT CHANGE		RANK	STATE	PERCENT CHANGE
10	Alabama	(5.0)		1	Nevada	36.8
NA	Alaska**	NA		2	Arizona	36.5
2	Arizona	36.5		3	Kansas	33.1
5	Arkansas	6.6		4	Oklahoma	13.6
15	California	(9.2)		5	Arkansas	6.6
27	Colorado	(22.4)		6	Connecticut	5.6
6	Connecticut	5.6		7	Delaware	2.6
7	Delaware	2.6		8	North Carolina	(1.2)
24	Florida	(16.7)		9	Wisconsin	(1.7)
29	Georgia	(26.1)		10	Alabama	(5.0)
NA	Hawaii**	NA		11	Missouri	(5.7)
NA	Idaho**	NA		12	Tennessee	(7.4)
30	Illinois	(27.9)		13	Mississippi	(7.5)
21	Indiana	(14.4)		14	Massachusetts	(7.7)
NA	Iowa**	NA		15	California	(9.2)
3	Kansas	33.1		16	Ohio	(10.4)
31	Kentucky	(28.7)		17	Washington	(11.0)
19	Louisiana	(12.7)		18	South Carolina	(12.3)
NA	Maine**	NA		19	Louisiana	(12.7)
22	Maryland	(16.0)		20	Texas	(13.7)
14	Massachusetts	(7.7)		21	Indiana	(14.4)
26	Michigan	(19.0)		22	Maryland	(16.0)
33	Minnesota	(51.3)		22	Virginia	(16.0)
13	Mississippi	(7.5)		24	Florida	(16.7)
11	Missouri	(5.7)		25	New Jersey	(17.9)
NA	Montana**	NA		26	Michigan	(19.0)
NA	Nebraska**	NA		27	Colorado	(22.4)
1	Nevada	36.8		28	Pennsylvania	(23.4)
NA	New Hampshire**	NA		29	Georgia	(26.1)
25	New Jersey	(17.9)		30	Illinois	(27.9)
NA	New Mexico**	NA		31	Kentucky	(28.7)
32	New York	(43.9)		32	New York	(43.9)
8	North Carolina	(1.2)		33	Minnesota	(51.3)
NA	North Dakota**	NA		NA	Alaska**	NA
16	Ohio	(10.4)		NA	Hawaii**	NA
4	Oklahoma	13.6		NA	Idaho**	NA
NA	Oregon**	NA		NA	Iowa**	NA
28	Pennsylvania	(23.4)		NA	Maine**	NA
NA	Rhode Island**	NA		NA	Montana**	NA
18	South Carolina	(12.3)		NA	Nebraska**	NA
NA	South Dakota**	NA		NA	New Hampshire**	NA
12	Tennessee	(7.4)		NA	New Mexico**	NA
20	Texas	(13.7)		NA	North Dakota**	NA
NA	Utah**	NA		NA	Oregon**	NA
NA	Vermont**	NA		NA	Rhode Island**	NA
22	Virginia	(16.0)		NA	South Dakota**	NA
17	Washington	(11.0)		NA	Utah**	NA
NA	West Virginia**	NA		NA	Vermont**	NA
9	Wisconsin	(1.7)		NA	West Virginia**	NA
NA	Wyoming**	NA		NA	Wyoming**	NA
					District of Columbia	(38.5)

Source: Morgan Quitno Press using data from US Dept of Health & Human Services, National Center for Health Statistics
"National Vital Statistics Reports" (Vol. 52, No. 3, September 18, 2003) and "Vital Statistics of the United States"
*Final data. Deaths of infants under 1 year old, exclusive of fetal deaths. Based on race of the mother.
**Not available, fewer than 20 black infant deaths.

Neonatal Deaths in 2001

National Total = 18,265 Deaths*

ALPHA ORDER

RANK	STATE	DEATHS	% of USA
19	Alabama	355	1.9%
46	Alaska	38	0.2%
17	Arizona	389	2.1%
31	Arkansas	173	0.9%
1	California	1,896	10.4%
24	Colorado	288	1.6%
29	Connecticut	195	1.1%
40	Delaware	82	0.4%
4	Florida	981	5.4%
6	Georgia	780	4.3%
42	Hawaii	68	0.4%
39	Idaho	84	0.5%
5	Illinois	954	5.2%
16	Indiana	407	2.2%
34	Iowa	130	0.7%
30	Kansas	181	1.0%
28	Kentucky	196	1.1%
15	Louisiana	417	2.3%
43	Maine	65	0.4%
13	Maryland	439	2.4%
22	Massachusetts	308	1.7%
8	Michigan	731	4.0%
26	Minnesota	236	1.3%
25	Mississippi	278	1.5%
18	Missouri	370	2.0%
44	Montana	48	0.3%
35	Nebraska	119	0.7%
38	Nevada	93	0.5%
46	New Hampshire	38	0.2%
11	New Jersey	501	2.7%
37	New Mexico	107	0.6%
3	New York	1,028	5.6%
10	North Carolina	703	3.8%
45	North Dakota	44	0.2%
7	Ohio	760	4.2%
27	Oklahoma	205	1.1%
32	Oregon	157	0.9%
9	Pennsylvania	728	4.0%
41	Rhode Island	70	0.4%
20	South Carolina	337	1.8%
48	South Dakota	37	0.2%
14	Tennessee	437	2.4%
2	Texas	1,345	7.4%
33	Utah	149	0.8%
50	Vermont	23	0.1%
12	Virginia	486	2.7%
23	Washington	292	1.6%
36	West Virginia	110	0.6%
21	Wisconsin	324	1.8%
49	Wyoming	24	0.1%

RANK ORDER

RANK	STATE	DEATHS	% of USA
1	California	1,896	10.4%
2	Texas	1,345	7.4%
3	New York	1,028	5.6%
4	Florida	981	5.4%
5	Illinois	954	5.2%
6	Georgia	780	4.3%
7	Ohio	760	4.2%
8	Michigan	731	4.0%
9	Pennsylvania	728	4.0%
10	North Carolina	703	3.8%
11	New Jersey	501	2.7%
12	Virginia	486	2.7%
13	Maryland	439	2.4%
14	Tennessee	437	2.4%
15	Louisiana	417	2.3%
16	Indiana	407	2.2%
17	Arizona	389	2.1%
18	Missouri	370	2.0%
19	Alabama	355	1.9%
20	South Carolina	337	1.8%
21	Wisconsin	324	1.8%
22	Massachusetts	308	1.7%
23	Washington	292	1.6%
24	Colorado	288	1.6%
25	Mississippi	278	1.5%
26	Minnesota	236	1.3%
27	Oklahoma	205	1.1%
28	Kentucky	196	1.1%
29	Connecticut	195	1.1%
30	Kansas	181	1.0%
31	Arkansas	173	0.9%
32	Oregon	157	0.9%
33	Utah	149	0.8%
34	Iowa	130	0.7%
35	Nebraska	119	0.7%
36	West Virginia	110	0.6%
37	New Mexico	107	0.6%
38	Nevada	93	0.5%
39	Idaho	84	0.5%
40	Delaware	82	0.4%
41	Rhode Island	70	0.4%
42	Hawaii	68	0.4%
43	Maine	65	0.4%
44	Montana	48	0.3%
45	North Dakota	44	0.2%
46	Alaska	38	0.2%
46	New Hampshire	38	0.2%
48	South Dakota	37	0.2%
49	Wyoming	24	0.1%
50	Vermont	23	0.1%
	District of Columbia	59	0.3%

Source: U.S. Department of Health and Human Services, National Center for Health Statistics
"National Vital Statistics Reports" (Vol. 52, No. 3, September 18, 2003)
*Final data. Deaths of infants under 28 days, exclusive of fetal deaths.

Neonatal Death Rate in 2001

National Rate = 4.5 Deaths per 1,000 Live Births*

ALPHA ORDER

RANK	STATE	RATE
6	Alabama	5.9
37	Alaska	3.8
27	Arizona	4.5
21	Arkansas	4.7
41	California	3.6
29	Colorado	4.3
26	Connecticut	4.6
1	Delaware	7.6
19	Florida	4.8
8	Georgia	5.8
33	Hawaii	4.0
31	Idaho	4.1
14	Illinois	5.2
21	Indiana	4.7
44	Iowa	3.5
21	Kansas	4.7
41	Kentucky	3.6
3	Louisiana	6.4
21	Maine	4.7
4	Maryland	6.0
37	Massachusetts	3.8
11	Michigan	5.5
44	Minnesota	3.5
2	Mississippi	6.6
17	Missouri	4.9
28	Montana	4.4
19	Nebraska	4.8
49	Nevada	3.0
50	New Hampshire	2.6
29	New Jersey	4.3
35	New Mexico	3.9
33	New York	4.0
6	North Carolina	5.9
8	North Dakota	5.8
16	Ohio	5.0
31	Oklahoma	4.1
44	Oregon	3.5
15	Pennsylvania	5.1
11	Rhode Island	5.5
4	South Carolina	6.0
44	South Dakota	3.5
10	Tennessee	5.6
39	Texas	3.7
48	Utah	3.1
41	Vermont	3.6
17	Virginia	4.9
39	Washington	3.7
13	West Virginia	5.4
21	Wisconsin	4.7
35	Wyoming	3.9

RANK ORDER

RANK	STATE	RATE
1	Delaware	7.6
2	Mississippi	6.6
3	Louisiana	6.4
4	Maryland	6.0
4	South Carolina	6.0
6	Alabama	5.9
6	North Carolina	5.9
8	Georgia	5.8
8	North Dakota	5.8
10	Tennessee	5.6
11	Michigan	5.5
11	Rhode Island	5.5
13	West Virginia	5.4
14	Illinois	5.2
15	Pennsylvania	5.1
16	Ohio	5.0
17	Missouri	4.9
17	Virginia	4.9
19	Florida	4.8
19	Nebraska	4.8
21	Arkansas	4.7
21	Indiana	4.7
21	Kansas	4.7
21	Maine	4.7
21	Wisconsin	4.7
26	Connecticut	4.6
27	Arizona	4.5
28	Montana	4.4
29	Colorado	4.3
29	New Jersey	4.3
31	Idaho	4.1
31	Oklahoma	4.1
33	Hawaii	4.0
33	New York	4.0
35	New Mexico	3.9
35	Wyoming	3.9
37	Alaska	3.8
37	Massachusetts	3.8
39	Texas	3.7
39	Washington	3.7
41	California	3.6
41	Kentucky	3.6
41	Vermont	3.6
44	Iowa	3.5
44	Minnesota	3.5
44	Oregon	3.5
44	South Dakota	3.5
48	Utah	3.1
49	Nevada	3.0
50	New Hampshire	2.6
	District of Columbia	7.7

Source: U.S. Department of Health and Human Services, National Center for Health Statistics
    "National Vital Statistics Reports" (Vol. 52, No. 3, September 18, 2003)
*Final data. Deaths of infants under 28 days, exclusive of fetal deaths.

White Neonatal Deaths in 2001

National Total = 12,013 Deaths*

ALPHA ORDER

RANK	STATE	DEATHS	% of USA
23	Alabama	171	1.4%
47	Alaska	24	0.2%
12	Arizona	317	2.6%
34	Arkansas	105	0.9%
1	California	1,438	12.0%
15	Colorado	251	2.1%
31	Connecticut	127	1.1%
42	Delaware	44	0.4%
5	Florida	544	4.5%
9	Georgia	357	3.0%
50	Hawaii	17	0.1%
38	Idaho	82	0.7%
4	Illinois	607	5.1%
11	Indiana	325	2.7%
32	Iowa	117	1.0%
29	Kansas	144	1.2%
24	Kentucky	169	1.4%
25	Louisiana	151	1.3%
40	Maine	59	0.5%
21	Maryland	191	1.6%
19	Massachusetts	240	2.0%
8	Michigan	447	3.7%
22	Minnesota	190	1.6%
36	Mississippi	97	0.8%
18	Missouri	241	2.0%
43	Montana	43	0.4%
33	Nebraska	106	0.9%
39	Nevada	69	0.6%
44	New Hampshire	35	0.3%
13	New Jersey	303	2.5%
37	New Mexico	92	0.8%
3	New York	664	5.5%
10	North Carolina	352	2.9%
44	North Dakota	35	0.3%
7	Ohio	516	4.3%
27	Oklahoma	146	1.2%
26	Oregon	147	1.2%
6	Pennsylvania	531	4.4%
41	Rhode Island	54	0.4%
30	South Carolina	137	1.1%
46	South Dakota	27	0.2%
14	Tennessee	255	2.1%
2	Texas	1,020	8.5%
27	Utah	146	1.2%
49	Vermont	23	0.2%
20	Virginia	236	2.0%
16	Washington	245	2.0%
35	West Virginia	102	0.8%
16	Wisconsin	245	2.0%
47	Wyoming	24	0.2%

RANK ORDER

RANK	STATE	DEATHS	% of USA
1	California	1,438	12.0%
2	Texas	1,020	8.5%
3	New York	664	5.5%
4	Illinois	607	5.1%
5	Florida	544	4.5%
6	Pennsylvania	531	4.4%
7	Ohio	516	4.3%
8	Michigan	447	3.7%
9	Georgia	357	3.0%
10	North Carolina	352	2.9%
11	Indiana	325	2.7%
12	Arizona	317	2.6%
13	New Jersey	303	2.5%
14	Tennessee	255	2.1%
15	Colorado	251	2.1%
16	Washington	245	2.0%
16	Wisconsin	245	2.0%
18	Missouri	241	2.0%
19	Massachusetts	240	2.0%
20	Virginia	236	2.0%
21	Maryland	191	1.6%
22	Minnesota	190	1.6%
23	Alabama	171	1.4%
24	Kentucky	169	1.4%
25	Louisiana	151	1.3%
26	Oregon	147	1.2%
27	Oklahoma	146	1.2%
27	Utah	146	1.2%
29	Kansas	144	1.2%
30	South Carolina	137	1.1%
31	Connecticut	127	1.1%
32	Iowa	117	1.0%
33	Nebraska	106	0.9%
34	Arkansas	105	0.9%
35	West Virginia	102	0.8%
36	Mississippi	97	0.8%
37	New Mexico	92	0.8%
38	Idaho	82	0.7%
39	Nevada	69	0.6%
40	Maine	59	0.5%
41	Rhode Island	54	0.4%
42	Delaware	44	0.4%
43	Montana	43	0.4%
44	New Hampshire	35	0.3%
44	North Dakota	35	0.3%
46	South Dakota	27	0.2%
47	Alaska	24	0.2%
47	Wyoming	24	0.2%
49	Vermont	23	0.2%
50	Hawaii	17	0.1%
	District of Columbia	5	0.0%

Source: U.S. Department of Health and Human Services, National Center for Health Statistics
"National Vital Statistics Reports" (Vol. 52, No. 3, September 18, 2003)
Final data. Deaths of infants under 28 days, exclusive of fetal deaths. Based on race of the mother.

White Neonatal Death Rate in 2001

National Rate = 3.8 White Neonatal Deaths per 1,000 White Live Births*

ALPHA ORDER

RANK	STATE	RATE
12	Alabama	4.2
28	Alaska	3.8
12	Arizona	4.2
32	Arkansas	3.6
41	California	3.4
20	Colorado	4.1
32	Connecticut	3.6
1	Delaware	5.7
32	Florida	3.6
12	Georgia	4.2
NA	Hawaii**	NA
20	Idaho	4.1
9	Illinois	4.3
9	Indiana	4.3
42	Iowa	3.3
12	Kansas	4.2
39	Kentucky	3.5
20	Louisiana	4.1
8	Maine	4.4
12	Maryland	4.2
39	Massachusetts	3.5
12	Michigan	4.2
42	Minnesota	3.3
9	Mississippi	4.3
27	Missouri	3.9
6	Montana	4.6
5	Nebraska	4.7
48	Nevada	2.6
49	New Hampshire	2.5
32	New Jersey	3.6
26	New Mexico	4.0
32	New York	3.6
20	North Carolina	4.1
2	North Dakota	5.3
20	Ohio	4.1
30	Oklahoma	3.7
32	Oregon	3.6
7	Pennsylvania	4.5
4	Rhode Island	4.9
28	South Carolina	3.8
46	South Dakota	3.2
12	Tennessee	4.2
42	Texas	3.3
46	Utah	3.2
30	Vermont	3.7
42	Virginia	3.3
32	Washington	3.6
3	West Virginia	5.2
20	Wisconsin	4.1
12	Wyoming	4.2

RANK ORDER

RANK	STATE	RATE
1	Delaware	5.7
2	North Dakota	5.3
3	West Virginia	5.2
4	Rhode Island	4.9
5	Nebraska	4.7
6	Montana	4.6
7	Pennsylvania	4.5
8	Maine	4.4
9	Illinois	4.3
9	Indiana	4.3
9	Mississippi	4.3
12	Alabama	4.2
12	Arizona	4.2
12	Georgia	4.2
12	Kansas	4.2
12	Maryland	4.2
12	Michigan	4.2
12	Tennessee	4.2
12	Wyoming	4.2
20	Colorado	4.1
20	Idaho	4.1
20	Louisiana	4.1
20	North Carolina	4.1
20	Ohio	4.1
20	Wisconsin	4.1
26	New Mexico	4.0
27	Missouri	3.9
28	Alaska	3.8
28	South Carolina	3.8
30	Oklahoma	3.7
30	Vermont	3.7
32	Arkansas	3.6
32	Connecticut	3.6
32	Florida	3.6
32	New Jersey	3.6
32	New York	3.6
32	Oregon	3.6
32	Washington	3.6
39	Kentucky	3.5
39	Massachusetts	3.5
41	California	3.4
42	Iowa	3.3
42	Minnesota	3.3
42	Texas	3.3
42	Virginia	3.3
46	South Dakota	3.2
46	Utah	3.2
48	Nevada	2.6
49	New Hampshire	2.5
NA	Hawaii**	NA
	District of Columbia**	NA

Source: U.S. Department of Health and Human Services, National Center for Health Statistics
"National Vital Statistics Reports" (Vol. 52, No. 3, September 18, 2003)
*Final data. Deaths of infants under 28 days, exclusive of fetal deaths. Based on race of the mother.
**Not available. Fewer than 20 white neonatal deaths.

Black Neonatal Deaths in 2001

National Total = 5,585 Deaths*

ALPHA ORDER					RANK ORDER			
RANK	STATE	DEATHS	% of USA		RANK	STATE	DEATHS	% of USA
16	Alabama	184	3.3%		1	Florida	426	7.6%
41	Alaska	2	0.0%		2	Georgia	400	7.2%
25	Arizona	42	0.8%		3	New York	337	6.0%
22	Arkansas	66	1.2%		4	North Carolina	320	5.7%
6	California	295	5.3%		5	Illinois	315	5.6%
29	Colorado	29	0.5%		6	California	295	5.3%
23	Connecticut	63	1.1%		7	Texas	292	5.2%
26	Delaware	38	0.7%		8	Michigan	268	4.8%
1	Florida	426	7.6%		9	Louisiana	256	4.6%
2	Georgia	400	7.2%		10	Virginia	238	4.3%
39	Hawaii	4	0.1%		11	Maryland	237	4.2%
43	Idaho	1	0.0%		11	Ohio	237	4.2%
5	Illinois	315	5.6%		13	South Carolina	199	3.6%
20	Indiana	80	1.4%		14	New Jersey	187	3.3%
34	Iowa	13	0.2%		15	Pennsylvania	186	3.3%
27	Kansas	34	0.6%		16	Alabama	184	3.3%
31	Kentucky	26	0.5%		17	Mississippi	180	3.2%
9	Louisiana	256	4.6%		18	Tennessee	176	3.2%
38	Maine	6	0.1%		19	Missouri	126	2.3%
11	Maryland	237	4.2%		20	Indiana	80	1.4%
24	Massachusetts	59	1.1%		21	Wisconsin	67	1.2%
8	Michigan	268	4.8%		22	Arkansas	66	1.2%
33	Minnesota	23	0.4%		23	Connecticut	63	1.1%
17	Mississippi	180	3.2%		24	Massachusetts	59	1.1%
19	Missouri	126	2.3%		25	Arizona	42	0.8%
47	Montana	0	0.0%		26	Delaware	38	0.7%
36	Nebraska	8	0.1%		27	Kansas	34	0.6%
32	Nevada	24	0.4%		27	Oklahoma	34	0.6%
47	New Hampshire	0	0.0%		29	Colorado	29	0.5%
14	New Jersey	187	3.3%		30	Washington	27	0.5%
39	New Mexico	4	0.1%		31	Kentucky	26	0.5%
3	New York	337	6.0%		32	Nevada	24	0.4%
4	North Carolina	320	5.7%		33	Minnesota	23	0.4%
43	North Dakota	1	0.0%		34	Iowa	13	0.2%
11	Ohio	237	4.2%		35	Rhode Island	10	0.2%
27	Oklahoma	34	0.6%		36	Nebraska	8	0.1%
41	Oregon	2	0.0%		36	West Virginia	8	0.1%
15	Pennsylvania	186	3.3%		38	Maine	6	0.1%
35	Rhode Island	10	0.2%		39	Hawaii	4	0.1%
13	South Carolina	199	3.6%		39	New Mexico	4	0.1%
43	South Dakota	1	0.0%		41	Alaska	2	0.0%
18	Tennessee	176	3.2%		41	Oregon	2	0.0%
7	Texas	292	5.2%		43	Idaho	1	0.0%
43	Utah	1	0.0%		43	North Dakota	1	0.0%
47	Vermont	0	0.0%		43	South Dakota	1	0.0%
10	Virginia	238	4.3%		43	Utah	1	0.0%
30	Washington	27	0.5%		47	Montana	0	0.0%
36	West Virginia	8	0.1%		47	New Hampshire	0	0.0%
21	Wisconsin	67	1.2%		47	Vermont	0	0.0%
47	Wyoming	0	0.0%		47	Wyoming	0	0.0%
					District of Columbia	53	0.9%

Source: U.S. Department of Health and Human Services, National Center for Health Statistics
   "National Vital Statistics Reports" (Vol. 52, No. 3, September 18, 2003)
*Final data. Deaths of infants under 28 days, exclusive of fetal deaths. Based on race of the mother.

Black Neonatal Death Rate in 2001

National Rate = 9.2 Black Neonatal Deaths per 1,000 Black Live Births*

ALPHA ORDER

RANK	STATE	RATE
15	Alabama	9.6
NA	Alaska**	NA
1	Arizona	15.2
24	Arkansas	8.9
25	California	8.7
13	Colorado	9.8
3	Connecticut	12.3
2	Delaware	14.0
23	Florida	9.0
21	Georgia	9.1
NA	Hawaii**	NA
NA	Idaho**	NA
17	Illinois	9.5
26	Indiana	8.3
NA	Iowa**	NA
4	Kansas	12.2
32	Kentucky	5.3
17	Louisiana	9.5
NA	Maine**	NA
13	Maryland	9.8
29	Massachusetts	7.2
5	Michigan	11.3
33	Minnesota	4.8
15	Mississippi	9.6
5	Missouri	11.3
NA	Montana**	NA
NA	Nebraska**	NA
17	Nevada	9.5
NA	New Hampshire**	NA
21	New Jersey	9.1
NA	New Mexico**	NA
31	New York	6.5
5	North Carolina	11.3
NA	North Dakota**	NA
11	Ohio	10.3
28	Oklahoma	7.4
NA	Oregon**	NA
20	Pennsylvania	9.2
NA	Rhode Island**	NA
10	South Carolina	10.5
NA	South Dakota**	NA
9	Tennessee	10.6
29	Texas	7.2
NA	Utah**	NA
NA	Vermont**	NA
8	Virginia	10.7
27	Washington	8.1
NA	West Virginia**	NA
12	Wisconsin	10.2
NA	Wyoming**	NA

RANK ORDER

RANK	STATE	RATE
1	Arizona	15.2
2	Delaware	14.0
3	Connecticut	12.3
4	Kansas	12.2
5	Michigan	11.3
5	Missouri	11.3
5	North Carolina	11.3
8	Virginia	10.7
9	Tennessee	10.6
10	South Carolina	10.5
11	Ohio	10.3
12	Wisconsin	10.2
13	Colorado	9.8
13	Maryland	9.8
15	Alabama	9.6
15	Mississippi	9.6
17	Illinois	9.5
17	Louisiana	9.5
17	Nevada	9.5
20	Pennsylvania	9.2
21	Georgia	9.1
21	New Jersey	9.1
23	Florida	9.0
24	Arkansas	8.9
25	California	8.7
26	Indiana	8.3
27	Washington	8.1
28	Oklahoma	7.4
29	Massachusetts	7.2
29	Texas	7.2
31	New York	6.5
32	Kentucky	5.3
33	Minnesota	4.8
NA	Alaska**	NA
NA	Hawaii**	NA
NA	Idaho**	NA
NA	Iowa**	NA
NA	Maine**	NA
NA	Montana**	NA
NA	Nebraska**	NA
NA	New Hampshire**	NA
NA	New Mexico**	NA
NA	North Dakota**	NA
NA	Oregon**	NA
NA	Rhode Island**	NA
NA	South Dakota**	NA
NA	Utah**	NA
NA	Vermont**	NA
NA	West Virginia**	NA
NA	Wyoming**	NA
	District of Columbia	10.9

Source: U.S. Department of Health and Human Services, National Center for Health Statistics
"National Vital Statistics Reports" (Vol. 52, No. 3, September 18, 2003)
*Final data. Deaths of infants under 28 days, exclusive of fetal deaths. Based on race of the mother.
**Not available. Fewer than 20 black neonatal deaths.

Deaths by AIDS in 2001

National Total = 14,175 Deaths*

ALPHA ORDER					RANK ORDER			
RANK	STATE	DEATHS	% of USA		RANK	STATE	DEATHS	% of USA
17	Alabama	214	1.5%		1	New York	2,085	14.7%
45	Alaska	7	0.0%		2	Florida	1,664	11.7%
21	Arizona	156	1.1%		3	California	1,505	10.6%
31	Arkansas	64	0.5%		4	Texas	1,055	7.4%
3	California	1,505	10.6%		5	New Jersey	785	5.5%
26	Colorado	93	0.7%		6	Georgia	722	5.1%
20	Connecticut	193	1.4%		7	Maryland	572	4.0%
30	Delaware	67	0.5%		8	Illinois	518	3.7%
2	Florida	1,664	11.7%		9	Pennsylvania	496	3.5%
6	Georgia	722	5.1%		10	North Carolina	464	3.3%
39	Hawaii	26	0.2%		11	Louisiana	404	2.9%
42	Idaho	12	0.1%		12	South Carolina	310	2.2%
8	Illinois	518	3.7%		13	Tennessee	277	2.0%
23	Indiana	119	0.8%		14	Virginia	275	1.9%
40	Iowa	18	0.1%		15	Michigan	255	1.8%
34	Kansas	39	0.3%		16	Massachusetts	249	1.8%
27	Kentucky	90	0.6%		17	Alabama	214	1.5%
11	Louisiana	404	2.9%		18	Ohio	207	1.5%
41	Maine	14	0.1%		19	Mississippi	202	1.4%
7	Maryland	572	4.0%		20	Connecticut	193	1.4%
16	Massachusetts	249	1.8%		21	Arizona	156	1.1%
15	Michigan	255	1.8%		22	Missouri	147	1.0%
33	Minnesota	53	0.4%		23	Indiana	119	0.8%
19	Mississippi	202	1.4%		24	Washington	113	0.8%
22	Missouri	147	1.0%		25	Oklahoma	99	0.7%
46	Montana	5	0.0%		26	Colorado	93	0.7%
36	Nebraska	33	0.2%		27	Kentucky	90	0.6%
28	Nevada	76	0.5%		28	Nevada	76	0.5%
44	New Hampshire	9	0.1%		29	Wisconsin	73	0.5%
5	New Jersey	785	5.5%		30	Delaware	67	0.5%
34	New Mexico	39	0.3%		31	Arkansas	64	0.5%
1	New York	2,085	14.7%		32	Oregon	63	0.4%
10	North Carolina	464	3.3%		33	Minnesota	53	0.4%
47	North Dakota	4	0.0%		34	Kansas	39	0.3%
18	Ohio	207	1.5%		34	New Mexico	39	0.3%
25	Oklahoma	99	0.7%		36	Nebraska	33	0.2%
32	Oregon	63	0.4%		37	Rhode Island	30	0.2%
9	Pennsylvania	496	3.5%		38	West Virginia	29	0.2%
37	Rhode Island	30	0.2%		39	Hawaii	26	0.2%
12	South Carolina	310	2.2%		40	Iowa	18	0.1%
47	South Dakota	4	0.0%		41	Maine	14	0.1%
13	Tennessee	277	2.0%		42	Idaho	12	0.1%
4	Texas	1,055	7.4%		42	Utah	12	0.1%
42	Utah	12	0.1%		44	New Hampshire	9	0.1%
47	Vermont	4	0.0%		45	Alaska	7	0.0%
14	Virginia	275	1.9%		46	Montana	5	0.0%
24	Washington	113	0.8%		47	North Dakota	4	0.0%
38	West Virginia	29	0.2%		47	South Dakota	4	0.0%
29	Wisconsin	73	0.5%		47	Vermont	4	0.0%
50	Wyoming	2	0.0%		50	Wyoming	2	0.0%
						District of Columbia	223	1.6%

Source: U.S. Department of Health and Human Services, National Center for Health Statistics
    "National Vital Statistics Reports" (Vol. 52, No. 3, September 18, 2003)
*AIDS is Acquired Immunodeficiency Syndrome. It is a specific group of diseases or conditions which are indicative
of severe immunosuppression related to infection with the Human Immunodeficiency Virus (HIV).

Death Rate by AIDS in 2001

National Rate = 5.0 Deaths per 100,000 Population*

ALPHA ORDER

RANK	STATE	RATE
13	Alabama	4.8
NA	Alaska**	NA
21	Arizona	2.9
26	Arkansas	2.4
15	California	4.3
28	Colorado	2.1
11	Connecticut	5.6
7	Delaware	8.4
3	Florida	10.2
6	Georgia	8.6
28	Hawaii	2.1
NA	Idaho**	NA
16	Illinois	4.1
31	Indiana	1.9
NA	Iowa**	NA
37	Kansas	1.4
27	Kentucky	2.2
5	Louisiana	9.0
NA	Maine**	NA
2	Maryland	10.6
18	Massachusetts	3.9
25	Michigan	2.5
39	Minnesota	1.1
9	Mississippi	7.1
24	Missouri	2.6
NA	Montana**	NA
31	Nebraska	1.9
20	Nevada	3.6
NA	New Hampshire**	NA
4	New Jersey	9.2
28	New Mexico	2.1
1	New York	10.9
10	North Carolina	5.7
NA	North Dakota**	NA
34	Ohio	1.8
21	Oklahoma	2.9
34	Oregon	1.8
17	Pennsylvania	4.0
23	Rhode Island	2.8
8	South Carolina	7.6
NA	South Dakota**	NA
13	Tennessee	4.8
12	Texas	4.9
NA	Utah**	NA
NA	Vermont**	NA
19	Virginia	3.8
31	Washington	1.9
36	West Virginia	1.6
37	Wisconsin	1.4
NA	Wyoming**	NA

RANK ORDER

RANK	STATE	RATE
1	New York	10.9
2	Maryland	10.6
3	Florida	10.2
4	New Jersey	9.2
5	Louisiana	9.0
6	Georgia	8.6
7	Delaware	8.4
8	South Carolina	7.6
9	Mississippi	7.1
10	North Carolina	5.7
11	Connecticut	5.6
12	Texas	4.9
13	Alabama	4.8
13	Tennessee	4.8
15	California	4.3
16	Illinois	4.1
17	Pennsylvania	4.0
18	Massachusetts	3.9
19	Virginia	3.8
20	Nevada	3.6
21	Arizona	2.9
21	Oklahoma	2.9
23	Rhode Island	2.8
24	Missouri	2.6
25	Michigan	2.5
26	Arkansas	2.4
27	Kentucky	2.2
28	Colorado	2.1
28	Hawaii	2.1
28	New Mexico	2.1
31	Indiana	1.9
31	Nebraska	1.9
31	Washington	1.9
34	Ohio	1.8
34	Oregon	1.8
36	West Virginia	1.6
37	Kansas	1.4
37	Wisconsin	1.4
39	Minnesota	1.1
NA	Alaska**	NA
NA	Idaho**	NA
NA	Iowa**	NA
NA	Maine**	NA
NA	Montana**	NA
NA	New Hampshire**	NA
NA	North Dakota**	NA
NA	South Dakota**	NA
NA	Utah**	NA
NA	Vermont**	NA
NA	Wyoming**	NA

District of Columbia 38.9

Source: U.S. Department of Health and Human Services, National Center for Health Statistics
"National Vital Statistics Reports" (Vol. 52, No. 3, September 18, 2003)
*AIDS is Acquired Immunodeficiency Syndrome. It is a specific group of diseases or conditions which are indicative of severe immunosuppression related to infection with the Human Immunodeficiency Virus (HIV). Not age-adjusted.
**Insufficient data to determine a reliable rate.

Age-Adjusted Death Rate by AIDS in 2001

National Rate = 5.0 Deaths per 100,000 Population*

ALPHA ORDER

RANK	STATE	RATE
13	Alabama	4.9
NA	Alaska**	NA
21	Arizona	3.1
25	Arkansas	2.5
15	California	4.4
30	Colorado	2.0
11	Connecticut	5.4
7	Delaware	8.3
2	Florida	10.4
6	Georgia	8.5
29	Hawaii	2.1
NA	Idaho**	NA
16	Illinois	4.2
30	Indiana	2.0
NA	Iowa**	NA
37	Kansas	1.5
27	Kentucky	2.2
4	Louisiana	9.3
NA	Maine**	NA
3	Maryland	10.1
18	Massachusetts	3.7
25	Michigan	2.5
39	Minnesota	1.0
9	Mississippi	7.4
24	Missouri	2.7
NA	Montana**	NA
30	Nebraska	2.0
20	Nevada	3.6
NA	New Hampshire**	NA
5	New Jersey	8.9
27	New Mexico	2.2
1	New York	10.7
10	North Carolina	5.6
NA	North Dakota**	NA
33	Ohio	1.9
22	Oklahoma	2.9
33	Oregon	1.9
17	Pennsylvania	4.0
23	Rhode Island	2.8
8	South Carolina	7.6
NA	South Dakota**	NA
14	Tennessee	4.8
12	Texas	5.1
NA	Utah**	NA
NA	Vermont**	NA
18	Virginia	3.7
35	Washington	1.8
36	West Virginia	1.7
38	Wisconsin	1.3
NA	Wyoming**	NA

RANK ORDER

RANK	STATE	RATE
1	New York	10.7
2	Florida	10.4
3	Maryland	10.1
4	Louisiana	9.3
5	New Jersey	8.9
6	Georgia	8.5
7	Delaware	8.3
8	South Carolina	7.6
9	Mississippi	7.4
10	North Carolina	5.6
11	Connecticut	5.4
12	Texas	5.1
13	Alabama	4.9
14	Tennessee	4.8
15	California	4.4
16	Illinois	4.2
17	Pennsylvania	4.0
18	Massachusetts	3.7
18	Virginia	3.7
20	Nevada	3.6
21	Arizona	3.1
22	Oklahoma	2.9
23	Rhode Island	2.8
24	Missouri	2.7
25	Arkansas	2.5
25	Michigan	2.5
27	Kentucky	2.2
27	New Mexico	2.2
29	Hawaii	2.1
30	Colorado	2.0
30	Indiana	2.0
30	Nebraska	2.0
33	Ohio	1.9
33	Oregon	1.9
35	Washington	1.8
36	West Virginia	1.7
37	Kansas	1.5
38	Wisconsin	1.3
39	Minnesota	1.0
NA	Alaska**	NA
NA	Idaho**	NA
NA	Iowa**	NA
NA	Maine**	NA
NA	Montana**	NA
NA	New Hampshire**	NA
NA	North Dakota**	NA
NA	South Dakota**	NA
NA	Utah**	NA
NA	Vermont**	NA
NA	Wyoming**	NA

District of Columbia   38.1

Source: U.S. Department of Health and Human Services, National Center for Health Statistics
    "National Vital Statistics Reports" (Vol. 52, No. 3, September 18, 2003)
*AIDS is Acquired Immunodeficiency Syndrome. It is a specific group of diseases or conditions which are indicative of severe immunosuppression related to infection with the Human Immunodeficiency Virus (HIV). Age-adjusted rates based on the year 2000 standard population.
**Insufficient data to determine a reliable rate.

Estimated Deaths by Cancer in 2004

National Estimated Total = 563,700 Deaths

ALPHA ORDER

RANK	STATE	DEATHS	% of USA
20	Alabama	10,000	1.8%
50	Alaska	780	0.1%
21	Arizona	9,710	1.7%
32	Arkansas	6,100	1.1%
1	California	55,340	9.8%
30	Colorado	6,390	1.1%
28	Connecticut	7,010	1.2%
45	Delaware	1,810	0.3%
2	Florida	40,090	7.1%
11	Georgia	14,600	2.6%
43	Hawaii	2,090	0.4%
42	Idaho	2,250	0.4%
6	Illinois	24,840	4.4%
13	Indiana	13,250	2.4%
29	Iowa	6,570	1.2%
33	Kansas	5,330	0.9%
23	Kentucky	9,360	1.7%
22	Louisiana	9,700	1.7%
38	Maine	3,100	0.5%
19	Maryland	10,430	1.9%
12	Massachusetts	13,620	2.4%
8	Michigan	19,870	3.5%
23	Minnesota	9,360	1.7%
31	Mississippi	6,230	1.1%
16	Missouri	12,480	2.2%
44	Montana	2,060	0.4%
36	Nebraska	3,410	0.6%
35	Nevada	4,530	0.8%
40	New Hampshire	2,590	0.5%
9	New Jersey	18,060	3.2%
37	New Mexico	3,110	0.6%
3	New York	36,340	6.4%
10	North Carolina	16,580	2.9%
47	North Dakota	1,340	0.2%
7	Ohio	24,480	4.3%
26	Oklahoma	7,640	1.4%
27	Oregon	7,120	1.3%
5	Pennsylvania	29,910	5.3%
41	Rhode Island	2,450	0.4%
25	South Carolina	8,860	1.6%
46	South Dakota	1,650	0.3%
15	Tennessee	12,710	2.3%
4	Texas	34,830	6.2%
39	Utah	2,620	0.5%
48	Vermont	1,300	0.2%
14	Virginia	12,850	2.3%
17	Washington	11,280	2.0%
34	West Virginia	4,710	0.8%
18	Wisconsin	10,780	1.9%
49	Wyoming	1,000	0.2%

RANK ORDER

RANK	STATE	DEATHS	% of USA
1	California	55,340	9.8%
2	Florida	40,090	7.1%
3	New York	36,340	6.4%
4	Texas	34,830	6.2%
5	Pennsylvania	29,910	5.3%
6	Illinois	24,840	4.4%
7	Ohio	24,480	4.3%
8	Michigan	19,870	3.5%
9	New Jersey	18,060	3.2%
10	North Carolina	16,580	2.9%
11	Georgia	14,600	2.6%
12	Massachusetts	13,620	2.4%
13	Indiana	13,250	2.4%
14	Virginia	12,850	2.3%
15	Tennessee	12,710	2.3%
16	Missouri	12,480	2.2%
17	Washington	11,280	2.0%
18	Wisconsin	10,780	1.9%
19	Maryland	10,430	1.9%
20	Alabama	10,000	1.8%
21	Arizona	9,710	1.7%
22	Louisiana	9,700	1.7%
23	Kentucky	9,360	1.7%
23	Minnesota	9,360	1.7%
25	South Carolina	8,860	1.6%
26	Oklahoma	7,640	1.4%
27	Oregon	7,120	1.3%
28	Connecticut	7,010	1.2%
29	Iowa	6,570	1.2%
30	Colorado	6,390	1.1%
31	Mississippi	6,230	1.1%
32	Arkansas	6,100	1.1%
33	Kansas	5,330	0.9%
34	West Virginia	4,710	0.8%
35	Nevada	4,530	0.8%
36	Nebraska	3,410	0.6%
37	New Mexico	3,110	0.6%
38	Maine	3,100	0.5%
39	Utah	2,620	0.5%
40	New Hampshire	2,590	0.5%
41	Rhode Island	2,450	0.4%
42	Idaho	2,250	0.4%
43	Hawaii	2,090	0.4%
44	Montana	2,060	0.4%
45	Delaware	1,810	0.3%
46	South Dakota	1,650	0.3%
47	North Dakota	1,340	0.2%
48	Vermont	1,300	0.2%
49	Wyoming	1,000	0.2%
50	Alaska	780	0.1%
	District of Columbia	1,180	0.2%

Source: American Cancer Society
"Cancer Facts & Figures 2004" (Copyright 2004, Reprinted with permission from the American Cancer Society)

Estimated Death Rate by Cancer in 2004

National Estimated Rate = 193.8 Deaths per 100,000 Population*

ALPHA ORDER

RANK	STATE	RATE
10	Alabama	222.2
49	Alaska	120.2
40	Arizona	174.0
8	Arkansas	223.8
47	California	156.0
48	Colorado	140.4
26	Connecticut	201.2
11	Delaware	221.4
4	Florida	235.6
42	Georgia	168.1
43	Hawaii	166.2
45	Idaho	164.7
33	Illinois	196.3
19	Indiana	213.9
9	Iowa	223.2
35	Kansas	195.7
6	Kentucky	227.3
17	Louisiana	215.7
3	Maine	237.4
37	Maryland	189.3
21	Massachusetts	211.7
31	Michigan	197.1
38	Minnesota	185.0
15	Mississippi	216.2
12	Missouri	218.8
7	Montana	224.5
34	Nebraska	196.1
25	Nevada	202.1
27	New Hampshire	201.1
24	New Jersey	209.1
44	New Mexico	165.9
36	New York	189.4
30	North Carolina	197.2
22	North Dakota	211.4
18	Ohio	214.1
13	Oklahoma	217.6
28	Oregon	200.0
2	Pennsylvania	241.9
5	Rhode Island	227.7
20	South Carolina	213.6
16	South Dakota	215.9
13	Tennessee	217.6
46	Texas	157.5
50	Utah	111.4
23	Vermont	210.0
40	Virginia	174.0
39	Washington	184.0
1	West Virginia	260.2
32	Wisconsin	197.0
29	Wyoming	199.5

RANK ORDER

RANK	STATE	RATE
1	West Virginia	260.2
2	Pennsylvania	241.9
3	Maine	237.4
4	Florida	235.6
5	Rhode Island	227.7
6	Kentucky	227.3
7	Montana	224.5
8	Arkansas	223.8
9	Iowa	223.2
10	Alabama	222.2
11	Delaware	221.4
12	Missouri	218.8
13	Oklahoma	217.6
13	Tennessee	217.6
15	Mississippi	216.2
16	South Dakota	215.9
17	Louisiana	215.7
18	Ohio	214.1
19	Indiana	213.9
20	South Carolina	213.6
21	Massachusetts	211.7
22	North Dakota	211.4
23	Vermont	210.0
24	New Jersey	209.1
25	Nevada	202.1
26	Connecticut	201.2
27	New Hampshire	201.1
28	Oregon	200.0
29	Wyoming	199.5
30	North Carolina	197.2
31	Michigan	197.1
32	Wisconsin	197.0
33	Illinois	196.3
34	Nebraska	196.1
35	Kansas	195.7
36	New York	189.4
37	Maryland	189.3
38	Minnesota	185.0
39	Washington	184.0
40	Arizona	174.0
40	Virginia	174.0
42	Georgia	168.1
43	Hawaii	166.2
44	New Mexico	165.9
45	Idaho	164.7
46	Texas	157.5
47	California	156.0
48	Colorado	140.4
49	Alaska	120.2
50	Utah	111.4

District of Columbia   209.4

Source: Morgan Quitno Press using data from American Cancer Society
"Cancer Facts & Figures 2004" (Copyright 2004, Reprinted with permission from the American Cancer Society)
*Rates calculated using 2003 Census resident population estimates. Not age-adjusted.

Age-Adjusted Death Rate by Cancer for Males in 2000

National Rate = 255.5 Deaths per 100,000 Male Population*

ALPHA ORDER

RANK	STATE	RATE
4	Alabama	294.3
35	Alaska	241.9
46	Arizona	217.9
8	Arkansas	281.4
45	California	225.2
47	Colorado	216.0
36	Connecticut	240.8
13	Delaware	273.0
38	Florida	240.4
10	Georgia	276.4
49	Hawaii	197.5
44	Idaho	226.6
19	Illinois	267.2
11	Indiana	275.6
30	Iowa	245.1
37	Kansas	240.7
3	Kentucky	301.8
2	Louisiana	308.2
17	Maine	268.5
13	Maryland	273.0
22	Massachusetts	265.0
25	Michigan	259.9
40	Minnesota	237.7
1	Mississippi	309.2
21	Missouri	265.9
32	Montana	244.3
43	Nebraska	233.6
28	Nevada	254.2
23	New Hampshire	262.3
24	New Jersey	261.4
48	New Mexico	212.4
33	New York	244.2
9	North Carolina	277.9
41	North Dakota	236.1
12	Ohio	273.6
18	Oklahoma	267.8
31	Oregon	244.4
20	Pennsylvania	266.6
16	Rhode Island	271.1
7	South Carolina	283.6
34	South Dakota	243.7
5	Tennessee	290.3
26	Texas	257.3
50	Utah	188.4
27	Vermont	255.8
15	Virginia	271.8
39	Washington	238.8
6	West Virginia	286.3
29	Wisconsin	247.8
42	Wyoming	234.7

RANK ORDER

RANK	STATE	RATE
1	Mississippi	309.2
2	Louisiana	308.2
3	Kentucky	301.8
4	Alabama	294.3
5	Tennessee	290.3
6	West Virginia	286.3
7	South Carolina	283.6
8	Arkansas	281.4
9	North Carolina	277.9
10	Georgia	276.4
11	Indiana	275.6
12	Ohio	273.6
13	Delaware	273.0
13	Maryland	273.0
15	Virginia	271.8
16	Rhode Island	271.1
17	Maine	268.5
18	Oklahoma	267.8
19	Illinois	267.2
20	Pennsylvania	266.6
21	Missouri	265.9
22	Massachusetts	265.0
23	New Hampshire	262.3
24	New Jersey	261.4
25	Michigan	259.9
26	Texas	257.3
27	Vermont	255.8
28	Nevada	254.2
29	Wisconsin	247.8
30	Iowa	245.1
31	Oregon	244.4
32	Montana	244.3
33	New York	244.2
34	South Dakota	243.7
35	Alaska	241.9
36	Connecticut	240.8
37	Kansas	240.7
38	Florida	240.4
39	Washington	238.8
40	Minnesota	237.7
41	North Dakota	236.1
42	Wyoming	234.7
43	Nebraska	233.6
44	Idaho	226.6
45	California	225.2
46	Arizona	217.9
47	Colorado	216.0
48	New Mexico	212.4
49	Hawaii	197.5
50	Utah	188.4
	District of Columbia	318.1

Source: American Cancer Society
   "Cancer Facts & Figures 2004" (Copyright 2004, Reprinted with permission from the American Cancer Society)
*For 1996 to 2000. Age-adjusted to the 2000 U.S. standard population.

Age-Adjusted Death Rate by Cancer for Females in 2000

National Rate = 168.3 Deaths per 100,000 Female Population*

ALPHA ORDER

RANK	STATE	RATE
28	Alabama	167.5
12	Alaska	177.4
46	Arizona	150.5
26	Arkansas	168.4
37	California	160.7
48	Colorado	148.4
30	Connecticut	166.4
1	Delaware	187.8
39	Florida	159.5
33	Georgia	163.4
49	Hawaii	129.5
45	Idaho	152.0
13	Illinois	177.0
11	Indiana	178.2
41	Iowa	158.5
40	Kansas	158.6
4	Kentucky	182.1
3	Louisiana	184.8
5	Maine	181.8
10	Maryland	179.0
15	Massachusetts	176.0
17	Michigan	173.2
38	Minnesota	160.2
24	Mississippi	170.2
18	Missouri	172.7
36	Montana	161.0
43	Nebraska	154.5
7	Nevada	179.9
14	New Hampshire	176.7
6	New Jersey	181.7
47	New Mexico	149.1
23	New York	170.3
32	North Carolina	163.9
44	North Dakota	152.4
8	Ohio	179.6
27	Oklahoma	168.1
21	Oregon	171.4
16	Pennsylvania	175.2
9	Rhode Island	179.5
29	South Carolina	167.2
42	South Dakota	157.3
20	Tennessee	172.2
35	Texas	162.7
50	Utah	128.0
22	Vermont	170.9
19	Virginia	172.4
25	Washington	168.8
2	West Virginia	186.9
34	Wisconsin	162.8
31	Wyoming	165.5

RANK ORDER

RANK	STATE	RATE
1	Delaware	187.8
2	West Virginia	186.9
3	Louisiana	184.8
4	Kentucky	182.1
5	Maine	181.8
6	New Jersey	181.7
7	Nevada	179.9
8	Ohio	179.6
9	Rhode Island	179.5
10	Maryland	179.0
11	Indiana	178.2
12	Alaska	177.4
13	Illinois	177.0
14	New Hampshire	176.7
15	Massachusetts	176.0
16	Pennsylvania	175.2
17	Michigan	173.2
18	Missouri	172.7
19	Virginia	172.4
20	Tennessee	172.2
21	Oregon	171.4
22	Vermont	170.9
23	New York	170.3
24	Mississippi	170.2
25	Washington	168.8
26	Arkansas	168.4
27	Oklahoma	168.1
28	Alabama	167.5
29	South Carolina	167.2
30	Connecticut	166.4
31	Wyoming	165.5
32	North Carolina	163.9
33	Georgia	163.4
34	Wisconsin	162.8
35	Texas	162.7
36	Montana	161.0
37	California	160.7
38	Minnesota	160.2
39	Florida	159.5
40	Kansas	158.6
41	Iowa	158.5
42	South Dakota	157.3
43	Nebraska	154.5
44	North Dakota	152.4
45	Idaho	152.0
46	Arizona	150.5
47	New Mexico	149.1
48	Colorado	148.4
49	Hawaii	129.5
50	Utah	128.0
	District of Columbia	199.8

Source: American Cancer Society
"Cancer Facts & Figures 2004" (Copyright 2004, Reprinted with permission from the American Cancer Society)
*For 1996 to 2000. Age-adjusted to the 2000 U.S. standard population.

Estimated Deaths by Brain Cancer in 2004

National Estimated Total = 12,690 Deaths

ALPHA ORDER

RANK	STATE	DEATHS	% of USA
22	Alabama	200	1.6%
NA	Alaska*	NA	NA
20	Arizona	240	1.9%
26	Arkansas	160	1.3%
1	California	1,440	11.3%
25	Colorado	180	1.4%
32	Connecticut	150	1.2%
NA	Delaware*	NA	NA
2	Florida	980	7.7%
17	Georgia	260	2.0%
NA	Hawaii*	NA	NA
39	Idaho	70	0.6%
7	Illinois	490	3.9%
14	Indiana	280	2.2%
26	Iowa	160	1.3%
33	Kansas	120	0.9%
26	Kentucky	160	1.3%
24	Louisiana	190	1.5%
36	Maine	80	0.6%
21	Maryland	210	1.7%
14	Massachusetts	280	2.2%
8	Michigan	450	3.5%
19	Minnesota	250	2.0%
26	Mississippi	160	1.3%
16	Missouri	270	2.1%
NA	Montana*	NA	NA
34	Nebraska	90	0.7%
36	Nevada	80	0.6%
39	New Hampshire	70	0.6%
10	New Jersey	320	2.5%
39	New Mexico	70	0.6%
4	New York	690	5.4%
10	North Carolina	320	2.5%
42	North Dakota	40	0.3%
6	Ohio	520	4.1%
26	Oklahoma	160	1.3%
26	Oregon	160	1.3%
5	Pennsylvania	570	4.5%
NA	Rhode Island*	NA	NA
22	South Carolina	200	1.6%
NA	South Dakota*	NA	NA
12	Tennessee	300	2.4%
3	Texas	940	7.4%
36	Utah	80	0.6%
NA	Vermont*	NA	NA
13	Virginia	290	2.3%
9	Washington	340	2.7%
34	West Virginia	90	0.7%
17	Wisconsin	260	2.0%
NA	Wyoming*	NA	NA

RANK ORDER

RANK	STATE	DEATHS	% of USA
1	California	1,440	11.3%
2	Florida	980	7.7%
3	Texas	940	7.4%
4	New York	690	5.4%
5	Pennsylvania	570	4.5%
6	Ohio	520	4.1%
7	Illinois	490	3.9%
8	Michigan	450	3.5%
9	Washington	340	2.7%
10	New Jersey	320	2.5%
10	North Carolina	320	2.5%
12	Tennessee	300	2.4%
13	Virginia	290	2.3%
14	Indiana	280	2.2%
14	Massachusetts	280	2.2%
16	Missouri	270	2.1%
17	Georgia	260	2.0%
17	Wisconsin	260	2.0%
19	Minnesota	250	2.0%
20	Arizona	240	1.9%
21	Maryland	210	1.7%
22	Alabama	200	1.6%
22	South Carolina	200	1.6%
24	Louisiana	190	1.5%
25	Colorado	180	1.4%
26	Arkansas	160	1.3%
26	Iowa	160	1.3%
26	Kentucky	160	1.3%
26	Mississippi	160	1.3%
26	Oklahoma	160	1.3%
26	Oregon	160	1.3%
32	Connecticut	150	1.2%
33	Kansas	120	0.9%
34	Nebraska	90	0.7%
34	West Virginia	90	0.7%
36	Maine	80	0.6%
36	Nevada	80	0.6%
36	Utah	80	0.6%
39	Idaho	70	0.6%
39	New Hampshire	70	0.6%
39	New Mexico	70	0.6%
42	North Dakota	40	0.3%
NA	Alaska*	NA	NA
NA	Delaware*	NA	NA
NA	Hawaii*	NA	NA
NA	Montana*	NA	NA
NA	Rhode Island*	NA	NA
NA	South Dakota*	NA	NA
NA	Vermont*	NA	NA
NA	Wyoming*	NA	NA
	District of Columbia*	NA	NA

Source: American Cancer Society
    "Cancer Facts & Figures 2004" (Copyright 2004, Reprinted with permission from the American Cancer Society)
*Fewer than 50 deaths.

Estimated Death Rate by Brain Cancer in 2004

National Estimated Rate = 4.4 Deaths per 100,000 Population*

ALPHA ORDER

RANK	STATE	RATE
23	Alabama	4.4
NA	Alaska**	NA
26	Arizona	4.3
3	Arkansas	5.9
30	California	4.1
31	Colorado	4.0
26	Connecticut	4.3
NA	Delaware**	NA
4	Florida	5.8
42	Georgia	3.0
NA	Hawaii**	NA
10	Idaho	5.1
32	Illinois	3.9
19	Indiana	4.5
7	Iowa	5.4
23	Kansas	4.4
32	Kentucky	3.9
28	Louisiana	4.2
2	Maine	6.1
35	Maryland	3.8
23	Massachusetts	4.4
19	Michigan	4.5
13	Minnesota	4.9
5	Mississippi	5.6
16	Missouri	4.7
NA	Montana**	NA
9	Nebraska	5.2
39	Nevada	3.6
7	New Hampshire	5.4
37	New Jersey	3.7
37	New Mexico	3.7
39	New York	3.6
35	North Carolina	3.8
1	North Dakota	6.3
19	Ohio	4.5
17	Oklahoma	4.6
19	Oregon	4.5
17	Pennsylvania	4.6
NA	Rhode Island**	NA
14	South Carolina	4.8
NA	South Dakota**	NA
10	Tennessee	5.1
28	Texas	4.2
41	Utah	3.4
NA	Vermont**	NA
32	Virginia	3.9
6	Washington	5.5
12	West Virginia	5.0
14	Wisconsin	4.8
NA	Wyoming**	NA

RANK ORDER

RANK	STATE	RATE
1	North Dakota	6.3
2	Maine	6.1
3	Arkansas	5.9
4	Florida	5.8
5	Mississippi	5.6
6	Washington	5.5
7	Iowa	5.4
7	New Hampshire	5.4
9	Nebraska	5.2
10	Idaho	5.1
10	Tennessee	5.1
12	West Virginia	5.0
13	Minnesota	4.9
14	South Carolina	4.8
14	Wisconsin	4.8
16	Missouri	4.7
17	Oklahoma	4.6
17	Pennsylvania	4.6
19	Indiana	4.5
19	Michigan	4.5
19	Ohio	4.5
19	Oregon	4.5
23	Alabama	4.4
23	Kansas	4.4
23	Massachusetts	4.4
26	Arizona	4.3
26	Connecticut	4.3
28	Louisiana	4.2
28	Texas	4.2
30	California	4.1
31	Colorado	4.0
32	Illinois	3.9
32	Kentucky	3.9
32	Virginia	3.9
35	Maryland	3.8
35	North Carolina	3.8
37	New Jersey	3.7
37	New Mexico	3.7
39	Nevada	3.6
39	New York	3.6
41	Utah	3.4
42	Georgia	3.0
NA	Alaska**	NA
NA	Delaware**	NA
NA	Hawaii**	NA
NA	Montana**	NA
NA	Rhode Island**	NA
NA	South Dakota**	NA
NA	Vermont**	NA
NA	Wyoming**	NA

District of Columbia**   NA

Source: Morgan Quitno Press using data from American Cancer Society
   "Cancer Facts & Figures 2004" (Copyright 2004, Reprinted with permission from the American Cancer Society)
Rates calculated using 2003 Census resident population estimates. Not age-adjusted.
**Fewer than 50 deaths.*

Estimated Deaths by Female Breast Cancer in 2004

National Estimated Total = 40,110 Deaths

ALPHA ORDER

RANK	STATE	DEATHS	% of USA
20	Alabama	740	1.8%
NA	Alaska*	NA	NA
20	Arizona	740	1.8%
32	Arkansas	380	0.9%
1	California	4,060	10.1%
29	Colorado	480	1.2%
27	Connecticut	530	1.3%
44	Delaware	130	0.3%
3	Florida	2,480	6.2%
11	Georgia	1,130	2.8%
43	Hawaii	140	0.3%
39	Idaho	170	0.4%
7	Illinois	1,790	4.5%
14	Indiana	890	2.2%
31	Iowa	430	1.1%
33	Kansas	350	0.9%
24	Kentucky	620	1.5%
22	Louisiana	730	1.8%
39	Maine	170	0.4%
17	Maryland	760	1.9%
13	Massachusetts	960	2.4%
9	Michigan	1,350	3.4%
23	Minnesota	670	1.7%
30	Mississippi	460	1.1%
15	Missouri	870	2.2%
45	Montana	110	0.3%
36	Nebraska	240	0.6%
34	Nevada	300	0.7%
39	New Hampshire	170	0.4%
8	New Jersey	1,480	3.7%
38	New Mexico	190	0.5%
2	New York	2,820	7.0%
12	North Carolina	1,090	2.7%
47	North Dakota	100	0.2%
6	Ohio	1,870	4.7%
26	Oklahoma	540	1.3%
28	Oregon	510	1.3%
5	Pennsylvania	2,080	5.2%
42	Rhode Island	160	0.4%
25	South Carolina	610	1.5%
47	South Dakota	100	0.2%
16	Tennessee	800	2.0%
4	Texas	2,410	6.0%
37	Utah	200	0.5%
45	Vermont	110	0.3%
10	Virginia	1,180	2.9%
18	Washington	750	1.9%
34	West Virginia	300	0.7%
18	Wisconsin	750	1.9%
NA	Wyoming*	NA	NA

RANK ORDER

RANK	STATE	DEATHS	% of USA
1	California	4,060	10.1%
2	New York	2,820	7.0%
3	Florida	2,480	6.2%
4	Texas	2,410	6.0%
5	Pennsylvania	2,080	5.2%
6	Ohio	1,870	4.7%
7	Illinois	1,790	4.5%
8	New Jersey	1,480	3.7%
9	Michigan	1,350	3.4%
10	Virginia	1,180	2.9%
11	Georgia	1,130	2.8%
12	North Carolina	1,090	2.7%
13	Massachusetts	960	2.4%
14	Indiana	890	2.2%
15	Missouri	870	2.2%
16	Tennessee	800	2.0%
17	Maryland	760	1.9%
18	Washington	750	1.9%
18	Wisconsin	750	1.9%
20	Alabama	740	1.8%
20	Arizona	740	1.8%
22	Louisiana	730	1.8%
23	Minnesota	670	1.7%
24	Kentucky	620	1.5%
25	South Carolina	610	1.5%
26	Oklahoma	540	1.3%
27	Connecticut	530	1.3%
28	Oregon	510	1.3%
29	Colorado	480	1.2%
30	Mississippi	460	1.1%
31	Iowa	430	1.1%
32	Arkansas	380	0.9%
33	Kansas	350	0.9%
34	Nevada	300	0.7%
34	West Virginia	300	0.7%
36	Nebraska	240	0.6%
37	Utah	200	0.5%
38	New Mexico	190	0.5%
39	Idaho	170	0.4%
39	Maine	170	0.4%
39	New Hampshire	170	0.4%
42	Rhode Island	160	0.4%
43	Hawaii	140	0.3%
44	Delaware	130	0.3%
45	Montana	110	0.3%
45	Vermont	110	0.3%
47	North Dakota	100	0.2%
47	South Dakota	100	0.2%
NA	Alaska*	NA	NA
NA	Wyoming*	NA	NA
	District of Columbia	110	0.3%

Source: American Cancer Society
    "Cancer Facts & Figures 2004" (Copyright 2004, Reprinted with permission from the American Cancer Society)
*Not available.

Age-Adjusted Death Rate by Female Breast Cancer in 2000

National Rate = 27.7 Deaths per 100,000 Female Population*

ALPHA ORDER

RANK	STATE	RATE
30	Alabama	26.5
44	Alaska	25.2
44	Arizona	25.2
42	Arkansas	25.4
30	California	26.5
48	Colorado	24.0
16	Connecticut	27.8
2	Delaware	31.2
40	Florida	25.6
23	Georgia	27.1
50	Hawaii	20.0
27	Idaho	26.6
3	Illinois	30.3
13	Indiana	28.4
30	Iowa	26.5
37	Kansas	26.2
19	Kentucky	27.3
4	Louisiana	30.2
34	Maine	26.4
7	Maryland	29.6
10	Massachusetts	28.7
13	Michigan	28.4
26	Minnesota	26.7
11	Mississippi	28.6
21	Missouri	27.2
47	Montana	24.9
40	Nebraska	25.6
34	Nevada	26.4
15	New Hampshire	28.1
1	New Jersey	31.3
42	New Mexico	25.4
5	New York	30.0
24	North Carolina	27.0
27	North Dakota	26.6
6	Ohio	29.8
25	Oklahoma	26.8
27	Oregon	26.6
7	Pennsylvania	29.6
9	Rhode Island	29.3
16	South Carolina	27.8
46	South Dakota	25.0
19	Tennessee	27.3
38	Texas	26.1
49	Utah	23.7
21	Vermont	27.2
11	Virginia	28.6
39	Washington	25.8
16	West Virginia	27.8
30	Wisconsin	26.5
36	Wyoming	26.3

RANK ORDER

RANK	STATE	RATE
1	New Jersey	31.3
2	Delaware	31.2
3	Illinois	30.3
4	Louisiana	30.2
5	New York	30.0
6	Ohio	29.8
7	Maryland	29.6
7	Pennsylvania	29.6
9	Rhode Island	29.3
10	Massachusetts	28.7
11	Mississippi	28.6
11	Virginia	28.6
13	Indiana	28.4
13	Michigan	28.4
15	New Hampshire	28.1
16	Connecticut	27.8
16	South Carolina	27.8
16	West Virginia	27.8
19	Kentucky	27.3
19	Tennessee	27.3
21	Missouri	27.2
21	Vermont	27.2
23	Georgia	27.1
24	North Carolina	27.0
25	Oklahoma	26.8
26	Minnesota	26.7
27	Idaho	26.6
27	North Dakota	26.6
27	Oregon	26.6
30	Alabama	26.5
30	California	26.5
30	Iowa	26.5
30	Wisconsin	26.5
34	Maine	26.4
34	Nevada	26.4
36	Wyoming	26.3
37	Kansas	26.2
38	Texas	26.1
39	Washington	25.8
40	Florida	25.6
40	Nebraska	25.6
42	Arkansas	25.4
42	New Mexico	25.4
44	Alaska	25.2
44	Arizona	25.2
46	South Dakota	25.0
47	Montana	24.9
48	Colorado	24.0
49	Utah	23.7
50	Hawaii	20.0

| | District of Columbia | 37.6 |

Source: American Cancer Society
"Cancer Facts & Figures 2004" (Copyright 2004, Reprinted with permission from the American Cancer Society)
*For 1996 to 2000. Age-adjusted to the 2000 U.S. standard population.

Estimated Deaths by Colon and Rectum Cancer in 2004

National Estimated Total = 56,730 Deaths

ALPHA ORDER

RANK	STATE	DEATHS	% of USA
22	Alabama	900	1.6%
50	Alaska	80	0.1%
21	Arizona	960	1.7%
30	Arkansas	630	1.1%
1	California	5,360	9.4%
31	Colorado	620	1.1%
29	Connecticut	660	1.2%
46	Delaware	160	0.3%
2	Florida	3,840	6.8%
15	Georgia	1,320	2.3%
43	Hawaii	200	0.4%
42	Idaho	210	0.4%
7	Illinois	2,580	4.5%
12	Indiana	1,360	2.4%
27	Iowa	710	1.3%
33	Kansas	570	1.0%
23	Kentucky	890	1.6%
20	Louisiana	990	1.7%
38	Maine	310	0.5%
18	Maryland	1,090	1.9%
12	Massachusetts	1,360	2.4%
8	Michigan	1,900	3.3%
25	Minnesota	850	1.5%
31	Mississippi	620	1.1%
16	Missouri	1,250	2.2%
45	Montana	180	0.3%
36	Nebraska	390	0.7%
35	Nevada	480	0.8%
39	New Hampshire	260	0.5%
9	New Jersey	1,840	3.2%
37	New Mexico	320	0.6%
3	New York	3,820	6.7%
10	North Carolina	1,590	2.8%
47	North Dakota	140	0.2%
6	Ohio	2,610	4.6%
26	Oklahoma	800	1.4%
28	Oregon	690	1.2%
5	Pennsylvania	3,310	5.8%
41	Rhode Island	250	0.4%
24	South Carolina	880	1.6%
44	South Dakota	190	0.3%
14	Tennessee	1,340	2.4%
4	Texas	3,560	6.3%
39	Utah	260	0.5%
48	Vermont	130	0.2%
11	Virginia	1,370	2.4%
19	Washington	1,050	1.9%
34	West Virginia	490	0.9%
17	Wisconsin	1,120	2.0%
49	Wyoming	110	0.2%

RANK ORDER

RANK	STATE	DEATHS	% of USA
1	California	5,360	9.4%
2	Florida	3,840	6.8%
3	New York	3,820	6.7%
4	Texas	3,560	6.3%
5	Pennsylvania	3,310	5.8%
6	Ohio	2,610	4.6%
7	Illinois	2,580	4.5%
8	Michigan	1,900	3.3%
9	New Jersey	1,840	3.2%
10	North Carolina	1,590	2.8%
11	Virginia	1,370	2.4%
12	Indiana	1,360	2.4%
12	Massachusetts	1,360	2.4%
14	Tennessee	1,340	2.4%
15	Georgia	1,320	2.3%
16	Missouri	1,250	2.2%
17	Wisconsin	1,120	2.0%
18	Maryland	1,090	1.9%
19	Washington	1,050	1.9%
20	Louisiana	990	1.7%
21	Arizona	960	1.7%
22	Alabama	900	1.6%
23	Kentucky	890	1.6%
24	South Carolina	880	1.6%
25	Minnesota	850	1.5%
26	Oklahoma	800	1.4%
27	Iowa	710	1.3%
28	Oregon	690	1.2%
29	Connecticut	660	1.2%
30	Arkansas	630	1.1%
31	Colorado	620	1.1%
31	Mississippi	620	1.1%
33	Kansas	570	1.0%
34	West Virginia	490	0.9%
35	Nevada	480	0.8%
36	Nebraska	390	0.7%
37	New Mexico	320	0.6%
38	Maine	310	0.5%
39	New Hampshire	260	0.5%
39	Utah	260	0.5%
41	Rhode Island	250	0.4%
42	Idaho	210	0.4%
43	Hawaii	200	0.4%
44	South Dakota	190	0.3%
45	Montana	180	0.3%
46	Delaware	160	0.3%
47	North Dakota	140	0.2%
48	Vermont	130	0.2%
49	Wyoming	110	0.2%
50	Alaska	80	0.1%
	District of Columbia	130	0.2%

Source: American Cancer Society
"Cancer Facts & Figures 2004" (Copyright 2004, Reprinted with permission from the American Cancer Society)

Estimated Death Rate by Colon and Rectum Cancer in 2004

National Estimated Rate = 19.5 Deaths per 100,000 Population*

<table>
<tr><td colspan="3">ALPHA ORDER</td><td colspan="3">RANK ORDER</td></tr>
<tr><th>RANK</th><th>STATE</th><th>RATE</th><th>RANK</th><th>STATE</th><th>RATE</th></tr>
<tr><td>29</td><td>Alabama</td><td>20.0</td><td>1</td><td>West Virginia</td><td>27.1</td></tr>
<tr><td>49</td><td>Alaska</td><td>12.3</td><td>2</td><td>Pennsylvania</td><td>26.8</td></tr>
<tr><td>39</td><td>Arizona</td><td>17.2</td><td>3</td><td>South Dakota</td><td>24.9</td></tr>
<tr><td>7</td><td>Arkansas</td><td>23.1</td><td>4</td><td>Iowa</td><td>24.1</td></tr>
<tr><td>47</td><td>California</td><td>15.1</td><td>5</td><td>Maine</td><td>23.7</td></tr>
<tr><td>48</td><td>Colorado</td><td>13.6</td><td>6</td><td>Rhode Island</td><td>23.2</td></tr>
<tr><td>35</td><td>Connecticut</td><td>18.9</td><td>7</td><td>Arkansas</td><td>23.1</td></tr>
<tr><td>32</td><td>Delaware</td><td>19.6</td><td>8</td><td>Tennessee</td><td>22.9</td></tr>
<tr><td>11</td><td>Florida</td><td>22.6</td><td>9</td><td>Ohio</td><td>22.8</td></tr>
<tr><td>46</td><td>Georgia</td><td>15.2</td><td>9</td><td>Oklahoma</td><td>22.8</td></tr>
<tr><td>44</td><td>Hawaii</td><td>15.9</td><td>11</td><td>Florida</td><td>22.6</td></tr>
<tr><td>45</td><td>Idaho</td><td>15.4</td><td>12</td><td>Nebraska</td><td>22.4</td></tr>
<tr><td>27</td><td>Illinois</td><td>20.4</td><td>13</td><td>North Dakota</td><td>22.1</td></tr>
<tr><td>14</td><td>Indiana</td><td>22.0</td><td>14</td><td>Indiana</td><td>22.0</td></tr>
<tr><td>4</td><td>Iowa</td><td>24.1</td><td>14</td><td>Louisiana</td><td>22.0</td></tr>
<tr><td>25</td><td>Kansas</td><td>20.9</td><td>16</td><td>Missouri</td><td>21.9</td></tr>
<tr><td>18</td><td>Kentucky</td><td>21.6</td><td>16</td><td>Wyoming</td><td>21.9</td></tr>
<tr><td>14</td><td>Louisiana</td><td>22.0</td><td>18</td><td>Kentucky</td><td>21.6</td></tr>
<tr><td>5</td><td>Maine</td><td>23.7</td><td>19</td><td>Mississippi</td><td>21.5</td></tr>
<tr><td>31</td><td>Maryland</td><td>19.8</td><td>20</td><td>Nevada</td><td>21.4</td></tr>
<tr><td>23</td><td>Massachusetts</td><td>21.1</td><td>21</td><td>New Jersey</td><td>21.3</td></tr>
<tr><td>37</td><td>Michigan</td><td>18.8</td><td>22</td><td>South Carolina</td><td>21.2</td></tr>
<tr><td>42</td><td>Minnesota</td><td>16.8</td><td>23</td><td>Massachusetts</td><td>21.1</td></tr>
<tr><td>19</td><td>Mississippi</td><td>21.5</td><td>24</td><td>Vermont</td><td>21.0</td></tr>
<tr><td>16</td><td>Missouri</td><td>21.9</td><td>25</td><td>Kansas</td><td>20.9</td></tr>
<tr><td>32</td><td>Montana</td><td>19.6</td><td>26</td><td>Wisconsin</td><td>20.5</td></tr>
<tr><td>12</td><td>Nebraska</td><td>22.4</td><td>27</td><td>Illinois</td><td>20.4</td></tr>
<tr><td>20</td><td>Nevada</td><td>21.4</td><td>28</td><td>New Hampshire</td><td>20.2</td></tr>
<tr><td>28</td><td>New Hampshire</td><td>20.2</td><td>29</td><td>Alabama</td><td>20.0</td></tr>
<tr><td>21</td><td>New Jersey</td><td>21.3</td><td>30</td><td>New York</td><td>19.9</td></tr>
<tr><td>40</td><td>New Mexico</td><td>17.1</td><td>31</td><td>Maryland</td><td>19.8</td></tr>
<tr><td>30</td><td>New York</td><td>19.9</td><td>32</td><td>Delaware</td><td>19.6</td></tr>
<tr><td>35</td><td>North Carolina</td><td>18.9</td><td>32</td><td>Montana</td><td>19.6</td></tr>
<tr><td>13</td><td>North Dakota</td><td>22.1</td><td>34</td><td>Oregon</td><td>19.4</td></tr>
<tr><td>9</td><td>Ohio</td><td>22.8</td><td>35</td><td>Connecticut</td><td>18.9</td></tr>
<tr><td>9</td><td>Oklahoma</td><td>22.8</td><td>35</td><td>North Carolina</td><td>18.9</td></tr>
<tr><td>34</td><td>Oregon</td><td>19.4</td><td>37</td><td>Michigan</td><td>18.8</td></tr>
<tr><td>2</td><td>Pennsylvania</td><td>26.8</td><td>38</td><td>Virginia</td><td>18.5</td></tr>
<tr><td>6</td><td>Rhode Island</td><td>23.2</td><td>39</td><td>Arizona</td><td>17.2</td></tr>
<tr><td>22</td><td>South Carolina</td><td>21.2</td><td>40</td><td>New Mexico</td><td>17.1</td></tr>
<tr><td>3</td><td>South Dakota</td><td>24.9</td><td>40</td><td>Washington</td><td>17.1</td></tr>
<tr><td>8</td><td>Tennessee</td><td>22.9</td><td>42</td><td>Minnesota</td><td>16.8</td></tr>
<tr><td>43</td><td>Texas</td><td>16.1</td><td>43</td><td>Texas</td><td>16.1</td></tr>
<tr><td>50</td><td>Utah</td><td>11.1</td><td>44</td><td>Hawaii</td><td>15.9</td></tr>
<tr><td>24</td><td>Vermont</td><td>21.0</td><td>45</td><td>Idaho</td><td>15.4</td></tr>
<tr><td>38</td><td>Virginia</td><td>18.5</td><td>46</td><td>Georgia</td><td>15.2</td></tr>
<tr><td>40</td><td>Washington</td><td>17.1</td><td>47</td><td>California</td><td>15.1</td></tr>
<tr><td>1</td><td>West Virginia</td><td>27.1</td><td>48</td><td>Colorado</td><td>13.6</td></tr>
<tr><td>26</td><td>Wisconsin</td><td>20.5</td><td>49</td><td>Alaska</td><td>12.3</td></tr>
<tr><td>16</td><td>Wyoming</td><td>21.9</td><td>50</td><td>Utah</td><td>11.1</td></tr>
<tr><td></td><td></td><td></td><td></td><td>District of Columbia</td><td>23.1</td></tr>
</table>

Source: Morgan Quitno Press using data from American Cancer Society
    "Cancer Facts & Figures 2004" (Copyright 2004, Reprinted with permission from the American Cancer Society)
Rates calculated using 2003 Census resident population estimates. Not age-adjusted.

Estimated Deaths by Leukemia in 2004

National Estimated Total = 23,300 Deaths

RANK	STATE	DEATHS	% of USA
23	Alabama	370	1.6%
NA	Alaska*	NA	NA
21	Arizona	410	1.8%
31	Arkansas	260	1.1%
1	California	2,260	9.7%
27	Colorado	310	1.3%
29	Connecticut	280	1.2%
44	Delaware	80	0.3%
2	Florida	1,740	7.5%
11	Georgia	550	2.4%
44	Hawaii	80	0.3%
39	Idaho	100	0.4%
6	Illinois	1,080	4.6%
11	Indiana	550	2.4%
26	Iowa	320	1.4%
32	Kansas	240	1.0%
25	Kentucky	330	1.4%
22	Louisiana	380	1.6%
39	Maine	100	0.4%
19	Maryland	450	1.9%
14	Massachusetts	530	2.3%
8	Michigan	840	3.6%
20	Minnesota	440	1.9%
33	Mississippi	210	0.9%
13	Missouri	540	2.3%
39	Montana	100	0.4%
36	Nebraska	160	0.7%
35	Nevada	180	0.8%
39	New Hampshire	100	0.4%
9	New Jersey	720	3.1%
38	New Mexico	120	0.5%
4	New York	1,470	6.3%
10	North Carolina	650	2.8%
47	North Dakota	70	0.3%
7	Ohio	1,010	4.3%
27	Oklahoma	310	1.3%
29	Oregon	280	1.2%
5	Pennsylvania	1,130	4.8%
43	Rhode Island	90	0.4%
24	South Carolina	340	1.5%
44	South Dakota	80	0.3%
17	Tennessee	510	2.2%
3	Texas	1,490	6.4%
37	Utah	150	0.6%
48	Vermont	50	0.2%
14	Virginia	530	2.3%
18	Washington	500	2.1%
34	West Virginia	190	0.8%
16	Wisconsin	520	2.2%
NA	Wyoming*	NA	NA

RANK	STATE	DEATHS	% of USA
1	California	2,260	9.7%
2	Florida	1,740	7.5%
3	Texas	1,490	6.4%
4	New York	1,470	6.3%
5	Pennsylvania	1,130	4.8%
6	Illinois	1,080	4.6%
7	Ohio	1,010	4.3%
8	Michigan	840	3.6%
9	New Jersey	720	3.1%
10	North Carolina	650	2.8%
11	Georgia	550	2.4%
11	Indiana	550	2.4%
13	Missouri	540	2.3%
14	Massachusetts	530	2.3%
14	Virginia	530	2.3%
16	Wisconsin	520	2.2%
17	Tennessee	510	2.2%
18	Washington	500	2.1%
19	Maryland	450	1.9%
20	Minnesota	440	1.9%
21	Arizona	410	1.8%
22	Louisiana	380	1.6%
23	Alabama	370	1.6%
24	South Carolina	340	1.5%
25	Kentucky	330	1.4%
26	Iowa	320	1.4%
27	Colorado	310	1.3%
27	Oklahoma	310	1.3%
29	Connecticut	280	1.2%
29	Oregon	280	1.2%
31	Arkansas	260	1.1%
32	Kansas	240	1.0%
33	Mississippi	210	0.9%
34	West Virginia	190	0.8%
35	Nevada	180	0.8%
36	Nebraska	160	0.7%
37	Utah	150	0.6%
38	New Mexico	120	0.5%
39	Idaho	100	0.4%
39	Maine	100	0.4%
39	Montana	100	0.4%
39	New Hampshire	100	0.4%
43	Rhode Island	90	0.4%
44	Delaware	80	0.3%
44	Hawaii	80	0.3%
44	South Dakota	80	0.3%
47	North Dakota	70	0.3%
48	Vermont	50	0.2%
NA	Alaska*	NA	NA
NA	Wyoming*	NA	NA
	District of Columbia*	NA	NA

Source: American Cancer Society
"Cancer Facts & Figures 2004" (Copyright 2004, Reprinted with permission from the American Cancer Society)
*Fewer than 50 deaths.

Estimated Death Rate by Leukemia in 2004

National Estimated Rate = 8.0 Deaths per 100,000 Population*

ALPHA ORDER

RANK	STATE	RATE
24	Alabama	8.2
NA	Alaska**	NA
38	Arizona	7.3
8	Arkansas	9.5
44	California	6.4
42	Colorado	6.8
30	Connecticut	8.0
7	Delaware	9.8
6	Florida	10.2
48	Georgia	6.3
44	Hawaii	6.4
38	Idaho	7.3
19	Illinois	8.5
13	Indiana	8.9
2	Iowa	10.9
14	Kansas	8.8
30	Kentucky	8.0
19	Louisiana	8.5
35	Maine	7.7
24	Maryland	8.2
24	Massachusetts	8.2
22	Michigan	8.3
17	Minnesota	8.7
38	Mississippi	7.3
8	Missouri	9.5
2	Montana	10.9
11	Nebraska	9.2
30	Nevada	8.0
34	New Hampshire	7.8
22	New Jersey	8.3
44	New Mexico	6.4
35	New York	7.7
35	North Carolina	7.7
1	North Dakota	11.0
14	Ohio	8.8
14	Oklahoma	8.8
33	Oregon	7.9
12	Pennsylvania	9.1
21	Rhode Island	8.4
24	South Carolina	8.2
4	South Dakota	10.5
17	Tennessee	8.7
43	Texas	6.7
44	Utah	6.4
29	Vermont	8.1
41	Virginia	7.2
24	Washington	8.2
4	West Virginia	10.5
8	Wisconsin	9.5
NA	Wyoming**	NA

RANK ORDER

RANK	STATE	RATE
1	North Dakota	11.0
2	Iowa	10.9
2	Montana	10.9
4	South Dakota	10.5
4	West Virginia	10.5
6	Florida	10.2
7	Delaware	9.8
8	Arkansas	9.5
8	Missouri	9.5
8	Wisconsin	9.5
11	Nebraska	9.2
12	Pennsylvania	9.1
13	Indiana	8.9
14	Kansas	8.8
14	Ohio	8.8
14	Oklahoma	8.8
17	Minnesota	8.7
17	Tennessee	8.7
19	Illinois	8.5
19	Louisiana	8.5
21	Rhode Island	8.4
22	Michigan	8.3
22	New Jersey	8.3
24	Alabama	8.2
24	Maryland	8.2
24	Massachusetts	8.2
24	South Carolina	8.2
24	Washington	8.2
29	Vermont	8.1
30	Connecticut	8.0
30	Kentucky	8.0
30	Nevada	8.0
33	Oregon	7.9
34	New Hampshire	7.8
35	Maine	7.7
35	New York	7.7
35	North Carolina	7.7
38	Arizona	7.3
38	Idaho	7.3
38	Mississippi	7.3
41	Virginia	7.2
42	Colorado	6.8
43	Texas	6.7
44	California	6.4
44	Hawaii	6.4
44	New Mexico	6.4
44	Utah	6.4
48	Georgia	6.3
NA	Alaska**	NA
NA	Wyoming**	NA
	District of Columbia**	NA

Source: Morgan Quitno Press using data from American Cancer Society
    "Cancer Facts & Figures 2004" (Copyright 2004, Reprinted with permission from the American Cancer Society)
Rates calculated using 2003 Census resident population estimates. Not age-adjusted.
**Fewer than 50 deaths.*

Estimated Deaths by Liver Cancer in 2004

National Estimated Total = 14,270 Deaths

ALPHA ORDER

RANK	STATE	DEATHS	% of USA
19	Alabama	260	1.8%
NA	Alaska*	NA	NA
19	Arizona	260	1.8%
23	Arkansas	200	1.4%
1	California	1,880	13.2%
29	Colorado	160	1.1%
28	Connecticut	170	1.2%
NA	Delaware*	NA	NA
3	Florida	1,030	7.2%
13	Georgia	300	2.1%
35	Hawaii	100	0.7%
NA	Idaho*	NA	NA
6	Illinois	650	4.6%
15	Indiana	280	2.0%
32	Iowa	110	0.8%
35	Kansas	100	0.7%
27	Kentucky	180	1.3%
15	Louisiana	280	2.0%
38	Maine	60	0.4%
22	Maryland	240	1.7%
11	Massachusetts	340	2.4%
8	Michigan	500	3.5%
24	Minnesota	190	1.3%
24	Mississippi	190	1.3%
17	Missouri	270	1.9%
NA	Montana*	NA	NA
NA	Nebraska*	NA	NA
32	Nevada	110	0.8%
38	New Hampshire	60	0.4%
9	New Jersey	480	3.4%
32	New Mexico	110	0.8%
4	New York	890	6.2%
10	North Carolina	350	2.5%
NA	North Dakota*	NA	NA
7	Ohio	520	3.6%
29	Oklahoma	160	1.1%
31	Oregon	150	1.1%
5	Pennsylvania	690	4.8%
38	Rhode Island	60	0.4%
24	South Carolina	190	1.3%
NA	South Dakota*	NA	NA
17	Tennessee	270	1.9%
2	Texas	1,120	7.8%
38	Utah	60	0.4%
NA	Vermont*	NA	NA
12	Virginia	320	2.2%
13	Washington	300	2.1%
35	West Virginia	100	0.7%
21	Wisconsin	250	1.8%
NA	Wyoming*	NA	NA

RANK ORDER

RANK	STATE	DEATHS	% of USA
1	California	1,880	13.2%
2	Texas	1,120	7.8%
3	Florida	1,030	7.2%
4	New York	890	6.2%
5	Pennsylvania	690	4.8%
6	Illinois	650	4.6%
7	Ohio	520	3.6%
8	Michigan	500	3.5%
9	New Jersey	480	3.4%
10	North Carolina	350	2.5%
11	Massachusetts	340	2.4%
12	Virginia	320	2.2%
13	Georgia	300	2.1%
13	Washington	300	2.1%
15	Indiana	280	2.0%
15	Louisiana	280	2.0%
17	Missouri	270	1.9%
17	Tennessee	270	1.9%
19	Alabama	260	1.8%
19	Arizona	260	1.8%
21	Wisconsin	250	1.8%
22	Maryland	240	1.7%
23	Arkansas	200	1.4%
24	Minnesota	190	1.3%
24	Mississippi	190	1.3%
24	South Carolina	190	1.3%
27	Kentucky	180	1.3%
28	Connecticut	170	1.2%
29	Colorado	160	1.1%
29	Oklahoma	160	1.1%
31	Oregon	150	1.1%
32	Iowa	110	0.8%
32	Nevada	110	0.8%
32	New Mexico	110	0.8%
35	Hawaii	100	0.7%
35	Kansas	100	0.7%
35	West Virginia	100	0.7%
38	Maine	60	0.4%
38	New Hampshire	60	0.4%
38	Rhode Island	60	0.4%
38	Utah	60	0.4%
NA	Alaska*	NA	NA
NA	Delaware*	NA	NA
NA	Idaho*	NA	NA
NA	Montana*	NA	NA
NA	Nebraska*	NA	NA
NA	North Dakota*	NA	NA
NA	South Dakota*	NA	NA
NA	Vermont*	NA	NA
NA	Wyoming*	NA	NA
	District of Columbia*	NA	NA

Source: American Cancer Society
"Cancer Facts & Figures 2004" (Copyright 2004, Reprinted with permission from the American Cancer Society)
*Fewer than 50 deaths.

Estimated Death Rate by Liver Cancer in 2004

National Estimated Rate = 4.9 Deaths per 100,000 Population*

ALPHA ORDER

RANK	STATE	RATE
7	Alabama	5.8
NA	Alaska**	NA
20	Arizona	4.7
2	Arkansas	7.3
12	California	5.3
39	Colorado	3.5
17	Connecticut	4.9
NA	Delaware**	NA
5	Florida	6.1
39	Georgia	3.5
1	Hawaii	8.0
NA	Idaho**	NA
14	Illinois	5.1
29	Indiana	4.5
37	Iowa	3.7
37	Kansas	3.7
31	Kentucky	4.4
4	Louisiana	6.2
23	Maine	4.6
31	Maryland	4.4
12	Massachusetts	5.3
16	Michigan	5.0
36	Minnesota	3.8
3	Mississippi	6.6
20	Missouri	4.7
NA	Montana**	NA
NA	Nebraska**	NA
17	Nevada	4.9
20	New Hampshire	4.7
8	New Jersey	5.6
6	New Mexico	5.9
23	New York	4.6
34	North Carolina	4.2
NA	North Dakota**	NA
29	Ohio	4.5
23	Oklahoma	4.6
34	Oregon	4.2
8	Pennsylvania	5.6
8	Rhode Island	5.6
23	South Carolina	4.6
NA	South Dakota**	NA
23	Tennessee	4.6
14	Texas	5.1
41	Utah	2.6
NA	Vermont**	NA
33	Virginia	4.3
17	Washington	4.9
11	West Virginia	5.5
23	Wisconsin	4.6
NA	Wyoming**	NA

RANK ORDER

RANK	STATE	RATE
1	Hawaii	8.0
2	Arkansas	7.3
3	Mississippi	6.6
4	Louisiana	6.2
5	Florida	6.1
6	New Mexico	5.9
7	Alabama	5.8
8	New Jersey	5.6
8	Pennsylvania	5.6
8	Rhode Island	5.6
11	West Virginia	5.5
12	California	5.3
12	Massachusetts	5.3
14	Illinois	5.1
14	Texas	5.1
16	Michigan	5.0
17	Connecticut	4.9
17	Nevada	4.9
17	Washington	4.9
20	Arizona	4.7
20	Missouri	4.7
20	New Hampshire	4.7
23	Maine	4.6
23	New York	4.6
23	Oklahoma	4.6
23	South Carolina	4.6
23	Tennessee	4.6
23	Wisconsin	4.6
29	Indiana	4.5
29	Ohio	4.5
31	Kentucky	4.4
31	Maryland	4.4
33	Virginia	4.3
34	North Carolina	4.2
34	Oregon	4.2
36	Minnesota	3.8
37	Iowa	3.7
37	Kansas	3.7
39	Colorado	3.5
39	Georgia	3.5
41	Utah	2.6
NA	Alaska**	NA
NA	Delaware**	NA
NA	Idaho**	NA
NA	Montana**	NA
NA	Nebraska**	NA
NA	North Dakota**	NA
NA	South Dakota**	NA
NA	Vermont**	NA
NA	Wyoming**	NA

District of Columbia** — NA

Source: Morgan Quitno Press using data from American Cancer Society
    "Cancer Facts & Figures 2004" (Copyright 2004, Reprinted with permission from the American Cancer Society)
*Rates calculated using 2003 Census resident population estimates. Not age-adjusted.
**Fewer than 50 deaths.

Estimated Deaths by Lung Cancer in 2004

National Estimated Total = 160,440 Deaths

ALPHA ORDER

RANK	STATE	DEATHS	% of USA
19	Alabama	3,090	1.9%
50	Alaska	220	0.1%
24	Arizona	2,550	1.6%
27	Arkansas	2,060	1.3%
1	California	14,450	9.0%
33	Colorado	1,610	1.0%
30	Connecticut	1,850	1.2%
44	Delaware	510	0.3%
2	Florida	12,360	7.7%
11	Georgia	4,660	2.9%
43	Hawaii	530	0.3%
41	Idaho	610	0.4%
7	Illinois	6,760	4.2%
13	Indiana	4,150	2.6%
31	Iowa	1,680	1.0%
34	Kansas	1,560	1.0%
17	Kentucky	3,380	2.1%
21	Louisiana	2,920	1.8%
37	Maine	880	0.5%
20	Maryland	2,940	1.8%
15	Massachusetts	3,740	2.3%
8	Michigan	5,690	3.5%
25	Minnesota	2,380	1.5%
27	Mississippi	2,060	1.3%
14	Missouri	3,780	2.4%
42	Montana	600	0.4%
36	Nebraska	960	0.6%
35	Nevada	1,450	0.9%
38	New Hampshire	740	0.5%
10	New Jersey	4,720	2.9%
40	New Mexico	690	0.4%
4	New York	9,250	5.8%
9	North Carolina	5,270	3.3%
48	North Dakota	330	0.2%
6	Ohio	7,130	4.4%
26	Oklahoma	2,370	1.5%
29	Oregon	1,980	1.2%
5	Pennsylvania	7,900	4.9%
39	Rhode Island	700	0.4%
23	South Carolina	2,720	1.7%
46	South Dakota	420	0.3%
12	Tennessee	4,320	2.7%
3	Texas	9,670	6.0%
45	Utah	440	0.3%
47	Vermont	370	0.2%
15	Virginia	3,740	2.3%
18	Washington	3,250	2.0%
32	West Virginia	1,640	1.0%
22	Wisconsin	2,820	1.8%
49	Wyoming	260	0.2%

RANK ORDER

RANK	STATE	DEATHS	% of USA
1	California	14,450	9.0%
2	Florida	12,360	7.7%
3	Texas	9,670	6.0%
4	New York	9,250	5.8%
5	Pennsylvania	7,900	4.9%
6	Ohio	7,130	4.4%
7	Illinois	6,760	4.2%
8	Michigan	5,690	3.5%
9	North Carolina	5,270	3.3%
10	New Jersey	4,720	2.9%
11	Georgia	4,660	2.9%
12	Tennessee	4,320	2.7%
13	Indiana	4,150	2.6%
14	Missouri	3,780	2.4%
15	Massachusetts	3,740	2.3%
15	Virginia	3,740	2.3%
17	Kentucky	3,380	2.1%
18	Washington	3,250	2.0%
19	Alabama	3,090	1.9%
20	Maryland	2,940	1.8%
21	Louisiana	2,920	1.8%
22	Wisconsin	2,820	1.8%
23	South Carolina	2,720	1.7%
24	Arizona	2,550	1.6%
25	Minnesota	2,380	1.5%
26	Oklahoma	2,370	1.5%
27	Arkansas	2,060	1.3%
27	Mississippi	2,060	1.3%
29	Oregon	1,980	1.2%
30	Connecticut	1,850	1.2%
31	Iowa	1,680	1.0%
32	West Virginia	1,640	1.0%
33	Colorado	1,610	1.0%
34	Kansas	1,560	1.0%
35	Nevada	1,450	0.9%
36	Nebraska	960	0.6%
37	Maine	880	0.5%
38	New Hampshire	740	0.5%
39	Rhode Island	700	0.4%
40	New Mexico	690	0.4%
41	Idaho	610	0.4%
42	Montana	600	0.4%
43	Hawaii	530	0.3%
44	Delaware	510	0.3%
45	Utah	440	0.3%
46	South Dakota	420	0.3%
47	Vermont	370	0.2%
48	North Dakota	330	0.2%
49	Wyoming	260	0.2%
50	Alaska	220	0.1%
	District of Columbia	280	0.2%

Source: American Cancer Society
   "Cancer Facts & Figures 2004" (Copyright 2004, Reprinted with permission from the American Cancer Society)

Estimated Death Rate by Lung Cancer in 2004

National Estimated Rate = 55.2 Deaths per 100,000 Population*

ALPHA ORDER

RANK	STATE	RATE
7	Alabama	68.7
49	Alaska	33.9
42	Arizona	45.7
3	Arkansas	75.6
46	California	40.7
48	Colorado	35.4
34	Connecticut	53.1
19	Delaware	62.4
5	Florida	72.6
31	Georgia	53.7
45	Hawaii	42.1
43	Idaho	44.6
32	Illinois	53.4
10	Indiana	67.0
25	Iowa	57.1
24	Kansas	57.3
2	Kentucky	82.1
15	Louisiana	64.9
9	Maine	67.4
32	Maryland	53.4
22	Massachusetts	58.1
26	Michigan	56.4
41	Minnesota	47.0
6	Mississippi	71.5
11	Missouri	66.3
13	Montana	65.4
28	Nebraska	55.2
16	Nevada	64.7
23	New Hampshire	57.5
30	New Jersey	54.6
47	New Mexico	36.8
40	New York	48.2
18	North Carolina	62.7
36	North Dakota	52.1
20	Ohio	62.3
8	Oklahoma	67.5
27	Oregon	55.6
17	Pennsylvania	63.9
14	Rhode Island	65.0
12	South Carolina	65.6
29	South Dakota	55.0
4	Tennessee	74.0
44	Texas	43.7
50	Utah	18.7
21	Vermont	59.8
39	Virginia	50.6
35	Washington	53.0
1	West Virginia	90.6
38	Wisconsin	51.5
37	Wyoming	51.9

RANK ORDER

RANK	STATE	RATE
1	West Virginia	90.6
2	Kentucky	82.1
3	Arkansas	75.6
4	Tennessee	74.0
5	Florida	72.6
6	Mississippi	71.5
7	Alabama	68.7
8	Oklahoma	67.5
9	Maine	67.4
10	Indiana	67.0
11	Missouri	66.3
12	South Carolina	65.6
13	Montana	65.4
14	Rhode Island	65.0
15	Louisiana	64.9
16	Nevada	64.7
17	Pennsylvania	63.9
18	North Carolina	62.7
19	Delaware	62.4
20	Ohio	62.3
21	Vermont	59.8
22	Massachusetts	58.1
23	New Hampshire	57.5
24	Kansas	57.3
25	Iowa	57.1
26	Michigan	56.4
27	Oregon	55.6
28	Nebraska	55.2
29	South Dakota	55.0
30	New Jersey	54.6
31	Georgia	53.7
32	Illinois	53.4
32	Maryland	53.4
34	Connecticut	53.1
35	Washington	53.0
36	North Dakota	52.1
37	Wyoming	51.9
38	Wisconsin	51.5
39	Virginia	50.6
40	New York	48.2
41	Minnesota	47.0
42	Arizona	45.7
43	Idaho	44.6
44	Texas	43.7
45	Hawaii	42.1
46	California	40.7
47	New Mexico	36.8
48	Colorado	35.4
49	Alaska	33.9
50	Utah	18.7

District of Columbia — 49.7

Source: Morgan Quitno Press using data from American Cancer Society
"Cancer Facts & Figures 2004" (Copyright 2004, Reprinted with permission from the American Cancer Society)
*Rates calculated using 2003 Census resident population estimates. Not age-adjusted.

Estimated Deaths by Non-Hodgkin's Lymphoma in 2004

National Estimated Total = 19,410 Deaths

ALPHA ORDER

RANK	STATE	DEATHS	% of USA
26	Alabama	300	1.5%
NA	Alaska*	NA	NA
23	Arizona	340	1.8%
30	Arkansas	230	1.2%
1	California	1,980	10.2%
27	Colorado	290	1.5%
28	Connecticut	270	1.4%
44	Delaware	70	0.4%
5	Florida	960	4.9%
14	Georgia	470	2.4%
40	Hawaii	90	0.5%
40	Idaho	90	0.5%
7	Illinois	810	4.2%
11	Indiana	510	2.6%
30	Iowa	230	1.2%
30	Kansas	230	1.2%
21	Kentucky	350	1.8%
21	Louisiana	350	1.8%
40	Maine	90	0.5%
20	Maryland	370	1.9%
19	Massachusetts	410	2.1%
8	Michigan	730	3.8%
15	Minnesota	460	2.4%
35	Mississippi	140	0.7%
12	Missouri	500	2.6%
44	Montana	70	0.4%
37	Nebraska	130	0.7%
34	Nevada	150	0.8%
NA	New Hampshire*	NA	NA
9	New Jersey	650	3.3%
38	New Mexico	110	0.6%
4	New York	990	5.1%
10	North Carolina	530	2.7%
NA	North Dakota*	NA	NA
6	Ohio	860	4.4%
28	Oklahoma	270	1.4%
24	Oregon	330	1.7%
2	Pennsylvania	1,080	5.6%
39	Rhode Island	100	0.5%
25	South Carolina	310	1.6%
43	South Dakota	80	0.4%
12	Tennessee	500	2.6%
3	Texas	1,060	5.5%
35	Utah	140	0.7%
46	Vermont	60	0.3%
18	Virginia	440	2.3%
15	Washington	460	2.4%
33	West Virginia	180	0.9%
15	Wisconsin	460	2.4%
NA	Wyoming*	NA	NA

RANK ORDER

RANK	STATE	DEATHS	% of USA
1	California	1,980	10.2%
2	Pennsylvania	1,080	5.6%
3	Texas	1,060	5.5%
4	New York	990	5.1%
5	Florida	960	4.9%
6	Ohio	860	4.4%
7	Illinois	810	4.2%
8	Michigan	730	3.8%
9	New Jersey	650	3.3%
10	North Carolina	530	2.7%
11	Indiana	510	2.6%
12	Missouri	500	2.6%
12	Tennessee	500	2.6%
14	Georgia	470	2.4%
15	Minnesota	460	2.4%
15	Washington	460	2.4%
15	Wisconsin	460	2.4%
18	Virginia	440	2.3%
19	Massachusetts	410	2.1%
20	Maryland	370	1.9%
21	Kentucky	350	1.8%
21	Louisiana	350	1.8%
23	Arizona	340	1.8%
24	Oregon	330	1.7%
25	South Carolina	310	1.6%
26	Alabama	300	1.5%
27	Colorado	290	1.5%
28	Connecticut	270	1.4%
28	Oklahoma	270	1.4%
30	Arkansas	230	1.2%
30	Iowa	230	1.2%
30	Kansas	230	1.2%
33	West Virginia	180	0.9%
34	Nevada	150	0.8%
35	Mississippi	140	0.7%
35	Utah	140	0.7%
37	Nebraska	130	0.7%
38	New Mexico	110	0.6%
39	Rhode Island	100	0.5%
40	Hawaii	90	0.5%
40	Idaho	90	0.5%
40	Maine	90	0.5%
43	South Dakota	80	0.4%
44	Delaware	70	0.4%
44	Montana	70	0.4%
46	Vermont	60	0.3%
NA	Alaska*	NA	NA
NA	New Hampshire*	NA	NA
NA	North Dakota*	NA	NA
NA	Wyoming*	NA	NA
	District of Columbia*	NA	NA

Source: American Cancer Society
"Cancer Facts & Figures 2004" (Copyright 2004, Reprinted with permission from the American Cancer Society)
*Fewer than 50 deaths.

Estimated Death Rate by Non-Hodgkin's Lymphoma in 2004

National Estimated Rate = 6.7 Deaths per 100,000 Population*

ALPHA ORDER				RANK ORDER		
RANK	**STATE**	**RATE**		**RANK**	**STATE**	**RATE**
29	Alabama	6.7		1	South Dakota	10.5
NA	Alaska**	NA		2	West Virginia	9.9
37	Arizona	6.1		3	Vermont	9.7
12	Arkansas	8.4		4	Oregon	9.3
41	California	5.6		4	Rhode Island	9.3
33	Colorado	6.4		6	Minnesota	9.1
16	Connecticut	7.8		7	Missouri	8.8
9	Delaware	8.6		8	Pennsylvania	8.7
41	Florida	5.6		9	Delaware	8.6
43	Georgia	5.4		9	Tennessee	8.6
26	Hawaii	7.2		11	Kentucky	8.5
32	Idaho	6.6		12	Arkansas	8.4
33	Illinois	6.4		12	Kansas	8.4
15	Indiana	8.2		12	Wisconsin	8.4
16	Iowa	7.8		15	Indiana	8.2
12	Kansas	8.4		16	Connecticut	7.8
11	Kentucky	8.5		16	Iowa	7.8
16	Louisiana	7.8		16	Louisiana	7.8
28	Maine	6.9		19	Oklahoma	7.7
29	Maryland	6.7		20	Montana	7.6
33	Massachusetts	6.4		21	Nebraska	7.5
26	Michigan	7.2		21	New Jersey	7.5
6	Minnesota	9.1		21	Ohio	7.5
45	Mississippi	4.9		21	South Carolina	7.5
7	Missouri	8.8		21	Washington	7.5
20	Montana	7.6		26	Hawaii	7.2
21	Nebraska	7.5		26	Michigan	7.2
29	Nevada	6.7		28	Maine	6.9
NA	New Hampshire**	NA		29	Alabama	6.7
21	New Jersey	7.5		29	Maryland	6.7
40	New Mexico	5.9		29	Nevada	6.7
44	New York	5.2		32	Idaho	6.6
36	North Carolina	6.3		33	Colorado	6.4
NA	North Dakota**	NA		33	Illinois	6.4
21	Ohio	7.5		33	Massachusetts	6.4
19	Oklahoma	7.7		36	North Carolina	6.3
4	Oregon	9.3		37	Arizona	6.1
8	Pennsylvania	8.7		38	Utah	6.0
4	Rhode Island	9.3		38	Virginia	6.0
21	South Carolina	7.5		40	New Mexico	5.9
1	South Dakota	10.5		41	California	5.6
9	Tennessee	8.6		41	Florida	5.6
46	Texas	4.8		43	Georgia	5.4
38	Utah	6.0		44	New York	5.2
3	Vermont	9.7		45	Mississippi	4.9
38	Virginia	6.0		46	Texas	4.8
21	Washington	7.5		NA	Alaska**	NA
2	West Virginia	9.9		NA	New Hampshire**	NA
12	Wisconsin	8.4		NA	North Dakota**	NA
NA	Wyoming**	NA		NA	Wyoming**	NA
				District of Columbia**		NA

Source: Morgan Quitno Press using data from American Cancer Society
"Cancer Facts & Figures 2004" (Copyright 2004, Reprinted with permission from the American Cancer Society)
Rates calculated using 2003 Census resident population estimates. Not age-adjusted.
**Fewer than 50 deaths.*

Estimated Deaths by Pancreatic Cancer in 2004

National Estimated Total = 31,270 Deaths

ALPHA ORDER

RANK	STATE	DEATHS	% of USA
22	Alabama	530	1.7%
NA	Alaska*	NA	NA
20	Arizona	560	1.8%
33	Arkansas	280	0.9%
1	California	3,020	9.7%
27	Colorado	380	1.2%
27	Connecticut	380	1.2%
44	Delaware	110	0.4%
2	Florida	2,270	7.3%
12	Georgia	750	2.4%
40	Hawaii	150	0.5%
43	Idaho	120	0.4%
6	Illinois	1,400	4.5%
15	Indiana	670	2.1%
27	Iowa	380	1.2%
32	Kansas	300	1.0%
25	Kentucky	410	1.3%
23	Louisiana	520	1.7%
37	Maine	170	0.5%
19	Maryland	590	1.9%
11	Massachusetts	830	2.7%
8	Michigan	1,120	3.6%
21	Minnesota	540	1.7%
31	Mississippi	320	1.0%
16	Missouri	660	2.1%
45	Montana	100	0.3%
36	Nebraska	180	0.6%
34	Nevada	220	0.7%
42	New Hampshire	140	0.4%
9	New Jersey	1,040	3.3%
37	New Mexico	170	0.5%
2	New York	2,270	7.3%
10	North Carolina	900	2.9%
47	North Dakota	90	0.3%
7	Ohio	1,290	4.1%
30	Oklahoma	360	1.2%
26	Oregon	400	1.3%
5	Pennsylvania	1,650	5.3%
39	Rhode Island	160	0.5%
24	South Carolina	500	1.6%
45	South Dakota	100	0.3%
16	Tennessee	660	2.1%
4	Texas	1,930	6.2%
40	Utah	150	0.5%
48	Vermont	70	0.2%
12	Virginia	750	2.4%
14	Washington	700	2.2%
35	West Virginia	190	0.6%
18	Wisconsin	630	2.0%
NA	Wyoming*	NA	NA

RANK ORDER

RANK	STATE	DEATHS	% of USA
1	California	3,020	9.7%
2	Florida	2,270	7.3%
2	New York	2,270	7.3%
4	Texas	1,930	6.2%
5	Pennsylvania	1,650	5.3%
6	Illinois	1,400	4.5%
7	Ohio	1,290	4.1%
8	Michigan	1,120	3.6%
9	New Jersey	1,040	3.3%
10	North Carolina	900	2.9%
11	Massachusetts	830	2.7%
12	Georgia	750	2.4%
12	Virginia	750	2.4%
14	Washington	700	2.2%
15	Indiana	670	2.1%
16	Missouri	660	2.1%
16	Tennessee	660	2.1%
18	Wisconsin	630	2.0%
19	Maryland	590	1.9%
20	Arizona	560	1.8%
21	Minnesota	540	1.7%
22	Alabama	530	1.7%
23	Louisiana	520	1.7%
24	South Carolina	500	1.6%
25	Kentucky	410	1.3%
26	Oregon	400	1.3%
27	Colorado	380	1.2%
27	Connecticut	380	1.2%
27	Iowa	380	1.2%
30	Oklahoma	360	1.2%
31	Mississippi	320	1.0%
32	Kansas	300	1.0%
33	Arkansas	280	0.9%
34	Nevada	220	0.7%
35	West Virginia	190	0.6%
36	Nebraska	180	0.6%
37	Maine	170	0.5%
37	New Mexico	170	0.5%
39	Rhode Island	160	0.5%
40	Hawaii	150	0.5%
40	Utah	150	0.5%
42	New Hampshire	140	0.4%
43	Idaho	120	0.4%
44	Delaware	110	0.4%
45	Montana	100	0.3%
45	South Dakota	100	0.3%
47	North Dakota	90	0.3%
48	Vermont	70	0.2%
NA	Alaska*	NA	NA
NA	Wyoming*	NA	NA
	District of Columbia	60	0.2%

Source: American Cancer Society
   "Cancer Facts & Figures 2004" (Copyright 2004, Reprinted with permission from the American Cancer Society)
*Fewer than 50 deaths.

Estimated Death Rate by Pancreatic Cancer in 2004

National Estimated Rate = 10.8 Deaths per 100,000 Population*

ALPHA ORDER

RANK	STATE	RATE
13	Alabama	11.8
NA	Alaska**	NA
39	Arizona	10.0
35	Arkansas	10.3
46	California	8.5
47	Colorado	8.4
27	Connecticut	10.9
3	Delaware	13.5
4	Florida	13.3
45	Georgia	8.6
12	Hawaii	11.9
43	Idaho	8.8
23	Illinois	11.1
30	Indiana	10.8
8	Iowa	12.9
26	Kansas	11.0
39	Kentucky	10.0
15	Louisiana	11.6
7	Maine	13.0
31	Maryland	10.7
8	Massachusetts	12.9
23	Michigan	11.1
31	Minnesota	10.7
23	Mississippi	11.1
15	Missouri	11.6
27	Montana	10.9
35	Nebraska	10.3
41	Nevada	9.8
27	New Hampshire	10.9
11	New Jersey	12.0
42	New Mexico	9.1
13	New York	11.8
31	North Carolina	10.7
2	North Dakota	14.2
19	Ohio	11.3
35	Oklahoma	10.3
22	Oregon	11.2
4	Pennsylvania	13.3
1	Rhode Island	14.9
10	South Carolina	12.1
6	South Dakota	13.1
19	Tennessee	11.3
44	Texas	8.7
48	Utah	6.4
19	Vermont	11.3
38	Virginia	10.2
18	Washington	11.4
34	West Virginia	10.5
17	Wisconsin	11.5
NA	Wyoming**	NA

RANK ORDER

RANK	STATE	RATE
1	Rhode Island	14.9
2	North Dakota	14.2
3	Delaware	13.5
4	Florida	13.3
4	Pennsylvania	13.3
6	South Dakota	13.1
7	Maine	13.0
8	Iowa	12.9
8	Massachusetts	12.9
10	South Carolina	12.1
11	New Jersey	12.0
12	Hawaii	11.9
13	Alabama	11.8
13	New York	11.8
15	Louisiana	11.6
15	Missouri	11.6
17	Wisconsin	11.5
18	Washington	11.4
19	Ohio	11.3
19	Tennessee	11.3
19	Vermont	11.3
22	Oregon	11.2
23	Illinois	11.1
23	Michigan	11.1
23	Mississippi	11.1
26	Kansas	11.0
27	Connecticut	10.9
27	Montana	10.9
27	New Hampshire	10.9
30	Indiana	10.8
31	Maryland	10.7
31	Minnesota	10.7
31	North Carolina	10.7
34	West Virginia	10.5
35	Arkansas	10.3
35	Nebraska	10.3
35	Oklahoma	10.3
38	Virginia	10.2
39	Arizona	10.0
39	Kentucky	10.0
41	Nevada	9.8
42	New Mexico	9.1
43	Idaho	8.8
44	Texas	8.7
45	Georgia	8.6
46	California	8.5
47	Colorado	8.4
48	Utah	6.4
NA	Alaska**	NA
NA	Wyoming**	NA

District of Columbia   10.6

Source: Morgan Quitno Press using data from American Cancer Society
    "Cancer Facts & Figures 2004" (Copyright 2004, Reprinted with permission from the American Cancer Society)
*Rates calculated using 2003 Census resident population estimates. Not age-adjusted.
**Fewer than 50 deaths.

Estimated Deaths by Prostate Cancer in 2004

National Estimated Total = 29,900 Deaths

ALPHA ORDER

RANK	STATE	DEATHS	% of USA
15	Alabama	630	2.1%
NA	Alaska*	NA	NA
21	Arizona	510	1.7%
33	Arkansas	280	0.9%
1	California	3,010	10.1%
32	Colorado	330	1.1%
26	Connecticut	430	1.4%
46	Delaware	90	0.3%
2	Florida	2,220	7.4%
11	Georgia	740	2.5%
42	Hawaii	130	0.4%
39	Idaho	140	0.5%
6	Illinois	1,290	4.3%
13	Indiana	700	2.3%
27	Iowa	410	1.4%
29	Kansas	350	1.2%
30	Kentucky	340	1.1%
23	Louisiana	480	1.6%
38	Maine	150	0.5%
20	Maryland	530	1.8%
11	Massachusetts	740	2.5%
8	Michigan	1,110	3.7%
19	Minnesota	550	1.8%
25	Mississippi	440	1.5%
24	Missouri	450	1.5%
39	Montana	140	0.5%
37	Nebraska	190	0.6%
34	Nevada	260	0.9%
42	New Hampshire	130	0.4%
9	New Jersey	1,030	3.4%
35	New Mexico	220	0.7%
3	New York	1,880	6.3%
10	North Carolina	930	3.1%
48	North Dakota	70	0.2%
7	Ohio	1,120	3.7%
30	Oklahoma	340	1.1%
28	Oregon	380	1.3%
5	Pennsylvania	1,560	5.2%
42	Rhode Island	130	0.4%
17	South Carolina	620	2.1%
45	South Dakota	120	0.4%
18	Tennessee	590	2.0%
4	Texas	1,760	5.9%
39	Utah	140	0.5%
49	Vermont	60	0.2%
14	Virginia	660	2.2%
15	Washington	630	2.1%
36	West Virginia	200	0.7%
22	Wisconsin	500	1.7%
47	Wyoming	80	0.3%

RANK ORDER

RANK	STATE	DEATHS	% of USA
1	California	3,010	10.1%
2	Florida	2,220	7.4%
3	New York	1,880	6.3%
4	Texas	1,760	5.9%
5	Pennsylvania	1,560	5.2%
6	Illinois	1,290	4.3%
7	Ohio	1,120	3.7%
8	Michigan	1,110	3.7%
9	New Jersey	1,030	3.4%
10	North Carolina	930	3.1%
11	Georgia	740	2.5%
11	Massachusetts	740	2.5%
13	Indiana	700	2.3%
14	Virginia	660	2.2%
15	Alabama	630	2.1%
15	Washington	630	2.1%
17	South Carolina	620	2.1%
18	Tennessee	590	2.0%
19	Minnesota	550	1.8%
20	Maryland	530	1.8%
21	Arizona	510	1.7%
22	Wisconsin	500	1.7%
23	Louisiana	480	1.6%
24	Missouri	450	1.5%
25	Mississippi	440	1.5%
26	Connecticut	430	1.4%
27	Iowa	410	1.4%
28	Oregon	380	1.3%
29	Kansas	350	1.2%
30	Kentucky	340	1.1%
30	Oklahoma	340	1.1%
32	Colorado	330	1.1%
33	Arkansas	280	0.9%
34	Nevada	260	0.9%
35	New Mexico	220	0.7%
36	West Virginia	200	0.7%
37	Nebraska	190	0.6%
38	Maine	150	0.5%
39	Idaho	140	0.5%
39	Montana	140	0.5%
39	Utah	140	0.5%
42	Hawaii	130	0.4%
42	New Hampshire	130	0.4%
42	Rhode Island	130	0.4%
45	South Dakota	120	0.4%
46	Delaware	90	0.3%
47	Wyoming	80	0.3%
48	North Dakota	70	0.2%
49	Vermont	60	0.2%
NA	Alaska*	NA	NA
	District of Columbia	80	0.3%

Source: American Cancer Society
"Cancer Facts & Figures 2004" (Copyright 2004, Reprinted with permission from the American Cancer Society)
*Fewer than 50 deaths.

Age-Adjusted Death Rate by Prostate Cancer in 2000

National Rate = 32.9 Deaths per 100,000 Male Population*

ALPHA ORDER

RANK ORDER

RANK	STATE	RATE
3	Alabama	41.0
49	Alaska	24.2
48	Arizona	28.2
13	Arkansas	34.9
45	California	29.4
40	Colorado	30.5
43	Connecticut	30.1
12	Delaware	35.2
47	Florida	28.4
4	Georgia	40.2
50	Hawaii	21.9
22	Idaho	34.0
15	Illinois	34.7
16	Indiana	34.6
30	Iowa	32.3
40	Kansas	30.5
22	Kentucky	34.0
5	Louisiana	39.7
39	Maine	30.6
9	Maryland	36.8
26	Massachusetts	33.0
18	Michigan	34.3
17	Minnesota	34.4
1	Mississippi	44.0
37	Missouri	30.9
14	Montana	34.8
46	Nebraska	28.6
42	Nevada	30.2
35	New Hampshire	31.2
28	New Jersey	32.9
33	New Mexico	31.7
34	New York	31.6
6	North Carolina	38.9
21	North Dakota	34.1
24	Ohio	33.9
38	Oklahoma	30.8
20	Oregon	34.2
25	Pennsylvania	33.6
26	Rhode Island	33.0
2	South Carolina	41.7
30	South Dakota	32.3
10	Tennessee	35.8
29	Texas	32.8
11	Utah	35.3
32	Vermont	32.1
7	Virginia	37.6
44	Washington	29.8
35	West Virginia	31.2
18	Wisconsin	34.3
8	Wyoming	37.4

RANK	STATE	RATE
1	Mississippi	44.0
2	South Carolina	41.7
3	Alabama	41.0
4	Georgia	40.2
5	Louisiana	39.7
6	North Carolina	38.9
7	Virginia	37.6
8	Wyoming	37.4
9	Maryland	36.8
10	Tennessee	35.8
11	Utah	35.3
12	Delaware	35.2
13	Arkansas	34.9
14	Montana	34.8
15	Illinois	34.7
16	Indiana	34.6
17	Minnesota	34.4
18	Michigan	34.3
18	Wisconsin	34.3
20	Oregon	34.2
21	North Dakota	34.1
22	Idaho	34.0
22	Kentucky	34.0
24	Ohio	33.9
25	Pennsylvania	33.6
26	Massachusetts	33.0
26	Rhode Island	33.0
28	New Jersey	32.9
29	Texas	32.8
30	Iowa	32.3
30	South Dakota	32.3
32	Vermont	32.1
33	New Mexico	31.7
34	New York	31.6
35	New Hampshire	31.2
35	West Virginia	31.2
37	Missouri	30.9
38	Oklahoma	30.8
39	Maine	30.6
40	Colorado	30.5
40	Kansas	30.5
42	Nevada	30.2
43	Connecticut	30.1
44	Washington	29.8
45	California	29.4
46	Nebraska	28.6
47	Florida	28.4
48	Arizona	28.2
49	Alaska	24.2
50	Hawaii	21.9

	District of Columbia	54.2

Source: American Cancer Society
"Cancer Facts & Figures 2004" (Copyright 2004, Reprinted with permission from the American Cancer Society)
*For 1996 to 2000. Age-adjusted to the 2000 U.S. standard population.

Estimated Deaths by Ovarian Cancer in 2004

National Estimated Total = 16,090 Deaths

ALPHA ORDER

RANK	STATE	DEATHS	% of USA
18	Alabama	320	2.0%
NA	Alaska*	NA	NA
20	Arizona	290	1.8%
33	Arkansas	150	0.9%
1	California	1,730	10.8%
26	Colorado	210	1.3%
28	Connecticut	200	1.2%
NA	Delaware*	NA	NA
2	Florida	1,120	7.0%
11	Georgia	430	2.7%
NA	Hawaii*	NA	NA
40	Idaho	80	0.5%
6	Illinois	660	4.1%
14	Indiana	380	2.4%
26	Iowa	210	1.3%
31	Kansas	160	1.0%
23	Kentucky	230	1.4%
23	Louisiana	230	1.4%
36	Maine	100	0.6%
19	Maryland	300	1.9%
15	Massachusetts	360	2.2%
8	Michigan	580	3.6%
21	Minnesota	270	1.7%
31	Mississippi	160	1.0%
16	Missouri	350	2.2%
NA	Montana*	NA	NA
37	Nebraska	90	0.6%
35	Nevada	110	0.7%
41	New Hampshire	60	0.4%
9	New Jersey	540	3.4%
37	New Mexico	90	0.6%
3	New York	1,080	6.7%
10	North Carolina	450	2.8%
NA	North Dakota*	NA	NA
6	Ohio	660	4.1%
29	Oklahoma	170	1.1%
23	Oregon	230	1.4%
5	Pennsylvania	910	5.7%
41	Rhode Island	60	0.4%
29	South Carolina	170	1.1%
41	South Dakota	60	0.4%
17	Tennessee	340	2.1%
4	Texas	960	6.0%
37	Utah	90	0.6%
NA	Vermont*	NA	NA
12	Virginia	400	2.5%
13	Washington	390	2.4%
34	West Virginia	140	0.9%
22	Wisconsin	260	1.6%
NA	Wyoming*	NA	NA

RANK ORDER

RANK	STATE	DEATHS	% of USA
1	California	1,730	10.8%
2	Florida	1,120	7.0%
3	New York	1,080	6.7%
4	Texas	960	6.0%
5	Pennsylvania	910	5.7%
6	Illinois	660	4.1%
6	Ohio	660	4.1%
8	Michigan	580	3.6%
9	New Jersey	540	3.4%
10	North Carolina	450	2.8%
11	Georgia	430	2.7%
12	Virginia	400	2.5%
13	Washington	390	2.4%
14	Indiana	380	2.4%
15	Massachusetts	360	2.2%
16	Missouri	350	2.2%
17	Tennessee	340	2.1%
18	Alabama	320	2.0%
19	Maryland	300	1.9%
20	Arizona	290	1.8%
21	Minnesota	270	1.7%
22	Wisconsin	260	1.6%
23	Kentucky	230	1.4%
23	Louisiana	230	1.4%
23	Oregon	230	1.4%
26	Colorado	210	1.3%
26	Iowa	210	1.3%
28	Connecticut	200	1.2%
29	Oklahoma	170	1.1%
29	South Carolina	170	1.1%
31	Kansas	160	1.0%
31	Mississippi	160	1.0%
33	Arkansas	150	0.9%
34	West Virginia	140	0.9%
35	Nevada	110	0.7%
36	Maine	100	0.6%
37	Nebraska	90	0.6%
37	New Mexico	90	0.6%
37	Utah	90	0.6%
40	Idaho	80	0.5%
41	New Hampshire	60	0.4%
41	Rhode Island	60	0.4%
41	South Dakota	60	0.4%
NA	Alaska*	NA	NA
NA	Delaware*	NA	NA
NA	Hawaii*	NA	NA
NA	Montana*	NA	NA
NA	North Dakota*	NA	NA
NA	Vermont*	NA	NA
NA	Wyoming*	NA	NA
	District of Columbia*	NA	NA

Source: American Cancer Society
"Cancer Facts & Figures 2004" (Copyright 2004, Reprinted with permission from the American Cancer Society)
*Fewer than 50 deaths.

Estimated Death Rate by Ovarian Cancer in 2004

National Estimated Rate = 11.0 Deaths per 100,000 Female Population*

ALPHA ORDER

RANK	STATE	RATE
6	Alabama	13.8
NA	Alaska**	NA
27	Arizona	10.6
21	Arkansas	10.8
35	California	9.8
38	Colorado	9.4
17	Connecticut	11.2
NA	Delaware**	NA
7	Florida	13.1
34	Georgia	9.9
NA	Hawaii**	NA
12	Idaho	12.0
30	Illinois	10.3
11	Indiana	12.1
5	Iowa	14.0
14	Kansas	11.7
19	Kentucky	11.0
33	Louisiana	10.0
2	Maine	15.1
27	Maryland	10.6
21	Massachusetts	10.8
16	Michigan	11.3
26	Minnesota	10.7
21	Mississippi	10.8
12	Missouri	12.0
NA	Montana**	NA
30	Nebraska	10.3
30	Nevada	10.3
40	New Hampshire	9.3
10	New Jersey	12.2
37	New Mexico	9.5
20	New York	10.9
27	North Carolina	10.6
NA	North Dakota**	NA
17	Ohio	11.2
36	Oklahoma	9.6
8	Oregon	13.0
4	Pennsylvania	14.3
21	Rhode Island	10.8
42	South Carolina	8.0
1	South Dakota	15.7
15	Tennessee	11.4
41	Texas	8.8
43	Utah	7.8
NA	Vermont**	NA
21	Virginia	10.8
9	Washington	12.8
2	West Virginia	15.1
38	Wisconsin	9.4
NA	Wyoming**	NA

RANK ORDER

RANK	STATE	RATE
1	South Dakota	15.7
2	Maine	15.1
2	West Virginia	15.1
4	Pennsylvania	14.3
5	Iowa	14.0
6	Alabama	13.8
7	Florida	13.1
8	Oregon	13.0
9	Washington	12.8
10	New Jersey	12.2
11	Indiana	12.1
12	Idaho	12.0
12	Missouri	12.0
14	Kansas	11.7
15	Tennessee	11.4
16	Michigan	11.3
17	Connecticut	11.2
17	Ohio	11.2
19	Kentucky	11.0
20	New York	10.9
21	Arkansas	10.8
21	Massachusetts	10.8
21	Mississippi	10.8
21	Rhode Island	10.8
21	Virginia	10.8
26	Minnesota	10.7
27	Arizona	10.6
27	Maryland	10.6
27	North Carolina	10.6
30	Illinois	10.3
30	Nebraska	10.3
30	Nevada	10.3
33	Louisiana	10.0
34	Georgia	9.9
35	California	9.8
36	Oklahoma	9.6
37	New Mexico	9.5
38	Colorado	9.4
38	Wisconsin	9.4
40	New Hampshire	9.3
41	Texas	8.8
42	South Carolina	8.0
43	Utah	7.8
NA	Alaska**	NA
NA	Delaware**	NA
NA	Hawaii**	NA
NA	Montana**	NA
NA	North Dakota**	NA
NA	Vermont**	NA
NA	Wyoming**	NA
	District of Columbia**	NA

Source: Morgan Quitno Press using data from American Cancer Society
    "Cancer Facts & Figures 2004" (Copyright 2004, Reprinted with permission from the American Cancer Society)
*Rates calculated using 2002 Census female population estimates. Not age-adjusted.
**Fewer than 50 deaths.

Deaths by Alzheimer's Disease in 2001

National Total = 53,852 Deaths*

ALPHA ORDER				RANK ORDER			
RANK	**STATE**	**DEATHS**	**% of USA**	**RANK**	**STATE**	**DEATHS**	**% of USA**
21	Alabama	1,103	2.0%	1	California	4,935	9.2%
50	Alaska	44	0.1%	2	Florida	3,643	6.8%
19	Arizona	1,108	2.1%	3	Texas	3,439	6.4%
33	Arkansas	452	0.8%	4	Pennsylvania	2,753	5.1%
1	California	4,935	9.2%	5	Ohio	2,367	4.4%
28	Colorado	852	1.6%	6	Illinois	2,163	4.0%
31	Connecticut	573	1.1%	7	Washington	2,050	3.8%
47	Delaware	135	0.3%	8	Michigan	1,803	3.3%
2	Florida	3,643	6.8%	9	North Carolina	1,786	3.3%
12	Georgia	1,419	2.6%	10	New York	1,705	3.2%
48	Hawaii	122	0.2%	11	Massachusetts	1,533	2.8%
40	Idaho	294	0.5%	12	Georgia	1,419	2.6%
6	Illinois	2,163	4.0%	13	New Jersey	1,376	2.6%
15	Indiana	1,231	2.3%	14	Wisconsin	1,269	2.4%
27	Iowa	863	1.6%	15	Indiana	1,231	2.3%
30	Kansas	642	1.2%	16	Virginia	1,184	2.2%
23	Kentucky	966	1.8%	17	Minnesota	1,173	2.2%
24	Louisiana	957	1.8%	18	Tennessee	1,148	2.1%
32	Maine	471	0.9%	19	Arizona	1,108	2.1%
25	Maryland	948	1.8%	20	Missouri	1,106	2.1%
11	Massachusetts	1,533	2.8%	21	Alabama	1,103	2.0%
8	Michigan	1,803	3.3%	22	Oregon	1,030	1.9%
17	Minnesota	1,173	2.2%	23	Kentucky	966	1.8%
34	Mississippi	449	0.8%	24	Louisiana	957	1.8%
20	Missouri	1,106	2.1%	25	Maryland	948	1.8%
42	Montana	249	0.5%	26	South Carolina	881	1.6%
35	Nebraska	430	0.8%	27	Iowa	863	1.6%
44	Nevada	211	0.4%	28	Colorado	852	1.6%
38	New Hampshire	305	0.6%	29	Oklahoma	682	1.3%
13	New Jersey	1,376	2.6%	30	Kansas	642	1.2%
39	New Mexico	297	0.6%	31	Connecticut	573	1.1%
10	New York	1,705	3.2%	32	Maine	471	0.9%
9	North Carolina	1,786	3.3%	33	Arkansas	452	0.8%
43	North Dakota	224	0.4%	34	Mississippi	449	0.8%
5	Ohio	2,367	4.4%	35	Nebraska	430	0.8%
29	Oklahoma	682	1.3%	36	West Virginia	398	0.7%
22	Oregon	1,030	1.9%	37	Utah	314	0.6%
4	Pennsylvania	2,753	5.1%	38	New Hampshire	305	0.6%
41	Rhode Island	251	0.5%	39	New Mexico	297	0.6%
26	South Carolina	881	1.6%	40	Idaho	294	0.5%
45	South Dakota	156	0.3%	41	Rhode Island	251	0.5%
18	Tennessee	1,148	2.1%	42	Montana	249	0.5%
3	Texas	3,439	6.4%	43	North Dakota	224	0.4%
37	Utah	314	0.6%	44	Nevada	211	0.4%
46	Vermont	149	0.3%	45	South Dakota	156	0.3%
16	Virginia	1,184	2.2%	46	Vermont	149	0.3%
7	Washington	2,050	3.8%	47	Delaware	135	0.3%
36	West Virginia	398	0.7%	48	Hawaii	122	0.2%
14	Wisconsin	1,269	2.4%	49	Wyoming	114	0.2%
49	Wyoming	114	0.2%	50	Alaska	44	0.1%
					District of Columbia	99	0.2%

Source: U.S. Department of Health and Human Services, National Center for Health Statistics
   "National Vital Statistics Reports" (Vol. 52, No. 3, September 18, 2003)
Final data by state of residence. A degenerative disease of the brain cells producing loss of memory and general
intellectual impairment. It usually affects people over age 65. As the disease progresses, a variety of symptoms may
become apparent, including confusion, irritability, Andd restlessness, as well as disorientation and impaired
judgment and concentration.

Death Rate by Alzheimer's Disease in 2001

National Rate = 18.9 Deaths per 100,000 Population*

ALPHA ORDER

RANK	STATE	RATE
8	Alabama	24.7
50	Alaska	6.9
25	Arizona	20.9
38	Arkansas	16.8
45	California	14.3
32	Colorado	19.2
39	Connecticut	16.7
36	Delaware	16.9
20	Florida	22.2
36	Georgia	16.9
48	Hawaii	9.9
19	Idaho	22.3
35	Illinois	17.3
28	Indiana	20.1
5	Iowa	29.4
12	Kansas	23.8
13	Kentucky	23.7
24	Louisiana	21.4
1	Maine	36.7
34	Maryland	17.6
11	Massachusetts	23.9
33	Michigan	18.0
15	Minnesota	23.5
44	Mississippi	15.7
31	Missouri	19.6
6	Montana	27.5
7	Nebraska	25.0
47	Nevada	10.1
10	New Hampshire	24.2
41	New Jersey	16.2
41	New Mexico	16.2
49	New York	8.9
22	North Carolina	21.8
2	North Dakota	35.2
26	Ohio	20.8
30	Oklahoma	19.7
4	Oregon	29.7
18	Pennsylvania	22.4
13	Rhode Island	23.7
23	South Carolina	21.7
27	South Dakota	20.6
29	Tennessee	20.0
43	Texas	16.1
46	Utah	13.8
9	Vermont	24.3
40	Virginia	16.5
3	Washington	34.2
21	West Virginia	22.1
15	Wisconsin	23.5
17	Wyoming	23.1

RANK ORDER

RANK	STATE	RATE
1	Maine	36.7
2	North Dakota	35.2
3	Washington	34.2
4	Oregon	29.7
5	Iowa	29.4
6	Montana	27.5
7	Nebraska	25.0
8	Alabama	24.7
9	Vermont	24.3
10	New Hampshire	24.2
11	Massachusetts	23.9
12	Kansas	23.8
13	Kentucky	23.7
13	Rhode Island	23.7
15	Minnesota	23.5
15	Wisconsin	23.5
17	Wyoming	23.1
18	Pennsylvania	22.4
19	Idaho	22.3
20	Florida	22.2
21	West Virginia	22.1
22	North Carolina	21.8
23	South Carolina	21.7
24	Louisiana	21.4
25	Arizona	20.9
26	Ohio	20.8
27	South Dakota	20.6
28	Indiana	20.1
29	Tennessee	20.0
30	Oklahoma	19.7
31	Missouri	19.6
32	Colorado	19.2
33	Michigan	18.0
34	Maryland	17.6
35	Illinois	17.3
36	Delaware	16.9
36	Georgia	16.9
38	Arkansas	16.8
39	Connecticut	16.7
40	Virginia	16.5
41	New Jersey	16.2
41	New Mexico	16.2
43	Texas	16.1
44	Mississippi	15.7
45	California	14.3
46	Utah	13.8
47	Nevada	10.1
48	Hawaii	9.9
49	New York	8.9
50	Alaska	6.9

| | District of Columbia | 17.3 |

Source: U.S. Department of Health and Human Services, National Center for Health Statistics
"National Vital Statistics Reports" (Vol. 52, No. 3, September 18, 2003)
Final data by state of residence. A degenerative disease of the brain cells producing loss of memory and general intellectual impairment. It usually affects people over age 65. As the disease progresses, a variety of symptoms may become apparent, including confusion, irritability, and restlessness, as well as disorientation and impaired judgment and concentration. Not age-adjusted.

Age-Adjusted Death Rate by Alzheimer's Disease in 2001

National Rate = 19.1 Deaths per 100,000 Population*

ALPHA ORDER

RANK	STATE	RATE
10	Alabama	24.6
31	Alaska	18.8
17	Arizona	22.1
45	Arkansas	15.1
41	California	16.9
4	Colorado	25.9
48	Connecticut	13.8
37	Delaware	17.6
43	Florida	16.1
15	Georgia	23.5
49	Hawaii	9.6
11	Idaho	24.4
39	Illinois	17.3
27	Indiana	20.2
19	Iowa	21.7
26	Kansas	20.3
8	Kentucky	24.7
13	Louisiana	24.2
2	Maine	30.9
27	Maryland	20.2
25	Massachusetts	20.5
34	Michigan	18.5
18	Minnesota	22.0
42	Mississippi	16.4
37	Missouri	17.6
8	Montana	24.7
22	Nebraska	20.8
47	Nevada	14.7
6	New Hampshire	25.0
46	New Jersey	15.0
36	New Mexico	18.3
50	New York	8.4
13	North Carolina	24.2
5	North Dakota	25.3
29	Ohio	19.7
32	Oklahoma	18.6
3	Oregon	27.2
40	Pennsylvania	17.2
35	Rhode Island	18.4
11	South Carolina	24.4
44	South Dakota	15.7
21	Tennessee	20.9
20	Texas	21.4
24	Utah	20.7
16	Vermont	22.9
30	Virginia	19.4
1	Washington	36.5
32	West Virginia	18.6
22	Wisconsin	20.8
6	Wyoming	25.0

RANK ORDER

RANK	STATE	RATE
1	Washington	36.5
2	Maine	30.9
3	Oregon	27.2
4	Colorado	25.9
5	North Dakota	25.3
6	New Hampshire	25.0
6	Wyoming	25.0
8	Kentucky	24.7
8	Montana	24.7
10	Alabama	24.6
11	Idaho	24.4
11	South Carolina	24.4
13	Louisiana	24.2
13	North Carolina	24.2
15	Georgia	23.5
16	Vermont	22.9
17	Arizona	22.1
18	Minnesota	22.0
19	Iowa	21.7
20	Texas	21.4
21	Tennessee	20.9
22	Nebraska	20.8
22	Wisconsin	20.8
24	Utah	20.7
25	Massachusetts	20.5
26	Kansas	20.3
27	Indiana	20.2
27	Maryland	20.2
29	Ohio	19.7
30	Virginia	19.4
31	Alaska	18.8
32	Oklahoma	18.6
32	West Virginia	18.6
34	Michigan	18.5
35	Rhode Island	18.4
36	New Mexico	18.3
37	Delaware	17.6
37	Missouri	17.6
39	Illinois	17.3
40	Pennsylvania	17.2
41	California	16.9
42	Mississippi	16.4
43	Florida	16.1
44	South Dakota	15.7
45	Arkansas	15.1
46	New Jersey	15.0
47	Nevada	14.7
48	Connecticut	13.8
49	Hawaii	9.6
50	New York	8.4
	District of Columbia	17.0

Source: U.S. Department of Health and Human Services, National Center for Health Statistics
   "National Vital Statistics Reports" (Vol. 52, No. 3, September 18, 2003)
*Final data by state of residence. A degenerative disease of the brain cells producing loss of memory and general intellectual impairment. It usually affects people over age 65. As the disease progresses, a variety of symptoms may become apparent, including confusion, irritability, and restlessness, as well as disorientation and impaired judgment and concentration. Age-adjusted rates based on the year 2000 standard population.

Deaths by Atherosclerosis in 2000

National Total = 14,393 Deaths*

ALPHA ORDER					RANK ORDER			
RANK	**STATE**	**DEATHS**	**% of USA**		**RANK**	**STATE**	**DEATHS**	**% of USA**
26	Alabama	190	1.3%		1	California	1,629	11.3%
50	Alaska	8	0.1%		2	Florida	1,044	7.3%
21	Arizona	237	1.6%		3	Texas	748	5.2%
33	Arkansas	125	0.9%		4	Michigan	662	4.6%
1	California	1,629	11.3%		5	Pennsylvania	646	4.5%
10	Colorado	475	3.3%		6	New York	606	4.2%
30	Connecticut	164	1.1%		7	Illinois	602	4.2%
49	Delaware	10	0.1%		8	Ohio	577	4.0%
2	Florida	1,044	7.3%		9	Georgia	499	3.5%
9	Georgia	499	3.5%		10	Colorado	475	3.3%
47	Hawaii	24	0.2%		11	Oklahoma	447	3.1%
44	Idaho	33	0.2%		12	New Jersey	393	2.7%
7	Illinois	602	4.2%		13	North Carolina	383	2.7%
17	Indiana	325	2.3%		14	Kansas	354	2.5%
19	Iowa	294	2.0%		15	Tennessee	338	2.3%
14	Kansas	354	2.5%		15	Washington	338	2.3%
29	Kentucky	167	1.2%		17	Indiana	325	2.3%
25	Louisiana	215	1.5%		18	Massachusetts	309	2.1%
43	Maine	54	0.4%		19	Iowa	294	2.0%
32	Maryland	158	1.1%		20	Missouri	278	1.9%
18	Massachusetts	309	2.1%		21	Arizona	237	1.6%
4	Michigan	662	4.6%		22	Wisconsin	236	1.6%
28	Minnesota	176	1.2%		23	Oregon	230	1.6%
37	Mississippi	89	0.6%		23	Virginia	230	1.6%
20	Missouri	278	1.9%		25	Louisiana	215	1.5%
39	Montana	72	0.5%		26	Alabama	190	1.3%
31	Nebraska	163	1.1%		27	West Virginia	188	1.3%
35	Nevada	93	0.6%		28	Minnesota	176	1.2%
40	New Hampshire	70	0.5%		29	Kentucky	167	1.2%
12	New Jersey	393	2.7%		30	Connecticut	164	1.1%
36	New Mexico	91	0.6%		31	Nebraska	163	1.1%
6	New York	606	4.2%		32	Maryland	158	1.1%
13	North Carolina	383	2.7%		33	Arkansas	125	0.9%
41	North Dakota	62	0.4%		34	South Carolina	111	0.8%
8	Ohio	577	4.0%		35	Nevada	93	0.6%
11	Oklahoma	447	3.1%		36	New Mexico	91	0.6%
23	Oregon	230	1.6%		37	Mississippi	89	0.6%
5	Pennsylvania	646	4.5%		38	Rhode Island	83	0.6%
38	Rhode Island	83	0.6%		39	Montana	72	0.5%
34	South Carolina	111	0.8%		40	New Hampshire	70	0.5%
46	South Dakota	27	0.2%		41	North Dakota	62	0.4%
15	Tennessee	338	2.3%		42	Utah	61	0.4%
3	Texas	748	5.2%		43	Maine	54	0.4%
42	Utah	61	0.4%		44	Idaho	33	0.2%
48	Vermont	21	0.1%		45	Wyoming	29	0.2%
23	Virginia	230	1.6%		46	South Dakota	27	0.2%
15	Washington	338	2.3%		47	Hawaii	24	0.2%
27	West Virginia	188	1.3%		48	Vermont	21	0.1%
22	Wisconsin	236	1.6%		49	Delaware	10	0.1%
45	Wyoming	29	0.2%		50	Alaska	8	0.1%
						District of Columbia	29	0.2%

Source: U.S. Department of Health and Human Services, National Center for Health Statistics
    (http://wonder.cdc.gov)
*Final data by state of residence. Atherosclerosis is a form of hardening of the arteries.

Death Rate by Atherosclerosis in 2000

National Rate = 5.1 Deaths per 100,000 Population*

ALPHA ORDER

RANK	STATE	RATE
34	Alabama	4.3
49	Alaska**	1.3
31	Arizona	4.6
29	Arkansas	4.7
24	California	4.8
3	Colorado	11.0
24	Connecticut	4.8
49	Delaware**	1.3
12	Florida	6.5
13	Georgia	6.1
48	Hawaii	2.0
47	Idaho	2.5
24	Illinois	4.8
18	Indiana	5.3
5	Iowa	10.0
1	Kansas	13.2
36	Kentucky	4.1
24	Louisiana	4.8
35	Maine	4.2
44	Maryland	3.0
23	Massachusetts	4.9
10	Michigan	6.7
37	Minnesota	3.6
43	Mississippi	3.1
21	Missouri	5.0
8	Montana	8.0
7	Nebraska	9.5
31	Nevada	4.6
16	New Hampshire	5.7
29	New Jersey	4.7
21	New Mexico	5.0
41	New York	3.2
24	North Carolina	4.8
6	North Dakota	9.7
20	Ohio	5.1
2	Oklahoma	12.9
10	Oregon	6.7
18	Pennsylvania	5.3
9	Rhode Island	7.9
45	South Carolina	2.8
37	South Dakota	3.6
14	Tennessee	5.9
37	Texas	3.6
46	Utah	2.7
40	Vermont	3.4
41	Virginia	3.2
16	Washington	5.7
4	West Virginia	10.4
33	Wisconsin	4.4
14	Wyoming	5.9

RANK ORDER

RANK	STATE	RATE
1	Kansas	13.2
2	Oklahoma	12.9
3	Colorado	11.0
4	West Virginia	10.4
5	Iowa	10.0
6	North Dakota	9.7
7	Nebraska	9.5
8	Montana	8.0
9	Rhode Island	7.9
10	Michigan	6.7
10	Oregon	6.7
12	Florida	6.5
13	Georgia	6.1
14	Tennessee	5.9
14	Wyoming	5.9
16	New Hampshire	5.7
16	Washington	5.7
18	Indiana	5.3
18	Pennsylvania	5.3
20	Ohio	5.1
21	Missouri	5.0
21	New Mexico	5.0
23	Massachusetts	4.9
24	California	4.8
24	Connecticut	4.8
24	Illinois	4.8
24	Louisiana	4.8
24	North Carolina	4.8
29	Arkansas	4.7
29	New Jersey	4.7
31	Arizona	4.6
31	Nevada	4.6
33	Wisconsin	4.4
34	Alabama	4.3
35	Maine	4.2
36	Kentucky	4.1
37	Minnesota	3.6
37	South Dakota	3.6
37	Texas	3.6
40	Vermont	3.4
41	New York	3.2
41	Virginia	3.2
43	Mississippi	3.1
44	Maryland	3.0
45	South Carolina	2.8
46	Utah	2.7
47	Idaho	2.5
48	Hawaii	2.0
49	Alaska**	1.3
49	Delaware**	1.3
	District of Columbia	5.1

Source: U.S. Department of Health and Human Services, National Center for Health Statistics
(http://wonder.cdc.gov)
*Final data by state of residence. Atherosclerosis is a form of hardening of the arteries. Not age-adjusted.
**Due to low numbers of deaths, rates for these states should be interpreted with caution.

Age-Adjusted Death Rate by Atherosclerosis in 2000

National Rate = 5.2 Deaths per 100,000 Population*

<table>
<tr><td colspan="3">ALPHA ORDER</td><td colspan="3">RANK ORDER</td></tr>
<tr><td>RANK</td><td>STATE</td><td>RATE</td><td>RANK</td><td>STATE</td><td>RATE</td></tr>
<tr><td>30</td><td>Alabama</td><td>4.3</td><td>1</td><td>Colorado</td><td>14.9</td></tr>
<tr><td>48</td><td>Alaska**</td><td>2.7</td><td>2</td><td>Oklahoma</td><td>12.3</td></tr>
<tr><td>23</td><td>Arizona</td><td>5.0</td><td>3</td><td>Kansas</td><td>11.3</td></tr>
<tr><td>33</td><td>Arkansas</td><td>4.2</td><td>4</td><td>West Virginia</td><td>9.0</td></tr>
<tr><td>18</td><td>California</td><td>5.8</td><td>5</td><td>Georgia</td><td>8.4</td></tr>
<tr><td>1</td><td>Colorado</td><td>14.9</td><td>6</td><td>Nebraska</td><td>8.0</td></tr>
<tr><td>36</td><td>Connecticut</td><td>4.1</td><td>7</td><td>Iowa</td><td>7.6</td></tr>
<tr><td>50</td><td>Delaware**</td><td>1.3</td><td>8</td><td>Montana</td><td>7.4</td></tr>
<tr><td>26</td><td>Florida</td><td>4.8</td><td>9</td><td>Michigan</td><td>7.0</td></tr>
<tr><td>5</td><td>Georgia</td><td>8.4</td><td>9</td><td>North Dakota</td><td>7.0</td></tr>
<tr><td>49</td><td>Hawaii</td><td>2.0</td><td>11</td><td>Nevada</td><td>6.7</td></tr>
<tr><td>47</td><td>Idaho</td><td>2.8</td><td>12</td><td>Wyoming</td><td>6.6</td></tr>
<tr><td>24</td><td>Illinois</td><td>4.9</td><td>13</td><td>Oregon</td><td>6.4</td></tr>
<tr><td>20</td><td>Indiana</td><td>5.5</td><td>14</td><td>Rhode Island</td><td>6.3</td></tr>
<tr><td>7</td><td>Iowa</td><td>7.6</td><td>14</td><td>Tennessee</td><td>6.3</td></tr>
<tr><td>3</td><td>Kansas</td><td>11.3</td><td>14</td><td>Washington</td><td>6.3</td></tr>
<tr><td>30</td><td>Kentucky</td><td>4.3</td><td>17</td><td>New Hampshire</td><td>6.0</td></tr>
<tr><td>20</td><td>Louisiana</td><td>5.5</td><td>18</td><td>California</td><td>5.8</td></tr>
<tr><td>39</td><td>Maine</td><td>3.7</td><td>18</td><td>New Mexico</td><td>5.8</td></tr>
<tr><td>40</td><td>Maryland</td><td>3.5</td><td>20</td><td>Indiana</td><td>5.5</td></tr>
<tr><td>30</td><td>Massachusetts</td><td>4.3</td><td>20</td><td>Louisiana</td><td>5.5</td></tr>
<tr><td>9</td><td>Michigan</td><td>7.0</td><td>22</td><td>North Carolina</td><td>5.3</td></tr>
<tr><td>41</td><td>Minnesota</td><td>3.4</td><td>23</td><td>Arizona</td><td>5.0</td></tr>
<tr><td>43</td><td>Mississippi</td><td>3.3</td><td>24</td><td>Illinois</td><td>4.9</td></tr>
<tr><td>28</td><td>Missouri</td><td>4.5</td><td>24</td><td>Ohio</td><td>4.9</td></tr>
<tr><td>8</td><td>Montana</td><td>7.4</td><td>26</td><td>Florida</td><td>4.8</td></tr>
<tr><td>6</td><td>Nebraska</td><td>8.0</td><td>26</td><td>Texas</td><td>4.8</td></tr>
<tr><td>11</td><td>Nevada</td><td>6.7</td><td>28</td><td>Missouri</td><td>4.5</td></tr>
<tr><td>17</td><td>New Hampshire</td><td>6.0</td><td>28</td><td>New Jersey</td><td>4.5</td></tr>
<tr><td>28</td><td>New Jersey</td><td>4.5</td><td>30</td><td>Alabama</td><td>4.3</td></tr>
<tr><td>18</td><td>New Mexico</td><td>5.8</td><td>30</td><td>Kentucky</td><td>4.3</td></tr>
<tr><td>44</td><td>New York</td><td>3.1</td><td>30</td><td>Massachusetts</td><td>4.3</td></tr>
<tr><td>22</td><td>North Carolina</td><td>5.3</td><td>33</td><td>Arkansas</td><td>4.2</td></tr>
<tr><td>9</td><td>North Dakota</td><td>7.0</td><td>33</td><td>Pennsylvania</td><td>4.2</td></tr>
<tr><td>24</td><td>Ohio</td><td>4.9</td><td>33</td><td>Utah</td><td>4.2</td></tr>
<tr><td>2</td><td>Oklahoma</td><td>12.3</td><td>36</td><td>Connecticut</td><td>4.1</td></tr>
<tr><td>13</td><td>Oregon</td><td>6.4</td><td>37</td><td>Wisconsin</td><td>4.0</td></tr>
<tr><td>33</td><td>Pennsylvania</td><td>4.2</td><td>38</td><td>Virginia</td><td>3.9</td></tr>
<tr><td>14</td><td>Rhode Island</td><td>6.3</td><td>39</td><td>Maine</td><td>3.7</td></tr>
<tr><td>44</td><td>South Carolina</td><td>3.1</td><td>40</td><td>Maryland</td><td>3.5</td></tr>
<tr><td>46</td><td>South Dakota</td><td>2.9</td><td>41</td><td>Minnesota</td><td>3.4</td></tr>
<tr><td>14</td><td>Tennessee</td><td>6.3</td><td>41</td><td>Vermont</td><td>3.4</td></tr>
<tr><td>26</td><td>Texas</td><td>4.8</td><td>43</td><td>Mississippi</td><td>3.3</td></tr>
<tr><td>33</td><td>Utah</td><td>4.2</td><td>44</td><td>New York</td><td>3.1</td></tr>
<tr><td>41</td><td>Vermont</td><td>3.4</td><td>44</td><td>South Carolina</td><td>3.1</td></tr>
<tr><td>38</td><td>Virginia</td><td>3.9</td><td>46</td><td>South Dakota</td><td>2.9</td></tr>
<tr><td>14</td><td>Washington</td><td>6.3</td><td>47</td><td>Idaho</td><td>2.8</td></tr>
<tr><td>4</td><td>West Virginia</td><td>9.0</td><td>48</td><td>Alaska**</td><td>2.7</td></tr>
<tr><td>37</td><td>Wisconsin</td><td>4.0</td><td>49</td><td>Hawaii</td><td>2.0</td></tr>
<tr><td>12</td><td>Wyoming</td><td>6.6</td><td>50</td><td>Delaware**</td><td>1.3</td></tr>
<tr><td></td><td></td><td></td><td></td><td>District of Columbia</td><td>5.1</td></tr>
</table>

Source: U.S. Department of Health and Human Services, National Center for Health Statistics
   (http://wonder.cdc.gov)

*Final data by state of residence. Atherosclerosis is a form of hardening of the arteries. Age-adjusted rates based on the year 2000 standard population.

**Due to low numbers of deaths, rates for these states should be interpreted with caution.

Deaths by Cerebrovascular Diseases in 2001

National Total = 163,538 Deaths*

ALPHA ORDER

RANK	STATE	DEATHS	% of USA	RANK	STATE	DEATHS	% of USA
19	Alabama	2,998	1.8%	1	California	18,088	11.1%
50	Alaska	158	0.1%	2	Texas	10,612	6.5%
26	Arizona	2,480	1.5%	3	Florida	10,414	6.4%
28	Arkansas	2,256	1.4%	4	Pennsylvania	8,619	5.3%
1	California	18,088	11.1%	5	New York	7,706	4.7%
33	Colorado	1,825	1.1%	6	Illinois	7,230	4.4%
30	Connecticut	2,003	1.2%	7	Ohio	6,891	4.2%
47	Delaware	383	0.2%	8	Michigan	5,701	3.5%
3	Florida	10,414	6.4%	9	North Carolina	5,401	3.3%
10	Georgia	4,312	2.6%	10	Georgia	4,312	2.6%
41	Hawaii	766	0.5%	11	Virginia	4,129	2.5%
40	Idaho	781	0.5%	12	Tennessee	4,037	2.5%
6	Illinois	7,230	4.4%	13	New Jersey	4,007	2.5%
14	Indiana	3,877	2.4%	14	Indiana	3,877	2.4%
29	Iowa	2,218	1.4%	15	Missouri	3,796	2.3%
32	Kansas	1,848	1.1%	16	Washington	3,765	2.3%
25	Kentucky	2,557	1.6%	17	Wisconsin	3,658	2.2%
23	Louisiana	2,638	1.6%	18	Massachusetts	3,535	2.2%
39	Maine	822	0.5%	19	Alabama	2,998	1.8%
20	Maryland	2,882	1.8%	20	Maryland	2,882	1.8%
18	Massachusetts	3,535	2.2%	21	South Carolina	2,832	1.7%
8	Michigan	5,701	3.5%	22	Minnesota	2,727	1.7%
22	Minnesota	2,727	1.7%	23	Louisiana	2,638	1.6%
31	Mississippi	1,935	1.2%	24	Oregon	2,588	1.6%
15	Missouri	3,796	2.3%	25	Kentucky	2,557	1.6%
44	Montana	578	0.4%	26	Arizona	2,480	1.5%
35	Nebraska	1,130	0.7%	27	Oklahoma	2,384	1.5%
36	Nevada	913	0.6%	28	Arkansas	2,256	1.4%
42	New Hampshire	633	0.4%	29	Iowa	2,218	1.4%
13	New Jersey	4,007	2.5%	30	Connecticut	2,003	1.2%
38	New Mexico	824	0.5%	31	Mississippi	1,935	1.2%
5	New York	7,706	4.7%	32	Kansas	1,848	1.1%
9	North Carolina	5,401	3.3%	33	Colorado	1,825	1.1%
45	North Dakota	507	0.3%	34	West Virginia	1,272	0.8%
7	Ohio	6,891	4.2%	35	Nebraska	1,130	0.7%
27	Oklahoma	2,384	1.5%	36	Nevada	913	0.6%
24	Oregon	2,588	1.6%	37	Utah	870	0.5%
4	Pennsylvania	8,619	5.3%	38	New Mexico	824	0.5%
43	Rhode Island	614	0.4%	39	Maine	822	0.5%
21	South Carolina	2,832	1.7%	40	Idaho	781	0.5%
46	South Dakota	490	0.3%	41	Hawaii	766	0.5%
12	Tennessee	4,037	2.5%	42	New Hampshire	633	0.4%
2	Texas	10,612	6.5%	43	Rhode Island	614	0.4%
37	Utah	870	0.5%	44	Montana	578	0.4%
48	Vermont	323	0.2%	45	North Dakota	507	0.3%
11	Virginia	4,129	2.5%	46	South Dakota	490	0.3%
16	Washington	3,765	2.3%	47	Delaware	383	0.2%
34	West Virginia	1,272	0.8%	48	Vermont	323	0.2%
17	Wisconsin	3,658	2.2%	49	Wyoming	260	0.2%
49	Wyoming	260	0.2%	50	Alaska	158	0.1%
					District of Columbia	265	0.2%

RANK ORDER

Source: U.S. Department of Health and Human Services, National Center for Health Statistics
    "National Vital Statistics Reports" (Vol. 52, No. 3, September 18, 2003)
*Final data by state of residence. Cerebrovascular diseases include stroke and other disorders of the blood
vessels of the brain.

Death Rate by Cerebrovascular Diseases in 2001

National Rate = 57.4 Deaths per 100,000 Population*

ALPHA ORDER

RANK	STATE	RATE
14	Alabama	67.1
50	Alaska	24.9
44	Arizona	46.7
1	Arkansas	83.7
38	California	52.3
47	Colorado	41.2
28	Connecticut	58.3
42	Delaware	48.1
20	Florida	63.6
39	Georgia	51.3
24	Hawaii	62.4
26	Idaho	59.1
30	Illinois	57.7
21	Indiana	63.3
3	Iowa	75.6
10	Kansas	68.4
22	Kentucky	62.8
27	Louisiana	59.0
18	Maine	64.0
35	Maryland	53.5
33	Massachusetts	55.2
32	Michigan	57.0
34	Minnesota	54.7
11	Mississippi	67.7
13	Missouri	67.3
19	Montana	63.8
16	Nebraska	65.7
46	Nevada	43.5
40	New Hampshire	50.3
43	New Jersey	47.1
45	New Mexico	45.0
48	New York	40.4
15	North Carolina	65.8
2	North Dakota	79.6
25	Ohio	60.5
9	Oklahoma	68.7
4	Oregon	74.5
7	Pennsylvania	70.1
29	Rhode Island	57.9
8	South Carolina	69.7
17	South Dakota	64.6
6	Tennessee	70.2
41	Texas	49.7
49	Utah	38.2
36	Vermont	52.7
31	Virginia	57.4
22	Washington	62.8
5	West Virginia	70.6
11	Wisconsin	67.7
36	Wyoming	52.7

RANK ORDER

RANK	STATE	RATE
1	Arkansas	83.7
2	North Dakota	79.6
3	Iowa	75.6
4	Oregon	74.5
5	West Virginia	70.6
6	Tennessee	70.2
7	Pennsylvania	70.1
8	South Carolina	69.7
9	Oklahoma	68.7
10	Kansas	68.4
11	Mississippi	67.7
11	Wisconsin	67.7
13	Missouri	67.3
14	Alabama	67.1
15	North Carolina	65.8
16	Nebraska	65.7
17	South Dakota	64.6
18	Maine	64.0
19	Montana	63.8
20	Florida	63.6
21	Indiana	63.3
22	Kentucky	62.8
22	Washington	62.8
24	Hawaii	62.4
25	Ohio	60.5
26	Idaho	59.1
27	Louisiana	59.0
28	Connecticut	58.3
29	Rhode Island	57.9
30	Illinois	57.7
31	Virginia	57.4
32	Michigan	57.0
33	Massachusetts	55.2
34	Minnesota	54.7
35	Maryland	53.5
36	Vermont	52.7
36	Wyoming	52.7
38	California	52.3
39	Georgia	51.3
40	New Hampshire	50.3
41	Texas	49.7
42	Delaware	48.1
43	New Jersey	47.1
44	Arizona	46.7
45	New Mexico	45.0
46	Nevada	43.5
47	Colorado	41.2
48	New York	40.4
49	Utah	38.2
50	Alaska	24.9
	District of Columbia	46.2

Source: U.S. Department of Health and Human Services, National Center for Health Statistics
   "National Vital Statistics Reports" (Vol. 52, No. 3, September 18, 2003)
*Final data by state of residence. Cerebrovascular diseases include stroke and other disorders of the blood vessels of the brain. Not age-adjusted.

Age-Adjusted Death Rate by Cerebrovascular Diseases in 2001

National Rate = 57.9 Deaths per 100,000 Population*

<table>
<tr><td colspan="3">ALPHA ORDER</td><td colspan="3">RANK ORDER</td></tr>
<tr><td>RANK</td><td>STATE</td><td>RATE</td><td>RANK</td><td>STATE</td><td>RATE</td></tr>
<tr><td>9</td><td>Alabama</td><td>66.0</td><td>1</td><td>Arkansas</td><td>75.9</td></tr>
<tr><td>29</td><td>Alaska</td><td>57.4</td><td>2</td><td>South Carolina</td><td>75.0</td></tr>
<tr><td>46</td><td>Arizona</td><td>48.2</td><td>3</td><td>Tennessee</td><td>72.3</td></tr>
<tr><td>1</td><td>Arkansas</td><td>75.9</td><td>4</td><td>North Carolina</td><td>71.3</td></tr>
<tr><td>19</td><td>California</td><td>61.2</td><td>5</td><td>Mississippi</td><td>70.5</td></tr>
<tr><td>37</td><td>Colorado</td><td>53.9</td><td>6</td><td>Oregon</td><td>69.5</td></tr>
<tr><td>42</td><td>Connecticut</td><td>49.6</td><td>7</td><td>Georgia</td><td>67.3</td></tr>
<tr><td>44</td><td>Delaware</td><td>49.2</td><td>8</td><td>Washington</td><td>67.2</td></tr>
<tr><td>47</td><td>Florida</td><td>47.6</td><td>9</td><td>Alabama</td><td>66.0</td></tr>
<tr><td>7</td><td>Georgia</td><td>67.3</td><td>10</td><td>Oklahoma</td><td>65.6</td></tr>
<tr><td>22</td><td>Hawaii</td><td>59.8</td><td>11</td><td>Virginia</td><td>65.4</td></tr>
<tr><td>13</td><td>Idaho</td><td>64.7</td><td>12</td><td>Louisiana</td><td>64.8</td></tr>
<tr><td>26</td><td>Illinois</td><td>58.4</td><td>13</td><td>Idaho</td><td>64.7</td></tr>
<tr><td>16</td><td>Indiana</td><td>63.7</td><td>14</td><td>Kentucky</td><td>64.4</td></tr>
<tr><td>25</td><td>Iowa</td><td>58.8</td><td>15</td><td>Texas</td><td>63.8</td></tr>
<tr><td>21</td><td>Kansas</td><td>60.3</td><td>16</td><td>Indiana</td><td>63.7</td></tr>
<tr><td>14</td><td>Kentucky</td><td>64.4</td><td>17</td><td>Wisconsin</td><td>61.7</td></tr>
<tr><td>12</td><td>Louisiana</td><td>64.8</td><td>18</td><td>Missouri</td><td>61.6</td></tr>
<tr><td>36</td><td>Maine</td><td>54.7</td><td>19</td><td>California</td><td>61.2</td></tr>
<tr><td>23</td><td>Maryland</td><td>59.6</td><td>20</td><td>North Dakota</td><td>60.4</td></tr>
<tr><td>45</td><td>Massachusetts</td><td>48.6</td><td>21</td><td>Kansas</td><td>60.3</td></tr>
<tr><td>27</td><td>Michigan</td><td>58.2</td><td>22</td><td>Hawaii</td><td>59.8</td></tr>
<tr><td>38</td><td>Minnesota</td><td>52.5</td><td>23</td><td>Maryland</td><td>59.6</td></tr>
<tr><td>5</td><td>Mississippi</td><td>70.5</td><td>24</td><td>West Virginia</td><td>59.4</td></tr>
<tr><td>18</td><td>Missouri</td><td>61.6</td><td>25</td><td>Iowa</td><td>58.8</td></tr>
<tr><td>28</td><td>Montana</td><td>57.6</td><td>26</td><td>Illinois</td><td>58.4</td></tr>
<tr><td>31</td><td>Nebraska</td><td>57.3</td><td>27</td><td>Michigan</td><td>58.2</td></tr>
<tr><td>35</td><td>Nevada</td><td>55.1</td><td>28</td><td>Montana</td><td>57.6</td></tr>
<tr><td>40</td><td>New Hampshire</td><td>52.0</td><td>29</td><td>Alaska</td><td>57.4</td></tr>
<tr><td>49</td><td>New Jersey</td><td>44.2</td><td>29</td><td>Ohio</td><td>57.4</td></tr>
<tr><td>42</td><td>New Mexico</td><td>49.6</td><td>31</td><td>Nebraska</td><td>57.3</td></tr>
<tr><td>50</td><td>New York</td><td>38.4</td><td>32</td><td>Utah</td><td>56.4</td></tr>
<tr><td>4</td><td>North Carolina</td><td>71.3</td><td>33</td><td>Wyoming</td><td>56.1</td></tr>
<tr><td>20</td><td>North Dakota</td><td>60.4</td><td>34</td><td>Pennsylvania</td><td>55.5</td></tr>
<tr><td>29</td><td>Ohio</td><td>57.4</td><td>35</td><td>Nevada</td><td>55.1</td></tr>
<tr><td>10</td><td>Oklahoma</td><td>65.6</td><td>36</td><td>Maine</td><td>54.7</td></tr>
<tr><td>6</td><td>Oregon</td><td>69.5</td><td>37</td><td>Colorado</td><td>53.9</td></tr>
<tr><td>34</td><td>Pennsylvania</td><td>55.5</td><td>38</td><td>Minnesota</td><td>52.5</td></tr>
<tr><td>48</td><td>Rhode Island</td><td>47.4</td><td>38</td><td>South Dakota</td><td>52.5</td></tr>
<tr><td>2</td><td>South Carolina</td><td>75.0</td><td>40</td><td>New Hampshire</td><td>52.0</td></tr>
<tr><td>38</td><td>South Dakota</td><td>52.5</td><td>41</td><td>Vermont</td><td>50.2</td></tr>
<tr><td>3</td><td>Tennessee</td><td>72.3</td><td>42</td><td>Connecticut</td><td>49.6</td></tr>
<tr><td>15</td><td>Texas</td><td>63.8</td><td>42</td><td>New Mexico</td><td>49.6</td></tr>
<tr><td>32</td><td>Utah</td><td>56.4</td><td>44</td><td>Delaware</td><td>49.2</td></tr>
<tr><td>41</td><td>Vermont</td><td>50.2</td><td>45</td><td>Massachusetts</td><td>48.6</td></tr>
<tr><td>11</td><td>Virginia</td><td>65.4</td><td>46</td><td>Arizona</td><td>48.2</td></tr>
<tr><td>8</td><td>Washington</td><td>67.2</td><td>47</td><td>Florida</td><td>47.6</td></tr>
<tr><td>24</td><td>West Virginia</td><td>59.4</td><td>48</td><td>Rhode Island</td><td>47.4</td></tr>
<tr><td>17</td><td>Wisconsin</td><td>61.7</td><td>49</td><td>New Jersey</td><td>44.2</td></tr>
<tr><td>33</td><td>Wyoming</td><td>56.1</td><td>50</td><td>New York</td><td>38.4</td></tr>
<tr><td></td><td></td><td></td><td></td><td>District of Columbia</td><td>46.4</td></tr>
</table>

Source: U.S. Department of Health and Human Services, National Center for Health Statistics
"National Vital Statistics Reports" (Vol. 52, No. 3, September 18, 2003)
*Final data by state of residence. Cerebrovascular diseases include stroke and other disorders of the blood
vessels of the brain. Age-adjusted rates based on the year 2000 standard population.

Deaths by Chronic Liver Disease and Cirrhosis in 2001

National Total = 27,035 Deaths*

ALPHA ORDER

RANK	STATE	DEATHS	% of USA
20	Alabama	445	1.6%
48	Alaska	57	0.2%
11	Arizona	661	2.4%
33	Arkansas	233	0.9%
1	California	3,692	13.7%
23	Colorado	420	1.6%
31	Connecticut	294	1.1%
46	Delaware	75	0.3%
3	Florida	2,013	7.4%
12	Georgia	654	2.4%
44	Hawaii	84	0.3%
40	Idaho	105	0.4%
6	Illinois	1,103	4.1%
19	Indiana	459	1.7%
34	Iowa	214	0.8%
36	Kansas	208	0.8%
24	Kentucky	387	1.4%
28	Louisiana	327	1.2%
39	Maine	111	0.4%
17	Maryland	481	1.8%
15	Massachusetts	556	2.1%
7	Michigan	1,058	3.9%
26	Minnesota	359	1.3%
32	Mississippi	265	1.0%
21	Missouri	439	1.6%
41	Montana	104	0.4%
42	Nebraska	103	0.4%
30	Nevada	297	1.1%
38	New Hampshire	121	0.4%
9	New Jersey	778	2.9%
29	New Mexico	302	1.1%
4	New York	1,488	5.5%
10	North Carolina	725	2.7%
47	North Dakota	62	0.2%
8	Ohio	1,027	3.8%
25	Oklahoma	363	1.3%
27	Oregon	339	1.3%
5	Pennsylvania	1,134	4.2%
43	Rhode Island	96	0.4%
18	South Carolina	461	1.7%
45	South Dakota	77	0.3%
13	Tennessee	613	2.3%
2	Texas	2,213	8.2%
37	Utah	138	0.5%
50	Vermont	37	0.1%
16	Virginia	531	2.0%
14	Washington	571	2.1%
35	West Virginia	212	0.8%
22	Wisconsin	431	1.6%
49	Wyoming	49	0.2%

RANK ORDER

RANK	STATE	DEATHS	% of USA
1	California	3,692	13.7%
2	Texas	2,213	8.2%
3	Florida	2,013	7.4%
4	New York	1,488	5.5%
5	Pennsylvania	1,134	4.2%
6	Illinois	1,103	4.1%
7	Michigan	1,058	3.9%
8	Ohio	1,027	3.8%
9	New Jersey	778	2.9%
10	North Carolina	725	2.7%
11	Arizona	661	2.4%
12	Georgia	654	2.4%
13	Tennessee	613	2.3%
14	Washington	571	2.1%
15	Massachusetts	556	2.1%
16	Virginia	531	2.0%
17	Maryland	481	1.8%
18	South Carolina	461	1.7%
19	Indiana	459	1.7%
20	Alabama	445	1.6%
21	Missouri	439	1.6%
22	Wisconsin	431	1.6%
23	Colorado	420	1.6%
24	Kentucky	387	1.4%
25	Oklahoma	363	1.3%
26	Minnesota	359	1.3%
27	Oregon	339	1.3%
28	Louisiana	327	1.2%
29	New Mexico	302	1.1%
30	Nevada	297	1.1%
31	Connecticut	294	1.1%
32	Mississippi	265	1.0%
33	Arkansas	233	0.9%
34	Iowa	214	0.8%
35	West Virginia	212	0.8%
36	Kansas	208	0.8%
37	Utah	138	0.5%
38	New Hampshire	121	0.4%
39	Maine	111	0.4%
40	Idaho	105	0.4%
41	Montana	104	0.4%
42	Nebraska	103	0.4%
43	Rhode Island	96	0.4%
44	Hawaii	84	0.3%
45	South Dakota	77	0.3%
46	Delaware	75	0.3%
47	North Dakota	62	0.2%
48	Alaska	57	0.2%
49	Wyoming	49	0.2%
50	Vermont	37	0.1%
	District of Columbia	63	0.2%

Source: U.S. Department of Health and Human Services, National Center for Health Statistics
    "National Vital Statistics Reports" (Vol. 52, No. 3, September 18, 2003)
*Final data by state of residence. Cirrhosis of the liver is characterized by the replacement of normal tissue with fibrous tissue and the loss of functional liver cells. It can result from alcohol abuse, nutritional deprivation, or infection especially by the hepatitis virus.

Death Rate by Chronic Liver Disease and Cirrhosis in 2001

National Rate = 9.5 Deaths per 100,000 Population*

ALPHA ORDER

RANK	STATE	RATE
14	Alabama	10.0
27	Alaska	9.0
3	Arizona	12.5
33	Arkansas	8.6
8	California	10.7
19	Colorado	9.5
33	Connecticut	8.6
22	Delaware	9.4
4	Florida	12.3
38	Georgia	7.8
47	Hawaii	6.8
36	Idaho	8.0
30	Illinois	8.8
42	Indiana	7.5
44	Iowa	7.3
41	Kansas	7.7
19	Kentucky	9.5
44	Louisiana	7.3
33	Maine	8.6
29	Maryland	8.9
32	Massachusetts	8.7
10	Michigan	10.6
46	Minnesota	7.2
23	Mississippi	9.3
38	Missouri	7.8
6	Montana	11.5
49	Nebraska	6.0
2	Nevada	14.2
18	New Hampshire	9.6
25	New Jersey	9.1
1	New Mexico	16.5
38	New York	7.8
30	North Carolina	8.8
17	North Dakota	9.7
27	Ohio	9.0
11	Oklahoma	10.5
16	Oregon	9.8
24	Pennsylvania	9.2
25	Rhode Island	9.1
7	South Carolina	11.3
13	South Dakota	10.2
8	Tennessee	10.7
12	Texas	10.4
48	Utah	6.1
49	Vermont	6.0
43	Virginia	7.4
19	Washington	9.5
5	West Virginia	11.8
36	Wisconsin	8.0
15	Wyoming	9.9

RANK ORDER

RANK	STATE	RATE
1	New Mexico	16.5
2	Nevada	14.2
3	Arizona	12.5
4	Florida	12.3
5	West Virginia	11.8
6	Montana	11.5
7	South Carolina	11.3
8	California	10.7
8	Tennessee	10.7
10	Michigan	10.6
11	Oklahoma	10.5
12	Texas	10.4
13	South Dakota	10.2
14	Alabama	10.0
15	Wyoming	9.9
16	Oregon	9.8
17	North Dakota	9.7
18	New Hampshire	9.6
19	Colorado	9.5
19	Kentucky	9.5
19	Washington	9.5
22	Delaware	9.4
23	Mississippi	9.3
24	Pennsylvania	9.2
25	New Jersey	9.1
25	Rhode Island	9.1
27	Alaska	9.0
27	Ohio	9.0
29	Maryland	8.9
30	Illinois	8.8
30	North Carolina	8.8
32	Massachusetts	8.7
33	Arkansas	8.6
33	Connecticut	8.6
33	Maine	8.6
36	Idaho	8.0
36	Wisconsin	8.0
38	Georgia	7.8
38	Missouri	7.8
38	New York	7.8
41	Kansas	7.7
42	Indiana	7.5
43	Virginia	7.4
44	Iowa	7.3
44	Louisiana	7.3
46	Minnesota	7.2
47	Hawaii	6.8
48	Utah	6.1
49	Nebraska	6.0
49	Vermont	6.0

| | District of Columbia | 11.0 |

Source: U.S. Department of Health and Human Services, National Center for Health Statistics
   "National Vital Statistics Reports" (Vol. 52, No. 3, September 18, 2003)
*Final data by state of residence. Cirrhosis of the liver is characterized by the replacement of normal tissue with fibrous tissue and the loss of functional liver cells. It can result from alcohol abuse, nutritional deprivation, or infection especially by the hepatitis virus. Not age-adjusted.

Age-Adjusted Death Rate by Chronic Liver Disease and Cirrhosis in 2001

National Rate = 9.5 Deaths per 100,000 Population*

ALPHA ORDER

RANK	STATE	RATE
18	Alabama	9.6
8	Alaska	10.7
3	Arizona	12.8
33	Arkansas	8.3
5	California	11.7
13	Colorado	10.2
37	Connecticut	8.0
24	Delaware	9.1
7	Florida	10.8
28	Georgia	8.7
48	Hawaii	6.4
31	Idaho	8.5
24	Illinois	9.1
43	Indiana	7.5
47	Iowa	6.8
39	Kansas	7.7
23	Kentucky	9.2
40	Louisiana	7.6
40	Maine	7.6
26	Maryland	9.0
33	Massachusetts	8.3
10	Michigan	10.5
46	Minnesota	7.3
18	Mississippi	9.6
43	Missouri	7.5
9	Montana	10.6
49	Nebraska	5.9
2	Nevada	14.5
18	New Hampshire	9.6
28	New Jersey	8.7
1	New Mexico	16.7
40	New York	7.6
27	North Carolina	8.9
22	North Dakota	9.3
28	Ohio	8.7
13	Oklahoma	10.2
21	Oregon	9.4
35	Pennsylvania	8.1
32	Rhode Island	8.4
6	South Carolina	11.2
15	South Dakota	10.1
11	Tennessee	10.4
4	Texas	11.8
35	Utah	8.1
50	Vermont	5.6
43	Virginia	7.5
16	Washington	9.8
12	West Virginia	10.3
38	Wisconsin	7.8
17	Wyoming	9.7

RANK ORDER

RANK	STATE	RATE
1	New Mexico	16.7
2	Nevada	14.5
3	Arizona	12.8
4	Texas	11.8
5	California	11.7
6	South Carolina	11.2
7	Florida	10.8
8	Alaska	10.7
9	Montana	10.6
10	Michigan	10.5
11	Tennessee	10.4
12	West Virginia	10.3
13	Colorado	10.2
13	Oklahoma	10.2
15	South Dakota	10.1
16	Washington	9.8
17	Wyoming	9.7
18	Alabama	9.6
18	Mississippi	9.6
18	New Hampshire	9.6
21	Oregon	9.4
22	North Dakota	9.3
23	Kentucky	9.2
24	Delaware	9.1
24	Illinois	9.1
26	Maryland	9.0
27	North Carolina	8.9
28	Georgia	8.7
28	New Jersey	8.7
28	Ohio	8.7
31	Idaho	8.5
32	Rhode Island	8.4
33	Arkansas	8.3
33	Massachusetts	8.3
35	Pennsylvania	8.1
35	Utah	8.1
37	Connecticut	8.0
38	Wisconsin	7.8
39	Kansas	7.7
40	Louisiana	7.6
40	Maine	7.6
40	New York	7.6
43	Indiana	7.5
43	Missouri	7.5
43	Virginia	7.5
46	Minnesota	7.3
47	Iowa	6.8
48	Hawaii	6.4
49	Nebraska	5.9
50	Vermont	5.6

District of Columbia	11.1

Source: U.S. Department of Health and Human Services, National Center for Health Statistics
    "National Vital Statistics Reports" (Vol. 52, No. 3, September 18, 2003)
*Final data by state of residence. Cirrhosis of the liver is characterized by the replacement of normal tissue with fibrous tissue and the loss of functional liver cells. It can result from alcohol abuse, nutritional deprivation, or infection especially by the hepatitis virus. Age-adjusted rates based on the year 2000 standard population.

Deaths by Chronic Lower Respiratory Diseases in 2001

National Total = 123,013 Deaths*

ALPHA ORDER

RANK	STATE	DEATHS	% of USA
21	Alabama	2,204	1.8%
50	Alaska	147	0.1%
18	Arizona	2,499	2.0%
32	Arkansas	1,368	1.1%
1	California	12,965	10.5%
25	Colorado	1,836	1.5%
30	Connecticut	1,486	1.2%
46	Delaware	306	0.2%
2	Florida	8,954	7.3%
11	Georgia	3,097	2.5%
48	Hawaii	280	0.2%
41	Idaho	581	0.5%
7	Illinois	4,776	3.9%
10	Indiana	3,136	2.5%
29	Iowa	1,552	1.3%
31	Kansas	1,444	1.2%
20	Kentucky	2,265	1.8%
26	Louisiana	1,763	1.4%
37	Maine	800	0.7%
24	Maryland	1,907	1.6%
15	Massachusetts	2,810	2.3%
8	Michigan	4,148	3.4%
23	Minnesota	1,909	1.6%
33	Mississippi	1,333	1.1%
14	Missouri	2,882	2.3%
40	Montana	583	0.5%
36	Nebraska	882	0.7%
35	Nevada	1,136	0.9%
39	New Hampshire	616	0.5%
13	New Jersey	2,911	2.4%
38	New Mexico	775	0.6%
4	New York	6,906	5.6%
9	North Carolina	3,514	2.9%
45	North Dakota	308	0.3%
5	Ohio	5,881	4.8%
22	Oklahoma	1,922	1.6%
28	Oregon	1,726	1.4%
6	Pennsylvania	5,845	4.8%
43	Rhode Island	511	0.4%
27	South Carolina	1,731	1.4%
44	South Dakota	362	0.3%
12	Tennessee	2,941	2.4%
3	Texas	7,739	6.3%
42	Utah	525	0.4%
47	Vermont	305	0.2%
16	Virginia	2,744	2.2%
17	Washington	2,634	2.1%
34	West Virginia	1,273	1.0%
19	Wisconsin	2,375	1.9%
49	Wyoming	270	0.2%

RANK ORDER

RANK	STATE	DEATHS	% of USA
1	California	12,965	10.5%
2	Florida	8,954	7.3%
3	Texas	7,739	6.3%
4	New York	6,906	5.6%
5	Ohio	5,881	4.8%
6	Pennsylvania	5,845	4.8%
7	Illinois	4,776	3.9%
8	Michigan	4,148	3.4%
9	North Carolina	3,514	2.9%
10	Indiana	3,136	2.5%
11	Georgia	3,097	2.5%
12	Tennessee	2,941	2.4%
13	New Jersey	2,911	2.4%
14	Missouri	2,882	2.3%
15	Massachusetts	2,810	2.3%
16	Virginia	2,744	2.2%
17	Washington	2,634	2.1%
18	Arizona	2,499	2.0%
19	Wisconsin	2,375	1.9%
20	Kentucky	2,265	1.8%
21	Alabama	2,204	1.8%
22	Oklahoma	1,922	1.6%
23	Minnesota	1,909	1.6%
24	Maryland	1,907	1.6%
25	Colorado	1,836	1.5%
26	Louisiana	1,763	1.4%
27	South Carolina	1,731	1.4%
28	Oregon	1,726	1.4%
29	Iowa	1,552	1.3%
30	Connecticut	1,486	1.2%
31	Kansas	1,444	1.2%
32	Arkansas	1,368	1.1%
33	Mississippi	1,333	1.1%
34	West Virginia	1,273	1.0%
35	Nevada	1,136	0.9%
36	Nebraska	882	0.7%
37	Maine	800	0.7%
38	New Mexico	775	0.6%
39	New Hampshire	616	0.5%
40	Montana	583	0.5%
41	Idaho	581	0.5%
42	Utah	525	0.4%
43	Rhode Island	511	0.4%
44	South Dakota	362	0.3%
45	North Dakota	308	0.3%
46	Delaware	306	0.2%
47	Vermont	305	0.2%
48	Hawaii	280	0.2%
49	Wyoming	270	0.2%
50	Alaska	147	0.1%
	District of Columbia	150	0.1%

Source: U.S. Department of Health and Human Services, National Center for Health Statistics
"National Vital Statistics Reports" (Vol. 52, No. 3, September 18, 2003)
*Final data by state of residence. Chronic lower respiratory diseases are diseases of the lungs including bronchitis, emphysema and asthma. Includes allied conditions.

Death Rate by Chronic Lower Respiratory Diseases in 2001

National Rate = 43.2 Deaths per 100,000 Population*

ALPHA ORDER

RANK	STATE	RATE
19	Alabama	49.3
48	Alaska	23.2
25	Arizona	47.1
16	Arkansas	50.8
42	California	37.5
36	Colorado	41.4
31	Connecticut	43.3
38	Delaware	38.4
6	Florida	54.7
43	Georgia	36.8
50	Hawaii	22.8
27	Idaho	44.0
40	Illinois	38.1
13	Indiana	51.2
10	Iowa	52.9
9	Kansas	53.4
4	Kentucky	55.7
37	Louisiana	39.4
3	Maine	62.3
46	Maryland	35.4
28	Massachusetts	43.9
35	Michigan	41.5
39	Minnesota	38.3
26	Mississippi	46.6
15	Missouri	51.1
2	Montana	64.4
12	Nebraska	51.3
8	Nevada	54.2
20	New Hampshire	48.9
47	New Jersey	34.2
34	New Mexico	42.3
44	New York	36.2
32	North Carolina	42.8
21	North Dakota	48.4
11	Ohio	51.6
5	Oklahoma	55.4
18	Oregon	49.7
24	Pennsylvania	47.5
22	Rhode Island	48.2
33	South Carolina	42.6
23	South Dakota	47.7
13	Tennessee	51.2
44	Texas	36.2
49	Utah	23.0
17	Vermont	49.8
40	Virginia	38.1
28	Washington	43.9
1	West Virginia	70.7
28	Wisconsin	43.9
6	Wyoming	54.7

RANK ORDER

RANK	STATE	RATE
1	West Virginia	70.7
2	Montana	64.4
3	Maine	62.3
4	Kentucky	55.7
5	Oklahoma	55.4
6	Florida	54.7
6	Wyoming	54.7
8	Nevada	54.2
9	Kansas	53.4
10	Iowa	52.9
11	Ohio	51.6
12	Nebraska	51.3
13	Indiana	51.2
13	Tennessee	51.2
15	Missouri	51.1
16	Arkansas	50.8
17	Vermont	49.8
18	Oregon	49.7
19	Alabama	49.3
20	New Hampshire	48.9
21	North Dakota	48.4
22	Rhode Island	48.2
23	South Dakota	47.7
24	Pennsylvania	47.5
25	Arizona	47.1
26	Mississippi	46.6
27	Idaho	44.0
28	Massachusetts	43.9
28	Washington	43.9
28	Wisconsin	43.9
31	Connecticut	43.3
32	North Carolina	42.8
33	South Carolina	42.6
34	New Mexico	42.3
35	Michigan	41.5
36	Colorado	41.4
37	Louisiana	39.4
38	Delaware	38.4
39	Minnesota	38.3
40	Illinois	38.1
40	Virginia	38.1
42	California	37.5
43	Georgia	36.8
44	New York	36.2
44	Texas	36.2
46	Maryland	35.4
47	New Jersey	34.2
48	Alaska	23.2
49	Utah	23.0
50	Hawaii	22.8
	District of Columbia	26.1

Source: U.S. Department of Health and Human Services, National Center for Health Statistics
    "National Vital Statistics Reports" (Vol. 52, No. 3, September 18, 2003)
*Final data by state of residence. Chronic lower respiratory diseases are diseases of the lungs including
bronchitis, emphysema and asthma. Includes allied conditions. Not age-adjusted.

Age-Adjusted Death Rate by Chronic Lower Respiratory Diseases in 2001

National Rate = 43.7 Deaths per 100,000 Population*

ALPHA ORDER

RANK	STATE	RATE
18	Alabama	48.0
13	Alaska	49.6
23	Arizona	47.3
25	Arkansas	46.2
30	California	43.9
7	Colorado	53.5
45	Connecticut	38.0
46	Delaware	37.9
37	Florida	40.9
19	Georgia	47.9
50	Hawaii	21.6
16	Idaho	48.4
41	Illinois	39.3
10	Indiana	51.9
31	Iowa	43.5
12	Kansas	49.9
5	Kentucky	56.2
32	Louisiana	43.0
6	Maine	54.1
42	Maryland	39.2
39	Massachusetts	39.7
34	Michigan	42.3
43	Minnesota	38.7
15	Mississippi	48.7
22	Missouri	47.7
2	Montana	59.1
24	Nebraska	46.5
1	Nevada	65.6
11	New Hampshire	50.8
49	New Jersey	32.4
27	New Mexico	45.6
47	New York	34.8
28	North Carolina	45.4
40	North Dakota	39.5
14	Ohio	49.0
8	Oklahoma	53.0
20	Oregon	47.8
44	Pennsylvania	38.2
38	Rhode Island	40.8
29	South Carolina	44.4
35	South Dakota	41.5
9	Tennessee	52.0
26	Texas	46.1
48	Utah	33.6
17	Vermont	48.1
33	Virginia	42.8
20	Washington	47.8
3	West Virginia	58.9
36	Wisconsin	41.4
4	Wyoming	57.5

RANK ORDER

RANK	STATE	RATE
1	Nevada	65.6
2	Montana	59.1
3	West Virginia	58.9
4	Wyoming	57.5
5	Kentucky	56.2
6	Maine	54.1
7	Colorado	53.5
8	Oklahoma	53.0
9	Tennessee	52.0
10	Indiana	51.9
11	New Hampshire	50.8
12	Kansas	49.9
13	Alaska	49.6
14	Ohio	49.0
15	Mississippi	48.7
16	Idaho	48.4
17	Vermont	48.1
18	Alabama	48.0
19	Georgia	47.9
20	Oregon	47.8
20	Washington	47.8
22	Missouri	47.7
23	Arizona	47.3
24	Nebraska	46.5
25	Arkansas	46.2
26	Texas	46.1
27	New Mexico	45.6
28	North Carolina	45.4
29	South Carolina	44.4
30	California	43.9
31	Iowa	43.5
32	Louisiana	43.0
33	Virginia	42.8
34	Michigan	42.3
35	South Dakota	41.5
36	Wisconsin	41.4
37	Florida	40.9
38	Rhode Island	40.8
39	Massachusetts	39.7
40	North Dakota	39.5
41	Illinois	39.3
42	Maryland	39.2
43	Minnesota	38.7
44	Pennsylvania	38.2
45	Connecticut	38.0
46	Delaware	37.9
47	New York	34.8
48	Utah	33.6
49	New Jersey	32.4
50	Hawaii	21.6
	District of Columbia	26.5

Source: U.S. Department of Health and Human Services, National Center for Health Statistics
   "National Vital Statistics Reports" (Vol. 52, No. 3, September 18, 2003)
*Final data by state of residence. Chronic lower respiratory diseases are diseases of the lungs including bronchitis, emphysema and asthma. Includes allied conditions. Age-adjusted rates based on the year 2000 standard population.

Deaths by Diabetes Mellitus in 2001

National Total = 71,372 Deaths*

ALPHA ORDER

RANK	STATE	DEATHS	% of USA
20	Alabama	1,344	1.9%
50	Alaska	80	0.1%
26	Arizona	1,058	1.5%
30	Arkansas	756	1.1%
1	California	6,395	9.0%
33	Colorado	667	0.9%
29	Connecticut	759	1.1%
44	Delaware	218	0.3%
3	Florida	4,631	6.5%
16	Georgia	1,475	2.1%
47	Hawaii	173	0.2%
40	Idaho	318	0.4%
7	Illinois	3,092	4.3%
13	Indiana	1,677	2.3%
32	Iowa	709	1.0%
31	Kansas	721	1.0%
23	Kentucky	1,099	1.5%
12	Louisiana	1,734	2.4%
38	Maine	398	0.6%
17	Maryland	1,458	2.0%
18	Massachusetts	1,422	2.0%
8	Michigan	2,655	3.7%
22	Minnesota	1,213	1.7%
34	Mississippi	661	0.9%
15	Missouri	1,535	2.2%
43	Montana	229	0.3%
37	Nebraska	400	0.6%
39	Nevada	322	0.5%
41	New Hampshire	291	0.4%
9	New Jersey	2,556	3.6%
35	New Mexico	538	0.8%
4	New York	3,844	5.4%
10	North Carolina	2,181	3.1%
46	North Dakota	196	0.3%
6	Ohio	3,750	5.3%
25	Oklahoma	1,065	1.5%
27	Oregon	1,011	1.4%
5	Pennsylvania	3,826	5.4%
42	Rhode Island	265	0.4%
24	South Carolina	1,088	1.5%
45	South Dakota	212	0.3%
11	Tennessee	1,746	2.4%
2	Texas	5,456	7.6%
36	Utah	509	0.7%
48	Vermont	155	0.2%
14	Virginia	1,613	2.3%
19	Washington	1,403	2.0%
28	West Virginia	802	1.1%
21	Wisconsin	1,337	1.9%
49	Wyoming	120	0.2%

RANK ORDER

RANK	STATE	DEATHS	% of USA
1	California	6,395	9.0%
2	Texas	5,456	7.6%
3	Florida	4,631	6.5%
4	New York	3,844	5.4%
5	Pennsylvania	3,826	5.4%
6	Ohio	3,750	5.3%
7	Illinois	3,092	4.3%
8	Michigan	2,655	3.7%
9	New Jersey	2,556	3.6%
10	North Carolina	2,181	3.1%
11	Tennessee	1,746	2.4%
12	Louisiana	1,734	2.4%
13	Indiana	1,677	2.3%
14	Virginia	1,613	2.3%
15	Missouri	1,535	2.2%
16	Georgia	1,475	2.1%
17	Maryland	1,458	2.0%
18	Massachusetts	1,422	2.0%
19	Washington	1,403	2.0%
20	Alabama	1,344	1.9%
21	Wisconsin	1,337	1.9%
22	Minnesota	1,213	1.7%
23	Kentucky	1,099	1.5%
24	South Carolina	1,088	1.5%
25	Oklahoma	1,065	1.5%
26	Arizona	1,058	1.5%
27	Oregon	1,011	1.4%
28	West Virginia	802	1.1%
29	Connecticut	759	1.1%
30	Arkansas	756	1.1%
31	Kansas	721	1.0%
32	Iowa	709	1.0%
33	Colorado	667	0.9%
34	Mississippi	661	0.9%
35	New Mexico	538	0.8%
36	Utah	509	0.7%
37	Nebraska	400	0.6%
38	Maine	398	0.6%
39	Nevada	322	0.5%
40	Idaho	318	0.4%
41	New Hampshire	291	0.4%
42	Rhode Island	265	0.4%
43	Montana	229	0.3%
44	Delaware	218	0.3%
45	South Dakota	212	0.3%
46	North Dakota	196	0.3%
47	Hawaii	173	0.2%
48	Vermont	155	0.2%
49	Wyoming	120	0.2%
50	Alaska	80	0.1%

| | District of Columbia | 209 | 0.3% |

Source: U.S. Department of Health and Human Services, National Center for Health Statistics
   "National Vital Statistics Reports" (Vol. 52, No. 3, September 18, 2003)
*Final data by state of residence. A severe, chronic form of diabetes caused by insufficient production of insulin
and resulting in abnormal metabolism of carbohydrates, fats, and proteins. The disease, which typically appears in
childhood or adolescence, is characterized by increased sugar levels in the blood and urine, excessive thirst and
frequent urination.

Death Rate by Diabetes Mellitus in 2001

National Rate = 25.1 Deaths per 100,000 Population*

ALPHA ORDER

RANK	STATE	RATE
9	Alabama	30.1
50	Alaska	12.6
44	Arizona	19.9
14	Arkansas	28.1
45	California	18.5
48	Colorado	15.1
42	Connecticut	22.1
16	Delaware	27.4
13	Florida	28.3
46	Georgia	17.5
49	Hawaii	14.1
34	Idaho	24.1
29	Illinois	24.7
16	Indiana	27.4
33	Iowa	24.2
22	Kansas	26.7
20	Kentucky	27.0
2	Louisiana	38.8
5	Maine	31.0
19	Maryland	27.1
41	Massachusetts	22.2
24	Michigan	26.5
31	Minnesota	24.3
37	Mississippi	23.1
18	Missouri	27.2
26	Montana	25.3
36	Nebraska	23.3
47	Nevada	15.3
37	New Hampshire	23.1
10	New Jersey	30.0
11	New Mexico	29.4
43	New York	20.1
23	North Carolina	26.6
6	North Dakota	30.8
3	Ohio	32.9
7	Oklahoma	30.7
12	Oregon	29.1
4	Pennsylvania	31.1
28	Rhode Island	25.0
21	South Carolina	26.8
15	South Dakota	28.0
8	Tennessee	30.4
25	Texas	25.5
40	Utah	22.3
26	Vermont	25.3
39	Virginia	22.4
35	Washington	23.4
1	West Virginia	44.5
29	Wisconsin	24.7
31	Wyoming	24.3

RANK ORDER

RANK	STATE	RATE
1	West Virginia	44.5
2	Louisiana	38.8
3	Ohio	32.9
4	Pennsylvania	31.1
5	Maine	31.0
6	North Dakota	30.8
7	Oklahoma	30.7
8	Tennessee	30.4
9	Alabama	30.1
10	New Jersey	30.0
11	New Mexico	29.4
12	Oregon	29.1
13	Florida	28.3
14	Arkansas	28.1
15	South Dakota	28.0
16	Delaware	27.4
16	Indiana	27.4
18	Missouri	27.2
19	Maryland	27.1
20	Kentucky	27.0
21	South Carolina	26.8
22	Kansas	26.7
23	North Carolina	26.6
24	Michigan	26.5
25	Texas	25.5
26	Montana	25.3
26	Vermont	25.3
28	Rhode Island	25.0
29	Illinois	24.7
29	Wisconsin	24.7
31	Minnesota	24.3
31	Wyoming	24.3
33	Iowa	24.2
34	Idaho	24.1
35	Washington	23.4
36	Nebraska	23.3
37	Mississippi	23.1
37	New Hampshire	23.1
39	Virginia	22.4
40	Utah	22.3
41	Massachusetts	22.2
42	Connecticut	22.1
43	New York	20.1
44	Arizona	19.9
45	California	18.5
46	Georgia	17.5
47	Nevada	15.3
48	Colorado	15.1
49	Hawaii	14.1
50	Alaska	12.6

District of Columbia	36.4

Source: U.S. Department of Health and Human Services, National Center for Health Statistics
   "National Vital Statistics Reports" (Vol. 52, No. 3, September 18, 2003)
*Final data by state of residence. A severe, chronic form of diabetes caused by insufficient production of insulin
and resulting in abnormal metabolism of carbohydrates, fats, and proteins. The disease, which typically appears in
childhood or adolescence, is characterized by increased sugar levels in the blood and urine, excessive thirst and
frequent urination. Not age-adjusted.

Age-Adjusted Death Rate by Diabetes Mellitus in 2001

National Rate = 25.3 Deaths per 100,000 Population*

ALPHA ORDER

RANK	STATE	RATE
9	Alabama	29.4
37	Alaska	22.6
44	Arizona	20.1
21	Arkansas	25.8
41	California	21.4
48	Colorado	18.7
46	Connecticut	19.6
16	Delaware	27.2
38	Florida	22.0
39	Georgia	21.9
50	Hawaii	13.3
20	Idaho	26.2
26	Illinois	25.4
14	Indiana	27.7
44	Iowa	20.1
28	Kansas	25.0
17	Kentucky	27.1
1	Louisiana	41.7
18	Maine	26.9
10	Maryland	29.2
43	Massachusetts	20.2
18	Michigan	26.9
30	Minnesota	24.3
32	Mississippi	24.1
24	Missouri	25.5
36	Montana	23.1
42	Nebraska	21.2
49	Nevada	17.6
34	New Hampshire	23.6
11	New Jersey	28.5
5	New Mexico	31.4
47	New York	19.4
13	North Carolina	27.8
22	North Dakota	25.7
5	Ohio	31.4
8	Oklahoma	29.5
12	Oregon	27.9
22	Pennsylvania	25.7
40	Rhode Island	21.7
15	South Carolina	27.5
31	South Dakota	24.2
7	Tennessee	30.6
4	Texas	31.6
3	Utah	31.9
32	Vermont	24.1
29	Virginia	24.5
27	Washington	25.1
2	West Virginia	37.6
35	Wisconsin	23.3
24	Wyoming	25.5

RANK ORDER

RANK	STATE	RATE
1	Louisiana	41.7
2	West Virginia	37.6
3	Utah	31.9
4	Texas	31.6
5	New Mexico	31.4
5	Ohio	31.4
7	Tennessee	30.6
8	Oklahoma	29.5
9	Alabama	29.4
10	Maryland	29.2
11	New Jersey	28.5
12	Oregon	27.9
13	North Carolina	27.8
14	Indiana	27.7
15	South Carolina	27.5
16	Delaware	27.2
17	Kentucky	27.1
18	Maine	26.9
18	Michigan	26.9
20	Idaho	26.2
21	Arkansas	25.8
22	North Dakota	25.7
22	Pennsylvania	25.7
24	Missouri	25.5
24	Wyoming	25.5
26	Illinois	25.4
27	Washington	25.1
28	Kansas	25.0
29	Virginia	24.5
30	Minnesota	24.3
31	South Dakota	24.2
32	Mississippi	24.1
32	Vermont	24.1
34	New Hampshire	23.6
35	Wisconsin	23.3
36	Montana	23.1
37	Alaska	22.6
38	Florida	22.0
39	Georgia	21.9
40	Rhode Island	21.7
41	California	21.4
42	Nebraska	21.2
43	Massachusetts	20.2
44	Arizona	20.1
44	Iowa	20.1
46	Connecticut	19.6
47	New York	19.4
48	Colorado	18.7
49	Nevada	17.6
50	Hawaii	13.3

District of Columbia	37.0

Source: U.S. Department of Health and Human Services, National Center for Health Statistics
     "National Vital Statistics Reports" (Vol. 52, No. 3, September 18, 2003)
*Final data by state of residence. A severe, chronic form of diabetes caused by insufficient production of insulin
and resulting in abnormal metabolism of carbohydrates, fats, and proteins. The disease, which typically appears in
childhood or adolescence, is characterized by increased sugar levels in the blood and urine, excessive thirst and
frequent urination. Age-adjusted rates based on the year 2000 standard population.

Deaths by Diseases of the Heart in 2001

National Total = 700,142 Deaths*

ALPHA ORDER

RANK	STATE	DEATHS	% of USA
17	Alabama	13,207	1.9%
50	Alaska	603	0.1%
24	Arizona	10,588	1.5%
29	Arkansas	8,263	1.2%
1	California	68,234	9.7%
34	Colorado	6,293	0.9%
28	Connecticut	8,582	1.2%
44	Delaware	2,033	0.3%
3	Florida	50,629	7.2%
11	Georgia	17,478	2.5%
43	Hawaii	2,310	0.3%
42	Idaho	2,489	0.4%
7	Illinois	30,990	4.4%
14	Indiana	15,682	2.2%
30	Iowa	8,250	1.2%
32	Kansas	6,716	1.0%
20	Kentucky	11,808	1.7%
21	Louisiana	11,474	1.6%
38	Maine	3,272	0.5%
19	Maryland	12,310	1.8%
15	Massachusetts	15,144	2.2%
8	Michigan	26,896	3.8%
27	Minnesota	8,760	1.3%
26	Mississippi	9,050	1.3%
12	Missouri	16,633	2.4%
46	Montana	1,970	0.3%
36	Nebraska	4,150	0.6%
35	Nevada	4,393	0.6%
41	New Hampshire	2,835	0.4%
9	New Jersey	22,704	3.2%
37	New Mexico	3,423	0.5%
2	New York	56,643	8.1%
10	North Carolina	18,792	2.7%
47	North Dakota	1,700	0.2%
6	Ohio	32,453	4.6%
23	Oklahoma	10,840	1.5%
31	Oregon	7,075	1.0%
5	Pennsylvania	39,438	5.6%
39	Rhode Island	3,076	0.4%
25	South Carolina	9,471	1.4%
45	South Dakota	1,985	0.3%
13	Tennessee	15,688	2.2%
4	Texas	43,199	6.2%
40	Utah	2,896	0.4%
48	Vermont	1,429	0.2%
16	Virginia	14,913	2.1%
22	Washington	11,281	1.6%
33	West Virginia	6,325	0.9%
18	Wisconsin	13,023	1.9%
49	Wyoming	985	0.1%

RANK ORDER

RANK	STATE	DEATHS	% of USA
1	California	68,234	9.7%
2	New York	56,643	8.1%
3	Florida	50,629	7.2%
4	Texas	43,199	6.2%
5	Pennsylvania	39,438	5.6%
6	Ohio	32,453	4.6%
7	Illinois	30,990	4.4%
8	Michigan	26,896	3.8%
9	New Jersey	22,704	3.2%
10	North Carolina	18,792	2.7%
11	Georgia	17,478	2.5%
12	Missouri	16,633	2.4%
13	Tennessee	15,688	2.2%
14	Indiana	15,682	2.2%
15	Massachusetts	15,144	2.2%
16	Virginia	14,913	2.1%
17	Alabama	13,207	1.9%
18	Wisconsin	13,023	1.9%
19	Maryland	12,310	1.8%
20	Kentucky	11,808	1.7%
21	Louisiana	11,474	1.6%
22	Washington	11,281	1.6%
23	Oklahoma	10,840	1.5%
24	Arizona	10,588	1.5%
25	South Carolina	9,471	1.4%
26	Mississippi	9,050	1.3%
27	Minnesota	8,760	1.3%
28	Connecticut	8,582	1.2%
29	Arkansas	8,263	1.2%
30	Iowa	8,250	1.2%
31	Oregon	7,075	1.0%
32	Kansas	6,716	1.0%
33	West Virginia	6,325	0.9%
34	Colorado	6,293	0.9%
35	Nevada	4,393	0.6%
36	Nebraska	4,150	0.6%
37	New Mexico	3,423	0.5%
38	Maine	3,272	0.5%
39	Rhode Island	3,076	0.4%
40	Utah	2,896	0.4%
41	New Hampshire	2,835	0.4%
42	Idaho	2,489	0.4%
43	Hawaii	2,310	0.3%
44	Delaware	2,033	0.3%
45	South Dakota	1,985	0.3%
46	Montana	1,970	0.3%
47	North Dakota	1,700	0.2%
48	Vermont	1,429	0.2%
49	Wyoming	985	0.1%
50	Alaska	603	0.1%
	District of Columbia	1,761	0.3%

Source: U.S. Department of Health and Human Services, National Center for Health Statistics
    "National Vital Statistics Reports" (Vol. 52, No. 3, September 18, 2003)
*Final data by state of residence.

Death Rate by Diseases of the Heart in 2001

National Rate = 245.8 Deaths per 100,000 Population*

ALPHA ORDER

RANK	STATE	RATE
8	Alabama	295.5
50	Alaska	95.2
40	Arizona	199.5
6	Arkansas	306.6
42	California	197.2
48	Colorado	142.0
23	Connecticut	249.9
21	Delaware	255.2
5	Florida	309.2
36	Georgia	207.9
44	Hawaii	188.3
43	Idaho	188.5
25	Illinois	247.5
20	Indiana	256.0
13	Iowa	281.4
24	Kansas	248.5
11	Kentucky	290.2
19	Louisiana	256.7
22	Maine	254.7
32	Maryland	228.6
28	Massachusetts	236.6
15	Michigan	268.8
47	Minnesota	175.7
3	Mississippi	316.5
9	Missouri	295.1
34	Montana	217.6
26	Nebraska	241.3
35	Nevada	209.4
33	New Hampshire	225.1
17	New Jersey	266.8
46	New Mexico	187.0
7	New York	296.8
31	North Carolina	229.0
16	North Dakota	267.1
12	Ohio	284.9
4	Oklahoma	312.4
38	Oregon	203.7
2	Pennsylvania	320.6
10	Rhode Island	290.3
29	South Carolina	233.2
18	South Dakota	261.8
14	Tennessee	272.9
39	Texas	202.1
49	Utah	127.1
30	Vermont	233.1
37	Virginia	207.2
45	Washington	188.2
1	West Virginia	351.2
27	Wisconsin	240.9
40	Wyoming	199.5

RANK ORDER

RANK	STATE	RATE
1	West Virginia	351.2
2	Pennsylvania	320.6
3	Mississippi	316.5
4	Oklahoma	312.4
5	Florida	309.2
6	Arkansas	306.6
7	New York	296.8
8	Alabama	295.5
9	Missouri	295.1
10	Rhode Island	290.3
11	Kentucky	290.2
12	Ohio	284.9
13	Iowa	281.4
14	Tennessee	272.9
15	Michigan	268.8
16	North Dakota	267.1
17	New Jersey	266.8
18	South Dakota	261.8
19	Louisiana	256.7
20	Indiana	256.0
21	Delaware	255.2
22	Maine	254.7
23	Connecticut	249.9
24	Kansas	248.5
25	Illinois	247.5
26	Nebraska	241.3
27	Wisconsin	240.9
28	Massachusetts	236.6
29	South Carolina	233.2
30	Vermont	233.1
31	North Carolina	229.0
32	Maryland	228.6
33	New Hampshire	225.1
34	Montana	217.6
35	Nevada	209.4
36	Georgia	207.9
37	Virginia	207.2
38	Oregon	203.7
39	Texas	202.1
40	Arizona	199.5
40	Wyoming	199.5
42	California	197.2
43	Idaho	188.5
44	Hawaii	188.3
45	Washington	188.2
46	New Mexico	187.0
47	Minnesota	175.7
48	Colorado	142.0
49	Utah	127.1
50	Alaska	95.2

District of Columbia   306.9

Source: U.S. Department of Health and Human Services, National Center for Health Statistics
   "National Vital Statistics Reports" (Vol. 52, No. 3, September 18, 2003)
Final data by state of residence. Not age-adjusted.

Age-Adjusted Death Rate by Diseases of the Heart in 2001

National Rate = 247.8 Deaths per 100,000 Population*

ALPHA ORDER

RANK	STATE	RATE
5	Alabama	289.3
46	Alaska	187.7
41	Arizona	204.5
8	Arkansas	279.1
28	California	230.4
48	Colorado	181.0
35	Connecticut	216.4
16	Delaware	257.2
25	Florida	233.2
13	Georgia	268.0
49	Hawaii	179.5
40	Idaho	205.1
20	Illinois	251.5
14	Indiana	258.0
29	Iowa	224.0
29	Kansas	224.0
4	Kentucky	294.0
7	Louisiana	280.1
33	Maine	218.8
19	Maryland	251.6
38	Massachusetts	210.4
10	Michigan	273.8
50	Minnesota	171.0
1	Mississippi	329.0
11	Missouri	271.9
44	Montana	197.9
36	Nebraska	210.9
17	Nevada	257.1
27	New Hampshire	230.9
21	New Jersey	250.8
42	New Mexico	203.4
6	New York	282.2
23	North Carolina	244.0
36	North Dakota	210.9
12	Ohio	271.0
2	Oklahoma	298.1
45	Oregon	191.6
15	Pennsylvania	257.8
24	Rhode Island	240.5
22	South Carolina	245.5
34	South Dakota	218.1
9	Tennessee	278.2
18	Texas	255.1
47	Utah	185.2
32	Vermont	221.4
26	Virginia	231.9
43	Washington	201.2
3	West Virginia	296.0
31	Wisconsin	222.3
39	Wyoming	209.5

RANK ORDER

RANK	STATE	RATE
1	Mississippi	329.0
2	Oklahoma	298.1
3	West Virginia	296.0
4	Kentucky	294.0
5	Alabama	289.3
6	New York	282.2
7	Louisiana	280.1
8	Arkansas	279.1
9	Tennessee	278.2
10	Michigan	273.8
11	Missouri	271.9
12	Ohio	271.0
13	Georgia	268.0
14	Indiana	258.0
15	Pennsylvania	257.8
16	Delaware	257.2
17	Nevada	257.1
18	Texas	255.1
19	Maryland	251.6
20	Illinois	251.5
21	New Jersey	250.8
22	South Carolina	245.5
23	North Carolina	244.0
24	Rhode Island	240.5
25	Florida	233.2
26	Virginia	231.9
27	New Hampshire	230.9
28	California	230.4
29	Iowa	224.0
29	Kansas	224.0
31	Wisconsin	222.3
32	Vermont	221.4
33	Maine	218.8
34	South Dakota	218.1
35	Connecticut	216.4
36	Nebraska	210.9
36	North Dakota	210.9
38	Massachusetts	210.4
39	Wyoming	209.5
40	Idaho	205.1
41	Arizona	204.5
42	New Mexico	203.4
43	Washington	201.2
44	Montana	197.9
45	Oregon	191.6
46	Alaska	187.7
47	Utah	185.2
48	Colorado	181.0
49	Hawaii	179.5
50	Minnesota	171.0

District of Columbia — 308.5

Source: U.S. Department of Health and Human Services, National Center for Health Statistics
"National Vital Statistics Reports" (Vol. 52, No. 3, September 18, 2003)
*Final data by state of residence. Age-adjusted rates based on the year 2000 standard population.

Deaths by Malignant Neoplasms in 2001

National Total = 553,768 Deaths*

ALPHA ORDER

RANK	STATE	DEATHS	% of USA
20	Alabama	9,801	1.8%
50	Alaska	689	0.1%
23	Arizona	9,143	1.7%
31	Arkansas	6,092	1.1%
1	California	53,924	9.7%
30	Colorado	6,145	1.1%
27	Connecticut	7,093	1.3%
45	Delaware	1,786	0.3%
2	Florida	39,090	7.1%
11	Georgia	13,818	2.5%
43	Hawaii	2,024	0.4%
42	Idaho	2,093	0.4%
7	Illinois	24,778	4.5%
14	Indiana	12,831	2.3%
29	Iowa	6,404	1.2%
33	Kansas	5,448	1.0%
22	Kentucky	9,358	1.7%
21	Louisiana	9,517	1.7%
37	Maine	3,045	0.5%
19	Maryland	10,322	1.9%
12	Massachusetts	13,750	2.5%
8	Michigan	19,689	3.6%
24	Minnesota	8,967	1.6%
32	Mississippi	5,958	1.1%
15	Missouri	12,365	2.2%
44	Montana	1,956	0.4%
36	Nebraska	3,389	0.6%
35	Nevada	3,815	0.7%
39	New Hampshire	2,398	0.4%
9	New Jersey	18,165	3.3%
38	New Mexico	2,900	0.5%
3	New York	36,975	6.7%
10	North Carolina	16,065	2.9%
47	North Dakota	1,391	0.3%
6	Ohio	24,804	4.5%
26	Oklahoma	7,411	1.3%
28	Oregon	7,057	1.3%
5	Pennsylvania	29,914	5.4%
39	Rhode Island	2,398	0.4%
25	South Carolina	8,272	1.5%
46	South Dakota	1,590	0.3%
16	Tennessee	12,229	2.2%
4	Texas	33,488	6.0%
41	Utah	2,313	0.4%
48	Vermont	1,249	0.2%
13	Virginia	13,345	2.4%
17	Washington	10,802	2.0%
34	West Virginia	4,685	0.8%
18	Wisconsin	10,777	1.9%
49	Wyoming	923	0.2%

RANK ORDER

RANK	STATE	DEATHS	% of USA
1	California	53,924	9.7%
2	Florida	39,090	7.1%
3	New York	36,975	6.7%
4	Texas	33,488	6.0%
5	Pennsylvania	29,914	5.4%
6	Ohio	24,804	4.5%
7	Illinois	24,778	4.5%
8	Michigan	19,689	3.6%
9	New Jersey	18,165	3.3%
10	North Carolina	16,065	2.9%
11	Georgia	13,818	2.5%
12	Massachusetts	13,750	2.5%
13	Virginia	13,345	2.4%
14	Indiana	12,831	2.3%
15	Missouri	12,365	2.2%
16	Tennessee	12,229	2.2%
17	Washington	10,802	2.0%
18	Wisconsin	10,777	1.9%
19	Maryland	10,322	1.9%
20	Alabama	9,801	1.8%
21	Louisiana	9,517	1.7%
22	Kentucky	9,358	1.7%
23	Arizona	9,143	1.7%
24	Minnesota	8,967	1.6%
25	South Carolina	8,272	1.5%
26	Oklahoma	7,411	1.3%
27	Connecticut	7,093	1.3%
28	Oregon	7,057	1.3%
29	Iowa	6,404	1.2%
30	Colorado	6,145	1.1%
31	Arkansas	6,092	1.1%
32	Mississippi	5,958	1.1%
33	Kansas	5,448	1.0%
34	West Virginia	4,685	0.8%
35	Nevada	3,815	0.7%
36	Nebraska	3,389	0.6%
37	Maine	3,045	0.5%
38	New Mexico	2,900	0.5%
39	New Hampshire	2,398	0.4%
39	Rhode Island	2,398	0.4%
41	Utah	2,313	0.4%
42	Idaho	2,093	0.4%
43	Hawaii	2,024	0.4%
44	Montana	1,956	0.4%
45	Delaware	1,786	0.3%
46	South Dakota	1,590	0.3%
47	North Dakota	1,391	0.3%
48	Vermont	1,249	0.2%
49	Wyoming	923	0.2%
50	Alaska	689	0.1%
	District of Columbia	1,327	0.2%

Source: U.S. Department of Health and Human Services, National Center for Health Statistics
"National Vital Statistics Reports" (Vol. 52, No. 3, September 18, 2003)
*Final data by state of residence. Neoplasms are abnormal tissue, tumors. Includes many cancers.

Death Rate by Malignant Neoplasms in 2001

National Rate = 194.4 Deaths per 100,000 Population*

ALPHA ORDER

RANK	STATE	RATE
9	Alabama	219.3
49	Alaska	108.7
41	Arizona	172.3
7	Arkansas	226.1
47	California	155.8
48	Colorado	138.7
23	Connecticut	206.5
8	Delaware	224.2
3	Florida	238.7
43	Georgia	164.4
42	Hawaii	165.0
44	Idaho	158.5
29	Illinois	197.9
21	Indiana	209.4
12	Iowa	218.4
27	Kansas	201.6
5	Kentucky	230.0
18	Louisiana	212.9
4	Maine	237.1
34	Maryland	191.6
15	Massachusetts	214.8
31	Michigan	196.8
40	Minnesota	179.9
22	Mississippi	208.3
9	Missouri	219.3
14	Montana	216.0
30	Nebraska	197.0
38	Nevada	181.9
35	New Hampshire	190.4
17	New Jersey	213.4
45	New Mexico	158.4
33	New York	193.7
32	North Carolina	195.8
11	North Dakota	218.5
13	Ohio	217.8
16	Oklahoma	213.6
26	Oregon	203.2
2	Pennsylvania	243.1
6	Rhode Island	226.3
25	South Carolina	203.6
20	South Dakota	209.7
19	Tennessee	212.7
46	Texas	156.7
50	Utah	101.5
24	Vermont	203.8
37	Virginia	185.4
39	Washington	180.2
1	West Virginia	260.1
28	Wisconsin	199.4
36	Wyoming	186.9

RANK ORDER

RANK	STATE	RATE
1	West Virginia	260.1
2	Pennsylvania	243.1
3	Florida	238.7
4	Maine	237.1
5	Kentucky	230.0
6	Rhode Island	226.3
7	Arkansas	226.1
8	Delaware	224.2
9	Alabama	219.3
9	Missouri	219.3
11	North Dakota	218.5
12	Iowa	218.4
13	Ohio	217.8
14	Montana	216.0
15	Massachusetts	214.8
16	Oklahoma	213.6
17	New Jersey	213.4
18	Louisiana	212.9
19	Tennessee	212.7
20	South Dakota	209.7
21	Indiana	209.4
22	Mississippi	208.3
23	Connecticut	206.5
24	Vermont	203.8
25	South Carolina	203.6
26	Oregon	203.2
27	Kansas	201.6
28	Wisconsin	199.4
29	Illinois	197.9
30	Nebraska	197.0
31	Michigan	196.8
32	North Carolina	195.8
33	New York	193.7
34	Maryland	191.6
35	New Hampshire	190.4
36	Wyoming	186.9
37	Virginia	185.4
38	Nevada	181.9
39	Washington	180.2
40	Minnesota	179.9
41	Arizona	172.3
42	Hawaii	165.0
43	Georgia	164.4
44	Idaho	158.5
45	New Mexico	158.4
46	Texas	156.7
47	California	155.8
48	Colorado	138.7
49	Alaska	108.7
50	Utah	101.5
	District of Columbia	231.3

Source: U.S. Department of Health and Human Services, National Center for Health Statistics
"National Vital Statistics Reports" (Vol. 52, No. 3, September 18, 2003)
*Final data by state of residence. Neoplasms are abnormal tissue, tumors. Includes many cancers. Not age-adjusted.

Age-Adjusted Death Rate by Malignant Neoplasms in 2001

National Rate = 196.0 Deaths per 100,000 Population*

ALPHA ORDER

RANK	STATE	RATE
7	Alabama	212.2
33	Alaska	192.6
45	Arizona	172.9
9	Arkansas	208.0
44	California	179.2
47	Colorado	169.6
40	Connecticut	187.2
3	Delaware	219.3
40	Florida	187.2
21	Georgia	202.1
49	Hawaii	155.9
46	Idaho	172.2
17	Illinois	204.5
8	Indiana	211.6
36	Iowa	188.7
30	Kansas	193.3
1	Kentucky	227.9
2	Louisiana	227.4
11	Maine	207.4
16	Maryland	204.6
24	Massachusetts	199.3
25	Michigan	199.0
43	Minnesota	183.1
5	Mississippi	216.3
12	Missouri	206.8
26	Montana	198.8
42	Nebraska	185.0
14	Nevada	205.9
29	New Hampshire	193.9
19	New Jersey	203.2
48	New Mexico	167.0
39	New York	187.7
20	North Carolina	202.5
37	North Dakota	188.4
10	Ohio	207.8
15	Oklahoma	205.2
27	Oregon	196.1
18	Pennsylvania	203.3
22	Rhode Island	200.6
12	South Carolina	206.8
38	South Dakota	187.9
6	Tennessee	212.5
34	Texas	191.0
50	Utah	143.4
28	Vermont	194.8
23	Virginia	199.9
30	Washington	193.3
4	West Virginia	218.7
35	Wisconsin	190.9
32	Wyoming	192.9

RANK ORDER

RANK	STATE	RATE
1	Kentucky	227.9
2	Louisiana	227.4
3	Delaware	219.3
4	West Virginia	218.7
5	Mississippi	216.3
6	Tennessee	212.5
7	Alabama	212.2
8	Indiana	211.6
9	Arkansas	208.0
10	Ohio	207.8
11	Maine	207.4
12	Missouri	206.8
12	South Carolina	206.8
14	Nevada	205.9
15	Oklahoma	205.2
16	Maryland	204.6
17	Illinois	204.5
18	Pennsylvania	203.3
19	New Jersey	203.2
20	North Carolina	202.5
21	Georgia	202.1
22	Rhode Island	200.6
23	Virginia	199.9
24	Massachusetts	199.3
25	Michigan	199.0
26	Montana	198.8
27	Oregon	196.1
28	Vermont	194.8
29	New Hampshire	193.9
30	Kansas	193.3
30	Washington	193.3
32	Wyoming	192.9
33	Alaska	192.6
34	Texas	191.0
35	Wisconsin	190.9
36	Iowa	188.7
37	North Dakota	188.4
38	South Dakota	187.9
39	New York	187.7
40	Connecticut	187.2
40	Florida	187.2
42	Nebraska	185.0
43	Minnesota	183.1
44	California	179.2
45	Arizona	172.9
46	Idaho	172.2
47	Colorado	169.6
48	New Mexico	167.0
49	Hawaii	155.9
50	Utah	143.4
	District of Columbia	235.3

Source: U.S. Department of Health and Human Services, National Center for Health Statistics
"National Vital Statistics Reports" (Vol. 52, No. 3, September 18, 2003)
*Final data by state of residence. Neoplasms are abnormal tissue, tumors. Includes many cancers. Age-adjusted rates based on the year 2000 standard population.

Deaths by Pneumonia and Influenza in 2001

National Total = 62,034 Deaths*

ALPHA ORDER					RANK ORDER			
RANK	STATE	DEATHS	% of USA		RANK	STATE	DEATHS	% of USA
20	Alabama	1,105	1.8%		1	California	8,129	13.1%
50	Alaska	36	0.1%		2	New York	5,085	8.2%
18	Arizona	1,133	1.8%		3	Texas	3,608	5.8%
30	Arkansas	735	1.2%		4	Florida	3,317	5.3%
1	California	8,129	13.1%		5	Pennsylvania	2,735	4.4%
31	Colorado	650	1.0%		6	Illinois	2,659	4.3%
26	Connecticut	854	1.4%		7	Ohio	2,401	3.9%
46	Delaware	181	0.3%		8	Michigan	2,076	3.3%
4	Florida	3,317	5.3%		9	New Jersey	1,893	3.1%
14	Georgia	1,515	2.4%		10	North Carolina	1,780	2.9%
43	Hawaii	207	0.3%		11	Massachusetts	1,770	2.9%
41	Idaho	239	0.4%		12	Tennessee	1,617	2.6%
6	Illinois	2,659	4.3%		13	Missouri	1,604	2.6%
17	Indiana	1,184	1.9%		14	Georgia	1,515	2.4%
25	Iowa	877	1.4%		15	Virginia	1,481	2.4%
33	Kansas	561	0.9%		16	Wisconsin	1,236	2.0%
19	Kentucky	1,114	1.8%		17	Indiana	1,184	1.9%
22	Louisiana	941	1.5%		18	Arizona	1,133	1.8%
40	Maine	269	0.4%		19	Kentucky	1,114	1.8%
23	Maryland	928	1.5%		20	Alabama	1,105	1.8%
11	Massachusetts	1,770	2.9%		21	Washington	965	1.6%
8	Michigan	2,076	3.3%		22	Louisiana	941	1.5%
27	Minnesota	828	1.3%		23	Maryland	928	1.5%
28	Mississippi	754	1.2%		24	Oklahoma	913	1.5%
13	Missouri	1,604	2.6%		25	Iowa	877	1.4%
44	Montana	193	0.3%		26	Connecticut	854	1.4%
38	Nebraska	296	0.5%		27	Minnesota	828	1.3%
37	Nevada	352	0.6%		28	Mississippi	754	1.2%
42	New Hampshire	216	0.3%		28	South Carolina	754	1.2%
9	New Jersey	1,893	3.1%		30	Arkansas	735	1.2%
36	New Mexico	398	0.6%		31	Colorado	650	1.0%
2	New York	5,085	8.2%		32	Oregon	575	0.9%
10	North Carolina	1,780	2.9%		33	Kansas	561	0.9%
47	North Dakota	162	0.3%		34	West Virginia	483	0.8%
7	Ohio	2,401	3.9%		35	Utah	411	0.7%
24	Oklahoma	913	1.5%		36	New Mexico	398	0.6%
32	Oregon	575	0.9%		37	Nevada	352	0.6%
5	Pennsylvania	2,735	4.4%		38	Nebraska	296	0.5%
39	Rhode Island	295	0.5%		39	Rhode Island	295	0.5%
28	South Carolina	754	1.2%		40	Maine	269	0.4%
45	South Dakota	188	0.3%		41	Idaho	239	0.4%
12	Tennessee	1,617	2.6%		42	New Hampshire	216	0.3%
3	Texas	3,608	5.8%		43	Hawaii	207	0.3%
35	Utah	411	0.7%		44	Montana	193	0.3%
48	Vermont	133	0.2%		45	South Dakota	188	0.3%
15	Virginia	1,481	2.4%		46	Delaware	181	0.3%
21	Washington	965	1.6%		47	North Dakota	162	0.3%
34	West Virginia	483	0.8%		48	Vermont	133	0.2%
16	Wisconsin	1,236	2.0%		49	Wyoming	112	0.2%
49	Wyoming	112	0.2%		50	Alaska	36	0.1%
						District of Columbia	86	0.1%

Source: U.S. Department of Health and Human Services, National Center for Health Statistics "National Vital Statistics Reports" (Vol. 52, No. 3, September 18, 2003)
*Final data by state of residence.

Death Rate by Pneumonia and Influenza in 2001

National Rate = 21.8 Deaths per 100,000 Population*

ALPHA ORDER

RANK	STATE	RATE
15	Alabama	24.7
50	Alaska	5.7
25	Arizona	21.3
7	Arkansas	27.3
16	California	23.5
49	Colorado	14.7
13	Connecticut	24.9
18	Delaware	22.7
34	Florida	20.3
38	Georgia	18.0
43	Hawaii	16.9
37	Idaho	18.1
27	Illinois	21.2
35	Indiana	19.3
1	Iowa	29.9
31	Kansas	20.8
6	Kentucky	27.4
29	Louisiana	21.0
30	Maine	20.9
40	Maryland	17.2
5	Massachusetts	27.7
32	Michigan	20.7
46	Minnesota	16.6
10	Mississippi	26.4
2	Missouri	28.5
25	Montana	21.3
40	Nebraska	17.2
45	Nevada	16.8
40	New Hampshire	17.2
20	New Jersey	22.2
22	New Mexico	21.7
9	New York	26.6
22	North Carolina	21.7
12	North Dakota	25.4
28	Ohio	21.1
11	Oklahoma	26.3
46	Oregon	16.6
20	Pennsylvania	22.2
4	Rhode Island	27.8
36	South Carolina	18.6
14	South Dakota	24.8
3	Tennessee	28.1
43	Texas	16.9
38	Utah	18.0
22	Vermont	21.7
33	Virginia	20.6
48	Washington	16.1
8	West Virginia	26.8
17	Wisconsin	22.9
18	Wyoming	22.7

RANK ORDER

RANK	STATE	RATE
1	Iowa	29.9
2	Missouri	28.5
3	Tennessee	28.1
4	Rhode Island	27.8
5	Massachusetts	27.7
6	Kentucky	27.4
7	Arkansas	27.3
8	West Virginia	26.8
9	New York	26.6
10	Mississippi	26.4
11	Oklahoma	26.3
12	North Dakota	25.4
13	Connecticut	24.9
14	South Dakota	24.8
15	Alabama	24.7
16	California	23.5
17	Wisconsin	22.9
18	Delaware	22.7
18	Wyoming	22.7
20	New Jersey	22.2
20	Pennsylvania	22.2
22	New Mexico	21.7
22	North Carolina	21.7
22	Vermont	21.7
25	Arizona	21.3
25	Montana	21.3
27	Illinois	21.2
28	Ohio	21.1
29	Louisiana	21.0
30	Maine	20.9
31	Kansas	20.8
32	Michigan	20.7
33	Virginia	20.6
34	Florida	20.3
35	Indiana	19.3
36	South Carolina	18.6
37	Idaho	18.1
38	Georgia	18.0
38	Utah	18.0
40	Maryland	17.2
40	Nebraska	17.2
40	New Hampshire	17.2
43	Hawaii	16.9
43	Texas	16.9
45	Nevada	16.8
46	Minnesota	16.6
46	Oregon	16.6
48	Washington	16.1
49	Colorado	14.7
50	Alaska	5.7
	District of Columbia	15.0

Source: U.S. Department of Health and Human Services, National Center for Health Statistics
"National Vital Statistics Reports" (Vol. 52, No. 3, September 18, 2003)
*Final data by state of residence. Not age-adjusted.

Age-Adjusted Death Rate by Pneumonia and Influenza in 2001

National Rate = 22.0 Deaths per 100,000 Population*

ALPHA ORDER

RANK	STATE	RATE
10	Alabama	24.4
50	Alaska	12.9
22	Arizona	22.1
9	Arkansas	24.8
3	California	27.6
38	Colorado	19.0
27	Connecticut	20.9
17	Delaware	23.4
48	Florida	15.2
12	Georgia	24.0
45	Hawaii	16.1
33	Idaho	19.6
25	Illinois	21.3
35	Indiana	19.4
19	Iowa	22.7
40	Kansas	18.2
2	Kentucky	28.2
17	Louisiana	23.4
41	Maine	17.8
36	Maryland	19.3
12	Massachusetts	24.0
26	Michigan	21.2
46	Minnesota	15.5
4	Mississippi	27.4
6	Missouri	25.8
37	Montana	19.2
49	Nebraska	14.5
23	Nevada	21.9
42	New Hampshire	17.7
28	New Jersey	20.8
12	New Mexico	24.0
7	New York	25.2
15	North Carolina	23.7
39	North Dakota	18.8
32	Ohio	20.0
8	Oklahoma	25.1
47	Oregon	15.3
43	Pennsylvania	17.6
21	Rhode Island	22.3
31	South Carolina	20.1
34	South Dakota	19.5
1	Tennessee	29.1
24	Texas	21.7
5	Utah	26.7
30	Vermont	20.4
15	Virginia	23.7
44	Washington	17.1
19	West Virginia	22.7
29	Wisconsin	20.5
11	Wyoming	24.1

RANK ORDER

RANK	STATE	RATE
1	Tennessee	29.1
2	Kentucky	28.2
3	California	27.6
4	Mississippi	27.4
5	Utah	26.7
6	Missouri	25.8
7	New York	25.2
8	Oklahoma	25.1
9	Arkansas	24.8
10	Alabama	24.4
11	Wyoming	24.1
12	Georgia	24.0
12	Massachusetts	24.0
12	New Mexico	24.0
15	North Carolina	23.7
15	Virginia	23.7
17	Delaware	23.4
17	Louisiana	23.4
19	Iowa	22.7
19	West Virginia	22.7
21	Rhode Island	22.3
22	Arizona	22.1
23	Nevada	21.9
24	Texas	21.7
25	Illinois	21.3
26	Michigan	21.2
27	Connecticut	20.9
28	New Jersey	20.8
29	Wisconsin	20.5
30	Vermont	20.4
31	South Carolina	20.1
32	Ohio	20.0
33	Idaho	19.6
34	South Dakota	19.5
35	Indiana	19.4
36	Maryland	19.3
37	Montana	19.2
38	Colorado	19.0
39	North Dakota	18.8
40	Kansas	18.2
41	Maine	17.8
42	New Hampshire	17.7
43	Pennsylvania	17.6
44	Washington	17.1
45	Hawaii	16.1
46	Minnesota	15.5
47	Oregon	15.3
48	Florida	15.2
49	Nebraska	14.5
50	Alaska	12.9
	District of Columbia	15.1

Source: U.S. Department of Health and Human Services, National Center for Health Statistics
"National Vital Statistics Reports" (Vol. 52, No. 3, September 18, 2003)
*Final data by state of residence. Age-adjusted rates based on the year 2000 standard population.

Deaths by Tuberculosis in 2000

National Total = 776 Deaths*

ALPHA ORDER

RANK	STATE	DEATHS	% of USA
17	Alabama	14	1.8%
35	Alaska	3	0.4%
14	Arizona	15	1.9%
24	Arkansas	10	1.3%
1	California	104	13.4%
31	Colorado	5	0.6%
25	Connecticut	7	0.9%
44	Delaware	1	0.1%
4	Florida	52	6.7%
6	Georgia	34	4.4%
35	Hawaii	3	0.4%
47	Idaho	0	0.0%
5	Illinois	47	6.1%
14	Indiana	15	1.9%
35	Iowa	3	0.4%
25	Kansas	7	0.9%
21	Kentucky	12	1.5%
11	Louisiana	25	3.2%
44	Maine	1	0.1%
25	Maryland	7	0.9%
19	Massachusetts	13	1.7%
8	Michigan	29	3.7%
33	Minnesota	4	0.5%
17	Mississippi	14	1.8%
19	Missouri	13	1.7%
35	Montana	3	0.4%
41	Nebraska	2	0.3%
35	Nevada	3	0.4%
47	New Hampshire	0	0.0%
9	New Jersey	28	3.6%
33	New Mexico	4	0.5%
3	New York	55	7.1%
7	North Carolina	32	4.1%
44	North Dakota	1	0.1%
10	Ohio	27	3.5%
21	Oklahoma	12	1.5%
30	Oregon	6	0.8%
12	Pennsylvania	23	3.0%
47	Rhode Island	0	0.0%
14	South Carolina	15	1.9%
41	South Dakota	2	0.3%
13	Tennessee	19	2.4%
2	Texas	67	8.6%
35	Utah	3	0.4%
41	Vermont	2	0.3%
23	Virginia	11	1.4%
25	Washington	7	0.9%
25	West Virginia	7	0.9%
31	Wisconsin	5	0.6%
47	Wyoming	0	0.0%

RANK ORDER

RANK	STATE	DEATHS	% of USA
1	California	104	13.4%
2	Texas	67	8.6%
3	New York	55	7.1%
4	Florida	52	6.7%
5	Illinois	47	6.1%
6	Georgia	34	4.4%
7	North Carolina	32	4.1%
8	Michigan	29	3.7%
9	New Jersey	28	3.6%
10	Ohio	27	3.5%
11	Louisiana	25	3.2%
12	Pennsylvania	23	3.0%
13	Tennessee	19	2.4%
14	Arizona	15	1.9%
14	Indiana	15	1.9%
14	South Carolina	15	1.9%
17	Alabama	14	1.8%
17	Mississippi	14	1.8%
19	Massachusetts	13	1.7%
19	Missouri	13	1.7%
21	Kentucky	12	1.5%
21	Oklahoma	12	1.5%
23	Virginia	11	1.4%
24	Arkansas	10	1.3%
25	Connecticut	7	0.9%
25	Kansas	7	0.9%
25	Maryland	7	0.9%
25	Washington	7	0.9%
25	West Virginia	7	0.9%
30	Oregon	6	0.8%
31	Colorado	5	0.6%
31	Wisconsin	5	0.6%
33	Minnesota	4	0.5%
33	New Mexico	4	0.5%
35	Alaska	3	0.4%
35	Hawaii	3	0.4%
35	Iowa	3	0.4%
35	Montana	3	0.4%
35	Nevada	3	0.4%
35	Utah	3	0.4%
41	Nebraska	2	0.3%
41	South Dakota	2	0.3%
41	Vermont	2	0.3%
44	Delaware	1	0.1%
44	Maine	1	0.1%
44	North Dakota	1	0.1%
47	Idaho	0	0.0%
47	New Hampshire	0	0.0%
47	Rhode Island	0	0.0%
47	Wyoming	0	0.0%
	District of Columbia	4	0.5%

Source: U.S. Department of Health and Human Services, National Center for Health Statistics
   (http://wonder.cdc.gov)
*By state of residence.

Death Rate by Tuberculosis in 2000

National Rate = 0.3 Deaths per 100,000 Population*

ALPHA ORDER

RANK	STATE	RATE
10	Alabama	0.3
2	Alaska	0.5
10	Arizona	0.3
4	Arkansas	0.4
10	California	0.3
36	Colorado	0.1
25	Connecticut	0.2
36	Delaware	0.1
10	Florida	0.3
4	Georgia	0.4
25	Hawaii	0.2
47	Idaho	0.0
4	Illinois	0.4
25	Indiana	0.2
36	Iowa	0.1
10	Kansas	0.3
10	Kentucky	0.3
1	Louisiana	0.6
36	Maine	0.1
36	Maryland	0.1
25	Massachusetts	0.2
10	Michigan	0.3
36	Minnesota	0.1
2	Mississippi	0.5
25	Missouri	0.2
10	Montana	0.3
36	Nebraska	0.1
36	Nevada	0.1
47	New Hampshire	0.0
10	New Jersey	0.3
25	New Mexico	0.2
10	New York	0.3
4	North Carolina	0.4
25	North Dakota	0.2
25	Ohio	0.2
10	Oklahoma	0.3
25	Oregon	0.2
25	Pennsylvania	0.2
47	Rhode Island	0.0
4	South Carolina	0.4
10	South Dakota	0.3
10	Tennessee	0.3
10	Texas	0.3
36	Utah	0.1
10	Vermont	0.3
25	Virginia	0.2
36	Washington	0.1
4	West Virginia	0.4
36	Wisconsin	0.1
47	Wyoming	0.0

RANK ORDER

RANK	STATE	RATE
1	Louisiana	0.6
2	Alaska	0.5
2	Mississippi	0.5
4	Arkansas	0.4
4	Georgia	0.4
4	Illinois	0.4
4	North Carolina	0.4
4	South Carolina	0.4
4	West Virginia	0.4
10	Alabama	0.3
10	Arizona	0.3
10	California	0.3
10	Florida	0.3
10	Kansas	0.3
10	Kentucky	0.3
10	Michigan	0.3
10	Montana	0.3
10	New Jersey	0.3
10	New York	0.3
10	Oklahoma	0.3
10	South Dakota	0.3
10	Tennessee	0.3
10	Texas	0.3
10	Vermont	0.3
25	Connecticut	0.2
25	Hawaii	0.2
25	Indiana	0.2
25	Massachusetts	0.2
25	Missouri	0.2
25	New Mexico	0.2
25	North Dakota	0.2
25	Ohio	0.2
25	Oregon	0.2
25	Pennsylvania	0.2
25	Virginia	0.2
36	Colorado	0.1
36	Delaware	0.1
36	Iowa	0.1
36	Maine	0.1
36	Maryland	0.1
36	Minnesota	0.1
36	Nebraska	0.1
36	Nevada	0.1
36	Utah	0.1
36	Washington	0.1
36	Wisconsin	0.1
47	Idaho	0.0
47	New Hampshire	0.0
47	Rhode Island	0.0
47	Wyoming	0.0
	District of Columbia	0.7

Source: U.S. Department of Health and Human Services, National Center for Health Statistics
(http://wonder.cdc.gov)
*By state of residence. Not age-adjusted. Due to low numbers of deaths, rates for all states should be interpreted with caution.

Age-Adjusted Death Rate by Tuberculosis in 2000

National Rate = 0.3 Deaths per 100,000 Population*

ALPHA ORDER

RANK	STATE	RATE
10	Alabama	0.3
1	Alaska	0.7
10	Arizona	0.3
10	Arkansas	0.3
5	California	0.4
25	Colorado	0.2
25	Connecticut	0.2
38	Delaware	0.1
10	Florida	0.3
3	Georgia	0.5
25	Hawaii	0.2
47	Idaho	0.0
5	Illinois	0.4
10	Indiana	0.3
38	Iowa	0.1
10	Kansas	0.3
10	Kentucky	0.3
2	Louisiana	0.6
38	Maine	0.1
38	Maryland	0.1
25	Massachusetts	0.2
10	Michigan	0.3
38	Minnesota	0.1
3	Mississippi	0.5
25	Missouri	0.2
10	Montana	0.3
38	Nebraska	0.1
25	Nevada	0.2
47	New Hampshire	0.0
10	New Jersey	0.3
25	New Mexico	0.2
10	New York	0.3
5	North Carolina	0.4
38	North Dakota	0.1
25	Ohio	0.2
10	Oklahoma	0.3
25	Oregon	0.2
25	Pennsylvania	0.2
47	Rhode Island	0.0
5	South Carolina	0.4
25	South Dakota	0.2
10	Tennessee	0.3
5	Texas	0.4
25	Utah	0.2
10	Vermont	0.3
25	Virginia	0.2
38	Washington	0.1
10	West Virginia	0.3
38	Wisconsin	0.1
47	Wyoming	0.0

RANK ORDER

RANK	STATE	RATE
1	Alaska	0.7
2	Louisiana	0.6
3	Georgia	0.5
3	Mississippi	0.5
5	California	0.4
5	Illinois	0.4
5	North Carolina	0.4
5	South Carolina	0.4
5	Texas	0.4
10	Alabama	0.3
10	Arizona	0.3
10	Arkansas	0.3
10	Florida	0.3
10	Indiana	0.3
10	Kansas	0.3
10	Kentucky	0.3
10	Michigan	0.3
10	Montana	0.3
10	New Jersey	0.3
10	New York	0.3
10	Oklahoma	0.3
10	Tennessee	0.3
10	Vermont	0.3
10	West Virginia	0.3
25	Colorado	0.2
25	Connecticut	0.2
25	Hawaii	0.2
25	Massachusetts	0.2
25	Missouri	0.2
25	Nevada	0.2
25	New Mexico	0.2
25	Ohio	0.2
25	Oregon	0.2
25	Pennsylvania	0.2
25	South Dakota	0.2
25	Utah	0.2
25	Virginia	0.2
38	Delaware	0.1
38	Iowa	0.1
38	Maine	0.1
38	Maryland	0.1
38	Minnesota	0.1
38	Nebraska	0.1
38	North Dakota	0.1
38	Washington	0.1
38	Wisconsin	0.1
47	Idaho	0.0
47	New Hampshire	0.0
47	Rhode Island	0.0
47	Wyoming	0.0
	District of Columbia	0.7

*Source: U.S. Department of Health and Human Services, National Center for Health Statistics
(http://wonder.cdc.gov)*
**By state of residence. Due to low numbers of deaths, rates for all states should be interpreted with caution.
Age-adjusted rates based on the year 2000 standard population.*

Deaths by Injury in 2000

National Total = 148,193 Deaths*

ALPHA ORDER					RANK ORDER			
RANK	STATE		DEATHS	% of USA	RANK	STATE	DEATHS	% of USA
17	Alabama		3,175	2.1%	1	California	13,850	9.3%
43	Alaska		537	0.4%	2	Texas	10,970	7.4%
13	Arizona		3,597	2.4%	3	Florida	9,421	6.4%
29	Arkansas		1,910	1.3%	4	Pennsylvania	6,709	4.5%
1	California		13,850	9.3%	5	New York	6,493	4.4%
24	Colorado		2,567	1.7%	6	Illinois	6,140	4.1%
31	Connecticut		1,612	1.1%	7	North Carolina	5,198	3.5%
47	Delaware		407	0.3%	8	Ohio	5,157	3.5%
3	Florida		9,421	6.4%	9	Michigan	5,144	3.5%
10	Georgia		4,703	3.2%	10	Georgia	4,703	3.2%
42	Hawaii		548	0.4%	11	Tennessee	4,027	2.7%
39	Idaho		725	0.5%	12	Virginia	3,660	2.5%
6	Illinois		6,140	4.1%	13	Arizona	3,597	2.4%
15	Indiana		3,279	2.2%	14	Missouri	3,539	2.4%
34	Iowa		1,443	1.0%	15	Indiana	3,279	2.2%
32	Kansas		1,542	1.0%	16	New Jersey	3,236	2.2%
23	Kentucky		2,588	1.7%	17	Alabama	3,175	2.1%
18	Louisiana		3,140	2.1%	18	Louisiana	3,140	2.1%
41	Maine		584	0.4%	19	Washington	3,112	2.1%
22	Maryland		2,750	1.9%	20	Wisconsin	2,965	2.0%
28	Massachusetts		2,261	1.5%	21	South Carolina	2,784	1.9%
9	Michigan		5,144	3.5%	22	Maryland	2,750	1.9%
25	Minnesota		2,339	1.6%	23	Kentucky	2,588	1.7%
27	Mississippi		2,301	1.6%	24	Colorado	2,567	1.7%
14	Missouri		3,539	2.4%	25	Minnesota	2,339	1.6%
40	Montana		704	0.5%	26	Oklahoma	2,313	1.6%
38	Nebraska		918	0.6%	27	Mississippi	2,301	1.6%
35	Nevada		1,324	0.9%	28	Massachusetts	2,261	1.5%
44	New Hampshire		472	0.3%	29	Arkansas	1,910	1.3%
16	New Jersey		3,236	2.2%	30	Oregon	1,898	1.3%
33	New Mexico		1,494	1.0%	31	Connecticut	1,612	1.1%
5	New York		6,493	4.4%	32	Kansas	1,542	1.0%
7	North Carolina		5,198	3.5%	33	New Mexico	1,494	1.0%
49	North Dakota		335	0.2%	34	Iowa	1,443	1.0%
8	Ohio		5,157	3.5%	35	Nevada	1,324	0.9%
26	Oklahoma		2,313	1.6%	36	West Virginia	1,198	0.8%
30	Oregon		1,898	1.3%	37	Utah	1,174	0.8%
4	Pennsylvania		6,709	4.5%	38	Nebraska	918	0.6%
46	Rhode Island		421	0.3%	39	Idaho	725	0.5%
21	South Carolina		2,784	1.9%	40	Montana	704	0.5%
45	South Dakota		437	0.3%	41	Maine	584	0.4%
11	Tennessee		4,027	2.7%	42	Hawaii	548	0.4%
2	Texas		10,970	7.4%	43	Alaska	537	0.4%
37	Utah		1,174	0.8%	44	New Hampshire	472	0.3%
50	Vermont		331	0.2%	45	South Dakota	437	0.3%
12	Virginia		3,660	2.5%	46	Rhode Island	421	0.3%
19	Washington		3,112	2.1%	47	Delaware	407	0.3%
36	West Virginia		1,198	0.8%	48	Wyoming	342	0.2%
20	Wisconsin		2,965	2.0%	49	North Dakota	335	0.2%
48	Wyoming		342	0.2%	50	Vermont	331	0.2%
						District of Columbia	419	0.3%

Source: U.S. Department of Health and Human Services, National Center for Health Statistics
(http://wonder.cdc.gov)
By state of residence. Injury as used here includes Accidents (including motor vehicle), Suicides, Homicides and "Other" undetermined.

Death Rate by Injury in 2000

National Rate = 52.6 Deaths per 100,000 Population*

ALPHA ORDER

RANK	STATE	RATE
6	Alabama	71.3
1	Alaska	85.6
9	Arizona	70.0
5	Arkansas	71.4
45	California	40.8
18	Colorado	59.6
41	Connecticut	47.3
34	Delaware	51.9
19	Florida	58.9
21	Georgia	57.4
44	Hawaii	45.2
23	Idaho	56.0
38	Illinois	49.4
28	Indiana	53.9
39	Iowa	49.3
22	Kansas	57.3
16	Kentucky	64.0
8	Louisiana	70.2
42	Maine	45.8
34	Maryland	51.9
49	Massachusetts	35.6
36	Michigan	51.7
40	Minnesota	47.5
3	Mississippi	80.8
17	Missouri	63.2
4	Montana	78.0
29	Nebraska	53.6
13	Nevada	66.2
48	New Hampshire	38.2
47	New Jersey	38.4
2	New Mexico	82.1
50	New York	34.2
15	North Carolina	64.5
33	North Dakota	52.2
43	Ohio	45.4
12	Oklahoma	67.0
24	Oregon	55.4
26	Pennsylvania	54.6
46	Rhode Island	40.1
10	South Carolina	69.4
20	South Dakota	57.9
7	Tennessee	70.7
31	Texas	52.5
31	Utah	52.5
27	Vermont	54.4
36	Virginia	51.7
30	Washington	52.8
13	West Virginia	66.2
25	Wisconsin	55.3
11	Wyoming	69.2

RANK ORDER

RANK	STATE	RATE
1	Alaska	85.6
2	New Mexico	82.1
3	Mississippi	80.8
4	Montana	78.0
5	Arkansas	71.4
6	Alabama	71.3
7	Tennessee	70.7
8	Louisiana	70.2
9	Arizona	70.0
10	South Carolina	69.4
11	Wyoming	69.2
12	Oklahoma	67.0
13	Nevada	66.2
13	West Virginia	66.2
15	North Carolina	64.5
16	Kentucky	64.0
17	Missouri	63.2
18	Colorado	59.6
19	Florida	58.9
20	South Dakota	57.9
21	Georgia	57.4
22	Kansas	57.3
23	Idaho	56.0
24	Oregon	55.4
25	Wisconsin	55.3
26	Pennsylvania	54.6
27	Vermont	54.4
28	Indiana	53.9
29	Nebraska	53.6
30	Washington	52.8
31	Texas	52.5
31	Utah	52.5
33	North Dakota	52.2
34	Delaware	51.9
34	Maryland	51.9
36	Michigan	51.7
36	Virginia	51.7
38	Illinois	49.4
39	Iowa	49.3
40	Minnesota	47.5
41	Connecticut	47.3
42	Maine	45.8
43	Ohio	45.4
44	Hawaii	45.2
45	California	40.8
46	Rhode Island	40.1
47	New Jersey	38.4
48	New Hampshire	38.2
49	Massachusetts	35.6
50	New York	34.2
	District of Columbia	73.1

Source: U.S. Department of Health and Human Services, National Center for Health Statistics
(http://wonder.cdc.gov)
*By state of residence. Injury as used here includes Accidents (including motor vehicle), Suicides, Homicides and
"Other" undetermined. Not age-adjusted.

Age-Adjusted Death Rate by Injury in 2000

National Rate = 52.7 Deaths per 100,000 Population*

ALPHA ORDER

RANK	STATE	RATE
5	Alabama	71.3
1	Alaska	94.4
6	Arizona	71.2
9	Arkansas	70.5
45	California	42.2
17	Colorado	62.6
41	Connecticut	45.6
34	Delaware	52.4
22	Florida	56.6
19	Georgia	60.4
43	Hawaii	44.9
21	Idaho	57.9
37	Illinois	49.6
27	Indiana	54.0
40	Iowa	46.2
24	Kansas	56.3
15	Kentucky	64.0
6	Louisiana	71.2
44	Maine	44.5
32	Maryland	52.5
49	Massachusetts	34.2
35	Michigan	52.2
39	Minnesota	46.9
3	Mississippi	81.7
18	Missouri	62.3
4	Montana	77.1
36	Nebraska	51.5
12	Nevada	68.4
46	New Hampshire	38.2
48	New Jersey	38.0
2	New Mexico	84.5
50	New York	33.8
14	North Carolina	65.2
38	North Dakota	48.8
42	Ohio	45.1
13	Oklahoma	66.7
26	Oregon	54.4
32	Pennsylvania	52.5
47	Rhode Island	38.1
11	South Carolina	70.1
22	South Dakota	56.6
8	Tennessee	70.9
25	Texas	54.9
20	Utah	59.0
29	Vermont	53.4
31	Virginia	53.0
29	Washington	53.4
15	West Virginia	64.0
28	Wisconsin	53.8
9	Wyoming	70.5

RANK ORDER

RANK	STATE	RATE
1	Alaska	94.4
2	New Mexico	84.5
3	Mississippi	81.7
4	Montana	77.1
5	Alabama	71.3
6	Arizona	71.2
6	Louisiana	71.2
8	Tennessee	70.9
9	Arkansas	70.5
9	Wyoming	70.5
11	South Carolina	70.1
12	Nevada	68.4
13	Oklahoma	66.7
14	North Carolina	65.2
15	Kentucky	64.0
15	West Virginia	64.0
17	Colorado	62.6
18	Missouri	62.3
19	Georgia	60.4
20	Utah	59.0
21	Idaho	57.9
22	Florida	56.6
22	South Dakota	56.6
24	Kansas	56.3
25	Texas	54.9
26	Oregon	54.4
27	Indiana	54.0
28	Wisconsin	53.8
29	Vermont	53.4
29	Washington	53.4
31	Virginia	53.0
32	Maryland	52.5
32	Pennsylvania	52.5
34	Delaware	52.4
35	Michigan	52.2
36	Nebraska	51.5
37	Illinois	49.6
38	North Dakota	48.8
39	Minnesota	46.9
40	Iowa	46.2
41	Connecticut	45.6
42	Ohio	45.1
43	Hawaii	44.9
44	Maine	44.5
45	California	42.2
46	New Hampshire	38.2
47	Rhode Island	38.1
48	New Jersey	38.0
49	Massachusetts	34.2
50	New York	33.8
	District of Columbia	69.9

Source: U.S. Department of Health and Human Services, National Center for Health Statistics
(http://wonder.cdc.gov)
*By state of residence. Injury as used here includes Accidents (including motor vehicle), Suicides, Homicides and "Other" undetermined. Age-adjusted rates based on the year 2000 standard population.

Deaths by Accidents in 2001

National Total = 101,537 Deaths*

ALPHA ORDER

RANK	STATE	DEATHS	% of USA
16	Alabama	2,211	2.2%
45	Alaska	345	0.3%
12	Arizona	2,475	2.4%
30	Arkansas	1,277	1.3%
1	California	8,132	8.0%
24	Colorado	1,720	1.7%
32	Connecticut	1,056	1.0%
47	Delaware	290	0.3%
3	Florida	6,969	6.9%
9	Georgia	3,396	3.3%
44	Hawaii	372	0.4%
39	Idaho	568	0.6%
6	Illinois	4,077	4.0%
17	Indiana	2,185	2.2%
33	Iowa	1,051	1.0%
31	Kansas	1,156	1.1%
21	Kentucky	1,990	2.0%
20	Louisiana	2,029	2.0%
40	Maine	490	0.5%
28	Maryland	1,339	1.3%
27	Massachusetts	1,506	1.5%
10	Michigan	3,291	3.2%
23	Minnesota	1,797	1.8%
26	Mississippi	1,571	1.5%
13	Missouri	2,455	2.4%
41	Montana	468	0.5%
38	Nebraska	633	0.6%
36	Nevada	739	0.7%
43	New Hampshire	374	0.4%
15	New Jersey	2,405	2.4%
34	New Mexico	1,020	1.0%
4	New York	4,982	4.9%
8	North Carolina	3,438	3.4%
49	North Dakota	238	0.2%
7	Ohio	3,857	3.8%
25	Oklahoma	1,700	1.7%
29	Oregon	1,313	1.3%
5	Pennsylvania	4,552	4.5%
46	Rhode Island	293	0.3%
22	South Carolina	1,960	1.9%
42	South Dakota	382	0.4%
11	Tennessee	2,709	2.7%
2	Texas	7,920	7.8%
37	Utah	643	0.6%
50	Vermont	230	0.2%
14	Virginia	2,432	2.4%
19	Washington	2,072	2.0%
35	West Virginia	834	0.8%
18	Wisconsin	2,100	2.1%
48	Wyoming	272	0.3%

RANK ORDER

RANK	STATE	DEATHS	% of USA
1	California	8,132	8.0%
2	Texas	7,920	7.8%
3	Florida	6,969	6.9%
4	New York	4,982	4.9%
5	Pennsylvania	4,552	4.5%
6	Illinois	4,077	4.0%
7	Ohio	3,857	3.8%
8	North Carolina	3,438	3.4%
9	Georgia	3,396	3.3%
10	Michigan	3,291	3.2%
11	Tennessee	2,709	2.7%
12	Arizona	2,475	2.4%
13	Missouri	2,455	2.4%
14	Virginia	2,432	2.4%
15	New Jersey	2,405	2.4%
16	Alabama	2,211	2.2%
17	Indiana	2,185	2.2%
18	Wisconsin	2,100	2.1%
19	Washington	2,072	2.0%
20	Louisiana	2,029	2.0%
21	Kentucky	1,990	2.0%
22	South Carolina	1,960	1.9%
23	Minnesota	1,797	1.8%
24	Colorado	1,720	1.7%
25	Oklahoma	1,700	1.7%
26	Mississippi	1,571	1.5%
27	Massachusetts	1,506	1.5%
28	Maryland	1,339	1.3%
29	Oregon	1,313	1.3%
30	Arkansas	1,277	1.3%
31	Kansas	1,156	1.1%
32	Connecticut	1,056	1.0%
33	Iowa	1,051	1.0%
34	New Mexico	1,020	1.0%
35	West Virginia	834	0.8%
36	Nevada	739	0.7%
37	Utah	643	0.6%
38	Nebraska	633	0.6%
39	Idaho	568	0.6%
40	Maine	490	0.5%
41	Montana	468	0.5%
42	South Dakota	382	0.4%
43	New Hampshire	374	0.4%
44	Hawaii	372	0.4%
45	Alaska	345	0.3%
46	Rhode Island	293	0.3%
47	Delaware	290	0.3%
48	Wyoming	272	0.3%
49	North Dakota	238	0.2%
50	Vermont	230	0.2%
	District of Columbia	223	0.2%

Source: U.S. Department of Health and Human Services, National Center for Health Statistics
   "National Vital Statistics Reports" (Vol. 52, No. 3, September 18, 2003)
Final data by state of residence. Includes motor vehicle deaths, poisoning, falls, drowning and other accidents.

Death Rate by Accidents in 2001

National Rate = 35.7 Deaths per 100,000 Population*

<u>ALPHA ORDER</u>

RANK	STATE	RATE
7	Alabama	49.5
4	Alaska	54.4
13	Arizona	46.6
11	Arkansas	47.4
49	California	23.5
22	Colorado	38.8
41	Connecticut	30.7
31	Delaware	36.4
19	Florida	42.6
21	Georgia	40.4
42	Hawaii	30.3
17	Idaho	43.0
40	Illinois	32.6
34	Indiana	35.7
33	Iowa	35.8
18	Kansas	42.8
9	Kentucky	48.9
15	Louisiana	45.4
24	Maine	38.1
48	Maryland	24.9
49	Massachusetts	23.5
39	Michigan	32.9
32	Minnesota	36.1
3	Mississippi	54.9
16	Missouri	43.5
5	Montana	51.7
30	Nebraska	36.8
35	Nevada	35.2
43	New Hampshire	29.7
44	New Jersey	28.3
1	New Mexico	55.7
47	New York	26.1
20	North Carolina	41.9
27	North Dakota	37.4
37	Ohio	33.9
8	Oklahoma	49.0
25	Oregon	37.8
29	Pennsylvania	37.0
46	Rhode Island	27.7
10	South Carolina	48.3
6	South Dakota	50.4
12	Tennessee	47.1
28	Texas	37.1
45	Utah	28.2
26	Vermont	37.5
38	Virginia	33.8
36	Washington	34.6
14	West Virginia	46.3
22	Wisconsin	38.8
2	Wyoming	55.1

<u>RANK ORDER</u>

RANK	STATE	RATE
1	New Mexico	55.7
2	Wyoming	55.1
3	Mississippi	54.9
4	Alaska	54.4
5	Montana	51.7
6	South Dakota	50.4
7	Alabama	49.5
8	Oklahoma	49.0
9	Kentucky	48.9
10	South Carolina	48.3
11	Arkansas	47.4
12	Tennessee	47.1
13	Arizona	46.6
14	West Virginia	46.3
15	Louisiana	45.4
16	Missouri	43.5
17	Idaho	43.0
18	Kansas	42.8
19	Florida	42.6
20	North Carolina	41.9
21	Georgia	40.4
22	Colorado	38.8
22	Wisconsin	38.8
24	Maine	38.1
25	Oregon	37.8
26	Vermont	37.5
27	North Dakota	37.4
28	Texas	37.1
29	Pennsylvania	37.0
30	Nebraska	36.8
31	Delaware	36.4
32	Minnesota	36.1
33	Iowa	35.8
34	Indiana	35.7
35	Nevada	35.2
36	Washington	34.6
37	Ohio	33.9
38	Virginia	33.8
39	Michigan	32.9
40	Illinois	32.6
41	Connecticut	30.7
42	Hawaii	30.3
43	New Hampshire	29.7
44	New Jersey	28.3
45	Utah	28.2
46	Rhode Island	27.7
47	New York	26.1
48	Maryland	24.9
49	California	23.5
49	Massachusetts	23.5
	District of Columbia	38.9

Source: U.S. Department of Health and Human Services, National Center for Health Statistics
"National Vital Statistics Reports" (Vol. 52, No. 3, September 18, 2003)
*Final data by state of residence. Includes motor vehicle deaths, poisoning, falls, drowning and other accidents. Not age-adjusted.

Age-Adjusted Death Rate by Accidents in 2001

National Rate = 35.7 Deaths per 100,000 Population*

ALPHA ORDER

RANK	STATE	RATE
6	Alabama	49.2
1	Alaska	60.4
10	Arizona	47.3
13	Arkansas	46.4
49	California	24.4
20	Colorado	41.5
44	Connecticut	29.5
28	Delaware	36.3
22	Florida	40.5
17	Georgia	43.6
43	Hawaii	29.7
16	Idaho	44.0
39	Illinois	32.7
30	Indiana	35.7
40	Iowa	32.3
21	Kansas	41.3
7	Kentucky	48.7
13	Louisiana	46.4
29	Maine	36.0
46	Maryland	25.7
50	Massachusetts	22.0
38	Michigan	33.1
31	Minnesota	35.2
3	Mississippi	55.6
19	Missouri	42.4
5	Montana	49.9
34	Nebraska	34.7
25	Nevada	37.2
42	New Hampshire	29.9
45	New Jersey	27.7
2	New Mexico	57.6
47	New York	25.6
18	North Carolina	42.6
36	North Dakota	33.8
37	Ohio	33.3
9	Oklahoma	48.3
26	Oregon	36.8
35	Pennsylvania	34.4
48	Rhode Island	25.1
7	South Carolina	48.7
12	South Dakota	47.0
11	Tennessee	47.1
23	Texas	39.5
40	Utah	32.3
27	Vermont	36.4
32	Virginia	35.1
32	Washington	35.1
15	West Virginia	44.6
24	Wisconsin	37.3
4	Wyoming	55.4

RANK ORDER

RANK	STATE	RATE
1	Alaska	60.4
2	New Mexico	57.6
3	Mississippi	55.6
4	Wyoming	55.4
5	Montana	49.9
6	Alabama	49.2
7	Kentucky	48.7
7	South Carolina	48.7
9	Oklahoma	48.3
10	Arizona	47.3
11	Tennessee	47.1
12	South Dakota	47.0
13	Arkansas	46.4
13	Louisiana	46.4
15	West Virginia	44.6
16	Idaho	44.0
17	Georgia	43.6
18	North Carolina	42.6
19	Missouri	42.4
20	Colorado	41.5
21	Kansas	41.3
22	Florida	40.5
23	Texas	39.5
24	Wisconsin	37.3
25	Nevada	37.2
26	Oregon	36.8
27	Vermont	36.4
28	Delaware	36.3
29	Maine	36.0
30	Indiana	35.7
31	Minnesota	35.2
32	Virginia	35.1
32	Washington	35.1
34	Nebraska	34.7
35	Pennsylvania	34.4
36	North Dakota	33.8
37	Ohio	33.3
38	Michigan	33.1
39	Illinois	32.7
40	Iowa	32.3
40	Utah	32.3
42	New Hampshire	29.9
43	Hawaii	29.7
44	Connecticut	29.5
45	New Jersey	27.7
46	Maryland	25.7
47	New York	25.6
48	Rhode Island	25.1
49	California	24.4
50	Massachusetts	22.0

District of Columbia	38.3

Source: U.S. Department of Health and Human Services, National Center for Health Statistics
    "National Vital Statistics Reports" (Vol. 52, No. 3, September 18, 2003)
*Final data by state of residence. Includes motor vehicle deaths, poisoning, falls, drowning and other accidents.
Age-adjusted rates based on the year 2000 standard population.

Deaths by Motor Vehicle Accidents in 2001

National Total = 43,788 Deaths*

RANK	STATE	DEATHS	% of USA
13	Alabama	1,037	2.4%
48	Alaska	103	0.2%
14	Arizona	1,020	2.3%
27	Arkansas	661	1.5%
2	California	3,932	9.0%
22	Colorado	758	1.7%
36	Connecticut	317	0.7%
46	Delaware	122	0.3%
3	Florida	3,094	7.1%
6	Georgia	1,628	3.7%
45	Hawaii	128	0.3%
39	Idaho	256	0.6%
7	Illinois	1,585	3.6%
17	Indiana	970	2.2%
32	Iowa	447	1.0%
30	Kansas	539	1.2%
19	Kentucky	861	2.0%
16	Louisiana	990	2.3%
41	Maine	200	0.5%
26	Maryland	703	1.6%
29	Massachusetts	565	1.3%
10	Michigan	1,431	3.3%
28	Minnesota	628	1.4%
20	Mississippi	825	1.9%
12	Missouri	1,105	2.5%
40	Montana	212	0.5%
38	Nebraska	271	0.6%
35	Nevada	331	0.8%
44	New Hampshire	136	0.3%
23	New Jersey	755	1.7%
33	New Mexico	430	1.0%
4	New York	1,678	3.8%
5	North Carolina	1,647	3.8%
47	North Dakota	115	0.3%
9	Ohio	1,470	3.4%
25	Oklahoma	728	1.7%
31	Oregon	506	1.2%
8	Pennsylvania	1,574	3.6%
49	Rhode Island	97	0.2%
15	South Carolina	999	2.3%
42	South Dakota	184	0.4%
11	Tennessee	1,305	3.0%
1	Texas	3,964	9.1%
37	Utah	299	0.7%
50	Vermont	88	0.2%
18	Virginia	961	2.2%
24	Washington	745	1.7%
34	West Virginia	373	0.9%
21	Wisconsin	821	1.9%
43	Wyoming	140	0.3%

RANK	STATE	DEATHS	% of USA
1	Texas	3,964	9.1%
2	California	3,932	9.0%
3	Florida	3,094	7.1%
4	New York	1,678	3.8%
5	North Carolina	1,647	3.8%
6	Georgia	1,628	3.7%
7	Illinois	1,585	3.6%
8	Pennsylvania	1,574	3.6%
9	Ohio	1,470	3.4%
10	Michigan	1,431	3.3%
11	Tennessee	1,305	3.0%
12	Missouri	1,105	2.5%
13	Alabama	1,037	2.4%
14	Arizona	1,020	2.3%
15	South Carolina	999	2.3%
16	Louisiana	990	2.3%
17	Indiana	970	2.2%
18	Virginia	961	2.2%
19	Kentucky	861	2.0%
20	Mississippi	825	1.9%
21	Wisconsin	821	1.9%
22	Colorado	758	1.7%
23	New Jersey	755	1.7%
24	Washington	745	1.7%
25	Oklahoma	728	1.7%
26	Maryland	703	1.6%
27	Arkansas	661	1.5%
28	Minnesota	628	1.4%
29	Massachusetts	565	1.3%
30	Kansas	539	1.2%
31	Oregon	506	1.2%
32	Iowa	447	1.0%
33	New Mexico	430	1.0%
34	West Virginia	373	0.9%
35	Nevada	331	0.8%
36	Connecticut	317	0.7%
37	Utah	299	0.7%
38	Nebraska	271	0.6%
39	Idaho	256	0.6%
40	Montana	212	0.5%
41	Maine	200	0.5%
42	South Dakota	184	0.4%
43	Wyoming	140	0.3%
44	New Hampshire	136	0.3%
45	Hawaii	128	0.3%
46	Delaware	122	0.3%
47	North Dakota	115	0.3%
48	Alaska	103	0.2%
49	Rhode Island	97	0.2%
50	Vermont	88	0.2%
	District of Columbia	54	0.1%

Source: U.S. Department of Health and Human Services, National Center for Health Statistics "National Vital Statistics Reports" (Vol. 52, No. 3, September 18, 2003)

Final data by state of residence. These numbers are compiled from death certificates by the Centers for Disease Control and Prevention. They may differ from motor vehicle deaths collected by the U.S. Department of Transportation from other sources.

Death Rate by Motor Vehicle Accidents in 2001

National Rate = 15.4 Deaths per 100,000 Population*

ALPHA ORDER			RANK ORDER		
RANK	STATE	RATE	RANK	STATE	RATE
8	Alabama	23.2	1	Mississippi	28.8
24	Alaska	16.3	2	Wyoming	28.4
19	Arizona	19.2	3	South Carolina	24.6
4	Arkansas	24.5	4	Arkansas	24.5
43	California	11.4	5	South Dakota	24.3
23	Colorado	17.1	6	New Mexico	23.5
46	Connecticut	9.2	7	Montana	23.4
29	Delaware	15.3	8	Alabama	23.2
20	Florida	18.9	9	Tennessee	22.7
17	Georgia	19.4	10	Louisiana	22.1
45	Hawaii	10.4	11	Kentucky	21.2
17	Idaho	19.4	12	Oklahoma	21.0
40	Illinois	12.7	13	West Virginia	20.7
25	Indiana	15.8	14	North Carolina	20.1
30	Iowa	15.2	15	Kansas	19.9
15	Kansas	19.9	16	Missouri	19.6
11	Kentucky	21.2	17	Georgia	19.4
10	Louisiana	22.1	17	Idaho	19.4
28	Maine	15.6	19	Arizona	19.2
36	Maryland	13.1	20	Florida	18.9
49	Massachusetts	8.8	21	Texas	18.5
34	Michigan	14.3	22	North Dakota	18.1
41	Minnesota	12.6	23	Colorado	17.1
1	Mississippi	28.8	24	Alaska	16.3
16	Missouri	19.6	25	Indiana	15.8
7	Montana	23.4	25	Nebraska	15.8
25	Nebraska	15.8	25	Nevada	15.8
25	Nevada	15.8	28	Maine	15.6
44	New Hampshire	10.8	29	Delaware	15.3
48	New Jersey	8.9	30	Iowa	15.2
6	New Mexico	23.5	30	Wisconsin	15.2
49	New York	8.8	32	Oregon	14.6
14	North Carolina	20.1	33	Vermont	14.4
22	North Dakota	18.1	34	Michigan	14.3
38	Ohio	12.9	35	Virginia	13.4
12	Oklahoma	21.0	36	Maryland	13.1
32	Oregon	14.6	36	Utah	13.1
39	Pennsylvania	12.8	38	Ohio	12.9
46	Rhode Island	9.2	39	Pennsylvania	12.8
3	South Carolina	24.6	40	Illinois	12.7
5	South Dakota	24.3	41	Minnesota	12.6
9	Tennessee	22.7	42	Washington	12.4
21	Texas	18.5	43	California	11.4
36	Utah	13.1	44	New Hampshire	10.8
33	Vermont	14.4	45	Hawaii	10.4
35	Virginia	13.4	46	Connecticut	9.2
42	Washington	12.4	46	Rhode Island	9.2
13	West Virginia	20.7	48	New Jersey	8.9
30	Wisconsin	15.2	49	Massachusetts	8.8
2	Wyoming	28.4	49	New York	8.8
				District of Columbia	9.4

Source: U.S. Department of Health and Human Services, National Center for Health Statistics
     "National Vital Statistics Reports" (Vol. 52, No. 3, September 18, 2003)
*Final data by state of residence. These numbers are compiled from death certificates by the Centers for Disease Control and Prevention. They may differ from motor vehicle deaths collected by the U.S. Department of Transportation from other sources. Not age-adjusted.

Age-Adjusted Death Rate by Motor Vehicle Accidents in 2001

National Rate = 15.3 Deaths per 100,000 Population*

ALPHA ORDER

RANK	STATE	RATE
8	Alabama	23.1
23	Alaska	17.4
17	Arizona	19.4
3	Arkansas	24.4
43	California	11.5
24	Colorado	17.2
46	Connecticut	9.4
28	Delaware	15.2
21	Florida	18.6
15	Georgia	19.7
45	Hawaii	10.3
19	Idaho	19.3
39	Illinois	12.7
26	Indiana	15.8
31	Iowa	14.9
16	Kansas	19.6
11	Kentucky	20.9
10	Louisiana	22.2
28	Maine	15.2
37	Maryland	13.3
49	Massachusetts	8.7
33	Michigan	14.3
40	Minnesota	12.6
1	Mississippi	28.9
17	Missouri	19.4
7	Montana	23.2
27	Nebraska	15.5
25	Nevada	16.2
44	New Hampshire	10.8
47	New Jersey	9.0
6	New Mexico	23.8
49	New York	8.7
14	North Carolina	20.1
22	North Dakota	17.5
38	Ohio	12.9
12	Oklahoma	20.8
32	Oregon	14.4
41	Pennsylvania	12.5
48	Rhode Island	8.8
4	South Carolina	24.3
5	South Dakota	24.0
9	Tennessee	22.5
20	Texas	18.9
35	Utah	13.6
34	Vermont	14.2
36	Virginia	13.5
41	Washington	12.5
13	West Virginia	20.6
30	Wisconsin	15.0
2	Wyoming	28.0

RANK ORDER

RANK	STATE	RATE
1	Mississippi	28.9
2	Wyoming	28.0
3	Arkansas	24.4
4	South Carolina	24.3
5	South Dakota	24.0
6	New Mexico	23.8
7	Montana	23.2
8	Alabama	23.1
9	Tennessee	22.5
10	Louisiana	22.2
11	Kentucky	20.9
12	Oklahoma	20.8
13	West Virginia	20.6
14	North Carolina	20.1
15	Georgia	19.7
16	Kansas	19.6
17	Arizona	19.4
17	Missouri	19.4
19	Idaho	19.3
20	Texas	18.9
21	Florida	18.6
22	North Dakota	17.5
23	Alaska	17.4
24	Colorado	17.2
25	Nevada	16.2
26	Indiana	15.8
27	Nebraska	15.5
28	Delaware	15.2
28	Maine	15.2
30	Wisconsin	15.0
31	Iowa	14.9
32	Oregon	14.4
33	Michigan	14.3
34	Vermont	14.2
35	Utah	13.6
36	Virginia	13.5
37	Maryland	13.3
38	Ohio	12.9
39	Illinois	12.7
40	Minnesota	12.6
41	Pennsylvania	12.5
41	Washington	12.5
43	California	11.5
44	New Hampshire	10.8
45	Hawaii	10.3
46	Connecticut	9.4
47	New Jersey	9.0
48	Rhode Island	8.8
49	Massachusetts	8.7
49	New York	8.7
	District of Columbia	9.2

Source: U.S. Department of Health and Human Services, National Center for Health Statistics
   "National Vital Statistics Reports" (Vol. 52, No. 3, September 18, 2003)
*Final data by state of residence. These numbers are compiled from death certificates by the Centers for Disease Control and Prevention. They may differ from motor vehicle deaths collected by the U.S. Department of Transportation from other sources. Age-adjusted rates based on the year 2000 standard population.

Deaths by Homicide in 2001

National Total = 20,308 Homicides*

ALPHA ORDER

RANK	STATE	HOMICIDES	% of USA
19	Alabama	425	2.1%
40	Alaska	38	0.2%
15	Arizona	494	2.4%
27	Arkansas	183	0.9%
2	California	2,223	10.9%
30	Colorado	169	0.8%
29	Connecticut	172	0.8%
43	Delaware	33	0.2%
6	Florida	969	4.8%
8	Georgia	681	3.4%
42	Hawaii	34	0.2%
39	Idaho	41	0.2%
4	Illinois	1,087	5.4%
17	Indiana	437	2.2%
37	Iowa	61	0.3%
31	Kansas	143	0.7%
23	Kentucky	221	1.1%
12	Louisiana	541	2.7%
46	Maine	21	0.1%
11	Maryland	555	2.7%
22	Massachusetts	246	1.2%
7	Michigan	689	3.4%
33	Minnesota	127	0.6%
21	Mississippi	326	1.6%
17	Missouri	437	2.2%
44	Montana	32	0.2%
38	Nebraska	44	0.2%
28	Nevada	175	0.9%
45	New Hampshire	28	0.1%
5	New Jersey	1,051	5.2%
32	New Mexico	130	0.6%
1	New York	2,818	13.9%
10	North Carolina	599	2.9%
50	North Dakota	9	0.0%
13	Ohio	524	2.6%
25	Oklahoma	210	1.0%
34	Oregon	100	0.5%
9	Pennsylvania	671	3.3%
41	Rhode Island	37	0.2%
20	South Carolina	350	1.7%
47	South Dakota	18	0.1%
16	Tennessee	454	2.2%
3	Texas	1,415	7.0%
35	Utah	77	0.4%
49	Vermont	14	0.1%
14	Virginia	509	2.5%
26	Washington	195	1.0%
36	West Virginia	68	0.3%
24	Wisconsin	214	1.1%
48	Wyoming	16	0.1%

RANK ORDER

RANK	STATE	HOMICIDES	% of USA
1	New York	2,818	13.9%
2	California	2,223	10.9%
3	Texas	1,415	7.0%
4	Illinois	1,087	5.4%
5	New Jersey	1,051	5.2%
6	Florida	969	4.8%
7	Michigan	689	3.4%
8	Georgia	681	3.4%
9	Pennsylvania	671	3.3%
10	North Carolina	599	2.9%
11	Maryland	555	2.7%
12	Louisiana	541	2.7%
13	Ohio	524	2.6%
14	Virginia	509	2.5%
15	Arizona	494	2.4%
16	Tennessee	454	2.2%
17	Indiana	437	2.2%
17	Missouri	437	2.2%
19	Alabama	425	2.1%
20	South Carolina	350	1.7%
21	Mississippi	326	1.6%
22	Massachusetts	246	1.2%
23	Kentucky	221	1.1%
24	Wisconsin	214	1.1%
25	Oklahoma	210	1.0%
26	Washington	195	1.0%
27	Arkansas	183	0.9%
28	Nevada	175	0.9%
29	Connecticut	172	0.8%
30	Colorado	169	0.8%
31	Kansas	143	0.7%
32	New Mexico	130	0.6%
33	Minnesota	127	0.6%
34	Oregon	100	0.5%
35	Utah	77	0.4%
36	West Virginia	68	0.3%
37	Iowa	61	0.3%
38	Nebraska	44	0.2%
39	Idaho	41	0.2%
40	Alaska	38	0.2%
41	Rhode Island	37	0.2%
42	Hawaii	34	0.2%
43	Delaware	33	0.2%
44	Montana	32	0.2%
45	New Hampshire	28	0.1%
46	Maine	21	0.1%
47	South Dakota	18	0.1%
48	Wyoming	16	0.1%
49	Vermont	14	0.1%
50	North Dakota	9	0.0%
	District of Columbia	197	1.0%

Source: U.S. Department of Health and Human Services, National Center for Health Statistics
"National Vital Statistics Reports" (Vol. 52, No. 3, September 18, 2003)
*By state of residence. Includes legal intervention. Homicide data shown here are collected by the Centers for Disease Control and Prevention based on death certificates and differ from murder data collected by the F.B.I. from other sources. Figures include deaths related to the attacks of September 11, 2001.

Death Rate by Homicide in 2001

National Rate = 7.1 Deaths per 100,000 Population*

ALPHA ORDER

RANK	STATE	RATE
6	Alabama	9.5
23	Alaska	6.0
7	Arizona	9.3
19	Arkansas	6.8
21	California	6.4
32	Colorado	3.8
28	Connecticut	5.0
30	Delaware	4.1
24	Florida	5.9
11	Georgia	8.1
41	Hawaii	2.8
39	Idaho	3.1
8	Illinois	8.7
15	Indiana	7.1
45	Iowa	2.1
27	Kansas	5.3
26	Kentucky	5.4
3	Louisiana	12.1
46	Maine	1.6
5	Maryland	10.3
32	Massachusetts	3.8
18	Michigan	6.9
43	Minnesota	2.5
4	Mississippi	11.4
13	Missouri	7.8
35	Montana	3.5
42	Nebraska	2.6
10	Nevada	8.3
44	New Hampshire	2.2
2	New Jersey	12.3
15	New Mexico	7.1
1	New York	14.8
14	North Carolina	7.3
NA	North Dakota**	NA
29	Ohio	4.6
22	Oklahoma	6.1
40	Oregon	2.9
25	Pennsylvania	5.5
35	Rhode Island	3.5
9	South Carolina	8.6
NA	South Dakota**	NA
12	Tennessee	7.9
20	Texas	6.6
37	Utah	3.4
NA	Vermont**	NA
15	Virginia	7.1
38	Washington	3.3
32	West Virginia	3.8
31	Wisconsin	4.0
NA	Wyoming**	NA

RANK ORDER

RANK	STATE	RATE
1	New York	14.8
2	New Jersey	12.3
3	Louisiana	12.1
4	Mississippi	11.4
5	Maryland	10.3
6	Alabama	9.5
7	Arizona	9.3
8	Illinois	8.7
9	South Carolina	8.6
10	Nevada	8.3
11	Georgia	8.1
12	Tennessee	7.9
13	Missouri	7.8
14	North Carolina	7.3
15	Indiana	7.1
15	New Mexico	7.1
15	Virginia	7.1
18	Michigan	6.9
19	Arkansas	6.8
20	Texas	6.6
21	California	6.4
22	Oklahoma	6.1
23	Alaska	6.0
24	Florida	5.9
25	Pennsylvania	5.5
26	Kentucky	5.4
27	Kansas	5.3
28	Connecticut	5.0
29	Ohio	4.6
30	Delaware	4.1
31	Wisconsin	4.0
32	Colorado	3.8
32	Massachusetts	3.8
32	West Virginia	3.8
35	Montana	3.5
35	Rhode Island	3.5
37	Utah	3.4
38	Washington	3.3
39	Idaho	3.1
40	Oregon	2.9
41	Hawaii	2.8
42	Nebraska	2.6
43	Minnesota	2.5
44	New Hampshire	2.2
45	Iowa	2.1
46	Maine	1.6
NA	North Dakota**	NA
NA	South Dakota**	NA
NA	Vermont**	NA
NA	Wyoming**	NA

| | District of Columbia | 34.3 |

*Source: U.S. Department of Health and Human Services, National Center for Health Statistics
"National Vital Statistics Reports" (Vol. 52, No. 3, September 18, 2003)*

By state of residence. Includes legal intervention. Homicide data shown here are collected by the Centers for Disease Control and Prevention based on death certificates and differ from murder data collected by the F.B.I. from other sources. Not age-adjusted. Figures include deaths related to the attacks of September 11, 2001.

**Insufficient data to determine a reliable rate.*

Age-Adjusted Death Rate by Homicide in 2001

National Rate = 7.1 Deaths per 100,000 Population*

ALPHA ORDER

RANK	STATE	RATE
6	Alabama	9.5
24	Alaska	5.7
7	Arizona	9.3
17	Arkansas	6.9
21	California	6.2
33	Colorado	3.7
28	Connecticut	5.1
30	Delaware	4.1
22	Florida	6.1
11	Georgia	7.8
41	Hawaii	2.8
39	Idaho	3.1
8	Illinois	8.6
14	Indiana	7.1
45	Iowa	2.1
26	Kansas	5.3
26	Kentucky	5.3
3	Louisiana	11.9
46	Maine	1.6
5	Maryland	10.4
32	Massachusetts	3.8
17	Michigan	6.9
43	Minnesota	2.5
4	Mississippi	11.4
11	Missouri	7.8
35	Montana	3.6
42	Nebraska	2.6
10	Nevada	8.4
44	New Hampshire	2.2
2	New Jersey	12.2
14	New Mexico	7.1
1	New York	14.5
14	North Carolina	7.1
NA	North Dakota**	NA
29	Ohio	4.7
23	Oklahoma	6.0
40	Oregon	2.9
24	Pennsylvania	5.7
36	Rhode Island	3.5
9	South Carolina	8.5
NA	South Dakota**	NA
11	Tennessee	7.8
20	Texas	6.4
37	Utah	3.4
NA	Vermont**	NA
17	Virginia	6.9
38	Washington	3.2
33	West Virginia	3.7
31	Wisconsin	3.9
NA	Wyoming**	NA

RANK ORDER

RANK	STATE	RATE
1	New York	14.5
2	New Jersey	12.2
3	Louisiana	11.9
4	Mississippi	11.4
5	Maryland	10.4
6	Alabama	9.5
7	Arizona	9.3
8	Illinois	8.6
9	South Carolina	8.5
10	Nevada	8.4
11	Georgia	7.8
11	Missouri	7.8
11	Tennessee	7.8
14	Indiana	7.1
14	New Mexico	7.1
14	North Carolina	7.1
17	Arkansas	6.9
17	Michigan	6.9
17	Virginia	6.9
20	Texas	6.4
21	California	6.2
22	Florida	6.1
23	Oklahoma	6.0
24	Alaska	5.7
24	Pennsylvania	5.7
26	Kansas	5.3
26	Kentucky	5.3
28	Connecticut	5.1
29	Ohio	4.7
30	Delaware	4.1
31	Wisconsin	3.9
32	Massachusetts	3.8
33	Colorado	3.7
33	West Virginia	3.7
35	Montana	3.6
36	Rhode Island	3.5
37	Utah	3.4
38	Washington	3.2
39	Idaho	3.1
40	Oregon	2.9
41	Hawaii	2.8
42	Nebraska	2.6
43	Minnesota	2.5
44	New Hampshire	2.2
45	Iowa	2.1
46	Maine	1.6
NA	North Dakota**	NA
NA	South Dakota**	NA
NA	Vermont**	NA
NA	Wyoming**	NA

District of Columbia	31.3

*Source: U.S. Department of Health and Human Services, National Center for Health Statistics
"National Vital Statistics Reports" (Vol. 52, No. 3, September 18, 2003)*

*By state of residence. Includes legal intervention. Homicide data shown here are collected by the Centers for Disease Control and Prevention based on death certificates and differ from murder data collected by the F.B.I. from other sources. Age-adjusted rates based on the year 2000 standard population. Figures include deaths related to the attacks of September 11, 2001. **Insufficient data to determine a reliable rate.*

Deaths by Suicide in 2001

National Total = 30,622 Suicides*

ALPHA ORDER				RANK ORDER			
RANK	STATE	SUICIDES	% of USA	RANK	STATE	SUICIDES	% of USA
21	Alabama	512	1.7%	1	California	2,831	9.2%
46	Alaska	102	0.3%	2	Florida	2,314	7.6%
12	Arizona	767	2.5%	3	Texas	2,225	7.3%
30	Arkansas	382	1.2%	4	Pennsylvania	1,276	4.2%
1	California	2,831	9.2%	5	New York	1,253	4.1%
14	Colorado	722	2.4%	6	Ohio	1,219	4.0%
37	Connecticut	283	0.9%	7	Illinois	1,139	3.7%
44	Delaware	108	0.4%	8	Michigan	1,051	3.4%
2	Florida	2,314	7.6%	9	North Carolina	997	3.3%
10	Georgia	935	3.1%	10	Georgia	935	3.1%
43	Hawaii	136	0.4%	11	Virginia	797	2.6%
38	Idaho	210	0.7%	12	Arizona	767	2.5%
7	Illinois	1,139	3.7%	13	Missouri	725	2.4%
15	Indiana	715	2.3%	14	Colorado	722	2.4%
34	Iowa	304	1.0%	15	Indiana	715	2.3%
35	Kansas	293	1.0%	16	Washington	712	2.3%
23	Kentucky	495	1.6%	17	Tennessee	711	2.3%
24	Louisiana	493	1.6%	18	Wisconsin	639	2.1%
42	Maine	161	0.5%	19	New Jersey	588	1.9%
27	Maryland	454	1.5%	20	Oklahoma	515	1.7%
28	Massachusetts	426	1.4%	21	Alabama	512	1.7%
8	Michigan	1,051	3.4%	22	Oregon	505	1.6%
25	Minnesota	480	1.6%	23	Kentucky	495	1.6%
32	Mississippi	328	1.1%	24	Louisiana	493	1.6%
13	Missouri	725	2.4%	25	Minnesota	480	1.6%
40	Montana	175	0.6%	26	South Carolina	467	1.5%
39	Nebraska	187	0.6%	27	Maryland	454	1.5%
29	Nevada	387	1.3%	28	Massachusetts	426	1.4%
41	New Hampshire	167	0.5%	29	Nevada	387	1.3%
19	New Jersey	588	1.9%	30	Arkansas	382	1.2%
31	New Mexico	362	1.2%	31	New Mexico	362	1.2%
5	New York	1,253	4.1%	32	Mississippi	328	1.1%
9	North Carolina	997	3.3%	33	Utah	321	1.0%
49	North Dakota	79	0.3%	34	Iowa	304	1.0%
6	Ohio	1,219	4.0%	35	Kansas	293	1.0%
20	Oklahoma	515	1.7%	36	West Virginia	286	0.9%
22	Oregon	505	1.6%	37	Connecticut	283	0.9%
4	Pennsylvania	1,276	4.2%	38	Idaho	210	0.7%
47	Rhode Island	88	0.3%	39	Nebraska	187	0.6%
26	South Carolina	467	1.5%	40	Montana	175	0.6%
45	South Dakota	105	0.3%	41	New Hampshire	167	0.5%
17	Tennessee	711	2.3%	42	Maine	161	0.5%
3	Texas	2,225	7.3%	43	Hawaii	136	0.4%
33	Utah	321	1.0%	44	Delaware	108	0.4%
50	Vermont	72	0.2%	45	South Dakota	105	0.3%
11	Virginia	797	2.6%	46	Alaska	102	0.3%
16	Washington	712	2.3%	47	Rhode Island	88	0.3%
36	West Virginia	286	0.9%	48	Wyoming	83	0.3%
18	Wisconsin	639	2.1%	49	North Dakota	79	0.3%
48	Wyoming	83	0.3%	50	Vermont	72	0.2%
					District of Columbia	40	0.1%

Source: U.S. Department of Health and Human Services, National Center for Health Statistics
"National Vital Statistics Reports" (Vol. 52, No. 3, September 18, 2003)
*Final data by state of residence.

Death Rate by Suicide in 2001

National Rate = 10.8 Suicides per 100,000 Population*

ALPHA ORDER				RANK ORDER		
RANK	STATE	RATE		RANK	STATE	RATE
28	Alabama	11.5		1	New Mexico	19.8
6	Alaska	16.1		2	Montana	19.3
10	Arizona	14.5		3	Nevada	18.4
12	Arkansas	14.2		4	Wyoming	16.8
46	California	8.2		5	Colorado	16.3
5	Colorado	16.3		6	Alaska	16.1
46	Connecticut	8.2		7	Idaho	15.9
16	Delaware	13.6		7	West Virginia	15.9
13	Florida	14.1		9	Oklahoma	14.8
31	Georgia	11.1		10	Arizona	14.5
31	Hawaii	11.1		10	Oregon	14.5
7	Idaho	15.9		12	Arkansas	14.2
43	Illinois	9.1		13	Florida	14.1
26	Indiana	11.7		13	Utah	14.1
39	Iowa	10.4		15	South Dakota	13.8
36	Kansas	10.8		16	Delaware	13.6
22	Kentucky	12.2		17	New Hampshire	13.3
34	Louisiana	11.0		18	Missouri	12.9
19	Maine	12.5		19	Maine	12.5
44	Maryland	8.4		20	North Dakota	12.4
49	Massachusetts	6.7		20	Tennessee	12.4
38	Michigan	10.5		22	Kentucky	12.2
42	Minnesota	9.6		23	North Carolina	12.1
28	Mississippi	11.5		24	Washington	11.9
18	Missouri	12.9		25	Wisconsin	11.8
2	Montana	19.3		26	Indiana	11.7
35	Nebraska	10.9		26	Vermont	11.7
3	Nevada	18.4		28	Alabama	11.5
17	New Hampshire	13.3		28	Mississippi	11.5
48	New Jersey	6.9		28	South Carolina	11.5
1	New Mexico	19.8		31	Georgia	11.1
50	New York	6.6		31	Hawaii	11.1
23	North Carolina	12.1		31	Virginia	11.1
20	North Dakota	12.4		34	Louisiana	11.0
37	Ohio	10.7		35	Nebraska	10.9
9	Oklahoma	14.8		36	Kansas	10.8
10	Oregon	14.5		37	Ohio	10.7
39	Pennsylvania	10.4		38	Michigan	10.5
45	Rhode Island	8.3		39	Iowa	10.4
28	South Carolina	11.5		39	Pennsylvania	10.4
15	South Dakota	13.8		39	Texas	10.4
20	Tennessee	12.4		42	Minnesota	9.6
39	Texas	10.4		43	Illinois	9.1
13	Utah	14.1		44	Maryland	8.4
26	Vermont	11.7		45	Rhode Island	8.3
31	Virginia	11.1		46	California	8.2
24	Washington	11.9		46	Connecticut	8.2
7	West Virginia	15.9		48	New Jersey	6.9
25	Wisconsin	11.8		49	Massachusetts	6.7
4	Wyoming	16.8		50	New York	6.6
					District of Columbia	7.0

Source: U.S. Department of Health and Human Services, National Center for Health Statistics
*   "National Vital Statistics Reports" (Vol. 52, No. 3, September 18, 2003)*
*Final data by state of residence. Not age-adjusted.

Age-Adjusted Death Rate by Suicide in 2001

National Rate = 10.7 Deaths per 100,000 Population*

ALPHA ORDER

RANK	STATE	RATE
29	Alabama	11.3
7	Alaska	15.9
11	Arizona	14.8
13	Arkansas	14.2
44	California	8.5
4	Colorado	16.5
46	Connecticut	8.2
16	Delaware	13.3
15	Florida	13.5
28	Georgia	11.4
34	Hawaii	10.9
6	Idaho	16.3
43	Illinois	9.1
25	Indiana	11.7
40	Iowa	10.1
34	Kansas	10.9
23	Kentucky	11.9
32	Louisiana	11.2
22	Maine	12.0
45	Maryland	8.4
49	Massachusetts	6.5
39	Michigan	10.5
42	Minnesota	9.6
25	Mississippi	11.7
18	Missouri	12.7
2	Montana	19.1
34	Nebraska	10.9
3	Nevada	18.8
17	New Hampshire	13.1
48	New Jersey	6.8
1	New Mexico	20.2
49	New York	6.5
21	North Carolina	12.1
18	North Dakota	12.7
38	Ohio	10.6
10	Oklahoma	14.9
12	Oregon	14.4
40	Pennsylvania	10.1
47	Rhode Island	8.0
29	South Carolina	11.3
14	South Dakota	13.9
20	Tennessee	12.2
34	Texas	10.9
8	Utah	15.4
29	Vermont	11.3
33	Virginia	11.0
24	Washington	11.8
9	West Virginia	15.0
25	Wisconsin	11.7
5	Wyoming	16.4

RANK ORDER

RANK	STATE	RATE
1	New Mexico	20.2
2	Montana	19.1
3	Nevada	18.8
4	Colorado	16.5
5	Wyoming	16.4
6	Idaho	16.3
7	Alaska	15.9
8	Utah	15.4
9	West Virginia	15.0
10	Oklahoma	14.9
11	Arizona	14.8
12	Oregon	14.4
13	Arkansas	14.2
14	South Dakota	13.9
15	Florida	13.5
16	Delaware	13.3
17	New Hampshire	13.1
18	Missouri	12.7
18	North Dakota	12.7
20	Tennessee	12.2
21	North Carolina	12.1
22	Maine	12.0
23	Kentucky	11.9
24	Washington	11.8
25	Indiana	11.7
25	Mississippi	11.7
25	Wisconsin	11.7
28	Georgia	11.4
29	Alabama	11.3
29	South Carolina	11.3
29	Vermont	11.3
32	Louisiana	11.2
33	Virginia	11.0
34	Hawaii	10.9
34	Kansas	10.9
34	Nebraska	10.9
34	Texas	10.9
38	Ohio	10.6
39	Michigan	10.5
40	Iowa	10.1
40	Pennsylvania	10.1
42	Minnesota	9.6
43	Illinois	9.1
44	California	8.5
45	Maryland	8.4
46	Connecticut	8.2
47	Rhode Island	8.0
48	New Jersey	6.8
49	Massachusetts	6.5
49	New York	6.5
	District of Columbia	6.5

Source: U.S. Department of Health and Human Services, National Center for Health Statistics
    "National Vital Statistics Reports" (Vol. 52, No. 3, September 18, 2003)
*Final data by state of residence. Age-adjusted rates based on the year 2000 standard population.

Alcohol-Induced Deaths in 2000

National Total = 19,358 Deaths*

ALPHA ORDER

RANK	STATE	DEATHS	% of USA
27	Alabama	232	1.2%
39	Alaska	100	0.5%
12	Arizona	466	2.4%
36	Arkansas	113	0.6%
1	California	3,361	17.4%
15	Colorado	443	2.3%
31	Connecticut	193	1.0%
47	Delaware	51	0.3%
2	Florida	1,317	6.8%
11	Georgia	479	2.5%
50	Hawaii	37	0.2%
38	Idaho	105	0.5%
8	Illinois	558	2.9%
19	Indiana	343	1.8%
34	Iowa	135	0.7%
35	Kansas	133	0.7%
26	Kentucky	261	1.3%
30	Louisiana	213	1.1%
40	Maine	97	0.5%
25	Maryland	290	1.5%
21	Massachusetts	337	1.7%
6	Michigan	669	3.5%
23	Minnesota	316	1.6%
32	Mississippi	163	0.8%
22	Missouri	326	1.7%
42	Montana	79	0.4%
45	Nebraska	67	0.3%
29	Nevada	217	1.1%
41	New Hampshire	90	0.5%
10	New Jersey	500	2.6%
20	New Mexico	339	1.8%
4	New York	1,137	5.9%
5	North Carolina	684	3.5%
48	North Dakota	49	0.3%
7	Ohio	578	3.0%
28	Oklahoma	229	1.2%
24	Oregon	312	1.6%
13	Pennsylvania	464	2.4%
43	Rhode Island	77	0.4%
14	South Carolina	448	2.3%
44	South Dakota	69	0.4%
17	Tennessee	379	2.0%
3	Texas	1,170	6.0%
37	Utah	112	0.6%
49	Vermont	38	0.2%
18	Virginia	353	1.8%
9	Washington	518	2.7%
33	West Virginia	144	0.7%
16	Wisconsin	392	2.0%
46	Wyoming	63	0.3%

RANK ORDER

RANK	STATE	DEATHS	% of USA
1	California	3,361	17.4%
2	Florida	1,317	6.8%
3	Texas	1,170	6.0%
4	New York	1,137	5.9%
5	North Carolina	684	3.5%
6	Michigan	669	3.5%
7	Ohio	578	3.0%
8	Illinois	558	2.9%
9	Washington	518	2.7%
10	New Jersey	500	2.6%
11	Georgia	479	2.5%
12	Arizona	466	2.4%
13	Pennsylvania	464	2.4%
14	South Carolina	448	2.3%
15	Colorado	443	2.3%
16	Wisconsin	392	2.0%
17	Tennessee	379	2.0%
18	Virginia	353	1.8%
19	Indiana	343	1.8%
20	New Mexico	339	1.8%
21	Massachusetts	337	1.7%
22	Missouri	326	1.7%
23	Minnesota	316	1.6%
24	Oregon	312	1.6%
25	Maryland	290	1.5%
26	Kentucky	261	1.3%
27	Alabama	232	1.2%
28	Oklahoma	229	1.2%
29	Nevada	217	1.1%
30	Louisiana	213	1.1%
31	Connecticut	193	1.0%
32	Mississippi	163	0.8%
33	West Virginia	144	0.7%
34	Iowa	135	0.7%
35	Kansas	133	0.7%
36	Arkansas	113	0.6%
37	Utah	112	0.6%
38	Idaho	105	0.5%
39	Alaska	100	0.5%
40	Maine	97	0.5%
41	New Hampshire	90	0.5%
42	Montana	79	0.4%
43	Rhode Island	77	0.4%
44	South Dakota	69	0.4%
45	Nebraska	67	0.3%
46	Wyoming	63	0.3%
47	Delaware	51	0.3%
48	North Dakota	49	0.3%
49	Vermont	38	0.2%
50	Hawaii	37	0.2%
	District of Columbia	112	0.6%

Source: U.S. Department of Health and Human Services, National Center for Health Statistics
(http://wonder.cdc.gov)

*By state of residence. Includes excessive blood level of alcohol, accidental poisoning by alcohol and the following alcohol-related causes: psychoses, dependence syndrome, polyneuropathy, cardiomyopathy, gastritis, chronic liver disease and cirrhosis. Excludes accidents, homicides and other causes indirectly related to alcohol use.

Death Rate by Alcohol-Induced Deaths in 2000

National Rate = 6.9 Deaths per 100,000 Population*

ALPHA ORDER

RANK	STATE	RATE
39	Alabama	5.2
2	Alaska	15.9
8	Arizona	9.1
47	Arkansas	4.2
7	California	9.9
6	Colorado	10.3
33	Connecticut	5.7
25	Delaware	6.5
14	Florida	8.2
31	Georgia	5.8
50	Hawaii	3.0
15	Idaho	8.1
46	Illinois	4.5
35	Indiana	5.6
45	Iowa	4.6
43	Kansas	4.9
25	Kentucky	6.5
44	Louisiana	4.8
17	Maine	7.6
37	Maryland	5.5
38	Massachusetts	5.3
22	Michigan	6.7
27	Minnesota	6.4
33	Mississippi	5.7
31	Missouri	5.8
11	Montana	8.8
48	Nebraska	3.9
5	Nevada	10.8
19	New Hampshire	7.3
30	New Jersey	5.9
1	New Mexico	18.6
29	New York	6.0
13	North Carolina	8.5
17	North Dakota	7.6
40	Ohio	5.1
24	Oklahoma	6.6
8	Oregon	9.1
49	Pennsylvania	3.8
19	Rhode Island	7.3
4	South Carolina	11.2
8	South Dakota	9.1
22	Tennessee	6.7
35	Texas	5.6
41	Utah	5.0
28	Vermont	6.2
41	Virginia	5.0
11	Washington	8.8
16	West Virginia	8.0
19	Wisconsin	7.3
3	Wyoming	12.8

RANK ORDER

RANK	STATE	RATE
1	New Mexico	18.6
2	Alaska	15.9
3	Wyoming	12.8
4	South Carolina	11.2
5	Nevada	10.8
6	Colorado	10.3
7	California	9.9
8	Arizona	9.1
8	Oregon	9.1
8	South Dakota	9.1
11	Montana	8.8
11	Washington	8.8
13	North Carolina	8.5
14	Florida	8.2
15	Idaho	8.1
16	West Virginia	8.0
17	Maine	7.6
17	North Dakota	7.6
19	New Hampshire	7.3
19	Rhode Island	7.3
19	Wisconsin	7.3
22	Michigan	6.7
22	Tennessee	6.7
24	Oklahoma	6.6
25	Delaware	6.5
25	Kentucky	6.5
27	Minnesota	6.4
28	Vermont	6.2
29	New York	6.0
30	New Jersey	5.9
31	Georgia	5.8
31	Missouri	5.8
33	Connecticut	5.7
33	Mississippi	5.7
35	Indiana	5.6
35	Texas	5.6
37	Maryland	5.5
38	Massachusetts	5.3
39	Alabama	5.2
40	Ohio	5.1
41	Utah	5.0
41	Virginia	5.0
43	Kansas	4.9
44	Louisiana	4.8
45	Iowa	4.6
46	Illinois	4.5
47	Arkansas	4.2
48	Nebraska	3.9
49	Pennsylvania	3.8
50	Hawaii	3.0

District of Columbia 19.5

Source: U.S. Department of Health and Human Services, National Center for Health Statistics
(http://wonder.cdc.gov)
*By state of residence. Includes excessive blood level of alcohol, accidental poisoning by alcohol and the following alcohol-related causes: psychoses, dependence syndrome, polyneuropathy, cardiomyopathy, gastritis, chronic liver disease and cirrhosis. Excludes accidents, homicides and other causes indirectly related to alcohol use. Not age-adjusted.

Drug-Induced Deaths in 2000

National Total = 19,698 Deaths*

ALPHA ORDER

RANK	STATE	DEATHS	% of USA
30	Alabama	232	1.2%
43	Alaska	54	0.3%
12	Arizona	559	2.8%
33	Arkansas	151	0.8%
1	California	2,301	11.7%
18	Colorado	372	1.9%
19	Connecticut	335	1.7%
42	Delaware	59	0.3%
2	Florida	1,237	6.3%
16	Georgia	428	2.2%
40	Hawaii	64	0.3%
39	Idaho	70	0.4%
5	Illinois	909	4.6%
23	Indiana	289	1.5%
37	Iowa	79	0.4%
36	Kansas	111	0.6%
28	Kentucky	257	1.3%
19	Louisiana	335	1.7%
41	Maine	62	0.3%
9	Maryland	657	3.3%
14	Massachusetts	484	2.5%
7	Michigan	870	4.4%
32	Minnesota	158	0.8%
34	Mississippi	123	0.6%
21	Missouri	326	1.7%
46	Montana	46	0.2%
44	Nebraska	52	0.3%
25	Nevada	281	1.4%
45	New Hampshire	48	0.2%
8	New Jersey	794	4.0%
26	New Mexico	279	1.4%
6	New York	901	4.6%
13	North Carolina	531	2.7%
50	North Dakota	16	0.1%
10	Ohio	625	3.2%
29	Oklahoma	249	1.3%
22	Oregon	305	1.5%
3	Pennsylvania	1,214	6.2%
38	Rhode Island	76	0.4%
23	South Carolina	289	1.5%
49	South Dakota	25	0.1%
17	Tennessee	426	2.2%
4	Texas	1,210	6.1%
31	Utah	224	1.1%
47	Vermont	37	0.2%
15	Virginia	441	2.2%
11	Washington	598	3.0%
35	West Virginia	122	0.6%
27	Wisconsin	277	1.4%
48	Wyoming	27	0.1%

RANK ORDER

RANK	STATE	DEATHS	% of USA
1	California	2,301	11.7%
2	Florida	1,237	6.3%
3	Pennsylvania	1,214	6.2%
4	Texas	1,210	6.1%
5	Illinois	909	4.6%
6	New York	901	4.6%
7	Michigan	870	4.4%
8	New Jersey	794	4.0%
9	Maryland	657	3.3%
10	Ohio	625	3.2%
11	Washington	598	3.0%
12	Arizona	559	2.8%
13	North Carolina	531	2.7%
14	Massachusetts	484	2.5%
15	Virginia	441	2.2%
16	Georgia	428	2.2%
17	Tennessee	426	2.2%
18	Colorado	372	1.9%
19	Connecticut	335	1.7%
19	Louisiana	335	1.7%
21	Missouri	326	1.7%
22	Oregon	305	1.5%
23	Indiana	289	1.5%
23	South Carolina	289	1.5%
25	Nevada	281	1.4%
26	New Mexico	279	1.4%
27	Wisconsin	277	1.4%
28	Kentucky	257	1.3%
29	Oklahoma	249	1.3%
30	Alabama	232	1.2%
31	Utah	224	1.1%
32	Minnesota	158	0.8%
33	Arkansas	151	0.8%
34	Mississippi	123	0.6%
35	West Virginia	122	0.6%
36	Kansas	111	0.6%
37	Iowa	79	0.4%
38	Rhode Island	76	0.4%
39	Idaho	70	0.4%
40	Hawaii	64	0.3%
41	Maine	62	0.3%
42	Delaware	59	0.3%
43	Alaska	54	0.3%
44	Nebraska	52	0.3%
45	New Hampshire	48	0.2%
46	Montana	46	0.2%
47	Vermont	37	0.2%
48	Wyoming	27	0.1%
49	South Dakota	25	0.1%
50	North Dakota	16	0.1%
	District of Columbia	83	0.4%

Source: U.S. Department of Health and Human Services, National Center for Health Statistics
(http://wonder.cdc.gov/)

*By state of residence. Includes drug psychoses, drug dependence, nondependent use excluding alcohol and tobacco, accidental poisoning or suicide by drugs, medicaments and biologicals. Excludes accidents, homicides and other causes indirectly related to drug use.

Death Rate from Drug-Induced Deaths in 2000

National Rate = 7.0 Deaths per 100,000 Population*

ALPHA ORDER

RANK	STATE	RATE
36	Alabama	5.2
12	Alaska	8.6
4	Arizona	10.9
31	Arkansas	5.6
23	California	6.8
12	Colorado	8.6
8	Connecticut	9.8
16	Delaware	7.5
14	Florida	7.7
36	Georgia	5.2
35	Hawaii	5.3
34	Idaho	5.4
19	Illinois	7.3
41	Indiana	4.8
49	Iowa	2.7
44	Kansas	4.1
26	Kentucky	6.4
16	Louisiana	7.5
40	Maine	4.9
3	Maryland	12.4
15	Massachusetts	7.6
11	Michigan	8.7
47	Minnesota	3.2
43	Mississippi	4.3
29	Missouri	5.8
39	Montana	5.1
48	Nebraska	3.0
2	Nevada	14.0
45	New Hampshire	3.9
9	New Jersey	9.4
1	New Mexico	15.3
42	New York	4.7
25	North Carolina	6.6
50	North Dakota**	2.5
32	Ohio	5.5
20	Oklahoma	7.2
10	Oregon	8.9
7	Pennsylvania	9.9
20	Rhode Island	7.2
20	South Carolina	7.2
46	South Dakota	3.3
16	Tennessee	7.5
29	Texas	5.8
6	Utah	10.0
28	Vermont	6.1
27	Virginia	6.2
5	Washington	10.1
24	West Virginia	6.7
36	Wisconsin	5.2
32	Wyoming	5.5

RANK ORDER

RANK	STATE	RATE
1	New Mexico	15.3
2	Nevada	14.0
3	Maryland	12.4
4	Arizona	10.9
5	Washington	10.1
6	Utah	10.0
7	Pennsylvania	9.9
8	Connecticut	9.8
9	New Jersey	9.4
10	Oregon	8.9
11	Michigan	8.7
12	Alaska	8.6
12	Colorado	8.6
14	Florida	7.7
15	Massachusetts	7.6
16	Delaware	7.5
16	Louisiana	7.5
16	Tennessee	7.5
19	Illinois	7.3
20	Oklahoma	7.2
20	Rhode Island	7.2
20	South Carolina	7.2
23	California	6.8
24	West Virginia	6.7
25	North Carolina	6.6
26	Kentucky	6.4
27	Virginia	6.2
28	Vermont	6.1
29	Missouri	5.8
29	Texas	5.8
31	Arkansas	5.6
32	Ohio	5.5
32	Wyoming	5.5
34	Idaho	5.4
35	Hawaii	5.3
36	Alabama	5.2
36	Georgia	5.2
36	Wisconsin	5.2
39	Montana	5.1
40	Maine	4.9
41	Indiana	4.8
42	New York	4.7
43	Mississippi	4.3
44	Kansas	4.1
45	New Hampshire	3.9
46	South Dakota	3.3
47	Minnesota	3.2
48	Nebraska	3.0
49	Iowa	2.7
50	North Dakota**	2.5

District of Columbia   14.5

Source: Morgan Quitno Press using data from U.S. Department of Health and Human Services
    (http://wonder.cdc.gov/)
*By state of residence. Includes drug psychoses, drug dependence, nondependent use excluding alcohol and tobacco, accidental poisoning or suicide by drugs, medicaments and biologicals. Excludes accidents, homicides and other causes indirectly related to drug use. Not age-adjusted.
**Due to low numbers of deaths, rates for this state should be interpreted with caution.

Occupational Fatalities in 2002

National Total = 5,524 Deaths*

ALPHA ORDER

RANK	STATE	DEATHS	% of USA
20	Alabama	102	1.8%
38	Alaska	42	0.8%
22	Arizona	101	1.8%
30	Arkansas	80	1.4%
1	California	478	8.7%
17	Colorado	123	2.2%
40	Connecticut	39	0.7%
48	Delaware	11	0.2%
3	Florida	354	6.4%
6	Georgia	197	3.6%
46	Hawaii	24	0.4%
40	Idaho	39	0.7%
7	Illinois	190	3.4%
15	Indiana	136	2.5%
33	Iowa	56	1.0%
26	Kansas	89	1.6%
12	Kentucky	146	2.6%
19	Louisiana	103	1.9%
44	Maine	30	0.5%
20	Maryland	102	1.8%
36	Massachusetts	46	0.8%
11	Michigan	151	2.7%
29	Minnesota	81	1.5%
23	Mississippi	94	1.7%
9	Missouri	175	3.2%
35	Montana	51	0.9%
27	Nebraska	83	1.5%
37	Nevada	45	0.8%
47	New Hampshire	19	0.3%
16	New Jersey	129	2.3%
31	New Mexico	63	1.1%
4	New York	238	4.3%
10	North Carolina	169	3.1%
45	North Dakota	25	0.5%
5	Ohio	202	3.7%
24	Oklahoma	92	1.7%
31	Oregon	63	1.1%
8	Pennsylvania	188	3.4%
50	Rhode Island	8	0.1%
18	South Carolina	107	1.9%
42	South Dakota	36	0.7%
14	Tennessee	140	2.5%
2	Texas	417	7.5%
34	Utah	52	0.9%
48	Vermont	11	0.2%
13	Virginia	142	2.6%
27	Washington	83	1.5%
39	West Virginia	40	0.7%
25	Wisconsin	91	1.6%
43	Wyoming	32	0.6%

RANK ORDER

RANK	STATE	DEATHS	% of USA
1	California	478	8.7%
2	Texas	417	7.5%
3	Florida	354	6.4%
4	New York	238	4.3%
5	Ohio	202	3.7%
6	Georgia	197	3.6%
7	Illinois	190	3.4%
8	Pennsylvania	188	3.4%
9	Missouri	175	3.2%
10	North Carolina	169	3.1%
11	Michigan	151	2.7%
12	Kentucky	146	2.6%
13	Virginia	142	2.6%
14	Tennessee	140	2.5%
15	Indiana	136	2.5%
16	New Jersey	129	2.3%
17	Colorado	123	2.2%
18	South Carolina	107	1.9%
19	Louisiana	103	1.9%
20	Alabama	102	1.8%
20	Maryland	102	1.8%
22	Arizona	101	1.8%
23	Mississippi	94	1.7%
24	Oklahoma	92	1.7%
25	Wisconsin	91	1.6%
26	Kansas	89	1.6%
27	Nebraska	83	1.5%
27	Washington	83	1.5%
29	Minnesota	81	1.5%
30	Arkansas	80	1.4%
31	New Mexico	63	1.1%
31	Oregon	63	1.1%
33	Iowa	56	1.0%
34	Utah	52	0.9%
35	Montana	51	0.9%
36	Massachusetts	46	0.8%
37	Nevada	45	0.8%
38	Alaska	42	0.8%
39	West Virginia	40	0.7%
40	Connecticut	39	0.7%
40	Idaho	39	0.7%
42	South Dakota	36	0.7%
43	Wyoming	32	0.6%
44	Maine	30	0.5%
45	North Dakota	25	0.5%
46	Hawaii	24	0.4%
47	New Hampshire	19	0.3%
48	Delaware	11	0.2%
48	Vermont	11	0.2%
50	Rhode Island	8	0.1%
	District of Columbia	8	0.1%

Source: U.S. Department of Labor, Bureau of Labor Statistics
    "National Census of Fatal Occupational Injuries, 2002" (press release, September 17, 2003)
*Includes one fatality that occurred within the territorial boundaries of the United States but for which a state of
incident could not be determined.

Occupational Fatality Rate in 2002

National Rate = 4.0 Deaths per 100,000 Workers*

ALPHA ORDER

RANK	STATE	RATE
19	Alabama	5.2
1	Alaska	14.1
30	Arizona	4.0
10	Arkansas	6.6
42	California	2.9
17	Colorado	5.4
48	Connecticut	2.3
46	Delaware	2.7
23	Florida	4.6
21	Georgia	4.8
26	Hawaii	4.3
13	Idaho	6.0
37	Illinois	3.2
25	Indiana	4.5
35	Iowa	3.5
10	Kansas	6.6
6	Kentucky	7.9
16	Louisiana	5.5
23	Maine	4.6
32	Maryland	3.7
50	Massachusetts	1.4
37	Michigan	3.2
42	Minnesota	2.9
7	Mississippi	7.8
12	Missouri	6.2
3	Montana	11.5
4	Nebraska	9.0
28	Nevada	4.2
45	New Hampshire	2.8
41	New Jersey	3.1
8	New Mexico	7.6
46	New York	2.7
26	North Carolina	4.3
9	North Dakota	7.5
32	Ohio	3.7
15	Oklahoma	5.7
32	Oregon	3.7
37	Pennsylvania	3.2
49	Rhode Island	1.5
14	South Carolina	5.8
5	South Dakota	8.8
20	Tennessee	5.0
29	Texas	4.1
22	Utah	4.7
36	Vermont	3.3
30	Virginia	4.0
42	Washington	2.9
18	West Virginia	5.3
37	Wisconsin	3.2
2	Wyoming	12.4

RANK ORDER

RANK	STATE	RATE
1	Alaska	14.1
2	Wyoming	12.4
3	Montana	11.5
4	Nebraska	9.0
5	South Dakota	8.8
6	Kentucky	7.9
7	Mississippi	7.8
8	New Mexico	7.6
9	North Dakota	7.5
10	Arkansas	6.6
10	Kansas	6.6
12	Missouri	6.2
13	Idaho	6.0
14	South Carolina	5.8
15	Oklahoma	5.7
16	Louisiana	5.5
17	Colorado	5.4
18	West Virginia	5.3
19	Alabama	5.2
20	Tennessee	5.0
21	Georgia	4.8
22	Utah	4.7
23	Florida	4.6
23	Maine	4.6
25	Indiana	4.5
26	Hawaii	4.3
26	North Carolina	4.3
28	Nevada	4.2
29	Texas	4.1
30	Arizona	4.0
30	Virginia	4.0
32	Maryland	3.7
32	Ohio	3.7
32	Oregon	3.7
35	Iowa	3.5
36	Vermont	3.3
37	Illinois	3.2
37	Michigan	3.2
37	Pennsylvania	3.2
37	Wisconsin	3.2
41	New Jersey	3.1
42	California	2.9
42	Minnesota	2.9
42	Washington	2.9
45	New Hampshire	2.8
46	Delaware	2.7
46	New York	2.7
48	Connecticut	2.3
49	Rhode Island	1.5
50	Massachusetts	1.4
	District of Columbia	2.8

Source: Morgan Quitno Press using data from U.S. Department of Labor, Bureau of Labor Statistics
"National Census of Fatal Occupational Injuries, 2002" (press release, September 17, 2003)
*Based on employed civilian labor force.

Years Lost by Premature Death in 2000

National Average = 7,578 Years Lost per 100,000 Population*

ALPHA ORDER

RANK	STATE	YEARS
3	Alabama	9,844
15	Alaska	8,144
21	Arizona	7,855
6	Arkansas	9,466
36	California	6,506
41	Colorado	6,448
37	Connecticut	6,499
13	Delaware	8,232
17	Florida	8,121
9	Georgia	8,924
43	Hawaii	6,321
35	Idaho	6,537
22	Illinois	7,777
19	Indiana	7,964
42	Iowa	6,354
29	Kansas	7,079
10	Kentucky	8,700
2	Louisiana	10,202
39	Maine	6,476
16	Maryland	8,138
48	Massachusetts	6,046
20	Michigan	7,878
50	Minnesota	5,762
1	Mississippi	11,017
14	Missouri	8,189
27	Montana	7,379
38	Nebraska	6,480
12	Nevada	8,390
49	New Hampshire	5,840
31	New Jersey	6,962
18	New Mexico	8,017
32	New York	6,869
11	North Carolina	8,616
45	North Dakota	6,273
24	Ohio	7,654
7	Oklahoma	9,048
33	Oregon	6,591
25	Pennsylvania	7,580
40	Rhode Island	6,471
4	South Carolina	9,597
30	South Dakota	7,013
5	Tennessee	9,488
23	Texas	7,658
47	Utah	6,109
46	Vermont	6,258
28	Virginia	7,314
44	Washington	6,283
8	West Virginia	8,972
34	Wisconsin	6,575
26	Wyoming	7,395

RANK ORDER

RANK	STATE	YEARS
1	Mississippi	11,017
2	Louisiana	10,202
3	Alabama	9,844
4	South Carolina	9,597
5	Tennessee	9,488
6	Arkansas	9,466
7	Oklahoma	9,048
8	West Virginia	8,972
9	Georgia	8,924
10	Kentucky	8,700
11	North Carolina	8,616
12	Nevada	8,390
13	Delaware	8,232
14	Missouri	8,189
15	Alaska	8,144
16	Maryland	8,138
17	Florida	8,121
18	New Mexico	8,017
19	Indiana	7,964
20	Michigan	7,878
21	Arizona	7,855
22	Illinois	7,777
23	Texas	7,658
24	Ohio	7,654
25	Pennsylvania	7,580
26	Wyoming	7,395
27	Montana	7,379
28	Virginia	7,314
29	Kansas	7,079
30	South Dakota	7,013
31	New Jersey	6,962
32	New York	6,869
33	Oregon	6,591
34	Wisconsin	6,575
35	Idaho	6,537
36	California	6,506
37	Connecticut	6,499
38	Nebraska	6,480
39	Maine	6,476
40	Rhode Island	6,471
41	Colorado	6,448
42	Iowa	6,354
43	Hawaii	6,321
44	Washington	6,283
45	North Dakota	6,273
46	Vermont	6,258
47	Utah	6,109
48	Massachusetts	6,046
49	New Hampshire	5,840
50	Minnesota	5,762

District of Columbia	13,366

Source: U.S. Department of Health and Human Services, National Center for Health Statistics unpublished data

*Age-adjusted years of potential life lost due to death before age 75.

Years Lost by Premature Death from Cancer in 2000

National Average = 1,674 Years Lost per 100,000 Population*

ALPHA ORDER				RANK ORDER		
RANK	STATE	YEARS		RANK	STATE	YEARS
8	Alabama	1,894		1	Mississippi	2,020
42	Alaska	1,462		2	Kentucky	2,000
37	Arizona	1,502		3	Louisiana	1,988
7	Arkansas	1,901		4	West Virginia	1,983
39	California	1,493		5	Tennessee	1,910
49	Colorado	1,303		6	South Carolina	1,909
40	Connecticut	1,482		7	Arkansas	1,901
23	Delaware	1,712		8	Alabama	1,894
16	Florida	1,733		9	Indiana	1,828
13	Georgia	1,776		10	Oklahoma	1,814
46	Hawaii	1,405		11	Missouri	1,794
44	Idaho	1,435		12	Ohio	1,784
14	Illinois	1,757		13	Georgia	1,776
9	Indiana	1,828		14	Illinois	1,757
30	Iowa	1,611		15	North Carolina	1,753
33	Kansas	1,545		16	Florida	1,733
2	Kentucky	2,000		17	Pennsylvania	1,723
3	Louisiana	1,988		18	Maryland	1,722
22	Maine	1,719		19	Nevada	1,721
18	Maryland	1,722		19	Virginia	1,721
25	Massachusetts	1,667		21	Michigan	1,720
21	Michigan	1,720		22	Maine	1,719
38	Minnesota	1,501		23	Delaware	1,712
1	Mississippi	2,020		24	Rhode Island	1,709
11	Missouri	1,794		25	Massachusetts	1,667
36	Montana	1,507		26	New Jersey	1,666
43	Nebraska	1,453		27	Texas	1,657
19	Nevada	1,721		28	New York	1,614
29	New Hampshire	1,613		29	New Hampshire	1,613
26	New Jersey	1,666		30	Iowa	1,611
48	New Mexico	1,352		31	Oregon	1,560
28	New York	1,614		32	Wisconsin	1,556
15	North Carolina	1,753		33	Kansas	1,545
47	North Dakota	1,391		34	Washington	1,533
12	Ohio	1,784		35	Vermont	1,513
10	Oklahoma	1,814		36	Montana	1,507
31	Oregon	1,560		37	Arizona	1,502
17	Pennsylvania	1,723		38	Minnesota	1,501
24	Rhode Island	1,709		39	California	1,493
6	South Carolina	1,909		40	Connecticut	1,482
41	South Dakota	1,476		41	South Dakota	1,476
5	Tennessee	1,910		42	Alaska	1,462
27	Texas	1,657		43	Nebraska	1,453
50	Utah	1,218		44	Idaho	1,435
35	Vermont	1,513		45	Wyoming	1,421
19	Virginia	1,721		46	Hawaii	1,405
34	Washington	1,533		47	North Dakota	1,391
4	West Virginia	1,983		48	New Mexico	1,352
32	Wisconsin	1,556		49	Colorado	1,303
45	Wyoming	1,421		50	Utah	1,218

	District of Columbia	2,181

Source: U.S. Department of Health and Human Services, National Center for Health Statistics
   unpublished data
*Age-adjusted years of potential life lost due to death before age 75.

Years Lost by Premature Death from Heart Disease in 2000

National Average = 1,253 Years Lost per 100,000 Population*

ALPHA ORDER

RANK	STATE	YEARS
2	Alabama	1,757
40	Alaska	959
30	Arizona	1,099
9	Arkansas	1,624
37	California	999
48	Colorado	829
34	Connecticut	1,081
21	Delaware	1,270
23	Florida	1,190
10	Georgia	1,547
25	Hawaii	1,159
42	Idaho	953
17	Illinois	1,365
15	Indiana	1,391
26	Iowa	1,133
32	Kansas	1,083
6	Kentucky	1,654
4	Louisiana	1,703
35	Maine	1,062
18	Maryland	1,335
38	Massachusetts	991
16	Michigan	1,382
50	Minnesota	767
1	Mississippi	2,097
12	Missouri	1,434
41	Montana	955
44	Nebraska	944
11	Nevada	1,487
43	New Hampshire	950
28	New Jersey	1,118
47	New Mexico	876
24	New York	1,183
13	North Carolina	1,416
27	North Dakota	1,128
14	Ohio	1,401
3	Oklahoma	1,704
46	Oregon	883
19	Pennsylvania	1,302
36	Rhode Island	1,058
7	South Carolina	1,638
29	South Dakota	1,103
5	Tennessee	1,683
20	Texas	1,297
49	Utah	798
39	Vermont	987
22	Virginia	1,251
45	Washington	937
8	West Virginia	1,629
31	Wisconsin	1,084
32	Wyoming	1,083

RANK ORDER

RANK	STATE	YEARS
1	Mississippi	2,097
2	Alabama	1,757
3	Oklahoma	1,704
4	Louisiana	1,703
5	Tennessee	1,683
6	Kentucky	1,654
7	South Carolina	1,638
8	West Virginia	1,629
9	Arkansas	1,624
10	Georgia	1,547
11	Nevada	1,487
12	Missouri	1,434
13	North Carolina	1,416
14	Ohio	1,401
15	Indiana	1,391
16	Michigan	1,382
17	Illinois	1,365
18	Maryland	1,335
19	Pennsylvania	1,302
20	Texas	1,297
21	Delaware	1,270
22	Virginia	1,251
23	Florida	1,190
24	New York	1,183
25	Hawaii	1,159
26	Iowa	1,133
27	North Dakota	1,128
28	New Jersey	1,118
29	South Dakota	1,103
30	Arizona	1,099
31	Wisconsin	1,084
32	Kansas	1,083
32	Wyoming	1,083
34	Connecticut	1,081
35	Maine	1,062
36	Rhode Island	1,058
37	California	999
38	Massachusetts	991
39	Vermont	987
40	Alaska	959
41	Montana	955
42	Idaho	953
43	New Hampshire	950
44	Nebraska	944
45	Washington	937
46	Oregon	883
47	New Mexico	876
48	Colorado	829
49	Utah	798
50	Minnesota	767

| | District of Columbia | 1,999 |

Source: U.S. Department of Health and Human Services, National Center for Health Statistics unpublished data

*Age-adjusted years of potential life lost due to death before age 75.

Years Lost by Premature Death from Homicide in 2000

National Average = 267 Years Lost per 100,000 Population*

ALPHA ORDER				RANK ORDER		
RANK	STATE	YEARS		RANK	STATE	YEARS
4	Alabama	436		1	Louisiana	609
17	Alaska	276		2	Mississippi	480
10	Arizona	339		3	Maryland	454
12	Arkansas	332		4	Alabama	436
18	California	270		5	New Mexico	391
34	Colorado	149		6	Illinois	374
36	Connecticut	137		7	Tennessee	368
38	Delaware	120		8	South Carolina	357
20	Florida	260		9	North Carolina	348
11	Georgia	338		10	Arizona	339
39	Hawaii	115		11	Georgia	338
44	Idaho	81		12	Arkansas	332
6	Illinois	374		12	Missouri	332
16	Indiana	286		14	Michigan	331
42	Iowa	95		15	Nevada	289
25	Kansas	241		16	Indiana	286
26	Kentucky	211		17	Alaska	276
1	Louisiana	609		18	California	270
NA	Maine**	NA		19	Texas	268
3	Maryland	454		20	Florida	260
43	Massachusetts	94		21	Virginia	259
14	Michigan	331		22	Pennsylvania	257
37	Minnesota	123		23	Oklahoma	243
2	Mississippi	480		24	New York	242
12	Missouri	332		25	Kansas	241
28	Montana	188		26	Kentucky	211
31	Nebraska	179		27	Rhode Island	191
15	Nevada	289		28	Montana	188
NA	New Hampshire**	NA		29	West Virginia	187
30	New Jersey	183		30	New Jersey	183
5	New Mexico	391		31	Nebraska	179
24	New York	242		32	Ohio	176
9	North Carolina	348		33	Wisconsin	152
NA	North Dakota**	NA		34	Colorado	149
32	Ohio	176		35	Washington	148
23	Oklahoma	243		36	Connecticut	137
39	Oregon	115		37	Minnesota	123
22	Pennsylvania	257		38	Delaware	120
27	Rhode Island	191		39	Hawaii	115
8	South Carolina	357		39	Oregon	115
NA	South Dakota**	NA		41	Utah	96
7	Tennessee	368		42	Iowa	95
19	Texas	268		43	Massachusetts	94
41	Utah	96		44	Idaho	81
NA	Vermont**	NA		NA	Maine**	NA
21	Virginia	259		NA	New Hampshire**	NA
35	Washington	148		NA	North Dakota**	NA
29	West Virginia	187		NA	South Dakota**	NA
33	Wisconsin	152		NA	Vermont**	NA
NA	Wyoming**	NA		NA	Wyoming**	NA

District of Columbia   1,402

*Source: U.S. Department of Health and Human Services, National Center for Health Statistics
unpublished data*
Age-adjusted years of potential life lost due to death before age 75.
**Data for states with fewer than 20 deaths from homicide for persons under 75 years of age are considered
unreliable and are not shown.*

Years Lost by Premature Death from Suicide in 2000

National Average = 335 Years Lost per 100,000 Population*

<table>
<tr><th colspan="3">ALPHA ORDER</th><th colspan="3">RANK ORDER</th></tr>
<tr><th>RANK</th><th>STATE</th><th>YEARS</th><th>RANK</th><th>STATE</th><th>YEARS</th></tr>
<tr><td>17</td><td>Alabama</td><td>417</td><td>1</td><td>Alaska</td><td>914</td></tr>
<tr><td>1</td><td>Alaska</td><td>914</td><td>2</td><td>New Mexico</td><td>630</td></tr>
<tr><td>7</td><td>Arizona</td><td>499</td><td>3</td><td>Nevada</td><td>615</td></tr>
<tr><td>14</td><td>Arkansas</td><td>426</td><td>4</td><td>Montana</td><td>596</td></tr>
<tr><td>46</td><td>California</td><td>257</td><td>5</td><td>Wyoming</td><td>537</td></tr>
<tr><td>10</td><td>Colorado</td><td>460</td><td>6</td><td>Oklahoma</td><td>504</td></tr>
<tr><td>44</td><td>Connecticut</td><td>284</td><td>7</td><td>Arizona</td><td>499</td></tr>
<tr><td>37</td><td>Delaware</td><td>327</td><td>8</td><td>Utah</td><td>488</td></tr>
<tr><td>28</td><td>Florida</td><td>375</td><td>9</td><td>South Dakota</td><td>477</td></tr>
<tr><td>36</td><td>Georgia</td><td>330</td><td>10</td><td>Colorado</td><td>460</td></tr>
<tr><td>29</td><td>Hawaii</td><td>374</td><td>11</td><td>West Virginia</td><td>447</td></tr>
<tr><td>15</td><td>Idaho</td><td>422</td><td>12</td><td>Oregon</td><td>433</td></tr>
<tr><td>45</td><td>Illinois</td><td>261</td><td>13</td><td>Maine</td><td>430</td></tr>
<tr><td>23</td><td>Indiana</td><td>384</td><td>14</td><td>Arkansas</td><td>426</td></tr>
<tr><td>33</td><td>Iowa</td><td>340</td><td>15</td><td>Idaho</td><td>422</td></tr>
<tr><td>20</td><td>Kansas</td><td>411</td><td>16</td><td>Missouri</td><td>418</td></tr>
<tr><td>17</td><td>Kentucky</td><td>417</td><td>17</td><td>Alabama</td><td>417</td></tr>
<tr><td>32</td><td>Louisiana</td><td>351</td><td>17</td><td>Kentucky</td><td>417</td></tr>
<tr><td>13</td><td>Maine</td><td>430</td><td>19</td><td>Tennessee</td><td>412</td></tr>
<tr><td>43</td><td>Maryland</td><td>294</td><td>20</td><td>Kansas</td><td>411</td></tr>
<tr><td>48</td><td>Massachusetts</td><td>209</td><td>21</td><td>Vermont</td><td>403</td></tr>
<tr><td>40</td><td>Michigan</td><td>316</td><td>22</td><td>North Carolina</td><td>392</td></tr>
<tr><td>41</td><td>Minnesota</td><td>311</td><td>23</td><td>Indiana</td><td>384</td></tr>
<tr><td>30</td><td>Mississippi</td><td>358</td><td>23</td><td>Nebraska</td><td>384</td></tr>
<tr><td>16</td><td>Missouri</td><td>418</td><td>23</td><td>Wisconsin</td><td>384</td></tr>
<tr><td>4</td><td>Montana</td><td>596</td><td>26</td><td>Washington</td><td>382</td></tr>
<tr><td>23</td><td>Nebraska</td><td>384</td><td>27</td><td>North Dakota</td><td>377</td></tr>
<tr><td>3</td><td>Nevada</td><td>615</td><td>28</td><td>Florida</td><td>375</td></tr>
<tr><td>37</td><td>New Hampshire</td><td>327</td><td>29</td><td>Hawaii</td><td>374</td></tr>
<tr><td>49</td><td>New Jersey</td><td>206</td><td>30</td><td>Mississippi</td><td>358</td></tr>
<tr><td>2</td><td>New Mexico</td><td>630</td><td>31</td><td>Pennsylvania</td><td>357</td></tr>
<tr><td>50</td><td>New York</td><td>195</td><td>32</td><td>Louisiana</td><td>351</td></tr>
<tr><td>22</td><td>North Carolina</td><td>392</td><td>33</td><td>Iowa</td><td>340</td></tr>
<tr><td>27</td><td>North Dakota</td><td>377</td><td>34</td><td>South Carolina</td><td>338</td></tr>
<tr><td>42</td><td>Ohio</td><td>305</td><td>35</td><td>Texas</td><td>332</td></tr>
<tr><td>6</td><td>Oklahoma</td><td>504</td><td>36</td><td>Georgia</td><td>330</td></tr>
<tr><td>12</td><td>Oregon</td><td>433</td><td>37</td><td>Delaware</td><td>327</td></tr>
<tr><td>31</td><td>Pennsylvania</td><td>357</td><td>37</td><td>New Hampshire</td><td>327</td></tr>
<tr><td>47</td><td>Rhode Island</td><td>244</td><td>39</td><td>Virginia</td><td>322</td></tr>
<tr><td>34</td><td>South Carolina</td><td>338</td><td>40</td><td>Michigan</td><td>316</td></tr>
<tr><td>9</td><td>South Dakota</td><td>477</td><td>41</td><td>Minnesota</td><td>311</td></tr>
<tr><td>19</td><td>Tennessee</td><td>412</td><td>42</td><td>Ohio</td><td>305</td></tr>
<tr><td>35</td><td>Texas</td><td>332</td><td>43</td><td>Maryland</td><td>294</td></tr>
<tr><td>8</td><td>Utah</td><td>488</td><td>44</td><td>Connecticut</td><td>284</td></tr>
<tr><td>21</td><td>Vermont</td><td>403</td><td>45</td><td>Illinois</td><td>261</td></tr>
<tr><td>39</td><td>Virginia</td><td>322</td><td>46</td><td>California</td><td>257</td></tr>
<tr><td>26</td><td>Washington</td><td>382</td><td>47</td><td>Rhode Island</td><td>244</td></tr>
<tr><td>11</td><td>West Virginia</td><td>447</td><td>48</td><td>Massachusetts</td><td>209</td></tr>
<tr><td>23</td><td>Wisconsin</td><td>384</td><td>49</td><td>New Jersey</td><td>206</td></tr>
<tr><td>5</td><td>Wyoming</td><td>537</td><td>50</td><td>New York</td><td>195</td></tr>
<tr><td></td><td></td><td></td><td></td><td>District of Columbia</td><td>134</td></tr>
</table>

Source: U.S. Department of Health and Human Services, National Center for Health Statistics
  unpublished data

*Age-adjusted years of potential life lost due to death before age 75.

Years Lost by Premature Death from Unintentional Injuries in 2000

National Average = 1,026 Years Lost per 100,000 Population*

ALPHA ORDER

RANK	STATE	YEARS
10	Alabama	1,490
1	Alaska	1,911
13	Arizona	1,377
9	Arkansas	1,500
43	California	771
25	Colorado	1,107
41	Connecticut	871
21	Delaware	1,174
18	Florida	1,245
22	Georgia	1,157
46	Hawaii	691
20	Idaho	1,191
30	Illinois	984
28	Indiana	1,006
38	Iowa	929
24	Kansas	1,125
12	Kentucky	1,419
8	Louisiana	1,502
34	Maine	949
47	Maryland	654
50	Massachusetts	441
33	Michigan	953
42	Minnesota	862
2	Mississippi	1,843
16	Missouri	1,279
4	Montana	1,674
37	Nebraska	931
19	Nevada	1,210
45	New Hampshire	741
44	New Jersey	752
3	New Mexico	1,718
48	New York	587
17	North Carolina	1,258
36	North Dakota	942
40	Ohio	888
14	Oklahoma	1,366
32	Oregon	976
27	Pennsylvania	1,052
49	Rhode Island	476
6	South Carolina	1,539
11	South Dakota	1,444
7	Tennessee	1,536
23	Texas	1,149
39	Utah	900
26	Vermont	1,085
35	Virginia	944
29	Washington	995
15	West Virginia	1,362
30	Wisconsin	984
5	Wyoming	1,605

RANK ORDER

RANK	STATE	YEARS
1	Alaska	1,911
2	Mississippi	1,843
3	New Mexico	1,718
4	Montana	1,674
5	Wyoming	1,605
6	South Carolina	1,539
7	Tennessee	1,536
8	Louisiana	1,502
9	Arkansas	1,500
10	Alabama	1,490
11	South Dakota	1,444
12	Kentucky	1,419
13	Arizona	1,377
14	Oklahoma	1,366
15	West Virginia	1,362
16	Missouri	1,279
17	North Carolina	1,258
18	Florida	1,245
19	Nevada	1,210
20	Idaho	1,191
21	Delaware	1,174
22	Georgia	1,157
23	Texas	1,149
24	Kansas	1,125
25	Colorado	1,107
26	Vermont	1,085
27	Pennsylvania	1,052
28	Indiana	1,006
29	Washington	995
30	Illinois	984
30	Wisconsin	984
32	Oregon	976
33	Michigan	953
34	Maine	949
35	Virginia	944
36	North Dakota	942
37	Nebraska	931
38	Iowa	929
39	Utah	900
40	Ohio	888
41	Connecticut	871
42	Minnesota	862
43	California	771
44	New Jersey	752
45	New Hampshire	741
46	Hawaii	691
47	Maryland	654
48	New York	587
49	Rhode Island	476
50	Massachusetts	441

District of Columbia	953

Source: U.S. Department of Health and Human Services, National Center for Health Statistics
    unpublished data
*Age-adjusted years of potential life lost due to death before age 75. Includes such subcategories as falls, drowning, fires/burns, poisonings and motor vehicle injuries.

III. FACILITIES

Community Hospitals in 2002

National Total = 4,927 Hospitals*

ALPHA ORDER

RANK	STATE	HOSPITALS	% of USA
19	Alabama	106	2.2%
47	Alaska	19	0.4%
31	Arizona	61	1.2%
23	Arkansas	87	1.8%
2	California	383	7.8%
29	Colorado	68	1.4%
42	Connecticut	35	0.7%
50	Delaware	6	0.1%
4	Florida	202	4.1%
8	Georgia	146	3.0%
45	Hawaii	25	0.5%
39	Idaho	39	0.8%
6	Illinois	192	3.9%
18	Indiana	112	2.3%
16	Iowa	116	2.4%
11	Kansas	132	2.7%
21	Kentucky	104	2.1%
12	Louisiana	128	2.6%
40	Maine	37	0.8%
36	Maryland	49	1.0%
28	Massachusetts	78	1.6%
9	Michigan	145	2.9%
10	Minnesota	133	2.7%
22	Mississippi	91	1.8%
15	Missouri	119	2.4%
34	Montana	53	1.1%
24	Nebraska	86	1.7%
44	Nevada	26	0.5%
43	New Hampshire	28	0.6%
27	New Jersey	81	1.6%
41	New Mexico	36	0.7%
3	New York	211	4.3%
17	North Carolina	113	2.3%
37	North Dakota	42	0.9%
7	Ohio	168	3.4%
20	Oklahoma	105	2.1%
32	Oregon	60	1.2%
5	Pennsylvania	201	4.1%
49	Rhode Island	11	0.2%
30	South Carolina	62	1.3%
35	South Dakota	51	1.0%
13	Tennessee	125	2.5%
1	Texas	416	8.4%
37	Utah	42	0.9%
48	Vermont	14	0.3%
24	Virginia	86	1.7%
24	Washington	86	1.7%
33	West Virginia	57	1.2%
14	Wisconsin	120	2.4%
46	Wyoming	24	0.5%

RANK ORDER

RANK	STATE	HOSPITALS	% of USA
1	Texas	416	8.4%
2	California	383	7.8%
3	New York	211	4.3%
4	Florida	202	4.1%
5	Pennsylvania	201	4.1%
6	Illinois	192	3.9%
7	Ohio	168	3.4%
8	Georgia	146	3.0%
9	Michigan	145	2.9%
10	Minnesota	133	2.7%
11	Kansas	132	2.7%
12	Louisiana	128	2.6%
13	Tennessee	125	2.5%
14	Wisconsin	120	2.4%
15	Missouri	119	2.4%
16	Iowa	116	2.4%
17	North Carolina	113	2.3%
18	Indiana	112	2.3%
19	Alabama	106	2.2%
20	Oklahoma	105	2.1%
21	Kentucky	104	2.1%
22	Mississippi	91	1.8%
23	Arkansas	87	1.8%
24	Nebraska	86	1.7%
24	Virginia	86	1.7%
24	Washington	86	1.7%
27	New Jersey	81	1.6%
28	Massachusetts	78	1.6%
29	Colorado	68	1.4%
30	South Carolina	62	1.3%
31	Arizona	61	1.2%
32	Oregon	60	1.2%
33	West Virginia	57	1.2%
34	Montana	53	1.1%
35	South Dakota	51	1.0%
36	Maryland	49	1.0%
37	North Dakota	42	0.9%
37	Utah	42	0.9%
39	Idaho	39	0.8%
40	Maine	37	0.8%
41	New Mexico	36	0.7%
42	Connecticut	35	0.7%
43	New Hampshire	28	0.6%
44	Nevada	26	0.5%
45	Hawaii	25	0.5%
46	Wyoming	24	0.5%
47	Alaska	19	0.4%
48	Vermont	14	0.3%
49	Rhode Island	11	0.2%
50	Delaware	6	0.1%
	District of Columbia	10	0.2%

Source: American Hospital Association (Chicago, IL)
    "Hospital Statistics" (2004 edition)

Community hospitals are all nonfederal, short-term, general and special hospitals whose facilities and services are available to the public.

Rate of Community Hospitals in 2002

National Rate = 1.7 Community Hospitals per 100,000 Population*

ALPHA ORDER

RANK	STATE	RATE
18	Alabama	2.4
11	Alaska	3.0
43	Arizona	1.1
8	Arkansas	3.2
43	California	1.1
32	Colorado	1.5
46	Connecticut	1.0
50	Delaware	0.7
39	Florida	1.2
29	Georgia	1.7
24	Hawaii	2.0
13	Idaho	2.9
32	Illinois	1.5
27	Indiana	1.8
7	Iowa	4.0
5	Kansas	4.9
17	Kentucky	2.5
13	Louisiana	2.9
13	Maine	2.9
48	Maryland	0.9
39	Massachusetts	1.2
36	Michigan	1.4
16	Minnesota	2.6
8	Mississippi	3.2
23	Missouri	2.1
3	Montana	5.8
4	Nebraska	5.0
39	Nevada	1.2
20	New Hampshire	2.2
48	New Jersey	0.9
25	New Mexico	1.9
43	New York	1.1
36	North Carolina	1.4
2	North Dakota	6.6
32	Ohio	1.5
11	Oklahoma	3.0
29	Oregon	1.7
31	Pennsylvania	1.6
46	Rhode Island	1.0
32	South Carolina	1.5
1	South Dakota	6.7
20	Tennessee	2.2
25	Texas	1.9
27	Utah	1.8
19	Vermont	2.3
39	Virginia	1.2
36	Washington	1.4
8	West Virginia	3.2
20	Wisconsin	2.2
6	Wyoming	4.8

RANK ORDER

RANK	STATE	RATE
1	South Dakota	6.7
2	North Dakota	6.6
3	Montana	5.8
4	Nebraska	5.0
5	Kansas	4.9
6	Wyoming	4.8
7	Iowa	4.0
8	Arkansas	3.2
8	Mississippi	3.2
8	West Virginia	3.2
11	Alaska	3.0
11	Oklahoma	3.0
13	Idaho	2.9
13	Louisiana	2.9
13	Maine	2.9
16	Minnesota	2.6
17	Kentucky	2.5
18	Alabama	2.4
19	Vermont	2.3
20	New Hampshire	2.2
20	Tennessee	2.2
20	Wisconsin	2.2
23	Missouri	2.1
24	Hawaii	2.0
25	New Mexico	1.9
25	Texas	1.9
27	Indiana	1.8
27	Utah	1.8
29	Georgia	1.7
29	Oregon	1.7
31	Pennsylvania	1.6
32	Colorado	1.5
32	Illinois	1.5
32	Ohio	1.5
32	South Carolina	1.5
36	Michigan	1.4
36	North Carolina	1.4
36	Washington	1.4
39	Florida	1.2
39	Massachusetts	1.2
39	Nevada	1.2
39	Virginia	1.2
43	Arizona	1.1
43	California	1.1
43	New York	1.1
46	Connecticut	1.0
46	Rhode Island	1.0
48	Maryland	0.9
48	New Jersey	0.9
50	Delaware	0.7
	District of Columbia	1.8

Source: Morgan Quitno Press using data from American Hospital Association (Chicago, IL)
   "Hospital Statistics" (2004 edition)
*Community hospitals are all nonfederal, short-term, general and special hospitals whose facilities and services are available to the public.

Community Hospitals per 1,000 Square Miles in 2002

National Rate = 1.4 Community Hospitals*

ALPHA ORDER

RANK	STATE	RATE
25	Alabama	2.1
50	Alaska**	0.0
43	Arizona	0.5
29	Arkansas	1.7
19	California	2.5
39	Colorado	0.7
4	Connecticut	7.2
12	Delaware	3.1
10	Florida	3.7
19	Georgia	2.5
9	Hawaii	3.9
43	Idaho	0.5
11	Illinois	3.5
12	Indiana	3.1
25	Iowa	2.1
32	Kansas	1.6
17	Kentucky	2.6
16	Louisiana	2.9
37	Maine	1.2
5	Maryland	5.0
3	Massachusetts	9.9
17	Michigan	2.6
29	Minnesota	1.7
28	Mississippi	1.9
29	Missouri	1.7
46	Montana	0.4
38	Nebraska	1.1
48	Nevada	0.2
12	New Hampshire	3.1
1	New Jersey	10.9
47	New Mexico	0.3
6	New York	4.5
22	North Carolina	2.3
41	North Dakota	0.6
8	Ohio	4.1
34	Oklahoma	1.5
41	Oregon	0.6
6	Pennsylvania	4.5
2	Rhode Island	10.5
25	South Carolina	2.1
39	South Dakota	0.7
15	Tennessee	3.0
32	Texas	1.6
43	Utah	0.5
34	Vermont	1.5
23	Virginia	2.2
36	Washington	1.3
21	West Virginia	2.4
23	Wisconsin	2.2
48	Wyoming	0.2

RANK ORDER

RANK	STATE	RATE
1	New Jersey	10.9
2	Rhode Island	10.5
3	Massachusetts	9.9
4	Connecticut	7.2
5	Maryland	5.0
6	New York	4.5
6	Pennsylvania	4.5
8	Ohio	4.1
9	Hawaii	3.9
10	Florida	3.7
11	Illinois	3.5
12	Delaware	3.1
12	Indiana	3.1
12	New Hampshire	3.1
15	Tennessee	3.0
16	Louisiana	2.9
17	Kentucky	2.6
17	Michigan	2.6
19	California	2.5
19	Georgia	2.5
21	West Virginia	2.4
22	North Carolina	2.3
23	Virginia	2.2
23	Wisconsin	2.2
25	Alabama	2.1
25	Iowa	2.1
25	South Carolina	2.1
28	Mississippi	1.9
29	Arkansas	1.7
29	Minnesota	1.7
29	Missouri	1.7
32	Kansas	1.6
32	Texas	1.6
34	Oklahoma	1.5
34	Vermont	1.5
36	Washington	1.3
37	Maine	1.2
38	Nebraska	1.1
39	Colorado	0.7
39	South Dakota	0.7
41	North Dakota	0.6
41	Oregon	0.6
43	Arizona	0.5
43	Idaho	0.5
43	Utah	0.5
46	Montana	0.4
47	New Mexico	0.3
48	Nevada	0.2
48	Wyoming	0.2
50	Alaska**	0.0

District of Columbia***   NA

Source: Morgan Quitno Press using data from American Hospital Association (Chicago, IL)
    "Hospital Statistics" (2004 edition)

*Based on 2000 Census land and water area figures. Community hospitals are nonfederal short-term general and other special hospitals, whose facilities and services are available to the public.

**Alaska has 19 community hospitals for its 571,949 square miles.

***The District of Columbia has 10 community hospitals for its 68 square miles.

Community Hospitals in Urban Areas in 2002

National Total = 2,749 Hospitals*

ALPHA ORDER

RANK	STATE	HOSPITALS	% of USA
16	Alabama	57	2.1%
48	Alaska	3	0.1%
20	Arizona	46	1.7%
28	Arkansas	31	1.1%
1	California	343	12.5%
26	Colorado	32	1.2%
29	Connecticut	29	1.1%
47	Delaware	4	0.1%
4	Florida	170	6.2%
13	Georgia	63	2.3%
39	Hawaii	13	0.5%
44	Idaho	6	0.2%
6	Illinois	120	4.4%
11	Indiana	67	2.4%
32	Iowa	21	0.8%
31	Kansas	25	0.9%
26	Kentucky	32	1.2%
10	Louisiana	77	2.8%
42	Maine	8	0.3%
23	Maryland	40	1.5%
11	Massachusetts	67	2.4%
8	Michigan	86	3.1%
20	Minnesota	46	1.7%
34	Mississippi	18	0.7%
14	Missouri	61	2.2%
46	Montana	5	0.2%
37	Nebraska	14	0.5%
36	Nevada	17	0.6%
40	New Hampshire	10	0.4%
9	New Jersey	81	2.9%
37	New Mexico	14	0.5%
3	New York	173	6.3%
18	North Carolina	51	1.9%
43	North Dakota	7	0.3%
7	Ohio	116	4.2%
24	Oklahoma	38	1.4%
29	Oregon	29	1.1%
5	Pennsylvania	158	5.7%
40	Rhode Island	10	0.4%
25	South Carolina	35	1.3%
44	South Dakota	6	0.2%
14	Tennessee	61	2.2%
2	Texas	255	9.3%
32	Utah	21	0.8%
49	Vermont	2	0.1%
18	Virginia	51	1.9%
22	Washington	45	1.6%
34	West Virginia	18	0.7%
17	Wisconsin	55	2.0%
49	Wyoming	2	0.1%

RANK ORDER

RANK	STATE	HOSPITALS	% of USA
1	California	343	12.5%
2	Texas	255	9.3%
3	New York	173	6.3%
4	Florida	170	6.2%
5	Pennsylvania	158	5.7%
6	Illinois	120	4.4%
7	Ohio	116	4.2%
8	Michigan	86	3.1%
9	New Jersey	81	2.9%
10	Louisiana	77	2.8%
11	Indiana	67	2.4%
11	Massachusetts	67	2.4%
13	Georgia	63	2.3%
14	Missouri	61	2.2%
14	Tennessee	61	2.2%
16	Alabama	57	2.1%
17	Wisconsin	55	2.0%
18	North Carolina	51	1.9%
18	Virginia	51	1.9%
20	Arizona	46	1.7%
20	Minnesota	46	1.7%
22	Washington	45	1.6%
23	Maryland	40	1.5%
24	Oklahoma	38	1.4%
25	South Carolina	35	1.3%
26	Colorado	32	1.2%
26	Kentucky	32	1.2%
28	Arkansas	31	1.1%
29	Connecticut	29	1.1%
29	Oregon	29	1.1%
31	Kansas	25	0.9%
32	Iowa	21	0.8%
32	Utah	21	0.8%
34	Mississippi	18	0.7%
34	West Virginia	18	0.7%
36	Nevada	17	0.6%
37	Nebraska	14	0.5%
37	New Mexico	14	0.5%
39	Hawaii	13	0.5%
40	New Hampshire	10	0.4%
40	Rhode Island	10	0.4%
42	Maine	8	0.3%
43	North Dakota	7	0.3%
44	Idaho	6	0.2%
44	South Dakota	6	0.2%
46	Montana	5	0.2%
47	Delaware	4	0.1%
48	Alaska	3	0.1%
49	Vermont	2	0.1%
49	Wyoming	2	0.1%
	District of Columbia	10	0.4%

Source: American Hospital Association (Chicago, IL)
   "Hospital Statistics" (2004 edition)
*Community hospitals are all nonfederal, short-term, general and special hospitals whose facilities and services are available to the public. Urban is defined as any area inside a metropolitan statistical area as defined by the U.S. Office of Management and Budget.

Percent of Community Hospitals in Urban Areas in 2002

National Percent = 55.8% of Community Hospitals*

ALPHA ORDER

RANK	STATE	PERCENT
21	Alabama	53.8
45	Alaska	15.8
10	Arizona	75.4
35	Arkansas	35.6
3	California	89.6
28	Colorado	47.1
6	Connecticut	82.9
12	Delaware	66.7
5	Florida	84.2
31	Georgia	43.2
23	Hawaii	52.0
46	Idaho	15.4
14	Illinois	62.5
17	Indiana	59.8
42	Iowa	18.1
41	Kansas	18.9
38	Kentucky	30.8
16	Louisiana	60.2
39	Maine	21.6
8	Maryland	81.6
4	Massachusetts	85.9
18	Michigan	59.3
36	Minnesota	34.6
40	Mississippi	19.8
24	Missouri	51.3
49	Montana	9.4
44	Nebraska	16.3
13	Nevada	65.4
34	New Hampshire	35.7
1	New Jersey	100.0
32	New Mexico	38.9
7	New York	82.0
30	North Carolina	45.1
43	North Dakota	16.7
11	Ohio	69.0
33	Oklahoma	36.2
27	Oregon	48.3
9	Pennsylvania	78.6
2	Rhode Island	90.9
20	South Carolina	56.5
48	South Dakota	11.8
26	Tennessee	48.8
15	Texas	61.3
25	Utah	50.0
47	Vermont	14.3
18	Virginia	59.3
22	Washington	52.3
37	West Virginia	31.6
29	Wisconsin	45.8
50	Wyoming	8.3

RANK ORDER

RANK	STATE	PERCENT
1	New Jersey	100.0
2	Rhode Island	90.9
3	California	89.6
4	Massachusetts	85.9
5	Florida	84.2
6	Connecticut	82.9
7	New York	82.0
8	Maryland	81.6
9	Pennsylvania	78.6
10	Arizona	75.4
11	Ohio	69.0
12	Delaware	66.7
13	Nevada	65.4
14	Illinois	62.5
15	Texas	61.3
16	Louisiana	60.2
17	Indiana	59.8
18	Michigan	59.3
18	Virginia	59.3
20	South Carolina	56.5
21	Alabama	53.8
22	Washington	52.3
23	Hawaii	52.0
24	Missouri	51.3
25	Utah	50.0
26	Tennessee	48.8
27	Oregon	48.3
28	Colorado	47.1
29	Wisconsin	45.8
30	North Carolina	45.1
31	Georgia	43.2
32	New Mexico	38.9
33	Oklahoma	36.2
34	New Hampshire	35.7
35	Arkansas	35.6
36	Minnesota	34.6
37	West Virginia	31.6
38	Kentucky	30.8
39	Maine	21.6
40	Mississippi	19.8
41	Kansas	18.9
42	Iowa	18.1
43	North Dakota	16.7
44	Nebraska	16.3
45	Alaska	15.8
46	Idaho	15.4
47	Vermont	14.3
48	South Dakota	11.8
49	Montana	9.4
50	Wyoming	8.3

District of Columbia   100.0

Source: Morgan Quitno Press using data from American Hospital Association (Chicago, IL)
    "Hospital Statistics" (2004 edition)
*Community hospitals are all nonfederal, short-term, general and special hospitals whose facilities and services are available to the public. Urban is defined as any area inside a metropolitan statistical area as defined by the U.S. Office of Management and Budget.

Community Hospitals in Rural Areas in 2002

National Total = 2,178 Hospitals*

ALPHA ORDER

RANK	STATE	HOSPITALS	% of USA
19	Alabama	49	2.2%
40	Alaska	16	0.7%
41	Arizona	15	0.7%
16	Arkansas	56	2.6%
25	California	40	1.8%
28	Colorado	36	1.7%
47	Connecticut	6	0.3%
48	Delaware	2	0.1%
32	Florida	32	1.5%
5	Georgia	83	3.8%
42	Hawaii	12	0.6%
31	Idaho	33	1.5%
7	Illinois	72	3.3%
21	Indiana	45	2.1%
3	Iowa	95	4.4%
2	Kansas	107	4.9%
7	Kentucky	72	3.3%
18	Louisiana	51	2.3%
34	Maine	29	1.3%
45	Maryland	9	0.4%
44	Massachusetts	11	0.5%
14	Michigan	59	2.7%
4	Minnesota	87	4.0%
6	Mississippi	73	3.4%
15	Missouri	58	2.7%
20	Montana	48	2.2%
7	Nebraska	72	3.3%
45	Nevada	9	0.4%
39	New Hampshire	18	0.8%
50	New Jersey	0	0.0%
36	New Mexico	22	1.0%
27	New York	38	1.7%
13	North Carolina	62	2.8%
29	North Dakota	35	1.6%
17	Ohio	52	2.4%
10	Oklahoma	67	3.1%
33	Oregon	31	1.4%
23	Pennsylvania	43	2.0%
49	Rhode Island	1	0.0%
35	South Carolina	27	1.2%
21	South Dakota	45	2.1%
12	Tennessee	64	2.9%
1	Texas	161	7.4%
38	Utah	21	1.0%
42	Vermont	12	0.6%
29	Virginia	35	1.6%
24	Washington	41	1.9%
26	West Virginia	39	1.8%
11	Wisconsin	65	3.0%
36	Wyoming	22	1.0%

RANK ORDER

RANK	STATE	HOSPITALS	% of USA
1	Texas	161	7.4%
2	Kansas	107	4.9%
3	Iowa	95	4.4%
4	Minnesota	87	4.0%
5	Georgia	83	3.8%
6	Mississippi	73	3.4%
7	Illinois	72	3.3%
7	Kentucky	72	3.3%
7	Nebraska	72	3.3%
10	Oklahoma	67	3.1%
11	Wisconsin	65	3.0%
12	Tennessee	64	2.9%
13	North Carolina	62	2.8%
14	Michigan	59	2.7%
15	Missouri	58	2.7%
16	Arkansas	56	2.6%
17	Ohio	52	2.4%
18	Louisiana	51	2.3%
19	Alabama	49	2.2%
20	Montana	48	2.2%
21	Indiana	45	2.1%
21	South Dakota	45	2.1%
23	Pennsylvania	43	2.0%
24	Washington	41	1.9%
25	California	40	1.8%
26	West Virginia	39	1.8%
27	New York	38	1.7%
28	Colorado	36	1.7%
29	North Dakota	35	1.6%
29	Virginia	35	1.6%
31	Idaho	33	1.5%
32	Florida	32	1.5%
33	Oregon	31	1.4%
34	Maine	29	1.3%
35	South Carolina	27	1.2%
36	New Mexico	22	1.0%
36	Wyoming	22	1.0%
38	Utah	21	1.0%
39	New Hampshire	18	0.8%
40	Alaska	16	0.7%
41	Arizona	15	0.7%
42	Hawaii	12	0.6%
42	Vermont	12	0.6%
44	Massachusetts	11	0.5%
45	Maryland	9	0.4%
45	Nevada	9	0.4%
47	Connecticut	6	0.3%
48	Delaware	2	0.1%
49	Rhode Island	1	0.0%
50	New Jersey	0	0.0%
	District of Columbia	0	0.0%

Source: American Hospital Association (Chicago, IL)
   "Hospital Statistics" (2004 edition)
*Community hospitals are all nonfederal, short-term, general and special hospitals whose facilities and services are available to the public. Rural is defined as any area outside a metropolitan statistical area as defined by the U.S. Office of Management and Budget.

Percent of Community Hospitals in Rural Areas in 2002

National Percent = 44.2% of Community Hospitals*

RANK	STATE	PERCENT
30	Alabama	46.2
6	Alaska	84.2
41	Arizona	24.6
16	Arkansas	64.4
48	California	10.4
23	Colorado	52.9
45	Connecticut	17.1
39	Delaware	33.3
46	Florida	15.8
20	Georgia	56.8
28	Hawaii	48.0
5	Idaho	84.6
37	Illinois	37.5
34	Indiana	40.2
9	Iowa	81.9
10	Kansas	81.1
13	Kentucky	69.2
35	Louisiana	39.8
12	Maine	78.4
43	Maryland	18.4
47	Massachusetts	14.1
32	Michigan	40.7
15	Minnesota	65.4
11	Mississippi	80.2
27	Missouri	48.7
2	Montana	90.6
7	Nebraska	83.7
38	Nevada	34.6
17	New Hampshire	64.3
50	New Jersey	0.0
19	New Mexico	61.1
44	New York	18.0
21	North Carolina	54.9
8	North Dakota	83.3
40	Ohio	31.0
18	Oklahoma	63.8
24	Oregon	51.7
42	Pennsylvania	21.4
49	Rhode Island	9.1
31	South Carolina	43.5
3	South Dakota	88.2
25	Tennessee	51.2
36	Texas	38.7
26	Utah	50.0
4	Vermont	85.7
32	Virginia	40.7
29	Washington	47.7
14	West Virginia	68.4
22	Wisconsin	54.2
1	Wyoming	91.7

RANK	STATE	PERCENT
1	Wyoming	91.7
2	Montana	90.6
3	South Dakota	88.2
4	Vermont	85.7
5	Idaho	84.6
6	Alaska	84.2
7	Nebraska	83.7
8	North Dakota	83.3
9	Iowa	81.9
10	Kansas	81.1
11	Mississippi	80.2
12	Maine	78.4
13	Kentucky	69.2
14	West Virginia	68.4
15	Minnesota	65.4
16	Arkansas	64.4
17	New Hampshire	64.3
18	Oklahoma	63.8
19	New Mexico	61.1
20	Georgia	56.8
21	North Carolina	54.9
22	Wisconsin	54.2
23	Colorado	52.9
24	Oregon	51.7
25	Tennessee	51.2
26	Utah	50.0
27	Missouri	48.7
28	Hawaii	48.0
29	Washington	47.7
30	Alabama	46.2
31	South Carolina	43.5
32	Michigan	40.7
32	Virginia	40.7
34	Indiana	40.2
35	Louisiana	39.8
36	Texas	38.7
37	Illinois	37.5
38	Nevada	34.6
39	Delaware	33.3
40	Ohio	31.0
41	Arizona	24.6
42	Pennsylvania	21.4
43	Maryland	18.4
44	New York	18.0
45	Connecticut	17.1
46	Florida	15.8
47	Massachusetts	14.1
48	California	10.4
49	Rhode Island	9.1
50	New Jersey	0.0

	District of Columbia	0.0

Source: Morgan Quitno Press using data from American Hospital Association (Chicago, IL)
    "Hospital Statistics" (2004 edition)
*Community hospitals are all nonfederal, short-term, general and special hospitals whose facilities and services are available to the public. Rural is defined as any area outside a metropolitan statistical area as defined by the U.S. Office of Management and Budget.

Nongovernment Not-For-Profit Hospitals in 2002

National Total = 3,025 Hospitals*

ALPHA ORDER				RANK ORDER			
RANK	STATE	HOSPITALS	% of USA	RANK	STATE	HOSPITALS	% of USA
32	Alabama	35	1.2%	1	California	217	7.2%
46	Alaska	11	0.4%	2	Pennsylvania	184	6.1%
31	Arizona	37	1.2%	3	New York	181	6.0%
22	Arkansas	51	1.7%	4	Texas	155	5.1%
1	California	217	7.2%	5	Illinois	154	5.1%
37	Colorado	32	1.1%	6	Ohio	141	4.7%
34	Connecticut	34	1.1%	7	Michigan	122	4.0%
49	Delaware	6	0.2%	8	Wisconsin	117	3.9%
10	Florida	86	2.8%	9	Minnesota	89	2.9%
17	Georgia	64	2.1%	10	Florida	86	2.8%
43	Hawaii	18	0.6%	11	New Jersey	76	2.5%
45	Idaho	13	0.4%	12	North Carolina	75	2.5%
5	Illinois	154	5.1%	13	Kentucky	73	2.4%
20	Indiana	58	1.9%	14	Massachusetts	68	2.2%
21	Iowa	57	1.9%	14	Missouri	68	2.2%
19	Kansas	62	2.0%	16	Virginia	67	2.2%
13	Kentucky	73	2.4%	17	Georgia	64	2.1%
32	Louisiana	35	1.2%	17	Tennessee	64	2.1%
34	Maine	34	1.1%	19	Kansas	62	2.0%
23	Maryland	46	1.5%	20	Indiana	58	1.9%
14	Massachusetts	68	2.2%	21	Iowa	57	1.9%
7	Michigan	122	4.0%	22	Arkansas	51	1.7%
9	Minnesota	89	2.9%	23	Maryland	46	1.5%
38	Mississippi	25	0.8%	23	Oklahoma	46	1.5%
14	Missouri	68	2.2%	25	Oregon	44	1.5%
27	Montana	43	1.4%	25	South Dakota	44	1.5%
27	Nebraska	43	1.4%	27	Montana	43	1.4%
48	Nevada	9	0.3%	27	Nebraska	43	1.4%
39	New Hampshire	24	0.8%	29	Washington	42	1.4%
11	New Jersey	76	2.5%	30	North Dakota	41	1.4%
42	New Mexico	19	0.6%	31	Arizona	37	1.2%
3	New York	181	6.0%	32	Alabama	35	1.2%
12	North Carolina	75	2.5%	32	Louisiana	35	1.2%
30	North Dakota	41	1.4%	34	Connecticut	34	1.1%
6	Ohio	141	4.7%	34	Maine	34	1.1%
23	Oklahoma	46	1.5%	36	West Virginia	33	1.1%
25	Oregon	44	1.5%	37	Colorado	32	1.1%
2	Pennsylvania	184	6.1%	38	Mississippi	25	0.8%
46	Rhode Island	11	0.4%	39	New Hampshire	24	0.8%
40	South Carolina	23	0.8%	40	South Carolina	23	0.8%
25	South Dakota	44	1.5%	41	Utah	22	0.7%
17	Tennessee	64	2.1%	42	New Mexico	19	0.6%
4	Texas	155	5.1%	43	Hawaii	18	0.6%
41	Utah	22	0.7%	44	Vermont	14	0.5%
44	Vermont	14	0.5%	45	Idaho	13	0.4%
16	Virginia	67	2.2%	46	Alaska	11	0.4%
29	Washington	42	1.4%	46	Rhode Island	11	0.4%
36	West Virginia	33	1.1%	48	Nevada	9	0.3%
8	Wisconsin	117	3.9%	49	Delaware	6	0.2%
50	Wyoming	5	0.2%	50	Wyoming	5	0.2%
					District of Columbia	7	0.2%

Source: American Hospital Association (Chicago, IL)
   "Hospital Statistics" (2004 edition)
*Nongovernment not-for-profit hospitals are a subset of community hospitals.

Investor-Owned (For-Profit) Hospitals in 2002

National Total = 766 Hospitals*

ALPHA ORDER

RANK	STATE	HOSPITALS	% of USA
5	Alabama	35	4.6%
38	Alaska	1	0.1%
10	Arizona	19	2.5%
9	Arkansas	21	2.7%
3	California	92	12.0%
21	Colorado	9	1.2%
43	Connecticut	0	0.0%
43	Delaware	0	0.0%
2	Florida	96	12.5%
7	Georgia	30	3.9%
43	Hawaii	0	0.0%
36	Idaho	2	0.3%
21	Illinois	9	1.2%
16	Indiana	14	1.8%
43	Iowa	0	0.0%
21	Kansas	9	1.2%
12	Kentucky	17	2.2%
4	Louisiana	41	5.4%
38	Maine	1	0.1%
33	Maryland	3	0.4%
26	Massachusetts	6	0.8%
27	Michigan	4	0.5%
43	Minnesota	0	0.0%
8	Mississippi	24	3.1%
13	Missouri	15	2.0%
43	Montana	0	0.0%
36	Nebraska	2	0.3%
20	Nevada	11	1.4%
27	New Hampshire	4	0.5%
33	New Jersey	3	0.4%
24	New Mexico	8	1.0%
27	New York	4	0.5%
24	North Carolina	8	1.0%
38	North Dakota	1	0.1%
27	Ohio	4	0.5%
13	Oklahoma	15	2.0%
27	Oregon	4	0.5%
13	Pennsylvania	15	2.0%
43	Rhode Island	0	0.0%
11	South Carolina	18	2.3%
38	South Dakota	1	0.1%
5	Tennessee	35	4.6%
1	Texas	132	17.2%
16	Utah	14	1.8%
43	Vermont	0	0.0%
16	Virginia	14	1.8%
27	Washington	4	0.5%
16	West Virginia	14	1.8%
38	Wisconsin	1	0.1%
33	Wyoming	3	0.4%

RANK ORDER

RANK	STATE	HOSPITALS	% of USA
1	Texas	132	17.2%
2	Florida	96	12.5%
3	California	92	12.0%
4	Louisiana	41	5.4%
5	Alabama	35	4.6%
5	Tennessee	35	4.6%
7	Georgia	30	3.9%
8	Mississippi	24	3.1%
9	Arkansas	21	2.7%
10	Arizona	19	2.5%
11	South Carolina	18	2.3%
12	Kentucky	17	2.2%
13	Missouri	15	2.0%
13	Oklahoma	15	2.0%
13	Pennsylvania	15	2.0%
16	Indiana	14	1.8%
16	Utah	14	1.8%
16	Virginia	14	1.8%
16	West Virginia	14	1.8%
20	Nevada	11	1.4%
21	Colorado	9	1.2%
21	Illinois	9	1.2%
21	Kansas	9	1.2%
24	New Mexico	8	1.0%
24	North Carolina	8	1.0%
26	Massachusetts	6	0.8%
27	Michigan	4	0.5%
27	New Hampshire	4	0.5%
27	New York	4	0.5%
27	Ohio	4	0.5%
27	Oregon	4	0.5%
27	Washington	4	0.5%
33	Maryland	3	0.4%
33	New Jersey	3	0.4%
33	Wyoming	3	0.4%
36	Idaho	2	0.3%
36	Nebraska	2	0.3%
38	Alaska	1	0.1%
38	Maine	1	0.1%
38	North Dakota	1	0.1%
38	South Dakota	1	0.1%
38	Wisconsin	1	0.1%
43	Connecticut	0	0.0%
43	Delaware	0	0.0%
43	Hawaii	0	0.0%
43	Iowa	0	0.0%
43	Minnesota	0	0.0%
43	Montana	0	0.0%
43	Rhode Island	0	0.0%
43	Vermont	0	0.0%
	District of Columbia	3	0.4%

Source: American Hospital Association (Chicago, IL)
"Hospital Statistics" (2004 edition)
Investor-owned (for-profit) hospitals are a subset of community hospitals.

State and Local Government-Owned Hospitals in 2002

National Total = 1,136 Hospitals*

ALPHA ORDER

RANK	STATE	HOSPITALS	% of USA
13	Alabama	36	3.2%
32	Alaska	7	0.6%
37	Arizona	5	0.4%
26	Arkansas	15	1.3%
2	California	74	6.5%
17	Colorado	27	2.4%
44	Connecticut	1	0.1%
45	Delaware	0	0.0%
23	Florida	20	1.8%
5	Georgia	52	4.6%
32	Hawaii	7	0.6%
20	Idaho	24	2.1%
16	Illinois	29	2.6%
11	Indiana	40	3.5%
4	Iowa	59	5.2%
3	Kansas	61	5.4%
27	Kentucky	14	1.2%
5	Louisiana	52	4.6%
40	Maine	2	0.2%
45	Maryland	0	0.0%
39	Massachusetts	4	0.4%
24	Michigan	19	1.7%
7	Minnesota	44	3.9%
9	Mississippi	42	3.7%
13	Missouri	36	3.2%
29	Montana	10	0.9%
10	Nebraska	41	3.6%
34	Nevada	6	0.5%
45	New Hampshire	0	0.0%
40	New Jersey	2	0.2%
31	New Mexico	9	0.8%
18	New York	26	2.3%
15	North Carolina	30	2.6%
45	North Dakota	0	0.0%
21	Ohio	23	2.0%
7	Oklahoma	44	3.9%
28	Oregon	12	1.1%
40	Pennsylvania	2	0.2%
45	Rhode Island	0	0.0%
22	South Carolina	21	1.8%
34	South Dakota	6	0.5%
18	Tennessee	26	2.3%
1	Texas	129	11.4%
34	Utah	6	0.5%
45	Vermont	0	0.0%
37	Virginia	5	0.4%
11	Washington	40	3.5%
29	West Virginia	10	0.9%
40	Wisconsin	2	0.2%
25	Wyoming	16	1.4%

RANK ORDER

RANK	STATE	HOSPITALS	% of USA
1	Texas	129	11.4%
2	California	74	6.5%
3	Kansas	61	5.4%
4	Iowa	59	5.2%
5	Georgia	52	4.6%
5	Louisiana	52	4.6%
7	Minnesota	44	3.9%
7	Oklahoma	44	3.9%
9	Mississippi	42	3.7%
10	Nebraska	41	3.6%
11	Indiana	40	3.5%
11	Washington	40	3.5%
13	Alabama	36	3.2%
13	Missouri	36	3.2%
15	North Carolina	30	2.6%
16	Illinois	29	2.6%
17	Colorado	27	2.4%
18	New York	26	2.3%
18	Tennessee	26	2.3%
20	Idaho	24	2.1%
21	Ohio	23	2.0%
22	South Carolina	21	1.8%
23	Florida	20	1.8%
24	Michigan	19	1.7%
25	Wyoming	16	1.4%
26	Arkansas	15	1.3%
27	Kentucky	14	1.2%
28	Oregon	12	1.1%
29	Montana	10	0.9%
29	West Virginia	10	0.9%
31	New Mexico	9	0.8%
32	Alaska	7	0.6%
32	Hawaii	7	0.6%
34	Nevada	6	0.5%
34	South Dakota	6	0.5%
34	Utah	6	0.5%
37	Arizona	5	0.4%
37	Virginia	5	0.4%
39	Massachusetts	4	0.4%
40	Maine	2	0.2%
40	New Jersey	2	0.2%
40	Pennsylvania	2	0.2%
40	Wisconsin	2	0.2%
44	Connecticut	1	0.1%
45	Delaware	0	0.0%
45	Maryland	0	0.0%
45	New Hampshire	0	0.0%
45	North Dakota	0	0.0%
45	Rhode Island	0	0.0%
45	Vermont	0	0.0%
	District of Columbia	0	0.0%

Source: American Hospital Association (Chicago, IL)
   "Hospital Statistics" (2004 edition)
*State and local government-owned hospitals are a subset of community hospitals.

Beds in Community Hospitals in 2002

National Total = 820,653 Beds*

ALPHA ORDER

RANK	STATE	BEDS	% of USA
19	Alabama	15,935	1.9%
50	Alaska	1,378	0.2%
28	Arizona	10,930	1.3%
30	Arkansas	9,942	1.2%
1	California	74,343	9.1%
31	Colorado	9,575	1.2%
34	Connecticut	7,714	0.9%
47	Delaware	2,014	0.2%
4	Florida	51,201	6.2%
9	Georgia	24,500	3.0%
44	Hawaii	3,191	0.4%
43	Idaho	3,349	0.4%
6	Illinois	36,309	4.4%
13	Indiana	18,961	2.3%
25	Iowa	11,267	1.4%
29	Kansas	10,850	1.3%
20	Kentucky	15,066	1.8%
15	Louisiana	17,867	2.2%
41	Maine	3,694	0.5%
23	Maryland	11,417	1.4%
18	Massachusetts	16,033	2.0%
8	Michigan	26,130	3.2%
17	Minnesota	16,659	2.0%
22	Mississippi	13,144	1.6%
14	Missouri	18,891	2.3%
39	Montana	4,263	0.5%
32	Nebraska	8,106	1.0%
37	Nevada	4,495	0.5%
45	New Hampshire	2,879	0.4%
10	New Jersey	24,094	2.9%
42	New Mexico	3,602	0.4%
2	New York	65,570	8.0%
11	North Carolina	23,583	2.9%
40	North Dakota	3,880	0.5%
7	Ohio	33,706	4.1%
26	Oklahoma	11,122	1.4%
35	Oregon	6,798	0.8%
5	Pennsylvania	40,534	4.9%
46	Rhode Island	2,428	0.3%
27	South Carolina	11,107	1.4%
36	South Dakota	4,624	0.6%
12	Tennessee	20,446	2.5%
3	Texas	56,833	6.9%
38	Utah	4,403	0.5%
49	Vermont	1,576	0.2%
16	Virginia	17,241	2.1%
24	Washington	11,338	1.4%
33	West Virginia	7,821	1.0%
21	Wisconsin	14,610	1.8%
48	Wyoming	1,882	0.2%

RANK ORDER

RANK	STATE	BEDS	% of USA
1	California	74,343	9.1%
2	New York	65,570	8.0%
3	Texas	56,833	6.9%
4	Florida	51,201	6.2%
5	Pennsylvania	40,534	4.9%
6	Illinois	36,309	4.4%
7	Ohio	33,706	4.1%
8	Michigan	26,130	3.2%
9	Georgia	24,500	3.0%
10	New Jersey	24,094	2.9%
11	North Carolina	23,583	2.9%
12	Tennessee	20,446	2.5%
13	Indiana	18,961	2.3%
14	Missouri	18,891	2.3%
15	Louisiana	17,867	2.2%
16	Virginia	17,241	2.1%
17	Minnesota	16,659	2.0%
18	Massachusetts	16,033	2.0%
19	Alabama	15,935	1.9%
20	Kentucky	15,066	1.8%
21	Wisconsin	14,610	1.8%
22	Mississippi	13,144	1.6%
23	Maryland	11,417	1.4%
24	Washington	11,338	1.4%
25	Iowa	11,267	1.4%
26	Oklahoma	11,122	1.4%
27	South Carolina	11,107	1.4%
28	Arizona	10,930	1.3%
29	Kansas	10,850	1.3%
30	Arkansas	9,942	1.2%
31	Colorado	9,575	1.2%
32	Nebraska	8,106	1.0%
33	West Virginia	7,821	1.0%
34	Connecticut	7,714	0.9%
35	Oregon	6,798	0.8%
36	South Dakota	4,624	0.6%
37	Nevada	4,495	0.5%
38	Utah	4,403	0.5%
39	Montana	4,263	0.5%
40	North Dakota	3,880	0.5%
41	Maine	3,694	0.5%
42	New Mexico	3,602	0.4%
43	Idaho	3,349	0.4%
44	Hawaii	3,191	0.4%
45	New Hampshire	2,879	0.4%
46	Rhode Island	2,428	0.3%
47	Delaware	2,014	0.2%
48	Wyoming	1,882	0.2%
49	Vermont	1,576	0.2%
50	Alaska	1,378	0.2%
	District of Columbia	3,352	0.4%

Source: American Hospital Association (Chicago, IL)
   "Hospital Statistics" (2004 edition)
*All nonfederal short-term general and other special hospitals, whose facilities and services are available to the public. Includes beds in hospital and nursing home units.

Rate of Beds in Community Hospitals in 2002

National Rate = 285 Beds per 100,000 Population*

ALPHA ORDER

RANK	STATE	RATE
13	Alabama	356
41	Alaska	215
46	Arizona	201
12	Arkansas	367
43	California	212
42	Colorado	213
40	Connecticut	223
34	Delaware	250
21	Florida	307
24	Georgia	287
32	Hawaii	257
36	Idaho	249
23	Illinois	288
20	Indiana	308
9	Iowa	384
7	Kansas	400
11	Kentucky	368
8	Louisiana	399
25	Maine	285
44	Maryland	209
34	Massachusetts	250
31	Michigan	260
17	Minnesota	332
5	Mississippi	459
16	Missouri	333
4	Montana	468
3	Nebraska	469
45	Nevada	207
39	New Hampshire	226
27	New Jersey	281
47	New Mexico	194
15	New York	343
26	North Carolina	284
1	North Dakota	612
22	Ohio	295
19	Oklahoma	319
48	Oregon	193
18	Pennsylvania	329
38	Rhode Island	227
28	South Carolina	271
2	South Dakota	608
14	Tennessee	353
30	Texas	261
49	Utah	190
33	Vermont	256
37	Virginia	237
50	Washington	187
6	West Virginia	433
29	Wisconsin	269
10	Wyoming	377

RANK ORDER

RANK	STATE	RATE
1	North Dakota	612
2	South Dakota	608
3	Nebraska	469
4	Montana	468
5	Mississippi	459
6	West Virginia	433
7	Kansas	400
8	Louisiana	399
9	Iowa	384
10	Wyoming	377
11	Kentucky	368
12	Arkansas	367
13	Alabama	356
14	Tennessee	353
15	New York	343
16	Missouri	333
17	Minnesota	332
18	Pennsylvania	329
19	Oklahoma	319
20	Indiana	308
21	Florida	307
22	Ohio	295
23	Illinois	288
24	Georgia	287
25	Maine	285
26	North Carolina	284
27	New Jersey	281
28	South Carolina	271
29	Wisconsin	269
30	Texas	261
31	Michigan	260
32	Hawaii	257
33	Vermont	256
34	Delaware	250
34	Massachusetts	250
36	Idaho	249
37	Virginia	237
38	Rhode Island	227
39	New Hampshire	226
40	Connecticut	223
41	Alaska	215
42	Colorado	213
43	California	212
44	Maryland	209
45	Nevada	207
46	Arizona	201
47	New Mexico	194
48	Oregon	193
49	Utah	190
50	Washington	187
	District of Columbia	589

Source: Morgan Quitno Press using data from American Hospital Association (Chicago, IL)
    "Hospital Statistics" (2004 edition)
*All nonfederal short-term general and other special hospitals, whose facilities and services are available to the public. Includes beds in hospital and nursing home units.

Average Number of Beds per Community Hospital in 2002

National Average = 167 Beds per Community Hospital*

ALPHA ORDER				RANK ORDER		
RANK	STATE	BEDS		RANK	STATE	BEDS
23	Alabama	150		1	Delaware	336
50	Alaska	73		2	New York	311
16	Arizona	179		3	New Jersey	297
34	Arkansas	114		4	Florida	253
13	California	194		5	Maryland	233
26	Colorado	141		6	Rhode Island	221
7	Connecticut	220		7	Connecticut	220
1	Delaware	336		8	North Carolina	209
4	Florida	253		9	Massachusetts	206
20	Georgia	168		10	Pennsylvania	202
31	Hawaii	128		11	Ohio	201
46	Idaho	86		12	Virginia	200
14	Illinois	189		13	California	194
19	Indiana	169		14	Illinois	189
42	Iowa	97		15	Michigan	180
47	Kansas	82		16	Arizona	179
24	Kentucky	145		16	South Carolina	179
27	Louisiana	140		18	Nevada	173
40	Maine	100		19	Indiana	169
5	Maryland	233		20	Georgia	168
9	Massachusetts	206		21	Tennessee	164
15	Michigan	180		22	Missouri	159
32	Minnesota	125		23	Alabama	150
25	Mississippi	144		24	Kentucky	145
22	Missouri	159		25	Mississippi	144
48	Montana	80		26	Colorado	141
43	Nebraska	94		27	Louisiana	140
18	Nevada	173		28	Texas	137
39	New Hampshire	103		28	West Virginia	137
3	New Jersey	297		30	Washington	132
40	New Mexico	100		31	Hawaii	128
2	New York	311		32	Minnesota	125
8	North Carolina	209		33	Wisconsin	122
44	North Dakota	92		34	Arkansas	114
11	Ohio	201		35	Oregon	113
37	Oklahoma	106		35	Vermont	113
35	Oregon	113		37	Oklahoma	106
10	Pennsylvania	202		38	Utah	105
6	Rhode Island	221		39	New Hampshire	103
16	South Carolina	179		40	Maine	100
45	South Dakota	91		40	New Mexico	100
21	Tennessee	164		42	Iowa	97
28	Texas	137		43	Nebraska	94
38	Utah	105		44	North Dakota	92
35	Vermont	113		45	South Dakota	91
12	Virginia	200		46	Idaho	86
30	Washington	132		47	Kansas	82
28	West Virginia	137		48	Montana	80
33	Wisconsin	122		49	Wyoming	78
49	Wyoming	78		50	Alaska	73
					District of Columbia	335

Source: Morgan Quitno Press using data from American Hospital Association (Chicago, IL)
    "Hospital Statistics" (2004 edition)

*All nonfederal short-term general and other special hospitals, whose facilities and services are available to the public. Includes beds in hospital and nursing home units.

Admissions to Community Hospitals in 2002

National Total = 34,478,280 Admissions*

ALPHA ORDER

RANK	STATE	ADMISSIONS	% of USA
18	Alabama	676,337	2.0%
50	Alaska	47,560	0.1%
22	Arizona	591,094	1.7%
29	Arkansas	383,509	1.1%
1	California	3,430,241	9.9%
27	Colorado	426,560	1.2%
30	Connecticut	375,686	1.1%
47	Delaware	93,275	0.3%
4	Florida	2,315,230	6.7%
11	Georgia	885,142	2.6%
43	Hawaii	111,498	0.3%
40	Idaho	123,046	0.4%
6	Illinois	1,615,269	4.7%
16	Indiana	715,936	2.1%
31	Iowa	370,968	1.1%
33	Kansas	328,987	1.0%
20	Kentucky	601,644	1.7%
17	Louisiana	692,011	2.0%
39	Maine	145,917	0.4%
19	Maryland	634,914	1.8%
14	Massachusetts	765,820	2.2%
8	Michigan	1,163,157	3.4%
21	Minnesota	598,852	1.7%
28	Mississippi	416,815	1.2%
12	Missouri	809,355	2.3%
44	Montana	106,758	0.3%
37	Nebraska	206,208	0.6%
35	Nevada	211,657	0.6%
42	New Hampshire	117,996	0.3%
9	New Jersey	1,094,781	3.2%
38	New Mexico	180,041	0.5%
3	New York	2,463,447	7.1%
10	North Carolina	966,722	2.8%
46	North Dakota	94,630	0.3%
7	Ohio	1,475,630	4.3%
26	Oklahoma	445,952	1.3%
32	Oregon	345,193	1.0%
5	Pennsylvania	1,798,243	5.2%
41	Rhode Island	122,741	0.4%
25	South Carolina	513,136	1.5%
45	South Dakota	100,141	0.3%
13	Tennessee	797,318	2.3%
2	Texas	2,533,821	7.3%
36	Utah	206,344	0.6%
48	Vermont	52,236	0.2%
15	Virginia	746,686	2.2%
24	Washington	518,562	1.5%
34	West Virginia	295,011	0.9%
23	Wisconsin	579,830	1.7%
49	Wyoming	49,201	0.1%

RANK ORDER

RANK	STATE	ADMISSIONS	% of USA
1	California	3,430,241	9.9%
2	Texas	2,533,821	7.3%
3	New York	2,463,447	7.1%
4	Florida	2,315,230	6.7%
5	Pennsylvania	1,798,243	5.2%
6	Illinois	1,615,269	4.7%
7	Ohio	1,475,630	4.3%
8	Michigan	1,163,157	3.4%
9	New Jersey	1,094,781	3.2%
10	North Carolina	966,722	2.8%
11	Georgia	885,142	2.6%
12	Missouri	809,355	2.3%
13	Tennessee	797,318	2.3%
14	Massachusetts	765,820	2.2%
15	Virginia	746,686	2.2%
16	Indiana	715,936	2.1%
17	Louisiana	692,011	2.0%
18	Alabama	676,337	2.0%
19	Maryland	634,914	1.8%
20	Kentucky	601,644	1.7%
21	Minnesota	598,852	1.7%
22	Arizona	591,094	1.7%
23	Wisconsin	579,830	1.7%
24	Washington	518,562	1.5%
25	South Carolina	513,136	1.5%
26	Oklahoma	445,952	1.3%
27	Colorado	426,560	1.2%
28	Mississippi	416,815	1.2%
29	Arkansas	383,509	1.1%
30	Connecticut	375,686	1.1%
31	Iowa	370,968	1.1%
32	Oregon	345,193	1.0%
33	Kansas	328,987	1.0%
34	West Virginia	295,011	0.9%
35	Nevada	211,657	0.6%
36	Utah	206,344	0.6%
37	Nebraska	206,208	0.6%
38	New Mexico	180,041	0.5%
39	Maine	145,917	0.4%
40	Idaho	123,046	0.4%
41	Rhode Island	122,741	0.4%
42	New Hampshire	117,996	0.3%
43	Hawaii	111,498	0.3%
44	Montana	106,758	0.3%
45	South Dakota	100,141	0.3%
46	North Dakota	94,630	0.3%
47	Delaware	93,275	0.3%
48	Vermont	52,236	0.2%
49	Wyoming	49,201	0.1%
50	Alaska	47,560	0.1%
	District of Columbia	137,172	0.4%

Source: American Hospital Association (Chicago, IL)
   "Hospital Statistics" (2004 edition)
*Admissions to all nonfederal short-term general and other special hospitals, whose facilities and services are available to the public. Includes admissions to hospital and nursing home units.

Inpatient Days in Community Hospitals in 2002

National Total = 196,690,099 Inpatient Days*

ALPHA ORDER				RANK ORDER			
RANK	STATE	DAYS	% of USA	RANK	STATE	DAYS	% of USA
21	Alabama	3,244,123	1.6%	1	California	18,591,536	9.5%
50	Alaska	300,060	0.2%	2	New York	18,394,472	9.4%
25	Arizona	2,544,370	1.3%	3	Texas	13,187,000	6.7%
32	Arkansas	2,110,323	1.1%	4	Florida	12,303,559	6.3%
1	California	18,591,536	9.5%	5	Pennsylvania	10,340,276	5.3%
30	Colorado	2,172,074	1.1%	6	Illinois	8,326,561	4.2%
29	Connecticut	2,239,055	1.1%	7	Ohio	7,657,394	3.9%
47	Delaware	546,058	0.3%	8	Michigan	6,296,654	3.2%
4	Florida	12,303,559	6.3%	9	New Jersey	6,190,443	3.1%
11	Georgia	5,774,911	2.9%	10	North Carolina	5,929,916	3.0%
41	Hawaii	866,160	0.4%	11	Georgia	5,774,911	2.9%
45	Idaho	648,640	0.3%	12	Tennessee	4,473,786	2.3%
6	Illinois	8,326,561	4.2%	13	Massachusetts	4,348,099	2.2%
17	Indiana	4,077,032	2.1%	14	Virginia	4,278,445	2.2%
27	Iowa	2,447,672	1.2%	15	Missouri	4,235,298	2.2%
31	Kansas	2,165,195	1.1%	16	Minnesota	4,162,994	2.1%
20	Kentucky	3,393,525	1.7%	17	Indiana	4,077,032	2.1%
18	Louisiana	3,873,634	2.0%	18	Louisiana	3,873,634	2.0%
39	Maine	889,005	0.5%	19	Wisconsin	3,396,381	1.7%
22	Maryland	3,049,647	1.6%	20	Kentucky	3,393,525	1.7%
13	Massachusetts	4,348,099	2.2%	21	Alabama	3,244,123	1.6%
8	Michigan	6,296,654	3.2%	22	Maryland	3,049,647	1.6%
16	Minnesota	4,162,994	2.1%	23	South Carolina	2,914,964	1.5%
24	Mississippi	2,745,516	1.4%	24	Mississippi	2,745,516	1.4%
15	Missouri	4,235,298	2.2%	25	Arizona	2,544,370	1.3%
37	Montana	1,071,834	0.5%	26	Washington	2,486,925	1.3%
34	Nebraska	1,723,683	0.9%	27	Iowa	2,447,672	1.2%
36	Nevada	1,110,583	0.6%	28	Oklahoma	2,371,009	1.2%
46	New Hampshire	646,838	0.3%	29	Connecticut	2,239,055	1.1%
9	New Jersey	6,190,443	3.1%	30	Colorado	2,172,074	1.1%
42	New Mexico	849,396	0.4%	31	Kansas	2,165,195	1.1%
2	New York	18,394,472	9.4%	32	Arkansas	2,110,323	1.1%
10	North Carolina	5,929,916	3.0%	33	West Virginia	1,775,869	0.9%
43	North Dakota	845,194	0.4%	34	Nebraska	1,723,683	0.9%
7	Ohio	7,657,394	3.9%	35	Oregon	1,511,420	0.8%
28	Oklahoma	2,371,009	1.2%	36	Nevada	1,110,583	0.6%
35	Oregon	1,511,420	0.8%	37	Montana	1,071,834	0.5%
5	Pennsylvania	10,340,276	5.3%	38	South Dakota	1,001,800	0.5%
44	Rhode Island	649,451	0.3%	39	Maine	889,005	0.5%
23	South Carolina	2,914,964	1.5%	40	Utah	876,524	0.4%
38	South Dakota	1,001,800	0.5%	41	Hawaii	866,160	0.4%
12	Tennessee	4,473,786	2.3%	42	New Mexico	849,396	0.4%
3	Texas	13,187,000	6.7%	43	North Dakota	845,194	0.4%
40	Utah	876,524	0.4%	44	Rhode Island	649,451	0.3%
49	Vermont	348,528	0.2%	45	Idaho	648,640	0.3%
14	Virginia	4,278,445	2.2%	46	New Hampshire	646,838	0.3%
26	Washington	2,486,925	1.3%	47	Delaware	546,058	0.3%
33	West Virginia	1,775,869	0.9%	48	Wyoming	370,143	0.2%
19	Wisconsin	3,396,381	1.7%	49	Vermont	348,528	0.2%
48	Wyoming	370,143	0.2%	50	Alaska	300,060	0.2%
					District of Columbia	936,124	0.5%

Source: American Hospital Association (Chicago, IL)
"Hospital Statistics" (2004 edition)

*Inpatient days in all nonfederal short-term general and other special hospitals, whose facilities and services are available to the public. Includes days in hospital and nursing home units.

Average Daily Census in Community Hospitals in 2002

National Average = 538,877 Inpatients*

ALPHA ORDER

RANK	STATE	INPATIENTS
21	Alabama	8,888
50	Alaska	822
25	Arizona	6,971
32	Arkansas	5,782
1	California	50,936
30	Colorado	5,951
29	Connecticut	6,134
47	Delaware	1,496
4	Florida	33,708
11	Georgia	15,822
41	Hawaii	2,373
45	Idaho	1,777
6	Illinois	22,812
17	Indiana	11,170
27	Iowa	6,706
31	Kansas	5,932
20	Kentucky	9,297
18	Louisiana	10,613
39	Maine	2,436
22	Maryland	8,355
13	Massachusetts	11,913
8	Michigan	17,251
16	Minnesota	11,405
24	Mississippi	7,522
15	Missouri	11,604
37	Montana	2,937
34	Nebraska	4,722
36	Nevada	3,043
46	New Hampshire	1,772
9	New Jersey	16,960
42	New Mexico	2,327
2	New York	50,396
10	North Carolina	16,246
43	North Dakota	2,316
7	Ohio	20,979
28	Oklahoma	6,496
35	Oregon	4,141
5	Pennsylvania	28,330
44	Rhode Island	1,779
23	South Carolina	7,986
38	South Dakota	2,745
12	Tennessee	12,257
3	Texas	36,129
40	Utah	2,401
49	Vermont	955
14	Virginia	11,722
26	Washington	6,813
33	West Virginia	4,865
19	Wisconsin	9,305
48	Wyoming	1,014

RANK ORDER

RANK	STATE	INPATIENTS
1	California	50,936
2	New York	50,396
3	Texas	36,129
4	Florida	33,708
5	Pennsylvania	28,330
6	Illinois	22,812
7	Ohio	20,979
8	Michigan	17,251
9	New Jersey	16,960
10	North Carolina	16,246
11	Georgia	15,822
12	Tennessee	12,257
13	Massachusetts	11,913
14	Virginia	11,722
15	Missouri	11,604
16	Minnesota	11,405
17	Indiana	11,170
18	Louisiana	10,613
19	Wisconsin	9,305
20	Kentucky	9,297
21	Alabama	8,888
22	Maryland	8,355
23	South Carolina	7,986
24	Mississippi	7,522
25	Arizona	6,971
26	Washington	6,813
27	Iowa	6,706
28	Oklahoma	6,496
29	Connecticut	6,134
30	Colorado	5,951
31	Kansas	5,932
32	Arkansas	5,782
33	West Virginia	4,865
34	Nebraska	4,722
35	Oregon	4,141
36	Nevada	3,043
37	Montana	2,937
38	South Dakota	2,745
39	Maine	2,436
40	Utah	2,401
41	Hawaii	2,373
42	New Mexico	2,327
43	North Dakota	2,316
44	Rhode Island	1,779
45	Idaho	1,777
46	New Hampshire	1,772
47	Delaware	1,496
48	Wyoming	1,014
49	Vermont	955
50	Alaska	822
	District of Columbia	2,565

Source: Morgan Quitno Press using data from American Hospital Association (Chicago, IL)
    "Hospital Statistics" (2004 edition)
*Average total of inpatients receiving care in all nonfederal short-term general and other special hospitals, whose facilities and services are available to the public. Excludes newborns.

Average Stay in Community Hospitals in 2002

National Average = 5.7 Days*

ALPHA ORDER

RANK	STATE	DAYS
44	Alabama	4.8
14	Alaska	6.3
49	Arizona	4.3
30	Arkansas	5.5
32	California	5.4
43	Colorado	5.1
17	Connecticut	6.0
19	Delaware	5.9
34	Florida	5.3
13	Georgia	6.5
5	Hawaii	7.8
34	Idaho	5.3
38	Illinois	5.2
22	Indiana	5.7
10	Iowa	6.6
10	Kansas	6.6
27	Kentucky	5.6
27	Louisiana	5.6
15	Maine	6.1
44	Maryland	4.8
22	Massachusetts	5.7
32	Michigan	5.4
8	Minnesota	7.0
10	Mississippi	6.6
38	Missouri	5.2
1	Montana	10.0
4	Nebraska	8.4
38	Nevada	5.2
30	New Hampshire	5.5
22	New Jersey	5.7
47	New Mexico	4.7
6	New York	7.5
15	North Carolina	6.1
3	North Dakota	8.9
38	Ohio	5.2
34	Oklahoma	5.3
48	Oregon	4.4
21	Pennsylvania	5.8
34	Rhode Island	5.3
22	South Carolina	5.7
1	South Dakota	10.0
27	Tennessee	5.6
38	Texas	5.2
50	Utah	4.2
9	Vermont	6.7
22	Virginia	5.7
44	Washington	4.8
17	West Virginia	6.0
19	Wisconsin	5.9
6	Wyoming	7.5

RANK ORDER

RANK	STATE	DAYS
1	Montana	10.0
1	South Dakota	10.0
3	North Dakota	8.9
4	Nebraska	8.4
5	Hawaii	7.8
6	New York	7.5
6	Wyoming	7.5
8	Minnesota	7.0
9	Vermont	6.7
10	Iowa	6.6
10	Kansas	6.6
10	Mississippi	6.6
13	Georgia	6.5
14	Alaska	6.3
15	Maine	6.1
15	North Carolina	6.1
17	Connecticut	6.0
17	West Virginia	6.0
19	Delaware	5.9
19	Wisconsin	5.9
21	Pennsylvania	5.8
22	Indiana	5.7
22	Massachusetts	5.7
22	New Jersey	5.7
22	South Carolina	5.7
22	Virginia	5.7
27	Kentucky	5.6
27	Louisiana	5.6
27	Tennessee	5.6
30	Arkansas	5.5
30	New Hampshire	5.5
32	California	5.4
32	Michigan	5.4
34	Florida	5.3
34	Idaho	5.3
34	Oklahoma	5.3
34	Rhode Island	5.3
38	Illinois	5.2
38	Missouri	5.2
38	Nevada	5.2
38	Ohio	5.2
38	Texas	5.2
43	Colorado	5.1
44	Alabama	4.8
44	Maryland	4.8
44	Washington	4.8
47	New Mexico	4.7
48	Oregon	4.4
49	Arizona	4.3
50	Utah	4.2

	District of Columbia	6.8

Source: American Hospital Association (Chicago, IL)
     "Hospital Statistics" (2004 edition)

*All nonfederal short-term general and other special hospitals, whose facilities and services are available to the public.

Occupancy Rate in Community Hospitals in 2002

National Rate = 65.7% of Community Hospital Beds Occupied*

ALPHA ORDER

RANK	STATE	PERCENT
46	Alabama	55.8
36	Alaska	59.7
22	Arizona	63.8
44	Arkansas	58.2
13	California	68.5
26	Colorado	62.2
1	Connecticut	79.5
4	Delaware	74.3
19	Florida	65.8
20	Georgia	64.6
3	Hawaii	74.4
50	Idaho	53.1
25	Illinois	62.8
41	Indiana	58.9
38	Iowa	59.5
47	Kansas	54.7
29	Kentucky	61.7
39	Louisiana	59.4
18	Maine	65.9
7	Maryland	73.2
4	Massachusetts	74.3
17	Michigan	66.0
13	Minnesota	68.5
45	Mississippi	57.2
31	Missouri	61.4
11	Montana	68.9
43	Nebraska	58.3
16	Nevada	67.7
30	New Hampshire	61.5
9	New Jersey	70.4
20	New Mexico	64.6
2	New York	76.9
11	North Carolina	68.9
36	North Dakota	59.7
26	Ohio	62.2
42	Oklahoma	58.4
32	Oregon	60.9
10	Pennsylvania	69.9
6	Rhode Island	73.3
8	South Carolina	71.9
39	South Dakota	59.4
35	Tennessee	59.9
24	Texas	63.6
48	Utah	54.5
33	Vermont	60.6
15	Virginia	68.0
34	Washington	60.1
26	West Virginia	62.2
23	Wisconsin	63.7
49	Wyoming	53.9

RANK ORDER

RANK	STATE	PERCENT
1	Connecticut	79.5
2	New York	76.9
3	Hawaii	74.4
4	Delaware	74.3
4	Massachusetts	74.3
6	Rhode Island	73.3
7	Maryland	73.2
8	South Carolina	71.9
9	New Jersey	70.4
10	Pennsylvania	69.9
11	Montana	68.9
11	North Carolina	68.9
13	California	68.5
13	Minnesota	68.5
15	Virginia	68.0
16	Nevada	67.7
17	Michigan	66.0
18	Maine	65.9
19	Florida	65.8
20	Georgia	64.6
20	New Mexico	64.6
22	Arizona	63.8
23	Wisconsin	63.7
24	Texas	63.6
25	Illinois	62.8
26	Colorado	62.2
26	Ohio	62.2
26	West Virginia	62.2
29	Kentucky	61.7
30	New Hampshire	61.5
31	Missouri	61.4
32	Oregon	60.9
33	Vermont	60.6
34	Washington	60.1
35	Tennessee	59.9
36	Alaska	59.7
36	North Dakota	59.7
38	Iowa	59.5
39	Louisiana	59.4
39	South Dakota	59.4
41	Indiana	58.9
42	Oklahoma	58.4
43	Nebraska	58.3
44	Arkansas	58.2
45	Mississippi	57.2
46	Alabama	55.8
47	Kansas	54.7
48	Utah	54.5
49	Wyoming	53.9
50	Idaho	53.1

District of Columbia   76.5

Source: Morgan Quitno Press using data from American Hospital Association (Chicago, IL) "Hospital Statistics" (2004 edition)

*Average daily census compared to number of community hospital beds.

Outpatient Visits to Community Hospitals in 2002

National Total = 556,404,212 Visits*

ALPHA ORDER

RANK	STATE	VISITS	% of USA
18	Alabama	10,045,515	1.8%
49	Alaska	1,337,616	0.2%
31	Arizona	5,136,881	0.9%
32	Arkansas	4,838,504	0.9%
1	California	53,333,448	9.6%
26	Colorado	7,012,498	1.3%
27	Connecticut	6,641,745	1.2%
45	Delaware	1,947,818	0.4%
8	Florida	22,490,291	4.0%
14	Georgia	12,483,943	2.2%
44	Hawaii	1,964,332	0.4%
42	Idaho	2,388,086	0.4%
6	Illinois	26,511,316	4.8%
12	Indiana	14,087,435	2.5%
21	Iowa	9,330,676	1.7%
30	Kansas	5,675,015	1.0%
23	Kentucky	8,646,112	1.6%
17	Louisiana	10,731,627	1.9%
37	Maine	3,731,261	0.7%
28	Maryland	6,464,183	1.2%
9	Massachusetts	19,024,487	3.4%
7	Michigan	25,866,365	4.6%
22	Minnesota	8,901,898	1.6%
36	Mississippi	3,996,380	0.7%
11	Missouri	14,904,088	2.7%
40	Montana	2,658,735	0.5%
38	Nebraska	3,467,037	0.6%
41	Nevada	2,462,224	0.4%
39	New Hampshire	3,022,907	0.5%
10	New Jersey	15,898,001	2.9%
35	New Mexico	4,187,662	0.8%
2	New York	46,760,534	8.4%
13	North Carolina	13,822,808	2.5%
46	North Dakota	1,916,774	0.3%
5	Ohio	28,355,387	5.1%
34	Oklahoma	4,802,763	0.9%
24	Oregon	8,176,178	1.5%
4	Pennsylvania	32,409,037	5.8%
43	Rhode Island	2,211,989	0.4%
25	South Carolina	7,266,845	1.3%
47	South Dakota	1,504,098	0.3%
19	Tennessee	9,951,741	1.8%
3	Texas	33,502,635	6.0%
33	Utah	4,814,311	0.9%
48	Vermont	1,470,528	0.3%
16	Virginia	10,789,497	1.9%
20	Washington	9,748,384	1.8%
29	West Virginia	5,685,408	1.0%
15	Wisconsin	11,612,237	2.1%
50	Wyoming	888,911	0.2%

RANK ORDER

RANK	STATE	VISITS	% of USA
1	California	53,333,448	9.6%
2	New York	46,760,534	8.4%
3	Texas	33,502,635	6.0%
4	Pennsylvania	32,409,037	5.8%
5	Ohio	28,355,387	5.1%
6	Illinois	26,511,316	4.8%
7	Michigan	25,866,365	4.6%
8	Florida	22,490,291	4.0%
9	Massachusetts	19,024,487	3.4%
10	New Jersey	15,898,001	2.9%
11	Missouri	14,904,088	2.7%
12	Indiana	14,087,435	2.5%
13	North Carolina	13,822,808	2.5%
14	Georgia	12,483,943	2.2%
15	Wisconsin	11,612,237	2.1%
16	Virginia	10,789,497	1.9%
17	Louisiana	10,731,627	1.9%
18	Alabama	10,045,515	1.8%
19	Tennessee	9,951,741	1.8%
20	Washington	9,748,384	1.8%
21	Iowa	9,330,676	1.7%
22	Minnesota	8,901,898	1.6%
23	Kentucky	8,646,112	1.6%
24	Oregon	8,176,178	1.5%
25	South Carolina	7,266,845	1.3%
26	Colorado	7,012,498	1.3%
27	Connecticut	6,641,745	1.2%
28	Maryland	6,464,183	1.2%
29	West Virginia	5,685,408	1.0%
30	Kansas	5,675,015	1.0%
31	Arizona	5,136,881	0.9%
32	Arkansas	4,838,504	0.9%
33	Utah	4,814,311	0.9%
34	Oklahoma	4,802,763	0.9%
35	New Mexico	4,187,662	0.8%
36	Mississippi	3,996,380	0.7%
37	Maine	3,731,261	0.7%
38	Nebraska	3,467,037	0.6%
39	New Hampshire	3,022,907	0.5%
40	Montana	2,658,735	0.5%
41	Nevada	2,462,224	0.4%
42	Idaho	2,388,086	0.4%
43	Rhode Island	2,211,989	0.4%
44	Hawaii	1,964,332	0.4%
45	Delaware	1,947,818	0.4%
46	North Dakota	1,916,774	0.3%
47	South Dakota	1,504,098	0.3%
48	Vermont	1,470,528	0.3%
49	Alaska	1,337,616	0.2%
50	Wyoming	888,911	0.2%
	District of Columbia	1,526,061	0.3%

Source: American Hospital Association (Chicago, IL)
   "Hospital Statistics" (2004 edition)
*All nonfederal short-term general and other special hospitals, whose facilities and services are available to the public. Includes emergency and other visits.

Emergency Outpatient Visits to Community Hospitals in 2002

National Total = 109,951,738 Visits*

ALPHA ORDER

RANK	STATE	VISITS	% of USA
18	Alabama	2,162,011	2.0%
47	Alaska	254,592	0.2%
25	Arizona	1,559,078	1.4%
30	Arkansas	1,224,053	1.1%
1	California	10,111,529	9.2%
27	Colorado	1,501,013	1.4%
28	Connecticut	1,392,274	1.3%
44	Delaware	305,634	0.3%
4	Florida	6,623,448	6.0%
10	Georgia	3,227,698	2.9%
43	Hawaii	311,713	0.3%
42	Idaho	445,100	0.4%
7	Illinois	4,699,328	4.3%
17	Indiana	2,437,268	2.2%
33	Iowa	1,072,319	1.0%
34	Kansas	940,408	0.9%
19	Kentucky	2,109,556	1.9%
16	Louisiana	2,468,832	2.2%
36	Maine	709,091	0.6%
20	Maryland	1,943,614	1.8%
12	Massachusetts	2,882,602	2.6%
8	Michigan	4,029,309	3.7%
24	Minnesota	1,605,237	1.5%
26	Mississippi	1,556,488	1.4%
15	Missouri	2,476,194	2.3%
46	Montana	276,829	0.3%
40	Nebraska	511,085	0.5%
38	Nevada	626,330	0.6%
39	New Hampshire	550,380	0.5%
11	New Jersey	2,940,592	2.7%
37	New Mexico	705,643	0.6%
3	New York	7,474,440	6.8%
9	North Carolina	3,322,226	3.0%
45	North Dakota	295,074	0.3%
5	Ohio	5,125,829	4.7%
29	Oklahoma	1,292,652	1.2%
31	Oregon	1,117,313	1.0%
6	Pennsylvania	5,059,150	4.6%
41	Rhode Island	468,530	0.4%
23	South Carolina	1,799,127	1.6%
50	South Dakota	208,068	0.2%
13	Tennessee	2,815,655	2.6%
2	Texas	8,243,642	7.5%
35	Utah	797,951	0.7%
48	Vermont	230,643	0.2%
14	Virginia	2,606,320	2.4%
21	Washington	1,936,458	1.8%
32	West Virginia	1,100,258	1.0%
22	Wisconsin	1,833,344	1.7%
49	Wyoming	212,868	0.2%

RANK ORDER

RANK	STATE	VISITS	% of USA
1	California	10,111,529	9.2%
2	Texas	8,243,642	7.5%
3	New York	7,474,440	6.8%
4	Florida	6,623,448	6.0%
5	Ohio	5,125,829	4.7%
6	Pennsylvania	5,059,150	4.6%
7	Illinois	4,699,328	4.3%
8	Michigan	4,029,309	3.7%
9	North Carolina	3,322,226	3.0%
10	Georgia	3,227,698	2.9%
11	New Jersey	2,940,592	2.7%
12	Massachusetts	2,882,602	2.6%
13	Tennessee	2,815,655	2.6%
14	Virginia	2,606,320	2.4%
15	Missouri	2,476,194	2.3%
16	Louisiana	2,468,832	2.2%
17	Indiana	2,437,268	2.2%
18	Alabama	2,162,011	2.0%
19	Kentucky	2,109,556	1.9%
20	Maryland	1,943,614	1.8%
21	Washington	1,936,458	1.8%
22	Wisconsin	1,833,344	1.7%
23	South Carolina	1,799,127	1.6%
24	Minnesota	1,605,237	1.5%
25	Arizona	1,559,078	1.4%
26	Mississippi	1,556,488	1.4%
27	Colorado	1,501,013	1.4%
28	Connecticut	1,392,274	1.3%
29	Oklahoma	1,292,652	1.2%
30	Arkansas	1,224,053	1.1%
31	Oregon	1,117,313	1.0%
32	West Virginia	1,100,258	1.0%
33	Iowa	1,072,319	1.0%
34	Kansas	940,408	0.9%
35	Utah	797,951	0.7%
36	Maine	709,091	0.6%
37	New Mexico	705,643	0.6%
38	Nevada	626,330	0.6%
39	New Hampshire	550,380	0.5%
40	Nebraska	511,085	0.5%
41	Rhode Island	468,530	0.4%
42	Idaho	445,100	0.4%
43	Hawaii	311,713	0.3%
44	Delaware	305,634	0.3%
45	North Dakota	295,074	0.3%
46	Montana	276,829	0.3%
47	Alaska	254,592	0.2%
48	Vermont	230,643	0.2%
49	Wyoming	212,868	0.2%
50	South Dakota	208,068	0.2%
	District of Columbia	352,942	0.3%

Source: American Hospital Association (Chicago, IL)
   "Hospital Statistics" (2004 edition)
*All nonfederal short-term general and other special hospitals, whose facilities and services are available to the public.

Surgical Operations in Community Hospitals in 2002

National Total = 27,576,675 Surgical Operations*

ALPHA ORDER

RANK	STATE	OPERATIONS	% of USA
20	Alabama	517,883	1.9%
48	Alaska	57,495	0.2%
26	Arizona	359,279	1.3%
32	Arkansas	278,792	1.0%
1	California	2,320,864	8.4%
27	Colorado	314,731	1.1%
29	Connecticut	299,309	1.1%
44	Delaware	96,683	0.4%
4	Florida	1,600,616	5.8%
10	Georgia	800,479	2.9%
45	Hawaii	84,557	0.3%
43	Idaho	101,442	0.4%
7	Illinois	1,174,945	4.3%
15	Indiana	615,920	2.2%
25	Iowa	409,982	1.5%
34	Kansas	244,669	0.9%
18	Kentucky	543,125	2.0%
21	Louisiana	467,940	1.7%
40	Maine	157,687	0.6%
19	Maryland	533,799	1.9%
13	Massachusetts	691,220	2.5%
8	Michigan	1,086,519	3.9%
22	Minnesota	458,224	1.7%
33	Mississippi	273,882	1.0%
16	Missouri	603,500	2.2%
47	Montana	71,135	0.3%
36	Nebraska	203,137	0.7%
39	Nevada	162,563	0.6%
42	New Hampshire	118,609	0.4%
12	New Jersey	720,160	2.6%
38	New Mexico	162,822	0.6%
2	New York	2,078,441	7.5%
9	North Carolina	811,408	2.9%
46	North Dakota	75,863	0.3%
6	Ohio	1,241,582	4.5%
30	Oklahoma	282,800	1.0%
28	Oregon	305,386	1.1%
5	Pennsylvania	1,521,334	5.5%
41	Rhode Island	142,776	0.5%
23	South Carolina	457,995	1.7%
37	South Dakota	195,126	0.7%
14	Tennessee	619,607	2.2%
3	Texas	1,846,170	6.7%
35	Utah	229,258	0.8%
49	Vermont	54,439	0.2%
11	Virginia	739,868	2.7%
24	Washington	443,595	1.6%
31	West Virginia	280,999	1.0%
17	Wisconsin	570,553	2.1%
50	Wyoming	41,590	0.2%

RANK ORDER

RANK	STATE	OPERATIONS	% of USA
1	California	2,320,864	8.4%
2	New York	2,078,441	7.5%
3	Texas	1,846,170	6.7%
4	Florida	1,600,616	5.8%
5	Pennsylvania	1,521,334	5.5%
6	Ohio	1,241,582	4.5%
7	Illinois	1,174,945	4.3%
8	Michigan	1,086,519	3.9%
9	North Carolina	811,408	2.9%
10	Georgia	800,479	2.9%
11	Virginia	739,868	2.7%
12	New Jersey	720,160	2.6%
13	Massachusetts	691,220	2.5%
14	Tennessee	619,607	2.2%
15	Indiana	615,920	2.2%
16	Missouri	603,500	2.2%
17	Wisconsin	570,553	2.1%
18	Kentucky	543,125	2.0%
19	Maryland	533,799	1.9%
20	Alabama	517,883	1.9%
21	Louisiana	467,940	1.7%
22	Minnesota	458,224	1.7%
23	South Carolina	457,995	1.7%
24	Washington	443,595	1.6%
25	Iowa	409,982	1.5%
26	Arizona	359,279	1.3%
27	Colorado	314,731	1.1%
28	Oregon	305,386	1.1%
29	Connecticut	299,309	1.1%
30	Oklahoma	282,800	1.0%
31	West Virginia	280,999	1.0%
32	Arkansas	278,792	1.0%
33	Mississippi	273,882	1.0%
34	Kansas	244,669	0.9%
35	Utah	229,258	0.8%
36	Nebraska	203,137	0.7%
37	South Dakota	195,126	0.7%
38	New Mexico	162,822	0.6%
39	Nevada	162,563	0.6%
40	Maine	157,687	0.6%
41	Rhode Island	142,776	0.5%
42	New Hampshire	118,609	0.4%
43	Idaho	101,442	0.4%
44	Delaware	96,683	0.4%
45	Hawaii	84,557	0.3%
46	North Dakota	75,863	0.3%
47	Montana	71,135	0.3%
48	Alaska	57,495	0.2%
49	Vermont	54,439	0.2%
50	Wyoming	41,590	0.2%
	District of Columbia	105,917	0.4%

Source: American Hospital Association (Chicago, IL)
    "Hospital Statistics" (2004 edition)
*Includes inpatient and outpatient surgeries.

Medicare and Medicaid Certified Facilities in 2004

National Total = 241,617 Facilities*

ALPHA ORDER

RANK	STATE	FACILITIES	% of USA
19	Alabama	4,243	1.8%
49	Alaska	555	0.2%
27	Arizona	3,469	1.4%
32	Arkansas	2,723	1.1%
1	California	23,691	9.8%
30	Colorado	3,110	1.3%
29	Connecticut	3,242	1.3%
47	Delaware	795	0.3%
3	Florida	15,518	6.4%
9	Georgia	7,437	3.1%
45	Hawaii	935	0.4%
40	Idaho	1,154	0.5%
6	Illinois	10,311	4.3%
11	Indiana	6,351	2.6%
26	Iowa	3,613	1.5%
28	Kansas	3,288	1.4%
24	Kentucky	3,880	1.6%
15	Louisiana	5,346	2.2%
38	Maine	1,347	0.6%
18	Maryland	4,361	1.8%
17	Massachusetts	4,559	1.9%
8	Michigan	7,843	3.2%
25	Minnesota	3,674	1.5%
31	Mississippi	2,807	1.2%
13	Missouri	5,880	2.4%
43	Montana	989	0.4%
35	Nebraska	2,022	0.8%
39	Nevada	1,320	0.5%
41	New Hampshire	1,128	0.5%
12	New Jersey	6,146	2.5%
36	New Mexico	1,589	0.7%
4	New York	12,549	5.2%
10	North Carolina	7,180	3.0%
46	North Dakota	854	0.4%
5	Ohio	11,491	4.8%
22	Oklahoma	3,887	1.6%
33	Oregon	2,543	1.1%
7	Pennsylvania	9,863	4.1%
44	Rhode Island	951	0.4%
21	South Carolina	3,953	1.6%
42	South Dakota	1,002	0.4%
14	Tennessee	5,405	2.2%
2	Texas	20,100	8.3%
37	Utah	1,452	0.6%
48	Vermont	557	0.2%
16	Virginia	5,259	2.2%
23	Washington	3,884	1.6%
34	West Virginia	2,155	0.9%
20	Wisconsin	4,026	1.7%
50	Wyoming	521	0.2%

RANK ORDER

RANK	STATE	FACILITIES	% of USA
1	California	23,691	9.8%
2	Texas	20,100	8.3%
3	Florida	15,518	6.4%
4	New York	12,549	5.2%
5	Ohio	11,491	4.8%
6	Illinois	10,311	4.3%
7	Pennsylvania	9,863	4.1%
8	Michigan	7,843	3.2%
9	Georgia	7,437	3.1%
10	North Carolina	7,180	3.0%
11	Indiana	6,351	2.6%
12	New Jersey	6,146	2.5%
13	Missouri	5,880	2.4%
14	Tennessee	5,405	2.2%
15	Louisiana	5,346	2.2%
16	Virginia	5,259	2.2%
17	Massachusetts	4,559	1.9%
18	Maryland	4,361	1.8%
19	Alabama	4,243	1.8%
20	Wisconsin	4,026	1.7%
21	South Carolina	3,953	1.6%
22	Oklahoma	3,887	1.6%
23	Washington	3,884	1.6%
24	Kentucky	3,880	1.6%
25	Minnesota	3,674	1.5%
26	Iowa	3,613	1.5%
27	Arizona	3,469	1.4%
28	Kansas	3,288	1.4%
29	Connecticut	3,242	1.3%
30	Colorado	3,110	1.3%
31	Mississippi	2,807	1.2%
32	Arkansas	2,723	1.1%
33	Oregon	2,543	1.1%
34	West Virginia	2,155	0.9%
35	Nebraska	2,022	0.8%
36	New Mexico	1,589	0.7%
37	Utah	1,452	0.6%
38	Maine	1,347	0.6%
39	Nevada	1,320	0.5%
40	Idaho	1,154	0.5%
41	New Hampshire	1,128	0.5%
42	South Dakota	1,002	0.4%
43	Montana	989	0.4%
44	Rhode Island	951	0.4%
45	Hawaii	935	0.4%
46	North Dakota	854	0.4%
47	Delaware	795	0.3%
48	Vermont	557	0.2%
49	Alaska	555	0.2%
50	Wyoming	521	0.2%
	District of Columbia	659	0.3%

Source: U.S. Department of Health and Human Services, Centers for Medicare and Medicaid Services
OSCAR Report 10 (January 7, 2004)

*Certified by CMS to participate in the Medicare/Medicaid programs. All provider groups including hospitals, home health agencies, rural health centers, community mental health centers, nursing facilities, outpatient physical therapy facilities, hospices and laboratories. National total does not include 1,357 certified facilities in U.S. territories.

Medicare and Medicaid Certified Hospitals in 2004

National Total = 6,000 Hospitals*

ALPHA ORDER

RANK	STATE	HOSPITALS	% of USA
19	Alabama	123	2.1%
47	Alaska	24	0.4%
29	Arizona	89	1.5%
24	Arkansas	108	1.8%
2	California	438	7.3%
30	Colorado	84	1.4%
41	Connecticut	46	0.8%
50	Delaware	10	0.2%
5	Florida	235	3.9%
9	Georgia	177	3.0%
46	Hawaii	27	0.5%
40	Idaho	47	0.8%
6	Illinois	216	3.6%
11	Indiana	157	2.6%
20	Iowa	119	2.0%
12	Kansas	152	2.5%
21	Kentucky	116	1.9%
7	Louisiana	214	3.6%
42	Maine	41	0.7%
34	Maryland	65	1.1%
22	Massachusetts	113	1.9%
10	Michigan	175	2.9%
15	Minnesota	147	2.5%
25	Mississippi	107	1.8%
18	Missouri	137	2.3%
35	Montana	64	1.1%
28	Nebraska	94	1.6%
42	Nevada	41	0.7%
44	New Hampshire	30	0.5%
25	New Jersey	107	1.8%
37	New Mexico	53	0.9%
3	New York	252	4.2%
17	North Carolina	139	2.3%
38	North Dakota	51	0.9%
8	Ohio	211	3.5%
14	Oklahoma	151	2.5%
36	Oregon	62	1.0%
4	Pennsylvania	246	4.1%
49	Rhode Island	15	0.3%
31	South Carolina	76	1.3%
32	South Dakota	67	1.1%
12	Tennessee	152	2.5%
1	Texas	497	8.3%
39	Utah	48	0.8%
48	Vermont	16	0.3%
23	Virginia	109	1.8%
27	Washington	101	1.7%
33	West Virginia	66	1.1%
16	Wisconsin	141	2.4%
44	Wyoming	30	0.5%

RANK ORDER

RANK	STATE	HOSPITALS	% of USA
1	Texas	497	8.3%
2	California	438	7.3%
3	New York	252	4.2%
4	Pennsylvania	246	4.1%
5	Florida	235	3.9%
6	Illinois	216	3.6%
7	Louisiana	214	3.6%
8	Ohio	211	3.5%
9	Georgia	177	3.0%
10	Michigan	175	2.9%
11	Indiana	157	2.6%
12	Kansas	152	2.5%
12	Tennessee	152	2.5%
14	Oklahoma	151	2.5%
15	Minnesota	147	2.5%
16	Wisconsin	141	2.4%
17	North Carolina	139	2.3%
18	Missouri	137	2.3%
19	Alabama	123	2.1%
20	Iowa	119	2.0%
21	Kentucky	116	1.9%
22	Massachusetts	113	1.9%
23	Virginia	109	1.8%
24	Arkansas	108	1.8%
25	Mississippi	107	1.8%
25	New Jersey	107	1.8%
27	Washington	101	1.7%
28	Nebraska	94	1.6%
29	Arizona	89	1.5%
30	Colorado	84	1.4%
31	South Carolina	76	1.3%
32	South Dakota	67	1.1%
33	West Virginia	66	1.1%
34	Maryland	65	1.1%
35	Montana	64	1.1%
36	Oregon	62	1.0%
37	New Mexico	53	0.9%
38	North Dakota	51	0.9%
39	Utah	48	0.8%
40	Idaho	47	0.8%
41	Connecticut	46	0.8%
42	Maine	41	0.7%
42	Nevada	41	0.7%
44	New Hampshire	30	0.5%
44	Wyoming	30	0.5%
46	Hawaii	27	0.5%
47	Alaska	24	0.4%
48	Vermont	16	0.3%
49	Rhode Island	15	0.3%
50	Delaware	10	0.2%
	District of Columbia	14	0.2%

*Source: U.S. Department of Health and Human Services, Centers for Medicare and Medicaid Services
OSCAR Database (January 7, 2004)*

*Certified by CMS to participate in the Medicare/Medicaid programs. Excludes licensed facilities that do not accept federal funding and facilities managed by the Department of Veterans Affairs. National total does not include 64 certified hospitals in U.S. territories.

Beds in Medicare and Medicaid Certified Hospitals in 2004

National Total = 940,645 Beds*

ALPHA ORDER

RANK	STATE	BEDS	% of USA
17	Alabama	19,936	2.1%
50	Alaska	1,509	0.2%
26	Arizona	12,844	1.4%
31	Arkansas	10,996	1.2%
1	California	82,366	8.8%
29	Colorado	11,551	1.2%
32	Connecticut	10,372	1.1%
47	Delaware	2,261	0.2%
4	Florida	53,517	5.7%
11	Georgia	24,932	2.7%
46	Hawaii	2,715	0.3%
44	Idaho	3,285	0.3%
5	Illinois	46,864	5.0%
15	Indiana	21,602	2.3%
28	Iowa	11,824	1.3%
30	Kansas	11,166	1.2%
20	Kentucky	17,372	1.8%
14	Louisiana	22,762	2.4%
39	Maine	4,063	0.4%
22	Maryland	16,104	1.7%
18	Massachusetts	19,420	2.1%
9	Michigan	29,984	3.2%
21	Minnesota	16,684	1.8%
25	Mississippi	12,859	1.4%
13	Missouri	24,134	2.6%
45	Montana	2,907	0.3%
35	Nebraska	6,669	0.7%
36	Nevada	5,386	0.6%
42	New Hampshire	3,389	0.4%
8	New Jersey	31,338	3.3%
38	New Mexico	5,011	0.5%
2	New York	73,989	7.9%
10	North Carolina	25,993	2.8%
43	North Dakota	3,301	0.4%
6	Ohio	46,129	4.9%
23	Oklahoma	14,679	1.6%
34	Oregon	7,867	0.8%
7	Pennsylvania	41,034	4.4%
40	Rhode Island	3,785	0.4%
27	South Carolina	12,637	1.3%
41	South Dakota	3,409	0.4%
12	Tennessee	24,781	2.6%
3	Texas	60,466	6.4%
37	Utah	5,089	0.5%
48	Vermont	2,048	0.2%
16	Virginia	21,236	2.3%
24	Washington	13,939	1.5%
33	West Virginia	9,388	1.0%
19	Wisconsin	19,023	2.0%
49	Wyoming	1,511	0.2%

RANK ORDER

RANK	STATE	BEDS	% of USA
1	California	82,366	8.8%
2	New York	73,989	7.9%
3	Texas	60,466	6.4%
4	Florida	53,517	5.7%
5	Illinois	46,864	5.0%
6	Ohio	46,129	4.9%
7	Pennsylvania	41,034	4.4%
8	New Jersey	31,338	3.3%
9	Michigan	29,984	3.2%
10	North Carolina	25,993	2.8%
11	Georgia	24,932	2.7%
12	Tennessee	24,781	2.6%
13	Missouri	24,134	2.6%
14	Louisiana	22,762	2.4%
15	Indiana	21,602	2.3%
16	Virginia	21,236	2.3%
17	Alabama	19,936	2.1%
18	Massachusetts	19,420	2.1%
19	Wisconsin	19,023	2.0%
20	Kentucky	17,372	1.8%
21	Minnesota	16,684	1.8%
22	Maryland	16,104	1.7%
23	Oklahoma	14,679	1.6%
24	Washington	13,939	1.5%
25	Mississippi	12,859	1.4%
26	Arizona	12,844	1.4%
27	South Carolina	12,637	1.3%
28	Iowa	11,824	1.3%
29	Colorado	11,551	1.2%
30	Kansas	11,166	1.2%
31	Arkansas	10,996	1.2%
32	Connecticut	10,372	1.1%
33	West Virginia	9,388	1.0%
34	Oregon	7,867	0.8%
35	Nebraska	6,669	0.7%
36	Nevada	5,386	0.6%
37	Utah	5,089	0.5%
38	New Mexico	5,011	0.5%
39	Maine	4,063	0.4%
40	Rhode Island	3,785	0.4%
41	South Dakota	3,409	0.4%
42	New Hampshire	3,389	0.4%
43	North Dakota	3,301	0.4%
44	Idaho	3,285	0.3%
45	Montana	2,907	0.3%
46	Hawaii	2,715	0.3%
47	Delaware	2,261	0.2%
48	Vermont	2,048	0.2%
49	Wyoming	1,511	0.2%
50	Alaska	1,509	0.2%
	District of Columbia	4,519	0.5%

Source: U.S. Department of Health and Human Services, Centers for Medicare and Medicaid Services OSCAR Database (January 7, 2004)

*Beds in hospitals certified by CMS to participate in the Medicare/Medicaid programs. Excludes licensed facilities that do not accept federal funding and facilities managed by the Department of Veterans Affairs. National total does not include 11,133 beds in U.S. territories.

Medicare and Medicaid Certified Children's Hospitals in 2004

National Total = 79 Hospitals*

ALPHA ORDER

RANK	STATE	HOSPITALS	% of USA
9	Alabama	2	2.5%
34	Alaska	0	0.0%
9	Arizona	2	2.5%
20	Arkansas	1	1.3%
1	California	9	11.4%
20	Colorado	1	1.3%
20	Connecticut	1	1.3%
20	Delaware	1	1.3%
9	Florida	2	2.5%
9	Georgia	2	2.5%
20	Hawaii	1	1.3%
34	Idaho	0	0.0%
9	Illinois	2	2.5%
20	Indiana	1	1.3%
34	Iowa	0	0.0%
20	Kansas	1	1.3%
34	Kentucky	0	0.0%
20	Louisiana	1	1.3%
34	Maine	0	0.0%
9	Maryland	2	2.5%
9	Massachusetts	2	2.5%
20	Michigan	1	1.3%
5	Minnesota	3	3.8%
34	Mississippi	0	0.0%
5	Missouri	3	3.8%
34	Montana	0	0.0%
9	Nebraska	2	2.5%
34	Nevada	0	0.0%
34	New Hampshire	0	0.0%
20	New Jersey	1	1.3%
20	New Mexico	1	1.3%
20	New York	1	1.3%
34	North Carolina	0	0.0%
34	North Dakota	0	0.0%
3	Ohio	7	8.9%
9	Oklahoma	2	2.5%
34	Oregon	0	0.0%
4	Pennsylvania	6	7.6%
34	Rhode Island	0	0.0%
34	South Carolina	0	0.0%
20	South Dakota	1	1.3%
9	Tennessee	2	2.5%
2	Texas	8	10.1%
20	Utah	1	1.3%
34	Vermont	0	0.0%
5	Virginia	3	3.8%
9	Washington	2	2.5%
34	West Virginia	0	0.0%
5	Wisconsin	3	3.8%
34	Wyoming	0	0.0%

RANK ORDER

RANK	STATE	HOSPITALS	% of USA
1	California	9	11.4%
2	Texas	8	10.1%
3	Ohio	7	8.9%
4	Pennsylvania	6	7.6%
5	Minnesota	3	3.8%
5	Missouri	3	3.8%
5	Virginia	3	3.8%
5	Wisconsin	3	3.8%
9	Alabama	2	2.5%
9	Arizona	2	2.5%
9	Florida	2	2.5%
9	Georgia	2	2.5%
9	Illinois	2	2.5%
9	Maryland	2	2.5%
9	Massachusetts	2	2.5%
9	Nebraska	2	2.5%
9	Oklahoma	2	2.5%
9	Tennessee	2	2.5%
9	Washington	2	2.5%
20	Arkansas	1	1.3%
20	Colorado	1	1.3%
20	Connecticut	1	1.3%
20	Delaware	1	1.3%
20	Hawaii	1	1.3%
20	Indiana	1	1.3%
20	Kansas	1	1.3%
20	Louisiana	1	1.3%
20	Michigan	1	1.3%
20	New Jersey	1	1.3%
20	New Mexico	1	1.3%
20	New York	1	1.3%
20	South Dakota	1	1.3%
20	Utah	1	1.3%
34	Alaska	0	0.0%
34	Idaho	0	0.0%
34	Iowa	0	0.0%
34	Kentucky	0	0.0%
34	Maine	0	0.0%
34	Mississippi	0	0.0%
34	Montana	0	0.0%
34	Nevada	0	0.0%
34	New Hampshire	0	0.0%
34	North Carolina	0	0.0%
34	North Dakota	0	0.0%
34	Oregon	0	0.0%
34	Rhode Island	0	0.0%
34	South Carolina	0	0.0%
34	Vermont	0	0.0%
34	West Virginia	0	0.0%
34	Wyoming	0	0.0%
	District of Columbia	1	1.3%

Source: U.S. Department of Health and Human Services, Centers for Medicare and Medicaid Services
    OSCAR Database (January 7, 2004)

*Certified by CMS to participate in the Medicare/Medicaid programs. National total does not include one facility in U.S. territories. Excludes licensed facilities that do not accept federal funding and facilities managed by the Department of Veterans Affairs.

Beds in Medicare and Medicaid Certified Children's Hospitals in 2004

National Total = 11,592 Beds*

ALPHA ORDER

RANK	STATE	BEDS	% of USA
9	Alabama	384	3.3%
34	Alaska	0	0.0%
19	Arizona	223	1.9%
13	Arkansas	280	2.4%
1	California	1,605	13.8%
16	Colorado	253	2.2%
26	Connecticut	97	0.8%
26	Delaware	97	0.8%
7	Florida	424	3.7%
8	Georgia	400	3.5%
20	Hawaii	201	1.7%
34	Idaho	0	0.0%
10	Illinois	351	3.0%
33	Indiana	20	0.2%
34	Iowa	0	0.0%
31	Kansas	34	0.3%
34	Kentucky	0	0.0%
21	Louisiana	188	1.6%
34	Maine	0	0.0%
24	Maryland	150	1.3%
6	Massachusetts	425	3.7%
18	Michigan	228	2.0%
11	Minnesota	329	2.8%
34	Mississippi	0	0.0%
5	Missouri	432	3.7%
34	Montana	0	0.0%
24	Nebraska	150	1.3%
34	Nevada	0	0.0%
34	New Hampshire	0	0.0%
30	New Jersey	74	0.6%
32	New Mexico	28	0.2%
29	New York	92	0.8%
34	North Carolina	0	0.0%
34	North Dakota	0	0.0%
2	Ohio	1,419	12.2%
23	Oklahoma	160	1.4%
34	Oregon	0	0.0%
4	Pennsylvania	679	5.9%
34	Rhode Island	0	0.0%
34	South Carolina	0	0.0%
28	South Dakota	96	0.8%
22	Tennessee	175	1.5%
3	Texas	1,285	11.1%
17	Utah	232	2.0%
34	Vermont	0	0.0%
12	Virginia	286	2.5%
14	Washington	276	2.4%
34	West Virginia	0	0.0%
14	Wisconsin	276	2.4%
34	Wyoming	0	0.0%

RANK ORDER

RANK	STATE	BEDS	% of USA
1	California	1,605	13.8%
2	Ohio	1,419	12.2%
3	Texas	1,285	11.1%
4	Pennsylvania	679	5.9%
5	Missouri	432	3.7%
6	Massachusetts	425	3.7%
7	Florida	424	3.7%
8	Georgia	400	3.5%
9	Alabama	384	3.3%
10	Illinois	351	3.0%
11	Minnesota	329	2.8%
12	Virginia	286	2.5%
13	Arkansas	280	2.4%
14	Washington	276	2.4%
14	Wisconsin	276	2.4%
16	Colorado	253	2.2%
17	Utah	232	2.0%
18	Michigan	228	2.0%
19	Arizona	223	1.9%
20	Hawaii	201	1.7%
21	Louisiana	188	1.6%
22	Tennessee	175	1.5%
23	Oklahoma	160	1.4%
24	Maryland	150	1.3%
24	Nebraska	150	1.3%
26	Connecticut	97	0.8%
26	Delaware	97	0.8%
28	South Dakota	96	0.8%
29	New York	92	0.8%
30	New Jersey	74	0.6%
31	Kansas	34	0.3%
32	New Mexico	28	0.2%
33	Indiana	20	0.2%
34	Alaska	0	0.0%
34	Idaho	0	0.0%
34	Iowa	0	0.0%
34	Kentucky	0	0.0%
34	Maine	0	0.0%
34	Mississippi	0	0.0%
34	Montana	0	0.0%
34	Nevada	0	0.0%
34	New Hampshire	0	0.0%
34	North Carolina	0	0.0%
34	North Dakota	0	0.0%
34	Oregon	0	0.0%
34	Rhode Island	0	0.0%
34	South Carolina	0	0.0%
34	Vermont	0	0.0%
34	West Virginia	0	0.0%
34	Wyoming	0	0.0%
	District of Columbia	243	2.1%

Source: U.S. Department of Health and Human Services, Centers for Medicare and Medicaid Services OSCAR Database (January 7, 2004)

*Beds in hospitals certified by CMS to participate in the Medicare/Medicaid programs. Excludes licensed facilities that do not accept federal funding and facilities managed by the Department of Veterans Affairs. National total does not include 215 beds in U.S. territories.

Medicare and Medicaid Certified Rehabilitation Hospitals in 2004

National Total = 217 Hospitals*

ALPHA ORDER

RANK	STATE	HOSPITALS	% of USA
6	Alabama	7	3.2%
41	Alaska	0	0.0%
16	Arizona	4	1.8%
10	Arkansas	6	2.8%
6	California	7	3.2%
25	Colorado	2	0.9%
31	Connecticut	1	0.5%
41	Delaware	0	0.0%
4	Florida	14	6.5%
25	Georgia	2	0.9%
31	Hawaii	1	0.5%
31	Idaho	1	0.5%
16	Illinois	4	1.8%
6	Indiana	7	3.2%
41	Iowa	0	0.0%
16	Kansas	4	1.8%
10	Kentucky	6	2.8%
2	Louisiana	26	12.0%
31	Maine	1	0.5%
25	Maryland	2	0.9%
6	Massachusetts	7	3.2%
14	Michigan	5	2.3%
31	Minnesota	1	0.5%
41	Mississippi	0	0.0%
24	Missouri	3	1.4%
41	Montana	0	0.0%
31	Nebraska	1	0.5%
16	Nevada	4	1.8%
25	New Hampshire	2	0.9%
5	New Jersey	10	4.6%
16	New Mexico	4	1.8%
16	New York	4	1.8%
25	North Carolina	2	0.9%
41	North Dakota	0	0.0%
25	Ohio	2	0.9%
16	Oklahoma	4	1.8%
41	Oregon	0	0.0%
3	Pennsylvania	18	8.3%
31	Rhode Island	1	0.5%
14	South Carolina	5	2.3%
41	South Dakota	0	0.0%
10	Tennessee	6	2.8%
1	Texas	29	13.4%
31	Utah	1	0.5%
41	Vermont	0	0.0%
16	Virginia	4	1.8%
31	Washington	1	0.5%
10	West Virginia	6	2.8%
31	Wisconsin	1	0.5%
41	Wyoming	0	0.0%

RANK ORDER

RANK	STATE	HOSPITALS	% of USA
1	Texas	29	13.4%
2	Louisiana	26	12.0%
3	Pennsylvania	18	8.3%
4	Florida	14	6.5%
5	New Jersey	10	4.6%
6	Alabama	7	3.2%
6	California	7	3.2%
6	Indiana	7	3.2%
6	Massachusetts	7	3.2%
10	Arkansas	6	2.8%
10	Kentucky	6	2.8%
10	Tennessee	6	2.8%
10	West Virginia	6	2.8%
14	Michigan	5	2.3%
14	South Carolina	5	2.3%
16	Arizona	4	1.8%
16	Illinois	4	1.8%
16	Kansas	4	1.8%
16	Nevada	4	1.8%
16	New Mexico	4	1.8%
16	New York	4	1.8%
16	Oklahoma	4	1.8%
16	Virginia	4	1.8%
24	Missouri	3	1.4%
25	Colorado	2	0.9%
25	Georgia	2	0.9%
25	Maryland	2	0.9%
25	New Hampshire	2	0.9%
25	North Carolina	2	0.9%
25	Ohio	2	0.9%
31	Connecticut	1	0.5%
31	Hawaii	1	0.5%
31	Idaho	1	0.5%
31	Maine	1	0.5%
31	Minnesota	1	0.5%
31	Nebraska	1	0.5%
31	Rhode Island	1	0.5%
31	Utah	1	0.5%
31	Washington	1	0.5%
31	Wisconsin	1	0.5%
41	Alaska	0	0.0%
41	Delaware	0	0.0%
41	Iowa	0	0.0%
41	Mississippi	0	0.0%
41	Montana	0	0.0%
41	North Dakota	0	0.0%
41	Oregon	0	0.0%
41	South Dakota	0	0.0%
41	Vermont	0	0.0%
41	Wyoming	0	0.0%
	District of Columbia	1	0.5%

Source: U.S. Department of Health and Human Services, Centers for Medicare and Medicaid Services
OSCAR Database (January 7, 2004)
*Certified by CMS to participate in the Medicare/Medicaid programs. Excludes licensed facilities that do not accept federal funding and facilities managed by the Department of Veterans Affairs. National total does not include one certified hospital in U.S. territories.

Beds in Medicare and Medicaid Certified Rehabilitation Hospitals in 2004

National Total = 13,830 Beds*

ALPHA ORDER

RANK	STATE	BEDS	% of USA
13	Alabama	351	2.5%
41	Alaska	0	0.0%
23	Arizona	209	1.5%
7	Arkansas	459	3.3%
10	California	411	3.0%
25	Colorado	186	1.3%
37	Connecticut	60	0.4%
41	Delaware	0	0.0%
3	Florida	1,029	7.4%
29	Georgia	116	0.8%
31	Hawaii	100	0.7%
39	Idaho	59	0.4%
11	Illinois	408	3.0%
8	Indiana	438	3.2%
41	Iowa	0	0.0%
18	Kansas	257	1.9%
14	Kentucky	328	2.4%
6	Louisiana	621	4.5%
31	Maine	100	0.7%
33	Maryland	99	0.7%
5	Massachusetts	742	5.4%
15	Michigan	315	2.3%
40	Minnesota	15	0.1%
41	Mississippi	0	0.0%
22	Missouri	220	1.6%
41	Montana	0	0.0%
37	Nebraska	60	0.4%
17	Nevada	272	2.0%
27	New Hampshire	152	1.1%
4	New Jersey	786	5.7%
26	New Mexico	156	1.1%
9	New York	428	3.1%
20	North Carolina	233	1.7%
41	North Dakota	0	0.0%
28	Ohio	145	1.0%
21	Oklahoma	227	1.6%
41	Oregon	0	0.0%
2	Pennsylvania	1,575	11.4%
35	Rhode Island	82	0.6%
16	South Carolina	274	2.0%
41	South Dakota	0	0.0%
12	Tennessee	370	2.7%
1	Texas	1,669	12.1%
34	Utah	84	0.6%
41	Vermont	0	0.0%
24	Virginia	205	1.5%
30	Washington	102	0.7%
19	West Virginia	246	1.8%
36	Wisconsin	81	0.6%
41	Wyoming	0	0.0%

RANK ORDER

RANK	STATE	BEDS	% of USA
1	Texas	1,669	12.1%
2	Pennsylvania	1,575	11.4%
3	Florida	1,029	7.4%
4	New Jersey	786	5.7%
5	Massachusetts	742	5.4%
6	Louisiana	621	4.5%
7	Arkansas	459	3.3%
8	Indiana	438	3.2%
9	New York	428	3.1%
10	California	411	3.0%
11	Illinois	408	3.0%
12	Tennessee	370	2.7%
13	Alabama	351	2.5%
14	Kentucky	328	2.4%
15	Michigan	315	2.3%
16	South Carolina	274	2.0%
17	Nevada	272	2.0%
18	Kansas	257	1.9%
19	West Virginia	246	1.8%
20	North Carolina	233	1.7%
21	Oklahoma	227	1.6%
22	Missouri	220	1.6%
23	Arizona	209	1.5%
24	Virginia	205	1.5%
25	Colorado	186	1.3%
26	New Mexico	156	1.1%
27	New Hampshire	152	1.1%
28	Ohio	145	1.0%
29	Georgia	116	0.8%
30	Washington	102	0.7%
31	Hawaii	100	0.7%
31	Maine	100	0.7%
33	Maryland	99	0.7%
34	Utah	84	0.6%
35	Rhode Island	82	0.6%
36	Wisconsin	81	0.6%
37	Connecticut	60	0.4%
37	Nebraska	60	0.4%
39	Idaho	59	0.4%
40	Minnesota	15	0.1%
41	Alaska	0	0.0%
41	Delaware	0	0.0%
41	Iowa	0	0.0%
41	Mississippi	0	0.0%
41	Montana	0	0.0%
41	North Dakota	0	0.0%
41	Oregon	0	0.0%
41	South Dakota	0	0.0%
41	Vermont	0	0.0%
41	Wyoming	0	0.0%
	District of Columbia	160	1.2%

Source: U.S. Department of Health and Human Services, Centers for Medicare and Medicaid Services
   OSCAR Database (January 7, 2004)
*Beds in hospitals certified by CMS to participate in the Medicare/Medicaid programs. Excludes licensed facilities that do not accept federal funding and facilities managed by the Department of Veterans Affairs. National total does not include 30 beds in U.S. territories.

Medicare and Medicaid Certified Psychiatric Hospitals in 2004

National Total = 474 Psychiatric Hospitals*

ALPHA ORDER

RANK	STATE	HOSPITALS	% of USA
22	Alabama	9	1.9%
43	Alaska	2	0.4%
27	Arizona	6	1.3%
19	Arkansas	10	2.1%
2	California	31	6.5%
27	Colorado	6	1.3%
24	Connecticut	8	1.7%
37	Delaware	3	0.6%
5	Florida	20	4.2%
12	Georgia	14	3.0%
49	Hawaii	1	0.2%
30	Idaho	5	1.1%
9	Illinois	16	3.4%
5	Indiana	20	4.2%
31	Iowa	4	0.8%
31	Kansas	4	0.8%
14	Kentucky	11	2.3%
7	Louisiana	18	3.8%
31	Maine	4	0.8%
19	Maryland	10	2.1%
8	Massachusetts	17	3.6%
22	Michigan	9	1.9%
25	Minnesota	7	1.5%
31	Mississippi	4	0.8%
13	Missouri	13	2.7%
43	Montana	2	0.4%
31	Nebraska	4	0.8%
37	Nevada	3	0.6%
43	New Hampshire	2	0.4%
9	New Jersey	16	3.4%
37	New Mexico	3	0.6%
3	New York	30	6.3%
19	North Carolina	10	2.1%
37	North Dakota	3	0.6%
11	Ohio	15	3.2%
14	Oklahoma	11	2.3%
37	Oregon	3	0.6%
4	Pennsylvania	24	5.1%
43	Rhode Island	2	0.4%
25	South Carolina	7	1.5%
49	South Dakota	1	0.2%
14	Tennessee	11	2.3%
1	Texas	33	7.0%
37	Utah	3	0.6%
43	Vermont	2	0.4%
14	Virginia	11	2.3%
27	Washington	6	1.3%
31	West Virginia	4	0.8%
14	Wisconsin	11	2.3%
43	Wyoming	2	0.4%

RANK ORDER

RANK	STATE	HOSPITALS	% of USA
1	Texas	33	7.0%
2	California	31	6.5%
3	New York	30	6.3%
4	Pennsylvania	24	5.1%
5	Florida	20	4.2%
5	Indiana	20	4.2%
7	Louisiana	18	3.8%
8	Massachusetts	17	3.6%
9	Illinois	16	3.4%
9	New Jersey	16	3.4%
11	Ohio	15	3.2%
12	Georgia	14	3.0%
13	Missouri	13	2.7%
14	Kentucky	11	2.3%
14	Oklahoma	11	2.3%
14	Tennessee	11	2.3%
14	Virginia	11	2.3%
14	Wisconsin	11	2.3%
19	Arkansas	10	2.1%
19	Maryland	10	2.1%
19	North Carolina	10	2.1%
22	Alabama	9	1.9%
22	Michigan	9	1.9%
24	Connecticut	8	1.7%
25	Minnesota	7	1.5%
25	South Carolina	7	1.5%
27	Arizona	6	1.3%
27	Colorado	6	1.3%
27	Washington	6	1.3%
30	Idaho	5	1.1%
31	Iowa	4	0.8%
31	Kansas	4	0.8%
31	Maine	4	0.8%
31	Mississippi	4	0.8%
31	Nebraska	4	0.8%
31	West Virginia	4	0.8%
37	Delaware	3	0.6%
37	Nevada	3	0.6%
37	New Mexico	3	0.6%
37	North Dakota	3	0.6%
37	Oregon	3	0.6%
37	Utah	3	0.6%
43	Alaska	2	0.4%
43	Montana	2	0.4%
43	New Hampshire	2	0.4%
43	Rhode Island	2	0.4%
43	Vermont	2	0.4%
43	Wyoming	2	0.4%
49	Hawaii	1	0.2%
49	South Dakota	1	0.2%
	District of Columbia	3	0.6%

Source: U.S. Department of Health and Human Services, Centers for Medicare and Medicaid Services
   OSCAR Database (January 7, 2004)

*Certified by CMS to participate in the Medicare/Medicaid programs. Excludes licensed facilities that do not accept federal funding and facilities managed by the Department of Veterans Affairs. National total does not include four certified psychiatric hospitals in U.S. territories.

Beds in Medicare and Medicaid Certified Psychiatric Hospitals in 2004

National Total = 56,268 Beds*

ALPHA ORDER

RANK	STATE	BEDS	% of USA
28	Alabama	625	1.1%
46	Alaska	169	0.3%
27	Arizona	768	1.4%
25	Arkansas	875	1.6%
8	California	2,208	3.9%
24	Colorado	879	1.6%
18	Connecticut	1,220	2.2%
40	Delaware	237	0.4%
6	Florida	2,459	4.4%
10	Georgia	1,600	2.8%
49	Hawaii	88	0.2%
43	Idaho	221	0.4%
9	Illinois	1,801	3.2%
17	Indiana	1,268	2.3%
36	Iowa	350	0.6%
31	Kansas	561	1.0%
16	Kentucky	1,291	2.3%
15	Louisiana	1,329	2.4%
34	Maine	369	0.7%
7	Maryland	2,282	4.1%
12	Massachusetts	1,480	2.6%
19	Michigan	1,199	2.1%
20	Minnesota	1,131	2.0%
37	Mississippi	296	0.5%
23	Missouri	946	1.7%
45	Montana	182	0.3%
30	Nebraska	567	1.0%
39	Nevada	268	0.5%
35	New Hampshire	356	0.6%
3	New Jersey	3,085	5.5%
42	New Mexico	223	0.4%
1	New York	6,607	11.7%
5	North Carolina	2,469	4.4%
41	North Dakota	229	0.4%
14	Ohio	1,418	2.5%
29	Oklahoma	576	1.0%
37	Oregon	296	0.5%
2	Pennsylvania	3,982	7.1%
47	Rhode Island	165	0.3%
26	South Carolina	802	1.4%
48	South Dakota	133	0.2%
22	Tennessee	1,036	1.8%
4	Texas	2,565	4.6%
33	Utah	391	0.7%
44	Vermont	205	0.4%
21	Virginia	1,092	1.9%
11	Washington	1,492	2.7%
32	West Virginia	485	0.9%
13	Wisconsin	1,419	2.5%
50	Wyoming	68	0.1%

RANK ORDER

RANK	STATE	BEDS	% of USA
1	New York	6,607	11.7%
2	Pennsylvania	3,982	7.1%
3	New Jersey	3,085	5.5%
4	Texas	2,565	4.6%
5	North Carolina	2,469	4.4%
6	Florida	2,459	4.4%
7	Maryland	2,282	4.1%
8	California	2,208	3.9%
9	Illinois	1,801	3.2%
10	Georgia	1,600	2.8%
11	Washington	1,492	2.7%
12	Massachusetts	1,480	2.6%
13	Wisconsin	1,419	2.5%
14	Ohio	1,418	2.5%
15	Louisiana	1,329	2.4%
16	Kentucky	1,291	2.3%
17	Indiana	1,268	2.3%
18	Connecticut	1,220	2.2%
19	Michigan	1,199	2.1%
20	Minnesota	1,131	2.0%
21	Virginia	1,092	1.9%
22	Tennessee	1,036	1.8%
23	Missouri	946	1.7%
24	Colorado	879	1.6%
25	Arkansas	875	1.6%
26	South Carolina	802	1.4%
27	Arizona	768	1.4%
28	Alabama	625	1.1%
29	Oklahoma	576	1.0%
30	Nebraska	567	1.0%
31	Kansas	561	1.0%
32	West Virginia	485	0.9%
33	Utah	391	0.7%
34	Maine	369	0.7%
35	New Hampshire	356	0.6%
36	Iowa	350	0.6%
37	Mississippi	296	0.5%
37	Oregon	296	0.5%
39	Nevada	268	0.5%
40	Delaware	237	0.4%
41	North Dakota	229	0.4%
42	New Mexico	223	0.4%
43	Idaho	221	0.4%
44	Vermont	205	0.4%
45	Montana	182	0.3%
46	Alaska	169	0.3%
47	Rhode Island	165	0.3%
48	South Dakota	133	0.2%
49	Hawaii	88	0.2%
50	Wyoming	68	0.1%
	District of Columbia	505	0.9%

Source: U.S. Department of Health and Human Services, Centers for Medicare and Medicaid Services
    OSCAR Database (January 7, 2004)
*Beds in hospitals certified by CMS to participate in the Medicare/Medicaid programs. Excludes licensed facilities
that do not accept federal funding and facilities managed by the Department of Veterans Affairs. National total
does not include 903 beds in U.S. territories.

Medicare and Medicaid Certified Community Mental Health Centers in 2004

National Total = 617 Centers*

ALPHA ORDER

RANK	STATE	CENTERS	% of USA
2	Alabama	70	11.3%
42	Alaska	0	0.0%
29	Arizona	3	0.5%
14	Arkansas	14	2.3%
8	California	20	3.2%
14	Colorado	14	2.3%
29	Connecticut	3	0.5%
42	Delaware	0	0.0%
1	Florida	103	16.7%
23	Georgia	9	1.5%
42	Hawaii	0	0.0%
42	Idaho	0	0.0%
18	Illinois	13	2.1%
22	Indiana	10	1.6%
25	Iowa	7	1.1%
12	Kansas	15	2.4%
20	Kentucky	12	1.9%
5	Louisiana	33	5.3%
42	Maine	0	0.0%
34	Maryland	2	0.3%
14	Massachusetts	14	2.3%
25	Michigan	7	1.1%
18	Minnesota	13	2.1%
27	Mississippi	5	0.8%
10	Missouri	17	2.8%
39	Montana	1	0.2%
39	Nebraska	1	0.2%
34	Nevada	2	0.3%
39	New Hampshire	1	0.2%
4	New Jersey	36	5.8%
12	New Mexico	15	2.4%
27	New York	5	0.8%
7	North Carolina	21	3.4%
42	North Dakota	0	0.0%
10	Ohio	17	2.8%
24	Oklahoma	8	1.3%
20	Oregon	12	1.9%
14	Pennsylvania	14	2.3%
42	Rhode Island	0	0.0%
34	South Carolina	2	0.3%
34	South Dakota	2	0.3%
8	Tennessee	20	3.2%
3	Texas	37	6.0%
34	Utah	2	0.3%
42	Vermont	0	0.0%
29	Virginia	3	0.5%
6	Washington	28	4.5%
29	West Virginia	3	0.5%
42	Wisconsin	0	0.0%
29	Wyoming	3	0.5%

RANK ORDER

RANK	STATE	CENTERS	% of USA
1	Florida	103	16.7%
2	Alabama	70	11.3%
3	Texas	37	6.0%
4	New Jersey	36	5.8%
5	Louisiana	33	5.3%
6	Washington	28	4.5%
7	North Carolina	21	3.4%
8	California	20	3.2%
8	Tennessee	20	3.2%
10	Missouri	17	2.8%
10	Ohio	17	2.8%
12	Kansas	15	2.4%
12	New Mexico	15	2.4%
14	Arkansas	14	2.3%
14	Colorado	14	2.3%
14	Massachusetts	14	2.3%
14	Pennsylvania	14	2.3%
18	Illinois	13	2.1%
18	Minnesota	13	2.1%
20	Kentucky	12	1.9%
20	Oregon	12	1.9%
22	Indiana	10	1.6%
23	Georgia	9	1.5%
24	Oklahoma	8	1.3%
25	Iowa	7	1.1%
25	Michigan	7	1.1%
27	Mississippi	5	0.8%
27	New York	5	0.8%
29	Arizona	3	0.5%
29	Connecticut	3	0.5%
29	Virginia	3	0.5%
29	West Virginia	3	0.5%
29	Wyoming	3	0.5%
34	Maryland	2	0.3%
34	Nevada	2	0.3%
34	South Carolina	2	0.3%
34	South Dakota	2	0.3%
34	Utah	2	0.3%
39	Montana	1	0.2%
39	Nebraska	1	0.2%
39	New Hampshire	1	0.2%
42	Alaska	0	0.0%
42	Delaware	0	0.0%
42	Hawaii	0	0.0%
42	Idaho	0	0.0%
42	Maine	0	0.0%
42	North Dakota	0	0.0%
42	Rhode Island	0	0.0%
42	Vermont	0	0.0%
42	Wisconsin	0	0.0%
	District of Columbia	0	0.0%

Source: U.S. Department of Health and Human Services, Centers for Medicare and Medicaid Services
OSCAR Report 10 (January 7, 2004)
*Certified by CMS to participate in the Medicare/Medicaid programs. Excludes licensed facilities that do not accept federal funding and facilities managed by the Department of Veterans Affairs. National total does not include nine certified mental health centers in U.S. territories.

Medicare and Medicaid Certified Outpatient Physical Therapy Facilities in 2004

National Total = 2,966 Facilities*

ALPHA ORDER

RANK ORDER

RANK	STATE	FACILITIES	% of USA		RANK	STATE	FACILITIES	% of USA
31	Alabama	24	0.8%		1	Florida	301	10.1%
35	Alaska	19	0.6%		2	Michigan	253	8.5%
27	Arizona	31	1.0%		3	Texas	212	7.1%
30	Arkansas	26	0.9%		4	California	206	6.9%
4	California	206	6.9%		5	Ohio	133	4.5%
20	Colorado	51	1.7%		6	Pennsylvania	132	4.5%
26	Connecticut	36	1.2%		7	Georgia	126	4.2%
36	Delaware	18	0.6%		8	Virginia	124	4.2%
1	Florida	301	10.1%		9	New Jersey	110	3.7%
7	Georgia	126	4.2%		10	Maryland	98	3.3%
45	Hawaii	7	0.2%		11	Tennessee	90	3.0%
40	Idaho	11	0.4%		12	Illinois	88	3.0%
12	Illinois	88	3.0%		13	Kentucky	82	2.8%
16	Indiana	57	1.9%		14	Missouri	60	2.0%
25	Iowa	42	1.4%		15	Wisconsin	58	2.0%
32	Kansas	23	0.8%		16	Indiana	57	1.9%
13	Kentucky	82	2.8%		17	South Carolina	56	1.9%
19	Louisiana	52	1.8%		18	Mississippi	53	1.8%
34	Maine	20	0.7%		19	Louisiana	52	1.8%
10	Maryland	98	3.3%		20	Colorado	51	1.7%
38	Massachusetts	12	0.4%		21	Minnesota	49	1.7%
2	Michigan	253	8.5%		21	North Carolina	49	1.7%
21	Minnesota	49	1.7%		23	Oklahoma	47	1.6%
18	Mississippi	53	1.8%		24	Washington	43	1.4%
14	Missouri	60	2.0%		25	Iowa	42	1.4%
41	Montana	9	0.3%		26	Connecticut	36	1.2%
41	Nebraska	9	0.3%		27	Arizona	31	1.0%
33	Nevada	22	0.7%		27	New Mexico	31	1.0%
38	New Hampshire	12	0.4%		29	New York	29	1.0%
9	New Jersey	110	3.7%		30	Arkansas	26	0.9%
27	New Mexico	31	1.0%		31	Alabama	24	0.8%
29	New York	29	1.0%		32	Kansas	23	0.8%
21	North Carolina	49	1.7%		33	Nevada	22	0.7%
47	North Dakota	5	0.2%		34	Maine	20	0.7%
5	Ohio	133	4.5%		35	Alaska	19	0.6%
23	Oklahoma	47	1.6%		36	Delaware	18	0.6%
36	Oregon	18	0.6%		36	Oregon	18	0.6%
6	Pennsylvania	132	4.5%		38	Massachusetts	12	0.4%
48	Rhode Island	3	0.1%		38	New Hampshire	12	0.4%
17	South Carolina	56	1.9%		40	Idaho	11	0.4%
46	South Dakota	6	0.2%		41	Montana	9	0.3%
11	Tennessee	90	3.0%		41	Nebraska	9	0.3%
3	Texas	212	7.1%		43	Utah	8	0.3%
43	Utah	8	0.3%		43	West Virginia	8	0.3%
50	Vermont	2	0.1%		45	Hawaii	7	0.2%
8	Virginia	124	4.2%		46	South Dakota	6	0.2%
24	Washington	43	1.4%		47	North Dakota	5	0.2%
43	West Virginia	8	0.3%		48	Rhode Island	3	0.1%
15	Wisconsin	58	2.0%		48	Wyoming	3	0.1%
48	Wyoming	3	0.1%		50	Vermont	2	0.1%
						District of Columbia	2	0.1%

Source: U.S. Department of Health and Human Services, Centers for Medicare and Medicaid Services
OSCAR Report 10 (January 7, 2004)

*Certified by CMS to participate in the Medicare/Medicaid programs. Excludes licensed facilities that do not accept federal funding and facilities managed by the Department of Veterans Affairs. National total does not include four certified outpatient physical therapy facilities in U.S. territories.

Medicare and Medicaid Certified Rural Health Clinics in 2004

National Total = 3,413 Rural Health Clinics*

ALPHA ORDER

RANK	STATE	CLINICS	% of USA
20	Alabama	62	1.8%
41	Alaska	6	0.2%
41	Arizona	6	0.2%
16	Arkansas	72	2.1%
3	California	243	7.1%
33	Colorado	33	1.0%
46	Connecticut	0	0.0%
46	Delaware	0	0.0%
7	Florida	150	4.4%
13	Georgia	101	3.0%
44	Hawaii	1	0.0%
29	Idaho	42	1.2%
4	Illinois	197	5.8%
24	Indiana	51	1.5%
9	Iowa	127	3.7%
5	Kansas	173	5.1%
11	Kentucky	107	3.1%
23	Louisiana	52	1.5%
27	Maine	46	1.3%
46	Maryland	0	0.0%
46	Massachusetts	0	0.0%
6	Michigan	158	4.6%
17	Minnesota	69	2.0%
8	Mississippi	131	3.8%
2	Missouri	249	7.3%
30	Montana	40	1.2%
15	Nebraska	79	2.3%
41	Nevada	6	0.2%
34	New Hampshire	19	0.6%
46	New Jersey	0	0.0%
39	New Mexico	10	0.3%
40	New York	9	0.3%
10	North Carolina	111	3.3%
18	North Dakota	64	1.9%
37	Ohio	16	0.5%
26	Oklahoma	48	1.4%
32	Oregon	36	1.1%
28	Pennsylvania	44	1.3%
44	Rhode Island	1	0.0%
14	South Carolina	93	2.7%
22	South Dakota	56	1.6%
31	Tennessee	37	1.1%
1	Texas	338	9.9%
38	Utah	14	0.4%
36	Vermont	18	0.5%
24	Virginia	51	1.5%
12	Washington	104	3.0%
19	West Virginia	63	1.8%
21	Wisconsin	61	1.8%
34	Wyoming	19	0.6%

RANK ORDER

RANK	STATE	CLINICS	% of USA
1	Texas	338	9.9%
2	Missouri	249	7.3%
3	California	243	7.1%
4	Illinois	197	5.8%
5	Kansas	173	5.1%
6	Michigan	158	4.6%
7	Florida	150	4.4%
8	Mississippi	131	3.8%
9	Iowa	127	3.7%
10	North Carolina	111	3.3%
11	Kentucky	107	3.1%
12	Washington	104	3.0%
13	Georgia	101	3.0%
14	South Carolina	93	2.7%
15	Nebraska	79	2.3%
16	Arkansas	72	2.1%
17	Minnesota	69	2.0%
18	North Dakota	64	1.9%
19	West Virginia	63	1.8%
20	Alabama	62	1.8%
21	Wisconsin	61	1.8%
22	South Dakota	56	1.6%
23	Louisiana	52	1.5%
24	Indiana	51	1.5%
24	Virginia	51	1.5%
26	Oklahoma	48	1.4%
27	Maine	46	1.3%
28	Pennsylvania	44	1.3%
29	Idaho	42	1.2%
30	Montana	40	1.2%
31	Tennessee	37	1.1%
32	Oregon	36	1.1%
33	Colorado	33	1.0%
34	New Hampshire	19	0.6%
34	Wyoming	19	0.6%
36	Vermont	18	0.5%
37	Ohio	16	0.5%
38	Utah	14	0.4%
39	New Mexico	10	0.3%
40	New York	9	0.3%
41	Alaska	6	0.2%
41	Arizona	6	0.2%
41	Nevada	6	0.2%
44	Hawaii	1	0.0%
44	Rhode Island	1	0.0%
46	Connecticut	0	0.0%
46	Delaware	0	0.0%
46	Maryland	0	0.0%
46	Massachusetts	0	0.0%
46	New Jersey	0	0.0%
	District of Columbia	0	0.0%

Source: U.S. Department of Health and Human Services, Centers for Medicare and Medicaid Services
   OSCAR Report 10 (January 7, 2004)

*Certified by CMS to participate in the Medicare/Medicaid programs. Excludes licensed facilities that do not accept federal funding and facilities managed by the Department of Veterans Affairs. There are no certified rural health centers in U.S. territories.

Medicare and Medicaid Certified Home Health Agencies in 2004

National Total = 7,188 Home Health Agencies*

ALPHA ORDER

RANK	STATE	AGENCIES	% of USA
18	Alabama	140	1.9%
47	Alaska	15	0.2%
30	Arizona	62	0.9%
13	Arkansas	174	2.4%
2	California	602	8.4%
21	Colorado	129	1.8%
26	Connecticut	84	1.2%
48	Delaware	14	0.2%
3	Florida	428	6.0%
25	Georgia	98	1.4%
48	Hawaii	14	0.2%
36	Idaho	49	0.7%
5	Illinois	298	4.1%
15	Indiana	161	2.2%
12	Iowa	180	2.5%
20	Kansas	132	1.8%
24	Kentucky	108	1.5%
7	Louisiana	228	3.2%
44	Maine	31	0.4%
40	Maryland	45	0.6%
23	Massachusetts	114	1.6%
9	Michigan	213	3.0%
8	Minnesota	223	3.1%
32	Mississippi	60	0.8%
16	Missouri	160	2.2%
39	Montana	46	0.6%
29	Nebraska	64	0.9%
40	Nevada	45	0.6%
42	New Hampshire	36	0.5%
35	New Jersey	52	0.7%
34	New Mexico	58	0.8%
10	New York	195	2.7%
14	North Carolina	169	2.4%
45	North Dakota	30	0.4%
4	Ohio	352	4.9%
11	Oklahoma	187	2.6%
33	Oregon	59	0.8%
6	Pennsylvania	282	3.9%
46	Rhode Island	21	0.3%
27	South Carolina	71	1.0%
37	South Dakota	47	0.7%
19	Tennessee	138	1.9%
1	Texas	1,061	14.8%
37	Utah	47	0.7%
50	Vermont	12	0.2%
17	Virginia	157	2.2%
31	Washington	61	0.8%
28	West Virginia	65	0.9%
22	Wisconsin	124	1.7%
43	Wyoming	32	0.4%

RANK ORDER

RANK	STATE	AGENCIES	% of USA
1	Texas	1,061	14.8%
2	California	602	8.4%
3	Florida	428	6.0%
4	Ohio	352	4.9%
5	Illinois	298	4.1%
6	Pennsylvania	282	3.9%
7	Louisiana	228	3.2%
8	Minnesota	223	3.1%
9	Michigan	213	3.0%
10	New York	195	2.7%
11	Oklahoma	187	2.6%
12	Iowa	180	2.5%
13	Arkansas	174	2.4%
14	North Carolina	169	2.4%
15	Indiana	161	2.2%
16	Missouri	160	2.2%
17	Virginia	157	2.2%
18	Alabama	140	1.9%
19	Tennessee	138	1.9%
20	Kansas	132	1.8%
21	Colorado	129	1.8%
22	Wisconsin	124	1.7%
23	Massachusetts	114	1.6%
24	Kentucky	108	1.5%
25	Georgia	98	1.4%
26	Connecticut	84	1.2%
27	South Carolina	71	1.0%
28	West Virginia	65	0.9%
29	Nebraska	64	0.9%
30	Arizona	62	0.9%
31	Washington	61	0.8%
32	Mississippi	60	0.8%
33	Oregon	59	0.8%
34	New Mexico	58	0.8%
35	New Jersey	52	0.7%
36	Idaho	49	0.7%
37	South Dakota	47	0.7%
37	Utah	47	0.7%
39	Montana	46	0.6%
40	Maryland	45	0.6%
40	Nevada	45	0.6%
42	New Hampshire	36	0.5%
43	Wyoming	32	0.4%
44	Maine	31	0.4%
45	North Dakota	30	0.4%
46	Rhode Island	21	0.3%
47	Alaska	15	0.2%
48	Delaware	14	0.2%
48	Hawaii	14	0.2%
50	Vermont	12	0.2%
	District of Columbia	15	0.2%

Source: U.S. Department of Health and Human Services, Centers for Medicare and Medicaid Services
   OSCAR Report 10 (January 7, 2004)

*Certified by CMS to participate in the Medicare/Medicaid programs. Excludes agencies that do not accept federal funding. National total does not include 51 certified home health agencies in U.S. territories. A home health agency provides health services to individuals in their homes for the purpose of promoting, maintaining or restoring health or maximizing the level of independence, while minimizing the effects of disability and illness.

Medicare and Medicaid Certified Hospices in 2004

National Total = 2,404 Hospices*

ALPHA ORDER

RANK	STATE	HOSPICES	% of USA
5	Alabama	94	3.9%
50	Alaska	3	0.1%
29	Arizona	36	1.5%
20	Arkansas	47	2.0%
1	California	167	6.9%
28	Colorado	39	1.6%
35	Connecticut	26	1.1%
48	Delaware	6	0.2%
22	Florida	44	1.8%
8	Georgia	89	3.7%
47	Hawaii	7	0.3%
35	Idaho	26	1.1%
7	Illinois	90	3.7%
12	Indiana	69	2.9%
13	Iowa	62	2.6%
25	Kansas	41	1.7%
35	Kentucky	26	1.1%
16	Louisiana	56	2.3%
41	Maine	17	0.7%
33	Maryland	28	1.2%
25	Massachusetts	41	1.7%
9	Michigan	85	3.5%
15	Minnesota	60	2.5%
14	Mississippi	61	2.5%
11	Missouri	70	2.9%
38	Montana	23	1.0%
32	Nebraska	30	1.2%
45	Nevada	10	0.4%
39	New Hampshire	19	0.8%
23	New Jersey	43	1.8%
30	New Mexico	32	1.3%
19	New York	51	2.1%
10	North Carolina	77	3.2%
43	North Dakota	15	0.6%
6	Ohio	91	3.8%
4	Oklahoma	95	4.0%
23	Oregon	43	1.8%
3	Pennsylvania	114	4.7%
48	Rhode Island	6	0.2%
27	South Carolina	40	1.7%
43	South Dakota	15	0.6%
21	Tennessee	45	1.9%
2	Texas	152	6.3%
33	Utah	28	1.2%
46	Vermont	9	0.4%
17	Virginia	54	2.2%
31	Washington	31	1.3%
39	West Virginia	19	0.8%
18	Wisconsin	52	2.2%
41	Wyoming	17	0.7%

RANK ORDER

RANK	STATE	HOSPICES	% of USA
1	California	167	6.9%
2	Texas	152	6.3%
3	Pennsylvania	114	4.7%
4	Oklahoma	95	4.0%
5	Alabama	94	3.9%
6	Ohio	91	3.8%
7	Illinois	90	3.7%
8	Georgia	89	3.7%
9	Michigan	85	3.5%
10	North Carolina	77	3.2%
11	Missouri	70	2.9%
12	Indiana	69	2.9%
13	Iowa	62	2.6%
14	Mississippi	61	2.5%
15	Minnesota	60	2.5%
16	Louisiana	56	2.3%
17	Virginia	54	2.2%
18	Wisconsin	52	2.2%
19	New York	51	2.1%
20	Arkansas	47	2.0%
21	Tennessee	45	1.9%
22	Florida	44	1.8%
23	New Jersey	43	1.8%
23	Oregon	43	1.8%
25	Kansas	41	1.7%
25	Massachusetts	41	1.7%
27	South Carolina	40	1.7%
28	Colorado	39	1.6%
29	Arizona	36	1.5%
30	New Mexico	32	1.3%
31	Washington	31	1.3%
32	Nebraska	30	1.2%
33	Maryland	28	1.2%
33	Utah	28	1.2%
35	Connecticut	26	1.1%
35	Idaho	26	1.1%
35	Kentucky	26	1.1%
38	Montana	23	1.0%
39	New Hampshire	19	0.8%
39	West Virginia	19	0.8%
41	Maine	17	0.7%
41	Wyoming	17	0.7%
43	North Dakota	15	0.6%
43	South Dakota	15	0.6%
45	Nevada	10	0.4%
46	Vermont	9	0.4%
47	Hawaii	7	0.3%
48	Delaware	6	0.2%
48	Rhode Island	6	0.2%
50	Alaska	3	0.1%
	District of Columbia	3	0.1%

Source: U.S. Department of Health and Human Services, Centers for Medicare and Medicaid Services
    OSCAR Report 10 (January 7, 2004)

Certified by CMS to participate in the Medicare/Medicaid programs. Excludes licensed facilities that do not accept federal funding and facilities managed by the Department of Veterans Affairs. National total does not include 35 certified hospices in U.S. territories. An hospice provides specialized services for terminally ill people and their families.

Hospice Patients in Residential Facilities in 2004

National Total = 37,705 Patients*

ALPHA ORDER

RANK	STATE	PATIENTS	% of USA
20	Alabama	452	1.2%
50	Alaska	0	0.0%
21	Arizona	439	1.2%
33	Arkansas	166	0.4%
5	California	1,716	4.6%
18	Colorado	609	1.6%
34	Connecticut	162	0.4%
47	Delaware	8	0.0%
2	Florida	5,574	14.8%
8	Georgia	1,086	2.9%
38	Hawaii	51	0.1%
44	Idaho	34	0.1%
12	Illinois	919	2.4%
10	Indiana	1,024	2.7%
19	Iowa	586	1.6%
24	Kansas	395	1.0%
11	Kentucky	981	2.6%
26	Louisiana	345	0.9%
39	Maine	48	0.1%
32	Maryland	170	0.5%
22	Massachusetts	418	1.1%
7	Michigan	1,463	3.9%
17	Minnesota	622	1.6%
31	Mississippi	175	0.5%
9	Missouri	1,065	2.8%
40	Montana	43	0.1%
13	Nebraska	789	2.1%
36	Nevada	79	0.2%
40	New Hampshire	43	0.1%
25	New Jersey	346	0.9%
35	New Mexico	91	0.2%
15	New York	755	2.0%
14	North Carolina	759	2.0%
37	North Dakota	60	0.2%
4	Ohio	2,774	7.4%
6	Oklahoma	1,588	4.2%
16	Oregon	751	2.0%
1	Pennsylvania	5,593	14.8%
49	Rhode Island	1	0.0%
28	South Carolina	318	0.8%
46	South Dakota	17	0.0%
30	Tennessee	237	0.6%
3	Texas	3,757	10.0%
29	Utah	294	0.8%
44	Vermont	34	0.1%
43	Virginia	36	0.1%
27	Washington	330	0.9%
40	West Virginia	43	0.1%
23	Wisconsin	409	1.1%
48	Wyoming	4	0.0%

RANK ORDER

RANK	STATE	PATIENTS	% of USA
1	Pennsylvania	5,593	14.8%
2	Florida	5,574	14.8%
3	Texas	3,757	10.0%
4	Ohio	2,774	7.4%
5	California	1,716	4.6%
6	Oklahoma	1,588	4.2%
7	Michigan	1,463	3.9%
8	Georgia	1,086	2.9%
9	Missouri	1,065	2.8%
10	Indiana	1,024	2.7%
11	Kentucky	981	2.6%
12	Illinois	919	2.4%
13	Nebraska	789	2.1%
14	North Carolina	759	2.0%
15	New York	755	2.0%
16	Oregon	751	2.0%
17	Minnesota	622	1.6%
18	Colorado	609	1.6%
19	Iowa	586	1.6%
20	Alabama	452	1.2%
21	Arizona	439	1.2%
22	Massachusetts	418	1.1%
23	Wisconsin	409	1.1%
24	Kansas	395	1.0%
25	New Jersey	346	0.9%
26	Louisiana	345	0.9%
27	Washington	330	0.9%
28	South Carolina	318	0.8%
29	Utah	294	0.8%
30	Tennessee	237	0.6%
31	Mississippi	175	0.5%
32	Maryland	170	0.5%
33	Arkansas	166	0.4%
34	Connecticut	162	0.4%
35	New Mexico	91	0.2%
36	Nevada	79	0.2%
37	North Dakota	60	0.2%
38	Hawaii	51	0.1%
39	Maine	48	0.1%
40	Montana	43	0.1%
40	New Hampshire	43	0.1%
40	West Virginia	43	0.1%
43	Virginia	36	0.1%
44	Idaho	34	0.1%
44	Vermont	34	0.1%
46	South Dakota	17	0.0%
47	Delaware	8	0.0%
48	Wyoming	4	0.0%
49	Rhode Island	1	0.0%
50	Alaska	0	0.0%
	District of Columbia	46	0.1%

Source: U.S. Department of Health and Human Services, Centers for Medicare and Medicaid Services OSCAR Database (January 7, 2004)

*Patients in facilities certified by CMS to participate in the Medicare/Medicaid programs. Excludes licensed facilities that do not accept federal funding and facilities managed by the Department of Veterans Affairs. National total does not include 27 patients in U.S. territories. An hospice provides specialized services for terminally ill people and their families.

Medicare and Medicaid Certified Nursing Care Facilities in 2004

National Total = 16,314 Nursing Care Facilities*

<table>
<tr><td colspan="4">ALPHA ORDER</td><td colspan="4">RANK ORDER</td></tr>
<tr><td>RANK</td><td>STATE</td><td>FACILITIES</td><td>% of USA</td><td>RANK</td><td>STATE</td><td>FACILITIES</td><td>% of USA</td></tr>
<tr><td>28</td><td>Alabama</td><td>228</td><td>1.4%</td><td>1</td><td>California</td><td>1,340</td><td>8.2%</td></tr>
<tr><td>50</td><td>Alaska</td><td>14</td><td>0.1%</td><td>2</td><td>Texas</td><td>1,145</td><td>7.0%</td></tr>
<tr><td>35</td><td>Arizona</td><td>135</td><td>0.8%</td><td>3</td><td>Ohio</td><td>991</td><td>6.1%</td></tr>
<tr><td>27</td><td>Arkansas</td><td>242</td><td>1.5%</td><td>4</td><td>Illinois</td><td>829</td><td>5.1%</td></tr>
<tr><td>1</td><td>California</td><td>1,340</td><td>8.2%</td><td>5</td><td>Pennsylvania</td><td>738</td><td>4.5%</td></tr>
<tr><td>30</td><td>Colorado</td><td>216</td><td>1.3%</td><td>6</td><td>Florida</td><td>692</td><td>4.2%</td></tr>
<tr><td>25</td><td>Connecticut</td><td>251</td><td>1.5%</td><td>7</td><td>New York</td><td>670</td><td>4.1%</td></tr>
<tr><td>48</td><td>Delaware</td><td>42</td><td>0.3%</td><td>8</td><td>Missouri</td><td>536</td><td>3.3%</td></tr>
<tr><td>6</td><td>Florida</td><td>692</td><td>4.2%</td><td>9</td><td>Indiana</td><td>520</td><td>3.2%</td></tr>
<tr><td>18</td><td>Georgia</td><td>362</td><td>2.2%</td><td>10</td><td>Massachusetts</td><td>481</td><td>2.9%</td></tr>
<tr><td>45</td><td>Hawaii</td><td>45</td><td>0.3%</td><td>11</td><td>Iowa</td><td>455</td><td>2.8%</td></tr>
<tr><td>43</td><td>Idaho</td><td>80</td><td>0.5%</td><td>12</td><td>Michigan</td><td>431</td><td>2.6%</td></tr>
<tr><td>4</td><td>Illinois</td><td>829</td><td>5.1%</td><td>13</td><td>Minnesota</td><td>422</td><td>2.6%</td></tr>
<tr><td>9</td><td>Indiana</td><td>520</td><td>3.2%</td><td>14</td><td>North Carolina</td><td>421</td><td>2.6%</td></tr>
<tr><td>11</td><td>Iowa</td><td>455</td><td>2.8%</td><td>15</td><td>Wisconsin</td><td>407</td><td>2.5%</td></tr>
<tr><td>16</td><td>Kansas</td><td>375</td><td>2.3%</td><td>16</td><td>Kansas</td><td>375</td><td>2.3%</td></tr>
<tr><td>22</td><td>Kentucky</td><td>295</td><td>1.8%</td><td>17</td><td>Oklahoma</td><td>369</td><td>2.3%</td></tr>
<tr><td>21</td><td>Louisiana</td><td>314</td><td>1.9%</td><td>18</td><td>Georgia</td><td>362</td><td>2.2%</td></tr>
<tr><td>36</td><td>Maine</td><td>120</td><td>0.7%</td><td>19</td><td>New Jersey</td><td>356</td><td>2.2%</td></tr>
<tr><td>26</td><td>Maryland</td><td>244</td><td>1.5%</td><td>20</td><td>Tennessee</td><td>337</td><td>2.1%</td></tr>
<tr><td>10</td><td>Massachusetts</td><td>481</td><td>2.9%</td><td>21</td><td>Louisiana</td><td>314</td><td>1.9%</td></tr>
<tr><td>12</td><td>Michigan</td><td>431</td><td>2.6%</td><td>22</td><td>Kentucky</td><td>295</td><td>1.8%</td></tr>
<tr><td>13</td><td>Minnesota</td><td>422</td><td>2.6%</td><td>23</td><td>Virginia</td><td>278</td><td>1.7%</td></tr>
<tr><td>31</td><td>Mississippi</td><td>204</td><td>1.3%</td><td>24</td><td>Washington</td><td>258</td><td>1.6%</td></tr>
<tr><td>8</td><td>Missouri</td><td>536</td><td>3.3%</td><td>25</td><td>Connecticut</td><td>251</td><td>1.5%</td></tr>
<tr><td>38</td><td>Montana</td><td>101</td><td>0.6%</td><td>26</td><td>Maryland</td><td>244</td><td>1.5%</td></tr>
<tr><td>28</td><td>Nebraska</td><td>228</td><td>1.4%</td><td>27</td><td>Arkansas</td><td>242</td><td>1.5%</td></tr>
<tr><td>46</td><td>Nevada</td><td>44</td><td>0.3%</td><td>28</td><td>Alabama</td><td>228</td><td>1.4%</td></tr>
<tr><td>43</td><td>New Hampshire</td><td>80</td><td>0.5%</td><td>28</td><td>Nebraska</td><td>228</td><td>1.4%</td></tr>
<tr><td>19</td><td>New Jersey</td><td>356</td><td>2.2%</td><td>30</td><td>Colorado</td><td>216</td><td>1.3%</td></tr>
<tr><td>42</td><td>New Mexico</td><td>81</td><td>0.5%</td><td>31</td><td>Mississippi</td><td>204</td><td>1.3%</td></tr>
<tr><td>7</td><td>New York</td><td>670</td><td>4.1%</td><td>32</td><td>South Carolina</td><td>178</td><td>1.1%</td></tr>
<tr><td>14</td><td>North Carolina</td><td>421</td><td>2.6%</td><td>33</td><td>Oregon</td><td>140</td><td>0.9%</td></tr>
<tr><td>41</td><td>North Dakota</td><td>83</td><td>0.5%</td><td>34</td><td>West Virginia</td><td>136</td><td>0.8%</td></tr>
<tr><td>3</td><td>Ohio</td><td>991</td><td>6.1%</td><td>35</td><td>Arizona</td><td>135</td><td>0.8%</td></tr>
<tr><td>17</td><td>Oklahoma</td><td>369</td><td>2.3%</td><td>36</td><td>Maine</td><td>120</td><td>0.7%</td></tr>
<tr><td>33</td><td>Oregon</td><td>140</td><td>0.9%</td><td>37</td><td>South Dakota</td><td>113</td><td>0.7%</td></tr>
<tr><td>5</td><td>Pennsylvania</td><td>738</td><td>4.5%</td><td>38</td><td>Montana</td><td>101</td><td>0.6%</td></tr>
<tr><td>39</td><td>Rhode Island</td><td>95</td><td>0.6%</td><td>39</td><td>Rhode Island</td><td>95</td><td>0.6%</td></tr>
<tr><td>32</td><td>South Carolina</td><td>178</td><td>1.1%</td><td>40</td><td>Utah</td><td>89</td><td>0.5%</td></tr>
<tr><td>37</td><td>South Dakota</td><td>113</td><td>0.7%</td><td>41</td><td>North Dakota</td><td>83</td><td>0.5%</td></tr>
<tr><td>20</td><td>Tennessee</td><td>337</td><td>2.1%</td><td>42</td><td>New Mexico</td><td>81</td><td>0.5%</td></tr>
<tr><td>2</td><td>Texas</td><td>1,145</td><td>7.0%</td><td>43</td><td>Idaho</td><td>80</td><td>0.5%</td></tr>
<tr><td>40</td><td>Utah</td><td>89</td><td>0.5%</td><td>43</td><td>New Hampshire</td><td>80</td><td>0.5%</td></tr>
<tr><td>47</td><td>Vermont</td><td>43</td><td>0.3%</td><td>45</td><td>Hawaii</td><td>45</td><td>0.3%</td></tr>
<tr><td>23</td><td>Virginia</td><td>278</td><td>1.7%</td><td>46</td><td>Nevada</td><td>44</td><td>0.3%</td></tr>
<tr><td>24</td><td>Washington</td><td>258</td><td>1.6%</td><td>47</td><td>Vermont</td><td>43</td><td>0.3%</td></tr>
<tr><td>34</td><td>West Virginia</td><td>136</td><td>0.8%</td><td>48</td><td>Delaware</td><td>42</td><td>0.3%</td></tr>
<tr><td>15</td><td>Wisconsin</td><td>407</td><td>2.5%</td><td>49</td><td>Wyoming</td><td>39</td><td>0.2%</td></tr>
<tr><td>49</td><td>Wyoming</td><td>39</td><td>0.2%</td><td>50</td><td>Alaska</td><td>14</td><td>0.1%</td></tr>
<tr><td></td><td></td><td></td><td></td><td></td><td>District of Columbia</td><td>21</td><td>0.1%</td></tr>
</table>

Source: U.S. Department of Health and Human Services, Centers for Medicare and Medicaid Services
OSCAR Database (January 7, 2004)

*Certified by CMS to participate in the Medicare/Medicaid programs. Excludes licensed facilities that do not accept federal funding and facilities managed by the Department of Veterans Affairs. National total does not include eight certified nursing facilities in U.S. territories.

Beds in Medicare and Medicaid Certified Nursing Care Facilities in 2004

National Total = 1,694,926 Beds*

ALPHA ORDER

RANK ORDER

RANK	STATE	BEDS	% of USA		RANK	STATE	BEDS	% of USA
24	Alabama	26,326	1.6%		1	California	125,456	7.4%
50	Alaska	738	0.0%		2	New York	121,878	7.2%
32	Arizona	16,046	0.9%		3	Texas	113,288	6.7%
27	Arkansas	24,505	1.4%		4	Illinois	99,598	5.9%
1	California	125,456	7.4%		5	Ohio	93,102	5.5%
29	Colorado	20,021	1.2%		6	Pennsylvania	90,504	5.3%
22	Connecticut	30,624	1.8%		7	Florida	81,652	4.8%
46	Delaware	4,394	0.3%		8	Massachusetts	51,836	3.1%
7	Florida	81,652	4.8%		9	New Jersey	50,520	3.0%
15	Georgia	40,037	2.4%		10	Missouri	50,131	3.0%
47	Hawaii	4,004	0.2%		11	Indiana	48,460	2.9%
44	Idaho	6,277	0.4%		12	Michigan	47,492	2.8%
4	Illinois	99,598	5.9%		13	North Carolina	42,558	2.5%
11	Indiana	48,460	2.9%		14	Wisconsin	41,914	2.5%
19	Iowa	33,537	2.0%		15	Georgia	40,037	2.4%
26	Kansas	24,665	1.5%		16	Minnesota	38,735	2.3%
25	Kentucky	25,286	1.5%		17	Louisiana	37,644	2.2%
17	Louisiana	37,644	2.2%		18	Tennessee	37,569	2.2%
38	Maine	7,505	0.4%		19	Iowa	33,537	2.0%
23	Maryland	29,386	1.7%		20	Oklahoma	32,238	1.9%
8	Massachusetts	51,836	3.1%		21	Virginia	30,765	1.8%
12	Michigan	47,492	2.8%		22	Connecticut	30,624	1.8%
16	Minnesota	38,735	2.3%		23	Maryland	29,386	1.7%
30	Mississippi	18,171	1.1%		24	Alabama	26,326	1.6%
10	Missouri	50,131	3.0%		25	Kentucky	25,286	1.5%
39	Montana	7,452	0.4%		26	Kansas	24,665	1.5%
33	Nebraska	15,673	0.9%		27	Arkansas	24,505	1.4%
45	Nevada	5,139	0.3%		28	Washington	22,990	1.4%
37	New Hampshire	7,691	0.5%		29	Colorado	20,021	1.2%
9	New Jersey	50,520	3.0%		30	Mississippi	18,171	1.1%
40	New Mexico	7,365	0.4%		31	South Carolina	17,687	1.0%
2	New York	121,878	7.2%		32	Arizona	16,046	0.9%
13	North Carolina	42,558	2.5%		33	Nebraska	15,673	0.9%
43	North Dakota	6,522	0.4%		34	Oregon	12,642	0.7%
5	Ohio	93,102	5.5%		35	West Virginia	11,027	0.7%
20	Oklahoma	32,238	1.9%		36	Rhode Island	9,523	0.6%
34	Oregon	12,642	0.7%		37	New Hampshire	7,691	0.5%
6	Pennsylvania	90,504	5.3%		38	Maine	7,505	0.4%
36	Rhode Island	9,523	0.6%		39	Montana	7,452	0.4%
31	South Carolina	17,687	1.0%		40	New Mexico	7,365	0.4%
41	South Dakota	7,364	0.4%		41	South Dakota	7,364	0.4%
18	Tennessee	37,569	2.2%		42	Utah	7,260	0.4%
3	Texas	113,288	6.7%		43	North Dakota	6,522	0.4%
42	Utah	7,260	0.4%		44	Idaho	6,277	0.4%
48	Vermont	3,554	0.2%		45	Nevada	5,139	0.3%
21	Virginia	30,765	1.8%		46	Delaware	4,394	0.3%
28	Washington	22,990	1.4%		47	Hawaii	4,004	0.2%
35	West Virginia	11,027	0.7%		48	Vermont	3,554	0.2%
14	Wisconsin	41,914	2.5%		49	Wyoming	3,061	0.2%
49	Wyoming	3,061	0.2%		50	Alaska	738	0.0%
						District of Columbia	3,114	0.2%

Source: U.S. Department of Health and Human Services, Centers for Medicare and Medicaid Services
OSCAR Database (January 7, 2004)
*Beds in nursing care facilities certified by CMS to participate in the Medicare/Medicaid programs. National total does not include 335 beds in U.S. territories.

Rate of Beds in Medicare and Medicaid Certified Nursing Care Facilities in 2004

National Rate = 369 Beds per 1,000 Population 85 Years and Older*

ALPHA ORDER

RANK	STATE	RATE
29	Alabama	369
46	Alaska	240
48	Arizona	207
3	Arkansas	501
43	California	266
27	Colorado	377
13	Connecticut	437
28	Delaware	372
47	Florida	227
19	Georgia	419
50	Hawaii	197
38	Idaho	319
8	Illinois	481
4	Indiana	493
5	Iowa	489
9	Kansas	458
22	Kentucky	413
1	Louisiana	613
41	Maine	300
25	Maryland	400
21	Massachusetts	414
39	Michigan	305
16	Minnesota	423
23	Mississippi	408
7	Missouri	487
10	Montana	450
12	Nebraska	441
44	Nevada	251
26	New Hampshire	385
33	New Jersey	339
42	New Mexico	285
31	New York	362
30	North Carolina	368
18	North Dakota	420
6	Ohio	488
2	Oklahoma	553
49	Oregon	200
32	Pennsylvania	350
19	Rhode Island	419
37	South Carolina	320
14	South Dakota	433
14	Tennessee	433
11	Texas	443
40	Utah	302
35	Vermont	330
36	Virginia	321
45	Washington	247
34	West Virginia	331
24	Wisconsin	406
17	Wyoming	421

RANK ORDER

RANK	STATE	RATE
1	Louisiana	613
2	Oklahoma	553
3	Arkansas	501
4	Indiana	493
5	Iowa	489
6	Ohio	488
7	Missouri	487
8	Illinois	481
9	Kansas	458
10	Montana	450
11	Texas	443
12	Nebraska	441
13	Connecticut	437
14	South Dakota	433
14	Tennessee	433
16	Minnesota	423
17	Wyoming	421
18	North Dakota	420
19	Georgia	419
19	Rhode Island	419
21	Massachusetts	414
22	Kentucky	413
23	Mississippi	408
24	Wisconsin	406
25	Maryland	400
26	New Hampshire	385
27	Colorado	377
28	Delaware	372
29	Alabama	369
30	North Carolina	368
31	New York	362
32	Pennsylvania	350
33	New Jersey	339
34	West Virginia	331
35	Vermont	330
36	Virginia	321
37	South Carolina	320
38	Idaho	319
39	Michigan	305
40	Utah	302
41	Maine	300
42	New Mexico	285
43	California	266
44	Nevada	251
45	Washington	247
46	Alaska	240
47	Florida	227
48	Arizona	207
49	Oregon	200
50	Hawaii	197
	District of Columbia	330

Source: MQ Press using data from U.S. Dept of Health & Human Services, Centers for Medicare and Medicaid Services
OSCAR Database (January 7, 2004)
*Beds in nursing care facilities certified by CMS to participate in the Medicare/Medicaid programs. National rate
does not include beds or population in U.S. territories. Calculated using 2002 Census population estimate.

Nursing Home Occupancy Rate in 2001

National Rate = 82.5% of Beds in Nursing Homes Occupied

ALPHA ORDER

RANK	STATE	RATE
8	Alabama	91.2
47	Alaska	72.3
35	Arizona	79.9
42	Arkansas	74.5
33	California	81.5
25	Colorado	83.8
4	Connecticut	91.9
27	Delaware	83.4
29	Florida	83.3
7	Georgia	91.3
6	Hawaii	91.4
46	Idaho	72.5
41	Illinois	75.5
43	Indiana	73.8
38	Iowa	78.0
34	Kansas	80.4
15	Kentucky	89.4
40	Louisiana	77.5
13	Maine	89.8
30	Maryland	83.1
14	Massachusetts	89.7
25	Michigan	83.8
2	Minnesota	93.2
12	Mississippi	89.9
48	Missouri	70.5
37	Montana	78.1
27	Nebraska	83.4
36	Nevada	79.6
11	New Hampshire	90.4
22	New Jersey	87.1
19	New Mexico	87.6
1	New York	93.9
18	North Carolina	87.9
3	North Dakota	92.9
39	Ohio	77.8
50	Oklahoma	69.1
44	Oregon	72.8
21	Pennsylvania	87.5
19	Rhode Island	87.6
17	South Carolina	88.6
4	South Dakota	91.9
16	Tennessee	88.9
49	Texas	69.3
44	Utah	72.8
9	Vermont	90.6
23	Virginia	86.4
31	Washington	82.7
9	West Virginia	90.6
24	Wisconsin	84.2
32	Wyoming	82.2

RANK ORDER

RANK	STATE	RATE
1	New York	93.9
2	Minnesota	93.2
3	North Dakota	92.9
4	Connecticut	91.9
4	South Dakota	91.9
6	Hawaii	91.4
7	Georgia	91.3
8	Alabama	91.2
9	Vermont	90.6
9	West Virginia	90.6
11	New Hampshire	90.4
12	Mississippi	89.9
13	Maine	89.8
14	Massachusetts	89.7
15	Kentucky	89.4
16	Tennessee	88.9
17	South Carolina	88.6
18	North Carolina	87.9
19	New Mexico	87.6
19	Rhode Island	87.6
21	Pennsylvania	87.5
22	New Jersey	87.1
23	Virginia	86.4
24	Wisconsin	84.2
25	Colorado	83.8
25	Michigan	83.8
27	Delaware	83.4
27	Nebraska	83.4
29	Florida	83.3
30	Maryland	83.1
31	Washington	82.7
32	Wyoming	82.2
33	California	81.5
34	Kansas	80.4
35	Arizona	79.9
36	Nevada	79.6
37	Montana	78.1
38	Iowa	78.0
39	Ohio	77.8
40	Louisiana	77.5
41	Illinois	75.5
42	Arkansas	74.5
43	Indiana	73.8
44	Oregon	72.8
44	Utah	72.8
46	Idaho	72.5
47	Alaska	72.3
48	Missouri	70.5
49	Texas	69.3
50	Oklahoma	69.1
	District of Columbia	91.3

Source: U.S. Department of Health and Human Services, Centers for Medicare and Medicaid Services
"Health, United States, 2003"

Nursing Home Resident Rate in 2000

National Rate = 349.1 Residents per 1,000 Population Age 85 and Older*

ALPHA ORDER

RANK	STATE	RATE
32	Alabama	343.1
45	Alaska	225.9
49	Arizona	193.4
17	Arkansas	415.5
44	California	250.1
29	Colorado	353.5
4	Connecticut	461.4
25	Delaware	369.7
47	Florida	208.4
16	Georgia	416.1
48	Hawaii	202.6
42	Idaho	257.0
9	Illinois	435.4
3	Indiana	462.3
6	Iowa	448.5
12	Kansas	429.4
21	Kentucky	390.1
1	Louisiana	523.8
37	Maine	313.0
24	Maryland	383.1
13	Massachusetts	426.8
39	Michigan	299.1
5	Minnesota	453.4
26	Mississippi	368.7
20	Missouri	391.5
22	Montana	389.5
7	Nebraska	441.5
46	Nevada	215.3
19	New Hampshire	392.6
33	New Jersey	337.0
40	New Mexico	279.0
27	New York	362.6
31	North Carolina	347.6
11	North Dakota	430.7
2	Ohio	463.5
15	Oklahoma	416.8
50	Oregon	173.9
30	Pennsylvania	353.1
10	Rhode Island	432.6
36	South Carolina	313.1
8	South Dakota	438.8
14	Tennessee	426.1
28	Texas	358.4
41	Utah	262.2
34	Vermont	335.0
38	Virginia	310.4
43	Washington	251.6
35	West Virginia	325.2
18	Wisconsin	406.9
23	Wyoming	386.8

RANK ORDER

RANK	STATE	RATE
1	Louisiana	523.8
2	Ohio	463.5
3	Indiana	462.3
4	Connecticut	461.4
5	Minnesota	453.4
6	Iowa	448.5
7	Nebraska	441.5
8	South Dakota	438.8
9	Illinois	435.4
10	Rhode Island	432.6
11	North Dakota	430.7
12	Kansas	429.4
13	Massachusetts	426.8
14	Tennessee	426.1
15	Oklahoma	416.8
16	Georgia	416.1
17	Arkansas	415.5
18	Wisconsin	406.9
19	New Hampshire	392.6
20	Missouri	391.5
21	Kentucky	390.1
22	Montana	389.5
23	Wyoming	386.8
24	Maryland	383.1
25	Delaware	369.7
26	Mississippi	368.7
27	New York	362.6
28	Texas	358.4
29	Colorado	353.5
30	Pennsylvania	353.1
31	North Carolina	347.6
32	Alabama	343.1
33	New Jersey	337.0
34	Vermont	335.0
35	West Virginia	325.2
36	South Carolina	313.1
37	Maine	313.0
38	Virginia	310.4
39	Michigan	299.1
40	New Mexico	279.0
41	Utah	262.2
42	Idaho	257.0
43	Washington	251.6
44	California	250.1
45	Alaska	225.9
46	Nevada	215.3
47	Florida	208.4
48	Hawaii	202.6
49	Arizona	193.4
50	Oregon	173.9
	District of Columbia	318.4

Source: U.S. Department of Health and Human Services, Centers for Medicare and Medicaid Services "Health, United States, 2002"

Number of nursing home residents (all ages) per 1,000 resident population 85 years of age and over.

Nursing Home Population in 2001

National Total = 1,469,001

ALPHA ORDER

RANK	STATE	POPULATION	% of USA
23	Alabama	23,538	1.6%
50	Alaska	638	0.0%
33	Arizona	13,455	0.9%
28	Arkansas	18,677	1.3%
2	California	105,923	7.2%
29	Colorado	16,855	1.1%
19	Connecticut	29,166	2.0%
46	Delaware	3,950	0.3%
7	Florida	70,029	4.8%
16	Georgia	36,356	2.5%
47	Hawaii	3,694	0.3%
44	Idaho	4,619	0.3%
5	Illinois	81,749	5.6%
10	Indiana	41,946	2.9%
20	Iowa	28,825	2.0%
26	Kansas	21,498	1.5%
24	Kentucky	22,776	1.6%
18	Louisiana	30,127	2.1%
37	Maine	7,189	0.5%
22	Maryland	25,361	1.7%
8	Massachusetts	48,876	3.3%
11	Michigan	41,508	2.8%
14	Minnesota	38,052	2.6%
31	Mississippi	15,696	1.1%
12	Missouri	38,706	2.6%
42	Montana	5,928	0.4%
32	Nebraska	14,492	1.0%
45	Nevada	4,036	0.3%
38	New Hampshire	7,126	0.5%
9	New Jersey	45,672	3.1%
40	New Mexico	6,364	0.4%
1	New York	114,141	7.8%
15	North Carolina	37,106	2.5%
41	North Dakota	6,279	0.4%
6	Ohio	80,930	5.5%
25	Oklahoma	22,640	1.5%
35	Oregon	9,444	0.6%
4	Pennsylvania	82,971	5.6%
36	Rhode Island	8,923	0.6%
30	South Carolina	16,117	1.1%
39	South Dakota	6,952	0.5%
17	Tennessee	34,588	2.4%
3	Texas	85,517	5.8%
43	Utah	5,592	0.4%
48	Vermont	3,293	0.2%
21	Virginia	26,875	1.8%
27	Washington	20,663	1.4%
34	West Virginia	10,304	0.7%
13	Wisconsin	38,430	2.6%
49	Wyoming	2,546	0.2%

RANK ORDER

RANK	STATE	POPULATION	% of USA
1	New York	114,141	7.8%
2	California	105,923	7.2%
3	Texas	85,517	5.8%
4	Pennsylvania	82,971	5.6%
5	Illinois	81,749	5.6%
6	Ohio	80,930	5.5%
7	Florida	70,029	4.8%
8	Massachusetts	48,876	3.3%
9	New Jersey	45,672	3.1%
10	Indiana	41,946	2.9%
11	Michigan	41,508	2.8%
12	Missouri	38,706	2.6%
13	Wisconsin	38,430	2.6%
14	Minnesota	38,052	2.6%
15	North Carolina	37,106	2.5%
16	Georgia	36,356	2.5%
17	Tennessee	34,588	2.4%
18	Louisiana	30,127	2.1%
19	Connecticut	29,166	2.0%
20	Iowa	28,825	2.0%
21	Virginia	26,875	1.8%
22	Maryland	25,361	1.7%
23	Alabama	23,538	1.6%
24	Kentucky	22,776	1.6%
25	Oklahoma	22,640	1.5%
26	Kansas	21,498	1.5%
27	Washington	20,663	1.4%
28	Arkansas	18,677	1.3%
29	Colorado	16,855	1.1%
30	South Carolina	16,117	1.1%
31	Mississippi	15,696	1.1%
32	Nebraska	14,492	1.0%
33	Arizona	13,455	0.9%
34	West Virginia	10,304	0.7%
35	Oregon	9,444	0.6%
36	Rhode Island	8,923	0.6%
37	Maine	7,189	0.5%
38	New Hampshire	7,126	0.5%
39	South Dakota	6,952	0.5%
40	New Mexico	6,364	0.4%
41	North Dakota	6,279	0.4%
42	Montana	5,928	0.4%
43	Utah	5,592	0.4%
44	Idaho	4,619	0.3%
45	Nevada	4,036	0.3%
46	Delaware	3,950	0.3%
47	Hawaii	3,694	0.3%
48	Vermont	3,293	0.2%
49	Wyoming	2,546	0.2%
50	Alaska	638	0.0%
	District of Columbia	2,863	0.2%

Source: U.S. Department of Health and Human Services, Centers for Medicare and Medicaid Services
   "Health, United States, 2003"

Health Care Establishments in 2001

National Total = 539,140 Establishments*

ALPHA ORDER

RANK	STATE	ESTABLISH'S	% of USA
27	Alabama	7,021	1.3%
48	Alaska	1,304	0.2%
20	Arizona	9,446	1.8%
32	Arkansas	4,697	0.9%
1	California	69,441	12.9%
21	Colorado	8,914	1.7%
25	Connecticut	7,362	1.4%
45	Delaware	1,484	0.3%
4	Florida	35,739	6.6%
10	Georgia	13,729	2.5%
41	Hawaii	2,548	0.5%
40	Idaho	2,591	0.5%
6	Illinois	21,881	4.1%
18	Indiana	10,047	1.9%
30	Iowa	5,315	1.0%
31	Kansas	5,083	0.9%
26	Kentucky	7,064	1.3%
23	Louisiana	8,145	1.5%
39	Maine	2,943	0.5%
15	Maryland	10,867	2.0%
11	Massachusetts	12,854	2.4%
8	Michigan	19,384	3.6%
22	Minnesota	8,634	1.6%
34	Mississippi	3,918	0.7%
16	Missouri	10,147	1.9%
44	Montana	2,031	0.4%
38	Nebraska	3,071	0.6%
35	Nevada	3,643	0.7%
43	New Hampshire	2,243	0.4%
9	New Jersey	19,083	3.5%
37	New Mexico	3,098	0.6%
2	New York	38,861	7.2%
12	North Carolina	12,797	2.4%
49	North Dakota	1,093	0.2%
7	Ohio	20,931	3.9%
28	Oklahoma	6,737	1.2%
24	Oregon	7,560	1.4%
5	Pennsylvania	25,744	4.8%
42	Rhode Island	2,332	0.4%
29	South Carolina	6,224	1.2%
46	South Dakota	1,428	0.3%
17	Tennessee	10,051	1.9%
3	Texas	37,008	6.9%
33	Utah	4,223	0.8%
47	Vermont	1,348	0.3%
14	Virginia	11,744	2.2%
13	Washington	11,811	2.2%
36	West Virginia	3,541	0.7%
19	Wisconsin	9,455	1.8%
50	Wyoming	1,070	0.2%

RANK ORDER

RANK	STATE	ESTABLISH'S	% of USA
1	California	69,441	12.9%
2	New York	38,861	7.2%
3	Texas	37,008	6.9%
4	Florida	35,739	6.6%
5	Pennsylvania	25,744	4.8%
6	Illinois	21,881	4.1%
7	Ohio	20,931	3.9%
8	Michigan	19,384	3.6%
9	New Jersey	19,083	3.5%
10	Georgia	13,729	2.5%
11	Massachusetts	12,854	2.4%
12	North Carolina	12,797	2.4%
13	Washington	11,811	2.2%
14	Virginia	11,744	2.2%
15	Maryland	10,867	2.0%
16	Missouri	10,147	1.9%
17	Tennessee	10,051	1.9%
18	Indiana	10,047	1.9%
19	Wisconsin	9,455	1.8%
20	Arizona	9,446	1.8%
21	Colorado	8,914	1.7%
22	Minnesota	8,634	1.6%
23	Louisiana	8,145	1.5%
24	Oregon	7,560	1.4%
25	Connecticut	7,362	1.4%
26	Kentucky	7,064	1.3%
27	Alabama	7,021	1.3%
28	Oklahoma	6,737	1.2%
29	South Carolina	6,224	1.2%
30	Iowa	5,315	1.0%
31	Kansas	5,083	0.9%
32	Arkansas	4,697	0.9%
33	Utah	4,223	0.8%
34	Mississippi	3,918	0.7%
35	Nevada	3,643	0.7%
36	West Virginia	3,541	0.7%
37	New Mexico	3,098	0.6%
38	Nebraska	3,071	0.6%
39	Maine	2,943	0.5%
40	Idaho	2,591	0.5%
41	Hawaii	2,548	0.5%
42	Rhode Island	2,332	0.4%
43	New Hampshire	2,243	0.4%
44	Montana	2,031	0.4%
45	Delaware	1,484	0.3%
46	South Dakota	1,428	0.3%
47	Vermont	1,348	0.3%
48	Alaska	1,304	0.2%
49	North Dakota	1,093	0.2%
50	Wyoming	1,070	0.2%
	District of Columbia	1,455	0.3%

Source: U.S. Bureau of the Census
    "County Business Patterns 2001 (NAICS)" (http://censtats.census.gov/cbpnaic/cbpnaic.shtml)
*Includes establishments exempt from as well as subject to the federal income tax. Includes those establishments within the North American Industry Classification System (NAICS) classifications 621 (ambulatory health care services), 622 (hospitals) and 623 (nursing and residential care facilities).

IV. FINANCE

IV. FINANCE (Continued)

Persons Not Covered by Health Insurance in 2002

National Total = 43,574,000 Uninsured

ALPHA ORDER

RANK	STATE	UNINSURED	% of USA
23	Alabama	564,000	1.3%
44	Alaska	119,000	0.3%
13	Arizona	916,000	2.1%
29	Arkansas	440,000	1.0%
1	California	6,398,000	14.7%
18	Colorado	720,000	1.7%
33	Connecticut	356,000	0.8%
48	Delaware	79,000	0.2%
4	Florida	2,843,000	6.5%
8	Georgia	1,354,000	3.1%
43	Hawaii	123,000	0.3%
38	Idaho	233,000	0.5%
5	Illinois	1,767,000	4.1%
16	Indiana	797,000	1.8%
36	Iowa	277,000	0.6%
35	Kansas	280,000	0.6%
24	Kentucky	548,000	1.3%
15	Louisiana	820,000	1.9%
40	Maine	144,000	0.3%
17	Maryland	730,000	1.7%
20	Massachusetts	644,000	1.5%
11	Michigan	1,158,000	2.7%
31	Minnesota	397,000	0.9%
28	Mississippi	465,000	1.1%
19	Missouri	646,000	1.5%
41	Montana	139,000	0.3%
39	Nebraska	174,000	0.4%
30	Nevada	418,000	1.0%
42	New Hampshire	125,000	0.3%
10	New Jersey	1,197,000	2.7%
32	New Mexico	388,000	0.9%
3	New York	3,042,000	7.0%
7	North Carolina	1,368,000	3.1%
49	North Dakota	69,000	0.2%
9	Ohio	1,344,000	3.1%
22	Oklahoma	601,000	1.4%
26	Oregon	511,000	1.2%
6	Pennsylvania	1,380,000	3.2%
45	Rhode Island	104,000	0.2%
27	South Carolina	500,000	1.1%
47	South Dakota	85,000	0.2%
21	Tennessee	614,000	1.4%
2	Texas	5,556,000	12.8%
34	Utah	310,000	0.7%
50	Vermont	66,000	0.2%
12	Virginia	962,000	2.2%
14	Washington	850,000	2.0%
37	West Virginia	255,000	0.6%
25	Wisconsin	538,000	1.2%
46	Wyoming	86,000	0.2%

RANK ORDER

RANK	STATE	UNINSURED	% of USA
1	California	6,398,000	14.7%
2	Texas	5,556,000	12.8%
3	New York	3,042,000	7.0%
4	Florida	2,843,000	6.5%
5	Illinois	1,767,000	4.1%
6	Pennsylvania	1,380,000	3.2%
7	North Carolina	1,368,000	3.1%
8	Georgia	1,354,000	3.1%
9	Ohio	1,344,000	3.1%
10	New Jersey	1,197,000	2.7%
11	Michigan	1,158,000	2.7%
12	Virginia	962,000	2.2%
13	Arizona	916,000	2.1%
14	Washington	850,000	2.0%
15	Louisiana	820,000	1.9%
16	Indiana	797,000	1.8%
17	Maryland	730,000	1.7%
18	Colorado	720,000	1.7%
19	Missouri	646,000	1.5%
20	Massachusetts	644,000	1.5%
21	Tennessee	614,000	1.4%
22	Oklahoma	601,000	1.4%
23	Alabama	564,000	1.3%
24	Kentucky	548,000	1.3%
25	Wisconsin	538,000	1.2%
26	Oregon	511,000	1.2%
27	South Carolina	500,000	1.1%
28	Mississippi	465,000	1.1%
29	Arkansas	440,000	1.0%
30	Nevada	418,000	1.0%
31	Minnesota	397,000	0.9%
32	New Mexico	388,000	0.9%
33	Connecticut	356,000	0.8%
34	Utah	310,000	0.7%
35	Kansas	280,000	0.6%
36	Iowa	277,000	0.6%
37	West Virginia	255,000	0.6%
38	Idaho	233,000	0.5%
39	Nebraska	174,000	0.4%
40	Maine	144,000	0.3%
41	Montana	139,000	0.3%
42	New Hampshire	125,000	0.3%
43	Hawaii	123,000	0.3%
44	Alaska	119,000	0.3%
45	Rhode Island	104,000	0.2%
46	Wyoming	86,000	0.2%
47	South Dakota	85,000	0.2%
48	Delaware	79,000	0.2%
49	North Dakota	69,000	0.2%
50	Vermont	66,000	0.2%
	District of Columbia	74,000	0.2%

Source: U.S. Bureau of the Census
"Health Insurance Coverage Status by State for All People: 2002"
(http://ferret.bls.census.gov/macro/032003/health/h06_000.htm)

Percent of Population Not Covered by Health Insurance in 2002

National Percent = 14.7% of Population*

ALPHA ORDER

RANK	STATE	PERCENT
26	Alabama	13.0
6	Alaska	17.8
9	Arizona	17.1
14	Arkansas	15.6
3	California	18.7
16	Colorado	15.3
39	Connecticut	10.2
44	Delaware	9.5
7	Florida	17.5
13	Georgia	15.7
40	Hawaii	9.7
10	Idaho	16.4
20	Illinois	13.9
28	Indiana	12.0
47	Iowa	8.6
33	Kansas	10.9
24	Kentucky	13.2
4	Louisiana	18.6
34	Maine	10.8
28	Maryland	12.0
46	Massachusetts	9.0
37	Michigan	10.4
50	Minnesota	8.0
14	Mississippi	15.6
37	Missouri	10.4
17	Montana	15.2
42	Nebraska	9.6
7	Nevada	17.5
45	New Hampshire	9.2
25	New Jersey	13.1
2	New Mexico	22.0
12	New York	15.8
18	North Carolina	14.9
35	North Dakota	10.7
31	Ohio	11.4
5	Oklahoma	18.2
23	Oregon	13.3
40	Pennsylvania	9.7
49	Rhode Island	8.3
27	South Carolina	12.3
36	South Dakota	10.6
32	Tennessee	11.0
1	Texas	24.1
21	Utah	13.6
42	Vermont	9.6
28	Virginia	12.0
21	Washington	13.6
19	West Virginia	14.0
48	Wisconsin	8.4
10	Wyoming	16.4

RANK ORDER

RANK	STATE	PERCENT
1	Texas	24.1
2	New Mexico	22.0
3	California	18.7
4	Louisiana	18.6
5	Oklahoma	18.2
6	Alaska	17.8
7	Florida	17.5
7	Nevada	17.5
9	Arizona	17.1
10	Idaho	16.4
10	Wyoming	16.4
12	New York	15.8
13	Georgia	15.7
14	Arkansas	15.6
14	Mississippi	15.6
16	Colorado	15.3
17	Montana	15.2
18	North Carolina	14.9
19	West Virginia	14.0
20	Illinois	13.9
21	Utah	13.6
21	Washington	13.6
23	Oregon	13.3
24	Kentucky	13.2
25	New Jersey	13.1
26	Alabama	13.0
27	South Carolina	12.3
28	Indiana	12.0
28	Maryland	12.0
28	Virginia	12.0
31	Ohio	11.4
32	Tennessee	11.0
33	Kansas	10.9
34	Maine	10.8
35	North Dakota	10.7
36	South Dakota	10.6
37	Michigan	10.4
37	Missouri	10.4
39	Connecticut	10.2
40	Hawaii	9.7
40	Pennsylvania	9.7
42	Nebraska	9.6
42	Vermont	9.6
44	Delaware	9.5
45	New Hampshire	9.2
46	Massachusetts	9.0
47	Iowa	8.6
48	Wisconsin	8.4
49	Rhode Island	8.3
50	Minnesota	8.0

District of Columbia	13.2

Source: U.S. Bureau of the Census
"Percent of People Without Health Insurance Coverage for the Entire Year by State"
(http://www.census.gov/hhes/hlthins/hlthin02/hi02t4.pdf)
Three-year average for 2000 through 2002.

Numerical Change in Persons Uninsured: 1998 to 2002

National Change = 707,000 Decrease

ALPHA ORDER

RANK	STATE	CHANGE
47	Alabama	(150,000)
21	Alaska	7,000
49	Arizona	(271,000)
33	Arkansas	(38,000)
50	California	(975,000)
7	Colorado	121,000
38	Connecticut	(56,000)
32	Delaware	(36,000)
2	Florida	279,000
15	Georgia	13,000
25	Hawaii	2,000
18	Idaho	8,000
40	Illinois	(75,000)
34	Indiana	(42,000)
16	Iowa	12,000
17	Kansas	10,000
23	Kentucky	3,000
23	Louisiana	3,000
29	Maine	(17,000)
43	Maryland	(107,000)
12	Massachusetts	17,000
48	Michigan	(170,000)
37	Minnesota	(51,000)
41	Mississippi	(89,000)
8	Missouri	76,000
34	Montana	(42,000)
11	Nebraska	19,000
10	Nevada	24,000
28	New Hampshire	(13,000)
45	New Jersey	(132,000)
25	New Mexico	2,000
46	New York	(135,000)
3	North Carolina	257,000
31	North Dakota	(23,000)
4	Ohio	175,000
25	Oklahoma	2,000
9	Oregon	30,000
6	Pennsylvania	132,000
18	Rhode Island	8,000
42	South Carolina	(94,000)
29	South Dakota	(17,000)
44	Tennessee	(110,000)
1	Texas	676,000
12	Utah	17,000
18	Vermont	8,000
14	Virginia	16,000
5	Washington	144,000
36	West Virginia	(47,000)
39	Wisconsin	(66,000)
22	Wyoming	4,000

RANK ORDER

RANK	STATE	CHANGE
1	Texas	676,000
2	Florida	279,000
3	North Carolina	257,000
4	Ohio	175,000
5	Washington	144,000
6	Pennsylvania	132,000
7	Colorado	121,000
8	Missouri	76,000
9	Oregon	30,000
10	Nevada	24,000
11	Nebraska	19,000
12	Massachusetts	17,000
12	Utah	17,000
14	Virginia	16,000
15	Georgia	13,000
16	Iowa	12,000
17	Kansas	10,000
18	Idaho	8,000
18	Rhode Island	8,000
18	Vermont	8,000
21	Alaska	7,000
22	Wyoming	4,000
23	Kentucky	3,000
23	Louisiana	3,000
25	Hawaii	2,000
25	New Mexico	2,000
25	Oklahoma	2,000
28	New Hampshire	(13,000)
29	Maine	(17,000)
29	South Dakota	(17,000)
31	North Dakota	(23,000)
32	Delaware	(36,000)
33	Arkansas	(38,000)
34	Indiana	(42,000)
34	Montana	(42,000)
36	West Virginia	(47,000)
37	Minnesota	(51,000)
38	Connecticut	(56,000)
39	Wisconsin	(66,000)
40	Illinois	(75,000)
41	Mississippi	(89,000)
42	South Carolina	(94,000)
43	Maryland	(107,000)
44	Tennessee	(110,000)
45	New Jersey	(132,000)
46	New York	(135,000)
47	Alabama	(150,000)
48	Michigan	(170,000)
49	Arizona	(271,000)
50	California	(975,000)

	District of Columbia	(13,000)

Source: Morgan Quitno Press using data from U.S. Bureau of the Census
"Health Insurance Historical Table 4" (http://www.census.gov/hhes/hlthins/historic/hihistt4.html) and
"Health Insurance Coverage Status by State for All People: 2002"
(http://ferret.bls.census.gov/macro/032003/health/h06_000.htm)

Percent Change in Persons Uninsured: 1998 to 2002

National Percent Change = 1.6% Decrease

ALPHA ORDER

RANK	STATE	PERCENT CHANGE
46	Alabama	(21.0)
12	Alaska	6.3
47	Arizona	(22.8)
31	Arkansas	(7.9)
39	California	(13.2)
3	Colorado	20.2
40	Connecticut	(13.6)
50	Delaware	(31.3)
9	Florida	10.9
23	Georgia	1.0
21	Hawaii	1.7
19	Idaho	3.6
28	Illinois	(4.1)
30	Indiana	(5.0)
17	Iowa	4.5
18	Kansas	3.7
24	Kentucky	0.6
26	Louisiana	0.4
34	Maine	(10.6)
37	Maryland	(12.8)
20	Massachusetts	2.7
37	Michigan	(12.8)
36	Minnesota	(11.4)
44	Mississippi	(16.1)
7	Missouri	13.3
48	Montana	(23.2)
8	Nebraska	12.3
14	Nevada	6.1
32	New Hampshire	(9.4)
33	New Jersey	(9.9)
25	New Mexico	0.5
29	New York	(4.2)
1	North Carolina	23.1
49	North Dakota	(25.0)
4	Ohio	15.0
27	Oklahoma	0.3
13	Oregon	6.2
10	Pennsylvania	10.6
11	Rhode Island	8.3
43	South Carolina	(15.8)
45	South Dakota	(16.7)
41	Tennessee	(15.2)
5	Texas	13.9
15	Utah	5.8
6	Vermont	13.8
21	Virginia	1.7
2	Washington	20.4
42	West Virginia	(15.6)
35	Wisconsin	(10.9)
16	Wyoming	4.9

RANK ORDER

RANK	STATE	PERCENT CHANGE
1	North Carolina	23.1
2	Washington	20.4
3	Colorado	20.2
4	Ohio	15.0
5	Texas	13.9
6	Vermont	13.8
7	Missouri	13.3
8	Nebraska	12.3
9	Florida	10.9
10	Pennsylvania	10.6
11	Rhode Island	8.3
12	Alaska	6.3
13	Oregon	6.2
14	Nevada	6.1
15	Utah	5.8
16	Wyoming	4.9
17	Iowa	4.5
18	Kansas	3.7
19	Idaho	3.6
20	Massachusetts	2.7
21	Hawaii	1.7
21	Virginia	1.7
23	Georgia	1.0
24	Kentucky	0.6
25	New Mexico	0.5
26	Louisiana	0.4
27	Oklahoma	0.3
28	Illinois	(4.1)
29	New York	(4.2)
30	Indiana	(5.0)
31	Arkansas	(7.9)
32	New Hampshire	(9.4)
33	New Jersey	(9.9)
34	Maine	(10.6)
35	Wisconsin	(10.9)
36	Minnesota	(11.4)
37	Maryland	(12.8)
37	Michigan	(12.8)
39	California	(13.2)
40	Connecticut	(13.6)
41	Tennessee	(15.2)
42	West Virginia	(15.6)
43	South Carolina	(15.8)
44	Mississippi	(16.1)
45	South Dakota	(16.7)
46	Alabama	(21.0)
47	Arizona	(22.8)
48	Montana	(23.2)
49	North Dakota	(25.0)
50	Delaware	(31.3)
	District of Columbia	(14.9)

Source: Morgan Quitno Press using data from U.S. Bureau of the Census
"Health Insurance Historical Table 4" (http://www.census.gov/hhes/hlthins/historic/hihistt4.html) and
"Health Insurance Coverage Status by State for All People: 2002"
(http://ferret.bls.census.gov/macro/032003/health/h06_000.htm)

Change in Percent of Population Uninsured: 1998 to 2002

National Percent Change = 8.1% Decrease*

ALPHA ORDER			RANK ORDER		
RANK	STATE	PERCENT CHANGE	RANK	STATE	PERCENT CHANGE
33	Alabama	(13.9)	1	Hawaii	11.5
3	Alaska	9.2	2	Washington	9.7
49	Arizona	(29.6)	3	Alaska	9.2
48	Arkansas	(27.8)	4	Illinois	7.8
30	California	(11.8)	5	Wyoming	7.2
13	Colorado	(1.9)	6	Utah	3.8
35	Connecticut	(14.3)	7	Oklahoma	2.8
50	Delaware	(30.7)	8	Ohio	2.7
20	Florida	(6.4)	9	New Mexico	0.0
28	Georgia	(10.8)	10	Indiana	(0.8)
1	Hawaii	11.5	11	Texas	(1.2)
18	Idaho	(5.2)	12	Kansas	(1.8)
4	Illinois	7.8	13	Colorado	(1.9)
10	Indiana	(0.8)	14	Pennsylvania	(3.0)
45	Iowa	(21.8)	15	Nevada	(3.3)
12	Kansas	(1.8)	16	North Carolina	(3.9)
28	Kentucky	(10.8)	17	Vermont	(5.0)
19	Louisiana	(5.6)	18	Idaho	(5.2)
40	Maine	(18.2)	19	Louisiana	(5.6)
31	Maryland	(13.0)	20	Florida	(6.4)
46	Massachusetts	(23.7)	21	Oregon	(7.0)
22	Michigan	(7.1)	22	Michigan	(7.1)
38	Minnesota	(16.7)	23	Nebraska	(7.7)
42	Mississippi	(20.0)	24	Virginia	(8.4)
34	Missouri	(14.0)	25	New York	(8.7)
32	Montana	(13.6)	26	South Dakota	(10.2)
23	Nebraska	(7.7)	27	Wisconsin	(10.6)
15	Nevada	(3.3)	28	Georgia	(10.8)
37	New Hampshire	(15.6)	28	Kentucky	(10.8)
44	New Jersey	(21.1)	30	California	(11.8)
9	New Mexico	0.0	31	Maryland	(13.0)
25	New York	(8.7)	32	Montana	(13.6)
16	North Carolina	(3.9)	33	Alabama	(13.9)
41	North Dakota	(18.3)	34	Missouri	(14.0)
8	Ohio	2.7	35	Connecticut	(14.3)
7	Oklahoma	2.8	36	West Virginia	(14.6)
21	Oregon	(7.0)	37	New Hampshire	(15.6)
14	Pennsylvania	(3.0)	38	Minnesota	(16.7)
39	Rhode Island	(17.0)	39	Rhode Island	(17.0)
47	South Carolina	(25.0)	40	Maine	(18.2)
26	South Dakota	(10.2)	41	North Dakota	(18.3)
43	Tennessee	(20.9)	42	Mississippi	(20.0)
11	Texas	(1.2)	43	Tennessee	(20.9)
6	Utah	3.8	44	New Jersey	(21.1)
17	Vermont	(5.0)	45	Iowa	(21.8)
24	Virginia	(8.4)	46	Massachusetts	(23.7)
2	Washington	9.7	47	South Carolina	(25.0)
36	West Virginia	(14.6)	48	Arkansas	(27.8)
27	Wisconsin	(10.6)	49	Arizona	(29.6)
5	Wyoming	7.2	50	Delaware	(30.7)
				District of Columbia	(17.5)

Source: Morgan Quitno Press using data from U.S. Bureau of the Census
"Health Insurance Historical Table 4" (http://www.census.gov/hhes/hlthins/historic/hihistt4.html) and
"Percent of People Without Health Insurance Coverage for the Entire Year by State"
(http://www.census.gov/hhes/hlthins/hlthin02/hi02t4.pdf)
*Based on three-year averages for 2000 through 2002 and 1996 through 1998.

Percent of Children Not Covered by Health Insurance in 2002

National Percent = 11.6% of Children*

RANK	STATE	PERCENT
21	Alabama	10.8
11	Alaska	13.3
4	Arizona	14.7
24	Arkansas	10.0
9	California	14.0
7	Colorado	14.4
33	Connecticut	8.1
27	Delaware	9.8
5	Florida	14.5
14	Georgia	12.3
37	Hawaii	7.4
10	Idaho	13.6
18	Illinois	11.3
27	Indiana	9.8
42	Iowa	5.9
33	Kansas	8.1
13	Kentucky	12.6
16	Louisiana	11.9
35	Maine	7.9
25	Maryland	9.9
42	Massachusetts	5.9
39	Michigan	6.9
44	Minnesota	5.8
20	Mississippi	10.9
47	Missouri	5.0
3	Montana	15.0
46	Nebraska	5.6
2	Nevada	19.7
48	New Hampshire	4.8
29	New Jersey	9.7
5	New Mexico	14.5
25	New York	9.9
12	North Carolina	12.7
37	North Dakota	7.4
32	Ohio	8.2
17	Oklahoma	11.6
18	Oregon	11.3
23	Pennsylvania	10.2
49	Rhode Island	4.7
39	South Carolina	6.9
36	South Dakota	7.7
41	Tennessee	6.8
1	Texas	22.4
30	Utah	9.3
45	Vermont	5.7
14	Virginia	12.3
31	Washington	9.0
22	West Virginia	10.3
50	Wisconsin	4.6
8	Wyoming	14.2

RANK	STATE	PERCENT
1	Texas	22.4
2	Nevada	19.7
3	Montana	15.0
4	Arizona	14.7
5	Florida	14.5
5	New Mexico	14.5
7	Colorado	14.4
8	Wyoming	14.2
9	California	14.0
10	Idaho	13.6
11	Alaska	13.3
12	North Carolina	12.7
13	Kentucky	12.6
14	Georgia	12.3
14	Virginia	12.3
16	Louisiana	11.9
17	Oklahoma	11.6
18	Illinois	11.3
18	Oregon	11.3
20	Mississippi	10.9
21	Alabama	10.8
22	West Virginia	10.3
23	Pennsylvania	10.2
24	Arkansas	10.0
25	Maryland	9.9
25	New York	9.9
27	Delaware	9.8
27	Indiana	9.8
29	New Jersey	9.7
30	Utah	9.3
31	Washington	9.0
32	Ohio	8.2
33	Connecticut	8.1
33	Kansas	8.1
35	Maine	7.9
36	South Dakota	7.7
37	Hawaii	7.4
37	North Dakota	7.4
39	Michigan	6.9
39	South Carolina	6.9
41	Tennessee	6.8
42	Iowa	5.9
42	Massachusetts	5.9
44	Minnesota	5.8
45	Vermont	5.7
46	Nebraska	5.6
47	Missouri	5.0
48	New Hampshire	4.8
49	Rhode Island	4.7
50	Wisconsin	4.6

	District of Columbia	8.6

Source: U.S. Bureau of the Census
"Health Insurance Historical Table 5" (http://www.census.gov/hhes/hlthins/historic/hihistt5.html)
*Children under 18 years old.

Persons Covered by Health Insurance in 2002

National Total = 242,360,000 Insured

ALPHA ORDER

RANK	STATE	INSURED	% of USA
22	Alabama	3,876,000	1.6%
49	Alaska	516,000	0.2%
21	Arizona	4,526,000	1.9%
33	Arkansas	2,252,000	0.9%
1	California	28,761,000	11.9%
23	Colorado	3,756,000	1.5%
27	Connecticut	3,027,000	1.2%
45	Delaware	719,000	0.3%
4	Florida	13,586,000	5.6%
10	Georgia	7,072,000	2.9%
41	Hawaii	1,101,000	0.5%
42	Idaho	1,067,000	0.4%
6	Illinois	10,737,000	4.4%
14	Indiana	5,303,000	2.2%
30	Iowa	2,626,000	1.1%
31	Kansas	2,404,000	1.0%
25	Kentucky	3,498,000	1.4%
24	Louisiana	3,627,000	1.5%
40	Maine	1,125,000	0.5%
19	Maryland	4,728,000	2.0%
13	Massachusetts	5,827,000	2.4%
8	Michigan	8,752,000	3.6%
20	Minnesota	4,657,000	1.9%
32	Mississippi	2,322,000	1.0%
17	Missouri	4,939,000	2.0%
44	Montana	767,000	0.3%
36	Nebraska	1,530,000	0.6%
35	Nevada	1,703,000	0.7%
39	New Hampshire	1,141,000	0.5%
9	New Jersey	7,408,000	3.1%
38	New Mexico	1,452,000	0.6%
2	New York	16,241,000	6.7%
11	North Carolina	6,794,000	2.8%
47	North Dakota	564,000	0.2%
7	Ohio	9,938,000	4.1%
29	Oklahoma	2,876,000	1.2%
28	Oregon	2,999,000	1.2%
5	Pennsylvania	10,809,000	4.5%
43	Rhode Island	952,000	0.4%
26	South Carolina	3,497,000	1.4%
46	South Dakota	659,000	0.3%
16	Tennessee	5,058,000	2.1%
3	Texas	15,973,000	6.6%
34	Utah	2,000,000	0.8%
48	Vermont	553,000	0.2%
12	Virginia	6,156,000	2.5%
15	Washington	5,151,000	2.1%
37	West Virginia	1,496,000	0.6%
18	Wisconsin	4,938,000	2.0%
50	Wyoming	402,000	0.2%

RANK ORDER

RANK	STATE	INSURED	% of USA
1	California	28,761,000	11.9%
2	New York	16,241,000	6.7%
3	Texas	15,973,000	6.6%
4	Florida	13,586,000	5.6%
5	Pennsylvania	10,809,000	4.5%
6	Illinois	10,737,000	4.4%
7	Ohio	9,938,000	4.1%
8	Michigan	8,752,000	3.6%
9	New Jersey	7,408,000	3.1%
10	Georgia	7,072,000	2.9%
11	North Carolina	6,794,000	2.8%
12	Virginia	6,156,000	2.5%
13	Massachusetts	5,827,000	2.4%
14	Indiana	5,303,000	2.2%
15	Washington	5,151,000	2.1%
16	Tennessee	5,058,000	2.1%
17	Missouri	4,939,000	2.0%
18	Wisconsin	4,938,000	2.0%
19	Maryland	4,728,000	2.0%
20	Minnesota	4,657,000	1.9%
21	Arizona	4,526,000	1.9%
22	Alabama	3,876,000	1.6%
23	Colorado	3,756,000	1.5%
24	Louisiana	3,627,000	1.5%
25	Kentucky	3,498,000	1.4%
26	South Carolina	3,497,000	1.4%
27	Connecticut	3,027,000	1.2%
28	Oregon	2,999,000	1.2%
29	Oklahoma	2,876,000	1.2%
30	Iowa	2,626,000	1.1%
31	Kansas	2,404,000	1.0%
32	Mississippi	2,322,000	1.0%
33	Arkansas	2,252,000	0.9%
34	Utah	2,000,000	0.8%
35	Nevada	1,703,000	0.7%
36	Nebraska	1,530,000	0.6%
37	West Virginia	1,496,000	0.6%
38	New Mexico	1,452,000	0.6%
39	New Hampshire	1,141,000	0.5%
40	Maine	1,125,000	0.5%
41	Hawaii	1,101,000	0.5%
42	Idaho	1,067,000	0.4%
43	Rhode Island	952,000	0.4%
44	Montana	767,000	0.3%
45	Delaware	719,000	0.3%
46	South Dakota	659,000	0.3%
47	North Dakota	564,000	0.2%
48	Vermont	553,000	0.2%
49	Alaska	516,000	0.2%
50	Wyoming	402,000	0.2%
	District of Columbia	498,000	0.2%

Source: U.S. Bureau of the Census
"Health Insurance Coverage Status by State for All People: 2002"
(http://ferret.bls.census.gov/macro/032003/health/h06_000.htm)

Percent of Population Covered by Health Insurance in 2002

National Percent = 85.3% of Population

ALPHA ORDER

RANK	STATE	PERCENT
25	Alabama	87.0
45	Alaska	82.2
42	Arizona	82.9
36	Arkansas	84.4
48	California	81.3
35	Colorado	84.7
12	Connecticut	89.8
7	Delaware	90.5
43	Florida	82.5
38	Georgia	84.3
10	Hawaii	90.3
40	Idaho	83.6
31	Illinois	86.1
21	Indiana	88.0
4	Iowa	91.4
18	Kansas	89.1
27	Kentucky	86.8
47	Louisiana	81.4
17	Maine	89.2
21	Maryland	88.0
5	Massachusetts	91.0
13	Michigan	89.6
1	Minnesota	92.0
36	Mississippi	84.4
13	Missouri	89.6
34	Montana	84.8
8	Nebraska	90.4
43	Nevada	82.5
6	New Hampshire	90.8
26	New Jersey	86.9
49	New Mexico	78.0
39	New York	84.2
33	North Carolina	85.1
16	North Dakota	89.3
20	Ohio	88.6
46	Oklahoma	81.8
28	Oregon	86.7
10	Pennsylvania	90.3
2	Rhode Island	91.7
24	South Carolina	87.7
15	South Dakota	89.4
19	Tennessee	89.0
50	Texas	75.9
29	Utah	86.4
8	Vermont	90.4
21	Virginia	88.0
29	Washington	86.4
32	West Virginia	86.0
3	Wisconsin	91.6
40	Wyoming	83.6

RANK ORDER

RANK	STATE	PERCENT
1	Minnesota	92.0
2	Rhode Island	91.7
3	Wisconsin	91.6
4	Iowa	91.4
5	Massachusetts	91.0
6	New Hampshire	90.8
7	Delaware	90.5
8	Nebraska	90.4
8	Vermont	90.4
10	Hawaii	90.3
10	Pennsylvania	90.3
12	Connecticut	89.8
13	Michigan	89.6
13	Missouri	89.6
15	South Dakota	89.4
16	North Dakota	89.3
17	Maine	89.2
18	Kansas	89.1
19	Tennessee	89.0
20	Ohio	88.6
21	Indiana	88.0
21	Maryland	88.0
21	Virginia	88.0
24	South Carolina	87.7
25	Alabama	87.0
26	New Jersey	86.9
27	Kentucky	86.8
28	Oregon	86.7
29	Utah	86.4
29	Washington	86.4
31	Illinois	86.1
32	West Virginia	86.0
33	North Carolina	85.1
34	Montana	84.8
35	Colorado	84.7
36	Arkansas	84.4
36	Mississippi	84.4
38	Georgia	84.3
39	New York	84.2
40	Idaho	83.6
40	Wyoming	83.6
42	Arizona	82.9
43	Florida	82.5
43	Nevada	82.5
45	Alaska	82.2
46	Oklahoma	81.8
47	Louisiana	81.4
48	California	81.3
49	New Mexico	78.0
50	Texas	75.9

District of Columbia   86.8

Source: Morgan Quitno Press using data from U.S. Bureau of the Census
"Percent of People Without Health Insurance Coverage for the Entire Year by State"
(http://www.census.gov/hhes/hlthins/hlthin02/hi02t4.pdf)
*Three-year average for 2000 through 2002.

Percent of Population Covered by Private Health Insurance in 2002

National Percent = 69.6% of Population

<table>
<tr><td colspan="4">ALPHA ORDER</td><td colspan="4">RANK ORDER</td></tr>
<tr><td>RANK</td><td>STATE</td><td>PERCENT</td><td></td><td>RANK</td><td>STATE</td><td>PERCENT</td></tr>
<tr><td>25</td><td>Alabama</td><td>70.8</td><td></td><td>1</td><td>Minnesota</td><td>82.3</td></tr>
<tr><td>45</td><td>Alaska</td><td>62.8</td><td></td><td>2</td><td>New Hampshire</td><td>80.2</td></tr>
<tr><td>41</td><td>Arizona</td><td>65.3</td><td></td><td>3</td><td>Iowa</td><td>79.7</td></tr>
<tr><td>46</td><td>Arkansas</td><td>61.1</td><td></td><td>4</td><td>Wisconsin</td><td>78.5</td></tr>
<tr><td>42</td><td>California</td><td>65.1</td><td></td><td>5</td><td>Kansas</td><td>77.6</td></tr>
<tr><td>24</td><td>Colorado</td><td>71.7</td><td></td><td>6</td><td>Connecticut</td><td>77.2</td></tr>
<tr><td>6</td><td>Connecticut</td><td>77.2</td><td></td><td>7</td><td>Maryland</td><td>77.0</td></tr>
<tr><td>12</td><td>Delaware</td><td>76.2</td><td></td><td>7</td><td>Nebraska</td><td>77.0</td></tr>
<tr><td>43</td><td>Florida</td><td>64.9</td><td></td><td>9</td><td>Ohio</td><td>76.6</td></tr>
<tr><td>28</td><td>Georgia</td><td>70.3</td><td></td><td>10</td><td>South Dakota</td><td>76.5</td></tr>
<tr><td>20</td><td>Hawaii</td><td>73.5</td><td></td><td>11</td><td>Pennsylvania</td><td>76.4</td></tr>
<tr><td>32</td><td>Idaho</td><td>69.5</td><td></td><td>12</td><td>Delaware</td><td>76.2</td></tr>
<tr><td>22</td><td>Illinois</td><td>72.7</td><td></td><td>13</td><td>Missouri</td><td>76.1</td></tr>
<tr><td>15</td><td>Indiana</td><td>75.9</td><td></td><td>14</td><td>North Dakota</td><td>76.0</td></tr>
<tr><td>3</td><td>Iowa</td><td>79.7</td><td></td><td>15</td><td>Indiana</td><td>75.9</td></tr>
<tr><td>5</td><td>Kansas</td><td>77.6</td><td></td><td>16</td><td>Michigan</td><td>75.6</td></tr>
<tr><td>30</td><td>Kentucky</td><td>69.9</td><td></td><td>17</td><td>Utah</td><td>75.5</td></tr>
<tr><td>48</td><td>Louisiana</td><td>60.8</td><td></td><td>18</td><td>New Jersey</td><td>74.1</td></tr>
<tr><td>31</td><td>Maine</td><td>69.7</td><td></td><td>19</td><td>Massachusetts</td><td>73.7</td></tr>
<tr><td>7</td><td>Maryland</td><td>77.0</td><td></td><td>20</td><td>Hawaii</td><td>73.5</td></tr>
<tr><td>19</td><td>Massachusetts</td><td>73.7</td><td></td><td>21</td><td>Virginia</td><td>73.1</td></tr>
<tr><td>16</td><td>Michigan</td><td>75.6</td><td></td><td>22</td><td>Illinois</td><td>72.7</td></tr>
<tr><td>1</td><td>Minnesota</td><td>82.3</td><td></td><td>23</td><td>Rhode Island</td><td>72.2</td></tr>
<tr><td>46</td><td>Mississippi</td><td>61.1</td><td></td><td>24</td><td>Colorado</td><td>71.7</td></tr>
<tr><td>13</td><td>Missouri</td><td>76.1</td><td></td><td>25</td><td>Alabama</td><td>70.8</td></tr>
<tr><td>36</td><td>Montana</td><td>68.3</td><td></td><td>26</td><td>Vermont</td><td>70.7</td></tr>
<tr><td>7</td><td>Nebraska</td><td>77.0</td><td></td><td>27</td><td>Oregon</td><td>70.5</td></tr>
<tr><td>33</td><td>Nevada</td><td>69.0</td><td></td><td>28</td><td>Georgia</td><td>70.3</td></tr>
<tr><td>2</td><td>New Hampshire</td><td>80.2</td><td></td><td>29</td><td>Washington</td><td>70.2</td></tr>
<tr><td>18</td><td>New Jersey</td><td>74.1</td><td></td><td>30</td><td>Kentucky</td><td>69.9</td></tr>
<tr><td>50</td><td>New Mexico</td><td>56.9</td><td></td><td>31</td><td>Maine</td><td>69.7</td></tr>
<tr><td>40</td><td>New York</td><td>65.5</td><td></td><td>32</td><td>Idaho</td><td>69.5</td></tr>
<tr><td>38</td><td>North Carolina</td><td>66.1</td><td></td><td>33</td><td>Nevada</td><td>69.0</td></tr>
<tr><td>14</td><td>North Dakota</td><td>76.0</td><td></td><td>34</td><td>Tennessee</td><td>68.5</td></tr>
<tr><td>9</td><td>Ohio</td><td>76.6</td><td></td><td>35</td><td>Wyoming</td><td>68.4</td></tr>
<tr><td>39</td><td>Oklahoma</td><td>65.6</td><td></td><td>36</td><td>Montana</td><td>68.3</td></tr>
<tr><td>27</td><td>Oregon</td><td>70.5</td><td></td><td>37</td><td>South Carolina</td><td>67.6</td></tr>
<tr><td>11</td><td>Pennsylvania</td><td>76.4</td><td></td><td>38</td><td>North Carolina</td><td>66.1</td></tr>
<tr><td>23</td><td>Rhode Island</td><td>72.2</td><td></td><td>39</td><td>Oklahoma</td><td>65.6</td></tr>
<tr><td>37</td><td>South Carolina</td><td>67.6</td><td></td><td>40</td><td>New York</td><td>65.5</td></tr>
<tr><td>10</td><td>South Dakota</td><td>76.5</td><td></td><td>41</td><td>Arizona</td><td>65.3</td></tr>
<tr><td>34</td><td>Tennessee</td><td>68.5</td><td></td><td>42</td><td>California</td><td>65.1</td></tr>
<tr><td>49</td><td>Texas</td><td>59.2</td><td></td><td>43</td><td>Florida</td><td>64.9</td></tr>
<tr><td>17</td><td>Utah</td><td>75.5</td><td></td><td>44</td><td>West Virginia</td><td>63.2</td></tr>
<tr><td>26</td><td>Vermont</td><td>70.7</td><td></td><td>45</td><td>Alaska</td><td>62.8</td></tr>
<tr><td>21</td><td>Virginia</td><td>73.1</td><td></td><td>46</td><td>Arkansas</td><td>61.1</td></tr>
<tr><td>29</td><td>Washington</td><td>70.2</td><td></td><td>46</td><td>Mississippi</td><td>61.1</td></tr>
<tr><td>44</td><td>West Virginia</td><td>63.2</td><td></td><td>48</td><td>Louisiana</td><td>60.8</td></tr>
<tr><td>4</td><td>Wisconsin</td><td>78.5</td><td></td><td>49</td><td>Texas</td><td>59.2</td></tr>
<tr><td>35</td><td>Wyoming</td><td>68.4</td><td></td><td>50</td><td>New Mexico</td><td>56.9</td></tr>
<tr><td></td><td></td><td></td><td></td><td colspan="2">District of Columbia</td><td>65.1</td></tr>
</table>

Source: U.S. Bureau of the Census
"Health Insurance Historical Table 4" (http://www.census.gov/hhes/hlthins/historic/hihistt4.html)

Percent of Population Covered by Employment-Based Health Insurance in 2002
National Percent = 61.3% of Population

ALPHA ORDER

RANK	STATE	PERCENT
21	Alabama	63.6
36	Alaska	58.8
43	Arizona	54.7
50	Arkansas	49.6
40	California	56.9
24	Colorado	62.7
7	Connecticut	68.8
5	Delaware	69.7
45	Florida	53.4
20	Georgia	64.7
8	Hawaii	67.6
31	Idaho	59.7
18	Illinois	64.9
10	Indiana	67.4
17	Iowa	65.6
18	Kansas	64.9
28	Kentucky	61.2
46	Louisiana	53.2
34	Maine	59.2
3	Maryland	70.8
14	Massachusetts	66.4
6	Michigan	68.9
2	Minnesota	71.3
44	Mississippi	54.5
14	Missouri	66.4
49	Montana	49.9
29	Nebraska	61.1
23	Nevada	63.1
1	New Hampshire	72.5
11	New Jersey	67.1
48	New Mexico	51.2
32	New York	59.5
39	North Carolina	58.1
38	North Dakota	58.5
4	Ohio	70.1
42	Oklahoma	56.4
30	Oregon	60.0
12	Pennsylvania	66.5
22	Rhode Island	63.3
33	South Carolina	59.4
27	South Dakota	61.3
35	Tennessee	59.0
47	Texas	52.6
14	Utah	66.4
24	Vermont	62.7
12	Virginia	66.5
26	Washington	61.5
41	West Virginia	56.7
8	Wisconsin	67.6
37	Wyoming	58.7

RANK ORDER

RANK	STATE	PERCENT
1	New Hampshire	72.5
2	Minnesota	71.3
3	Maryland	70.8
4	Ohio	70.1
5	Delaware	69.7
6	Michigan	68.9
7	Connecticut	68.8
8	Hawaii	67.6
8	Wisconsin	67.6
10	Indiana	67.4
11	New Jersey	67.1
12	Pennsylvania	66.5
12	Virginia	66.5
14	Massachusetts	66.4
14	Missouri	66.4
14	Utah	66.4
17	Iowa	65.6
18	Illinois	64.9
18	Kansas	64.9
20	Georgia	64.7
21	Alabama	63.6
22	Rhode Island	63.3
23	Nevada	63.1
24	Colorado	62.7
24	Vermont	62.7
26	Washington	61.5
27	South Dakota	61.3
28	Kentucky	61.2
29	Nebraska	61.1
30	Oregon	60.0
31	Idaho	59.7
32	New York	59.5
33	South Carolina	59.4
34	Maine	59.2
35	Tennessee	59.0
36	Alaska	58.8
37	Wyoming	58.7
38	North Dakota	58.5
39	North Carolina	58.1
40	California	56.9
41	West Virginia	56.7
42	Oklahoma	56.4
43	Arizona	54.7
44	Mississippi	54.5
45	Florida	53.4
46	Louisiana	53.2
47	Texas	52.6
48	New Mexico	51.2
49	Montana	49.9
50	Arkansas	49.6
	District of Columbia	58.7

Source: U.S. Bureau of the Census
"Health Insurance Historical Table 4" (http://www.census.gov/hhes/hlthins/historic/hihistt4.html)

Percent of Population Covered by Direct Purchase Health Insurance in 2002

National Percent = 9.3% of Population*

<table>
<tr><td colspan="3">ALPHA ORDER</td><td colspan="3">RANK ORDER</td></tr>
<tr><td>RANK</td><td>STATE</td><td>PERCENT</td><td>RANK</td><td>STATE</td><td>PERCENT</td></tr>
<tr><td>34</td><td>Alabama</td><td>8.7</td><td>1</td><td>Montana</td><td>18.7</td></tr>
<tr><td>50</td><td>Alaska</td><td>6.0</td><td>2</td><td>North Dakota</td><td>18.6</td></tr>
<tr><td>11</td><td>Arizona</td><td>11.7</td><td>3</td><td>Iowa</td><td>17.5</td></tr>
<tr><td>7</td><td>Arkansas</td><td>12.9</td><td>4</td><td>South Dakota</td><td>17.2</td></tr>
<tr><td>31</td><td>California</td><td>9.0</td><td>5</td><td>Nebraska</td><td>15.7</td></tr>
<tr><td>24</td><td>Colorado</td><td>9.8</td><td>6</td><td>Kansas</td><td>13.5</td></tr>
<tr><td>24</td><td>Connecticut</td><td>9.8</td><td>7</td><td>Arkansas</td><td>12.9</td></tr>
<tr><td>41</td><td>Delaware</td><td>7.5</td><td>8</td><td>Oregon</td><td>12.1</td></tr>
<tr><td>9</td><td>Florida</td><td>12.0</td><td>9</td><td>Florida</td><td>12.0</td></tr>
<tr><td>36</td><td>Georgia</td><td>8.2</td><td>10</td><td>Idaho</td><td>11.8</td></tr>
<tr><td>42</td><td>Hawaii</td><td>7.3</td><td>11</td><td>Arizona</td><td>11.7</td></tr>
<tr><td>10</td><td>Idaho</td><td>11.8</td><td>12</td><td>Wisconsin</td><td>11.4</td></tr>
<tr><td>30</td><td>Illinois</td><td>9.1</td><td>13</td><td>Minnesota</td><td>11.3</td></tr>
<tr><td>22</td><td>Indiana</td><td>10.1</td><td>14</td><td>Maine</td><td>11.2</td></tr>
<tr><td>3</td><td>Iowa</td><td>17.5</td><td>15</td><td>Wyoming</td><td>11.1</td></tr>
<tr><td>6</td><td>Kansas</td><td>13.5</td><td>16</td><td>Missouri</td><td>10.9</td></tr>
<tr><td>21</td><td>Kentucky</td><td>10.2</td><td>16</td><td>Tennessee</td><td>10.9</td></tr>
<tr><td>32</td><td>Louisiana</td><td>8.9</td><td>18</td><td>Pennsylvania</td><td>10.8</td></tr>
<tr><td>14</td><td>Maine</td><td>11.2</td><td>19</td><td>Washington</td><td>10.6</td></tr>
<tr><td>47</td><td>Maryland</td><td>6.8</td><td>20</td><td>Oklahoma</td><td>10.5</td></tr>
<tr><td>43</td><td>Massachusetts</td><td>7.1</td><td>21</td><td>Kentucky</td><td>10.2</td></tr>
<tr><td>49</td><td>Michigan</td><td>6.5</td><td>22</td><td>Indiana</td><td>10.1</td></tr>
<tr><td>13</td><td>Minnesota</td><td>11.3</td><td>23</td><td>Utah</td><td>10.0</td></tr>
<tr><td>35</td><td>Mississippi</td><td>8.3</td><td>24</td><td>Colorado</td><td>9.8</td></tr>
<tr><td>16</td><td>Missouri</td><td>10.9</td><td>24</td><td>Connecticut</td><td>9.8</td></tr>
<tr><td>1</td><td>Montana</td><td>18.7</td><td>26</td><td>North Carolina</td><td>9.6</td></tr>
<tr><td>5</td><td>Nebraska</td><td>15.7</td><td>26</td><td>Rhode Island</td><td>9.6</td></tr>
<tr><td>48</td><td>Nevada</td><td>6.6</td><td>28</td><td>South Carolina</td><td>9.5</td></tr>
<tr><td>32</td><td>New Hampshire</td><td>8.9</td><td>29</td><td>Vermont</td><td>9.2</td></tr>
<tr><td>39</td><td>New Jersey</td><td>7.8</td><td>30</td><td>Illinois</td><td>9.1</td></tr>
<tr><td>43</td><td>New Mexico</td><td>7.1</td><td>31</td><td>California</td><td>9.0</td></tr>
<tr><td>43</td><td>New York</td><td>7.1</td><td>32</td><td>Louisiana</td><td>8.9</td></tr>
<tr><td>26</td><td>North Carolina</td><td>9.6</td><td>32</td><td>New Hampshire</td><td>8.9</td></tr>
<tr><td>2</td><td>North Dakota</td><td>18.6</td><td>34</td><td>Alabama</td><td>8.7</td></tr>
<tr><td>39</td><td>Ohio</td><td>7.8</td><td>35</td><td>Mississippi</td><td>8.3</td></tr>
<tr><td>20</td><td>Oklahoma</td><td>10.5</td><td>36</td><td>Georgia</td><td>8.2</td></tr>
<tr><td>8</td><td>Oregon</td><td>12.1</td><td>37</td><td>Virginia</td><td>8.1</td></tr>
<tr><td>18</td><td>Pennsylvania</td><td>10.8</td><td>38</td><td>West Virginia</td><td>7.9</td></tr>
<tr><td>26</td><td>Rhode Island</td><td>9.6</td><td>39</td><td>New Jersey</td><td>7.8</td></tr>
<tr><td>28</td><td>South Carolina</td><td>9.5</td><td>39</td><td>Ohio</td><td>7.8</td></tr>
<tr><td>4</td><td>South Dakota</td><td>17.2</td><td>41</td><td>Delaware</td><td>7.5</td></tr>
<tr><td>16</td><td>Tennessee</td><td>10.9</td><td>42</td><td>Hawaii</td><td>7.3</td></tr>
<tr><td>43</td><td>Texas</td><td>7.1</td><td>43</td><td>Massachusetts</td><td>7.1</td></tr>
<tr><td>23</td><td>Utah</td><td>10.0</td><td>43</td><td>New Mexico</td><td>7.1</td></tr>
<tr><td>29</td><td>Vermont</td><td>9.2</td><td>43</td><td>New York</td><td>7.1</td></tr>
<tr><td>37</td><td>Virginia</td><td>8.1</td><td>43</td><td>Texas</td><td>7.1</td></tr>
<tr><td>19</td><td>Washington</td><td>10.6</td><td>47</td><td>Maryland</td><td>6.8</td></tr>
<tr><td>38</td><td>West Virginia</td><td>7.9</td><td>48</td><td>Nevada</td><td>6.6</td></tr>
<tr><td>12</td><td>Wisconsin</td><td>11.4</td><td>49</td><td>Michigan</td><td>6.5</td></tr>
<tr><td>15</td><td>Wyoming</td><td>11.1</td><td>50</td><td>Alaska</td><td>6.0</td></tr>
<tr><td></td><td></td><td></td><td></td><td>District of Columbia</td><td>7.0</td></tr>
</table>

Source: U.S. Bureau of the Census
  "Health Insurance Historical Table 4" (http://www.census.gov/hhes/hlthins/historic/hihistt4.html)
*Insurance purchased directly instead of through employment.

Percent of Population Covered by Government Health Insurance in 2002

National Percent = 28.5% of Population*

RANK	STATE	PERCENT
19	Alabama	31.2
10	Alaska	35.6
14	Arizona	33.5
2	Arkansas	40.3
29	California	27.9
39	Colorado	25.3
32	Connecticut	27.8
27	Delaware	28.5
12	Florida	34.1
43	Georgia	24.2
15	Hawaii	33.1
36	Idaho	26.3
45	Illinois	23.4
46	Indiana	23.0
35	Iowa	27.1
24	Kansas	29.2
8	Kentucky	35.8
13	Louisiana	33.8
3	Maine	38.5
48	Maryland	22.4
29	Massachusetts	27.9
38	Michigan	25.5
44	Minnesota	23.6
4	Mississippi	37.9
34	Missouri	27.3
7	Montana	36.1
33	Nebraska	27.7
47	Nevada	22.5
49	New Hampshire	22.3
42	New Jersey	24.8
5	New Mexico	37.7
20	New York	30.4
18	North Carolina	31.6
24	North Dakota	29.2
40	Ohio	25.1
16	Oklahoma	32.4
21	Oregon	30.0
28	Pennsylvania	28.3
16	Rhode Island	32.4
6	South Carolina	36.8
26	South Dakota	28.6
8	Tennessee	35.8
37	Texas	25.7
50	Utah	20.4
11	Vermont	34.3
22	Virginia	29.6
23	Washington	29.4
1	West Virginia	42.1
41	Wisconsin	25.0
29	Wyoming	27.9

RANK	STATE	PERCENT
1	West Virginia	42.1
2	Arkansas	40.3
3	Maine	38.5
4	Mississippi	37.9
5	New Mexico	37.7
6	South Carolina	36.8
7	Montana	36.1
8	Kentucky	35.8
8	Tennessee	35.8
10	Alaska	35.6
11	Vermont	34.3
12	Florida	34.1
13	Louisiana	33.8
14	Arizona	33.5
15	Hawaii	33.1
16	Oklahoma	32.4
16	Rhode Island	32.4
18	North Carolina	31.6
19	Alabama	31.2
20	New York	30.4
21	Oregon	30.0
22	Virginia	29.6
23	Washington	29.4
24	Kansas	29.2
24	North Dakota	29.2
26	South Dakota	28.6
27	Delaware	28.5
28	Pennsylvania	28.3
29	California	27.9
29	Massachusetts	27.9
29	Wyoming	27.9
32	Connecticut	27.8
33	Nebraska	27.7
34	Missouri	27.3
35	Iowa	27.1
36	Idaho	26.3
37	Texas	25.7
38	Michigan	25.5
39	Colorado	25.3
40	Ohio	25.1
41	Wisconsin	25.0
42	New Jersey	24.8
43	Georgia	24.2
44	Minnesota	23.6
45	Illinois	23.4
46	Indiana	23.0
47	Nevada	22.5
48	Maryland	22.4
49	New Hampshire	22.3
50	Utah	20.4

	District of Columbia	33.1

Source: Morgan Quitno Press using data from U.S. Bureau of the Census
"Health Insurance Historical Table 4" (http://www.census.gov/hhes/hlthins/historic/hihistt4.html)
*Includes Medicaid, Medicare and military health care.

Percent of Population Covered by Military Health Insurance in 2002

National Percent = 3.5% of Population*

ALPHA ORDER

RANK	STATE	PERCENT
24	Alabama	3.9
1	Alaska	12.8
8	Arizona	6.7
5	Arkansas	7.5
35	California	3.0
8	Colorado	6.7
38	Connecticut	2.4
27	Delaware	3.7
14	Florida	5.0
27	Georgia	3.7
3	Hawaii	8.5
32	Idaho	3.4
49	Illinois	1.1
45	Indiana	1.6
36	Iowa	2.6
6	Kansas	7.2
4	Kentucky	8.4
17	Louisiana	4.7
21	Maine	4.4
24	Maryland	3.9
42	Massachusetts	2.2
50	Michigan	0.9
39	Minnesota	2.3
24	Mississippi	3.9
32	Missouri	3.4
7	Montana	6.8
22	Nebraska	4.0
22	Nevada	4.0
34	New Hampshire	3.2
48	New Jersey	1.2
17	New Mexico	4.7
47	New York	1.4
11	North Carolina	5.5
11	North Dakota	5.5
43	Ohio	1.9
10	Oklahoma	5.9
30	Oregon	3.6
43	Pennsylvania	1.9
45	Rhode Island	1.6
19	South Carolina	4.6
14	South Dakota	5.0
27	Tennessee	3.7
31	Texas	3.5
36	Utah	2.6
39	Vermont	2.3
2	Virginia	10.1
14	Washington	5.0
19	West Virginia	4.6
39	Wisconsin	2.3
13	Wyoming	5.3

RANK ORDER

RANK	STATE	PERCENT
1	Alaska	12.8
2	Virginia	10.1
3	Hawaii	8.5
4	Kentucky	8.4
5	Arkansas	7.5
6	Kansas	7.2
7	Montana	6.8
8	Arizona	6.7
8	Colorado	6.7
10	Oklahoma	5.9
11	North Carolina	5.5
11	North Dakota	5.5
13	Wyoming	5.3
14	Florida	5.0
14	South Dakota	5.0
14	Washington	5.0
17	Louisiana	4.7
17	New Mexico	4.7
19	South Carolina	4.6
19	West Virginia	4.6
21	Maine	4.4
22	Nebraska	4.0
22	Nevada	4.0
24	Alabama	3.9
24	Maryland	3.9
24	Mississippi	3.9
27	Delaware	3.7
27	Georgia	3.7
27	Tennessee	3.7
30	Oregon	3.6
31	Texas	3.5
32	Idaho	3.4
32	Missouri	3.4
34	New Hampshire	3.2
35	California	3.0
36	Iowa	2.6
36	Utah	2.6
38	Connecticut	2.4
39	Minnesota	2.3
39	Vermont	2.3
39	Wisconsin	2.3
42	Massachusetts	2.2
43	Ohio	1.9
43	Pennsylvania	1.9
45	Indiana	1.6
45	Rhode Island	1.6
47	New York	1.4
48	New Jersey	1.2
49	Illinois	1.1
50	Michigan	0.9

District of Columbia   2.0

Source: U.S. Bureau of the Census
   "Health Insurance Historical Table 4" (http://www.census.gov/hhes/hlthins/historic/hihistt4.html)
*Includes CHAMPUS (Comprehensive Health and Medical Plan for Uniformed Services)/Tricare, Veterans and military health care.

Percent of Children Covered by Health Insurance in 2002

National Percent = 88.4% of Children*

ALPHA ORDER

RANK ORDER

RANK	STATE	PERCENT	RANK	STATE	PERCENT
30	Alabama	89.2	1	Wisconsin	95.4
40	Alaska	86.7	2	Rhode Island	95.3
47	Arizona	85.3	3	New Hampshire	95.2
27	Arkansas	90.0	4	Missouri	95.0
42	California	86.0	5	Nebraska	94.4
44	Colorado	85.6	6	Vermont	94.3
17	Connecticut	91.9	7	Minnesota	94.2
23	Delaware	90.2	8	Iowa	94.1
45	Florida	85.5	8	Massachusetts	94.1
36	Georgia	87.7	10	Tennessee	93.2
13	Hawaii	92.6	11	Michigan	93.1
41	Idaho	86.4	11	South Carolina	93.1
32	Illinois	88.7	13	Hawaii	92.6
23	Indiana	90.2	13	North Dakota	92.6
8	Iowa	94.1	15	South Dakota	92.3
17	Kansas	91.9	16	Maine	92.1
38	Kentucky	87.4	17	Connecticut	91.9
35	Louisiana	88.1	17	Kansas	91.9
16	Maine	92.1	19	Ohio	91.8
25	Maryland	90.1	20	Washington	91.0
8	Massachusetts	94.1	21	Utah	90.7
11	Michigan	93.1	22	New Jersey	90.3
7	Minnesota	94.2	23	Delaware	90.2
31	Mississippi	89.1	23	Indiana	90.2
4	Missouri	95.0	25	Maryland	90.1
48	Montana	85.0	25	New York	90.1
5	Nebraska	94.4	27	Arkansas	90.0
49	Nevada	80.3	28	Pennsylvania	89.8
3	New Hampshire	95.2	29	West Virginia	89.7
22	New Jersey	90.3	30	Alabama	89.2
45	New Mexico	85.5	31	Mississippi	89.1
25	New York	90.1	32	Illinois	88.7
39	North Carolina	87.3	32	Oregon	88.7
13	North Dakota	92.6	34	Oklahoma	88.4
19	Ohio	91.8	35	Louisiana	88.1
34	Oklahoma	88.4	36	Georgia	87.7
32	Oregon	88.7	36	Virginia	87.7
28	Pennsylvania	89.8	38	Kentucky	87.4
2	Rhode Island	95.3	39	North Carolina	87.3
11	South Carolina	93.1	40	Alaska	86.7
15	South Dakota	92.3	41	Idaho	86.4
10	Tennessee	93.2	42	California	86.0
50	Texas	77.6	43	Wyoming	85.8
21	Utah	90.7	44	Colorado	85.6
6	Vermont	94.3	45	Florida	85.5
36	Virginia	87.7	45	New Mexico	85.5
20	Washington	91.0	47	Arizona	85.3
29	West Virginia	89.7	48	Montana	85.0
1	Wisconsin	95.4	49	Nevada	80.3
43	Wyoming	85.8	50	Texas	77.6
				District of Columbia	91.4

Source: U.S. Bureau of the Census
   "Health Insurance Historical Table 5" (http://www.census.gov/hhes/hlthins/historic/hihistt5.html)
Children under 18 covered by either private or government health insurance.

Percent of Children Covered by Private Health Insurance in 2002

National Percent = 67.5% of Children*

ALPHA ORDER

RANK	STATE	PERCENT
25	Alabama	70.8
44	Alaska	59.6
40	Arizona	62.0
49	Arkansas	54.7
39	California	62.3
23	Colorado	71.0
7	Connecticut	77.2
19	Delaware	72.7
36	Florida	64.2
31	Georgia	67.2
22	Hawaii	71.4
28	Idaho	68.6
21	Illinois	71.5
8	Indiana	76.7
3	Iowa	79.8
12	Kansas	75.6
42	Kentucky	61.4
46	Louisiana	55.7
29	Maine	68.5
5	Maryland	78.1
15	Massachusetts	74.7
13	Michigan	74.9
2	Minnesota	81.4
45	Mississippi	56.4
9	Missouri	76.1
41	Montana	61.9
18	Nebraska	73.6
26	Nevada	70.5
1	New Hampshire	83.7
10	New Jersey	76.0
50	New Mexico	51.5
37	New York	63.1
43	North Carolina	59.7
17	North Dakota	73.9
6	Ohio	77.5
38	Oklahoma	62.8
23	Oregon	71.0
16	Pennsylvania	74.6
26	Rhode Island	70.5
34	South Carolina	65.4
10	South Dakota	76.0
35	Tennessee	64.9
48	Texas	54.8
13	Utah	74.9
30	Vermont	67.4
20	Virginia	72.1
31	Washington	67.2
47	West Virginia	55.3
4	Wisconsin	79.0
33	Wyoming	66.9

RANK ORDER

RANK	STATE	PERCENT
1	New Hampshire	83.7
2	Minnesota	81.4
3	Iowa	79.8
4	Wisconsin	79.0
5	Maryland	78.1
6	Ohio	77.5
7	Connecticut	77.2
8	Indiana	76.7
9	Missouri	76.1
10	New Jersey	76.0
10	South Dakota	76.0
12	Kansas	75.6
13	Michigan	74.9
13	Utah	74.9
15	Massachusetts	74.7
16	Pennsylvania	74.6
17	North Dakota	73.9
18	Nebraska	73.6
19	Delaware	72.7
20	Virginia	72.1
21	Illinois	71.5
22	Hawaii	71.4
23	Colorado	71.0
23	Oregon	71.0
25	Alabama	70.8
26	Nevada	70.5
26	Rhode Island	70.5
28	Idaho	68.6
29	Maine	68.5
30	Vermont	67.4
31	Georgia	67.2
31	Washington	67.2
33	Wyoming	66.9
34	South Carolina	65.4
35	Tennessee	64.9
36	Florida	64.2
37	New York	63.1
38	Oklahoma	62.8
39	California	62.3
40	Arizona	62.0
41	Montana	61.9
42	Kentucky	61.4
43	North Carolina	59.7
44	Alaska	59.6
45	Mississippi	56.4
46	Louisiana	55.7
47	West Virginia	55.3
48	Texas	54.8
49	Arkansas	54.7
50	New Mexico	51.5
	District of Columbia	50.1

Source: U.S. Bureau of the Census
  "Health Insurance Historical Table 5" (http://www.census.gov/hhes/hlthins/historic/hihistt5.html)
*Children under 18. Private health insurance is either employment-based or direct purchase.

Percent of Children Covered by Employment-Based Health Insurance in 2002

National Percent = 63.0% of Children*

	ALPHA ORDER			RANK ORDER	
RANK	STATE	PERCENT	RANK	STATE	PERCENT
18	Alabama	67.9	1	New Hampshire	79.3
37	Alaska	57.7	2	Minnesota	76.4
40	Arizona	57.0	3	Maryland	74.9
50	Arkansas	48.8	4	Ohio	74.7
40	California	57.0	5	Wisconsin	73.8
23	Colorado	66.3	6	Connecticut	73.2
6	Connecticut	73.2	6	New Jersey	73.2
15	Delaware	69.3	8	Iowa	72.4
38	Florida	57.2	9	Michigan	72.2
27	Georgia	64.1	10	Massachusetts	71.6
19	Hawaii	67.8	11	Indiana	71.2
31	Idaho	62.4	12	Missouri	70.8
21	Illinois	67.3	13	Pennsylvania	70.5
11	Indiana	71.2	14	Kansas	70.1
8	Iowa	72.4	15	Delaware	69.3
14	Kansas	70.1	16	South Dakota	68.4
42	Kentucky	56.6	17	Virginia	68.1
46	Louisiana	51.6	18	Alabama	67.9
28	Maine	63.5	19	Hawaii	67.8
3	Maryland	74.9	20	Utah	67.7
10	Massachusetts	71.6	21	Illinois	67.3
9	Michigan	72.2	22	Rhode Island	67.0
2	Minnesota	76.4	23	Colorado	66.3
45	Mississippi	52.9	24	Nebraska	66.0
12	Missouri	70.8	25	Nevada	65.8
47	Montana	51.2	26	North Dakota	64.5
24	Nebraska	66.0	27	Georgia	64.1
25	Nevada	65.8	28	Maine	63.5
1	New Hampshire	79.3	29	Vermont	63.4
6	New Jersey	73.2	30	Washington	62.8
49	New Mexico	49.7	31	Idaho	62.4
35	New York	59.2	32	Wyoming	62.3
43	North Carolina	56.2	33	Oregon	62.2
26	North Dakota	64.5	34	South Carolina	61.7
4	Ohio	74.7	35	New York	59.2
38	Oklahoma	57.2	36	Tennessee	59.1
33	Oregon	62.2	37	Alaska	57.7
13	Pennsylvania	70.5	38	Florida	57.2
22	Rhode Island	67.0	38	Oklahoma	57.2
34	South Carolina	61.7	40	Arizona	57.0
16	South Dakota	68.4	40	California	57.0
36	Tennessee	59.1	42	Kentucky	56.6
47	Texas	51.2	43	North Carolina	56.2
20	Utah	67.7	44	West Virginia	53.0
29	Vermont	63.4	45	Mississippi	52.9
17	Virginia	68.1	46	Louisiana	51.6
30	Washington	62.8	47	Montana	51.2
44	West Virginia	53.0	47	Texas	51.2
5	Wisconsin	73.8	49	New Mexico	49.7
32	Wyoming	62.3	50	Arkansas	48.8
				District of Columbia	47.9

Source: U.S. Bureau of the Census
        "Health Insurance Historical Table 5" (http://www.census.gov/hhes/hlthins/historic/hihistt5.html)
*Children under 18. Employment-based health insurance is a form of private health insurance.

Percent of Children Covered by Direct Purchase Health Insurance in 2002

National Percent = 5.3% of Children*

ALPHA ORDER			RANK ORDER		
RANK	STATE	PERCENT	RANK	STATE	PERCENT
42	Alabama	3.6	1	Montana	11.4
47	Alaska	3.2	2	Oregon	11.2
12	Arizona	6.8	3	North Dakota	10.8
7	Arkansas	8.4	4	Iowa	10.6
16	California	6.2	5	South Dakota	9.4
19	Colorado	5.6	6	Utah	9.0
29	Connecticut	4.5	7	Arkansas	8.4
42	Delaware	3.6	8	Idaho	8.3
14	Florida	6.7	9	Tennessee	7.9
37	Georgia	4.2	10	Nebraska	7.6
33	Hawaii	4.3	11	Missouri	7.2
8	Idaho	8.3	12	Arizona	6.8
27	Illinois	4.6	12	Oklahoma	6.8
15	Indiana	6.6	14	Florida	6.7
4	Iowa	10.6	15	Indiana	6.6
17	Kansas	5.9	16	California	6.2
31	Kentucky	4.4	17	Kansas	5.9
40	Louisiana	3.8	18	Washington	5.8
23	Maine	4.8	19	Colorado	5.6
44	Maryland	3.4	20	Wisconsin	5.5
48	Massachusetts	3.0	21	North Carolina	5.2
44	Michigan	3.4	22	Wyoming	5.0
27	Minnesota	4.6	23	Maine	4.8
33	Mississippi	4.3	23	Texas	4.8
11	Missouri	7.2	23	Vermont	4.8
1	Montana	11.4	26	Virginia	4.7
10	Nebraska	7.6	27	Illinois	4.6
33	Nevada	4.3	27	Minnesota	4.6
41	New Hampshire	3.7	29	Connecticut	4.5
44	New Jersey	3.4	29	Pennsylvania	4.5
49	New Mexico	2.5	31	Kentucky	4.4
31	New York	4.4	31	New York	4.4
21	North Carolina	5.2	33	Hawaii	4.3
3	North Dakota	10.8	33	Mississippi	4.3
39	Ohio	3.9	33	Nevada	4.3
12	Oklahoma	6.8	33	Rhode Island	4.3
2	Oregon	11.2	37	Georgia	4.2
29	Pennsylvania	4.5	38	South Carolina	4.0
33	Rhode Island	4.3	39	Ohio	3.9
38	South Carolina	4.0	40	Louisiana	3.8
5	South Dakota	9.4	41	New Hampshire	3.7
9	Tennessee	7.9	42	Alabama	3.6
23	Texas	4.8	42	Delaware	3.6
6	Utah	9.0	44	Maryland	3.4
23	Vermont	4.8	44	Michigan	3.4
26	Virginia	4.7	44	New Jersey	3.4
18	Washington	5.8	47	Alaska	3.2
50	West Virginia	2.4	48	Massachusetts	3.0
20	Wisconsin	5.5	49	New Mexico	2.5
22	Wyoming	5.0	50	West Virginia	2.4
				District of Columbia	1.4

Source: U.S. Bureau of the Census
   "Health Insurance Historical Table 5" (http://www.census.gov/hhes/hlthins/historic/hihistt5.html)
*Children under 18. Direct purchase health insurance is a form of private health insurance.

Percent of Children Covered by Government Health Insurance in 2002

National Percent = 27.5% of Children*

ALPHA ORDER				RANK ORDER		
RANK	STATE	PERCENT		RANK	STATE	PERCENT
31	Alabama	24.8		1	Mississippi	44.1
2	Alaska	43.3		2	Alaska	43.3
21	Arizona	29.4		2	Arkansas	43.3
2	Arkansas	43.3		2	Vermont	43.3
19	California	29.8		5	New Mexico	43.0
40	Colorado	21.4		6	West Virginia	42.4
41	Connecticut	21.2		7	Louisiana	39.9
36	Delaware	23.2		8	South Carolina	38.2
25	Florida	27.4		9	Tennessee	37.8
24	Georgia	27.9		10	North Carolina	36.3
17	Hawaii	30.8		11	Maine	36.0
31	Idaho	24.8		12	Kentucky	35.0
45	Illinois	19.8		13	Rhode Island	32.7
48	Indiana	18.1		14	Oklahoma	32.4
34	Iowa	23.4		15	Washington	31.7
27	Kansas	26.2		16	New York	31.6
12	Kentucky	35.0		17	Hawaii	30.8
7	Louisiana	39.9		18	Montana	30.4
11	Maine	36.0		19	California	29.8
49	Maryland	17.3		20	Texas	29.5
34	Massachusetts	23.4		21	Arizona	29.4
29	Michigan	25.9		21	Missouri	29.4
46	Minnesota	19.0		21	Nebraska	29.4
1	Mississippi	44.1		24	Georgia	27.9
21	Missouri	29.4		25	Florida	27.4
18	Montana	30.4		26	Wyoming	26.8
21	Nebraska	29.4		27	Kansas	26.2
50	Nevada	13.6		27	South Dakota	26.2
47	New Hampshire	18.7		29	Michigan	25.9
43	New Jersey	20.3		29	Oregon	25.9
5	New Mexico	43.0		31	Alabama	24.8
16	New York	31.6		31	Idaho	24.8
10	North Carolina	36.3		33	North Dakota	24.0
33	North Dakota	24.0		34	Iowa	23.4
39	Ohio	21.6		34	Massachusetts	23.4
14	Oklahoma	32.4		36	Delaware	23.2
29	Oregon	25.9		37	Wisconsin	23.1
42	Pennsylvania	21.0		38	Virginia	22.7
13	Rhode Island	32.7		39	Ohio	21.6
8	South Carolina	38.2		40	Colorado	21.4
27	South Dakota	26.2		41	Connecticut	21.2
9	Tennessee	37.8		42	Pennsylvania	21.0
20	Texas	29.5		43	New Jersey	20.3
44	Utah	20.2		44	Utah	20.2
2	Vermont	43.3		45	Illinois	19.8
38	Virginia	22.7		46	Minnesota	19.0
15	Washington	31.7		47	New Hampshire	18.7
6	West Virginia	42.4		48	Indiana	18.1
37	Wisconsin	23.1		49	Maryland	17.3
26	Wyoming	26.8		50	Nevada	13.6
				District of Columbia		46.9

Source: U.S. Bureau of the Census
   "Health Insurance Historical Table 5" (http://www.census.gov/hhes/hlthins/historic/hihistt5.html)
Children under 18. Government health insurance is Medicaid, Medicare or military health care.

Percent of Children Covered by Military Health Care in 2002

National Percent = 2.9% of Children*

ALPHA ORDER

RANK	STATE	PERCENT
25	Alabama	2.7
1	Alaska	12.7
10	Arizona	4.7
8	Arkansas	4.9
25	California	2.7
6	Colorado	7.9
24	Connecticut	3.2
32	Delaware	2.1
18	Florida	3.8
20	Georgia	3.6
2	Hawaii	10.8
25	Idaho	2.7
50	Illinois	0.4
45	Indiana	1.1
37	Iowa	1.9
3	Kansas	8.8
4	Kentucky	8.3
35	Louisiana	2.0
23	Maine	3.3
14	Maryland	4.3
30	Massachusetts	2.3
48	Michigan	0.8
35	Minnesota	2.0
20	Mississippi	3.6
18	Missouri	3.8
16	Montana	3.9
13	Nebraska	4.6
38	Nevada	1.8
41	New Hampshire	1.4
47	New Jersey	0.9
29	New Mexico	2.4
42	New York	1.2
7	North Carolina	7.8
8	North Dakota	4.9
42	Ohio	1.2
10	Oklahoma	4.7
32	Oregon	2.1
48	Pennsylvania	0.8
42	Rhode Island	1.2
39	South Carolina	1.6
22	South Dakota	3.4
16	Tennessee	3.9
28	Texas	2.5
39	Utah	1.6
32	Vermont	2.1
4	Virginia	8.3
10	Washington	4.7
30	West Virginia	2.3
46	Wisconsin	1.0
15	Wyoming	4.0

RANK ORDER

RANK	STATE	PERCENT
1	Alaska	12.7
2	Hawaii	10.8
3	Kansas	8.8
4	Kentucky	8.3
4	Virginia	8.3
6	Colorado	7.9
7	North Carolina	7.8
8	Arkansas	4.9
8	North Dakota	4.9
10	Arizona	4.7
10	Oklahoma	4.7
10	Washington	4.7
13	Nebraska	4.6
14	Maryland	4.3
15	Wyoming	4.0
16	Montana	3.9
16	Tennessee	3.9
18	Florida	3.8
18	Missouri	3.8
20	Georgia	3.6
20	Mississippi	3.6
22	South Dakota	3.4
23	Maine	3.3
24	Connecticut	3.2
25	Alabama	2.7
25	California	2.7
25	Idaho	2.7
28	Texas	2.5
29	New Mexico	2.4
30	Massachusetts	2.3
30	West Virginia	2.3
32	Delaware	2.1
32	Oregon	2.1
32	Vermont	2.1
35	Louisiana	2.0
35	Minnesota	2.0
37	Iowa	1.9
38	Nevada	1.8
39	South Carolina	1.6
39	Utah	1.6
41	New Hampshire	1.4
42	New York	1.2
42	Ohio	1.2
42	Rhode Island	1.2
45	Indiana	1.1
46	Wisconsin	1.0
47	New Jersey	0.9
48	Michigan	0.8
48	Pennsylvania	0.8
50	Illinois	0.4
	District of Columbia	0.0

Source: U.S. Bureau of the Census
  "Health Insurance Historical Table 5" (http://www.census.gov/hhes/hlthins/historic/hihistt5.html)
*Children under 18 years old. Military health care is a form of government insurance.

Percent of Children Covered by Medicaid in 2002

National Percent = 23.9% of Children*

ALPHA ORDER

RANK	STATE	PERCENT
33	Alabama	20.6
12	Alaska	30.0
22	Arizona	24.5
6	Arkansas	35.9
16	California	26.4
48	Colorado	12.7
42	Connecticut	17.5
32	Delaware	20.9
26	Florida	23.0
24	Georgia	23.6
39	Hawaii	18.7
28	Idaho	21.9
37	Illinois	19.2
46	Indiana	16.1
33	Iowa	20.6
43	Kansas	17.1
19	Kentucky	25.0
5	Louisiana	37.0
10	Maine	30.7
49	Maryland	12.6
31	Massachusetts	21.1
21	Michigan	24.7
44	Minnesota	16.9
2	Mississippi	39.5
19	Missouri	25.0
18	Montana	25.6
23	Nebraska	24.4
50	Nevada	11.4
45	New Hampshire	16.8
41	New Jersey	18.1
2	New Mexico	39.5
11	New York	30.1
14	North Carolina	27.0
38	North Dakota	18.9
35	Ohio	19.6
13	Oklahoma	27.3
25	Oregon	23.2
36	Pennsylvania	19.5
9	Rhode Island	31.2
8	South Carolina	33.2
29	South Dakota	21.8
7	Tennessee	33.9
17	Texas	26.0
40	Utah	18.2
1	Vermont	40.9
47	Virginia	14.2
15	Washington	26.7
4	West Virginia	38.7
30	Wisconsin	21.5
27	Wyoming	22.2

RANK ORDER

RANK	STATE	PERCENT
1	Vermont	40.9
2	Mississippi	39.5
2	New Mexico	39.5
4	West Virginia	38.7
5	Louisiana	37.0
6	Arkansas	35.9
7	Tennessee	33.9
8	South Carolina	33.2
9	Rhode Island	31.2
10	Maine	30.7
11	New York	30.1
12	Alaska	30.0
13	Oklahoma	27.3
14	North Carolina	27.0
15	Washington	26.7
16	California	26.4
17	Texas	26.0
18	Montana	25.6
19	Kentucky	25.0
19	Missouri	25.0
21	Michigan	24.7
22	Arizona	24.5
23	Nebraska	24.4
24	Georgia	23.6
25	Oregon	23.2
26	Florida	23.0
27	Wyoming	22.2
28	Idaho	21.9
29	South Dakota	21.8
30	Wisconsin	21.5
31	Massachusetts	21.1
32	Delaware	20.9
33	Alabama	20.6
33	Iowa	20.6
35	Ohio	19.6
36	Pennsylvania	19.5
37	Illinois	19.2
38	North Dakota	18.9
39	Hawaii	18.7
40	Utah	18.2
41	New Jersey	18.1
42	Connecticut	17.5
43	Kansas	17.1
44	Minnesota	16.9
45	New Hampshire	16.8
46	Indiana	16.1
47	Virginia	14.2
48	Colorado	12.7
49	Maryland	12.6
50	Nevada	11.4

District of Columbia   45.2

Source: U.S. Bureau of the Census
    "Health Insurance Historical Table 5" (http://www.census.gov/hhes/hlthins/historic/hihistt5.html)
*Children under 18 years old. Medicaid is a form of government insurance.

State Children's Health Insurance Program (SCHIP) Enrollment in 2002

National Total = 5,315,229 Children*

ALPHA ORDER

RANK	STATE	CHILDREN	% of USA
17	Alabama	83,359	1.6%
33	Alaska	22,291	0.4%
14	Arizona	92,705	1.7%
48	Arkansas	1,912	0.0%
1	California	856,994	16.1%
25	Colorado	51,826	1.0%
34	Connecticut	21,346	0.4%
41	Delaware	9,691	0.2%
4	Florida	368,180	6.9%
5	Georgia	221,005	4.2%
43	Hawaii	8,474	0.2%
37	Idaho	16,895	0.3%
20	Illinois	68,032	1.3%
22	Indiana	66,225	1.2%
30	Iowa	34,506	0.6%
27	Kansas	40,783	0.8%
13	Kentucky	93,941	1.8%
15	Louisiana	87,675	1.6%
32	Maine	22,586	0.4%
8	Maryland	125,180	2.4%
11	Massachusetts	116,699	2.2%
18	Michigan	71,882	1.4%
NA	Minnesota**	NA	NA
23	Mississippi	64,805	1.2%
12	Missouri	112,004	2.1%
39	Montana	13,875	0.3%
38	Nebraska	16,227	0.3%
28	Nevada	37,878	0.7%
44	New Hampshire	8,138	0.2%
10	New Jersey	117,053	2.2%
35	New Mexico	19,940	0.4%
2	New York	807,145	15.2%
9	North Carolina	120,090	2.3%
47	North Dakota	4,463	0.1%
6	Ohio	183,034	3.4%
16	Oklahoma	84,490	1.6%
26	Oregon	42,976	0.8%
7	Pennsylvania	148,689	2.8%
36	Rhode Island	19,515	0.4%
19	South Carolina	68,928	1.3%
40	South Dakota	11,183	0.2%
NA	Tennessee**	NA	NA
3	Texas	727,452	13.7%
31	Utah	33,808	0.6%
45	Vermont	6,162	0.1%
21	Virginia	67,974	1.3%
42	Washington	8,754	0.2%
29	West Virginia	35,949	0.7%
24	Wisconsin	62,391	1.2%
46	Wyoming	5,059	0.1%

RANK ORDER

RANK	STATE	CHILDREN	% of USA
1	California	856,994	16.1%
2	New York	807,145	15.2%
3	Texas	727,452	13.7%
4	Florida	368,180	6.9%
5	Georgia	221,005	4.2%
6	Ohio	183,034	3.4%
7	Pennsylvania	148,689	2.8%
8	Maryland	125,180	2.4%
9	North Carolina	120,090	2.3%
10	New Jersey	117,053	2.2%
11	Massachusetts	116,699	2.2%
12	Missouri	112,004	2.1%
13	Kentucky	93,941	1.8%
14	Arizona	92,705	1.7%
15	Louisiana	87,675	1.6%
16	Oklahoma	84,490	1.6%
17	Alabama	83,359	1.6%
18	Michigan	71,882	1.4%
19	South Carolina	68,928	1.3%
20	Illinois	68,032	1.3%
21	Virginia	67,974	1.3%
22	Indiana	66,225	1.2%
23	Mississippi	64,805	1.2%
24	Wisconsin	62,391	1.2%
25	Colorado	51,826	1.0%
26	Oregon	42,976	0.8%
27	Kansas	40,783	0.8%
28	Nevada	37,878	0.7%
29	West Virginia	35,949	0.7%
30	Iowa	34,506	0.6%
31	Utah	33,808	0.6%
32	Maine	22,586	0.4%
33	Alaska	22,291	0.4%
34	Connecticut	21,346	0.4%
35	New Mexico	19,940	0.4%
36	Rhode Island	19,515	0.4%
37	Idaho	16,895	0.3%
38	Nebraska	16,227	0.3%
39	Montana	13,875	0.3%
40	South Dakota	11,183	0.2%
41	Delaware	9,691	0.2%
42	Washington	8,754	0.2%
43	Hawaii	8,474	0.2%
44	New Hampshire	8,138	0.2%
45	Vermont	6,162	0.1%
46	Wyoming	5,059	0.1%
47	North Dakota	4,463	0.1%
48	Arkansas	1,912	0.0%
NA	Minnesota**	NA	NA
NA	Tennessee**	NA	NA
	District of Columbia	5,060	0.1%

Source: U.S. Department of Health and Human Services, Centers for Medicare and Medicaid Services
  "Children's Health Insurance Program" (http://www.cms.gov/schip/schip02.pdf)
*Preliminary for fiscal year 2002. The State Children's Health Insurance Program (SCHIP) was created in 1997 to help states expand health insurance to children whose families earn too much to qualify for Medicaid, yet not enough to afford private health insurance.
**Not reported.

Percent Change in State Children's Health Insurance Program (SCHIP) Enrollment: 2001 to 2002
National Percent Change = 15.0% Increase*

ALPHA ORDER | | | RANK ORDER | | |

RANK	STATE	PERCENT CHANGE	RANK	STATE	PERCENT CHANGE
15	Alabama	22.3	1	Oklahoma	117.4
40	Alaska	2.1	2	New Mexico	92.7
34	Arizona	6.7	3	Delaware	74.1
48	Arkansas	(33.7)	4	Iowa	48.3
14	California	22.9	5	Texas	45.2
27	Colorado	13.2	6	Kentucky	37.6
25	Connecticut	14.6	7	New Hampshire	36.0
3	Delaware	74.1	8	Nevada	35.2
13	Florida	23.3	9	North Dakota	31.1
16	Georgia	20.9	10	Louisiana	26.0
19	Hawaii	18.7	11	South Dakota	23.7
41	Idaho	0.0	12	Mississippi	23.6
47	Illinois	(18.5)	13	Florida	23.3
22	Indiana	16.2	14	California	22.9
4	Iowa	48.3	15	Alabama	22.3
18	Kansas	19.0	16	Georgia	20.9
6	Kentucky	37.6	17	North Carolina	20.1
10	Louisiana	26.0	18	Kansas	19.0
46	Maine	(16.4)	19	Hawaii	18.7
26	Maryland	13.8	20	New Jersey	17.2
33	Massachusetts	7.7	21	Nebraska	16.5
43	Michigan	(5.6)	22	Indiana	16.2
NA	Minnesota**	NA	23	Vermont	15.1
12	Mississippi	23.6	24	Washington	14.9
36	Missouri	4.7	25	Connecticut	14.6
39	Montana	2.6	26	Maryland	13.8
21	Nebraska	16.5	27	Colorado	13.2
8	Nevada	35.2	28	Ohio	12.7
7	New Hampshire	36.0	29	Rhode Island	12.2
20	New Jersey	17.2	30	Wisconsin	9.1
2	New Mexico	92.7	31	Wyoming	8.7
45	New York	(7.5)	32	West Virginia	8.5
17	North Carolina	20.1	33	Massachusetts	7.7
9	North Dakota	31.1	34	Arizona	6.7
28	Ohio	12.7	35	Pennsylvania	5.3
1	Oklahoma	117.4	36	Missouri	4.7
38	Oregon	3.6	37	South Carolina	4.1
35	Pennsylvania	5.3	38	Oregon	3.6
29	Rhode Island	12.2	39	Montana	2.6
37	South Carolina	4.1	40	Alaska	2.1
11	South Dakota	23.7	41	Idaho	0.0
NA	Tennessee**	NA	42	Utah	(2.4)
5	Texas	45.2	43	Michigan	(5.6)
42	Utah	(2.4)	44	Virginia	(7.0)
23	Vermont	15.1	45	New York	(7.5)
44	Virginia	(7.0)	46	Maine	(16.4)
24	Washington	14.9	47	Illinois	(18.5)
32	West Virginia	8.5	48	Arkansas	(33.7)
30	Wisconsin	9.1	NA	Minnesota**	NA
31	Wyoming	8.7	NA	Tennessee**	NA
				District of Columbia	80.3

Source: MQ Press using data from U.S. Dept of Health & Human Services, Centers for Medicare and Medicaid Services "Children's Health Insurance Program" (http://www.cms.gov/schip/schip02.pdf)

*Preliminary for fiscal year 2002. The State Children's Health Insurance Program (SCHIP) was created in 1997 to help states expand health insurance to children whose families earn too much to qualify for Medicaid, yet not enough to afford private health insurance.

**Not reported.

Percent of Children Enrolled in State Children's Health Insurance Program (SCHIP) in 2002
National Percent = 7.4% of Children 17 Years and Younger*

ALPHA ORDER

RANK	STATE	PERCENT
16	Alabama	7.4
3	Alaska	11.7
19	Arizona	6.8
48	Arkansas	0.3
8	California	9.3
30	Colorado	4.7
45	Connecticut	2.5
29	Delaware	5.0
5	Florida	10.1
4	Georgia	10.2
41	Hawaii	2.9
33	Idaho	4.6
46	Illinois	2.1
35	Indiana	4.2
30	Iowa	4.7
24	Kansas	5.7
7	Kentucky	9.4
18	Louisiana	7.2
15	Maine	7.5
9	Maryland	9.2
13	Massachusetts	7.8
42	Michigan	2.8
NA	Minnesota**	NA
11	Mississippi	8.4
13	Missouri	7.8
23	Montana	6.0
40	Nebraska	3.6
16	Nevada	7.4
44	New Hampshire	2.6
25	New Jersey	5.6
37	New Mexico	3.9
1	New York	17.2
22	North Carolina	6.1
42	North Dakota	2.8
21	Ohio	6.3
6	Oklahoma	9.5
27	Oregon	5.1
27	Pennsylvania	5.1
12	Rhode Island	7.9
19	South Carolina	6.8
26	South Dakota	5.5
NA	Tennessee**	NA
2	Texas	12.4
30	Utah	4.7
35	Vermont	4.2
37	Virginia	3.9
47	Washington	0.6
10	West Virginia	8.9
33	Wisconsin	4.6
37	Wyoming	3.9

RANK ORDER

RANK	STATE	PERCENT
1	New York	17.2
2	Texas	12.4
3	Alaska	11.7
4	Georgia	10.2
5	Florida	10.1
6	Oklahoma	9.5
7	Kentucky	9.4
8	California	9.3
9	Maryland	9.2
10	West Virginia	8.9
11	Mississippi	8.4
12	Rhode Island	7.9
13	Massachusetts	7.8
13	Missouri	7.8
15	Maine	7.5
16	Alabama	7.4
16	Nevada	7.4
18	Louisiana	7.2
19	Arizona	6.8
19	South Carolina	6.8
21	Ohio	6.3
22	North Carolina	6.1
23	Montana	6.0
24	Kansas	5.7
25	New Jersey	5.6
26	South Dakota	5.5
27	Oregon	5.1
27	Pennsylvania	5.1
29	Delaware	5.0
30	Colorado	4.7
30	Iowa	4.7
30	Utah	4.7
33	Idaho	4.6
33	Wisconsin	4.6
35	Indiana	4.2
35	Vermont	4.2
37	New Mexico	3.9
37	Virginia	3.9
37	Wyoming	3.9
40	Nebraska	3.6
41	Hawaii	2.9
42	Michigan	2.8
42	North Dakota	2.8
44	New Hampshire	2.6
45	Connecticut	2.5
46	Illinois	2.1
47	Washington	0.6
48	Arkansas	0.3
NA	Minnesota**	NA
NA	Tennessee**	NA
	District of Columbia	4.4

Source: MQ Press using data from U.S. Dept of Health & Human Services, Centers for Medicare and Medicaid Services "Children's Health Insurance Program" (http://www.cms.gov/schip/schip02.pdf)

*For fiscal year 2002. The State Children's Health Insurance Program (SCHIP) was created in 1997 to help states expand health insurance to children whose families earn too much to qualify for Medicaid, yet not enough to afford private health insurance. Calculated using 2000 Census population counts.

State Children's Health Insurance Program (SCHIP) Allotments in 2003

National Total = $3,142,125,000*

ALPHA ORDER

RANK	STATE	ALLOTMENTS	% of USA
17	Alabama	$51,972,697	1.7%
45	Alaska	7,430,455	0.2%
10	Arizona	87,709,090	2.8%
28	Arkansas	34,154,500	1.1%
1	California	548,807,933	17.5%
26	Colorado	37,914,522	1.2%
35	Connecticut	24,361,434	0.8%
44	Delaware	8,686,068	0.3%
4	Florida	171,990,713	5.5%
8	Georgia	96,976,597	3.1%
42	Hawaii	9,647,963	0.3%
38	Idaho	16,795,479	0.5%
5	Illinois	132,153,277	4.2%
15	Indiana	53,709,869	1.7%
36	Iowa	21,368,268	0.7%
34	Kansas	24,443,683	0.8%
25	Kentucky	37,984,461	1.2%
13	Louisiana	61,290,629	2.0%
41	Maine	9,688,881	0.3%
29	Maryland	33,648,564	1.1%
19	Massachusetts	46,201,047	1.5%
9	Michigan	95,696,032	3.0%
31	Minnesota	30,626,504	1.0%
27	Mississippi	37,672,898	1.2%
22	Missouri	43,424,901	1.4%
40	Montana	11,326,534	0.4%
39	Nebraska	15,414,316	0.5%
32	Nevada	30,436,463	1.0%
43	New Hampshire	8,903,739	0.3%
12	New Jersey	69,346,099	2.2%
30	New Mexico	32,788,606	1.0%
3	New York	227,517,050	7.2%
11	North Carolina	81,748,254	2.6%
49	North Dakota	5,436,695	0.2%
6	Ohio	114,614,244	3.6%
20	Oklahoma	44,621,756	1.4%
24	Oregon	40,708,703	1.3%
7	Pennsylvania	100,845,639	3.2%
46	Rhode Island	7,318,673	0.2%
23	South Carolina	43,402,180	1.4%
47	South Dakota	6,151,723	0.2%
14	Tennessee	58,354,512	1.9%
2	Texas	311,503,988	9.9%
33	Utah	24,693,700	0.8%
50	Vermont	3,813,156	0.1%
16	Virginia	53,437,771	1.7%
18	Washington	50,326,484	1.6%
37	West Virginia	18,550,788	0.6%
21	Wisconsin	43,824,792	1.4%
48	Wyoming	5,480,750	0.2%

RANK ORDER

RANK	STATE	ALLOTMENTS	% of USA
1	California	$548,807,933	17.5%
2	Texas	311,503,988	9.9%
3	New York	227,517,050	7.2%
4	Florida	171,990,713	5.5%
5	Illinois	132,153,277	4.2%
6	Ohio	114,614,244	3.6%
7	Pennsylvania	100,845,639	3.2%
8	Georgia	96,976,597	3.1%
9	Michigan	95,696,032	3.0%
10	Arizona	87,709,090	2.8%
11	North Carolina	81,748,254	2.6%
12	New Jersey	69,346,099	2.2%
13	Louisiana	61,290,629	2.0%
14	Tennessee	58,354,512	1.9%
15	Indiana	53,709,869	1.7%
16	Virginia	53,437,771	1.7%
17	Alabama	51,972,697	1.7%
18	Washington	50,326,484	1.6%
19	Massachusetts	46,201,047	1.5%
20	Oklahoma	44,621,756	1.4%
21	Wisconsin	43,824,792	1.4%
22	Missouri	43,424,901	1.4%
23	South Carolina	43,402,180	1.4%
24	Oregon	40,708,703	1.3%
25	Kentucky	37,984,461	1.2%
26	Colorado	37,914,522	1.2%
27	Mississippi	37,672,898	1.2%
28	Arkansas	34,154,500	1.1%
29	Maryland	33,648,564	1.1%
30	New Mexico	32,788,606	1.0%
31	Minnesota	30,626,504	1.0%
32	Nevada	30,436,463	1.0%
33	Utah	24,693,700	0.8%
34	Kansas	24,443,683	0.8%
35	Connecticut	24,361,434	0.8%
36	Iowa	21,368,268	0.7%
37	West Virginia	18,550,788	0.6%
38	Idaho	16,795,479	0.5%
39	Nebraska	15,414,316	0.5%
40	Montana	11,326,534	0.4%
41	Maine	9,688,881	0.3%
42	Hawaii	9,647,963	0.3%
43	New Hampshire	8,903,739	0.3%
44	Delaware	8,686,068	0.3%
45	Alaska	7,430,455	0.2%
46	Rhode Island	7,318,673	0.2%
47	South Dakota	6,151,723	0.2%
48	Wyoming	5,480,750	0.2%
49	North Dakota	5,436,695	0.2%
50	Vermont	3,813,156	0.1%
	District of Columbia	7,201,920	0.2%

Source: U.S. Department of Health and Human Services, Centers for Medicare and Medicaid Services
  "SCHIP Allotments" (http://www.cms.gov/schip/regulations/allotments/)
*For fiscal year 2003. Allotments are distributed based on the number of low-income children and health care cost factors in each state. States have three years to spend their SCHIP allotments. SCHIP was created in 1997 to help states expand health insurance to children whose families earn too much to qualify for Medicaid, yet not enough to afford private health insurance. Total does not include $33,075,000 in allotments to U.S. territories.

Per Capita State Children's Health Insurance Program (SCHIP) Allotments in 2003
National Per Capita = $10.80*

ALPHA ORDER

RANK	STATE	PER CAPITA
13	Alabama	$11.55
14	Alaska	11.45
2	Arizona	15.72
9	Arkansas	12.53
3	California	15.47
33	Colorado	8.33
45	Connecticut	6.99
18	Delaware	10.63
23	Florida	10.11
16	Georgia	11.17
39	Hawaii	7.67
11	Idaho	12.29
21	Illinois	10.44
31	Indiana	8.67
42	Iowa	7.26
29	Kansas	8.98
28	Kentucky	9.22
5	Louisiana	13.63
41	Maine	7.42
49	Maryland	6.11
44	Massachusetts	7.18
27	Michigan	9.49
50	Minnesota	6.05
7	Mississippi	13.08
40	Missouri	7.61
10	Montana	12.34
30	Nebraska	8.86
6	Nevada	13.58
46	New Hampshire	6.91
37	New Jersey	8.03
1	New Mexico	17.49
12	New York	11.86
26	North Carolina	9.72
32	North Dakota	8.58
24	Ohio	10.02
8	Oklahoma	12.71
15	Oregon	11.44
35	Pennsylvania	8.16
47	Rhode Island	6.80
20	South Carolina	10.47
36	South Dakota	8.05
25	Tennessee	9.99
4	Texas	14.08
19	Utah	10.50
48	Vermont	6.16
43	Virginia	7.23
34	Washington	8.21
22	West Virginia	10.25
38	Wisconsin	8.01
17	Wyoming	10.93

RANK ORDER

RANK	STATE	PER CAPITA
1	New Mexico	$17.49
2	Arizona	15.72
3	California	15.47
4	Texas	14.08
5	Louisiana	13.63
6	Nevada	13.58
7	Mississippi	13.08
8	Oklahoma	12.71
9	Arkansas	12.53
10	Montana	12.34
11	Idaho	12.29
12	New York	11.86
13	Alabama	11.55
14	Alaska	11.45
15	Oregon	11.44
16	Georgia	11.17
17	Wyoming	10.93
18	Delaware	10.63
19	Utah	10.50
20	South Carolina	10.47
21	Illinois	10.44
22	West Virginia	10.25
23	Florida	10.11
24	Ohio	10.02
25	Tennessee	9.99
26	North Carolina	9.72
27	Michigan	9.49
28	Kentucky	9.22
29	Kansas	8.98
30	Nebraska	8.86
31	Indiana	8.67
32	North Dakota	8.58
33	Colorado	8.33
34	Washington	8.21
35	Pennsylvania	8.16
36	South Dakota	8.05
37	New Jersey	8.03
38	Wisconsin	8.01
39	Hawaii	7.67
40	Missouri	7.61
41	Maine	7.42
42	Iowa	7.26
43	Virginia	7.23
44	Massachusetts	7.18
45	Connecticut	6.99
46	New Hampshire	6.91
47	Rhode Island	6.80
48	Vermont	6.16
49	Maryland	6.11
50	Minnesota	6.05

| | District of Columbia | 12.78 |

Source: Morgan Quitno Press using data from U.S. Dept of HHS, Centers for Medicare and Medicaid Services "SCHIP Allotments" (http://www.cms.gov/schip/regulations/allotments/)

*For fiscal year 2003. Allotments are distributed based on the number of low-income children and health care cost factors in each state. States have three years to spend their SCHIP allotments. SCHIP was created in 1997 to help states expand health insurance to children whose families earn too much to qualify for Medicaid, yet not enough to afford private health insurance. National per capita does not include allotments to U.S. territories.

Expenditures for State Children's Health Insurance Program (SCHIP) in 2001

National Total = $3,825,815,526*

RANK	STATE	EXPENDITURES	% of USA
21	Alabama	$52,726,132	1.4%
26	Alaska	32,703,546	0.9%
16	Arizona	63,107,549	1.6%
49	Arkansas	3,041,237	0.1%
2	California	472,725,298	12.4%
28	Colorado	32,219,993	0.8%
34	Connecticut	20,276,440	0.5%
46	Delaware	3,522,910	0.1%
4	Florida	280,423,871	7.3%
9	Georgia	107,394,549	2.8%
44	Hawaii	4,494,374	0.1%
38	Idaho	16,329,656	0.4%
18	Illinois	60,172,536	1.6%
12	Indiana	81,661,975	2.1%
25	Iowa	33,630,995	0.9%
24	Kansas	34,226,716	0.9%
11	Kentucky	85,961,492	2.2%
22	Louisiana	50,017,975	1.3%
36	Maine	18,534,011	0.5%
6	Maryland	142,892,096	3.7%
13	Massachusetts	77,925,866	2.0%
20	Michigan	54,139,320	1.4%
50	Minnesota	1,050,703	0.0%
19	Mississippi	58,491,668	1.5%
15	Missouri	71,929,237	1.9%
37	Montana	17,078,586	0.4%
39	Nebraska	13,147,172	0.3%
32	Nevada	22,193,839	0.6%
43	New Hampshire	4,549,414	0.1%
5	New Jersey	198,281,030	5.2%
40	New Mexico	9,825,870	0.3%
1	New York	528,852,081	13.8%
10	North Carolina	96,119,888	2.5%
48	North Dakota	3,139,322	0.1%
7	Ohio	140,430,524	3.7%
27	Oklahoma	32,430,733	0.8%
33	Oregon	20,545,897	0.5%
8	Pennsylvania	134,241,636	3.5%
30	Rhode Island	27,115,190	0.7%
17	South Carolina	61,187,513	1.6%
42	South Dakota	6,720,328	0.2%
35	Tennessee	19,341,379	0.5%
3	Texas	364,665,345	9.5%
29	Utah	28,195,260	0.7%
47	Vermont	3,175,394	0.1%
23	Virginia	43,630,115	1.1%
41	Washington	8,447,279	0.2%
31	West Virginia	26,827,504	0.7%
14	Wisconsin	77,751,531	2.0%
45	Wyoming	3,936,548	0.1%

RANK	STATE	EXPENDITURES	% of USA
1	New York	$528,852,081	13.8%
2	California	472,725,298	12.4%
3	Texas	364,665,345	9.5%
4	Florida	280,423,871	7.3%
5	New Jersey	198,281,030	5.2%
6	Maryland	142,092,096	3.7%
7	Ohio	140,430,524	3.7%
8	Pennsylvania	134,241,636	3.5%
9	Georgia	107,394,549	2.8%
10	North Carolina	96,119,888	2.5%
11	Kentucky	85,961,492	2.2%
12	Indiana	81,661,975	2.1%
13	Massachusetts	77,925,866	2.0%
14	Wisconsin	77,751,531	2.0%
15	Missouri	71,929,237	1.9%
16	Arizona	63,107,549	1.6%
17	South Carolina	61,187,513	1.6%
18	Illinois	60,172,536	1.6%
19	Mississippi	58,491,668	1.5%
20	Michigan	54,139,320	1.4%
21	Alabama	52,726,132	1.4%
22	Louisiana	50,017,975	1.3%
23	Virginia	43,630,115	1.1%
24	Kansas	34,226,716	0.9%
25	Iowa	33,630,995	0.9%
26	Alaska	32,703,546	0.9%
27	Oklahoma	32,430,733	0.8%
28	Colorado	32,219,993	0.8%
29	Utah	28,195,260	0.7%
30	Rhode Island	27,115,190	0.7%
31	West Virginia	26,827,504	0.7%
32	Nevada	22,193,839	0.6%
33	Oregon	20,545,897	0.5%
34	Connecticut	20,276,440	0.5%
35	Tennessee	19,341,379	0.5%
36	Maine	18,534,011	0.5%
37	Montana	17,078,586	0.4%
38	Idaho	16,329,656	0.4%
39	Nebraska	13,147,172	0.3%
40	New Mexico	9,825,870	0.3%
41	Washington	8,447,279	0.2%
42	South Dakota	6,720,328	0.2%
43	New Hampshire	4,549,414	0.1%
44	Hawaii	4,494,374	0.1%
45	Wyoming	3,936,548	0.1%
46	Delaware	3,522,910	0.1%
47	Vermont	3,175,394	0.1%
48	North Dakota	3,139,322	0.1%
49	Arkansas	3,041,237	0.1%
50	Minnesota	1,050,703	0.0%
	District of Columbia	6,679,004	0.2%

Source: U.S. Department of Health and Human Services, Centers for Medicare and Medicaid Services "Net Reported Medicaid and SCHIP Expenditures" (http://www.cms.gov/medicaid/mbes/sttotal.pdf)
For fiscal year 2001. National total includes $67,706,998 spent in U.S. territories. The State Children's Health Insurance Program (SCHIP) was created in 1997 to help states expand health insurance to children whose families earn too much to qualify for Medicaid, yet not enough to afford private health insurance.

Per Capita Expenditures for State Children's Health Insurance Program (SCHIP) in 2001
National Per Capita = $13.17*

ALPHA ORDER

RANK	STATE	PER CAPITA
25	Alabama	$11.80
1	Alaska	51.61
24	Arizona	11.89
49	Arkansas	1.13
15	California	13.66
35	Colorado	7.27
38	Connecticut	5.90
44	Delaware	4.42
9	Florida	17.13
17	Georgia	12.78
45	Hawaii	3.66
20	Idaho	12.37
43	Illinois	4.81
16	Indiana	13.33
27	Iowa	11.47
19	Kansas	12.67
6	Kentucky	21.13
28	Louisiana	11.19
13	Maine	14.43
3	Maryland	26.53
23	Massachusetts	12.17
39	Michigan	5.41
50	Minnesota	0.21
7	Mississippi	20.45
18	Missouri	12.76
8	Montana	18.86
34	Nebraska	7.64
30	Nevada	10.58
46	New Hampshire	3.61
5	New Jersey	23.30
40	New Mexico	5.37
2	New York	27.71
26	North Carolina	11.71
42	North Dakota	4.93
22	Ohio	12.33
31	Oklahoma	9.35
37	Oregon	5.92
29	Pennsylvania	10.91
4	Rhode Island	25.59
11	South Carolina	15.06
32	South Dakota	8.86
47	Tennessee	3.36
10	Texas	17.06
20	Utah	12.37
41	Vermont	5.18
36	Virginia	6.06
48	Washington	1.41
12	West Virginia	14.90
14	Wisconsin	14.38
33	Wyoming	7.97

RANK ORDER

RANK	STATE	PER CAPITA
1	Alaska	$51.61
2	New York	27.71
3	Maryland	26.53
4	Rhode Island	25.59
5	New Jersey	23.30
6	Kentucky	21.13
7	Mississippi	20.45
8	Montana	18.86
9	Florida	17.13
10	Texas	17.06
11	South Carolina	15.06
12	West Virginia	14.90
13	Maine	14.43
14	Wisconsin	14.38
15	California	13.66
16	Indiana	13.33
17	Georgia	12.78
18	Missouri	12.76
19	Kansas	12.67
20	Idaho	12.37
20	Utah	12.37
22	Ohio	12.33
23	Massachusetts	12.17
24	Arizona	11.89
25	Alabama	11.80
26	North Carolina	11.71
27	Iowa	11.47
28	Louisiana	11.19
29	Pennsylvania	10.91
30	Nevada	10.58
31	Oklahoma	9.35
32	South Dakota	8.86
33	Wyoming	7.97
34	Nebraska	7.64
35	Colorado	7.27
36	Virginia	6.06
37	Oregon	5.92
38	Connecticut	5.90
39	Michigan	5.41
40	New Mexico	5.37
41	Vermont	5.18
42	North Dakota	4.93
43	Illinois	4.81
44	Delaware	4.42
45	Hawaii	3.66
46	New Hampshire	3.61
47	Tennessee	3.36
48	Washington	1.41
49	Arkansas	1.13
50	Minnesota	0.21

District of Columbia 11.64

Source: MQ Press using data from U.S. Dept of Health & Human Services, Centers for Medicare and Medicaid Services "Net Reported Medicaid and SCHIP Expenditures" (http://www.cms.gov/medicaid/mbes/sttotal.pdf)
*For fiscal year 2001. National figure does not include expenditures or population in U.S. territories. The State Children's Health Insurance Program (SCHIP) was created in 1997 to help states expand health insurance to children whose families earn too much to qualify for Medicaid, yet not enough to afford private health insurance.

Expenditures per State Children's Health Insurance Program (SCHIP) Participant in 2001
National Per Participant = $813*

ALPHA ORDER

RANK	STATE	PER PARTICIPANT
31	Alabama	$773
5	Alaska	1,498
35	Arizona	727
15	Arkansas	1,055
42	California	678
40	Colorado	704
14	Connecticut	1,088
44	Delaware	633
22	Florida	939
49	Georgia	588
45	Hawaii	630
17	Idaho	966
36	Illinois	721
7	Indiana	1,433
6	Iowa	1,445
16	Kansas	998
11	Kentucky	1,259
37	Louisiana	719
41	Maine	686
9	Maryland	1,299
37	Massachusetts	719
39	Michigan	711
1	Minnesota	21,443
12	Mississippi	1,115
43	Missouri	673
10	Montana	1,263
21	Nebraska	944
30	Nevada	792
32	New Hampshire	761
3	New Jersey	1,986
20	New Mexico	950
46	New York	606
18	North Carolina	961
24	North Dakota	922
25	Ohio	864
27	Oklahoma	835
50	Oregon	495
19	Pennsylvania	951
4	Rhode Island	1,559
23	South Carolina	925
33	South Dakota	743
2	Tennessee	2,245
34	Texas	728
28	Utah	814
48	Vermont	593
47	Virginia	597
13	Washington	1,108
29	West Virginia	809
8	Wisconsin	1,360
26	Wyoming	846

RANK ORDER

RANK	STATE	PER PARTICIPANT
1	Minnesota	$21,443
2	Tennessee	2,245
3	New Jersey	1,986
4	Rhode Island	1,559
5	Alaska	1,498
6	Iowa	1,445
7	Indiana	1,433
8	Wisconsin	1,360
9	Maryland	1,299
10	Montana	1,263
11	Kentucky	1,259
12	Mississippi	1,115
13	Washington	1,108
14	Connecticut	1,088
15	Arkansas	1,055
16	Kansas	998
17	Idaho	966
18	North Carolina	961
19	Pennsylvania	951
20	New Mexico	950
21	Nebraska	944
22	Florida	939
23	South Carolina	925
24	North Dakota	922
25	Ohio	864
26	Wyoming	846
27	Oklahoma	835
28	Utah	814
29	West Virginia	809
30	Nevada	792
31	Alabama	773
32	New Hampshire	761
33	South Dakota	743
34	Texas	728
35	Arizona	727
36	Illinois	721
37	Louisiana	719
37	Massachusetts	719
39	Michigan	711
40	Colorado	704
41	Maine	686
42	California	678
43	Missouri	673
44	Delaware	633
45	Hawaii	630
46	New York	606
47	Virginia	597
48	Vermont	593
49	Georgia	588
50	Oregon	495

District of Columbia   2,379

Source: MQ Press using data from U.S. Dept of Health & Human Services, Centers for Medicare and Medicaid Services "Net Reported Medicaid and SCHIP Expenditures" (http://www.cms.gov/medicaid/mbes/sttotal.pdf)
*For fiscal year 2001. National figure does not include expenditures or participants in U.S. territories. The State Children's Health Insurance Program (SCHIP) was created in 1997 to help states expand health insurance to children whose families earn too much to qualify for Medicaid, yet not enough to afford private health insurance.

Health Maintenance Organizations (HMOs) in 2003

National Total = 450 HMOs*

RANK	STATE	HMOs	% of USA
32	Alabama	4	0.9%
50	Alaska	0	0.0%
15	Arizona	10	2.2%
38	Arkansas	3	0.7%
1	California	28	6.2%
13	Colorado	12	2.7%
22	Connecticut	7	1.6%
32	Delaware	4	0.9%
3	Florida	25	5.6%
17	Georgia	9	2.0%
38	Hawaii	3	0.7%
38	Idaho	3	0.7%
11	Illinois	14	3.1%
13	Indiana	12	2.7%
32	Iowa	4	0.9%
28	Kansas	5	1.1%
26	Kentucky	6	1.3%
22	Louisiana	7	1.6%
32	Maine	4	0.9%
17	Maryland	9	2.0%
17	Massachusetts	9	2.0%
3	Michigan	25	5.6%
21	Minnesota	8	1.8%
44	Mississippi	2	0.4%
8	Missouri	17	3.8%
44	Montana	2	0.4%
32	Nebraska	4	0.9%
26	Nevada	6	1.3%
38	New Hampshire	3	0.7%
12	New Jersey	13	2.9%
28	New Mexico	5	1.1%
2	New York	27	6.0%
17	North Carolina	9	2.0%
48	North Dakota	1	0.2%
6	Ohio	22	4.9%
22	Oklahoma	7	1.6%
28	Oregon	5	1.1%
9	Pennsylvania	16	3.6%
38	Rhode Island	3	0.7%
32	South Carolina	4	0.9%
38	South Dakota	3	0.7%
10	Tennessee	15	3.3%
3	Texas	25	5.6%
22	Utah	7	1.6%
44	Vermont	2	0.4%
15	Virginia	10	2.2%
28	Washington	5	1.1%
44	West Virginia	2	0.4%
7	Wisconsin	18	4.0%
48	Wyoming	1	0.2%

RANK	STATE	HMOs	% of USA
1	California	28	6.2%
2	New York	27	6.0%
3	Florida	25	5.6%
3	Michigan	25	5.6%
3	Texas	25	5.6%
6	Ohio	22	4.9%
7	Wisconsin	18	4.0%
8	Missouri	17	3.8%
9	Pennsylvania	16	3.6%
10	Tennessee	15	3.3%
11	Illinois	14	3.1%
12	New Jersey	13	2.9%
13	Colorado	12	2.7%
13	Indiana	12	2.7%
15	Arizona	10	2.2%
15	Virginia	10	2.2%
17	Georgia	9	2.0%
17	Maryland	9	2.0%
17	Massachusetts	9	2.0%
17	North Carolina	9	2.0%
21	Minnesota	8	1.8%
22	Connecticut	7	1.6%
22	Louisiana	7	1.6%
22	Oklahoma	7	1.6%
22	Utah	7	1.6%
26	Kentucky	6	1.3%
26	Nevada	6	1.3%
28	Kansas	5	1.1%
28	New Mexico	5	1.1%
28	Oregon	5	1.1%
28	Washington	5	1.1%
32	Alabama	4	0.9%
32	Delaware	4	0.9%
32	Iowa	4	0.9%
32	Maine	4	0.9%
32	Nebraska	4	0.9%
32	South Carolina	4	0.9%
38	Arkansas	3	0.7%
38	Hawaii	3	0.7%
38	Idaho	3	0.7%
38	New Hampshire	3	0.7%
38	Rhode Island	3	0.7%
38	South Dakota	3	0.7%
44	Mississippi	2	0.4%
44	Montana	2	0.4%
44	Vermont	2	0.4%
44	West Virginia	2	0.4%
48	North Dakota	1	0.2%
48	Wyoming	1	0.2%
50	Alaska	0	0.0%
	District of Columbia	5	1.1%

Source: InterStudy Publications (St. Paul, MN)
   "HMO Industry Report 13.2"
As of January 1, 2003. Total does not include one HMO in Guam and three in Puerto Rico. Health plans are allocated to states based upon their primary service areas. This means each plan is counted once. However, many plans serve more than one state.

Enrollees in Health Maintenance Organizations (HMOs) in 2003

National Total = 70,084,991 Enrollees*

ALPHA ORDER

RANK	STATE	ENROLLEES	% of USA
40	Alabama	170,700	0.2%
50	Alaska	0	0.0%
19	Arizona	1,161,477	1.7%
38	Arkansas	192,297	0.3%
1	California	17,026,183	24.3%
15	Colorado	1,365,883	1.9%
16	Connecticut	1,306,341	1.9%
42	Delaware	123,441	0.2%
3	Florida	4,339,360	6.2%
20	Georgia	1,150,988	1.6%
31	Hawaii	373,538	0.5%
46	Idaho	38,219	0.1%
10	Illinois	1,851,827	2.6%
25	Indiana	731,430	1.0%
34	Iowa	278,879	0.4%
37	Kansas	210,656	0.3%
17	Kentucky	1,277,659	1.8%
28	Louisiana	547,496	0.8%
35	Maine	273,563	0.4%
12	Maryland**	1,669,639	2.4%
7	Massachusetts	2,489,277	3.6%
6	Michigan	2,612,558	3.7%
14	Minnesota	1,386,187	2.0%
47	Mississippi	23,935	0.0%
11	Missouri	1,829,603	2.6%
45	Montana	47,088	0.1%
41	Nebraska	151,858	0.2%
30	Nevada	458,531	0.7%
33	New Hampshire	330,859	0.5%
8	New Jersey	2,322,649	3.3%
27	New Mexico	561,835	0.8%
2	New York	6,207,150	8.9%
22	North Carolina	962,563	1.4%
49	North Dakota	2,239	0.0%
9	Ohio	2,123,322	3.0%
29	Oklahoma	486,229	0.7%
24	Oregon	851,307	1.2%
4	Pennsylvania	3,911,001	5.6%
32	Rhode Island	338,657	0.5%
36	South Carolina	266,296	0.4%
43	South Dakota	80,752	0.1%
21	Tennessee	1,046,144	1.5%
5	Texas	2,789,326	4.0%
26	Utah	599,546	0.9%
44	Vermont	61,040	0.1%
18	Virginia**	1,202,706	1.7%
23	Washington	917,419	1.3%
39	West Virginia**	182,680	0.3%
13	Wisconsin	1,581,948	2.3%
48	Wyoming	12,000	0.0%

RANK ORDER

RANK	STATE	ENROLLEES	% of USA
1	California	17,026,183	24.3%
2	New York	6,207,150	8.9%
3	Florida	4,339,360	6.2%
4	Pennsylvania	3,911,001	5.6%
5	Texas	2,789,326	4.0%
6	Michigan	2,612,558	3.7%
7	Massachusetts	2,489,277	3.6%
8	New Jersey	2,322,649	3.3%
9	Ohio	2,123,322	3.0%
10	Illinois	1,851,827	2.6%
11	Missouri	1,829,603	2.6%
12	Maryland**	1,669,639	2.4%
13	Wisconsin	1,581,948	2.3%
14	Minnesota	1,386,187	2.0%
15	Colorado	1,365,883	1.9%
16	Connecticut	1,306,341	1.9%
17	Kentucky	1,277,659	1.8%
18	Virginia**	1,202,706	1.7%
19	Arizona	1,161,477	1.7%
20	Georgia	1,150,988	1.6%
21	Tennessee	1,046,144	1.5%
22	North Carolina	962,563	1.4%
23	Washington	917,419	1.3%
24	Oregon	851,307	1.2%
25	Indiana	731,430	1.0%
26	Utah	599,546	0.9%
27	New Mexico	561,835	0.8%
28	Louisiana	547,496	0.8%
29	Oklahoma	486,229	0.7%
30	Nevada	458,531	0.7%
31	Hawaii	373,538	0.5%
32	Rhode Island	338,657	0.5%
33	New Hampshire	330,859	0.5%
34	Iowa	278,879	0.4%
35	Maine	273,563	0.4%
36	South Carolina	266,296	0.4%
37	Kansas	210,656	0.3%
38	Arkansas	192,297	0.3%
39	West Virginia**	182,680	0.3%
40	Alabama	170,700	0.2%
41	Nebraska	151,858	0.2%
42	Delaware	123,441	0.2%
43	South Dakota	80,752	0.1%
44	Vermont	61,040	0.1%
45	Montana	47,088	0.1%
46	Idaho	38,219	0.1%
47	Mississippi	23,935	0.0%
48	Wyoming	12,000	0.0%
49	North Dakota	2,239	0.0%
50	Alaska	0	0.0%
	District of Columbia	158,710	0.2%

Source: InterStudy Publications (St. Paul, MN)
   "HMO Industry Report 13.2"

*As of January 1, 2003. Total does not include 1,758,316 enrollees in U.S. territories.
**Maryland, Virginia and West Virginia include partial enrollment from five HMOs serving the Washington, DC metropolitan area.

Percent Change in Enrollees in Health Maintenance Organizations (HMOs): 2002 to 2003
National Percent Change = 5.6% Decrease*

ALPHA ORDER

RANK	STATE	PERCENT CHANGE
44	Alabama	(18.2)
NA	Alaska**	NA
40	Arizona	(15.0)
26	Arkansas	(7.5)
17	California	(2.3)
23	Colorado	(6.1)
13	Connecticut	(0.4)
47	Delaware	(32.5)
32	Florida	(11.2)
30	Georgia	(9.7)
25	Hawaii	(7.0)
15	Idaho	(1.8)
41	Illinois	(17.5)
3	Indiana	11.9
1	Iowa	86.5
49	Kansas	(40.9)
14	Kentucky	(1.3)
37	Louisiana	(12.6)
32	Maine	(11.2)
31	Maryland	(10.9)
27	Massachusetts	(7.9)
8	Michigan	2.4
7	Minnesota	3.8
48	Mississippi	(40.5)
6	Missouri	4.1
29	Montana	(9.6)
9	Nebraska	2.1
19	Nevada	(2.9)
38	New Hampshire	(13.2)
34	New Jersey	(11.4)
4	New Mexico	5.8
19	New York	(2.9)
46	North Carolina	(20.5)
18	North Dakota	(2.6)
39	Ohio	(13.7)
22	Oklahoma	(5.2)
45	Oregon	(18.6)
10	Pennsylvania	1.9
28	Rhode Island	(8.2)
43	South Carolina	(17.7)
24	South Dakota	(6.9)
15	Tennessee	(1.8)
36	Texas	(12.3)
41	Utah	(17.5)
21	Vermont	(4.7)
5	Virginia	4.4
35	Washington	(12.0)
11	West Virginia	0.9
12	Wisconsin	(0.2)
2	Wyoming	18.8

RANK ORDER

RANK	STATE	PERCENT CHANGE
1	Iowa	86.5
2	Wyoming	18.8
3	Indiana	11.9
4	New Mexico	5.8
5	Virginia	4.4
6	Missouri	4.1
7	Minnesota	3.8
8	Michigan	2.4
9	Nebraska	2.1
10	Pennsylvania	1.9
11	West Virginia	0.9
12	Wisconsin	(0.2)
13	Connecticut	(0.4)
14	Kentucky	(1.3)
15	Idaho	(1.8)
15	Tennessee	(1.8)
17	California	(2.3)
18	North Dakota	(2.6)
19	Nevada	(2.9)
19	New York	(2.9)
21	Vermont	(4.7)
22	Oklahoma	(5.2)
23	Colorado	(6.1)
24	South Dakota	(6.9)
25	Hawaii	(7.0)
26	Arkansas	(7.5)
27	Massachusetts	(7.9)
28	Rhode Island	(8.2)
29	Montana	(9.6)
30	Georgia	(9.7)
31	Maryland	(10.9)
32	Florida	(11.2)
32	Maine	(11.2)
34	New Jersey	(11.4)
35	Washington	(12.0)
36	Texas	(12.3)
37	Louisiana	(12.6)
38	New Hampshire	(13.2)
39	Ohio	(13.7)
40	Arizona	(15.0)
41	Illinois	(17.5)
41	Utah	(17.5)
43	South Carolina	(17.7)
44	Alabama	(18.2)
45	Oregon	(18.6)
46	North Carolina	(20.5)
47	Delaware	(32.5)
48	Mississippi	(40.5)
49	Kansas	(40.9)
NA	Alaska**	NA
	District of Columbia	0.2

Source: InterStudy Publications (St. Paul, MN)
    "HMO Industry Report 13.2"
*As of January 1, 2003. National rate does not include enrollees in U.S. territories.
**Not applicable.

Percent of Population Enrolled in Health Maintenance Organizations (HMOs) in 2003
National Percent = 24.1% Enrolled in HMOs*

ALPHA ORDER

RANK	STATE	PERCENT
45	Alabama	3.8
50	Alaska	0.0
22	Arizona	20.8
42	Arkansas	7.1
1	California	48.0
10	Colorado	30.0
3	Connecticut	37.5
27	Delaware	15.1
18	Florida	25.5
31	Georgia	13.3
12	Hawaii	29.7
46	Idaho	2.8
29	Illinois	14.6
34	Indiana	11.8
39	Iowa	9.5
41	Kansas	7.7
8	Kentucky	31.0
33	Louisiana	12.2
21	Maine	21.0
9	Maryland	30.3
2	Massachusetts	38.7
16	Michigan	25.9
14	Minnesota	27.4
48	Mississippi	0.8
5	Missouri	32.1
44	Montana	5.1
40	Nebraska	8.7
23	Nevada	20.5
17	New Hampshire	25.7
15	New Jersey	26.9
10	New Mexico	30.0
4	New York	32.3
35	North Carolina	11.4
49	North Dakota	0.4
24	Ohio	18.6
30	Oklahoma	13.8
20	Oregon	23.9
6	Pennsylvania	31.6
7	Rhode Island	31.5
43	South Carolina	6.4
36	South Dakota	10.6
25	Tennessee	17.9
32	Texas	12.6
18	Utah	25.5
38	Vermont	9.9
26	Virginia	16.3
28	Washington	15.0
37	West Virginia	10.1
13	Wisconsin	28.9
47	Wyoming	2.4

RANK ORDER

RANK	STATE	PERCENT
1	California	48.0
2	Massachusetts	38.7
3	Connecticut	37.5
4	New York	32.3
5	Missouri	32.1
6	Pennsylvania	31.6
7	Rhode Island	31.5
8	Kentucky	31.0
9	Maryland	30.3
10	Colorado	30.0
10	New Mexico	30.0
12	Hawaii	29.7
13	Wisconsin	28.9
14	Minnesota	27.4
15	New Jersey	26.9
16	Michigan	25.9
17	New Hampshire	25.7
18	Florida	25.5
18	Utah	25.5
20	Oregon	23.9
21	Maine	21.0
22	Arizona	20.8
23	Nevada	20.5
24	Ohio	18.6
25	Tennessee	17.9
26	Virginia	16.3
27	Delaware	15.1
28	Washington	15.0
29	Illinois	14.6
30	Oklahoma	13.8
31	Georgia	13.3
32	Texas	12.6
33	Louisiana	12.2
34	Indiana	11.8
35	North Carolina	11.4
36	South Dakota	10.6
37	West Virginia	10.1
38	Vermont	9.9
39	Iowa	9.5
40	Nebraska	8.7
41	Kansas	7.7
42	Arkansas	7.1
43	South Carolina	6.4
44	Montana	5.1
45	Alabama	3.8
46	Idaho	2.8
47	Wyoming	2.4
48	Mississippi	0.8
49	North Dakota	0.4
50	Alaska	0.0

	District of Columbia	28.2

Source: Morgan Quitno Press using data from InterStudy Publications (St. Paul, MN)
    "HMO Industry Report 13.2"

*As of January 1, 2003. Calculated using Census 2003 population estimates. National percent does not include enrollees or population in U.S. territories.

Percent of Insured Population Enrolled in
Health Maintenance Organizations (HMOs) in 2003
National Percent = 28.9% of Insured are Enrolled in HMOs*

ALPHA ORDER

RANK	STATE	PERCENT
45	Alabama	4.4
50	Alaska	0.0
22	Arizona	25.7
42	Arkansas	8.5
1	California	59.2
8	Colorado	36.4
2	Connecticut	43.2
29	Delaware	17.2
14	Florida	31.9
32	Georgia	16.3
12	Hawaii	33.9
46	Idaho	3.6
29	Illinois	17.2
35	Indiana	13.8
39	Iowa	10.6
41	Kansas	8.8
7	Kentucky	36.5
33	Louisiana	15.1
23	Maine	24.3
11	Maryland	35.3
3	Massachusetts	42.7
17	Michigan	29.9
18	Minnesota	29.8
48	Mississippi	1.0
6	Missouri	37.0
44	Montana	6.1
40	Nebraska	9.9
21	Nevada	26.9
19	New Hampshire	29.0
15	New Jersey	31.4
4	New Mexico	38.7
5	New York	38.2
34	North Carolina	14.2
49	North Dakota	0.4
24	Ohio	21.4
31	Oklahoma	16.9
20	Oregon	28.4
9	Pennsylvania	36.2
10	Rhode Island	35.6
43	South Carolina	7.6
36	South Dakota	12.3
25	Tennessee	20.7
28	Texas	17.5
16	Utah	30.0
38	Vermont	11.0
26	Virginia	19.5
27	Washington	17.8
37	West Virginia	12.2
13	Wisconsin	32.0
47	Wyoming	3.0

RANK ORDER

RANK	STATE	PERCENT
1	California	59.2
2	Connecticut	43.2
3	Massachusetts	42.7
4	New Mexico	38.7
5	New York	38.2
6	Missouri	37.0
7	Kentucky	36.5
8	Colorado	36.4
9	Pennsylvania	36.2
10	Rhode Island	35.6
11	Maryland	35.3
12	Hawaii	33.9
13	Wisconsin	32.0
14	Florida	31.9
15	New Jersey	31.4
16	Utah	30.0
17	Michigan	29.9
18	Minnesota	29.8
19	New Hampshire	29.0
20	Oregon	28.4
21	Nevada	26.9
22	Arizona	25.7
23	Maine	24.3
24	Ohio	21.4
25	Tennessee	20.7
26	Virginia	19.5
27	Washington	17.8
28	Texas	17.5
29	Delaware	17.2
29	Illinois	17.2
31	Oklahoma	16.9
32	Georgia	16.3
33	Louisiana	15.1
34	North Carolina	14.2
35	Indiana	13.8
36	South Dakota	12.3
37	West Virginia	12.2
38	Vermont	11.0
39	Iowa	10.6
40	Nebraska	9.9
41	Kansas	8.8
42	Arkansas	8.5
43	South Carolina	7.6
44	Montana	6.1
45	Alabama	4.4
46	Idaho	3.6
47	Wyoming	3.0
48	Mississippi	1.0
49	North Dakota	0.4
50	Alaska	0.0
	District of Columbia	31.9

Source: Morgan Quitno Press using data from InterStudy Publications (Minneapolis, MN)
     "HMO Industry Report 13.2"
*As of January 1, 2003. Calculated using estimated number of insured as of 2002 from the U.S. Census Bureau.

Medicare Enrollees in 2002

National Total = 40,488,878 Enrollees*

ALPHA ORDER

RANK	STATE	ENROLLEES	% of USA
20	Alabama	705,555	1.7%
50	Alaska	45,788	0.1%
19	Arizona	708,210	1.7%
31	Arkansas	446,152	1.1%
1	California	4,009,429	9.9%
29	Colorado	483,706	1.2%
26	Connecticut	518,344	1.3%
46	Delaware	116,363	0.3%
2	Florida	2,876,168	7.1%
12	Georgia	951,439	2.3%
43	Hawaii	171,259	0.4%
41	Idaho	172,787	0.4%
7	Illinois	1,645,851	4.1%
15	Indiana	865,366	2.1%
30	Iowa	479,455	1.2%
33	Kansas	391,782	1.0%
23	Kentucky	637,212	1.6%
24	Louisiana	611,863	1.5%
38	Maine	222,917	0.6%
22	Maryland	663,739	1.6%
11	Massachusetts	963,270	2.4%
8	Michigan	1,426,169	3.5%
21	Minnesota	667,407	1.6%
32	Mississippi	429,046	1.1%
14	Missouri	873,816	2.2%
44	Montana	140,156	0.3%
36	Nebraska	255,862	0.6%
35	Nevada	261,371	0.6%
40	New Hampshire	175,828	0.4%
9	New Jersey	1,212,966	3.0%
37	New Mexico	243,922	0.6%
3	New York	2,746,660	6.8%
10	North Carolina	1,178,169	2.9%
47	North Dakota	103,208	0.3%
6	Ohio	1,712,918	4.2%
27	Oklahoma	514,542	1.3%
28	Oregon	503,783	1.2%
5	Pennsylvania	2,100,640	5.2%
42	Rhode Island	172,106	0.4%
25	South Carolina	592,039	1.5%
45	South Dakota	120,720	0.3%
16	Tennessee	855,278	2.1%
4	Texas	2,338,394	5.8%
39	Utah	214,881	0.5%
48	Vermont	91,382	0.2%
13	Virginia	926,579	2.3%
18	Washington	759,088	1.9%
34	West Virginia	343,210	0.8%
17	Wisconsin	794,181	2.0%
49	Wyoming	67,356	0.2%

RANK ORDER

RANK	STATE	ENROLLEES	% of USA
1	California	4,009,429	9.9%
2	Florida	2,876,168	7.1%
3	New York	2,746,660	6.8%
4	Texas	2,338,394	5.8%
5	Pennsylvania	2,100,640	5.2%
6	Ohio	1,712,918	4.2%
7	Illinois	1,645,851	4.1%
8	Michigan	1,426,169	3.5%
9	New Jersey	1,212,966	3.0%
10	North Carolina	1,178,169	2.9%
11	Massachusetts	963,270	2.4%
12	Georgia	951,439	2.3%
13	Virginia	926,579	2.3%
14	Missouri	873,816	2.2%
15	Indiana	865,366	2.1%
16	Tennessee	855,278	2.1%
17	Wisconsin	794,181	2.0%
18	Washington	759,088	1.9%
19	Arizona	708,210	1.7%
20	Alabama	705,555	1.7%
21	Minnesota	667,407	1.6%
22	Maryland	663,739	1.6%
23	Kentucky	637,212	1.6%
24	Louisiana	611,863	1.5%
25	South Carolina	592,039	1.5%
26	Connecticut	518,344	1.3%
27	Oklahoma	514,542	1.3%
28	Oregon	503,783	1.2%
29	Colorado	483,706	1.2%
30	Iowa	479,455	1.2%
31	Arkansas	446,152	1.1%
32	Mississippi	429,046	1.1%
33	Kansas	391,782	1.0%
34	West Virginia	343,210	0.8%
35	Nevada	261,371	0.6%
36	Nebraska	255,862	0.6%
37	New Mexico	243,922	0.6%
38	Maine	222,917	0.6%
39	Utah	214,881	0.5%
40	New Hampshire	175,828	0.4%
41	Idaho	172,787	0.4%
42	Rhode Island	172,106	0.4%
43	Hawaii	171,259	0.4%
44	Montana	140,156	0.3%
45	South Dakota	120,720	0.3%
46	Delaware	116,363	0.3%
47	North Dakota	103,208	0.3%
48	Vermont	91,382	0.2%
49	Wyoming	67,356	0.2%
50	Alaska	45,788	0.1%
	District of Columbia	74,175	0.2%

Source: U.S. Department of Health and Human Services, Centers for Medicare and Medicaid Services
"Medicare Enrollment" (http://www.cms.gov/statistics/enrollment/stenrtrend99_02.asp)
*As of July 2002. Includes aged and disabled enrollees. Total includes 561,768 enrollees in Puerto Rico and 344,603 enrollees in other outlying areas, foreign countries or whose address is unknown.

Percent Change in Medicare Enrollees: 2001 to 2002

National Percent Change = 1.1% Increase

<table>
<tr><td colspan="3">ALPHA ORDER</td><td colspan="3">RANK ORDER</td></tr>
<tr><td>RANK</td><td>STATE</td><td>PERCENT CHANGE</td><td>RANK</td><td>STATE</td><td>PERCENT CHANGE</td></tr>
<tr><td>19</td><td>Alabama</td><td>1.5</td><td>1</td><td>Alaska</td><td>4.3</td></tr>
<tr><td>1</td><td>Alaska</td><td>4.3</td><td>2</td><td>Nevada</td><td>4.1</td></tr>
<tr><td>3</td><td>Arizona</td><td>2.5</td><td>3</td><td>Arizona</td><td>2.5</td></tr>
<tr><td>31</td><td>Arkansas</td><td>1.0</td><td>3</td><td>Idaho</td><td>2.5</td></tr>
<tr><td>22</td><td>California</td><td>1.4</td><td>5</td><td>New Mexico</td><td>2.3</td></tr>
<tr><td>13</td><td>Colorado</td><td>1.7</td><td>6</td><td>Delaware</td><td>2.1</td></tr>
<tr><td>41</td><td>Connecticut</td><td>0.4</td><td>6</td><td>South Carolina</td><td>2.1</td></tr>
<tr><td>6</td><td>Delaware</td><td>2.1</td><td>6</td><td>Utah</td><td>2.1</td></tr>
<tr><td>25</td><td>Florida</td><td>1.3</td><td>9</td><td>North Carolina</td><td>2.0</td></tr>
<tr><td>10</td><td>Georgia</td><td>1.9</td><td>10</td><td>Georgia</td><td>1.9</td></tr>
<tr><td>13</td><td>Hawaii</td><td>1.7</td><td>11</td><td>New Hampshire</td><td>1.8</td></tr>
<tr><td>3</td><td>Idaho</td><td>2.5</td><td>11</td><td>Virginia</td><td>1.8</td></tr>
<tr><td>41</td><td>Illinois</td><td>0.4</td><td>13</td><td>Colorado</td><td>1.7</td></tr>
<tr><td>33</td><td>Indiana</td><td>0.8</td><td>13</td><td>Hawaii</td><td>1.7</td></tr>
<tr><td>45</td><td>Iowa</td><td>0.3</td><td>13</td><td>Texas</td><td>1.7</td></tr>
<tr><td>46</td><td>Kansas</td><td>0.2</td><td>13</td><td>Washington</td><td>1.7</td></tr>
<tr><td>28</td><td>Kentucky</td><td>1.2</td><td>17</td><td>Maine</td><td>1.6</td></tr>
<tr><td>29</td><td>Louisiana</td><td>1.1</td><td>17</td><td>Oregon</td><td>1.6</td></tr>
<tr><td>17</td><td>Maine</td><td>1.6</td><td>19</td><td>Alabama</td><td>1.5</td></tr>
<tr><td>22</td><td>Maryland</td><td>1.4</td><td>19</td><td>Tennessee</td><td>1.5</td></tr>
<tr><td>46</td><td>Massachusetts</td><td>0.2</td><td>19</td><td>Vermont</td><td>1.5</td></tr>
<tr><td>33</td><td>Michigan</td><td>0.8</td><td>22</td><td>California</td><td>1.4</td></tr>
<tr><td>29</td><td>Minnesota</td><td>1.1</td><td>22</td><td>Maryland</td><td>1.4</td></tr>
<tr><td>25</td><td>Mississippi</td><td>1.3</td><td>22</td><td>Wyoming</td><td>1.4</td></tr>
<tr><td>33</td><td>Missouri</td><td>0.8</td><td>25</td><td>Florida</td><td>1.3</td></tr>
<tr><td>25</td><td>Montana</td><td>1.3</td><td>25</td><td>Mississippi</td><td>1.3</td></tr>
<tr><td>40</td><td>Nebraska</td><td>0.5</td><td>25</td><td>Montana</td><td>1.3</td></tr>
<tr><td>2</td><td>Nevada</td><td>4.1</td><td>28</td><td>Kentucky</td><td>1.2</td></tr>
<tr><td>11</td><td>New Hampshire</td><td>1.8</td><td>29</td><td>Louisiana</td><td>1.1</td></tr>
<tr><td>41</td><td>New Jersey</td><td>0.4</td><td>29</td><td>Minnesota</td><td>1.1</td></tr>
<tr><td>5</td><td>New Mexico</td><td>2.3</td><td>31</td><td>Arkansas</td><td>1.0</td></tr>
<tr><td>38</td><td>New York</td><td>0.6</td><td>31</td><td>West Virginia</td><td>1.0</td></tr>
<tr><td>9</td><td>North Carolina</td><td>2.0</td><td>33</td><td>Indiana</td><td>0.8</td></tr>
<tr><td>50</td><td>North Dakota</td><td>0.1</td><td>33</td><td>Michigan</td><td>0.8</td></tr>
<tr><td>41</td><td>Ohio</td><td>0.4</td><td>33</td><td>Missouri</td><td>0.8</td></tr>
<tr><td>33</td><td>Oklahoma</td><td>0.8</td><td>33</td><td>Oklahoma</td><td>0.8</td></tr>
<tr><td>17</td><td>Oregon</td><td>1.6</td><td>33</td><td>Wisconsin</td><td>0.8</td></tr>
<tr><td>46</td><td>Pennsylvania</td><td>0.2</td><td>38</td><td>New York</td><td>0.6</td></tr>
<tr><td>46</td><td>Rhode Island</td><td>0.2</td><td>38</td><td>South Dakota</td><td>0.6</td></tr>
<tr><td>6</td><td>South Carolina</td><td>2.1</td><td>40</td><td>Nebraska</td><td>0.5</td></tr>
<tr><td>38</td><td>South Dakota</td><td>0.6</td><td>41</td><td>Connecticut</td><td>0.4</td></tr>
<tr><td>19</td><td>Tennessee</td><td>1.5</td><td>41</td><td>Illinois</td><td>0.4</td></tr>
<tr><td>13</td><td>Texas</td><td>1.7</td><td>41</td><td>New Jersey</td><td>0.4</td></tr>
<tr><td>6</td><td>Utah</td><td>2.1</td><td>41</td><td>Ohio</td><td>0.4</td></tr>
<tr><td>19</td><td>Vermont</td><td>1.5</td><td>45</td><td>Iowa</td><td>0.3</td></tr>
<tr><td>11</td><td>Virginia</td><td>1.8</td><td>46</td><td>Kansas</td><td>0.2</td></tr>
<tr><td>13</td><td>Washington</td><td>1.7</td><td>46</td><td>Massachusetts</td><td>0.2</td></tr>
<tr><td>31</td><td>West Virginia</td><td>1.0</td><td>46</td><td>Pennsylvania</td><td>0.2</td></tr>
<tr><td>33</td><td>Wisconsin</td><td>0.8</td><td>46</td><td>Rhode Island</td><td>0.2</td></tr>
<tr><td>22</td><td>Wyoming</td><td>1.4</td><td>50</td><td>North Dakota</td><td>0.1</td></tr>
</table>

District of Columbia   (0.7)

Source: U.S. Department of Health and Human Services, Centers for Medicare and Medicaid Services
"Medicare Enrollment" (http://www.cms.gov/statistics/enrollment/stenrtrend99_02.asp)

Percent of Population Enrolled in Medicare in 2002

National Percent = 13.7% of Population*

ALPHA ORDER

RANK	STATE	PERCENT
10	Alabama	15.8
50	Alaska	7.1
39	Arizona	13.0
5	Arkansas	16.5
45	California	11.5
48	Colorado	10.7
14	Connecticut	15.0
23	Delaware	14.4
2	Florida	17.2
46	Georgia	11.1
32	Hawaii	13.8
40	Idaho	12.9
38	Illinois	13.1
30	Indiana	14.1
6	Iowa	16.3
23	Kansas	14.4
11	Kentucky	15.6
34	Louisiana	13.7
2	Maine	17.2
43	Maryland	12.2
14	Massachusetts	15.0
28	Michigan	14.2
36	Minnesota	13.3
14	Mississippi	15.0
12	Missouri	15.4
12	Montana	15.4
18	Nebraska	14.8
44	Nevada	12.1
32	New Hampshire	13.8
30	New Jersey	14.1
37	New Mexico	13.2
23	New York	14.4
28	North Carolina	14.2
6	North Dakota	16.3
14	Ohio	15.0
21	Oklahoma	14.7
27	Oregon	14.3
4	Pennsylvania	17.0
8	Rhode Island	16.1
23	South Carolina	14.4
9	South Dakota	15.9
18	Tennessee	14.8
47	Texas	10.8
49	Utah	9.3
18	Vermont	14.8
41	Virginia	12.7
42	Washington	12.5
1	West Virginia	19.0
22	Wisconsin	14.6
35	Wyoming	13.5

RANK ORDER

RANK	STATE	PERCENT
1	West Virginia	19.0
2	Florida	17.2
2	Maine	17.2
4	Pennsylvania	17.0
5	Arkansas	16.5
6	Iowa	16.3
6	North Dakota	16.3
8	Rhode Island	16.1
9	South Dakota	15.9
10	Alabama	15.8
11	Kentucky	15.6
12	Missouri	15.4
12	Montana	15.4
14	Connecticut	15.0
14	Massachusetts	15.0
14	Mississippi	15.0
14	Ohio	15.0
18	Nebraska	14.8
18	Tennessee	14.8
18	Vermont	14.8
21	Oklahoma	14.7
22	Wisconsin	14.6
23	Delaware	14.4
23	Kansas	14.4
23	New York	14.4
23	South Carolina	14.4
27	Oregon	14.3
28	Michigan	14.2
28	North Carolina	14.2
30	Indiana	14.1
30	New Jersey	14.1
32	Hawaii	13.8
32	New Hampshire	13.8
34	Louisiana	13.7
35	Wyoming	13.5
36	Minnesota	13.3
37	New Mexico	13.2
38	Illinois	13.1
39	Arizona	13.0
40	Idaho	12.9
41	Virginia	12.7
42	Washington	12.5
43	Maryland	12.2
44	Nevada	12.1
45	California	11.5
46	Georgia	11.1
47	Texas	10.8
48	Colorado	10.7
49	Utah	9.3
50	Alaska	7.1
	District of Columbia	13.0

Source: MQ Press using data from U.S. Dept of Health & Human Services, Centers for Medicare and Medicaid Services
"Medicare Enrollment" (http://www.cms.gov/statistics/enrollment/stenrtrend99_02.asp)
*For fiscal year 2002. Includes aged and disabled enrollees. National rate includes only residents of the 50 states and the District of Columbia.

Medicare Managed Care Enrollees in 2003

National Total = 5,304,299 Enrollees*

RANK	STATE	ENROLLEES	% of USA
23	Alabama	38,767	0.7%
42	Alaska	0	0.0%
6	Arizona	206,422	3.9%
42	Arkansas	0	0.0%
1	California	1,356,897	25.6%
10	Colorado	134,791	2.5%
27	Connecticut	29,108	0.5%
42	Delaware	0	0.0%
2	Florida	542,748	10.2%
26	Georgia	35,819	0.7%
19	Hawaii	59,848	1.1%
32	Idaho	14,611	0.3%
16	Illinois	79,330	1.5%
31	Indiana	16,953	0.3%
34	Iowa	8,318	0.2%
41	Kansas	64	0.0%
36	Kentucky	1,401	0.0%
18	Louisiana	65,458	1.2%
42	Maine	0	0.0%
25	Maryland	37,465	0.7%
8	Massachusetts	171,758	3.2%
29	Michigan	23,138	0.4%
14	Minnesota	89,230	1.7%
39	Mississippi	755	0.0%
11	Missouri	134,261	2.5%
42	Montana	0	0.0%
33	Nebraska	9,095	0.2%
15	Nevada	81,418	1.5%
37	New Hampshire	1,120	0.0%
13	New Jersey	90,709	1.7%
24	New Mexico	37,643	0.7%
4	New York	477,271	9.0%
21	North Carolina	46,801	0.9%
40	North Dakota	624	0.0%
5	Ohio	240,806	4.5%
22	Oklahoma	38,926	0.7%
7	Oregon	184,368	3.5%
3	Pennsylvania	503,337	9.5%
20	Rhode Island	57,891	1.1%
42	South Carolina	0	0.0%
42	South Dakota	0	0.0%
17	Tennessee	65,546	1.2%
9	Texas	161,114	3.0%
30	Utah	17,400	0.3%
42	Vermont	0	0.0%
35	Virginia	2,861	0.1%
12	Washington	132,909	2.5%
38	West Virginia	762	0.0%
28	Wisconsin	28,200	0.5%
42	Wyoming	0	0.0%

RANK	STATE	ENROLLEES	% of USA
1	California	1,356,897	25.6%
2	Florida	542,748	10.2%
3	Pennsylvania	503,337	9.5%
4	New York	477,271	9.0%
5	Ohio	240,806	4.5%
6	Arizona	206,422	3.9%
7	Oregon	184,368	3.5%
8	Massachusetts	171,758	3.2%
9	Texas	161,114	3.0%
10	Colorado	134,791	2.5%
11	Missouri	134,261	2.5%
12	Washington	132,909	2.5%
13	New Jersey	90,709	1.7%
14	Minnesota	89,230	1.7%
15	Nevada	81,418	1.5%
16	Illinois	79,330	1.5%
17	Tennessee	65,546	1.2%
18	Louisiana	65,458	1.2%
19	Hawaii	59,848	1.1%
20	Rhode Island	57,891	1.1%
21	North Carolina	46,801	0.9%
22	Oklahoma	38,926	0.7%
23	Alabama	38,767	0.7%
24	New Mexico	37,643	0.7%
25	Maryland	37,465	0.7%
26	Georgia	35,819	0.7%
27	Connecticut	29,108	0.5%
28	Wisconsin	28,200	0.5%
29	Michigan	23,138	0.4%
30	Utah	17,400	0.3%
31	Indiana	16,953	0.3%
32	Idaho	14,611	0.3%
33	Nebraska	9,095	0.2%
34	Iowa	8,318	0.2%
35	Virginia	2,861	0.1%
36	Kentucky	1,401	0.0%
37	New Hampshire	1,120	0.0%
38	West Virginia	762	0.0%
39	Mississippi	755	0.0%
40	North Dakota	624	0.0%
41	Kansas	64	0.0%
42	Alaska	0	0.0%
42	Arkansas	0	0.0%
42	Delaware	0	0.0%
42	Maine	0	0.0%
42	Montana	0	0.0%
42	South Carolina	0	0.0%
42	South Dakota	0	0.0%
42	Vermont	0	0.0%
42	Wyoming	0	0.0%
	District of Columbia	0	0.0%

Source: U.S. Department of Health and Human Services, Centers for Medicare and Medicaid Services
  "2003 Data Compendium" (http://www.cms.gov/researchers/pubs/datacompendium/)
*As of August 2003. Includes M + C, Cost, Health Care Prepayment Plans (HCPP) and other demo plans. National total includes 51,095 enrollees in the United Mine Workers' plan not shown separately by state.

Percent of Medicare Enrollees in Managed Care Programs in 2003

National Percent = 13% of Medicare Enrollees*

ALPHA ORDER

RANK	STATE	PERCENT
26	Alabama	5
37	Alaska	0
6	Arizona	29
37	Arkansas	0
3	California	34
7	Colorado	28
24	Connecticut	6
37	Delaware	0
9	Florida	19
28	Georgia	4
2	Hawaii	35
18	Idaho	8
26	Illinois	5
32	Indiana	2
32	Iowa	2
37	Kansas	0
37	Kentucky	0
17	Louisiana	11
37	Maine	0
24	Maryland	6
10	Massachusetts	18
32	Michigan	2
16	Minnesota	13
37	Mississippi	0
13	Missouri	15
37	Montana	0
28	Nebraska	4
5	Nevada	31
35	New Hampshire	1
18	New Jersey	8
13	New Mexico	15
11	New York	17
28	North Carolina	4
35	North Dakota	1
15	Ohio	14
18	Oklahoma	8
1	Oregon	36
8	Pennsylvania	24
3	Rhode Island	34
37	South Carolina	0
37	South Dakota	0
18	Tennessee	8
23	Texas	7
18	Utah	8
37	Vermont	0
37	Virginia	0
11	Washington	17
37	West Virginia	0
28	Wisconsin	4
37	Wyoming	0

RANK ORDER

RANK	STATE	PERCENT
1	Oregon	36
2	Hawaii	35
3	California	34
3	Rhode Island	34
5	Nevada	31
6	Arizona	29
7	Colorado	28
8	Pennsylvania	24
9	Florida	19
10	Massachusetts	18
11	New York	17
11	Washington	17
13	Missouri	15
13	New Mexico	15
15	Ohio	14
16	Minnesota	13
17	Louisiana	11
18	Idaho	8
18	New Jersey	8
18	Oklahoma	8
18	Tennessee	8
18	Utah	8
23	Texas	7
24	Connecticut	6
24	Maryland	6
26	Alabama	5
26	Illinois	5
28	Georgia	4
28	Nebraska	4
28	North Carolina	4
28	Wisconsin	4
32	Indiana	2
32	Iowa	2
32	Michigan	2
35	New Hampshire	1
35	North Dakota	1
37	Alaska	0
37	Arkansas	0
37	Delaware	0
37	Kansas	0
37	Kentucky	0
37	Maine	0
37	Mississippi	0
37	Montana	0
37	South Carolina	0
37	South Dakota	0
37	Vermont	0
37	Virginia	0
37	West Virginia	0
37	Wyoming	0
	District of Columbia	0

*Source: U.S. Department of Health and Human Services, Centers for Medicare and Medicaid Services
"2003 Data Compendium" (http://www.cms.gov/researchers/pubs/datacompendium/)*
*As of August 2003. Includes M + C, Cost, Health Care Prepayment Plans (HCPP) and other demo plans. National figure includes enrollees in the United Mine Workers' plan not shown separately by state.

Medicare Physicians in 2002

National Total = 888,061 Physicians*

ALPHA ORDER

RANK	STATE	PHYSICIANS	% of USA
29	Alabama	10,021	1.1%
49	Alaska	1,816	0.2%
23	Arizona	13,860	1.6%
31	Arkansas	8,331	0.9%
1	California	93,909	10.6%
22	Colorado	13,969	1.6%
24	Connecticut	12,749	1.4%
48	Delaware	2,496	0.3%
5	Florida	46,697	5.3%
12	Georgia	22,157	2.5%
41	Hawaii**	4,192	0.5%
43	Idaho	3,385	0.4%
8	Illinois	33,797	3.8%
20	Indiana	17,237	1.9%
28	Iowa	10,230	1.2%
30	Kansas	8,526	1.0%
25	Kentucky	11,530	1.3%
21	Louisiana	15,238	1.7%
34	Maine	5,904	0.7%
14	Maryland	20,486	2.3%
6	Massachusetts	35,160	4.0%
9	Michigan	30,658	3.5%
19	Minnesota	17,433	2.0%
35	Mississippi	5,787	0.7%
15	Missouri	18,907	2.1%
44	Montana	3,080	0.3%
38	Nebraska	5,431	0.6%
40	Nevada	4,650	0.5%
37	New Hampshire	5,433	0.6%
10	New Jersey	30,251	3.4%
39	New Mexico	4,757	0.5%
2	New York	71,535	8.1%
11	North Carolina	23,932	2.7%
46	North Dakota	2,732	0.3%
7	Ohio	35,040	3.9%
32	Oklahoma	8,258	0.9%
26	Oregon	11,398	1.3%
4	Pennsylvania	46,953	5.3%
42	Rhode Island	3,632	0.4%
27	South Carolina	11,106	1.3%
47	South Dakota	2,559	0.3%
16	Tennessee	18,322	2.1%
3	Texas	50,291	5.7%
33	Utah	6,041	0.7%
45	Vermont	2,830	0.3%
17	Virginia	18,211	2.1%
13	Washington	21,306	2.4%
36	West Virginia	5,534	0.6%
18	Wisconsin	17,944	2.0%
50	Wyoming	1,554	0.2%

RANK ORDER

RANK	STATE	PHYSICIANS	% of USA
1	California	93,909	10.6%
2	New York	71,535	8.1%
3	Texas	50,291	5.7%
4	Pennsylvania	46,953	5.3%
5	Florida	46,697	5.3%
6	Massachusetts	35,160	4.0%
7	Ohio	35,040	3.9%
8	Illinois	33,797	3.8%
9	Michigan	30,658	3.5%
10	New Jersey	30,251	3.4%
11	North Carolina	23,932	2.7%
12	Georgia	22,157	2.5%
13	Washington	21,306	2.4%
14	Maryland	20,486	2.3%
15	Missouri	18,907	2.1%
16	Tennessee	18,322	2.1%
17	Virginia	18,211	2.1%
18	Wisconsin	17,944	2.0%
19	Minnesota	17,433	2.0%
20	Indiana	17,237	1.9%
21	Louisiana	15,238	1.7%
22	Colorado	13,969	1.6%
23	Arizona	13,860	1.6%
24	Connecticut	12,749	1.4%
25	Kentucky	11,530	1.3%
26	Oregon	11,398	1.3%
27	South Carolina	11,106	1.3%
28	Iowa	10,230	1.2%
29	Alabama	10,021	1.1%
30	Kansas	8,526	1.0%
31	Arkansas	8,331	0.9%
32	Oklahoma	8,258	0.9%
33	Utah	6,041	0.7%
34	Maine	5,904	0.7%
35	Mississippi	5,787	0.7%
36	West Virginia	5,534	0.6%
37	New Hampshire	5,433	0.6%
38	Nebraska	5,431	0.6%
39	New Mexico	4,757	0.5%
40	Nevada	4,650	0.5%
41	Hawaii**	4,192	0.5%
42	Rhode Island	3,632	0.4%
43	Idaho	3,385	0.4%
44	Montana	3,080	0.3%
45	Vermont	2,830	0.3%
46	North Dakota	2,732	0.3%
47	South Dakota	2,559	0.3%
48	Delaware	2,496	0.3%
49	Alaska	1,816	0.2%
50	Wyoming	1,554	0.2%
	District of Columbia	4,402	0.5%

Source: U.S. Department of Health and Human Services, Centers for Medicare and Medicaid Services
    "2002 Data Compendium" (http://www.cms.gov/researchers/pubs/datacompendium/)
*Medicare Part B. "Physicians" include MD, DO, DDM, DDS, DPM, OD and CH. National total includes 6,214 physicians in Puerto Rico and the Virgin Islands.
**Physicians for Guam are included in Hawaii's total.

Percent of Physicians Participating in Medicare in 2002

National Percent = 89.3% of Physicians Participate in Medicare*

	ALPHA ORDER				RANK ORDER	
RANK	STATE	PERCENT		RANK	STATE	PERCENT
6	Alabama	96.1		1	North Dakota	97.2
43	Alaska	86.1		2	Michigan	96.9
34	Arizona	90.6		3	Nevada	96.2
9	Arkansas	95.5		3	Utah	96.2
49	California	78.6		3	Washington	96.2
37	Colorado	89.5		6	Alabama	96.1
35	Connecticut	90.5		7	Pennsylvania	95.8
30	Delaware	92.0		8	Missouri	95.6
22	Florida	92.9		9	Arkansas	95.5
33	Georgia	90.8		9	Ohio	95.5
15	Hawaii	94.3		11	Vermont	94.9
47	Idaho	80.8		12	West Virginia	94.8
24	Illinois	92.6		13	Kansas	94.6
45	Indiana	85.5		14	Wisconsin	94.5
16	Iowa	94.2		15	Hawaii	94.3
13	Kansas	94.6		16	Iowa	94.2
20	Kentucky	93.7		17	Maryland	94.1
26	Louisiana	92.3		18	Oklahoma	93.9
20	Maine	93.7		19	Nebraska	93.8
17	Maryland	94.1		20	Kentucky	93.7
28	Massachusetts	92.1		20	Maine	93.7
2	Michigan	96.9		22	Florida	92.9
48	Minnesota	80.4		23	Oregon	92.8
44	Mississippi	85.6		24	Illinois	92.6
8	Missouri	95.6		24	New Mexico	92.6
36	Montana	89.9		26	Louisiana	92.3
19	Nebraska	93.8		27	Tennessee	92.2
3	Nevada	96.2		28	Massachusetts	92.1
31	New Hampshire	91.1		28	South Carolina	92.1
42	New Jersey	87.4		30	Delaware	92.0
24	New Mexico	92.6		31	New Hampshire	91.1
46	New York	81.2		31	North Carolina	91.1
31	North Carolina	91.1		33	Georgia	90.8
1	North Dakota	97.2		34	Arizona	90.6
9	Ohio	95.5		35	Connecticut	90.5
18	Oklahoma	93.9		36	Montana	89.9
23	Oregon	92.8		37	Colorado	89.5
7	Pennsylvania	95.8		38	South Dakota	89.3
50	Rhode Island	75.6		39	Virginia	88.6
28	South Carolina	92.1		40	Texas	88.0
38	South Dakota	89.3		41	Wyoming	87.7
27	Tennessee	92.2		42	New Jersey	87.4
40	Texas	88.0		43	Alaska	86.1
3	Utah	96.2		44	Mississippi	85.6
11	Vermont	94.9		45	Indiana	85.5
39	Virginia	88.6		46	New York	81.2
3	Washington	96.2		47	Idaho	80.8
12	West Virginia	94.8		48	Minnesota	80.4
14	Wisconsin	94.5		49	California	78.6
41	Wyoming	87.7		50	Rhode Island	75.6

			District of Columbia	90.8

Source: U.S. Department of Health and Human Services, Centers for Medicare and Medicaid Services
"2002 Data Compendium" (http://www.cms.gov/researchers/pubs/datacompendium/)
*As of January 1, 2002. Refers to Medicare Part B. Physicians include MD's, DO's, limited license practitioners and non-physician practitioners.

Medicare Benefit Payments in 2001

National Total = $236,492,552,000*

ALPHA ORDER

RANK	STATE	BENEFITS	% of USA
18	Alabama	$4,270,957,000	1.8%
50	Alaska	169,288,000	0.1%
23	Arizona	3,322,292,000	1.4%
28	Arkansas	2,420,406,000	1.0%
1	California	24,858,719,000	10.5%
27	Colorado	2,698,488,000	1.1%
26	Connecticut	3,117,052,000	1.3%
47	Delaware	500,000,000	0.2%
2	Florida	21,580,488,000	9.1%
17	Georgia	4,397,178,000	1.9%
42	Hawaii	717,998,000	0.3%
41	Idaho	741,441,000	0.3%
7	Illinois	8,001,947,000	3.4%
13	Indiana	4,999,250,000	2.1%
34	Iowa	1,632,032,000	0.7%
31	Kansas	2,141,312,000	0.9%
21	Kentucky	3,640,057,000	1.5%
14	Louisiana	4,902,926,000	2.1%
40	Maine	875,798,000	0.4%
16	Maryland	4,611,432,000	1.9%
11	Massachusetts	5,963,041,000	2.5%
8	Michigan	7,012,604,000	3.0%
25	Minnesota	3,136,907,000	1.3%
32	Mississippi	2,140,391,000	0.9%
15	Missouri	4,755,402,000	2.0%
44	Montana	663,416,000	0.3%
35	Nebraska	1,366,977,000	0.6%
36	Nevada	1,272,774,000	0.5%
43	New Hampshire	714,188,000	0.3%
9	New Jersey	6,885,642,000	2.9%
39	New Mexico	879,540,000	0.4%
3	New York	20,436,630,000	8.6%
10	North Carolina	6,797,677,000	2.9%
46	North Dakota	562,654,000	0.2%
6	Ohio	10,685,164,000	4.5%
29	Oklahoma	2,343,403,000	1.0%
30	Oregon	2,181,557,000	0.9%
5	Pennsylvania	15,141,847,000	6.4%
37	Rhode Island	1,146,888,000	0.5%
22	South Carolina	3,356,574,000	1.4%
45	South Dakota	622,092,000	0.3%
12	Tennessee	5,545,549,000	2.3%
4	Texas	16,336,061,000	6.9%
38	Utah	1,077,334,000	0.5%
48	Vermont	361,871,000	0.2%
20	Virginia	3,897,031,000	1.6%
24	Washington	3,209,406,000	1.4%
33	West Virginia	1,822,039,000	0.8%
19	Wisconsin	3,961,455,000	1.7%
49	Wyoming	281,639,000	0.1%

RANK ORDER

RANK	STATE	BENEFITS	% of USA
1	California	$24,858,719,000	10.5%
2	Florida	21,580,488,000	9.1%
3	New York	20,436,630,000	8.6%
4	Texas	16,336,061,000	6.9%
5	Pennsylvania	15,141,847,000	6.4%
6	Ohio	10,685,164,000	4.5%
7	Illinois	8,001,947,000	3.4%
8	Michigan	7,012,604,000	3.0%
9	New Jersey	6,885,642,000	2.9%
10	North Carolina	6,797,677,000	2.9%
11	Massachusetts	5,963,041,000	2.5%
12	Tennessee	5,545,549,000	2.3%
13	Indiana	4,999,250,000	2.1%
14	Louisiana	4,902,926,000	2.1%
15	Missouri	4,755,402,000	2.0%
16	Maryland	4,611,432,000	1.9%
17	Georgia	4,397,178,000	1.9%
18	Alabama	4,270,957,000	1.8%
19	Wisconsin	3,961,455,000	1.7%
20	Virginia	3,897,031,000	1.6%
21	Kentucky	3,640,057,000	1.5%
22	South Carolina	3,356,574,000	1.4%
23	Arizona	3,322,292,000	1.4%
24	Washington	3,209,406,000	1.4%
25	Minnesota	3,136,907,000	1.3%
26	Connecticut	3,117,052,000	1.3%
27	Colorado	2,698,488,000	1.1%
28	Arkansas	2,420,406,000	1.0%
29	Oklahoma	2,343,403,000	1.0%
30	Oregon	2,181,557,000	0.9%
31	Kansas	2,141,312,000	0.9%
32	Mississippi	2,140,391,000	0.9%
33	West Virginia	1,822,039,000	0.8%
34	Iowa	1,632,032,000	0.7%
35	Nebraska	1,366,977,000	0.6%
36	Nevada	1,272,774,000	0.5%
37	Rhode Island	1,146,888,000	0.5%
38	Utah	1,077,334,000	0.5%
39	New Mexico	879,540,000	0.4%
40	Maine	875,798,000	0.4%
41	Idaho	741,441,000	0.3%
42	Hawaii	717,998,000	0.3%
43	New Hampshire	714,188,000	0.3%
44	Montana	663,416,000	0.3%
45	South Dakota	622,092,000	0.3%
46	North Dakota	562,654,000	0.2%
47	Delaware	500,000,000	0.2%
48	Vermont	361,871,000	0.2%
49	Wyoming	281,639,000	0.1%
50	Alaska	169,288,000	0.1%
	District of Columbia	792,265,000	0.3%

Source: U.S. Department of Health and Human Services, Centers for Medicare and Medicaid Services
"Medicare Estimated Benefit Payments by State" (www.cms.gov/statistics/feeforservice/BenefitPayments01.pdf)
For fiscal year 2001. Includes payments to aged and disabled enrollees. Total includes $1,454,823,000 in payments to enrollees in Puerto Rico and $88,652,000 to enrollees in "other outlying areas."

Per Capita Medicare Benefit Payments in 2001

National Per Capita = $823*

ALPHA ORDER				RANK ORDER		
RANK	STATE	PER CAPITA		RANK	STATE	PER CAPITA
8	Alabama	$956		1	Florida	$1,318
50	Alaska	267		2	Pennsylvania	1,231
36	Arizona	626		3	Louisiana	1,097
12	Arkansas	898		4	Rhode Island	1,082
28	California	718		5	New York	1,071
37	Colorado	609		6	West Virginia	1,012
11	Connecticut	908		7	Tennessee	965
34	Delaware	628		8	Alabama	956
1	Florida	1,318		9	Ohio	938
47	Georgia	523		10	Massachusetts	932
40	Hawaii	585		11	Connecticut	908
43	Idaho	561		12	Arkansas	898
32	Illinois	639		13	Kentucky	895
20	Indiana	816		14	North Dakota	884
44	Iowa	557		15	Maryland	856
23	Kansas	792		16	Missouri	844
13	Kentucky	895		17	North Carolina	828
3	Louisiana	1,097		18	South Carolina	826
30	Maine	682		19	South Dakota	820
15	Maryland	856		20	Indiana	816
10	Massachusetts	932		21	New Jersey	809
29	Michigan	701		22	Nebraska	795
33	Minnesota	629		23	Kansas	792
25	Mississippi	748		24	Texas	764
16	Missouri	844		25	Mississippi	748
26	Montana	733		26	Montana	733
22	Nebraska	795		26	Wisconsin	733
38	Nevada	607		28	California	718
42	New Hampshire	567		29	Michigan	701
21	New Jersey	809		30	Maine	682
48	New Mexico	480		31	Oklahoma	675
5	New York	1,071		32	Illinois	639
17	North Carolina	828		33	Minnesota	629
14	North Dakota	884		34	Delaware	628
9	Ohio	938		34	Oregon	628
31	Oklahoma	675		36	Arizona	626
34	Oregon	628		37	Colorado	609
2	Pennsylvania	1,231		38	Nevada	607
4	Rhode Island	1,082		39	Vermont	590
18	South Carolina	826		40	Hawaii	585
19	South Dakota	820		41	Wyoming	570
7	Tennessee	965		42	New Hampshire	567
24	Texas	764		43	Idaho	561
49	Utah	473		44	Iowa	557
39	Vermont	590		45	Virginia	541
45	Virginia	541		46	Washington	535
46	Washington	535		47	Georgia	523
6	West Virginia	1,012		48	New Mexico	480
26	Wisconsin	733		49	Utah	473
41	Wyoming	570		50	Alaska	267
					District of Columbia	1,381

Source: MQ Press using data from U.S. Dept of Health & Human Services, Centers for Medicare and Medicaid Services "Medicare Estimated Benefit Payments by State" (www.cms.gov/statistics/feeforservice/BenefitPayments01.pdf)
*For fiscal year 2001. Includes aged and disabled enrollees. National rate does not include payments or enrollees in Puerto Rico and in "other outlying areas." Payments are based on the state of the provider or plan. Thus data showing payments per capita should be viewed as estimates and interpreted with caution.

Percent Change in Medicare Benefit Payments: 1997 to 2001

National Percent Change = 14.2% Increase*

ALPHA ORDER

RANK	STATE	PERCENT CHANGE
22	Alabama	19.2
37	Alaska	4.1
39	Arizona	3.5
10	Arkansas	27.0
30	California	12.5
17	Colorado	21.8
40	Connecticut	1.1
34	Delaware	6.1
15	Florida	23.1
48	Georgia	(6.9)
32	Hawaii	9.5
6	Idaho	31.2
45	Illinois	(3.7)
16	Indiana	22.5
47	Iowa	(6.1)
11	Kansas	26.6
12	Kentucky	26.0
27	Louisiana	14.4
43	Maine	(0.4)
2	Maryland	34.1
49	Massachusetts	(7.6)
46	Michigan	(5.2)
26	Minnesota	14.8
44	Mississippi	(3.3)
38	Missouri	3.8
3	Montana	33.8
5	Nebraska	32.8
29	Nevada	13.3
42	New Hampshire	0.1
36	New Jersey	4.8
41	New Mexico	0.7
14	New York	24.2
3	North Carolina	33.8
21	North Dakota	20.1
13	Ohio	24.9
50	Oklahoma	(12.5)
25	Oregon	15.6
18	Pennsylvania	21.7
24	Rhode Island	16.0
1	South Carolina	41.8
8	South Dakota	30.6
23	Tennessee	17.5
27	Texas	14.4
19	Utah	21.5
31	Vermont	10.3
33	Virginia	7.2
35	Washington	5.8
20	West Virginia	21.2
9	Wisconsin	27.4
7	Wyoming	30.7

RANK ORDER

RANK	STATE	PERCENT CHANGE
1	South Carolina	41.8
2	Maryland	34.1
3	Montana	33.8
3	North Carolina	33.8
5	Nebraska	32.8
6	Idaho	31.2
7	Wyoming	30.7
8	South Dakota	30.6
9	Wisconsin	27.4
10	Arkansas	27.0
11	Kansas	26.6
12	Kentucky	26.0
13	Ohio	24.9
14	New York	24.2
15	Florida	23.1
16	Indiana	22.5
17	Colorado	21.8
18	Pennsylvania	21.7
19	Utah	21.5
20	West Virginia	21.2
21	North Dakota	20.1
22	Alabama	19.2
23	Tennessee	17.5
24	Rhode Island	16.0
25	Oregon	15.6
26	Minnesota	14.8
27	Louisiana	14.4
27	Texas	14.4
29	Nevada	13.3
30	California	12.5
31	Vermont	10.3
32	Hawaii	9.5
33	Virginia	7.2
34	Delaware	6.1
35	Washington	5.8
36	New Jersey	4.8
37	Alaska	4.1
38	Missouri	3.8
39	Arizona	3.5
40	Connecticut	1.1
41	New Mexico	0.7
42	New Hampshire	0.1
43	Maine	(0.4)
44	Mississippi	(3.3)
45	Illinois	(3.7)
46	Michigan	(5.2)
47	Iowa	(6.1)
48	Georgia	(6.9)
49	Massachusetts	(7.6)
50	Oklahoma	(12.5)
	District of Columbia	(37.3)

Source: Morgan Quitno Press using data from U.S. Department of HHS, Centers for Medicare and Medicaid Services
"Medicare Estimated Benefit Payments by State" (www.cms.gov/statistics/feeforservice/BenefitPayments01.pdf)
*For fiscal years 1997 and 2001. Includes payments to aged and disabled enrollees. Total includes payments to
enrollees in Puerto Rico and to enrollees in "other outlying areas."

Medicare Payments per Enrollee in 2001

National Rate = $6,003*

ALPHA ORDER

RANK	STATE	PER ENROLLEE
12	Alabama	$6,144
48	Alaska	3,864
33	Arizona	4,811
21	Arkansas	5,478
9	California	6,285
19	Colorado	5,674
13	Connecticut	6,037
40	Delaware	4,387
2	Florida	7,603
36	Georgia	4,713
43	Hawaii	4,266
39	Idaho	4,399
32	Illinois	4,879
15	Indiana	5,826
50	Iowa	3,414
22	Kansas	5,475
17	Kentucky	5,781
1	Louisiana	8,099
47	Maine	3,993
6	Maryland	7,045
11	Massachusetts	6,202
31	Michigan	4,959
35	Minnesota	4,750
29	Mississippi	5,055
20	Missouri	5,486
34	Montana	4,798
24	Nebraska	5,367
28	Nevada	5,080
45	New Hampshire	4,135
18	New Jersey	5,702
49	New Mexico	3,689
3	New York	7,489
14	North Carolina	5,886
23	North Dakota	5,456
10	Ohio	6,266
37	Oklahoma	4,590
38	Oregon	4,401
4	Pennsylvania	7,226
7	Rhode Island	6,675
16	South Carolina	5,791
26	South Dakota	5,183
8	Tennessee	6,584
5	Texas	7,104
27	Utah	5,120
46	Vermont	4,019
42	Virginia	4,285
41	Washington	4,303
25	West Virginia	5,361
30	Wisconsin	5,031
44	Wyoming	4,239

RANK ORDER

RANK	STATE	PER ENROLLEE
1	Louisiana	$8,099
2	Florida	7,603
3	New York	7,489
4	Pennsylvania	7,226
5	Texas	7,104
6	Maryland	7,045
7	Rhode Island	6,675
8	Tennessee	6,584
9	California	6,285
10	Ohio	6,266
11	Massachusetts	6,202
12	Alabama	6,144
13	Connecticut	6,037
14	North Carolina	5,886
15	Indiana	5,826
16	South Carolina	5,791
17	Kentucky	5,781
18	New Jersey	5,702
19	Colorado	5,674
20	Missouri	5,486
21	Arkansas	5,478
22	Kansas	5,475
23	North Dakota	5,456
24	Nebraska	5,367
25	West Virginia	5,361
26	South Dakota	5,183
27	Utah	5,120
28	Nevada	5,080
29	Mississippi	5,055
30	Wisconsin	5,031
31	Michigan	4,959
32	Illinois	4,879
33	Arizona	4,811
34	Montana	4,798
35	Minnesota	4,750
36	Georgia	4,713
37	Oklahoma	4,590
38	Oregon	4,401
39	Idaho	4,399
40	Delaware	4,387
41	Washington	4,303
42	Virginia	4,285
43	Hawaii	4,266
44	Wyoming	4,239
45	New Hampshire	4,135
46	Vermont	4,019
47	Maine	3,993
48	Alaska	3,864
49	New Mexico	3,689
50	Iowa	3,414

| | District of Columbia | 10,606 |

Source: MQ Press using data from U.S. Dept of Health & Human Services, Centers for Medicare and Medicaid Services "Medicare Estimated Benefit Payments by State" (www.cms.gov/statistics/feeforservice/BenefitPayments01.pdf)
*For fiscal year 2001. Includes aged and disabled enrollees. National rate does not include payments or enrollees in Puerto Rico and in "other outlying areas." Payments are based on the state of the provider or plan. Thus data showing payments per beneficiary should be viewed as estimates and interpreted with caution.

Percent Change in Medicare Benefit Payments per Enrollee: 1997 to 2001

National Percent Change = 11.1% Increase*

ALPHA ORDER				RANK ORDER		
RANK	STATE	PERCENT CHANGE		RANK	STATE	PERCENT CHANGE
22	Alabama	13.2		1	Nebraska	30.7
48	Alaska	(12.6)		2	South Carolina	30.4
40	Arizona	(5.3)		3	Montana	28.6
9	Arkansas	23.4		4	South Dakota	28.1
29	California	6.0		5	Maryland	26.5
21	Colorado	13.3		6	Kansas	25.1
36	Connecticut	(0.6)		7	Wisconsin	24.6
37	Delaware	(1.9)		8	North Carolina	24.2
19	Florida	17.3		9	Arkansas	23.4
49	Georgia	(13.6)		10	Wyoming	23.2
32	Hawaii	1.5		11	Ohio	23.0
12	Idaho	21.0		12	Idaho	21.0
39	Illinois	(4.9)		12	New York	21.0
17	Indiana	18.9		14	Pennsylvania	20.7
43	Iowa	(6.6)		15	Kentucky	20.3
6	Kansas	25.1		16	North Dakota	19.9
15	Kentucky	20.3		17	Indiana	18.9
24	Louisiana	11.6		18	West Virginia	18.4
41	Maine	(5.5)		19	Florida	17.3
5	Maryland	26.5		20	Rhode Island	14.1
47	Massachusetts	(9.2)		21	Colorado	13.3
46	Michigan	(8.3)		22	Alabama	13.2
25	Minnesota	11.0		23	Utah	12.6
45	Mississippi	(7.2)		24	Louisiana	11.6
33	Missouri	1.0		25	Minnesota	11.0
3	Montana	28.6		26	Oregon	10.9
1	Nebraska	30.7		27	Tennessee	10.7
38	Nevada	(4.1)		28	Texas	7.2
42	New Hampshire	(6.3)		29	California	6.0
31	New Jersey	2.4		30	Vermont	4.9
44	New Mexico	(6.7)		31	New Jersey	2.4
12	New York	21.0		32	Hawaii	1.5
8	North Carolina	24.2		33	Missouri	1.0
16	North Dakota	19.9		34	Washington	0.3
11	Ohio	23.0		35	Virginia	(0.2)
50	Oklahoma	(15.1)		36	Connecticut	(0.6)
26	Oregon	10.9		37	Delaware	(1.9)
14	Pennsylvania	20.7		38	Nevada	(4.1)
20	Rhode Island	14.1		39	Illinois	(4.9)
2	South Carolina	30.4		40	Arizona	(5.3)
4	South Dakota	28.1		41	Maine	(5.5)
27	Tennessee	10.7		42	New Hampshire	(6.3)
28	Texas	7.2		43	Iowa	(6.6)
23	Utah	12.6		44	New Mexico	(6.7)
30	Vermont	4.9		45	Mississippi	(7.2)
35	Virginia	(0.2)		46	Michigan	(8.3)
34	Washington	0.3		47	Massachusetts	(9.2)
18	West Virginia	18.4		48	Alaska	(12.6)
7	Wisconsin	24.6		49	Georgia	(13.6)
10	Wyoming	23.2		50	Oklahoma	(15.1)
					District of Columbia	(36.1)

Source: Morgan Quitno Press using data from U.S. Department of HHS, Centers for Medicare and Medicaid Services
"Medicare Estimated Benefit Payments by State" (www.cms.gov/statistics/feeforservice/BenefitPayments01.pdf)
*For fiscal years 1997 and 2001. Includes payments to aged and disabled enrollees. Total includes payments to enrollees in Puerto Rico and to enrollees in "other outlying areas."

Medicaid Enrollment in 2002

National Total = 41,149,422 Enrollees*

ALPHA ORDER

RANK	STATE	ENROLLEES	% of USA
19	Alabama	735,706	1.8%
45	Alaska	91,698	0.2%
16	Arizona	821,748	2.0%
27	Arkansas	526,877	1.3%
1	California	6,190,430	15.0%
32	Colorado	313,183	0.8%
31	Connecticut	385,239	0.9%
44	Delaware	124,828	0.3%
4	Florida	2,109,603	5.1%
9	Georgia	1,323,205	3.2%
38	Hawaii	177,531	0.4%
42	Idaho	151,390	0.4%
5	Illinois	1,695,647	4.1%
20	Indiana	686,712	1.7%
34	Iowa	265,042	0.6%
35	Kansas	235,797	0.6%
24	Kentucky	604,120	1.5%
15	Louisiana	833,918	2.0%
36	Maine	221,230	0.5%
22	Maryland	662,755	1.6%
12	Massachusetts	962,342	2.3%
10	Michigan	1,191,456	2.9%
25	Minnesota	556,386	1.4%
23	Mississippi	650,800	1.6%
14	Missouri	930,232	2.3%
48	Montana	76,482	0.2%
37	Nebraska	211,712	0.5%
41	Nevada	164,388	0.4%
47	New Hampshire	90,028	0.2%
18	New Jersey	759,644	1.8%
30	New Mexico	389,298	0.9%
2	New York	3,388,931	8.2%
11	North Carolina	1,052,041	2.6%
50	North Dakota	52,913	0.1%
6	Ohio	1,545,000	3.8%
28	Oklahoma	462,533	1.1%
29	Oregon	427,547	1.0%
7	Pennsylvania	1,458,694	3.5%
39	Rhode Island	175,500	0.4%
17	South Carolina	771,490	1.9%
46	South Dakota	90,766	0.2%
8	Tennessee	1,324,011	3.2%
3	Texas	2,412,854	5.9%
40	Utah	170,775	0.4%
43	Vermont	132,502	0.3%
26	Virginia	530,423	1.3%
13	Washington	946,329	2.3%
33	West Virginia	288,072	0.7%
21	Wisconsin	676,395	1.6%
49	Wyoming	54,656	0.1%

RANK ORDER

RANK	STATE	ENROLLEES	% of USA
1	California	6,190,430	15.0%
2	New York	3,388,931	8.2%
3	Texas	2,412,854	5.9%
4	Florida	2,109,603	5.1%
5	Illinois	1,695,647	4.1%
6	Ohio	1,545,000	3.8%
7	Pennsylvania	1,458,694	3.5%
8	Tennessee	1,324,011	3.2%
9	Georgia	1,323,205	3.2%
10	Michigan	1,191,456	2.9%
11	North Carolina	1,052,041	2.6%
12	Massachusetts	962,342	2.3%
13	Washington	946,329	2.3%
14	Missouri	930,232	2.3%
15	Louisiana	833,918	2.0%
16	Arizona	821,748	2.0%
17	South Carolina	771,490	1.9%
18	New Jersey	759,644	1.8%
19	Alabama	735,706	1.8%
20	Indiana	686,712	1.7%
21	Wisconsin	676,395	1.6%
22	Maryland	662,755	1.6%
23	Mississippi	650,800	1.6%
24	Kentucky	604,120	1.5%
25	Minnesota	556,386	1.4%
26	Virginia	530,423	1.3%
27	Arkansas	526,877	1.3%
28	Oklahoma	462,533	1.1%
29	Oregon	427,547	1.0%
30	New Mexico	389,298	0.9%
31	Connecticut	385,239	0.9%
32	Colorado	313,183	0.8%
33	West Virginia	288,072	0.7%
34	Iowa	265,042	0.6%
35	Kansas	235,797	0.6%
36	Maine	221,230	0.5%
37	Nebraska	211,712	0.5%
38	Hawaii	177,531	0.4%
39	Rhode Island	175,500	0.4%
40	Utah	170,775	0.4%
41	Nevada	164,388	0.4%
42	Idaho	151,390	0.4%
43	Vermont	132,502	0.3%
44	Delaware	124,828	0.3%
45	Alaska	91,698	0.2%
46	South Dakota	90,766	0.2%
47	New Hampshire	90,028	0.2%
48	Montana	76,482	0.2%
49	Wyoming	54,656	0.1%
50	North Dakota	52,913	0.1%
	District of Columbia	128,837	0.3%

Source: U.S. Department of Health and Human Services, Centers for Medicare and Medicaid Services
   "Medicaid Managed Care State Enrollment" (http://www.cms.gov/medicaid/managedcare/mmcpr02.pdf)
*As of December 31, 2002.   National total includes 919,726 Medicaid enrollees in Puerto Rico and the Virgin Islands.

Percent of Population Enrolled in Medicaid in 2002

National Percent = 14.0% of Population*

ALPHA ORDER

RANK	STATE	PERCENT
11	Alabama	16.4
22	Alaska	14.2
18	Arizona	15.1
5	Arkansas	19.4
9	California	17.6
50	Colorado	6.9
36	Connecticut	11.1
16	Delaware	15.5
26	Florida	12.6
16	Georgia	15.5
21	Hawaii	14.3
35	Idaho	11.3
23	Illinois	13.5
36	Indiana	11.1
41	Iowa	9.0
43	Kansas	8.7
20	Kentucky	14.8
7	Louisiana	18.6
10	Maine	17.1
30	Maryland	12.1
19	Massachusetts	15.0
32	Michigan	11.9
36	Minnesota	11.1
2	Mississippi	22.7
11	Missouri	16.4
44	Montana	8.4
29	Nebraska	12.2
46	Nevada	7.6
49	New Hampshire	7.1
42	New Jersey	8.8
4	New Mexico	21.0
8	New York	17.7
26	North Carolina	12.6
45	North Dakota	8.3
23	Ohio	13.5
25	Oklahoma	13.2
30	Oregon	12.1
34	Pennsylvania	11.8
11	Rhode Island	16.4
6	South Carolina	18.8
32	South Dakota	11.9
1	Tennessee	22.8
36	Texas	11.1
47	Utah	7.4
3	Vermont	21.5
48	Virginia	7.3
15	Washington	15.6
14	West Virginia	16.0
28	Wisconsin	12.4
40	Wyoming	11.0

RANK ORDER

RANK	STATE	PERCENT
1	Tennessee	22.8
2	Mississippi	22.7
3	Vermont	21.5
4	New Mexico	21.0
5	Arkansas	19.4
6	South Carolina	18.8
7	Louisiana	18.6
8	New York	17.7
9	California	17.6
10	Maine	17.1
11	Alabama	16.4
11	Missouri	16.4
11	Rhode Island	16.4
14	West Virginia	16.0
15	Washington	15.6
16	Delaware	15.5
16	Georgia	15.5
18	Arizona	15.1
19	Massachusetts	15.0
20	Kentucky	14.8
21	Hawaii	14.3
22	Alaska	14.2
23	Illinois	13.5
23	Ohio	13.5
25	Oklahoma	13.2
26	Florida	12.6
26	North Carolina	12.6
28	Wisconsin	12.4
29	Nebraska	12.2
30	Maryland	12.1
30	Oregon	12.1
32	Michigan	11.9
32	South Dakota	11.9
34	Pennsylvania	11.8
35	Idaho	11.3
36	Connecticut	11.1
36	Indiana	11.1
36	Minnesota	11.1
36	Texas	11.1
40	Wyoming	11.0
41	Iowa	9.0
42	New Jersey	8.8
43	Kansas	8.7
44	Montana	8.4
45	North Dakota	8.3
46	Nevada	7.6
47	Utah	7.4
48	Virginia	7.3
49	New Hampshire	7.1
50	Colorado	6.9

| | District of Columbia | 22.6 |

Source: MQ Press using data from U.S. Dept of Health & Human Services, Centers for Medicare and Medicaid Services
"Medicaid Managed Care State Enrollment" (http://www.cms.gov/medicaid/managedcare/mmcpr02.pdf)
*As of December 31, 2002. National percent does not include recipients or population in U.S. territories.

Medicaid Managed Care Enrollment in 2002

National Total = 23,624,461 Enrollees*

<table>
<tr><td colspan="4">ALPHA ORDER</td><td colspan="4">RANK ORDER</td></tr>
<tr><th>RANK</th><th>STATE</th><th>ENROLLEES</th><th>% of USA</th><th>RANK</th><th>STATE</th><th>ENROLLEES</th><th>% of USA</th></tr>
<tr><td>17</td><td>Alabama</td><td>417,519</td><td>1.8%</td><td>1</td><td>California</td><td>3,279,796</td><td>13.9%</td></tr>
<tr><td>48</td><td>Alaska</td><td>0</td><td>0.0%</td><td>2</td><td>New York</td><td>1,512,491</td><td>6.4%</td></tr>
<tr><td>10</td><td>Arizona</td><td>757,837</td><td>3.2%</td><td>3</td><td>Tennessee</td><td>1,324,011</td><td>5.6%</td></tr>
<tr><td>26</td><td>Arkansas</td><td>306,247</td><td>1.3%</td><td>4</td><td>Florida</td><td>1,321,714</td><td>5.6%</td></tr>
<tr><td>1</td><td>California</td><td>3,279,796</td><td>13.9%</td><td>5</td><td>Pennsylvania</td><td>1,152,109</td><td>4.9%</td></tr>
<tr><td>27</td><td>Colorado</td><td>292,080</td><td>1.2%</td><td>6</td><td>Texas</td><td>945,869</td><td>4.0%</td></tr>
<tr><td>28</td><td>Connecticut</td><td>291,016</td><td>1.2%</td><td>7</td><td>Georgia</td><td>928,728</td><td>3.9%</td></tr>
<tr><td>39</td><td>Delaware</td><td>94,395</td><td>0.4%</td><td>8</td><td>Washington</td><td>897,940</td><td>3.8%</td></tr>
<tr><td>4</td><td>Florida</td><td>1,321,714</td><td>5.6%</td><td>9</td><td>Michigan</td><td>894,060</td><td>3.8%</td></tr>
<tr><td>7</td><td>Georgia</td><td>928,728</td><td>3.9%</td><td>10</td><td>Arizona</td><td>757,837</td><td>3.2%</td></tr>
<tr><td>34</td><td>Hawaii</td><td>140,594</td><td>0.6%</td><td>11</td><td>North Carolina</td><td>733,839</td><td>3.1%</td></tr>
<tr><td>42</td><td>Idaho</td><td>77,506</td><td>0.3%</td><td>12</td><td>Massachusetts</td><td>613,972</td><td>2.6%</td></tr>
<tr><td>36</td><td>Illinois</td><td>125,898</td><td>0.5%</td><td>13</td><td>New Jersey</td><td>525,937</td><td>2.2%</td></tr>
<tr><td>15</td><td>Indiana</td><td>465,662</td><td>2.0%</td><td>14</td><td>Kentucky</td><td>511,292</td><td>2.2%</td></tr>
<tr><td>30</td><td>Iowa</td><td>236,075</td><td>1.0%</td><td>15</td><td>Indiana</td><td>465,662</td><td>2.0%</td></tr>
<tr><td>35</td><td>Kansas</td><td>138,365</td><td>0.6%</td><td>16</td><td>Maryland</td><td>465,543</td><td>2.0%</td></tr>
<tr><td>14</td><td>Kentucky</td><td>511,292</td><td>2.2%</td><td>17</td><td>Alabama</td><td>417,519</td><td>1.8%</td></tr>
<tr><td>25</td><td>Louisiana</td><td>310,152</td><td>1.3%</td><td>18</td><td>Missouri</td><td>413,008</td><td>1.7%</td></tr>
<tr><td>37</td><td>Maine</td><td>117,946</td><td>0.5%</td><td>19</td><td>Ohio</td><td>403,497</td><td>1.7%</td></tr>
<tr><td>16</td><td>Maryland</td><td>465,543</td><td>2.0%</td><td>20</td><td>Minnesota</td><td>386,472</td><td>1.6%</td></tr>
<tr><td>12</td><td>Massachusetts</td><td>613,972</td><td>2.6%</td><td>21</td><td>Oregon</td><td>372,756</td><td>1.6%</td></tr>
<tr><td>9</td><td>Michigan</td><td>894,060</td><td>3.8%</td><td>22</td><td>Oklahoma</td><td>333,127</td><td>1.4%</td></tr>
<tr><td>20</td><td>Minnesota</td><td>386,472</td><td>1.6%</td><td>23</td><td>Wisconsin</td><td>328,638</td><td>1.4%</td></tr>
<tr><td>48</td><td>Mississippi</td><td>0</td><td>0.0%</td><td>24</td><td>Virginia</td><td>327,390</td><td>1.4%</td></tr>
<tr><td>18</td><td>Missouri</td><td>413,008</td><td>1.7%</td><td>25</td><td>Louisiana</td><td>310,152</td><td>1.3%</td></tr>
<tr><td>45</td><td>Montana</td><td>52,237</td><td>0.2%</td><td>26</td><td>Arkansas</td><td>306,247</td><td>1.3%</td></tr>
<tr><td>32</td><td>Nebraska</td><td>157,988</td><td>0.7%</td><td>27</td><td>Colorado</td><td>292,080</td><td>1.2%</td></tr>
<tr><td>44</td><td>Nevada</td><td>72,398</td><td>0.3%</td><td>28</td><td>Connecticut</td><td>291,016</td><td>1.2%</td></tr>
<tr><td>47</td><td>New Hampshire</td><td>10,925</td><td>0.0%</td><td>29</td><td>New Mexico</td><td>249,565</td><td>1.1%</td></tr>
<tr><td>13</td><td>New Jersey</td><td>525,937</td><td>2.2%</td><td>30</td><td>Iowa</td><td>236,075</td><td>1.0%</td></tr>
<tr><td>29</td><td>New Mexico</td><td>249,565</td><td>1.1%</td><td>31</td><td>Utah</td><td>159,773</td><td>0.7%</td></tr>
<tr><td>2</td><td>New York</td><td>1,512,491</td><td>6.4%</td><td>32</td><td>Nebraska</td><td>157,988</td><td>0.7%</td></tr>
<tr><td>11</td><td>North Carolina</td><td>733,839</td><td>3.1%</td><td>33</td><td>West Virginia</td><td>142,186</td><td>0.6%</td></tr>
<tr><td>46</td><td>North Dakota</td><td>32,906</td><td>0.1%</td><td>34</td><td>Hawaii</td><td>140,594</td><td>0.6%</td></tr>
<tr><td>19</td><td>Ohio</td><td>403,497</td><td>1.7%</td><td>35</td><td>Kansas</td><td>138,365</td><td>0.6%</td></tr>
<tr><td>22</td><td>Oklahoma</td><td>333,127</td><td>1.4%</td><td>36</td><td>Illinois</td><td>125,898</td><td>0.5%</td></tr>
<tr><td>21</td><td>Oregon</td><td>372,756</td><td>1.6%</td><td>37</td><td>Maine</td><td>117,946</td><td>0.5%</td></tr>
<tr><td>5</td><td>Pennsylvania</td><td>1,152,109</td><td>4.9%</td><td>38</td><td>Rhode Island</td><td>117,493</td><td>0.5%</td></tr>
<tr><td>38</td><td>Rhode Island</td><td>117,493</td><td>0.5%</td><td>39</td><td>Delaware</td><td>94,395</td><td>0.4%</td></tr>
<tr><td>43</td><td>South Carolina</td><td>74,386</td><td>0.3%</td><td>40</td><td>South Dakota</td><td>89,564</td><td>0.4%</td></tr>
<tr><td>40</td><td>South Dakota</td><td>89,564</td><td>0.4%</td><td>41</td><td>Vermont</td><td>82,714</td><td>0.4%</td></tr>
<tr><td>3</td><td>Tennessee</td><td>1,324,011</td><td>5.6%</td><td>42</td><td>Idaho</td><td>77,506</td><td>0.3%</td></tr>
<tr><td>6</td><td>Texas</td><td>945,869</td><td>4.0%</td><td>43</td><td>South Carolina</td><td>74,386</td><td>0.3%</td></tr>
<tr><td>31</td><td>Utah</td><td>159,773</td><td>0.7%</td><td>44</td><td>Nevada</td><td>72,398</td><td>0.3%</td></tr>
<tr><td>41</td><td>Vermont</td><td>82,714</td><td>0.4%</td><td>45</td><td>Montana</td><td>52,237</td><td>0.2%</td></tr>
<tr><td>24</td><td>Virginia</td><td>327,390</td><td>1.4%</td><td>46</td><td>North Dakota</td><td>32,906</td><td>0.1%</td></tr>
<tr><td>8</td><td>Washington</td><td>897,940</td><td>3.8%</td><td>47</td><td>New Hampshire</td><td>10,925</td><td>0.0%</td></tr>
<tr><td>33</td><td>West Virginia</td><td>142,186</td><td>0.6%</td><td>48</td><td>Alaska</td><td>0</td><td>0.0%</td></tr>
<tr><td>23</td><td>Wisconsin</td><td>328,638</td><td>1.4%</td><td>48</td><td>Mississippi</td><td>0</td><td>0.0%</td></tr>
<tr><td>48</td><td>Wyoming</td><td>0</td><td>0.0%</td><td>48</td><td>Wyoming</td><td>0</td><td>0.0%</td></tr>
<tr><td></td><td></td><td></td><td></td><td colspan="2">District of Columbia</td><td>84,200</td><td>0.4%</td></tr>
</table>

Source: U.S. Department of Health and Human Services, Centers for Medicare and Medicaid Services
"Medicaid Managed Care State Enrollment" (http://www.cms.gov/medicaid/managedcare/mmcpr02.pdf)
*As of December 31, 2002. Enrollment in state health care reform programs that expand eligibility beyond traditional Medicaid standards. National total includes 854,645 Medicaid managed care enrollees in Puerto Rico.

Percent of Medicaid Enrollees in Managed Care in 2002

National Percent = 57.4% of Medicaid Enrollees*

RANK	STATE	PERCENT
33	Alabama	56.8
48	Alaska	0.0
6	Arizona	92.2
32	Arkansas	58.1
35	California	53.0
5	Colorado	93.3
13	Connecticut	75.5
12	Delaware	75.6
27	Florida	62.7
17	Georgia	70.2
10	Hawaii	79.2
36	Idaho	51.2
47	Illinois	7.4
23	Indiana	67.8
7	Iowa	89.1
31	Kansas	58.7
9	Kentucky	84.6
43	Louisiana	37.2
34	Maine	53.3
17	Maryland	70.2
26	Massachusetts	63.8
14	Michigan	75.0
20	Minnesota	69.5
48	Mississippi	0.0
40	Missouri	44.4
22	Montana	68.3
15	Nebraska	74.6
41	Nevada	44.0
45	New Hampshire	12.1
21	New Jersey	69.2
25	New Mexico	64.1
39	New York	44.6
19	North Carolina	69.8
29	North Dakota	62.2
44	Ohio	26.1
16	Oklahoma	72.0
8	Oregon	87.2
11	Pennsylvania	79.0
24	Rhode Island	67.0
46	South Carolina	9.6
2	South Dakota	98.7
1	Tennessee	100.0
42	Texas	39.2
4	Utah	93.6
28	Vermont	62.4
30	Virginia	61.7
3	Washington	94.9
37	West Virginia	49.4
38	Wisconsin	48.6
48	Wyoming	0.0

RANK	STATE	PERCENT
1	Tennessee	100.0
2	South Dakota	98.7
3	Washington	94.9
4	Utah	93.6
5	Colorado	93.3
6	Arizona	92.2
7	Iowa	89.1
8	Oregon	87.2
9	Kentucky	84.6
10	Hawaii	79.2
11	Pennsylvania	79.0
12	Delaware	75.6
13	Connecticut	75.5
14	Michigan	75.0
15	Nebraska	74.6
16	Oklahoma	72.0
17	Georgia	70.2
17	Maryland	70.2
19	North Carolina	69.8
20	Minnesota	69.5
21	New Jersey	69.2
22	Montana	68.3
23	Indiana	67.8
24	Rhode Island	67.0
25	New Mexico	64.1
26	Massachusetts	63.8
27	Florida	62.7
28	Vermont	62.4
29	North Dakota	62.2
30	Virginia	61.7
31	Kansas	58.7
32	Arkansas	58.1
33	Alabama	56.8
34	Maine	53.3
35	California	53.0
36	Idaho	51.2
37	West Virginia	49.4
38	Wisconsin	48.6
39	New York	44.6
40	Missouri	44.4
41	Nevada	44.0
42	Texas	39.2
43	Louisiana	37.2
44	Ohio	26.1
45	New Hampshire	12.1
46	South Carolina	9.6
47	Illinois	7.4
48	Alaska	0.0
48	Mississippi	0.0
48	Wyoming	0.0
	District of Columbia	65.4

Source: U.S. Department of Health and Human Services, Centers for Medicare and Medicaid Services
"Medicaid Managed Care State Enrollment" (http://www.cms.gov/medicaid/managedcare/mmcpr02.pdf)
As of December 31, 2002. Enrollment in state health care reform programs that expand eligibility beyond traditional Medicaid standards. National percent includes Medicaid enrollees in Puerto Rico and the Virgin Islands.

Medicaid Expenditures in 2002

National Total = $246,283,943,000*

ALPHA ORDER

ALPHA ORDER

RANK	STATE	EXPENDITURES	% of USA
26	Alabama	$3,093,271,000	1.3%
44	Alaska	685,773,000	0.3%
23	Arizona	3,541,599,000	1.4%
32	Arkansas	2,237,818,000	0.9%
2	California	26,890,541,000	10.9%
30	Colorado	2,323,069,000	0.9%
24	Connecticut	3,456,339,000	1.4%
46	Delaware	634,046,000	0.3%
5	Florida	9,871,508,000	4.0%
12	Georgia	6,241,211,000	2.5%
43	Hawaii	740,007,000	0.3%
42	Idaho	773,535,000	0.3%
7	Illinois	8,809,060,000	3.6%
17	Indiana	4,448,318,000	1.8%
28	Iowa	2,575,146,000	1.0%
33	Kansas	1,836,717,000	0.7%
21	Kentucky	3,763,204,000	1.5%
16	Louisiana	4,885,972,000	2.0%
36	Maine	1,430,109,000	0.6%
22	Maryland	3,613,476,000	1.5%
8	Massachusetts	8,063,005,000	3.3%
10	Michigan	7,562,053,000	3.1%
18	Minnesota	4,414,511,000	1.8%
27	Mississippi	2,877,014,000	1.2%
14	Missouri	5,360,608,000	2.2%
47	Montana	571,456,000	0.2%
38	Nebraska	1,339,132,000	0.5%
41	Nevada	808,198,000	0.3%
39	New Hampshire	1,016,095,000	0.4%
9	New Jersey	7,745,878,000	3.1%
34	New Mexico	1,776,812,000	0.7%
1	New York	36,295,107,000	14.7%
11	North Carolina	6,723,599,000	2.7%
49	North Dakota	461,402,000	0.2%
6	Ohio	9,658,041,000	3.9%
31	Oklahoma	2,260,404,000	0.9%
29	Oregon	2,571,561,000	1.0%
4	Pennsylvania	12,130,925,000	4.9%
37	Rhode Island	1,358,501,000	0.6%
25	South Carolina	3,292,901,000	1.3%
48	South Dakota	549,884,000	0.2%
13	Tennessee	5,787,079,000	2.3%
3	Texas	13,523,486,000	5.5%
40	Utah	984,161,000	0.4%
45	Vermont	660,732,000	0.3%
20	Virginia	3,812,166,000	1.5%
15	Washington	5,168,512,000	2.1%
35	West Virginia	1,584,166,000	0.6%
19	Wisconsin	4,193,175,000	1.7%
50	Wyoming	274,565,000	0.1%

RANK ORDER

RANK	STATE	EXPENDITURES	% of USA
1	New York	$36,295,107,000	14.7%
2	California	26,890,541,000	10.9%
3	Texas	13,523,486,000	5.5%
4	Pennsylvania	12,130,925,000	4.9%
5	Florida	9,871,508,000	4.0%
6	Ohio	9,658,041,000	3.9%
7	Illinois	8,809,060,000	3.6%
8	Massachusetts	8,063,005,000	3.3%
9	New Jersey	7,745,878,000	3.1%
10	Michigan	7,562,053,000	3.1%
11	North Carolina	6,723,599,000	2.7%
12	Georgia	6,241,211,000	2.5%
13	Tennessee	5,787,079,000	2.3%
14	Missouri	5,360,608,000	2.2%
15	Washington	5,168,512,000	2.1%
16	Louisiana	4,885,972,000	2.0%
17	Indiana	4,448,318,000	1.8%
18	Minnesota	4,414,511,000	1.8%
19	Wisconsin	4,193,175,000	1.7%
20	Virginia	3,812,166,000	1.5%
21	Kentucky	3,763,204,000	1.5%
22	Maryland	3,613,476,000	1.5%
23	Arizona	3,541,599,000	1.4%
24	Connecticut	3,456,339,000	1.4%
25	South Carolina	3,292,901,000	1.3%
26	Alabama	3,093,271,000	1.3%
27	Mississippi	2,877,014,000	1.2%
28	Iowa	2,575,146,000	1.0%
29	Oregon	2,571,561,000	1.0%
30	Colorado	2,323,069,000	0.9%
31	Oklahoma	2,260,404,000	0.9%
32	Arkansas	2,237,818,000	0.9%
33	Kansas	1,836,717,000	0.7%
34	New Mexico	1,776,812,000	0.7%
35	West Virginia	1,584,166,000	0.6%
36	Maine	1,430,109,000	0.6%
37	Rhode Island	1,358,501,000	0.6%
38	Nebraska	1,339,132,000	0.5%
39	New Hampshire	1,016,095,000	0.4%
40	Utah	984,161,000	0.4%
41	Nevada	808,198,000	0.3%
42	Idaho	773,535,000	0.3%
43	Hawaii	740,007,000	0.3%
44	Alaska	685,773,000	0.3%
45	Vermont	660,732,000	0.3%
46	Delaware	634,046,000	0.3%
47	Montana	571,456,000	0.2%
48	South Dakota	549,884,000	0.2%
49	North Dakota	461,402,000	0.2%
50	Wyoming	274,565,000	0.1%
	District of Columbia	1,021,773,000	0.4%

Source: U.S. Department of Health and Human Services, Centers for Medicare and Medicaid Services
   "Medicaid Financial Statistics Tables (HCFA-64 Report)"
*For fiscal year 2002. National total includes $586,322,000 in expenditures in U.S. territories. Includes Medical Assistance Payments and Administrative Costs.

Per Capita Medicaid Expenditures in 2002

National Per Capita = $852*

<table>
<tr><td colspan="3">ALPHA ORDER</td><td colspan="3">RANK ORDER</td></tr>
<tr><td>RANK</td><td>STATE</td><td>PER CAPITA</td><td>RANK</td><td>STATE</td><td>PER CAPITA</td></tr>
<tr><td>36</td><td>Alabama</td><td>$689</td><td>1</td><td>New York</td><td>$1,895</td></tr>
<tr><td>7</td><td>Alaska</td><td>1,065</td><td>2</td><td>Rhode Island</td><td>1,270</td></tr>
<tr><td>39</td><td>Arizona</td><td>649</td><td>3</td><td>Massachusetts</td><td>1,254</td></tr>
<tr><td>21</td><td>Arkansas</td><td>826</td><td>4</td><td>Maine</td><td>1,105</td></tr>
<tr><td>28</td><td>California</td><td>766</td><td>5</td><td>Louisiana</td><td>1,090</td></tr>
<tr><td>48</td><td>Colorado</td><td>515</td><td>6</td><td>Vermont</td><td>1,072</td></tr>
<tr><td>9</td><td>Connecticut</td><td>999</td><td>7</td><td>Alaska</td><td>1,065</td></tr>
<tr><td>25</td><td>Delaware</td><td>785</td><td>8</td><td>Mississippi</td><td>1,002</td></tr>
<tr><td>44</td><td>Florida</td><td>591</td><td>9</td><td>Connecticut</td><td>999</td></tr>
<tr><td>31</td><td>Georgia</td><td>729</td><td>10</td><td>Tennessee</td><td>998</td></tr>
<tr><td>43</td><td>Hawaii</td><td>594</td><td>11</td><td>Pennsylvania</td><td>983</td></tr>
<tr><td>45</td><td>Idaho</td><td>577</td><td>12</td><td>New Mexico</td><td>958</td></tr>
<tr><td>35</td><td>Illinois</td><td>699</td><td>13</td><td>Missouri</td><td>945</td></tr>
<tr><td>34</td><td>Indiana</td><td>722</td><td>14</td><td>Kentucky</td><td>919</td></tr>
<tr><td>18</td><td>Iowa</td><td>877</td><td>15</td><td>New Jersey</td><td>902</td></tr>
<tr><td>37</td><td>Kansas</td><td>676</td><td>16</td><td>Minnesota</td><td>879</td></tr>
<tr><td>14</td><td>Kentucky</td><td>919</td><td>16</td><td>West Virginia</td><td>879</td></tr>
<tr><td>5</td><td>Louisiana</td><td>1,090</td><td>18</td><td>Iowa</td><td>877</td></tr>
<tr><td>4</td><td>Maine</td><td>1,105</td><td>19</td><td>Washington</td><td>852</td></tr>
<tr><td>38</td><td>Maryland</td><td>662</td><td>20</td><td>Ohio</td><td>846</td></tr>
<tr><td>3</td><td>Massachusetts</td><td>1,254</td><td>21</td><td>Arkansas</td><td>826</td></tr>
<tr><td>29</td><td>Michigan</td><td>752</td><td>22</td><td>North Carolina</td><td>808</td></tr>
<tr><td>16</td><td>Minnesota</td><td>879</td><td>23</td><td>South Carolina</td><td>802</td></tr>
<tr><td>8</td><td>Mississippi</td><td>1,002</td><td>24</td><td>New Hampshire</td><td>797</td></tr>
<tr><td>13</td><td>Missouri</td><td>945</td><td>25</td><td>Delaware</td><td>785</td></tr>
<tr><td>41</td><td>Montana</td><td>628</td><td>26</td><td>Nebraska</td><td>774</td></tr>
<tr><td>26</td><td>Nebraska</td><td>774</td><td>27</td><td>Wisconsin</td><td>771</td></tr>
<tr><td>50</td><td>Nevada</td><td>372</td><td>28</td><td>California</td><td>766</td></tr>
<tr><td>24</td><td>New Hampshire</td><td>797</td><td>29</td><td>Michigan</td><td>752</td></tr>
<tr><td>15</td><td>New Jersey</td><td>902</td><td>30</td><td>Oregon</td><td>730</td></tr>
<tr><td>12</td><td>New Mexico</td><td>958</td><td>31</td><td>Georgia</td><td>729</td></tr>
<tr><td>1</td><td>New York</td><td>1,895</td><td>32</td><td>North Dakota</td><td>728</td></tr>
<tr><td>22</td><td>North Carolina</td><td>808</td><td>33</td><td>South Dakota</td><td>723</td></tr>
<tr><td>32</td><td>North Dakota</td><td>728</td><td>34</td><td>Indiana</td><td>722</td></tr>
<tr><td>20</td><td>Ohio</td><td>846</td><td>35</td><td>Illinois</td><td>699</td></tr>
<tr><td>40</td><td>Oklahoma</td><td>647</td><td>36</td><td>Alabama</td><td>689</td></tr>
<tr><td>30</td><td>Oregon</td><td>730</td><td>37</td><td>Kansas</td><td>676</td></tr>
<tr><td>11</td><td>Pennsylvania</td><td>983</td><td>38</td><td>Maryland</td><td>662</td></tr>
<tr><td>2</td><td>Rhode Island</td><td>1,270</td><td>39</td><td>Arizona</td><td>649</td></tr>
<tr><td>23</td><td>South Carolina</td><td>802</td><td>40</td><td>Oklahoma</td><td>647</td></tr>
<tr><td>33</td><td>South Dakota</td><td>723</td><td>41</td><td>Montana</td><td>628</td></tr>
<tr><td>10</td><td>Tennessee</td><td>998</td><td>42</td><td>Texas</td><td>621</td></tr>
<tr><td>42</td><td>Texas</td><td>621</td><td>43</td><td>Hawaii</td><td>594</td></tr>
<tr><td>49</td><td>Utah</td><td>425</td><td>44</td><td>Florida</td><td>591</td></tr>
<tr><td>6</td><td>Vermont</td><td>1,072</td><td>45</td><td>Idaho</td><td>577</td></tr>
<tr><td>47</td><td>Virginia</td><td>523</td><td>46</td><td>Wyoming</td><td>551</td></tr>
<tr><td>19</td><td>Washington</td><td>852</td><td>47</td><td>Virginia</td><td>523</td></tr>
<tr><td>16</td><td>West Virginia</td><td>879</td><td>48</td><td>Colorado</td><td>515</td></tr>
<tr><td>27</td><td>Wisconsin</td><td>771</td><td>49</td><td>Utah</td><td>425</td></tr>
<tr><td>46</td><td>Wyoming</td><td>551</td><td>50</td><td>Nevada</td><td>372</td></tr>
<tr><td></td><td></td><td></td><td></td><td>District of Columbia</td><td>1,790</td></tr>
</table>

Source: MQ Press using data from U.S. Dept of Health & Human Services, Centers for Medicare and Medicaid Services
   "Medicaid Financial Statistics Tables (HCFA-64 Report)"
*For fiscal year 2002. National figure does not include expenditures or enrollees in U.S. territories. Includes
Medical Assistance Payments and Administrative Costs.

Percent Change in Medicaid Expenditures: 1998 to 2002

National Percent Change = 38.9% Increase*

ALPHA ORDER				RANK ORDER		
RANK	STATE	PERCENT CHANGE		RANK	STATE	PERCENT CHANGE
42	Alabama	30.1		1	Iowa	82.0
3	Alaska	72.5		2	Arizona	77.2
2	Arizona	77.2		3	Alaska	72.5
14	Arkansas	49.9		4	Georgia	67.1
32	California	37.5		5	Mississippi	66.9
29	Colorado	39.2		6	Idaho	66.3
49	Connecticut	18.1		7	Indiana	66.2
22	Delaware	43.3		7	New Mexico	66.2
16	Florida	49.3		9	Kansas	58.8
4	Georgia	67.1		10	Missouri	57.5
48	Hawaii	20.0		11	Virginia	54.8
6	Idaho	66.3		12	Oklahoma	54.4
46	Illinois	24.8		13	Vermont	53.6
7	Indiana	66.2		14	Arkansas	49.9
1	Iowa	82.0		14	South Dakota	49.9
9	Kansas	58.8		16	Florida	49.3
27	Kentucky	40.5		16	Louisiana	49.3
16	Louisiana	49.3		16	Nebraska	49.3
45	Maine	26.9		19	Nevada	49.1
43	Maryland	29.8		20	Wisconsin	45.6
23	Massachusetts	42.4		21	Washington	43.9
47	Michigan	21.6		22	Delaware	43.3
30	Minnesota	38.3		23	Massachusetts	42.4
5	Mississippi	66.9		24	North Carolina	42.1
10	Missouri	57.5		25	Ohio	41.5
32	Montana	37.5		26	Tennessee	41.3
16	Nebraska	49.3		27	Kentucky	40.5
19	Nevada	49.1		28	South Carolina	40.2
39	New Hampshire	31.4		29	Colorado	39.2
36	New Jersey	35.5		30	Minnesota	38.3
7	New Mexico	66.2		31	Oregon	38.2
44	New York	29.7		32	California	37.5
24	North Carolina	42.1		32	Montana	37.5
38	North Dakota	34.0		34	Pennsylvania	37.1
25	Ohio	41.5		35	Rhode Island	36.2
12	Oklahoma	54.4		36	New Jersey	35.5
31	Oregon	38.2		37	Utah	34.9
34	Pennsylvania	37.1		38	North Dakota	34.0
35	Rhode Island	36.2		39	New Hampshire	31.4
28	South Carolina	40.2		40	Wyoming	30.8
14	South Dakota	49.9		41	Texas	30.6
26	Tennessee	41.3		42	Alabama	30.1
41	Texas	30.6		43	Maryland	29.8
37	Utah	34.9		44	New York	29.7
13	Vermont	53.6		45	Maine	26.9
11	Virginia	54.8		46	Illinois	24.8
21	Washington	43.9		47	Michigan	21.6
50	West Virginia	12.3		48	Hawaii	20.0
20	Wisconsin	45.6		49	Connecticut	18.1
40	Wyoming	30.8		50	West Virginia	12.3
					District of Columbia	12.7

Source: MQ Press using data from U.S. Dept of Health & Human Services, Centers for Medicare and Medicaid Services
"Medicaid Financial Statistics Tables (HCFA-64 Report)"
*For fiscal years 2002 and 1998. National figure includes expenditures in U.S. territories.

Medicaid Expenditures per Enrollee in 2002

National Rate = $5,985 per Enrollee*

ALPHA ORDER

RANK	STATE	PER ENROLLEE
49	Alabama	$4,204
12	Alaska	7,479
46	Arizona	4,310
48	Arkansas	4,247
45	California	4,344
14	Colorado	7,418
5	Connecticut	8,972
35	Delaware	5,079
41	Florida	4,679
40	Georgia	4,717
50	Hawaii	4,168
34	Idaho	5,110
33	Illinois	5,195
16	Indiana	6,478
4	Iowa	9,716
10	Kansas	7,789
22	Kentucky	6,229
26	Louisiana	5,859
17	Maine	6,464
32	Maryland	5,452
7	Massachusetts	8,379
19	Michigan	6,347
9	Minnesota	7,934
43	Mississippi	4,421
27	Missouri	5,763
13	Montana	7,472
20	Nebraska	6,325
38	Nevada	4,916
1	New Hampshire	11,286
3	New Jersey	10,197
42	New Mexico	4,564
2	New York	10,710
18	North Carolina	6,391
6	North Dakota	8,720
21	Ohio	6,251
39	Oklahoma	4,887
25	Oregon	6,015
8	Pennsylvania	8,316
11	Rhode Island	7,741
47	South Carolina	4,268
24	South Dakota	6,058
44	Tennessee	4,371
29	Texas	5,605
27	Utah	5,763
37	Vermont	4,987
15	Virginia	7,187
31	Washington	5,462
30	West Virginia	5,499
23	Wisconsin	6,199
36	Wyoming	5,024

RANK ORDER

RANK	STATE	PER ENROLLEE
1	New Hampshire	$11,286
2	New York	10,710
3	New Jersey	10,197
4	Iowa	9,716
5	Connecticut	8,972
6	North Dakota	8,720
7	Massachusetts	8,379
8	Pennsylvania	8,316
9	Minnesota	7,934
10	Kansas	7,789
11	Rhode Island	7,741
12	Alaska	7,479
13	Montana	7,472
14	Colorado	7,418
15	Virginia	7,187
16	Indiana	6,478
17	Maine	6,464
18	North Carolina	6,391
19	Michigan	6,347
20	Nebraska	6,325
21	Ohio	6,251
22	Kentucky	6,229
23	Wisconsin	6,199
24	South Dakota	6,058
25	Oregon	6,015
26	Louisiana	5,859
27	Missouri	5,763
27	Utah	5,763
29	Texas	5,605
30	West Virginia	5,499
31	Washington	5,462
32	Maryland	5,452
33	Illinois	5,195
34	Idaho	5,110
35	Delaware	5,079
36	Wyoming	5,024
37	Vermont	4,987
38	Nevada	4,916
39	Oklahoma	4,887
40	Georgia	4,717
41	Florida	4,679
42	New Mexico	4,564
43	Mississippi	4,421
44	Tennessee	4,371
45	California	4,344
46	Arizona	4,310
47	South Carolina	4,268
48	Arkansas	4,247
49	Alabama	4,204
50	Hawaii	4,168
	District of Columbia	7,931

Source: MQ Press using data from U.S. Dept of Health & Human Services, Centers for Medicare and Medicaid Services
"Medicaid Financial Statistics Tables (HCFA-64 Report)"
*For fiscal year 2002. National figure includes expenditures and enrollees in U.S. territories. Includes Medical Assistance Payments and Administrative Costs.

Percent Change in Expenditures per Medicaid Enrollee: 1998 to 2002

National Percent Change = 5.1% Increase*

ALPHA ORDER

RANK	STATE	PERCENT CHANGE
44	Alabama	(9.6)
13	Alaska	14.6
42	Arizona	(7.6)
33	Arkansas	(0.5)
16	California	9.7
35	Colorado	(4.3)
37	Connecticut	(5.1)
39	Delaware	(6.6)
30	Florida	1.9
12	Georgia	14.8
23	Hawaii	8.4
46	Idaho	(14.6)
36	Illinois	(4.5)
23	Indiana	8.4
2	Iowa	42.5
15	Kansas	14.3
8	Kentucky	19.0
28	Louisiana	4.1
43	Maine	(7.8)
41	Maryland	(7.0)
5	Massachusetts	27.3
20	Michigan	8.9
29	Minnesota	3.9
31	Mississippi	1.6
22	Missouri	8.5
9	Montana	18.8
11	Nebraska	15.0
50	Nevada	(21.8)
19	New Hampshire	9.2
16	New Jersey	9.7
10	New Mexico	16.1
47	New York	(14.8)
18	North Carolina	9.6
25	North Dakota	7.4
38	Ohio	(5.9)
13	Oklahoma	14.6
7	Oregon	21.4
6	Pennsylvania	23.5
40	Rhode Island	(6.9)
45	South Carolina	(14.2)
21	South Dakota	8.8
3	Tennessee	37.5
32	Texas	(0.1)
34	Utah	(1.2)
4	Vermont	27.7
1	Virginia	43.5
26	Washington	6.5
27	West Virginia	5.3
48	Wisconsin	(15.0)
49	Wyoming	(16.5)

RANK ORDER

RANK	STATE	PERCENT CHANGE
1	Virginia	43.5
2	Iowa	42.5
3	Tennessee	37.5
4	Vermont	27.7
5	Massachusetts	27.3
6	Pennsylvania	23.5
7	Oregon	21.4
8	Kentucky	19.0
9	Montana	18.8
10	New Mexico	16.1
11	Nebraska	15.0
12	Georgia	14.8
13	Alaska	14.6
13	Oklahoma	14.6
15	Kansas	14.3
16	California	9.7
16	New Jersey	9.7
18	North Carolina	9.6
19	New Hampshire	9.2
20	Michigan	8.9
21	South Dakota	8.8
22	Missouri	8.5
23	Hawaii	8.4
23	Indiana	8.4
25	North Dakota	7.4
26	Washington	6.5
27	West Virginia	5.3
28	Louisiana	4.1
29	Minnesota	3.9
30	Florida	1.9
31	Mississippi	1.6
32	Texas	(0.1)
33	Arkansas	(0.5)
34	Utah	(1.2)
35	Colorado	(4.3)
36	Illinois	(4.5)
37	Connecticut	(5.1)
38	Ohio	(5.9)
39	Delaware	(6.6)
40	Rhode Island	(6.9)
41	Maryland	(7.0)
42	Arizona	(7.6)
43	Maine	(7.8)
44	Alabama	(9.6)
45	South Carolina	(14.2)
46	Idaho	(14.6)
47	New York	(14.8)
48	Wisconsin	(15.0)
49	Wyoming	(16.5)
50	Nevada	(21.8)

District of Columbia   1.3

Source: MQ Press using data from U.S. Dept of Health & Human Services, Centers for Medicare and Medicaid Services "Medicaid Financial Statistics Tables (HCFA-64 Report)"
For fiscal years 2002 and 1998. National figure includes expenditures and enrollees in U.S. territories.

Federal Medicaid Matching Fund Rate for 2004

National Average = 72.68% of States' Funds Matched by Federal Government*

<table>
<tr><td colspan="3">ALPHA ORDER</td><td colspan="3">RANK ORDER</td></tr>
<tr><td>RANK</td><td>STATE</td><td>RATE</td><td>RANK</td><td>STATE</td><td>RATE</td></tr>
<tr><td>8</td><td>Alabama</td><td>79.53</td><td>1</td><td>Mississippi</td><td>83.96</td></tr>
<tr><td>33</td><td>Alaska</td><td>70.87</td><td>2</td><td>West Virginia</td><td>82.63</td></tr>
<tr><td>14</td><td>Arizona</td><td>77.08</td><td>3</td><td>New Mexico</td><td>82.40</td></tr>
<tr><td>4</td><td>Arkansas</td><td>82.27</td><td>4</td><td>Arkansas</td><td>82.27</td></tr>
<tr><td>38</td><td>California</td><td>65.00</td><td>5</td><td>Montana</td><td>81.00</td></tr>
<tr><td>38</td><td>Colorado</td><td>65.00</td><td>6</td><td>Utah</td><td>80.20</td></tr>
<tr><td>38</td><td>Connecticut</td><td>65.00</td><td>7</td><td>Louisiana</td><td>80.14</td></tr>
<tr><td>38</td><td>Delaware</td><td>65.00</td><td>8</td><td>Alabama</td><td>79.53</td></tr>
<tr><td>30</td><td>Florida</td><td>71.25</td><td>9</td><td>Idaho</td><td>79.32</td></tr>
<tr><td>28</td><td>Georgia</td><td>71.71</td><td>10</td><td>Oklahoma</td><td>79.17</td></tr>
<tr><td>31</td><td>Hawaii</td><td>71.23</td><td>11</td><td>Kentucky</td><td>79.06</td></tr>
<tr><td>9</td><td>Idaho</td><td>79.32</td><td>12</td><td>South Carolina</td><td>78.90</td></tr>
<tr><td>38</td><td>Illinois</td><td>65.00</td><td>13</td><td>North Dakota</td><td>77.82</td></tr>
<tr><td>20</td><td>Indiana</td><td>73.62</td><td>14</td><td>Arizona</td><td>77.08</td></tr>
<tr><td>18</td><td>Iowa</td><td>74.75</td><td>15</td><td>Maine</td><td>76.21</td></tr>
<tr><td>23</td><td>Kansas</td><td>72.57</td><td>16</td><td>South Dakota</td><td>75.97</td></tr>
<tr><td>11</td><td>Kentucky</td><td>79.06</td><td>17</td><td>Tennessee</td><td>75.08</td></tr>
<tr><td>7</td><td>Louisiana</td><td>80.14</td><td>18</td><td>Iowa</td><td>74.75</td></tr>
<tr><td>15</td><td>Maine</td><td>76.21</td><td>19</td><td>North Carolina</td><td>74.00</td></tr>
<tr><td>38</td><td>Maryland</td><td>65.00</td><td>20</td><td>Indiana</td><td>73.62</td></tr>
<tr><td>38</td><td>Massachusetts</td><td>65.00</td><td>21</td><td>Missouri</td><td>73.03</td></tr>
<tr><td>35</td><td>Michigan</td><td>69.12</td><td>22</td><td>Vermont</td><td>72.94</td></tr>
<tr><td>38</td><td>Minnesota</td><td>65.00</td><td>23</td><td>Kansas</td><td>72.57</td></tr>
<tr><td>1</td><td>Mississippi</td><td>83.96</td><td>23</td><td>Oregon</td><td>72.57</td></tr>
<tr><td>21</td><td>Missouri</td><td>73.03</td><td>25</td><td>Texas</td><td>72.15</td></tr>
<tr><td>5</td><td>Montana</td><td>81.00</td><td>26</td><td>Nebraska</td><td>71.92</td></tr>
<tr><td>26</td><td>Nebraska</td><td>71.92</td><td>27</td><td>Wyoming</td><td>71.84</td></tr>
<tr><td>36</td><td>Nevada</td><td>68.45</td><td>28</td><td>Georgia</td><td>71.71</td></tr>
<tr><td>38</td><td>New Hampshire</td><td>65.00</td><td>29</td><td>Ohio</td><td>71.46</td></tr>
<tr><td>38</td><td>New Jersey</td><td>65.00</td><td>30</td><td>Florida</td><td>71.25</td></tr>
<tr><td>3</td><td>New Mexico</td><td>82.40</td><td>31</td><td>Hawaii</td><td>71.23</td></tr>
<tr><td>38</td><td>New York</td><td>65.00</td><td>32</td><td>Wisconsin</td><td>70.89</td></tr>
<tr><td>19</td><td>North Carolina</td><td>74.00</td><td>33</td><td>Alaska</td><td>70.87</td></tr>
<tr><td>13</td><td>North Dakota</td><td>77.82</td><td>34</td><td>Rhode Island</td><td>69.22</td></tr>
<tr><td>29</td><td>Ohio</td><td>71.46</td><td>35</td><td>Michigan</td><td>69.12</td></tr>
<tr><td>10</td><td>Oklahoma</td><td>79.17</td><td>36</td><td>Nevada</td><td>68.45</td></tr>
<tr><td>23</td><td>Oregon</td><td>72.57</td><td>37</td><td>Pennsylvania</td><td>68.33</td></tr>
<tr><td>37</td><td>Pennsylvania</td><td>68.33</td><td>38</td><td>California</td><td>65.00</td></tr>
<tr><td>34</td><td>Rhode Island</td><td>69.22</td><td>38</td><td>Colorado</td><td>65.00</td></tr>
<tr><td>12</td><td>South Carolina</td><td>78.90</td><td>38</td><td>Connecticut</td><td>65.00</td></tr>
<tr><td>16</td><td>South Dakota</td><td>75.97</td><td>38</td><td>Delaware</td><td>65.00</td></tr>
<tr><td>17</td><td>Tennessee</td><td>75.08</td><td>38</td><td>Illinois</td><td>65.00</td></tr>
<tr><td>25</td><td>Texas</td><td>72.15</td><td>38</td><td>Maryland</td><td>65.00</td></tr>
<tr><td>6</td><td>Utah</td><td>80.20</td><td>38</td><td>Massachusetts</td><td>65.00</td></tr>
<tr><td>22</td><td>Vermont</td><td>72.94</td><td>38</td><td>Minnesota</td><td>65.00</td></tr>
<tr><td>38</td><td>Virginia</td><td>65.00</td><td>38</td><td>New Hampshire</td><td>65.00</td></tr>
<tr><td>38</td><td>Washington</td><td>65.00</td><td>38</td><td>New Jersey</td><td>65.00</td></tr>
<tr><td>2</td><td>West Virginia</td><td>82.63</td><td>38</td><td>New York</td><td>65.00</td></tr>
<tr><td>32</td><td>Wisconsin</td><td>70.89</td><td>38</td><td>Virginia</td><td>65.00</td></tr>
<tr><td>27</td><td>Wyoming</td><td>71.84</td><td>38</td><td>Washington</td><td>65.00</td></tr>
<tr><td></td><td></td><td></td><td></td><td>District of Columbia</td><td>79.00</td></tr>
</table>

Source: U.S. Department of Health and Human Services, Centers for Medicare and Medicaid Services
    "Enhanced Federal Medical Assistance Percentages" (http://aspe.os.dhhs.gov/health/fmap04.htm)
For fiscal year 2004. These are "enhanced" matching rates established by the Children's Health Insurance
Program, signed into law in August 1997. Sixty-five percent is the minimum. National average is a simple average of
the 51 individual rates and is not weighted for population or funds.

Projected National Health Care Expenditures in 2004

Total Health Care Expenditures = $1,778,800,000,000*

The 1998 health care expenditures broken down to the state level and shown in this book were released in August of 2000 and updated in 2002. The Centers for Medicare and Medicaid Services (CMS) plan to update these numbers but no updates were available as we went to press.

Given the high level of interest in health care finance data, we have assembled a table showing the most recent national level health care expenditure projections. We will continue to monitor CMS data releases and will include the state expenditure updates in forthcoming editions.

	PROJECTED EXPENDITURES IN 2004	PROJECTED PERCENT CHANGE: 2003 TO 2004
Total Health Care Expenditures	$1,778,800,000,000	7.0
Per Capita Total Health Care Expenditures	$6,117	
Personal Health Care Expenditures	$1,526,400,000,000	7.1
Per Capita Personal Health Care Expenditures	$5,249	
Hospital Care Expenditures	$542,000,000,000	6.0
Per Capita Hospital Care Expenditures	$1,864	
Physician Services Expenditures	$381,400,000,000	6.9
Per Capita Physician Services Expenditures	$1,312	
Dental Services Expenditures	$78,200,000,000	5.6
Per Capita Dental Services Expenditures	$269	
Other Professional Services	$51,300,000,000	7.7
Per Capita Other Professional Services	$176	
Home Health Care Expenditures	$40,900,000,000	6.9
Per Capita Home Health Care Expenditures	$141	
Prescription Drugs	$204,700,000,000	12.4
Per Capita Prescription Drugs	$704	
Nursing Home Care	$113,300,000,000	4.8
Per Capita Nursing Home Care	$390	
Other Personal Care Expenditures	$57,300,000,000	12.0
Per Capita Other Personal Care Expenditures	$197	

Source: U.S. Department of Health and Human Services, Centers for Medicare and Medicaid Services
  "National Health Expenditure Amounts and Average Annual Percent Change, by Type of Expenditure"
    http://www.cms.hhs.gov/statistics/nhe/projections-2002/t2.asp
*Per Capita figures calculated by Morgan Quitno Press using 2003 Census population estimates.
For definitions see the corresponding 1998 state tables in this chapter.

Personal Health Care Expenditures in 1998

National Total = $1,016,129,000,000*

ALPHA ORDER

ALPHA ORDER

RANK	STATE	EXPENDITURES	% of USA
22	Alabama	$15,611,000,000	1.5%
48	Alaska	2,085,000,000	0.2%
24	Arizona	15,010,000,000	1.5%
33	Arkansas	8,532,000,000	0.8%
1	California	112,848,000,000	11.1%
26	Colorado	13,552,000,000	1.3%
23	Connecticut	15,336,000,000	1.5%
44	Delaware	3,070,000,000	0.3%
4	Florida	60,306,000,000	5.9%
11	Georgia	27,213,000,000	2.7%
41	Hawaii	4,579,000,000	0.5%
43	Idaho	3,419,000,000	0.3%
6	Illinois	44,170,000,000	4.3%
15	Indiana	21,221,000,000	2.1%
30	Iowa	10,192,000,000	1.0%
31	Kansas	9,309,000,000	0.9%
25	Kentucky	14,471,000,000	1.4%
21	Louisiana	16,434,000,000	1.6%
39	Maine	4,895,000,000	0.5%
19	Maryland	19,507,000,000	1.9%
10	Massachusetts	30,198,000,000	3.0%
8	Michigan	35,256,000,000	3.5%
17	Minnesota	19,989,000,000	2.0%
32	Mississippi	9,034,000,000	0.9%
16	Missouri	21,150,000,000	2.1%
45	Montana	2,855,000,000	0.3%
35	Nebraska	6,109,000,000	0.6%
37	Nevada	5,581,000,000	0.5%
40	New Hampshire	4,610,000,000	0.5%
9	New Jersey	32,772,000,000	3.2%
38	New Mexico	5,364,000,000	0.5%
2	New York	85,156,000,000	8.4%
12	North Carolina	26,853,000,000	2.6%
47	North Dakota	2,669,000,000	0.3%
7	Ohio	41,798,000,000	4.1%
29	Oklahoma	10,897,000,000	1.1%
28	Oregon	10,950,000,000	1.1%
5	Pennsylvania	50,760,000,000	5.0%
42	Rhode Island	4,400,000,000	0.4%
27	South Carolina	13,006,000,000	1.3%
46	South Dakota	2,774,000,000	0.3%
14	Tennessee	21,798,000,000	2.1%
3	Texas	68,385,000,000	6.7%
36	Utah	5,933,000,000	0.6%
49	Vermont	2,052,000,000	0.2%
13	Virginia	22,158,000,000	2.2%
20	Washington	19,331,000,000	1.9%
34	West Virginia	7,015,000,000	0.7%
18	Wisconsin	19,806,000,000	1.9%
50	Wyoming	1,398,000,000	0.1%

RANK ORDER

RANK	STATE	EXPENDITURES	% of USA
1	California	$112,848,000,000	11.1%
2	New York	85,156,000,000	8.4%
3	Texas	68,385,000,000	6.7%
4	Florida	60,306,000,000	5.9%
5	Pennsylvania	50,760,000,000	5.0%
6	Illinois	44,170,000,000	4.3%
7	Ohio	41,798,000,000	4.1%
8	Michigan	35,256,000,000	3.5%
9	New Jersey	32,772,000,000	3.2%
10	Massachusetts	30,198,000,000	3.0%
11	Georgia	27,213,000,000	2.7%
12	North Carolina	26,853,000,000	2.6%
13	Virginia	22,158,000,000	2.2%
14	Tennessee	21,798,000,000	2.1%
15	Indiana	21,221,000,000	2.1%
16	Missouri	21,150,000,000	2.1%
17	Minnesota	19,989,000,000	2.0%
18	Wisconsin	19,806,000,000	1.9%
19	Maryland	19,507,000,000	1.9%
20	Washington	19,331,000,000	1.9%
21	Louisiana	16,434,000,000	1.6%
22	Alabama	15,611,000,000	1.5%
23	Connecticut	15,336,000,000	1.5%
24	Arizona	15,010,000,000	1.5%
25	Kentucky	14,471,000,000	1.4%
26	Colorado	13,552,000,000	1.3%
27	South Carolina	13,006,000,000	1.3%
28	Oregon	10,950,000,000	1.1%
29	Oklahoma	10,897,000,000	1.1%
30	Iowa	10,192,000,000	1.0%
31	Kansas	9,309,000,000	0.9%
32	Mississippi	9,034,000,000	0.9%
33	Arkansas	8,532,000,000	0.8%
34	West Virginia	7,015,000,000	0.7%
35	Nebraska	6,109,000,000	0.6%
36	Utah	5,933,000,000	0.6%
37	Nevada	5,581,000,000	0.5%
38	New Mexico	5,364,000,000	0.5%
39	Maine	4,895,000,000	0.5%
40	New Hampshire	4,610,000,000	0.5%
41	Hawaii	4,579,000,000	0.5%
42	Rhode Island	4,400,000,000	0.4%
43	Idaho	3,419,000,000	0.3%
44	Delaware	3,070,000,000	0.3%
45	Montana	2,855,000,000	0.3%
46	South Dakota	2,774,000,000	0.3%
47	North Dakota	2,669,000,000	0.3%
48	Alaska	2,085,000,000	0.2%
49	Vermont	2,052,000,000	0.2%
50	Wyoming	1,398,000,000	0.1%
	District of Columbia	4,312,000,000	0.4%

Source: U.S. Department of Health and Human Services, Centers for Medicare and Medicaid Services
"State Health Care Expenditures" (http://www.cms.hhs.gov/statistics/nhe/)
*By state of provider. Includes hospital care, physician services, dental services, home health care, drugs, vision products, nursing home care and other personal health care services and products. Revised figures.

Health Care Expenditures as a Percent of Gross State Product in 1998

National Percent = 11.6% of Total Gross State Product*

RANK	STATE	PERCENT
8	Alabama	14.2
49	Alaska	8.5
32	Arizona	11.3
9	Arkansas	13.9
43	California	10.0
45	Colorado	9.7
36	Connecticut	10.7
47	Delaware	9.4
5	Florida	14.5
36	Georgia	10.7
30	Hawaii	11.6
35	Idaho	11.0
40	Illinois	10.4
25	Indiana	12.0
21	Iowa	12.3
23	Kansas	12.1
12	Kentucky	13.4
12	Louisiana	13.4
3	Maine	15.2
27	Maryland	11.9
20	Massachusetts	12.5
25	Michigan	12.0
21	Minnesota	12.3
4	Mississippi	14.6
16	Missouri	12.9
6	Montana	14.3
27	Nebraska	11.9
48	Nevada	8.7
31	New Hampshire	11.4
41	New Jersey	10.3
33	New Mexico	11.1
29	New York	11.8
33	North Carolina	11.1
2	North Dakota	15.7
23	Ohio	12.1
15	Oklahoma	13.3
39	Oregon	10.6
9	Pennsylvania	13.9
6	Rhode Island	14.3
17	South Carolina	12.8
11	South Dakota	13.5
12	Tennessee	13.4
36	Texas	10.7
43	Utah	10.0
18	Vermont	12.6
45	Virginia	9.7
42	Washington	10.1
1	West Virginia	18.0
18	Wisconsin	12.6
49	Wyoming	8.5

RANK	STATE	PERCENT
1	West Virginia	18.0
2	North Dakota	15.7
3	Maine	15.2
4	Mississippi	14.6
5	Florida	14.5
6	Montana	14.3
6	Rhode Island	14.3
8	Alabama	14.2
9	Arkansas	13.9
9	Pennsylvania	13.9
11	South Dakota	13.5
12	Kentucky	13.4
12	Louisiana	13.4
12	Tennessee	13.4
15	Oklahoma	13.3
16	Missouri	12.9
17	South Carolina	12.8
18	Vermont	12.6
18	Wisconsin	12.6
20	Massachusetts	12.5
21	Iowa	12.3
21	Minnesota	12.3
23	Kansas	12.1
23	Ohio	12.1
25	Indiana	12.0
25	Michigan	12.0
27	Maryland	11.9
27	Nebraska	11.9
29	New York	11.8
30	Hawaii	11.6
31	New Hampshire	11.4
32	Arizona	11.3
33	New Mexico	11.1
33	North Carolina	11.1
35	Idaho	11.0
36	Connecticut	10.7
36	Georgia	10.7
36	Texas	10.7
39	Oregon	10.6
40	Illinois	10.4
41	New Jersey	10.3
42	Washington	10.1
43	California	10.0
43	Utah	10.0
45	Colorado	9.7
45	Virginia	9.7
47	Delaware	9.4
48	Nevada	8.7
49	Alaska	8.5
49	Wyoming	8.5

	District of Columbia	8.3

Source: MQ Press using data from U.S. Dept of Health & Human Services, Centers for Medicare and Medicaid Services "State Health Care Expenditures" (http://www.cms.hhs.gov/statistics/nhe/)

*By state of provider. Includes hospital care, physician services, dental services, home health care, drugs, vision products, nursing home care and other personal health care services and products. Revised figures.

Per Capita Personal Health Care Expenditures in 1998

National Per Capita = $3,760*

ALPHA ORDER

RANK	STATE	PER CAPITA
27	Alabama	$3,588
37	Alaska	3,389
45	Arizona	3,216
39	Arkansas	3,361
34	California	3,453
35	Colorado	3,414
3	Connecticut	4,686
8	Delaware	4,126
10	Florida	4,045
28	Georgia	3,564
16	Hawaii	3,846
50	Idaho	2,778
24	Illinois	3,660
25	Indiana	3,592
29	Iowa	3,562
31	Kansas	3,528
22	Kentucky	3,678
20	Louisiana	3,767
12	Maine	3,924
17	Maryland	3,802
1	Massachusetts	4,915
26	Michigan	3,590
5	Minnesota	4,229
41	Mississippi	3,283
13	Missouri	3,890
44	Montana	3,246
22	Nebraska	3,678
46	Nevada	3,201
14	New Hampshire	3,888
9	New Jersey	4,048
47	New Mexico	3,094
2	New York	4,689
30	North Carolina	3,559
7	North Dakota	4,185
21	Ohio	3,719
43	Oklahoma	3,263
40	Oregon	3,336
5	Pennsylvania	4,229
4	Rhode Island	4,455
38	South Carolina	3,387
18	South Dakota	3,796
11	Tennessee	4,012
33	Texas	3,469
49	Utah	2,824
32	Vermont	3,475
42	Virginia	3,264
36	Washington	3,399
15	West Virginia	3,872
19	Wisconsin	3,793
48	Wyoming	2,912

RANK ORDER

RANK	STATE	PER CAPITA
1	Massachusetts	$4,915
2	New York	4,689
3	Connecticut	4,686
4	Rhode Island	4,455
5	Minnesota	4,229
5	Pennsylvania	4,229
7	North Dakota	4,185
8	Delaware	4,126
9	New Jersey	4,048
10	Florida	4,045
11	Tennessee	4,012
12	Maine	3,924
13	Missouri	3,890
14	New Hampshire	3,888
15	West Virginia	3,872
16	Hawaii	3,846
17	Maryland	3,802
18	South Dakota	3,796
19	Wisconsin	3,793
20	Louisiana	3,767
21	Ohio	3,719
22	Kentucky	3,678
22	Nebraska	3,678
24	Illinois	3,660
25	Indiana	3,592
26	Michigan	3,590
27	Alabama	3,588
28	Georgia	3,564
29	Iowa	3,562
30	North Carolina	3,559
31	Kansas	3,528
32	Vermont	3,475
33	Texas	3,469
34	California	3,453
35	Colorado	3,414
36	Washington	3,399
37	Alaska	3,389
38	South Carolina	3,387
39	Arkansas	3,361
40	Oregon	3,336
41	Mississippi	3,283
42	Virginia	3,264
43	Oklahoma	3,263
44	Montana	3,246
45	Arizona	3,216
46	Nevada	3,201
47	New Mexico	3,094
48	Wyoming	2,912
49	Utah	2,824
50	Idaho	2,778
	District of Columbia	8,270

Source: MQ Press using data from U.S. Dept of Health & Human Services, Centers for Medicare and Medicaid Services "State Health Care Expenditures" (http://www.cms.hhs.gov/statistics/nhe/)
*By state of provider. Per capita calculated using resident population. These figures may be skewed due to residents crossing state borders for care. Includes hospital care, physician services, dental services, home health care, drugs, vision products, nursing home care and other personal health care services and products. Revised figures

Expenditures for Hospital Care in 1998

National Total = $379,834,000,000*

ALPHA ORDER

RANK	STATE	EXPENDITURES	% of USA
22	Alabama	$6,169,000,000	1.6%
48	Alaska	909,000,000	0.2%
25	Arizona	5,199,000,000	1.4%
33	Arkansas	3,394,000,000	0.9%
1	California	37,717,000,000	9.9%
27	Colorado	4,729,000,000	1.2%
26	Connecticut	4,798,000,000	1.3%
47	Delaware	1,142,000,000	0.3%
4	Florida	20,313,000,000	5.3%
12	Georgia	10,381,000,000	2.7%
40	Hawaii	1,697,000,000	0.4%
44	Idaho	1,266,000,000	0.3%
6	Illinois	17,856,000,000	4.7%
15	Indiana	8,474,000,000	2.2%
29	Iowa	4,077,000,000	1.1%
32	Kansas	3,498,000,000	0.9%
23	Kentucky	5,783,000,000	1.5%
19	Louisiana	7,070,000,000	1.9%
39	Maine	1,818,000,000	0.5%
17	Maryland	7,178,000,000	1.9%
9	Massachusetts	11,464,000,000	3.0%
8	Michigan	14,246,000,000	3.8%
21	Minnesota	6,209,000,000	1.6%
30	Mississippi	4,000,000,000	1.1%
13	Missouri	9,063,000,000	2.4%
45	Montana	1,245,000,000	0.3%
35	Nebraska	2,611,000,000	0.7%
38	Nevada	1,843,000,000	0.5%
42	New Hampshire	1,510,000,000	0.4%
10	New Jersey	11,260,000,000	3.0%
36	New Mexico	2,336,000,000	0.6%
2	New York	31,990,000,000	8.4%
11	North Carolina	10,513,000,000	2.8%
43	North Dakota	1,271,000,000	0.3%
7	Ohio	15,985,000,000	4.2%
28	Oklahoma	4,127,000,000	1.1%
31	Oregon	3,652,000,000	1.0%
5	Pennsylvania	19,634,000,000	5.2%
41	Rhode Island	1,591,000,000	0.4%
24	South Carolina	5,399,000,000	1.4%
46	South Dakota	1,200,000,000	0.3%
16	Tennessee	8,049,000,000	2.1%
3	Texas	25,952,000,000	6.8%
37	Utah	2,261,000,000	0.6%
49	Vermont	698,000,000	0.2%
14	Virginia	8,585,000,000	2.3%
20	Washington	6,415,000,000	1.7%
34	West Virginia	2,932,000,000	0.8%
18	Wisconsin	7,108,000,000	1.9%
50	Wyoming	573,000,000	0.2%

RANK ORDER

RANK	STATE	EXPENDITURES	% of USA
1	California	$37,717,000,000	9.9%
2	New York	31,990,000,000	8.4%
3	Texas	25,952,000,000	6.8%
4	Florida	20,313,000,000	5.3%
5	Pennsylvania	19,634,000,000	5.2%
6	Illinois	17,856,000,000	4.7%
7	Ohio	15,985,000,000	4.2%
8	Michigan	14,246,000,000	3.8%
9	Massachusetts	11,464,000,000	3.0%
10	New Jersey	11,260,000,000	3.0%
11	North Carolina	10,513,000,000	2.8%
12	Georgia	10,381,000,000	2.7%
13	Missouri	9,063,000,000	2.4%
14	Virginia	8,585,000,000	2.3%
15	Indiana	8,474,000,000	2.2%
16	Tennessee	8,049,000,000	2.1%
17	Maryland	7,178,000,000	1.9%
18	Wisconsin	7,108,000,000	1.9%
19	Louisiana	7,070,000,000	1.9%
20	Washington	6,415,000,000	1.7%
21	Minnesota	6,209,000,000	1.6%
22	Alabama	6,169,000,000	1.6%
23	Kentucky	5,783,000,000	1.5%
24	South Carolina	5,399,000,000	1.4%
25	Arizona	5,199,000,000	1.4%
26	Connecticut	4,798,000,000	1.3%
27	Colorado	4,729,000,000	1.2%
28	Oklahoma	4,127,000,000	1.1%
29	Iowa	4,077,000,000	1.1%
30	Mississippi	4,000,000,000	1.1%
31	Oregon	3,652,000,000	1.0%
32	Kansas	3,498,000,000	0.9%
33	Arkansas	3,394,000,000	0.9%
34	West Virginia	2,932,000,000	0.8%
35	Nebraska	2,611,000,000	0.7%
36	New Mexico	2,336,000,000	0.6%
37	Utah	2,261,000,000	0.6%
38	Nevada	1,843,000,000	0.5%
39	Maine	1,818,000,000	0.5%
40	Hawaii	1,697,000,000	0.4%
41	Rhode Island	1,591,000,000	0.4%
42	New Hampshire	1,510,000,000	0.4%
43	North Dakota	1,271,000,000	0.3%
44	Idaho	1,266,000,000	0.3%
45	Montana	1,245,000,000	0.3%
46	South Dakota	1,200,000,000	0.3%
47	Delaware	1,142,000,000	0.3%
48	Alaska	909,000,000	0.2%
49	Vermont	698,000,000	0.2%
50	Wyoming	573,000,000	0.2%
	District of Columbia	2,644,000,000	0.7%

Source: U.S. Department of Health and Human Services, Centers for Medicare and Medicaid Services
    "State Health Care Expenditures" (http://www.cms.hhs.gov/statistics/nhe/)
*By state of provider. Revised figures

Percent of Total Personal Health Care Expenditures
Spent on Hospital Care in 1998
National Percent = 37.4%*

ALPHA ORDER

RANK	STATE	PERCENT
19	Alabama	39.5
3	Alaska	43.6
40	Arizona	34.6
18	Arkansas	39.8
44	California	33.4
39	Colorado	34.9
49	Connecticut	31.3
31	Delaware	37.2
43	Florida	33.7
24	Georgia	38.1
32	Hawaii	37.1
34	Idaho	37.0
13	Illinois	40.4
17	Indiana	39.9
15	Iowa	40.0
29	Kansas	37.6
15	Kentucky	40.0
7	Louisiana	43.0
32	Maine	37.1
36	Maryland	36.8
26	Massachusetts	38.0
13	Michigan	40.4
50	Minnesota	31.1
2	Mississippi	44.3
8	Missouri	42.9
3	Montana	43.6
9	Nebraska	42.7
47	Nevada	33.0
48	New Hampshire	32.8
41	New Jersey	34.4
5	New Mexico	43.5
29	New York	37.6
20	North Carolina	39.2
1	North Dakota	47.6
23	Ohio	38.2
27	Oklahoma	37.9
44	Oregon	33.4
21	Pennsylvania	38.7
37	Rhode Island	36.2
11	South Carolina	41.5
6	South Dakota	43.3
35	Tennessee	36.9
27	Texas	37.9
24	Utah	38.1
42	Vermont	34.0
21	Virginia	38.7
46	Washington	33.2
10	West Virginia	41.8
38	Wisconsin	35.9
12	Wyoming	41.0

RANK ORDER

RANK	STATE	PERCENT
1	North Dakota	47.6
2	Mississippi	44.3
3	Alaska	43.6
3	Montana	43.6
5	New Mexico	43.5
6	South Dakota	43.3
7	Louisiana	43.0
8	Missouri	42.9
9	Nebraska	42.7
10	West Virginia	41.8
11	South Carolina	41.5
12	Wyoming	41.0
13	Illinois	40.4
13	Michigan	40.4
15	Iowa	40.0
15	Kentucky	40.0
17	Indiana	39.9
18	Arkansas	39.8
19	Alabama	39.5
20	North Carolina	39.2
21	Pennsylvania	38.7
21	Virginia	38.7
23	Ohio	38.2
24	Georgia	38.1
24	Utah	38.1
26	Massachusetts	38.0
27	Oklahoma	37.9
27	Texas	37.9
29	Kansas	37.6
29	New York	37.6
31	Delaware	37.2
32	Hawaii	37.1
32	Maine	37.1
34	Idaho	37.0
35	Tennessee	36.9
36	Maryland	36.8
37	Rhode Island	36.2
38	Wisconsin	35.9
39	Colorado	34.9
40	Arizona	34.6
41	New Jersey	34.4
42	Vermont	34.0
43	Florida	33.7
44	California	33.4
44	Oregon	33.4
46	Washington	33.2
47	Nevada	33.0
48	New Hampshire	32.8
49	Connecticut	31.3
50	Minnesota	31.1
	District of Columbia	61.3

Source: MQ Press using data from U.S. Dept of Health & Human Services, Centers for Medicare and Medicaid Services
"State Health Care Expenditures" (http://www.cms.hhs.gov/statistics/nhe/)
*By state of provider. Revised figures.

Per Capita Expenditures for Hospital Care in 1998

National Per Capita = $1,406*

ALPHA ORDER

RANK	STATE	PER CAPITA
24	Alabama	$1,418
14	Alaska	1,478
46	Arizona	1,114
34	Arkansas	1,337
44	California	1,154
42	Colorado	1,191
16	Connecticut	1,466
11	Delaware	1,535
30	Florida	1,363
32	Georgia	1,359
21	Hawaii	1,425
50	Idaho	1,028
13	Illinois	1,479
20	Indiana	1,434
21	Iowa	1,425
35	Kansas	1,326
15	Kentucky	1,470
7	Louisiana	1,621
17	Maine	1,457
27	Maryland	1,399
2	Massachusetts	1,866
19	Michigan	1,451
37	Minnesota	1,314
18	Mississippi	1,454
4	Missouri	1,667
25	Montana	1,416
10	Nebraska	1,572
49	Nevada	1,057
38	New Hampshire	1,273
29	New Jersey	1,391
33	New Mexico	1,348
3	New York	1,762
28	North Carolina	1,393
1	North Dakota	1,993
23	Ohio	1,422
40	Oklahoma	1,236
47	Oregon	1,113
6	Pennsylvania	1,636
9	Rhode Island	1,611
26	South Carolina	1,406
5	South Dakota	1,642
12	Tennessee	1,482
36	Texas	1,317
48	Utah	1,076
43	Vermont	1,182
39	Virginia	1,265
45	Washington	1,128
8	West Virginia	1,618
31	Wisconsin	1,361
41	Wyoming	1,194

RANK ORDER

RANK	STATE	PER CAPITA
1	North Dakota	$1,993
2	Massachusetts	1,866
3	New York	1,762
4	Missouri	1,667
5	South Dakota	1,642
6	Pennsylvania	1,636
7	Louisiana	1,621
8	West Virginia	1,618
9	Rhode Island	1,611
10	Nebraska	1,572
11	Delaware	1,535
12	Tennessee	1,482
13	Illinois	1,479
14	Alaska	1,478
15	Kentucky	1,470
16	Connecticut	1,466
17	Maine	1,457
18	Mississippi	1,454
19	Michigan	1,451
20	Indiana	1,434
21	Hawaii	1,425
21	Iowa	1,425
23	Ohio	1,422
24	Alabama	1,418
25	Montana	1,416
26	South Carolina	1,406
27	Maryland	1,399
28	North Carolina	1,393
29	New Jersey	1,391
30	Florida	1,363
31	Wisconsin	1,361
32	Georgia	1,359
33	New Mexico	1,348
34	Arkansas	1,337
35	Kansas	1,326
36	Texas	1,317
37	Minnesota	1,314
38	New Hampshire	1,273
39	Virginia	1,265
40	Oklahoma	1,236
41	Wyoming	1,194
42	Colorado	1,191
43	Vermont	1,182
44	California	1,154
45	Washington	1,128
46	Arizona	1,114
47	Oregon	1,113
48	Utah	1,076
49	Nevada	1,057
50	Idaho	1,028

District of Columbia	5,071

Source: MQ Press using data from U.S. Dept of Health & Human Services, Centers for Medicare and Medicaid Services "State Health Care Expenditures" (http://www.cms.hhs.gov/statistics/nhe/)
*By state of provider. Per capita calculated using resident population. These figures may be skewed due to residents crossing state borders for care. Revised figures.

Expenditures for Physician and Other Professional Services in 1998

National Total = $296,102,000,000*

ALPHA ORDER

RANK	STATE	EXPENDITURES	% of USA
22	Alabama	$4,609,000,000	1.6%
48	Alaska	568,000,000	0.2%
21	Arizona	5,135,000,000	1.7%
32	Arkansas	2,225,000,000	0.8%
1	California	44,239,000,000	14.9%
23	Colorado	4,314,000,000	1.5%
24	Connecticut	4,292,000,000	1.4%
44	Delaware	792,000,000	0.3%
4	Florida	18,985,000,000	6.4%
10	Georgia	8,510,000,000	2.9%
37	Hawaii	1,594,000,000	0.5%
43	Idaho	935,000,000	0.3%
6	Illinois	11,975,000,000	4.0%
19	Indiana	5,613,000,000	1.9%
31	Iowa	2,457,000,000	0.8%
30	Kansas	2,538,000,000	0.9%
26	Kentucky	3,785,000,000	1.3%
25	Louisiana	4,249,000,000	1.4%
41	Maine	1,219,000,000	0.4%
16	Maryland	5,978,000,000	2.0%
11	Massachusetts	8,322,000,000	2.8%
9	Michigan	9,186,000,000	3.1%
12	Minnesota	7,183,000,000	2.4%
33	Mississippi	2,212,000,000	0.7%
20	Missouri	5,310,000,000	1.8%
46	Montana	695,000,000	0.2%
40	Nebraska	1,367,000,000	0.5%
34	Nevada	1,918,000,000	0.6%
39	New Hampshire	1,405,000,000	0.5%
8	New Jersey	9,506,000,000	3.2%
38	New Mexico	1,415,000,000	0.5%
2	New York	20,103,000,000	6.8%
13	North Carolina	7,106,000,000	2.4%
47	North Dakota	612,000,000	0.2%
7	Ohio	11,024,000,000	3.7%
29	Oklahoma	2,978,000,000	1.0%
27	Oregon	3,285,000,000	1.1%
5	Pennsylvania	13,434,000,000	4.5%
42	Rhode Island	1,095,000,000	0.4%
28	South Carolina	3,254,000,000	1.1%
45	South Dakota	747,000,000	0.3%
14	Tennessee	6,719,000,000	2.3%
3	Texas	20,071,000,000	6.8%
36	Utah	1,648,000,000	0.6%
49	Vermont	563,000,000	0.2%
15	Virginia	6,265,000,000	2.1%
17	Washington	5,908,000,000	2.0%
35	West Virginia	1,793,000,000	0.6%
18	Wisconsin	5,844,000,000	2.0%
50	Wyoming	343,000,000	0.1%

RANK ORDER

RANK	STATE	EXPENDITURES	% of USA
1	California	$44,239,000,000	14.9%
2	New York	20,103,000,000	6.8%
3	Texas	20,071,000,000	6.8%
4	Florida	18,985,000,000	6.4%
5	Pennsylvania	13,434,000,000	4.5%
6	Illinois	11,975,000,000	4.0%
7	Ohio	11,024,000,000	3.7%
8	New Jersey	9,506,000,000	3.2%
9	Michigan	9,186,000,000	3.1%
10	Georgia	8,510,000,000	2.9%
11	Massachusetts	8,322,000,000	2.8%
12	Minnesota	7,183,000,000	2.4%
13	North Carolina	7,106,000,000	2.4%
14	Tennessee	6,719,000,000	2.3%
15	Virginia	6,265,000,000	2.1%
16	Maryland	5,978,000,000	2.0%
17	Washington	5,908,000,000	2.0%
18	Wisconsin	5,844,000,000	2.0%
19	Indiana	5,613,000,000	1.9%
20	Missouri	5,310,000,000	1.8%
21	Arizona	5,135,000,000	1.7%
22	Alabama	4,609,000,000	1.6%
23	Colorado	4,314,000,000	1.5%
24	Connecticut	4,292,000,000	1.4%
25	Louisiana	4,249,000,000	1.4%
26	Kentucky	3,785,000,000	1.3%
27	Oregon	3,285,000,000	1.1%
28	South Carolina	3,254,000,000	1.1%
29	Oklahoma	2,978,000,000	1.0%
30	Kansas	2,538,000,000	0.9%
31	Iowa	2,457,000,000	0.8%
32	Arkansas	2,225,000,000	0.8%
33	Mississippi	2,212,000,000	0.7%
34	Nevada	1,918,000,000	0.6%
35	West Virginia	1,793,000,000	0.6%
36	Utah	1,648,000,000	0.6%
37	Hawaii	1,594,000,000	0.5%
38	New Mexico	1,415,000,000	0.5%
39	New Hampshire	1,405,000,000	0.5%
40	Nebraska	1,367,000,000	0.5%
41	Maine	1,219,000,000	0.4%
42	Rhode Island	1,095,000,000	0.4%
43	Idaho	935,000,000	0.3%
44	Delaware	792,000,000	0.3%
45	South Dakota	747,000,000	0.3%
46	Montana	695,000,000	0.2%
47	North Dakota	612,000,000	0.2%
48	Alaska	568,000,000	0.2%
49	Vermont	563,000,000	0.2%
50	Wyoming	343,000,000	0.1%
	District of Columbia	781,000,000	0.3%

Source: U.S. Department of Health and Human Services, Centers for Medicare and Medicaid Services
"State Health Care Expenditures" (http://www.cms.hhs.gov/statistics/nhe/)

*By state of provider. Includes "other professional services" previously listed as a separate category. These include services of licensed professionals such as chiropractors, optometrists, podiatrists and independently practicing nurses. Also includes specialty clinics, independently billing laboratories and Medicare ambulance services. Revised figures.

Percent of Total Personal Health Care Expenditures
Spent on Physician and Other Professional Services in 1998
National Percent = 29.1%*

RANK	STATE	PERCENT
14	Alabama	29.5
26	Alaska	27.2
5	Arizona	34.2
35	Arkansas	26.1
1	California	39.2
6	Colorado	31.8
19	Connecticut	28.0
38	Delaware	25.8
7	Florida	31.5
8	Georgia	31.3
3	Hawaii	34.8
23	Idaho	27.3
27	Illinois	27.1
29	Indiana	26.5
47	Iowa	24.1
23	Kansas	27.3
34	Kentucky	26.2
37	Louisiana	25.9
42	Maine	24.9
10	Maryland	30.6
21	Massachusetts	27.6
35	Michigan	26.1
2	Minnesota	35.9
44	Mississippi	24.5
40	Missouri	25.1
46	Montana	24.3
50	Nebraska	22.4
4	Nevada	34.4
12	New Hampshire	30.5
17	New Jersey	29.0
32	New Mexico	26.4
48	New York	23.6
29	North Carolina	26.5
49	North Dakota	22.9
32	Ohio	26.4
23	Oklahoma	27.3
13	Oregon	30.0
29	Pennsylvania	26.5
42	Rhode Island	24.9
41	South Carolina	25.0
28	South Dakota	26.9
9	Tennessee	30.8
16	Texas	29.4
20	Utah	27.8
22	Vermont	27.4
18	Virginia	28.3
10	Washington	30.6
39	West Virginia	25.6
14	Wisconsin	29.5
44	Wyoming	24.5

RANK	STATE	PERCENT
1	California	39.2
2	Minnesota	35.9
3	Hawaii	34.8
4	Nevada	34.4
5	Arizona	34.2
6	Colorado	31.8
7	Florida	31.5
8	Georgia	31.3
9	Tennessee	30.8
10	Maryland	30.6
10	Washington	30.6
12	New Hampshire	30.5
13	Oregon	30.0
14	Alabama	29.5
14	Wisconsin	29.5
16	Texas	29.4
17	New Jersey	29.0
18	Virginia	28.3
19	Connecticut	28.0
20	Utah	27.8
21	Massachusetts	27.6
22	Vermont	27.4
23	Idaho	27.3
23	Kansas	27.3
23	Oklahoma	27.3
26	Alaska	27.2
27	Illinois	27.1
28	South Dakota	26.9
29	Indiana	26.5
29	North Carolina	26.5
29	Pennsylvania	26.5
32	New Mexico	26.4
32	Ohio	26.4
34	Kentucky	26.2
35	Arkansas	26.1
35	Michigan	26.1
37	Louisiana	25.9
38	Delaware	25.8
39	West Virginia	25.6
40	Missouri	25.1
41	South Carolina	25.0
42	Maine	24.9
42	Rhode Island	24.9
44	Mississippi	24.5
44	Wyoming	24.5
46	Montana	24.3
47	Iowa	24.1
48	New York	23.6
49	North Dakota	22.9
50	Nebraska	22.4

District of Columbia 18.1

Source: MQ Press using data from U.S. Dept of Health & Human Services, Centers for Medicare and Medicaid Services "State Health Care Expenditures" (http://www.cms.hhs.gov/statistics/nhe/)

*By state of provider. Includes "other professional services" previously listed as a separate category. These include services of licensed professionals such as chiropractors, optometrists, podiatrists and independently practicing nurses. Also includes specialty clinics, independently billing laboratories and Medicare ambulance services. Revised figures.

Per Capita Expenditures for Physician and Other Professional Services in 1998

National Per Capita = $1,096*

ALPHA ORDER

RANK	STATE	PER CAPITA
20	Alabama	$1,059
38	Alaska	923
16	Arizona	1,100
41	Arkansas	877
2	California	1,354
18	Colorado	1,087
5	Connecticut	1,312
19	Delaware	1,064
6	Florida	1,273
13	Georgia	1,114
4	Hawaii	1,339
49	Idaho	760
25	Illinois	992
35	Indiana	950
42	Iowa	859
31	Kansas	962
31	Kentucky	962
30	Louisiana	974
28	Maine	977
10	Maryland	1,165
2	Massachusetts	1,354
37	Michigan	935
1	Minnesota	1,520
46	Mississippi	804
28	Missouri	977
47	Montana	790
44	Nebraska	823
16	Nevada	1,100
8	New Hampshire	1,185
9	New Jersey	1,174
45	New Mexico	816
15	New York	1,107
36	North Carolina	942
33	North Dakota	960
27	Ohio	981
40	Oklahoma	892
24	Oregon	1,001
11	Pennsylvania	1,119
14	Rhode Island	1,109
43	South Carolina	847
22	South Dakota	1,022
7	Tennessee	1,237
23	Texas	1,018
48	Utah	785
34	Vermont	953
38	Virginia	923
21	Washington	1,039
26	West Virginia	990
11	Wisconsin	1,119
50	Wyoming	715

RANK ORDER

RANK	STATE	PER CAPITA
1	Minnesota	$1,520
2	California	1,354
2	Massachusetts	1,354
4	Hawaii	1,339
5	Connecticut	1,312
6	Florida	1,273
7	Tennessee	1,237
8	New Hampshire	1,185
9	New Jersey	1,174
10	Maryland	1,165
11	Pennsylvania	1,119
11	Wisconsin	1,119
13	Georgia	1,114
14	Rhode Island	1,109
15	New York	1,107
16	Arizona	1,100
16	Nevada	1,100
18	Colorado	1,087
19	Delaware	1,064
20	Alabama	1,059
21	Washington	1,039
22	South Dakota	1,022
23	Texas	1,018
24	Oregon	1,001
25	Illinois	992
26	West Virginia	990
27	Ohio	981
28	Maine	977
28	Missouri	977
30	Louisiana	974
31	Kansas	962
31	Kentucky	962
33	North Dakota	960
34	Vermont	953
35	Indiana	950
36	North Carolina	942
37	Michigan	935
38	Alaska	923
38	Virginia	923
40	Oklahoma	892
41	Arkansas	877
42	Iowa	859
43	South Carolina	847
44	Nebraska	823
45	New Mexico	816
46	Mississippi	804
47	Montana	790
48	Utah	785
49	Idaho	760
50	Wyoming	715

| | District of Columbia | 1,498 |

Source: MQ Press using data from U.S. Dept of Health & Human Services, Centers for Medicare and Medicaid Services
 "State Health Care Expenditures" (http://www.cms.hhs.gov/statistics/nhe/)
*By state of provider. Per capita calculated using resident population. These figures may be skewed due to residents
crossing state borders for care. Includes "other professional services" previously listed as a separate category.
Services include licensed professionals such as chiropractors, optometrists, podiatrists and independently
practicing nurses. Revised figures.

Expenditures for Drugs and
Other Medical Non-Durables in 1998
National Total = $121,906,000,000*

ALPHA ORDER

RANK	STATE	EXPENDITURES	% of USA
21	Alabama	$2,049,000,000	1.7%
49	Alaska	221,000,000	0.2%
20	Arizona	2,066,000,000	1.7%
32	Arkansas	1,177,000,000	1.0%
1	California	11,604,000,000	9.5%
27	Colorado	1,546,000,000	1.3%
26	Connecticut	1,705,000,000	1.4%
44	Delaware	390,000,000	0.3%
4	Florida	8,226,000,000	6.7%
11	Georgia	3,367,000,000	2.8%
41	Hawaii	514,000,000	0.4%
43	Idaho	474,000,000	0.4%
6	Illinois	5,174,000,000	4.2%
15	Indiana	2,649,000,000	2.2%
31	Iowa	1,219,000,000	1.0%
33	Kansas	1,087,000,000	0.9%
24	Kentucky	1,966,000,000	1.6%
23	Louisiana	1,992,000,000	1.6%
39	Maine	559,000,000	0.5%
18	Maryland	2,304,000,000	1.9%
13	Massachusetts	2,882,000,000	2.4%
8	Michigan	4,884,000,000	4.0%
22	Minnesota	2,004,000,000	1.6%
30	Mississippi	1,222,000,000	1.0%
16	Missouri	2,403,000,000	2.0%
45	Montana	349,000,000	0.3%
37	Nebraska	791,000,000	0.6%
36	Nevada	825,000,000	0.7%
40	New Hampshire	539,000,000	0.4%
9	New Jersey	4,564,000,000	3.7%
38	New Mexico	630,000,000	0.5%
2	New York	8,940,000,000	7.3%
10	North Carolina	3,411,000,000	2.8%
47	North Dakota	250,000,000	0.2%
7	Ohio	5,027,000,000	4.1%
28	Oklahoma	1,418,000,000	1.2%
29	Oregon	1,386,000,000	1.1%
5	Pennsylvania	6,162,000,000	5.1%
42	Rhode Island	505,000,000	0.4%
25	South Carolina	1,721,000,000	1.4%
46	South Dakota	268,000,000	0.2%
14	Tennessee	2,751,000,000	2.3%
3	Texas	8,672,000,000	7.1%
35	Utah	828,000,000	0.7%
48	Vermont	237,000,000	0.2%
12	Virginia	2,947,000,000	2.4%
17	Washington	2,365,000,000	1.9%
34	West Virginia	949,000,000	0.8%
19	Wisconsin	2,269,000,000	1.9%
50	Wyoming	178,000,000	0.1%

RANK ORDER

RANK	STATE	EXPENDITURES	% of USA
1	California	$11,604,000,000	9.5%
2	New York	8,940,000,000	7.3%
3	Texas	8,672,000,000	7.1%
4	Florida	8,226,000,000	6.7%
5	Pennsylvania	6,162,000,000	5.1%
6	Illinois	5,174,000,000	4.2%
7	Ohio	5,027,000,000	4.1%
8	Michigan	4,884,000,000	4.0%
9	New Jersey	4,564,000,000	3.7%
10	North Carolina	3,411,000,000	2.8%
11	Georgia	3,367,000,000	2.8%
12	Virginia	2,947,000,000	2.4%
13	Massachusetts	2,882,000,000	2.4%
14	Tennessee	2,751,000,000	2.3%
15	Indiana	2,649,000,000	2.2%
16	Missouri	2,403,000,000	2.0%
17	Washington	2,365,000,000	1.9%
18	Maryland	2,304,000,000	1.9%
19	Wisconsin	2,269,000,000	1.9%
20	Arizona	2,066,000,000	1.7%
21	Alabama	2,049,000,000	1.7%
22	Minnesota	2,004,000,000	1.6%
23	Louisiana	1,992,000,000	1.6%
24	Kentucky	1,966,000,000	1.6%
25	South Carolina	1,721,000,000	1.4%
26	Connecticut	1,705,000,000	1.4%
27	Colorado	1,546,000,000	1.3%
28	Oklahoma	1,418,000,000	1.2%
29	Oregon	1,386,000,000	1.1%
30	Mississippi	1,222,000,000	1.0%
31	Iowa	1,219,000,000	1.0%
32	Arkansas	1,177,000,000	1.0%
33	Kansas	1,087,000,000	0.9%
34	West Virginia	949,000,000	0.8%
35	Utah	828,000,000	0.7%
36	Nevada	825,000,000	0.7%
37	Nebraska	791,000,000	0.6%
38	New Mexico	630,000,000	0.5%
39	Maine	559,000,000	0.5%
40	New Hampshire	539,000,000	0.4%
41	Hawaii	514,000,000	0.4%
42	Rhode Island	505,000,000	0.4%
43	Idaho	474,000,000	0.4%
44	Delaware	390,000,000	0.3%
45	Montana	349,000,000	0.3%
46	South Dakota	268,000,000	0.2%
47	North Dakota	250,000,000	0.2%
48	Vermont	237,000,000	0.2%
49	Alaska	221,000,000	0.2%
50	Wyoming	178,000,000	0.1%
	District of Columbia	239,000,000	0.2%

Source: U.S. Department of Health and Human Services, Centers for Medicare and Medicaid Services
  "State Health Care Expenditures" (http://www.cms.hhs.gov/statistics/nhe/)
Purchases in retail outlets. By state of outlet. Includes prescription drugs, over-the-counter drugs and sundries.
Revised figures.

Percent of Total Personal Health Care Expenditures
Spent on Drugs and Other Medical Non-Durables in 1998
National Percent = 12.0%*

ALPHA ORDER

RANK	STATE	PERCENT
14	Alabama	13.1
44	Alaska	10.6
6	Arizona	13.8
6	Arkansas	13.8
46	California	10.3
39	Colorado	11.4
43	Connecticut	11.1
17	Delaware	12.7
8	Florida	13.6
24	Georgia	12.4
42	Hawaii	11.2
3	Idaho	13.9
32	Illinois	11.7
23	Indiana	12.5
29	Iowa	12.0
32	Kansas	11.7
8	Kentucky	13.6
27	Louisiana	12.1
39	Maine	11.4
31	Maryland	11.8
49	Massachusetts	9.5
3	Michigan	13.9
47	Minnesota	10.0
10	Mississippi	13.5
39	Missouri	11.4
25	Montana	12.2
16	Nebraska	12.9
1	Nevada	14.8
32	New Hampshire	11.7
3	New Jersey	13.9
32	New Mexico	11.7
45	New York	10.5
17	North Carolina	12.7
50	North Dakota	9.4
29	Ohio	12.0
15	Oklahoma	13.0
17	Oregon	12.7
27	Pennsylvania	12.1
36	Rhode Island	11.5
13	South Carolina	13.2
48	South Dakota	9.7
22	Tennessee	12.6
17	Texas	12.7
2	Utah	14.0
36	Vermont	11.5
12	Virginia	13.3
25	Washington	12.2
10	West Virginia	13.5
36	Wisconsin	11.5
17	Wyoming	12.7

RANK ORDER

RANK	STATE	PERCENT
1	Nevada	14.8
2	Utah	14.0
3	Idaho	13.9
3	Michigan	13.9
3	New Jersey	13.9
6	Arizona	13.8
6	Arkansas	13.8
8	Florida	13.6
8	Kentucky	13.6
10	Mississippi	13.5
10	West Virginia	13.5
12	Virginia	13.3
13	South Carolina	13.2
14	Alabama	13.1
15	Oklahoma	13.0
16	Nebraska	12.9
17	Delaware	12.7
17	North Carolina	12.7
17	Oregon	12.7
17	Texas	12.7
17	Wyoming	12.7
22	Tennessee	12.6
23	Indiana	12.5
24	Georgia	12.4
25	Montana	12.2
25	Washington	12.2
27	Louisiana	12.1
27	Pennsylvania	12.1
29	Iowa	12.0
29	Ohio	12.0
31	Maryland	11.8
32	Illinois	11.7
32	Kansas	11.7
32	New Hampshire	11.7
32	New Mexico	11.7
36	Rhode Island	11.5
36	Vermont	11.5
36	Wisconsin	11.5
39	Colorado	11.4
39	Maine	11.4
39	Missouri	11.4
42	Hawaii	11.2
43	Connecticut	11.1
44	Alaska	10.6
45	New York	10.5
46	California	10.3
47	Minnesota	10.0
48	South Dakota	9.7
49	Massachusetts	9.5
50	North Dakota	9.4

District of Columbia	5.5

Source: MQ Press using data from U.S. Dept of Health & Human Services, Centers for Medicare and Medicaid Services
"State Health Care Expenditures" (http://www.cms.hhs.gov/statistics/nhe/)
*Purchases in retail outlets. By state of outlet. Includes prescription drugs, over-the-counter drugs and sundries.
Revised figures.

Per Capita Expenditures for Drugs and Other Medical Non-Durables in 1998
National Per Capita = $451*

ALPHA ORDER

RANK	STATE	PER CAPITA
14	Alabama	$471
49	Alaska	359
26	Arizona	443
16	Arkansas	464
50	California	355
44	Colorado	390
5	Connecticut	521
3	Delaware	524
2	Florida	552
28	Georgia	441
32	Hawaii	432
45	Idaho	385
33	Illinois	429
21	Indiana	448
34	Iowa	426
39	Kansas	412
9	Kentucky	500
17	Louisiana	457
21	Maine	448
20	Maryland	449
15	Massachusetts	469
10	Michigan	497
36	Minnesota	424
25	Mississippi	444
27	Missouri	442
41	Montana	397
12	Nebraska	476
13	Nevada	473
18	New Hampshire	455
1	New Jersey	564
48	New Mexico	363
11	New York	492
19	North Carolina	452
43	North Dakota	392
24	Ohio	447
35	Oklahoma	425
37	Oregon	422
6	Pennsylvania	513
7	Rhode Island	511
21	South Carolina	448
47	South Dakota	367
8	Tennessee	506
29	Texas	440
42	Utah	394
40	Vermont	401
30	Virginia	434
38	Washington	416
3	West Virginia	524
30	Wisconsin	434
46	Wyoming	371

RANK ORDER

RANK	STATE	PER CAPITA
1	New Jersey	$564
2	Florida	552
3	Delaware	524
3	West Virginia	524
5	Connecticut	521
6	Pennsylvania	513
7	Rhode Island	511
8	Tennessee	506
9	Kentucky	500
10	Michigan	497
11	New York	492
12	Nebraska	476
13	Nevada	473
14	Alabama	471
15	Massachusetts	469
16	Arkansas	464
17	Louisiana	457
18	New Hampshire	455
19	North Carolina	452
20	Maryland	449
21	Indiana	448
21	Maine	448
21	South Carolina	448
24	Ohio	447
25	Mississippi	444
26	Arizona	443
27	Missouri	442
28	Georgia	441
29	Texas	440
30	Virginia	434
30	Wisconsin	434
32	Hawaii	432
33	Illinois	429
34	Iowa	426
35	Oklahoma	425
36	Minnesota	424
37	Oregon	422
38	Washington	416
39	Kansas	412
40	Vermont	401
41	Montana	397
42	Utah	394
43	North Dakota	392
44	Colorado	390
45	Idaho	385
46	Wyoming	371
47	South Dakota	367
48	New Mexico	363
49	Alaska	359
50	California	355
	District of Columbia	458

Source: MQ Press using data from U.S. Dept of Health & Human Services, Centers for Medicare and Medicaid Services "State Health Care Expenditures" (http://www.cms.hhs.gov/statistics/nhe/)
*Purchases in retail outlets. By state of outlet. Includes prescription drugs, over-the-counter drugs and sundries. Per capita calculated using resident population. These figures may be skewed due to residents crossing state borders to make purchases. Revised figures.

Expenditures for Prescription Drugs in 1998

National Total = $90,648,000,000*

ALPHA ORDER

RANK	STATE	EXPENDITURES	% of USA
21	Alabama	$1,552,000,000	1.7%
49	Alaska	133,000,000	0.1%
24	Arizona	1,397,000,000	1.5%
32	Arkansas	903,000,000	1.0%
1	California	7,537,000,000	8.3%
28	Colorado	970,000,000	1.1%
25	Connecticut	1,354,000,000	1.5%
44	Delaware	300,000,000	0.3%
3	Florida	6,204,000,000	6.8%
11	Georgia	2,460,000,000	2.7%
43	Hawaii	311,000,000	0.3%
42	Idaho	334,000,000	0.4%
6	Illinois	3,964,000,000	4.4%
15	Indiana	2,058,000,000	2.3%
30	Iowa	945,000,000	1.0%
33	Kansas	854,000,000	0.9%
20	Kentucky	1,564,000,000	1.7%
22	Louisiana	1,507,000,000	1.7%
38	Maine	456,000,000	0.5%
18	Maryland	1,678,000,000	1.9%
12	Massachusetts	2,172,000,000	2.4%
8	Michigan	3,885,000,000	4.3%
23	Minnesota	1,491,000,000	1.6%
29	Mississippi	962,000,000	1.1%
16	Missouri	1,814,000,000	2.0%
45	Montana	234,000,000	0.3%
35	Nebraska	626,000,000	0.7%
37	Nevada	478,000,000	0.5%
41	New Hampshire	391,000,000	0.4%
9	New Jersey	3,545,000,000	3.9%
39	New Mexico	402,000,000	0.4%
2	New York	7,122,000,000	7.9%
10	North Carolina	2,566,000,000	2.8%
47	North Dakota	192,000,000	0.2%
7	Ohio	3,898,000,000	4.3%
27	Oklahoma	1,056,000,000	1.2%
31	Oregon	918,000,000	1.0%
5	Pennsylvania	5,035,000,000	5.6%
40	Rhode Island	400,000,000	0.4%
26	South Carolina	1,315,000,000	1.5%
46	South Dakota	201,000,000	0.2%
14	Tennessee	2,129,000,000	2.3%
4	Texas	6,023,000,000	6.6%
36	Utah	564,000,000	0.6%
48	Vermont	183,000,000	0.2%
13	Virginia	2,130,000,000	2.3%
19	Washington	1,603,000,000	1.8%
34	West Virginia	776,000,000	0.9%
17	Wisconsin	1,745,000,000	1.9%
49	Wyoming	133,000,000	0.1%

RANK ORDER

RANK	STATE	EXPENDITURES	% of USA
1	California	$7,537,000,000	8.3%
2	New York	7,122,000,000	7.9%
3	Florida	6,204,000,000	6.8%
4	Texas	6,023,000,000	6.6%
5	Pennsylvania	5,035,000,000	5.6%
6	Illinois	3,964,000,000	4.4%
7	Ohio	3,898,000,000	4.3%
8	Michigan	3,885,000,000	4.3%
9	New Jersey	3,545,000,000	3.9%
10	North Carolina	2,566,000,000	2.8%
11	Georgia	2,460,000,000	2.7%
12	Massachusetts	2,172,000,000	2.4%
13	Virginia	2,130,000,000	2.3%
14	Tennessee	2,129,000,000	2.3%
15	Indiana	2,058,000,000	2.3%
16	Missouri	1,814,000,000	2.0%
17	Wisconsin	1,745,000,000	1.9%
18	Maryland	1,678,000,000	1.9%
19	Washington	1,603,000,000	1.8%
20	Kentucky	1,564,000,000	1.7%
21	Alabama	1,552,000,000	1.7%
22	Louisiana	1,507,000,000	1.7%
23	Minnesota	1,491,000,000	1.6%
24	Arizona	1,397,000,000	1.5%
25	Connecticut	1,354,000,000	1.5%
26	South Carolina	1,315,000,000	1.5%
27	Oklahoma	1,056,000,000	1.2%
28	Colorado	970,000,000	1.1%
29	Mississippi	962,000,000	1.1%
30	Iowa	945,000,000	1.0%
31	Oregon	918,000,000	1.0%
32	Arkansas	903,000,000	1.0%
33	Kansas	854,000,000	0.9%
34	West Virginia	776,000,000	0.9%
35	Nebraska	626,000,000	0.7%
36	Utah	564,000,000	0.6%
37	Nevada	478,000,000	0.5%
38	Maine	456,000,000	0.5%
39	New Mexico	402,000,000	0.4%
40	Rhode Island	400,000,000	0.4%
41	New Hampshire	391,000,000	0.4%
42	Idaho	334,000,000	0.4%
43	Hawaii	311,000,000	0.3%
44	Delaware	300,000,000	0.3%
45	Montana	234,000,000	0.3%
46	South Dakota	201,000,000	0.2%
47	North Dakota	192,000,000	0.2%
48	Vermont	183,000,000	0.2%
49	Alaska	133,000,000	0.1%
49	Wyoming	133,000,000	0.1%
	District of Columbia	180,000,000	0.2%

Source: U.S. Department of Health and Human Services, Centers for Medicare and Medicaid Services
   "State Health Care Expenditures" (http://www.cms.hhs.gov/statistics/nhe/)
*Purchases in retail outlets. By state of outlet. Revised figures.

Percent of Total Personal Health Care Expenditures
Spent on Prescription Drugs in 1998
National Percent = 8.9%*

ALPHA ORDER

RANK	STATE	PERCENT
10	Alabama	9.9
50	Alaska	6.4
21	Arizona	9.3
5	Arkansas	10.6
49	California	6.7
44	Colorado	7.2
31	Connecticut	8.8
12	Delaware	9.8
7	Florida	10.3
28	Georgia	9.0
48	Hawaii	6.8
12	Idaho	9.8
28	Illinois	9.0
15	Indiana	9.7
21	Iowa	9.3
25	Kansas	9.2
3	Kentucky	10.8
25	Louisiana	9.2
21	Maine	9.3
34	Maryland	8.6
44	Massachusetts	7.2
2	Michigan	11.0
42	Minnesota	7.5
5	Mississippi	10.6
34	Missouri	8.6
41	Montana	8.2
8	Nebraska	10.2
34	Nevada	8.6
37	New Hampshire	8.5
3	New Jersey	10.8
42	New Mexico	7.5
38	New York	8.4
17	North Carolina	9.6
44	North Dakota	7.2
21	Ohio	9.3
15	Oklahoma	9.7
38	Oregon	8.4
10	Pennsylvania	9.9
27	Rhode Island	9.1
9	South Carolina	10.1
44	South Dakota	7.2
12	Tennessee	9.8
31	Texas	8.8
19	Utah	9.5
30	Vermont	8.9
17	Virginia	9.6
40	Washington	8.3
1	West Virginia	11.1
31	Wisconsin	8.8
19	Wyoming	9.5

RANK ORDER

RANK	STATE	PERCENT
1	West Virginia	11.1
2	Michigan	11.0
3	Kentucky	10.8
3	New Jersey	10.8
5	Arkansas	10.6
5	Mississippi	10.6
7	Florida	10.3
8	Nebraska	10.2
9	South Carolina	10.1
10	Alabama	9.9
10	Pennsylvania	9.9
12	Delaware	9.8
12	Idaho	9.8
12	Tennessee	9.8
15	Indiana	9.7
15	Oklahoma	9.7
17	North Carolina	9.6
17	Virginia	9.6
19	Utah	9.5
19	Wyoming	9.5
21	Arizona	9.3
21	Iowa	9.3
21	Maine	9.3
21	Ohio	9.3
25	Kansas	9.2
25	Louisiana	9.2
27	Rhode Island	9.1
28	Georgia	9.0
28	Illinois	9.0
30	Vermont	8.9
31	Connecticut	8.8
31	Texas	8.8
31	Wisconsin	8.8
34	Maryland	8.6
34	Missouri	8.6
34	Nevada	8.6
37	New Hampshire	8.5
38	New York	8.4
38	Oregon	8.4
40	Washington	8.3
41	Montana	8.2
42	Minnesota	7.5
42	New Mexico	7.5
44	Colorado	7.2
44	Massachusetts	7.2
44	North Dakota	7.2
44	South Dakota	7.2
48	Hawaii	6.8
49	California	6.7
50	Alaska	6.4

District of Columbia		4.2

Source: MQ Press using data from U.S. Dept of Health & Human Services, Centers for Medicare and Medicaid Services
"State Health Care Expenditures" (http://www.cms.hhs.gov/statistics/nhe/)
*Purchases in retail outlets. By state of outlet. Revised figures.

Per Capita Expenditures for Prescription Drugs in 1998

National Per Capita = $335*

RANK	STATE	PER CAPITA
14	Alabama	$357
50	Alaska	216
37	Arizona	299
15	Arkansas	356
49	California	231
47	Colorado	244
5	Connecticut	414
7	Delaware	403
4	Florida	416
30	Georgia	322
46	Hawaii	261
43	Idaho	271
27	Illinois	328
18	Indiana	348
25	Iowa	330
29	Kansas	324
8	Kentucky	398
20	Louisiana	345
13	Maine	366
28	Maryland	327
16	Massachusetts	353
9	Michigan	396
32	Minnesota	315
17	Mississippi	350
23	Missouri	334
45	Montana	266
12	Nebraska	377
42	Nevada	274
25	New Hampshire	330
1	New Jersey	438
48	New Mexico	232
10	New York	392
22	North Carolina	340
36	North Dakota	301
19	Ohio	347
31	Oklahoma	316
39	Oregon	280
3	Pennsylvania	420
6	Rhode Island	405
21	South Carolina	342
41	South Dakota	275
10	Tennessee	392
35	Texas	306
44	Utah	268
34	Vermont	310
33	Virginia	314
38	Washington	282
2	West Virginia	428
23	Wisconsin	334
40	Wyoming	277

RANK	STATE	PER CAPITA
1	New Jersey	$438
2	West Virginia	428
3	Pennsylvania	420
4	Florida	416
5	Connecticut	414
6	Rhode Island	405
7	Delaware	403
8	Kentucky	398
9	Michigan	396
10	New York	392
10	Tennessee	392
12	Nebraska	377
13	Maine	366
14	Alabama	357
15	Arkansas	356
16	Massachusetts	353
17	Mississippi	350
18	Indiana	348
19	Ohio	347
20	Louisiana	345
21	South Carolina	342
22	North Carolina	340
23	Missouri	334
23	Wisconsin	334
25	Iowa	330
25	New Hampshire	330
27	Illinois	328
28	Maryland	327
29	Kansas	324
30	Georgia	322
31	Oklahoma	316
32	Minnesota	315
33	Virginia	314
34	Vermont	310
35	Texas	306
36	North Dakota	301
37	Arizona	299
38	Washington	282
39	Oregon	280
40	Wyoming	277
41	South Dakota	275
42	Nevada	274
43	Idaho	271
44	Utah	268
45	Montana	266
46	Hawaii	261
47	Colorado	244
48	New Mexico	232
49	California	231
50	Alaska	216
	District of Columbia	345

Source: MQ Press using data from U.S. Dept of Health & Human Services, Centers for Medicare and Medicaid Services "State Health Care Expenditures" (http://www.cms.hhs.gov/statistics/nhe/)
*Purchases in retail outlets. By state of outlet. Revised figures.

Expenditures for Dental Services in 1998

National Total = $53,829,000,000*

ALPHA ORDER

RANK	STATE	EXPENDITURES	% of USA
26	Alabama	$652,000,000	1.2%
44	Alaska	173,000,000	0.3%
24	Arizona	867,000,000	1.6%
33	Arkansas	392,000,000	0.7%
1	California	7,999,000,000	14.9%
19	Colorado	944,000,000	1.8%
22	Connecticut	896,000,000	1.7%
45	Delaware	155,000,000	0.3%
4	Florida	2,957,000,000	5.5%
12	Georgia	1,381,000,000	2.6%
36	Hawaii	284,000,000	0.5%
40	Idaho	253,000,000	0.5%
5	Illinois	2,283,000,000	4.2%
18	Indiana	1,021,000,000	1.9%
31	Iowa	482,000,000	0.9%
30	Kansas	484,000,000	0.9%
28	Kentucky	533,000,000	1.0%
25	Louisiana	703,000,000	1.3%
41	Maine	233,000,000	0.4%
17	Maryland	1,047,000,000	1.9%
11	Massachusetts	1,472,000,000	2.7%
7	Michigan	2,141,000,000	4.0%
16	Minnesota	1,052,000,000	2.0%
35	Mississippi	317,000,000	0.6%
23	Missouri	877,000,000	1.6%
46	Montana	151,000,000	0.3%
38	Nebraska	274,000,000	0.5%
34	Nevada	391,000,000	0.7%
37	New Hampshire	283,000,000	0.5%
9	New Jersey	1,917,000,000	3.6%
39	New Mexico	268,000,000	0.5%
2	New York	3,698,000,000	6.9%
13	North Carolina	1,323,000,000	2.5%
49	North Dakota	110,000,000	0.2%
8	Ohio	1,978,000,000	3.7%
29	Oklahoma	505,000,000	0.9%
21	Oregon	902,000,000	1.7%
6	Pennsylvania	2,237,000,000	4.2%
43	Rhode Island	217,000,000	0.4%
27	South Carolina	591,000,000	1.1%
48	South Dakota	121,000,000	0.2%
20	Tennessee	927,000,000	1.7%
3	Texas	3,218,000,000	6.0%
32	Utah	461,000,000	0.9%
47	Vermont	127,000,000	0.2%
14	Virginia	1,272,000,000	2.4%
10	Washington	1,722,000,000	3.2%
42	West Virginia	221,000,000	0.4%
15	Wisconsin	1,089,000,000	2.0%
50	Wyoming	76,000,000	0.1%

RANK ORDER

RANK	STATE	EXPENDITURES	% of USA
1	California	$7,999,000,000	14.9%
2	New York	3,698,000,000	6.9%
3	Texas	3,218,000,000	6.0%
4	Florida	2,957,000,000	5.5%
5	Illinois	2,283,000,000	4.2%
6	Pennsylvania	2,237,000,000	4.2%
7	Michigan	2,141,000,000	4.0%
8	Ohio	1,978,000,000	3.7%
9	New Jersey	1,917,000,000	3.6%
10	Washington	1,722,000,000	3.2%
11	Massachusetts	1,472,000,000	2.7%
12	Georgia	1,381,000,000	2.6%
13	North Carolina	1,323,000,000	2.5%
14	Virginia	1,272,000,000	2.4%
15	Wisconsin	1,089,000,000	2.0%
16	Minnesota	1,052,000,000	2.0%
17	Maryland	1,047,000,000	1.9%
18	Indiana	1,021,000,000	1.9%
19	Colorado	944,000,000	1.8%
20	Tennessee	927,000,000	1.7%
21	Oregon	902,000,000	1.7%
22	Connecticut	896,000,000	1.7%
23	Missouri	877,000,000	1.6%
24	Arizona	867,000,000	1.6%
25	Louisiana	703,000,000	1.3%
26	Alabama	652,000,000	1.2%
27	South Carolina	591,000,000	1.1%
28	Kentucky	533,000,000	1.0%
29	Oklahoma	505,000,000	0.9%
30	Kansas	484,000,000	0.9%
31	Iowa	482,000,000	0.9%
32	Utah	461,000,000	0.9%
33	Arkansas	392,000,000	0.7%
34	Nevada	391,000,000	0.7%
35	Mississippi	317,000,000	0.6%
36	Hawaii	284,000,000	0.5%
37	New Hampshire	283,000,000	0.5%
38	Nebraska	274,000,000	0.5%
39	New Mexico	268,000,000	0.5%
40	Idaho	253,000,000	0.5%
41	Maine	233,000,000	0.4%
42	West Virginia	221,000,000	0.4%
43	Rhode Island	217,000,000	0.4%
44	Alaska	173,000,000	0.3%
45	Delaware	155,000,000	0.3%
46	Montana	151,000,000	0.3%
47	Vermont	127,000,000	0.2%
48	South Dakota	121,000,000	0.2%
49	North Dakota	110,000,000	0.2%
50	Wyoming	76,000,000	0.1%
	District of Columbia	151,000,000	0.3%

Source: U.S. Department of Health and Human Services, Centers for Medicare and Medicaid Services
    "State Health Care Expenditures" (http://www.cms.hhs.gov/statistics/nhe/)
*By state of provider. Revised figures.

Percent of Total Personal Health Care Expenditures
Spent on Dental Services in 1998
National Percent = 5.3%*

RANK	STATE	PERCENT
45	Alabama	4.2
2	Alaska	8.3
13	Arizona	5.8
36	Arkansas	4.6
6	California	7.1
7	Colorado	7.0
13	Connecticut	5.8
25	Delaware	5.0
27	Florida	4.9
24	Georgia	5.1
9	Hawaii	6.2
5	Idaho	7.4
22	Illinois	5.2
31	Indiana	4.8
33	Iowa	4.7
22	Kansas	5.2
48	Kentucky	3.7
42	Louisiana	4.3
31	Maine	4.8
18	Maryland	5.4
27	Massachusetts	4.9
11	Michigan	6.1
20	Minnesota	5.3
49	Mississippi	3.5
46	Missouri	4.1
20	Montana	5.3
38	Nebraska	4.5
7	Nevada	7.0
11	New Hampshire	6.1
13	New Jersey	5.8
25	New Mexico	5.0
42	New York	4.3
27	North Carolina	4.9
46	North Dakota	4.1
33	Ohio	4.7
36	Oklahoma	4.6
3	Oregon	8.2
40	Pennsylvania	4.4
27	Rhode Island	4.9
38	South Carolina	4.5
40	South Dakota	4.4
42	Tennessee	4.3
33	Texas	4.7
4	Utah	7.8
9	Vermont	6.2
16	Virginia	5.7
1	Washington	8.9
50	West Virginia	3.2
17	Wisconsin	5.5
18	Wyoming	5.4

RANK	STATE	PERCENT
1	Washington	8.9
2	Alaska	8.3
3	Oregon	8.2
4	Utah	7.8
5	Idaho	7.4
6	California	7.1
7	Colorado	7.0
7	Nevada	7.0
9	Hawaii	6.2
9	Vermont	6.2
11	Michigan	6.1
11	New Hampshire	6.1
13	Arizona	5.8
13	Connecticut	5.8
13	New Jersey	5.8
16	Virginia	5.7
17	Wisconsin	5.5
18	Maryland	5.4
18	Wyoming	5.4
20	Minnesota	5.3
20	Montana	5.3
22	Illinois	5.2
22	Kansas	5.2
24	Georgia	5.1
25	Delaware	5.0
25	New Mexico	5.0
27	Florida	4.9
27	Massachusetts	4.9
27	North Carolina	4.9
27	Rhode Island	4.9
31	Indiana	4.8
31	Maine	4.8
33	Iowa	4.7
33	Ohio	4.7
33	Texas	4.7
36	Arkansas	4.6
36	Oklahoma	4.6
38	Nebraska	4.5
38	South Carolina	4.5
40	Pennsylvania	4.4
40	South Dakota	4.4
42	Louisiana	4.3
42	New York	4.3
42	Tennessee	4.3
45	Alabama	4.2
46	Missouri	4.1
46	North Dakota	4.1
48	Kentucky	3.7
49	Mississippi	3.5
50	West Virginia	3.2

District of Columbia   3.5

Source: MQ Press using data from U.S. Dept of Health & Human Services, Centers for Medicare and Medicaid Services
"State Health Care Expenditures" (http://www.cms.hhs.gov/statistics/nhe/)
*By state of provider. Revised figures.

Per Capita Expenditures for Dental Services in 1998

National Per Capita = $199*

RANK	STATE	PER CAPITA
47	Alabama	$150
2	Alaska	281
26	Arizona	186
44	Arkansas	154
5	California	245
9	Colorado	238
4	Connecticut	274
18	Delaware	208
22	Florida	198
29	Georgia	181
7	Hawaii	239
19	Idaho	206
23	Illinois	189
32	Indiana	173
36	Iowa	168
28	Kansas	183
48	Kentucky	135
40	Louisiana	161
24	Maine	187
20	Maryland	204
6	Massachusetts	240
15	Michigan	218
12	Minnesota	223
50	Mississippi	115
40	Missouri	161
33	Montana	172
38	Nebraska	165
11	Nevada	224
7	New Hampshire	239
10	New Jersey	237
43	New Mexico	155
20	New York	204
31	North Carolina	175
33	North Dakota	172
30	Ohio	176
46	Oklahoma	151
3	Oregon	275
26	Pennsylvania	186
13	Rhode Island	220
44	South Carolina	154
37	South Dakota	166
35	Tennessee	171
39	Texas	163
14	Utah	219
16	Vermont	215
24	Virginia	187
1	Washington	303
49	West Virginia	122
17	Wisconsin	209
42	Wyoming	158

RANK	STATE	PER CAPITA
1	Washington	$303
2	Alaska	281
3	Oregon	275
4	Connecticut	274
5	California	245
6	Massachusetts	240
7	Hawaii	239
7	New Hampshire	239
9	Colorado	238
10	New Jersey	237
11	Nevada	224
12	Minnesota	223
13	Rhode Island	220
14	Utah	219
15	Michigan	218
16	Vermont	215
17	Wisconsin	209
18	Delaware	208
19	Idaho	206
20	Maryland	204
20	New York	204
22	Florida	198
23	Illinois	189
24	Maine	187
24	Virginia	187
26	Arizona	186
26	Pennsylvania	186
28	Kansas	183
29	Georgia	181
30	Ohio	176
31	North Carolina	175
32	Indiana	173
33	Montana	172
33	North Dakota	172
35	Tennessee	171
36	Iowa	168
37	South Dakota	166
38	Nebraska	165
39	Texas	163
40	Louisiana	161
40	Missouri	161
42	Wyoming	158
43	New Mexico	155
44	Arkansas	154
44	South Carolina	154
46	Oklahoma	151
47	Alabama	150
48	Kentucky	135
49	West Virginia	122
50	Mississippi	115
	District of Columbia	290

Source: MQ Press using data from U.S. Dept of Health & Human Services, Centers for Medicare and Medicaid Services
"State Health Care Expenditures" (http://www.cms.hhs.gov/statistics/nhe/)
*By state of provider. Per capita calculated using resident population. These figures may be skewed due to
residents crossing state borders for care. Revised figures.

Expenditures for Other Personal Health Care Services in 1998

National Total = $31,878,000,000*

ALPHA ORDER

RANK	STATE	EXPENDITURES	% of USA
26	Alabama	$411,000,000	1.3%
45	Alaska	125,000,000	0.4%
34	Arizona	305,000,000	1.0%
35	Arkansas	238,000,000	0.7%
3	California	2,056,000,000	6.4%
22	Colorado	468,000,000	1.5%
21	Connecticut	550,000,000	1.7%
43	Delaware	142,000,000	0.4%
5	Florida	1,537,000,000	4.8%
13	Georgia	786,000,000	2.5%
42	Hawaii	149,000,000	0.5%
46	Idaho	108,000,000	0.3%
6	Illinois	1,324,000,000	4.2%
27	Indiana	384,000,000	1.2%
31	Iowa	345,000,000	1.1%
24	Kansas	434,000,000	1.4%
25	Kentucky	430,000,000	1.3%
30	Louisiana	347,000,000	1.1%
32	Maine	343,000,000	1.1%
18	Maryland	593,000,000	1.9%
7	Massachusetts	1,145,000,000	3.6%
10	Michigan	872,000,000	2.7%
11	Minnesota	814,000,000	2.6%
38	Mississippi	210,000,000	0.7%
17	Missouri	648,000,000	2.0%
48	Montana	94,000,000	0.3%
39	Nebraska	179,000,000	0.6%
44	Nevada	137,000,000	0.4%
37	New Hampshire	235,000,000	0.7%
12	New Jersey	801,000,000	2.5%
35	New Mexico	238,000,000	0.7%
1	New York	4,447,000,000	14.0%
9	North Carolina	881,000,000	2.8%
49	North Dakota	84,000,000	0.3%
8	Ohio	935,000,000	2.9%
28	Oklahoma	383,000,000	1.2%
20	Oregon	566,000,000	1.8%
4	Pennsylvania	1,613,000,000	5.1%
29	Rhode Island	354,000,000	1.1%
19	South Carolina	575,000,000	1.8%
47	South Dakota	101,000,000	0.3%
23	Tennessee	463,000,000	1.5%
2	Texas	2,089,000,000	6.6%
40	Utah	178,000,000	0.6%
41	Vermont	154,000,000	0.5%
15	Virginia	668,000,000	2.1%
14	Washington	719,000,000	2.3%
33	West Virginia	331,000,000	1.0%
16	Wisconsin	661,000,000	2.1%
50	Wyoming	69,000,000	0.2%

RANK ORDER

RANK	STATE	EXPENDITURES	% of USA
1	New York	$4,447,000,000	14.0%
2	Texas	2,089,000,000	6.6%
3	California	2,056,000,000	6.4%
4	Pennsylvania	1,613,000,000	5.1%
5	Florida	1,537,000,000	4.8%
6	Illinois	1,324,000,000	4.2%
7	Massachusetts	1,145,000,000	3.6%
8	Ohio	935,000,000	2.9%
9	North Carolina	881,000,000	2.8%
10	Michigan	872,000,000	2.7%
11	Minnesota	814,000,000	2.6%
12	New Jersey	801,000,000	2.5%
13	Georgia	786,000,000	2.5%
14	Washington	719,000,000	2.3%
15	Virginia	668,000,000	2.1%
16	Wisconsin	661,000,000	2.1%
17	Missouri	648,000,000	2.0%
18	Maryland	593,000,000	1.9%
19	South Carolina	575,000,000	1.8%
20	Oregon	566,000,000	1.8%
21	Connecticut	550,000,000	1.7%
22	Colorado	468,000,000	1.5%
23	Tennessee	463,000,000	1.5%
24	Kansas	434,000,000	1.4%
25	Kentucky	430,000,000	1.3%
26	Alabama	411,000,000	1.3%
27	Indiana	384,000,000	1.2%
28	Oklahoma	383,000,000	1.2%
29	Rhode Island	354,000,000	1.1%
30	Louisiana	347,000,000	1.1%
31	Iowa	345,000,000	1.1%
32	Maine	343,000,000	1.1%
33	West Virginia	331,000,000	1.0%
34	Arizona	305,000,000	1.0%
35	Arkansas	238,000,000	0.7%
35	New Mexico	238,000,000	0.7%
37	New Hampshire	235,000,000	0.7%
38	Mississippi	210,000,000	0.7%
39	Nebraska	179,000,000	0.6%
40	Utah	178,000,000	0.6%
41	Vermont	154,000,000	0.5%
42	Hawaii	149,000,000	0.5%
43	Delaware	142,000,000	0.4%
44	Nevada	137,000,000	0.4%
45	Alaska	125,000,000	0.4%
46	Idaho	108,000,000	0.3%
47	South Dakota	101,000,000	0.3%
48	Montana	94,000,000	0.3%
49	North Dakota	84,000,000	0.3%
50	Wyoming	69,000,000	0.2%
	District of Columbia	157,000,000	0.5%

Source: U.S. Department of Health and Human Services, Centers for Medicare and Medicaid Services
"State Health Care Expenditures" (http://www.cms.hhs.gov/statistics/nhe/)
*By state of provider. Includes on-site services provided by employers for the health care needs of their employees.
Also includes shipboard facilities and field stations operated by the U.S. Department of Defense; certain state and
local maternal and child health programs; school health programs and federal agency programs targeting, military
personnel, Native Americans and persons with dependency and mental-health-related problems. Revised figures.

Percent of Total Personal Health Care Expenditures
Spent on Other Personal Health Care Services in 1998
National Percent = 3.1%*

ALPHA ORDER

RANK	STATE	PERCENT
39	Alabama	2.6
4	Alaska	6.0
48	Arizona	2.0
38	Arkansas	2.8
49	California	1.8
19	Colorado	3.5
17	Connecticut	3.6
11	Delaware	4.6
40	Florida	2.5
36	Georgia	2.9
22	Hawaii	3.3
26	Idaho	3.2
31	Illinois	3.0
49	Indiana	1.8
21	Iowa	3.4
9	Kansas	4.7
31	Kentucky	3.0
46	Louisiana	2.1
3	Maine	7.0
31	Maryland	3.0
15	Massachusetts	3.8
40	Michigan	2.5
14	Minnesota	4.1
44	Mississippi	2.3
28	Missouri	3.1
22	Montana	3.3
36	Nebraska	2.9
40	Nevada	2.5
7	New Hampshire	5.1
43	New Jersey	2.4
12	New Mexico	4.4
5	New York	5.2
22	North Carolina	3.3
28	North Dakota	3.1
45	Ohio	2.2
19	Oklahoma	3.5
5	Oregon	5.2
26	Pennsylvania	3.2
1	Rhode Island	8.0
12	South Carolina	4.4
17	South Dakota	3.6
46	Tennessee	2.1
28	Texas	3.1
31	Utah	3.0
2	Vermont	7.5
31	Virginia	3.0
16	Washington	3.7
9	West Virginia	4.7
22	Wisconsin	3.3
8	Wyoming	4.9

RANK ORDER

RANK	STATE	PERCENT
1	Rhode Island	8.0
2	Vermont	7.5
3	Maine	7.0
4	Alaska	6.0
5	New York	5.2
5	Oregon	5.2
7	New Hampshire	5.1
8	Wyoming	4.9
9	Kansas	4.7
9	West Virginia	4.7
11	Delaware	4.6
12	New Mexico	4.4
12	South Carolina	4.4
14	Minnesota	4.1
15	Massachusetts	3.8
16	Washington	3.7
17	Connecticut	3.6
17	South Dakota	3.6
19	Colorado	3.5
19	Oklahoma	3.5
21	Iowa	3.4
22	Hawaii	3.3
22	Montana	3.3
22	North Carolina	3.3
22	Wisconsin	3.3
26	Idaho	3.2
26	Pennsylvania	3.2
28	Missouri	3.1
28	North Dakota	3.1
28	Texas	3.1
31	Illinois	3.0
31	Kentucky	3.0
31	Maryland	3.0
31	Utah	3.0
31	Virginia	3.0
36	Georgia	2.9
36	Nebraska	2.9
38	Arkansas	2.8
39	Alabama	2.6
40	Florida	2.5
40	Michigan	2.5
40	Nevada	2.5
43	New Jersey	2.4
44	Mississippi	2.3
45	Ohio	2.2
46	Louisiana	2.1
46	Tennessee	2.1
48	Arizona	2.0
49	California	1.8
49	Indiana	1.8

| | District of Columbia | 3.6 |

Source: MQ Press using data from U.S. Dept of Health & Human Services, Centers for Medicare and Medicaid Services "State Health Care Expenditures" (http://www.cms.hhs.gov/statistics/nhe/)

*By state of provider. Includes on-site services provided by employers for the health care needs of their employees. Also includes shipboard facilities and field stations operated by the U.S. Department of Defense; certain state and local maternal and child health programs; school health programs hend federal agency programs targeting, military personnel, Native Americans and persons with dependency and mental-health-related problems. Revised figures.

Per Capita Expenditures for Other Personal Health Care Services in 1998

National Per Capita = $118*

<table>
<tr><td colspan="3">ALPHA ORDER</td><td colspan="3">RANK ORDER</td></tr>
<tr><td>RANK</td><td>STATE</td><td>PER CAPITA</td><td>RANK</td><td>STATE</td><td>PER CAPITA</td></tr>
<tr><td>38</td><td>Alabama</td><td>$94</td><td>1</td><td>Rhode Island</td><td>$358</td></tr>
<tr><td>5</td><td>Alaska</td><td>203</td><td>2</td><td>Maine</td><td>275</td></tr>
<tr><td>48</td><td>Arizona</td><td>65</td><td>3</td><td>Vermont</td><td>261</td></tr>
<tr><td>38</td><td>Arkansas</td><td>94</td><td>4</td><td>New York</td><td>245</td></tr>
<tr><td>50</td><td>California</td><td>63</td><td>5</td><td>Alaska</td><td>203</td></tr>
<tr><td>25</td><td>Colorado</td><td>118</td><td>6</td><td>New Hampshire</td><td>198</td></tr>
<tr><td>12</td><td>Connecticut</td><td>168</td><td>7</td><td>Delaware</td><td>191</td></tr>
<tr><td>7</td><td>Delaware</td><td>191</td><td>8</td><td>Massachusetts</td><td>186</td></tr>
<tr><td>34</td><td>Florida</td><td>103</td><td>9</td><td>West Virginia</td><td>183</td></tr>
<tr><td>34</td><td>Georgia</td><td>103</td><td>10</td><td>Minnesota</td><td>172</td></tr>
<tr><td>22</td><td>Hawaii</td><td>125</td><td>10</td><td>Oregon</td><td>172</td></tr>
<tr><td>41</td><td>Idaho</td><td>88</td><td>12</td><td>Connecticut</td><td>168</td></tr>
<tr><td>29</td><td>Illinois</td><td>110</td><td>13</td><td>Kansas</td><td>164</td></tr>
<tr><td>48</td><td>Indiana</td><td>65</td><td>14</td><td>South Carolina</td><td>150</td></tr>
<tr><td>23</td><td>Iowa</td><td>121</td><td>15</td><td>Wyoming</td><td>144</td></tr>
<tr><td>13</td><td>Kansas</td><td>164</td><td>16</td><td>South Dakota</td><td>138</td></tr>
<tr><td>30</td><td>Kentucky</td><td>109</td><td>17</td><td>New Mexico</td><td>137</td></tr>
<tr><td>45</td><td>Louisiana</td><td>80</td><td>18</td><td>Pennsylvania</td><td>134</td></tr>
<tr><td>2</td><td>Maine</td><td>275</td><td>19</td><td>North Dakota</td><td>132</td></tr>
<tr><td>27</td><td>Maryland</td><td>116</td><td>20</td><td>Wisconsin</td><td>127</td></tr>
<tr><td>8</td><td>Massachusetts</td><td>186</td><td>21</td><td>Washington</td><td>126</td></tr>
<tr><td>40</td><td>Michigan</td><td>89</td><td>22</td><td>Hawaii</td><td>125</td></tr>
<tr><td>10</td><td>Minnesota</td><td>172</td><td>23</td><td>Iowa</td><td>121</td></tr>
<tr><td>47</td><td>Mississippi</td><td>76</td><td>24</td><td>Missouri</td><td>119</td></tr>
<tr><td>24</td><td>Missouri</td><td>119</td><td>25</td><td>Colorado</td><td>118</td></tr>
<tr><td>32</td><td>Montana</td><td>107</td><td>26</td><td>North Carolina</td><td>117</td></tr>
<tr><td>31</td><td>Nebraska</td><td>108</td><td>27</td><td>Maryland</td><td>116</td></tr>
<tr><td>46</td><td>Nevada</td><td>79</td><td>28</td><td>Oklahoma</td><td>115</td></tr>
<tr><td>6</td><td>New Hampshire</td><td>198</td><td>29</td><td>Illinois</td><td>110</td></tr>
<tr><td>36</td><td>New Jersey</td><td>99</td><td>30</td><td>Kentucky</td><td>109</td></tr>
<tr><td>17</td><td>New Mexico</td><td>137</td><td>31</td><td>Nebraska</td><td>108</td></tr>
<tr><td>4</td><td>New York</td><td>245</td><td>32</td><td>Montana</td><td>107</td></tr>
<tr><td>26</td><td>North Carolina</td><td>117</td><td>33</td><td>Texas</td><td>106</td></tr>
<tr><td>19</td><td>North Dakota</td><td>132</td><td>34</td><td>Florida</td><td>103</td></tr>
<tr><td>44</td><td>Ohio</td><td>83</td><td>34</td><td>Georgia</td><td>103</td></tr>
<tr><td>28</td><td>Oklahoma</td><td>115</td><td>36</td><td>New Jersey</td><td>99</td></tr>
<tr><td>10</td><td>Oregon</td><td>172</td><td>37</td><td>Virginia</td><td>98</td></tr>
<tr><td>18</td><td>Pennsylvania</td><td>134</td><td>38</td><td>Alabama</td><td>94</td></tr>
<tr><td>1</td><td>Rhode Island</td><td>358</td><td>38</td><td>Arkansas</td><td>94</td></tr>
<tr><td>14</td><td>South Carolina</td><td>150</td><td>40</td><td>Michigan</td><td>89</td></tr>
<tr><td>16</td><td>South Dakota</td><td>138</td><td>41</td><td>Idaho</td><td>88</td></tr>
<tr><td>42</td><td>Tennessee</td><td>85</td><td>42</td><td>Tennessee</td><td>85</td></tr>
<tr><td>33</td><td>Texas</td><td>106</td><td>42</td><td>Utah</td><td>85</td></tr>
<tr><td>42</td><td>Utah</td><td>85</td><td>44</td><td>Ohio</td><td>83</td></tr>
<tr><td>3</td><td>Vermont</td><td>261</td><td>45</td><td>Louisiana</td><td>80</td></tr>
<tr><td>37</td><td>Virginia</td><td>98</td><td>46</td><td>Nevada</td><td>79</td></tr>
<tr><td>21</td><td>Washington</td><td>126</td><td>47</td><td>Mississippi</td><td>76</td></tr>
<tr><td>9</td><td>West Virginia</td><td>183</td><td>48</td><td>Arizona</td><td>65</td></tr>
<tr><td>20</td><td>Wisconsin</td><td>127</td><td>48</td><td>Indiana</td><td>65</td></tr>
<tr><td>15</td><td>Wyoming</td><td>144</td><td>50</td><td>California</td><td>63</td></tr>
<tr><td></td><td></td><td></td><td></td><td>District of Columbia</td><td>301</td></tr>
</table>

Source: MQ Press using data from U.S. Dept of Health & Human Services, Centers for Medicare and Medicaid Services
"State Health Care Expenditures" (http://www.cms.hhs.gov/statistics/nhe)

*By state of provider. Includes on-site services provided by employers for the health care needs of their employees. Also includes shipboard facilities and field stations operated by the U.S. Department of Defense; certain state and local maternal and child health programs; school health programs and federal agency programs targeting, military personnel, Native Americans and persons with dependency and mental-health-related problems. Revised figures.

Expenditures for Home Health Care in 1998

National Total = $29,255,000,000*

<table>
<tr><td colspan="4">ALPHA ORDER</td><td colspan="4">RANK ORDER</td></tr>
<tr><th>RANK</th><th>STATE</th><th>EXPENDITURES</th><th>% of USA</th><th>RANK</th><th>STATE</th><th>EXPENDITURES</th><th>% of USA</th></tr>
<tr><td>19</td><td>Alabama</td><td>$470,000,000</td><td>1.6%</td><td>1</td><td>New York</td><td>$4,292,000,000</td><td>14.7%</td></tr>
<tr><td>50</td><td>Alaska</td><td>9,000,000</td><td>0.0%</td><td>2</td><td>Texas</td><td>2,862,000,000</td><td>9.8%</td></tr>
<tr><td>27</td><td>Arizona</td><td>331,000,000</td><td>1.1%</td><td>3</td><td>Florida</td><td>2,225,000,000</td><td>7.6%</td></tr>
<tr><td>31</td><td>Arkansas</td><td>242,000,000</td><td>0.8%</td><td>4</td><td>California</td><td>1,951,000,000</td><td>6.7%</td></tr>
<tr><td>4</td><td>California</td><td>1,951,000,000</td><td>6.7%</td><td>5</td><td>Ohio</td><td>1,224,000,000</td><td>4.2%</td></tr>
<tr><td>28</td><td>Colorado</td><td>324,000,000</td><td>1.1%</td><td>6</td><td>Pennsylvania</td><td>1,109,000,000</td><td>3.8%</td></tr>
<tr><td>15</td><td>Connecticut</td><td>599,000,000</td><td>2.0%</td><td>7</td><td>Massachusetts</td><td>999,000,000</td><td>3.4%</td></tr>
<tr><td>41</td><td>Delaware</td><td>110,000,000</td><td>0.4%</td><td>8</td><td>Illinois</td><td>972,000,000</td><td>3.3%</td></tr>
<tr><td>3</td><td>Florida</td><td>2,225,000,000</td><td>7.6%</td><td>9</td><td>New Jersey</td><td>938,000,000</td><td>3.2%</td></tr>
<tr><td>12</td><td>Georgia</td><td>810,000,000</td><td>2.8%</td><td>10</td><td>North Carolina</td><td>934,000,000</td><td>3.2%</td></tr>
<tr><td>44</td><td>Hawaii</td><td>60,000,000</td><td>0.2%</td><td>11</td><td>Michigan</td><td>841,000,000</td><td>2.9%</td></tr>
<tr><td>44</td><td>Idaho</td><td>60,000,000</td><td>0.2%</td><td>12</td><td>Georgia</td><td>810,000,000</td><td>2.8%</td></tr>
<tr><td>8</td><td>Illinois</td><td>972,000,000</td><td>3.3%</td><td>13</td><td>Louisiana</td><td>629,000,000</td><td>2.2%</td></tr>
<tr><td>21</td><td>Indiana</td><td>415,000,000</td><td>1.4%</td><td>14</td><td>Tennessee</td><td>617,000,000</td><td>2.1%</td></tr>
<tr><td>30</td><td>Iowa</td><td>248,000,000</td><td>0.8%</td><td>15</td><td>Connecticut</td><td>599,000,000</td><td>2.0%</td></tr>
<tr><td>32</td><td>Kansas</td><td>220,000,000</td><td>0.8%</td><td>16</td><td>Missouri</td><td>567,000,000</td><td>1.9%</td></tr>
<tr><td>17</td><td>Kentucky</td><td>506,000,000</td><td>1.7%</td><td>17</td><td>Kentucky</td><td>506,000,000</td><td>1.7%</td></tr>
<tr><td>13</td><td>Louisiana</td><td>629,000,000</td><td>2.2%</td><td>18</td><td>Virginia</td><td>484,000,000</td><td>1.7%</td></tr>
<tr><td>33</td><td>Maine</td><td>188,000,000</td><td>0.6%</td><td>19</td><td>Alabama</td><td>470,000,000</td><td>1.6%</td></tr>
<tr><td>25</td><td>Maryland</td><td>390,000,000</td><td>1.3%</td><td>20</td><td>Minnesota</td><td>419,000,000</td><td>1.4%</td></tr>
<tr><td>7</td><td>Massachusetts</td><td>999,000,000</td><td>3.4%</td><td>21</td><td>Indiana</td><td>415,000,000</td><td>1.4%</td></tr>
<tr><td>11</td><td>Michigan</td><td>841,000,000</td><td>2.9%</td><td>22</td><td>Wisconsin</td><td>393,000,000</td><td>1.3%</td></tr>
<tr><td>20</td><td>Minnesota</td><td>419,000,000</td><td>1.4%</td><td>23</td><td>Oklahoma</td><td>391,000,000</td><td>1.3%</td></tr>
<tr><td>29</td><td>Mississippi</td><td>293,000,000</td><td>1.0%</td><td>23</td><td>South Carolina</td><td>391,000,000</td><td>1.3%</td></tr>
<tr><td>16</td><td>Missouri</td><td>567,000,000</td><td>1.9%</td><td>25</td><td>Maryland</td><td>390,000,000</td><td>1.3%</td></tr>
<tr><td>46</td><td>Montana</td><td>56,000,000</td><td>0.2%</td><td>26</td><td>Washington</td><td>365,000,000</td><td>1.2%</td></tr>
<tr><td>42</td><td>Nebraska</td><td>71,000,000</td><td>0.2%</td><td>27</td><td>Arizona</td><td>331,000,000</td><td>1.1%</td></tr>
<tr><td>35</td><td>Nevada</td><td>180,000,000</td><td>0.6%</td><td>28</td><td>Colorado</td><td>324,000,000</td><td>1.1%</td></tr>
<tr><td>37</td><td>New Hampshire</td><td>145,000,000</td><td>0.5%</td><td>29</td><td>Mississippi</td><td>293,000,000</td><td>1.0%</td></tr>
<tr><td>9</td><td>New Jersey</td><td>938,000,000</td><td>3.2%</td><td>30</td><td>Iowa</td><td>248,000,000</td><td>0.8%</td></tr>
<tr><td>38</td><td>New Mexico</td><td>143,000,000</td><td>0.5%</td><td>31</td><td>Arkansas</td><td>242,000,000</td><td>0.8%</td></tr>
<tr><td>1</td><td>New York</td><td>4,292,000,000</td><td>14.7%</td><td>32</td><td>Kansas</td><td>220,000,000</td><td>0.8%</td></tr>
<tr><td>10</td><td>North Carolina</td><td>934,000,000</td><td>3.2%</td><td>33</td><td>Maine</td><td>188,000,000</td><td>0.6%</td></tr>
<tr><td>48</td><td>North Dakota</td><td>20,000,000</td><td>0.1%</td><td>34</td><td>West Virginia</td><td>187,000,000</td><td>0.6%</td></tr>
<tr><td>5</td><td>Ohio</td><td>1,224,000,000</td><td>4.2%</td><td>35</td><td>Nevada</td><td>180,000,000</td><td>0.6%</td></tr>
<tr><td>23</td><td>Oklahoma</td><td>391,000,000</td><td>1.3%</td><td>36</td><td>Oregon</td><td>151,000,000</td><td>0.5%</td></tr>
<tr><td>36</td><td>Oregon</td><td>151,000,000</td><td>0.5%</td><td>37</td><td>New Hampshire</td><td>145,000,000</td><td>0.5%</td></tr>
<tr><td>6</td><td>Pennsylvania</td><td>1,109,000,000</td><td>3.8%</td><td>38</td><td>New Mexico</td><td>143,000,000</td><td>0.5%</td></tr>
<tr><td>40</td><td>Rhode Island</td><td>134,000,000</td><td>0.5%</td><td>39</td><td>Utah</td><td>136,000,000</td><td>0.5%</td></tr>
<tr><td>23</td><td>South Carolina</td><td>391,000,000</td><td>1.3%</td><td>40</td><td>Rhode Island</td><td>134,000,000</td><td>0.5%</td></tr>
<tr><td>49</td><td>South Dakota</td><td>11,000,000</td><td>0.0%</td><td>41</td><td>Delaware</td><td>110,000,000</td><td>0.4%</td></tr>
<tr><td>14</td><td>Tennessee</td><td>617,000,000</td><td>2.1%</td><td>42</td><td>Nebraska</td><td>71,000,000</td><td>0.2%</td></tr>
<tr><td>2</td><td>Texas</td><td>2,862,000,000</td><td>9.8%</td><td>43</td><td>Vermont</td><td>68,000,000</td><td>0.2%</td></tr>
<tr><td>39</td><td>Utah</td><td>136,000,000</td><td>0.5%</td><td>44</td><td>Hawaii</td><td>60,000,000</td><td>0.2%</td></tr>
<tr><td>43</td><td>Vermont</td><td>68,000,000</td><td>0.2%</td><td>44</td><td>Idaho</td><td>60,000,000</td><td>0.2%</td></tr>
<tr><td>18</td><td>Virginia</td><td>484,000,000</td><td>1.7%</td><td>46</td><td>Montana</td><td>56,000,000</td><td>0.2%</td></tr>
<tr><td>26</td><td>Washington</td><td>365,000,000</td><td>1.2%</td><td>47</td><td>Wyoming</td><td>24,000,000</td><td>0.1%</td></tr>
<tr><td>34</td><td>West Virginia</td><td>187,000,000</td><td>0.6%</td><td>48</td><td>North Dakota</td><td>20,000,000</td><td>0.1%</td></tr>
<tr><td>22</td><td>Wisconsin</td><td>393,000,000</td><td>1.3%</td><td>49</td><td>South Dakota</td><td>11,000,000</td><td>0.0%</td></tr>
<tr><td>47</td><td>Wyoming</td><td>24,000,000</td><td>0.1%</td><td>50</td><td>Alaska</td><td>9,000,000</td><td>0.0%</td></tr>
<tr><td></td><td></td><td></td><td></td><td></td><td>District of Columbia</td><td>54,000,000</td><td>0.2%</td></tr>
</table>

Source: U.S. Department of Health and Human Services, Centers for Medicare and Medicaid Services
    "State Health Care Expenditures" (http://www.cms.hhs.gov/statistics/nhe/)
*By state of provider. Includes spending for services and products by public and private freestanding home health agencies. Excludes home health care services provided by hospital-based agencies which are included in hospital expenditures. Revised figures.

Percent of Total Personal Health Care Expenditures
Spent on Home Health Care in 1998
National Percent = 2.9%*

ALPHA ORDER

RANK	STATE	PERCENT
16	Alabama	3.0
49	Alaska	0.4
32	Arizona	2.2
22	Arkansas	2.8
43	California	1.7
27	Colorado	2.4
3	Connecticut	3.9
7	Delaware	3.6
6	Florida	3.7
16	Georgia	3.0
46	Hawaii	1.3
42	Idaho	1.8
32	Illinois	2.2
37	Indiana	2.0
27	Iowa	2.4
27	Kansas	2.4
9	Kentucky	3.5
4	Louisiana	3.8
4	Maine	3.8
37	Maryland	2.0
11	Massachusetts	3.3
27	Michigan	2.4
36	Minnesota	2.1
13	Mississippi	3.2
24	Missouri	2.7
37	Montana	2.0
47	Nebraska	1.2
13	Nevada	3.2
15	New Hampshire	3.1
20	New Jersey	2.9
24	New Mexico	2.7
1	New York	5.0
9	North Carolina	3.5
48	North Dakota	0.7
20	Ohio	2.9
7	Oklahoma	3.6
45	Oregon	1.4
32	Pennsylvania	2.2
16	Rhode Island	3.0
16	South Carolina	3.0
49	South Dakota	0.4
22	Tennessee	2.8
2	Texas	4.2
31	Utah	2.3
11	Vermont	3.3
32	Virginia	2.2
41	Washington	1.9
24	West Virginia	2.7
37	Wisconsin	2.0
43	Wyoming	1.7

RANK ORDER

RANK	STATE	PERCENT
1	New York	5.0
2	Texas	4.2
3	Connecticut	3.9
4	Louisiana	3.8
4	Maine	3.8
6	Florida	3.7
7	Delaware	3.6
7	Oklahoma	3.6
9	Kentucky	3.5
9	North Carolina	3.5
11	Massachusetts	3.3
11	Vermont	3.3
13	Mississippi	3.2
13	Nevada	3.2
15	New Hampshire	3.1
16	Alabama	3.0
16	Georgia	3.0
16	Rhode Island	3.0
16	South Carolina	3.0
20	New Jersey	2.9
20	Ohio	2.9
22	Arkansas	2.8
22	Tennessee	2.8
24	Missouri	2.7
24	New Mexico	2.7
24	West Virginia	2.7
27	Colorado	2.4
27	Iowa	2.4
27	Kansas	2.4
27	Michigan	2.4
31	Utah	2.3
32	Arizona	2.2
32	Illinois	2.2
32	Pennsylvania	2.2
32	Virginia	2.2
36	Minnesota	2.1
37	Indiana	2.0
37	Maryland	2.0
37	Montana	2.0
37	Wisconsin	2.0
41	Washington	1.9
42	Idaho	1.8
43	California	1.7
43	Wyoming	1.7
45	Oregon	1.4
46	Hawaii	1.3
47	Nebraska	1.2
48	North Dakota	0.7
49	Alaska	0.4
49	South Dakota	0.4
	District of Columbia	1.3

Source: MQ Press using data from U.S. Dept of Health & Human Services, Centers for Medicare and Medicaid Services
"State Health Care Expenditures" (http://www.cms.hhs.gov/statistics/nhel)
*By state of provider. Includes spending for services and products by public and private freestanding home health agencies. Excludes home health care services provided by hospital-based agencies which are included in hospital expenditures. Revised figures.

Per Capita Expenditures for Home Health Care in 1998

National Per Capita = $108*

ALPHA ORDER

ALPHA ORDER

RANK	STATE	PER CAPITA
18	Alabama	$108
49	Alaska	15
36	Arizona	71
25	Arkansas	95
42	California	60
31	Colorado	82
2	Connecticut	183
6	Delaware	148
5	Florida	149
19	Georgia	106
43	Hawaii	50
45	Idaho	49
33	Illinois	81
38	Indiana	70
28	Iowa	87
30	Kansas	83
10	Kentucky	129
8	Louisiana	144
4	Maine	151
34	Maryland	76
3	Massachusetts	163
29	Michigan	86
27	Minnesota	89
19	Mississippi	106
21	Missouri	104
40	Montana	64
47	Nebraska	43
22	Nevada	103
12	New Hampshire	122
14	New Jersey	116
31	New Mexico	82
1	New York	236
11	North Carolina	124
48	North Dakota	31
17	Ohio	109
13	Oklahoma	117
46	Oregon	46
26	Pennsylvania	92
9	Rhode Island	136
24	South Carolina	102
49	South Dakota	15
16	Tennessee	114
7	Texas	145
39	Utah	65
15	Vermont	115
36	Virginia	71
40	Washington	64
22	West Virginia	103
35	Wisconsin	75
43	Wyoming	50

RANK ORDER

RANK	STATE	PER CAPITA
1	New York	$236
2	Connecticut	183
3	Massachusetts	163
4	Maine	151
5	Florida	149
6	Delaware	148
7	Texas	145
8	Louisiana	144
9	Rhode Island	136
10	Kentucky	129
11	North Carolina	124
12	New Hampshire	122
13	Oklahoma	117
14	New Jersey	116
15	Vermont	115
16	Tennessee	114
17	Ohio	109
18	Alabama	108
19	Georgia	106
19	Mississippi	106
21	Missouri	104
22	Nevada	103
22	West Virginia	103
24	South Carolina	102
25	Arkansas	95
26	Pennsylvania	92
27	Minnesota	89
28	Iowa	87
29	Michigan	86
30	Kansas	83
31	Colorado	82
31	New Mexico	82
33	Illinois	81
34	Maryland	76
35	Wisconsin	75
36	Arizona	71
36	Virginia	71
38	Indiana	70
39	Utah	65
40	Montana	64
40	Washington	64
42	California	60
43	Hawaii	50
43	Wyoming	50
45	Idaho	49
46	Oregon	46
47	Nebraska	43
48	North Dakota	31
49	Alaska	15
49	South Dakota	15

District of Columbia   104

Source: MQ Press using data from U.S. Dept of Health & Human Services, Centers for Medicare and Medicaid Services "State Health Care Expenditures" (http://www.cms.hhs.gov/statistics/nhe/)

*By state of provider. Includes spending for services and products by public and private freestanding home health agencies. Excludes home health care services provided by hospital-based agencies which are included in hospital expenditures. Revised figures.

Expenditures for Vision Products and Other Medical Durables in 1998

National Total = $15,499,000,000*

ALPHA ORDER

RANK	STATE	EXPENDITURES	% of USA
25	Alabama	$186,000,000	1.2%
46	Alaska	38,000,000	0.2%
22	Arizona	267,000,000	1.7%
36	Arkansas	87,000,000	0.6%
1	California	1,656,000,000	10.7%
18	Colorado	323,000,000	2.1%
23	Connecticut	231,000,000	1.5%
43	Delaware	49,000,000	0.3%
2	Florida	1,184,000,000	7.6%
10	Georgia	432,000,000	2.8%
38	Hawaii	78,000,000	0.5%
41	Idaho	59,000,000	0.4%
6	Illinois	662,000,000	4.3%
17	Indiana	328,000,000	2.1%
27	Iowa	177,000,000	1.1%
31	Kansas	128,000,000	0.8%
26	Kentucky	185,000,000	1.2%
24	Louisiana	198,000,000	1.3%
42	Maine	58,000,000	0.4%
19	Maryland	322,000,000	2.1%
12	Massachusetts	347,000,000	2.2%
8	Michigan	626,000,000	4.0%
14	Minnesota	343,000,000	2.2%
35	Mississippi	93,000,000	0.6%
20	Missouri	280,000,000	1.8%
44	Montana	41,000,000	0.3%
34	Nebraska	119,000,000	0.8%
32	Nevada	123,000,000	0.8%
40	New Hampshire	68,000,000	0.4%
9	New Jersey	552,000,000	3.6%
39	New Mexico	77,000,000	0.5%
4	New York	1,099,000,000	7.1%
15	North Carolina	338,000,000	2.2%
47	North Dakota	35,000,000	0.2%
7	Ohio	647,000,000	4.2%
30	Oklahoma	142,000,000	0.9%
28	Oregon	169,000,000	1.1%
5	Pennsylvania	688,000,000	4.4%
47	Rhode Island	35,000,000	0.2%
29	South Carolina	168,000,000	1.1%
45	South Dakota	40,000,000	0.3%
21	Tennessee	271,000,000	1.7%
3	Texas	1,176,000,000	7.6%
33	Utah	121,000,000	0.8%
49	Vermont	29,000,000	0.2%
11	Virginia	392,000,000	2.5%
13	Washington	346,000,000	2.2%
36	West Virginia	87,000,000	0.6%
16	Wisconsin	333,000,000	2.1%
50	Wyoming	22,000,000	0.1%

RANK ORDER

RANK	STATE	EXPENDITURES	% of USA
1	California	$1,656,000,000	10.7%
2	Florida	1,184,000,000	7.6%
3	Texas	1,176,000,000	7.6%
4	New York	1,099,000,000	7.1%
5	Pennsylvania	688,000,000	4.4%
6	Illinois	662,000,000	4.3%
7	Ohio	647,000,000	4.2%
8	Michigan	626,000,000	4.0%
9	New Jersey	552,000,000	3.6%
10	Georgia	432,000,000	2.8%
11	Virginia	392,000,000	2.5%
12	Massachusetts	347,000,000	2.2%
13	Washington	346,000,000	2.2%
14	Minnesota	343,000,000	2.2%
15	North Carolina	338,000,000	2.2%
16	Wisconsin	333,000,000	2.1%
17	Indiana	328,000,000	2.1%
18	Colorado	323,000,000	2.1%
19	Maryland	322,000,000	2.1%
20	Missouri	280,000,000	1.8%
21	Tennessee	271,000,000	1.7%
22	Arizona	267,000,000	1.7%
23	Connecticut	231,000,000	1.5%
24	Louisiana	198,000,000	1.3%
25	Alabama	186,000,000	1.2%
26	Kentucky	185,000,000	1.2%
27	Iowa	177,000,000	1.1%
28	Oregon	169,000,000	1.1%
29	South Carolina	168,000,000	1.1%
30	Oklahoma	142,000,000	0.9%
31	Kansas	128,000,000	0.8%
32	Nevada	123,000,000	0.8%
33	Utah	121,000,000	0.8%
34	Nebraska	119,000,000	0.8%
35	Mississippi	93,000,000	0.6%
36	Arkansas	87,000,000	0.6%
36	West Virginia	87,000,000	0.6%
38	Hawaii	78,000,000	0.5%
39	New Mexico	77,000,000	0.5%
40	New Hampshire	68,000,000	0.4%
41	Idaho	59,000,000	0.4%
42	Maine	58,000,000	0.4%
43	Delaware	49,000,000	0.3%
44	Montana	41,000,000	0.3%
45	South Dakota	40,000,000	0.3%
46	Alaska	38,000,000	0.2%
47	North Dakota	35,000,000	0.2%
47	Rhode Island	35,000,000	0.2%
49	Vermont	29,000,000	0.2%
50	Wyoming	22,000,000	0.1%
	District of Columbia	42,000,000	0.3%

*Source: U.S. Department of Health and Human Services, Centers for Medicare and Medicaid Services
"State Health Care Expenditures" (http://www.cms.hhs.gov/statistics/nhe/)*
By state of provider. Includes eyeglasses, hearing aids, surgical appliances and supplies, bulk and cylinder oxygen and medical equipment rentals. Revised figures.

Percent of Total Personal Health Care Expenditures
Spent on Vision Products and Other Medical Durables in 1998
National Percent = 1.5%*

ALPHA ORDER

RANK	STATE	PERCENT
42	Alabama	1.2
6	Alaska	1.8
6	Arizona	1.8
48	Arkansas	1.0
22	California	1.5
1	Colorado	2.4
22	Connecticut	1.5
19	Delaware	1.6
3	Florida	2.0
19	Georgia	1.6
11	Hawaii	1.7
11	Idaho	1.7
22	Illinois	1.5
22	Indiana	1.5
11	Iowa	1.7
29	Kansas	1.4
35	Kentucky	1.3
42	Louisiana	1.2
42	Maine	1.2
11	Maryland	1.7
47	Massachusetts	1.1
6	Michigan	1.8
11	Minnesota	1.7
48	Mississippi	1.0
35	Missouri	1.3
29	Montana	1.4
5	Nebraska	1.9
2	Nevada	2.2
22	New Hampshire	1.5
11	New Jersey	1.7
29	New Mexico	1.4
35	New York	1.3
35	North Carolina	1.3
35	North Dakota	1.3
22	Ohio	1.5
35	Oklahoma	1.3
22	Oregon	1.5
29	Pennsylvania	1.4
50	Rhode Island	0.8
35	South Carolina	1.3
29	South Dakota	1.4
42	Tennessee	1.2
11	Texas	1.7
3	Utah	2.0
29	Vermont	1.4
6	Virginia	1.8
6	Washington	1.8
42	West Virginia	1.2
11	Wisconsin	1.7
19	Wyoming	1.6

RANK ORDER

RANK	STATE	PERCENT
1	Colorado	2.4
2	Nevada	2.2
3	Florida	2.0
3	Utah	2.0
5	Nebraska	1.9
6	Alaska	1.8
6	Arizona	1.8
6	Michigan	1.8
6	Virginia	1.8
6	Washington	1.8
11	Hawaii	1.7
11	Idaho	1.7
11	Iowa	1.7
11	Maryland	1.7
11	Minnesota	1.7
11	New Jersey	1.7
11	Texas	1.7
11	Wisconsin	1.7
19	Delaware	1.6
19	Georgia	1.6
19	Wyoming	1.6
22	California	1.5
22	Connecticut	1.5
22	Illinois	1.5
22	Indiana	1.5
22	New Hampshire	1.5
22	Ohio	1.5
22	Oregon	1.5
29	Kansas	1.4
29	Montana	1.4
29	New Mexico	1.4
29	Pennsylvania	1.4
29	South Dakota	1.4
29	Vermont	1.4
35	Kentucky	1.3
35	Missouri	1.3
35	New York	1.3
35	North Carolina	1.3
35	North Dakota	1.3
35	Oklahoma	1.3
35	South Carolina	1.3
42	Alabama	1.2
42	Louisiana	1.2
42	Maine	1.2
42	Tennessee	1.2
42	West Virginia	1.2
47	Massachusetts	1.1
48	Arkansas	1.0
48	Mississippi	1.0
50	Rhode Island	0.8

	District of Columbia	1.0

Source: MQ Press using data from U.S. Dept of Health & Human Services, Centers for Medicare and Medicaid Services
"State Health Care Expenditures" (http://www.cms.hhs.gov/statistics/nhe/)
*By state of provider. Includes eyeglasses, hearing aids, surgical appliances and supplies, bulk and cylinder oxygen and medical equipment rentals. Revised figures.

Per Capita Expenditures for Vision Products and Other Medical Durables in 1998

National Per Capita = $57*

ALPHA ORDER				RANK ORDER		
RANK	STATE	PER CAPITA		RANK	STATE	PER CAPITA
46	Alabama	$43		1	Colorado	$81
13	Alaska	62		2	Florida	79
21	Arizona	57		3	Minnesota	73
49	Arkansas	34		4	Nebraska	72
30	California	51		5	Connecticut	71
1	Colorado	81		5	Nevada	71
5	Connecticut	71		7	New Jersey	68
8	Delaware	66		8	Delaware	66
2	Florida	79		8	Hawaii	66
21	Georgia	57		10	Michigan	64
8	Hawaii	66		10	Wisconsin	64
36	Idaho	48		12	Maryland	63
27	Illinois	55		13	Alaska	62
25	Indiana	56		13	Iowa	62
13	Iowa	62		15	New York	61
34	Kansas	49		15	Washington	61
38	Kentucky	47		17	Texas	60
42	Louisiana	45		18	Ohio	58
40	Maine	46		18	Utah	58
12	Maryland	63		18	Virginia	58
25	Massachusetts	56		21	Arizona	57
10	Michigan	64		21	Georgia	57
3	Minnesota	73		21	New Hampshire	57
49	Mississippi	34		21	Pennsylvania	57
30	Missouri	51		25	Indiana	56
38	Montana	47		25	Massachusetts	56
4	Nebraska	72		27	Illinois	55
5	Nevada	71		27	North Dakota	55
21	New Hampshire	57		27	South Dakota	55
7	New Jersey	68		30	California	51
44	New Mexico	44		30	Missouri	51
15	New York	61		30	Oregon	51
42	North Carolina	45		33	Tennessee	50
27	North Dakota	55		34	Kansas	49
18	Ohio	58		34	Vermont	49
46	Oklahoma	43		36	Idaho	48
30	Oregon	51		36	West Virginia	48
21	Pennsylvania	57		38	Kentucky	47
48	Rhode Island	35		38	Montana	47
44	South Carolina	44		40	Maine	46
27	South Dakota	55		40	Wyoming	46
33	Tennessee	50		42	Louisiana	45
17	Texas	60		42	North Carolina	45
18	Utah	58		44	New Mexico	44
34	Vermont	49		44	South Carolina	44
18	Virginia	58		46	Alabama	43
15	Washington	61		46	Oklahoma	43
36	West Virginia	48		48	Rhode Island	35
10	Wisconsin	64		49	Arkansas	34
40	Wyoming	46		49	Mississippi	34
					District of Columbia	81

Source: MQ Press using data from U.S. Dept of Health & Human Services, Centers for Medicare and Medicaid Services
"State Health Care Expenditures" (http://www.cms.hhs.gov/statistics/nhe/)
*By state of provider. Includes eyeglasses, hearing aids, surgical appliances and supplies, bulk and cylinder oxygen and medical equipment rentals. Revised figures.

Expenditures for Nursing Home Care in 1998

National Total = $87,826,000,000*

ALPHA ORDER

RANK	STATE	EXPENDITURES	% of USA
25	Alabama	$1,064,000,000	1.2%
50	Alaska	42,000,000	0.0%
30	Arizona	839,000,000	1.0%
32	Arkansas	776,000,000	0.9%
3	California	5,626,000,000	6.4%
29	Colorado	904,000,000	1.0%
13	Connecticut	2,264,000,000	2.6%
40	Delaware	290,000,000	0.3%
5	Florida	4,880,000,000	5.6%
20	Georgia	1,545,000,000	1.8%
46	Hawaii	204,000,000	0.2%
43	Idaho	264,000,000	0.3%
7	Illinois	3,924,000,000	4.5%
12	Indiana	2,337,000,000	2.7%
24	Iowa	1,186,000,000	1.4%
27	Kansas	920,000,000	1.0%
22	Kentucky	1,283,000,000	1.5%
23	Louisiana	1,248,000,000	1.4%
36	Maine	476,000,000	0.5%
18	Maryland	1,695,000,000	1.9%
8	Massachusetts	3,568,000,000	4.1%
10	Michigan	2,459,000,000	2.8%
17	Minnesota	1,964,000,000	2.2%
34	Mississippi	687,000,000	0.8%
15	Missouri	2,002,000,000	2.3%
45	Montana	222,000,000	0.3%
33	Nebraska	697,000,000	0.8%
48	Nevada	164,000,000	0.2%
38	New Hampshire	425,000,000	0.5%
9	New Jersey	3,233,000,000	3.7%
44	New Mexico	257,000,000	0.3%
1	New York	10,586,000,000	12.1%
11	North Carolina	2,347,000,000	2.7%
41	North Dakota	287,000,000	0.3%
4	Ohio	4,978,000,000	5.7%
26	Oklahoma	954,000,000	1.1%
31	Oregon	838,000,000	1.0%
2	Pennsylvania	5,883,000,000	6.7%
37	Rhode Island	468,000,000	0.5%
28	South Carolina	907,000,000	1.0%
42	South Dakota	286,000,000	0.3%
16	Tennessee	2,001,000,000	2.3%
6	Texas	4,346,000,000	4.9%
39	Utah	300,000,000	0.3%
47	Vermont	177,000,000	0.2%
19	Virginia	1,546,000,000	1.8%
21	Washington	1,492,000,000	1.7%
35	West Virginia	515,000,000	0.6%
14	Wisconsin	2,110,000,000	2.4%
49	Wyoming	113,000,000	0.1%

RANK ORDER

RANK	STATE	EXPENDITURES	% of USA
1	New York	$10,586,000,000	12.1%
2	Pennsylvania	5,883,000,000	6.7%
3	California	5,626,000,000	6.4%
4	Ohio	4,978,000,000	5.7%
5	Florida	4,880,000,000	5.6%
6	Texas	4,346,000,000	4.9%
7	Illinois	3,924,000,000	4.5%
8	Massachusetts	3,568,000,000	4.1%
9	New Jersey	3,233,000,000	3.7%
10	Michigan	2,459,000,000	2.8%
11	North Carolina	2,347,000,000	2.7%
12	Indiana	2,337,000,000	2.7%
13	Connecticut	2,264,000,000	2.6%
14	Wisconsin	2,110,000,000	2.4%
15	Missouri	2,002,000,000	2.3%
16	Tennessee	2,001,000,000	2.3%
17	Minnesota	1,964,000,000	2.2%
18	Maryland	1,695,000,000	1.9%
19	Virginia	1,546,000,000	1.8%
20	Georgia	1,545,000,000	1.8%
21	Washington	1,492,000,000	1.7%
22	Kentucky	1,283,000,000	1.5%
23	Louisiana	1,248,000,000	1.4%
24	Iowa	1,186,000,000	1.4%
25	Alabama	1,064,000,000	1.2%
26	Oklahoma	954,000,000	1.1%
27	Kansas	920,000,000	1.0%
28	South Carolina	907,000,000	1.0%
29	Colorado	904,000,000	1.0%
30	Arizona	839,000,000	1.0%
31	Oregon	838,000,000	1.0%
32	Arkansas	776,000,000	0.9%
33	Nebraska	697,000,000	0.8%
34	Mississippi	687,000,000	0.8%
35	West Virginia	515,000,000	0.6%
36	Maine	476,000,000	0.5%
37	Rhode Island	468,000,000	0.5%
38	New Hampshire	425,000,000	0.5%
39	Utah	300,000,000	0.3%
40	Delaware	290,000,000	0.3%
41	North Dakota	287,000,000	0.3%
42	South Dakota	286,000,000	0.3%
43	Idaho	264,000,000	0.3%
44	New Mexico	257,000,000	0.3%
45	Montana	222,000,000	0.3%
46	Hawaii	204,000,000	0.2%
47	Vermont	177,000,000	0.2%
48	Nevada	164,000,000	0.2%
49	Wyoming	113,000,000	0.1%
50	Alaska	42,000,000	0.0%
	District of Columbia	245,000,000	0.3%

Source: U.S. Department of Health and Human Services, Centers for Medicare and Medicaid Services
"State Health Care Expenditures" (http://www.cms.hhs.gov/statistics/nhe/)
By state of provider. Includes freestanding nursing and personal-care facilities. Includes Medicare- and Medicaid-certified skilled nursing and intermediate care facilities as well as facilities that are not certified. Excludes hospital-based facilities as they are counted in hospital care expenditures. Revised figures.

Percent of Total Personal Health Care Expenditures
Spent on Nursing Home Care in 1998
National Percent = 8.6%*

ALPHA ORDER				RANK ORDER		
RANK	STATE	PERCENT		RANK	STATE	PERCENT
40	Alabama	6.8		1	Connecticut	14.8
50	Alaska	2.0		2	New York	12.4
44	Arizona	5.6		3	Ohio	11.9
21	Arkansas	9.1		4	Massachusetts	11.8
46	California	5.0		5	Iowa	11.6
41	Colorado	6.7		5	Pennsylvania	11.6
1	Connecticut	14.8		7	Nebraska	11.4
18	Delaware	9.4		8	Indiana	11.0
28	Florida	8.1		9	North Dakota	10.8
43	Georgia	5.7		10	Wisconsin	10.7
48	Hawaii	4.5		11	Rhode Island	10.6
31	Idaho	7.7		12	South Dakota	10.3
22	Illinois	8.9		13	Kansas	9.9
8	Indiana	11.0		13	New Jersey	9.9
5	Iowa	11.6		15	Minnesota	9.8
13	Kansas	9.9		16	Maine	9.7
22	Kentucky	8.9		17	Missouri	9.5
34	Louisiana	7.6		18	Delaware	9.4
16	Maine	9.7		19	New Hampshire	9.2
25	Maryland	8.7		19	Tennessee	9.2
4	Massachusetts	11.8		21	Arkansas	9.1
37	Michigan	7.0		22	Illinois	8.9
15	Minnesota	9.8		22	Kentucky	8.9
34	Mississippi	7.6		24	Oklahoma	8.8
17	Missouri	9.5		25	Maryland	8.7
30	Montana	7.8		25	North Carolina	8.7
7	Nebraska	11.4		27	Vermont	8.6
49	Nevada	2.9		28	Florida	8.1
19	New Hampshire	9.2		28	Wyoming	8.1
13	New Jersey	9.9		30	Montana	7.8
47	New Mexico	4.8		31	Idaho	7.7
2	New York	12.4		31	Oregon	7.7
25	North Carolina	8.7		31	Washington	7.7
9	North Dakota	10.8		34	Louisiana	7.6
3	Ohio	11.9		34	Mississippi	7.6
24	Oklahoma	8.8		36	West Virginia	7.3
31	Oregon	7.7		37	Michigan	7.0
5	Pennsylvania	11.6		37	South Carolina	7.0
11	Rhode Island	10.6		37	Virginia	7.0
37	South Carolina	7.0		40	Alabama	6.8
12	South Dakota	10.3		41	Colorado	6.7
19	Tennessee	9.2		42	Texas	6.4
42	Texas	6.4		43	Georgia	5.7
45	Utah	5.1		44	Arizona	5.6
27	Vermont	8.6		45	Utah	5.1
37	Virginia	7.0		46	California	5.0
31	Washington	7.7		47	New Mexico	4.8
36	West Virginia	7.3		48	Hawaii	4.5
10	Wisconsin	10.7		49	Nevada	2.9
28	Wyoming	8.1		50	Alaska	2.0

District of Columbia   5.7

Source: MQ Press using data from U.S. Dept of Health & Human Services, Centers for Medicare and Medicaid Services
"State Health Care Expenditures" (http://www.cms.hhs.gov/statistics/nhe/)
*By state of provider. Includes freestanding nursing and personal-care facilities. Includes Medicare- and Medicaid-certified skilled nursing and intermediate care facilities as well as facilities that are not certified. Excludes hospital-based facilities as they are counted in hospital care expenditures. Revised figures.

Per Capita Expenditures for Nursing Home Care in 1998

National Per Capita = $325*

<table>
<tr><td colspan="3">ALPHA ORDER</td><td colspan="3">RANK ORDER</td></tr>
<tr><td>RANK</td><td>STATE</td><td>PER CAPITA</td><td>RANK</td><td>STATE</td><td>PER CAPITA</td></tr>
<tr><td>36</td><td>Alabama</td><td>$245</td><td>1</td><td>Connecticut</td><td>$692</td></tr>
<tr><td>50</td><td>Alaska</td><td>68</td><td>2</td><td>New York</td><td>583</td></tr>
<tr><td>44</td><td>Arizona</td><td>180</td><td>3</td><td>Massachusetts</td><td>581</td></tr>
<tr><td>26</td><td>Arkansas</td><td>306</td><td>4</td><td>Pennsylvania</td><td>490</td></tr>
<tr><td>45</td><td>California</td><td>172</td><td>5</td><td>Rhode Island</td><td>474</td></tr>
<tr><td>39</td><td>Colorado</td><td>228</td><td>6</td><td>North Dakota</td><td>450</td></tr>
<tr><td>1</td><td>Connecticut</td><td>692</td><td>7</td><td>Ohio</td><td>443</td></tr>
<tr><td>15</td><td>Delaware</td><td>390</td><td>8</td><td>Nebraska</td><td>420</td></tr>
<tr><td>22</td><td>Florida</td><td>327</td><td>9</td><td>Minnesota</td><td>416</td></tr>
<tr><td>43</td><td>Georgia</td><td>202</td><td>10</td><td>Iowa</td><td>415</td></tr>
<tr><td>46</td><td>Hawaii</td><td>171</td><td>11</td><td>Wisconsin</td><td>404</td></tr>
<tr><td>42</td><td>Idaho</td><td>214</td><td>12</td><td>New Jersey</td><td>399</td></tr>
<tr><td>24</td><td>Illinois</td><td>325</td><td>13</td><td>Indiana</td><td>396</td></tr>
<tr><td>13</td><td>Indiana</td><td>396</td><td>14</td><td>South Dakota</td><td>391</td></tr>
<tr><td>10</td><td>Iowa</td><td>415</td><td>15</td><td>Delaware</td><td>390</td></tr>
<tr><td>20</td><td>Kansas</td><td>349</td><td>16</td><td>Maine</td><td>382</td></tr>
<tr><td>23</td><td>Kentucky</td><td>326</td><td>17</td><td>Missouri</td><td>368</td></tr>
<tr><td>28</td><td>Louisiana</td><td>286</td><td>17</td><td>Tennessee</td><td>368</td></tr>
<tr><td>16</td><td>Maine</td><td>382</td><td>19</td><td>New Hampshire</td><td>358</td></tr>
<tr><td>21</td><td>Maryland</td><td>330</td><td>20</td><td>Kansas</td><td>349</td></tr>
<tr><td>3</td><td>Massachusetts</td><td>581</td><td>21</td><td>Maryland</td><td>330</td></tr>
<tr><td>34</td><td>Michigan</td><td>250</td><td>22</td><td>Florida</td><td>327</td></tr>
<tr><td>9</td><td>Minnesota</td><td>416</td><td>23</td><td>Kentucky</td><td>326</td></tr>
<tr><td>34</td><td>Mississippi</td><td>250</td><td>24</td><td>Illinois</td><td>325</td></tr>
<tr><td>17</td><td>Missouri</td><td>368</td><td>25</td><td>North Carolina</td><td>311</td></tr>
<tr><td>33</td><td>Montana</td><td>252</td><td>26</td><td>Arkansas</td><td>306</td></tr>
<tr><td>8</td><td>Nebraska</td><td>420</td><td>27</td><td>Vermont</td><td>300</td></tr>
<tr><td>49</td><td>Nevada</td><td>94</td><td>28</td><td>Louisiana</td><td>286</td></tr>
<tr><td>19</td><td>New Hampshire</td><td>358</td><td>28</td><td>Oklahoma</td><td>286</td></tr>
<tr><td>12</td><td>New Jersey</td><td>399</td><td>30</td><td>West Virginia</td><td>284</td></tr>
<tr><td>47</td><td>New Mexico</td><td>148</td><td>31</td><td>Washington</td><td>262</td></tr>
<tr><td>2</td><td>New York</td><td>583</td><td>32</td><td>Oregon</td><td>255</td></tr>
<tr><td>25</td><td>North Carolina</td><td>311</td><td>33</td><td>Montana</td><td>252</td></tr>
<tr><td>6</td><td>North Dakota</td><td>450</td><td>34</td><td>Michigan</td><td>250</td></tr>
<tr><td>7</td><td>Ohio</td><td>443</td><td>34</td><td>Mississippi</td><td>250</td></tr>
<tr><td>28</td><td>Oklahoma</td><td>286</td><td>36</td><td>Alabama</td><td>245</td></tr>
<tr><td>32</td><td>Oregon</td><td>255</td><td>37</td><td>South Carolina</td><td>236</td></tr>
<tr><td>4</td><td>Pennsylvania</td><td>490</td><td>38</td><td>Wyoming</td><td>235</td></tr>
<tr><td>5</td><td>Rhode Island</td><td>474</td><td>39</td><td>Colorado</td><td>228</td></tr>
<tr><td>37</td><td>South Carolina</td><td>236</td><td>39</td><td>Virginia</td><td>228</td></tr>
<tr><td>14</td><td>South Dakota</td><td>391</td><td>41</td><td>Texas</td><td>220</td></tr>
<tr><td>17</td><td>Tennessee</td><td>368</td><td>42</td><td>Idaho</td><td>214</td></tr>
<tr><td>41</td><td>Texas</td><td>220</td><td>43</td><td>Georgia</td><td>202</td></tr>
<tr><td>48</td><td>Utah</td><td>143</td><td>44</td><td>Arizona</td><td>180</td></tr>
<tr><td>27</td><td>Vermont</td><td>300</td><td>45</td><td>California</td><td>172</td></tr>
<tr><td>39</td><td>Virginia</td><td>228</td><td>46</td><td>Hawaii</td><td>171</td></tr>
<tr><td>31</td><td>Washington</td><td>262</td><td>47</td><td>New Mexico</td><td>148</td></tr>
<tr><td>30</td><td>West Virginia</td><td>284</td><td>48</td><td>Utah</td><td>143</td></tr>
<tr><td>11</td><td>Wisconsin</td><td>404</td><td>49</td><td>Nevada</td><td>94</td></tr>
<tr><td>38</td><td>Wyoming</td><td>235</td><td>50</td><td>Alaska</td><td>68</td></tr>
<tr><td></td><td></td><td></td><td></td><td>District of Columbia</td><td>470</td></tr>
</table>

Source: MQ Press using data from U.S. Dept of Health & Human Services, Centers for Medicare and Medicaid Services
"State Health Care Expenditures" (http://www.cms.hhs.gov/statistics/nhe/)
*By state of provider. Includes freestanding nursing and personal-care facilities. Includes Medicare- and
Medicaid-certified skilled nursing and intermediate care facilities as well as facilities that are not certified.
Excludes hospital-based facilities as they are counted in hospital care expenditures. Revised figures.

State Government Expenditures for Hospitals in 2001

National Total = $34,538,400,000*

ALPHA ORDER

RANK	STATE	EXPENDITURES	% of USA
12	Alabama	$1,074,849,000	3.1%
49	Alaska	18,734,000	0.1%
39	Arizona	84,634,000	0.2%
28	Arkansas	353,476,000	1.0%
1	California	4,121,426,000	11.9%
35	Colorado	157,390,000	0.5%
11	Connecticut	1,130,604,000	3.3%
41	Delaware	66,546,000	0.2%
30	Florida	218,976,000	0.6%
17	Georgia	745,701,000	2.2%
33	Hawaii	170,918,000	0.5%
46	Idaho	43,079,000	0.1%
15	Illinois	881,347,000	2.6%
29	Indiana	256,527,000	0.7%
18	Iowa	726,692,000	2.1%
38	Kansas	102,742,000	0.3%
23	Kentucky	490,685,000	1.4%
6	Louisiana	1,341,034,000	3.9%
47	Maine	42,739,000	0.1%
27	Maryland	365,404,000	1.1%
22	Massachusetts	510,744,000	1.5%
9	Michigan	1,247,150,000	3.6%
31	Minnesota	211,154,000	0.6%
20	Mississippi	690,264,000	2.0%
19	Missouri	711,157,000	2.1%
42	Montana	47,272,000	0.1%
32	Nebraska	177,365,000	0.5%
37	Nevada	117,135,000	0.3%
43	New Hampshire	44,227,000	0.1%
8	New Jersey	1,257,365,000	3.6%
25	New Mexico	368,272,000	1.1%
2	New York	3,281,523,000	9.5%
7	North Carolina	1,266,440,000	3.7%
44	North Dakota	44,212,000	0.1%
10	Ohio	1,198,907,000	3.5%
34	Oklahoma	166,664,000	0.5%
13	Oregon	982,096,000	2.8%
4	Pennsylvania	1,676,160,000	4.9%
36	Rhode Island	135,791,000	0.4%
16	South Carolina	847,267,000	2.5%
45	South Dakota	43,589,000	0.1%
26	Tennessee	365,594,000	1.1%
3	Texas	3,032,440,000	8.8%
24	Utah	420,128,000	1.2%
50	Vermont	9,205,000	0.0%
5	Virginia	1,667,367,000	4.8%
14	Washington	926,711,000	2.7%
40	West Virginia	74,653,000	0.2%
21	Wisconsin	593,927,000	1.7%
48	Wyoming	30,118,000	0.1%

RANK ORDER

RANK	STATE	EXPENDITURES	% of USA
1	California	$4,121,426,000	11.9%
2	New York	3,281,523,000	9.5%
3	Texas	3,032,440,000	8.8%
4	Pennsylvania	1,676,160,000	4.9%
5	Virginia	1,667,367,000	4.8%
6	Louisiana	1,341,034,000	3.9%
7	North Carolina	1,266,440,000	3.7%
8	New Jersey	1,257,365,000	3.6%
9	Michigan	1,247,150,000	3.6%
10	Ohio	1,198,907,000	3.5%
11	Connecticut	1,130,604,000	3.3%
12	Alabama	1,074,849,000	3.1%
13	Oregon	982,096,000	2.8%
14	Washington	926,711,000	2.7%
15	Illinois	881,347,000	2.6%
16	South Carolina	847,267,000	2.5%
17	Georgia	745,701,000	2.2%
18	Iowa	726,692,000	2.1%
19	Missouri	711,157,000	2.1%
20	Mississippi	690,264,000	2.0%
21	Wisconsin	593,927,000	1.7%
22	Massachusetts	510,744,000	1.5%
23	Kentucky	490,685,000	1.4%
24	Utah	420,128,000	1.2%
25	New Mexico	368,272,000	1.1%
26	Tennessee	365,594,000	1.1%
27	Maryland	365,404,000	1.1%
28	Arkansas	353,476,000	1.0%
29	Indiana	256,527,000	0.7%
30	Florida	218,976,000	0.6%
31	Minnesota	211,154,000	0.6%
32	Nebraska	177,365,000	0.5%
33	Hawaii	170,918,000	0.5%
34	Oklahoma	166,664,000	0.5%
35	Colorado	157,390,000	0.5%
36	Rhode Island	135,791,000	0.4%
37	Nevada	117,135,000	0.3%
38	Kansas	102,742,000	0.3%
39	Arizona	84,634,000	0.2%
40	West Virginia	74,653,000	0.2%
41	Delaware	66,546,000	0.2%
42	Montana	47,272,000	0.1%
43	New Hampshire	44,227,000	0.1%
44	North Dakota	44,212,000	0.1%
45	South Dakota	43,589,000	0.1%
46	Idaho	43,079,000	0.1%
47	Maine	42,739,000	0.1%
48	Wyoming	30,118,000	0.1%
49	Alaska	18,734,000	0.1%
50	Vermont	9,205,000	0.0%
	District of Columbia**	NA	NA

Source: U.S. Bureau of the Census, Governments Division
  "State Government Finances: 2001" (http://www.census.gov/govs/www/state01.html)
*Financing, construction, acquisition, maintenance or operation of hospital facilities, provision of hospital care and support of public or private hospitals.
**Not applicable.

Per Capita State Government Expenditures for Hospitals in 2001

National Per Capita = $121*

ALPHA ORDER

RANK	STATE	PER CAPITA
6	Alabama	$241
47	Alaska	30
48	Arizona	16
18	Arkansas	131
23	California	119
43	Colorado	36
1	Connecticut	329
28	Delaware	84
50	Florida	13
27	Georgia	89
16	Hawaii	140
45	Idaho	33
30	Illinois	70
39	Indiana	42
4	Iowa	248
42	Kansas	38
22	Kentucky	121
2	Louisiana	300
45	Maine	33
32	Maryland	68
29	Massachusetts	80
21	Michigan	125
39	Minnesota	42
5	Mississippi	242
20	Missouri	126
37	Montana	52
26	Nebraska	103
36	Nevada	56
44	New Hampshire	35
14	New Jersey	148
9	New Mexico	201
11	New York	172
12	North Carolina	155
31	North Dakota	69
25	Ohio	105
38	Oklahoma	48
3	Oregon	283
17	Pennsylvania	136
19	Rhode Island	128
8	South Carolina	209
35	South Dakota	57
33	Tennessee	64
15	Texas	142
10	Utah	184
49	Vermont	15
7	Virginia	232
12	Washington	155
41	West Virginia	41
24	Wisconsin	110
34	Wyoming	61

RANK ORDER

RANK	STATE	PER CAPITA
1	Connecticut	$329
2	Louisiana	300
3	Oregon	283
4	Iowa	248
5	Mississippi	242
6	Alabama	241
7	Virginia	232
8	South Carolina	209
9	New Mexico	201
10	Utah	184
11	New York	172
12	North Carolina	155
12	Washington	155
14	New Jersey	148
15	Texas	142
16	Hawaii	140
17	Pennsylvania	136
18	Arkansas	131
19	Rhode Island	128
20	Missouri	126
21	Michigan	125
22	Kentucky	121
23	California	119
24	Wisconsin	110
25	Ohio	105
26	Nebraska	103
27	Georgia	89
28	Delaware	84
29	Massachusetts	80
30	Illinois	70
31	North Dakota	69
32	Maryland	68
33	Tennessee	64
34	Wyoming	61
35	South Dakota	57
36	Nevada	56
37	Montana	52
38	Oklahoma	48
39	Indiana	42
39	Minnesota	42
41	West Virginia	41
42	Kansas	38
43	Colorado	36
44	New Hampshire	35
45	Idaho	33
45	Maine	33
47	Alaska	30
48	Arizona	16
49	Vermont	15
50	Florida	13

District of Columbia**   NA

Source: Morgan Quitno Press using data from U.S. Bureau of the Census, Governments Division
    "State Government Finances: 2001" (http://www.census.gov/govs/www/state01.html)
*Financing, construction, acquisition, maintenance or operation of hospital facilities, provision of hospital care and support of public or private hospitals.
**Not applicable.

Percent of State Government Expenditures Used for Hospitals in 2001

National Percent = 5.0%*

ALPHA ORDER

RANK	STATE	PERCENT
4	Alabama	9.6
50	Alaska	0.3
47	Arizona	0.9
20	Arkansas	5.1
16	California	5.4
40	Colorado	1.6
7	Connecticut	8.8
35	Delaware	2.1
48	Florida	0.7
23	Georgia	4.3
30	Hawaii	2.8
44	Idaho	1.4
28	Illinois	3.2
38	Indiana	1.9
6	Iowa	9.2
40	Kansas	1.6
25	Kentucky	4.1
1	Louisiana	12.6
46	Maine	1.0
31	Maryland	2.6
33	Massachusetts	2.3
18	Michigan	5.2
43	Minnesota	1.5
5	Mississippi	9.5
15	Missouri	5.8
39	Montana	1.7
23	Nebraska	4.3
27	Nevada	3.3
40	New Hampshire	1.6
14	New Jersey	5.9
12	New Mexico	6.3
13	New York	6.0
11	North Carolina	6.5
35	North Dakota	2.1
21	Ohio	4.9
31	Oklahoma	2.6
2	Oregon	10.3
18	Pennsylvania	5.2
26	Rhode Island	3.4
8	South Carolina	7.4
34	South Dakota	2.2
29	Tennessee	2.9
8	Texas	7.4
10	Utah	6.6
49	Vermont	0.4
3	Virginia	9.8
16	Washington	5.4
44	West Virginia	1.4
22	Wisconsin	4.6
37	Wyoming	2.0

RANK ORDER

RANK	STATE	PERCENT
1	Louisiana	12.6
2	Oregon	10.3
3	Virginia	9.8
4	Alabama	9.6
5	Mississippi	9.5
6	Iowa	9.2
7	Connecticut	8.8
8	South Carolina	7.4
8	Texas	7.4
10	Utah	6.6
11	North Carolina	6.5
12	New Mexico	6.3
13	New York	6.0
14	New Jersey	5.9
15	Missouri	5.8
16	California	5.4
16	Washington	5.4
18	Michigan	5.2
18	Pennsylvania	5.2
20	Arkansas	5.1
21	Ohio	4.9
22	Wisconsin	4.6
23	Georgia	4.3
23	Nebraska	4.3
25	Kentucky	4.1
26	Rhode Island	3.4
27	Nevada	3.3
28	Illinois	3.2
29	Tennessee	2.9
30	Hawaii	2.8
31	Maryland	2.6
31	Oklahoma	2.6
33	Massachusetts	2.3
34	South Dakota	2.2
35	Delaware	2.1
35	North Dakota	2.1
37	Wyoming	2.0
38	Indiana	1.9
39	Montana	1.7
40	Colorado	1.6
40	Kansas	1.6
40	New Hampshire	1.6
43	Minnesota	1.5
44	Idaho	1.4
44	West Virginia	1.4
46	Maine	1.0
47	Arizona	0.9
48	Florida	0.7
49	Vermont	0.4
50	Alaska	0.3

District of Columbia** — NA

Source: Morgan Quitno Press using data from U.S. Bureau of the Census, Governments Division
"State Government Finances: 2001" (http://www.census.gov/govs/www/state01.html)
*As a percent of direct general expenditures. Financing, construction, acquisition, maintenance or operation of hospital facilities, provision of hospital care and support of public or private hospitals.
**Not applicable.

State Government Expenditures for Health Programs in 2001

National Total = $43,716,400,000*

ALPHA ORDER

RANK	STATE	EXPENDITURES	% of USA
19	Alabama	$644,288,000	1.5%
41	Alaska	162,273,000	0.4%
12	Arizona	954,431,000	2.2%
35	Arkansas	298,356,000	0.7%
1	California	6,522,891,000	15.3%
34	Colorado	309,353,000	0.7%
21	Connecticut	549,848,000	1.3%
38	Delaware	242,769,000	0.6%
4	Florida	2,566,357,000	6.0%
13	Georgia	931,213,000	2.2%
29	Hawaii	391,234,000	0.9%
46	Idaho	103,705,000	0.2%
5	Illinois	2,331,657,000	5.5%
23	Indiana	529,616,000	1.2%
40	Iowa	223,521,000	0.5%
28	Kansas	469,867,000	1.1%
25	Kentucky	493,424,000	1.2%
27	Louisiana	471,732,000	1.1%
33	Maine	317,168,000	0.7%
11	Maryland	1,199,211,000	2.8%
6	Massachusetts	1,811,736,000	4.2%
3	Michigan	2,721,049,000	6.4%
26	Minnesota	473,095,000	1.1%
36	Mississippi	281,956,000	0.7%
20	Missouri	612,744,000	1.4%
39	Montana	233,868,000	0.5%
32	Nebraska	323,252,000	0.8%
42	Nevada	146,394,000	0.3%
44	New Hampshire	141,764,000	0.3%
15	New Jersey	905,061,000	2.1%
31	New Mexico	323,794,000	0.8%
2	New York	4,249,606,000	9.9%
14	North Carolina	922,880,000	2.2%
50	North Dakota	50,017,000	0.1%
7	Ohio	1,757,178,000	4.1%
30	Oklahoma	379,888,000	0.9%
24	Oregon	528,364,000	1.2%
9	Pennsylvania	1,655,602,000	3.9%
45	Rhode Island	137,275,000	0.3%
18	South Carolina	680,276,000	1.6%
49	South Dakota	67,183,000	0.2%
17	Tennessee	706,657,000	1.7%
8	Texas	1,725,889,000	4.0%
37	Utah	277,794,000	0.7%
48	Vermont	77,440,000	0.2%
16	Virginia	706,790,000	1.7%
10	Washington	1,313,199,000	3.1%
43	West Virginia	145,136,000	0.3%
22	Wisconsin	549,415,000	1.3%
47	Wyoming	98,184,000	0.2%

RANK ORDER

RANK	STATE	EXPENDITURES	% of USA
1	California	$6,522,891,000	15.3%
2	New York	4,249,606,000	9.9%
3	Michigan	2,721,049,000	6.4%
4	Florida	2,566,357,000	6.0%
5	Illinois	2,331,657,000	5.5%
6	Massachusetts	1,811,736,000	4.2%
7	Ohio	1,757,178,000	4.1%
8	Texas	1,725,889,000	4.0%
9	Pennsylvania	1,655,602,000	3.9%
10	Washington	1,313,199,000	3.1%
11	Maryland	1,199,211,000	2.8%
12	Arizona	954,431,000	2.2%
13	Georgia	931,213,000	2.2%
14	North Carolina	922,880,000	2.2%
15	New Jersey	905,061,000	2.1%
16	Virginia	706,790,000	1.7%
17	Tennessee	706,657,000	1.7%
18	South Carolina	680,276,000	1.6%
19	Alabama	644,288,000	1.5%
20	Missouri	612,744,000	1.4%
21	Connecticut	549,848,000	1.3%
22	Wisconsin	549,415,000	1.3%
23	Indiana	529,616,000	1.2%
24	Oregon	528,364,000	1.2%
25	Kentucky	493,424,000	1.2%
26	Minnesota	473,095,000	1.1%
27	Louisiana	471,732,000	1.1%
28	Kansas	469,867,000	1.1%
29	Hawaii	391,234,000	0.9%
30	Oklahoma	379,888,000	0.9%
31	New Mexico	323,794,000	0.8%
32	Nebraska	323,252,000	0.8%
33	Maine	317,168,000	0.7%
34	Colorado	309,353,000	0.7%
35	Arkansas	298,356,000	0.7%
36	Mississippi	281,956,000	0.7%
37	Utah	277,794,000	0.7%
38	Delaware	242,769,000	0.6%
39	Montana	233,868,000	0.5%
40	Iowa	223,521,000	0.5%
41	Alaska	162,273,000	0.4%
42	Nevada	146,394,000	0.3%
43	West Virginia	145,136,000	0.3%
44	New Hampshire	141,764,000	0.3%
45	Rhode Island	137,275,000	0.3%
46	Idaho	103,705,000	0.2%
47	Wyoming	98,184,000	0.2%
48	Vermont	77,440,000	0.2%
49	South Dakota	67,183,000	0.2%
50	North Dakota	50,017,000	0.1%
	District of Columbia**	NA	NA

Source: U.S. Bureau of the Census, Governments Division
"State Government Finances: 2001" (http://www.census.gov/govs/www/state01.html)
*Includes outpatient health services other than hospital care, research and education, categorical health programs, treatment and immunization clinics, nursing and environmental health activities. Includes capital expenditures.
**Not applicable.

Per Capita State Government Expenditures for Health Programs in 2001

National Per Capita = $153*

ALPHA ORDER

RANK	STATE	PER CAPITA
23	Alabama	$144
6	Alaska	256
15	Arizona	180
32	Arkansas	111
12	California	189
49	Colorado	70
19	Connecticut	160
2	Delaware	305
20	Florida	157
32	Georgia	111
1	Hawaii	319
47	Idaho	78
14	Illinois	186
43	Indiana	86
48	Iowa	76
17	Kansas	174
29	Kentucky	121
36	Louisiana	106
7	Maine	247
8	Maryland	223
3	Massachusetts	283
4	Michigan	272
41	Minnesota	95
39	Mississippi	99
35	Missouri	109
5	Montana	258
13	Nebraska	188
49	Nevada	70
30	New Hampshire	113
36	New Jersey	106
16	New Mexico	177
8	New York	223
30	North Carolina	113
46	North Dakota	79
21	Ohio	154
34	Oklahoma	110
22	Oregon	152
24	Pennsylvania	135
25	Rhode Island	130
18	South Carolina	168
42	South Dakota	89
27	Tennessee	123
44	Texas	81
28	Utah	122
26	Vermont	126
40	Virginia	98
10	Washington	219
44	West Virginia	81
38	Wisconsin	102
11	Wyoming	199

RANK ORDER

RANK	STATE	PER CAPITA
1	Hawaii	$319
2	Delaware	305
3	Massachusetts	283
4	Michigan	272
5	Montana	258
6	Alaska	256
7	Maine	247
8	Maryland	223
8	New York	223
10	Washington	219
11	Wyoming	199
12	California	189
13	Nebraska	188
14	Illinois	186
15	Arizona	180
16	New Mexico	177
17	Kansas	174
18	South Carolina	168
19	Connecticut	160
20	Florida	157
21	Ohio	154
22	Oregon	152
23	Alabama	144
24	Pennsylvania	135
25	Rhode Island	130
26	Vermont	126
27	Tennessee	123
28	Utah	122
29	Kentucky	121
30	New Hampshire	113
30	North Carolina	113
32	Arkansas	111
32	Georgia	111
34	Oklahoma	110
35	Missouri	109
36	Louisiana	106
36	New Jersey	106
38	Wisconsin	102
39	Mississippi	99
40	Virginia	98
41	Minnesota	95
42	South Dakota	89
43	Indiana	86
44	Texas	81
44	West Virginia	81
46	North Dakota	79
47	Idaho	78
48	Iowa	76
49	Colorado	70
49	Nevada	70
	District of Columbia**	NA

Source: Morgan Quitno Press using data from U.S. Bureau of the Census, Governments Division
"State Government Finances: 2001" (http://www.census.gov/govs/www/state01.html)
*Includes outpatient health services other than hospital care, research and education, categorical health programs, treatment and immunization clinics, nursing and environmental health activities. Includes capital expenditures.
**Not applicable.

Percent of State Government Expenditures Used for Health Programs in 2001

National Percent = 6.3%*

ALPHA ORDER

RANK	STATE	PERCENT
20	Alabama	5.8
50	Alaska	2.2
2	Arizona	10.5
30	Arkansas	4.3
3	California	8.6
46	Colorado	3.2
30	Connecticut	4.3
11	Delaware	7.7
7	Florida	8.1
24	Georgia	5.4
16	Hawaii	6.5
42	Idaho	3.4
4	Illinois	8.5
39	Indiana	4.0
47	Iowa	2.8
14	Kansas	7.3
37	Kentucky	4.1
29	Louisiana	4.4
13	Maine	7.5
6	Maryland	8.4
8	Massachusetts	8.0
1	Michigan	11.3
42	Minnesota	3.4
40	Mississippi	3.9
26	Missouri	5.0
4	Montana	8.5
9	Nebraska	7.8
37	Nevada	4.1
26	New Hampshire	5.0
34	New Jersey	4.2
23	New Mexico	5.5
9	New York	7.8
28	North Carolina	4.7
49	North Dakota	2.4
15	Ohio	7.2
18	Oklahoma	6.0
21	Oregon	5.6
25	Pennsylvania	5.1
41	Rhode Island	3.5
19	South Carolina	5.9
45	South Dakota	3.3
21	Tennessee	5.6
34	Texas	4.2
30	Utah	4.3
42	Vermont	3.4
34	Virginia	4.2
11	Washington	7.7
47	West Virginia	2.8
30	Wisconsin	4.3
16	Wyoming	6.5

RANK ORDER

RANK	STATE	PERCENT
1	Michigan	11.3
2	Arizona	10.5
3	California	8.6
4	Illinois	8.5
4	Montana	8.5
6	Maryland	8.4
7	Florida	8.1
8	Massachusetts	8.0
9	Nebraska	7.8
9	New York	7.8
11	Delaware	7.7
11	Washington	7.7
13	Maine	7.5
14	Kansas	7.3
15	Ohio	7.2
16	Hawaii	6.5
16	Wyoming	6.5
18	Oklahoma	6.0
19	South Carolina	5.9
20	Alabama	5.8
21	Oregon	5.6
21	Tennessee	5.6
23	New Mexico	5.5
24	Georgia	5.4
25	Pennsylvania	5.1
26	Missouri	5.0
26	New Hampshire	5.0
28	North Carolina	4.7
29	Louisiana	4.4
30	Arkansas	4.3
30	Connecticut	4.3
30	Utah	4.3
30	Wisconsin	4.3
34	New Jersey	4.2
34	Texas	4.2
34	Virginia	4.2
37	Kentucky	4.1
37	Nevada	4.1
39	Indiana	4.0
40	Mississippi	3.9
41	Rhode Island	3.5
42	Idaho	3.4
42	Minnesota	3.4
42	Vermont	3.4
45	South Dakota	3.3
46	Colorado	3.2
47	Iowa	2.8
47	West Virginia	2.8
49	North Dakota	2.4
50	Alaska	2.2

District of Columbia**	NA

Source: Morgan Quitno Press using data from U.S. Bureau of the Census, Governments Division
   "State Government Finances: 2001" (http://www.census.gov/govs/www/state01.html)
*As a percent of direct general expenditures. Includes outpatient health services other than hospital care, research and education, categorical health programs, treatment and immunization clinics, nursing and environmental health activities. Includes capital expenditures.
**Not applicable.

State and Local Government Expenditures for Hospitals in 2000

National Total = $75,975,990,000*

ALPHA ORDER

RANK	STATE	EXPENDITURES	% of USA
7	Alabama	$2,783,320,000	3.7%
45	Alaska	75,496,000	0.1%
34	Arizona	450,879,000	0.6%
29	Arkansas	654,059,000	0.9%
1	California	9,158,683,000	12.1%
26	Colorado	867,948,000	1.1%
23	Connecticut	1,145,790,000	1.5%
47	Delaware	62,968,000	0.1%
4	Florida	4,170,079,000	5.5%
8	Georgia	2,494,273,000	3.3%
41	Hawaii	192,039,000	0.3%
38	Idaho	373,138,000	0.5%
12	Illinois	1,956,580,000	2.6%
11	Indiana	2,031,205,000	2.7%
21	Iowa	1,304,188,000	1.7%
32	Kansas	525,924,000	0.7%
31	Kentucky	553,180,000	0.7%
6	Louisiana	2,822,725,000	3.7%
43	Maine	103,942,000	0.1%
39	Maryland	360,644,000	0.5%
28	Massachusetts	679,197,000	0.9%
16	Michigan	1,676,070,000	2.2%
24	Minnesota	1,110,804,000	1.5%
14	Mississippi	1,815,109,000	2.4%
19	Missouri	1,376,403,000	1.8%
44	Montana	96,618,000	0.1%
36	Nebraska	399,480,000	0.5%
30	Nevada	564,940,000	0.7%
48	New Hampshire	43,798,000	0.1%
20	New Jersey	1,313,512,000	1.7%
33	New Mexico	483,327,000	0.6%
2	New York	8,075,704,000	10.6%
5	North Carolina	3,823,391,000	5.0%
49	North Dakota	42,548,000	0.1%
9	Ohio	2,210,529,000	2.9%
25	Oklahoma	910,771,000	1.2%
22	Oregon	1,252,602,000	1.6%
18	Pennsylvania	1,553,450,000	2.0%
42	Rhode Island	121,570,000	0.2%
10	South Carolina	2,184,262,000	2.9%
46	South Dakota	71,823,000	0.1%
13	Tennessee	1,897,280,000	2.5%
3	Texas	6,535,751,000	8.6%
35	Utah	445,959,000	0.6%
50	Vermont	2,941,000	0.0%
15	Virginia	1,698,036,000	2.2%
17	Washington	1,614,194,000	2.1%
40	West Virginia	343,014,000	0.5%
27	Wisconsin	812,666,000	1.1%
37	Wyoming	373,784,000	0.5%

RANK ORDER

RANK	STATE	EXPENDITURES	% of USA
1	California	$9,158,683,000	12.1%
2	New York	8,075,704,000	10.6%
3	Texas	6,535,751,000	8.6%
4	Florida	4,170,079,000	5.5%
5	North Carolina	3,823,391,000	5.0%
6	Louisiana	2,822,725,000	3.7%
7	Alabama	2,783,320,000	3.7%
8	Georgia	2,494,273,000	3.3%
9	Ohio	2,210,529,000	2.9%
10	South Carolina	2,184,262,000	2.9%
11	Indiana	2,031,205,000	2.7%
12	Illinois	1,956,580,000	2.6%
13	Tennessee	1,897,280,000	2.5%
14	Mississippi	1,815,109,000	2.4%
15	Virginia	1,698,036,000	2.2%
16	Michigan	1,676,070,000	2.2%
17	Washington	1,614,194,000	2.1%
18	Pennsylvania	1,553,450,000	2.0%
19	Missouri	1,376,403,000	1.8%
20	New Jersey	1,313,512,000	1.7%
21	Iowa	1,304,188,000	1.7%
22	Oregon	1,252,602,000	1.6%
23	Connecticut	1,145,790,000	1.5%
24	Minnesota	1,110,804,000	1.5%
25	Oklahoma	910,771,000	1.2%
26	Colorado	867,948,000	1.1%
27	Wisconsin	812,666,000	1.1%
28	Massachusetts	679,197,000	0.9%
29	Arkansas	654,059,000	0.9%
30	Nevada	564,940,000	0.7%
31	Kentucky	553,180,000	0.7%
32	Kansas	525,924,000	0.7%
33	New Mexico	483,327,000	0.6%
34	Arizona	450,879,000	0.6%
35	Utah	445,959,000	0.6%
36	Nebraska	399,480,000	0.5%
37	Wyoming	373,784,000	0.5%
38	Idaho	373,138,000	0.5%
39	Maryland	360,644,000	0.5%
40	West Virginia	343,014,000	0.5%
41	Hawaii	192,039,000	0.3%
42	Rhode Island	121,570,000	0.2%
43	Maine	103,942,000	0.1%
44	Montana	96,618,000	0.1%
45	Alaska	75,496,000	0.1%
46	South Dakota	71,823,000	0.1%
47	Delaware	62,968,000	0.1%
48	New Hampshire	43,798,000	0.1%
49	North Dakota	42,548,000	0.1%
50	Vermont	2,941,000	0.0%
	District of Columbia	359,397,000	0.5%

Source: U.S. Bureau of the Census, Governments Division
"State and Local Government Finances: 1999-2000" (http://www.census.gov/govs/www/estimate00.html)
*Financing, construction, acquisition, maintenance or operation of hospital facilities, provision of hospital care and support of public or private hospitals.

Per Capita State and Local Government Expenditures for Hospitals in 2000

National Per Capita = $269*

ALPHA ORDER

RANK	STATE	PER CAPITA
4	Alabama	$625
39	Alaska	120
44	Arizona	87
23	Arkansas	244
18	California	269
27	Colorado	201
10	Connecticut	336
46	Delaware	80
21	Florida	260
14	Georgia	303
33	Hawaii	158
15	Idaho	287
34	Illinois	157
11	Indiana	333
7	Iowa	445
29	Kansas	195
37	Kentucky	137
3	Louisiana	632
45	Maine	81
47	Maryland	68
41	Massachusetts	107
32	Michigan	168
26	Minnesota	225
2	Mississippi	637
22	Missouri	246
41	Montana	107
25	Nebraska	233
16	Nevada	280
49	New Hampshire	35
35	New Jersey	156
19	New Mexico	265
8	New York	425
6	North Carolina	473
48	North Dakota	66
29	Ohio	195
20	Oklahoma	264
9	Oregon	365
38	Pennsylvania	126
40	Rhode Island	116
5	South Carolina	543
43	South Dakota	95
11	Tennessee	333
13	Texas	312
28	Utah	199
50	Vermont	5
24	Virginia	239
17	Washington	273
31	West Virginia	190
36	Wisconsin	151
1	Wyoming	757

RANK ORDER

RANK	STATE	PER CAPITA
1	Wyoming	$757
2	Mississippi	637
3	Louisiana	632
4	Alabama	625
5	South Carolina	543
6	North Carolina	473
7	Iowa	445
8	New York	425
9	Oregon	365
10	Connecticut	336
11	Indiana	333
11	Tennessee	333
13	Texas	312
14	Georgia	303
15	Idaho	287
16	Nevada	280
17	Washington	273
18	California	269
19	New Mexico	265
20	Oklahoma	264
21	Florida	260
22	Missouri	246
23	Arkansas	244
24	Virginia	239
25	Nebraska	233
26	Minnesota	225
27	Colorado	201
28	Utah	199
29	Kansas	195
29	Ohio	195
31	West Virginia	190
32	Michigan	168
33	Hawaii	158
34	Illinois	157
35	New Jersey	156
36	Wisconsin	151
37	Kentucky	137
38	Pennsylvania	126
39	Alaska	120
40	Rhode Island	116
41	Massachusetts	107
41	Montana	107
43	South Dakota	95
44	Arizona	87
45	Maine	81
46	Delaware	80
47	Maryland	68
48	North Dakota	66
49	New Hampshire	35
50	Vermont	5

District of Columbia	629

Source: Morgan Quitno Press using data from U.S. Bureau of the Census, Governments Division
"State and Local Government Finances: 1999-2000" (http://www.census.gov/govs/www/estimate00.html)
*Financing, construction, acquisition, maintenance or operation of hospital facilities, provision of hospital care and support of public or private hospitals.

Percent of State and Local Government Expenditures
Used for Hospitals in 2000
National Percent = 5.1%*

ALPHA ORDER

RANK	STATE	PERCENT
3	Alabama	12.6
48	Alaska	1.0
42	Arizona	1.9
15	Arkansas	5.9
25	California	4.7
28	Colorado	3.9
20	Connecticut	5.3
45	Delaware	1.3
18	Florida	5.5
11	Georgia	6.6
36	Hawaii	2.6
13	Idaho	6.4
33	Illinois	3.0
9	Indiana	7.1
7	Iowa	8.4
26	Kansas	4.1
34	Kentucky	2.9
2	Louisiana	12.7
44	Maine	1.5
45	Maryland	1.3
43	Massachusetts	1.8
32	Michigan	3.1
31	Minnesota	3.6
1	Mississippi	13.0
18	Missouri	5.5
40	Montana	2.1
22	Nebraska	4.8
16	Nevada	5.8
49	New Hampshire	0.8
35	New Jersey	2.8
22	New Mexico	4.8
16	New York	5.8
6	North Carolina	9.5
47	North Dakota	1.2
30	Ohio	3.8
11	Oklahoma	6.6
14	Oregon	6.2
38	Pennsylvania	2.4
39	Rhode Island	2.2
5	South Carolina	10.8
40	South Dakota	2.1
8	Tennessee	7.5
10	Texas	6.8
27	Utah	4.0
50	Vermont	0.1
21	Virginia	4.9
22	Washington	4.8
28	West Virginia	3.9
36	Wisconsin	2.6
4	Wyoming	11.2

RANK ORDER

RANK	STATE	PERCENT
1	Mississippi	13.0
2	Louisiana	12.7
3	Alabama	12.6
4	Wyoming	11.2
5	South Carolina	10.8
6	North Carolina	9.5
7	Iowa	8.4
8	Tennessee	7.5
9	Indiana	7.1
10	Texas	6.8
11	Georgia	6.6
11	Oklahoma	6.6
13	Idaho	6.4
14	Oregon	6.2
15	Arkansas	5.9
16	Nevada	5.8
16	New York	5.8
18	Florida	5.5
18	Missouri	5.5
20	Connecticut	5.3
21	Virginia	4.9
22	Nebraska	4.8
22	New Mexico	4.8
22	Washington	4.8
25	California	4.7
26	Kansas	4.1
27	Utah	4.0
28	Colorado	3.9
28	West Virginia	3.9
30	Ohio	3.8
31	Minnesota	3.6
32	Michigan	3.1
33	Illinois	3.0
34	Kentucky	2.9
35	New Jersey	2.8
36	Hawaii	2.6
36	Wisconsin	2.6
38	Pennsylvania	2.4
39	Rhode Island	2.2
40	Montana	2.1
40	South Dakota	2.1
42	Arizona	1.9
43	Massachusetts	1.8
44	Maine	1.5
45	Delaware	1.3
45	Maryland	1.3
47	North Dakota	1.2
48	Alaska	1.0
49	New Hampshire	0.8
50	Vermont	0.1

District of Columbia 7.0

Source: Morgan Quitno Press using data from U.S. Bureau of the Census, Governments Division
   "State and Local Government Finances: 1999-2000" (http://www.census.gov/govs/www/estimate00.html)
*Financing, construction, acquisition, maintenance or operation of hospital facilities, provision of hospital care and
support of public or private hospitals.

State and Local Government Expenditures for Health Programs in 2000

National Total = $51,365,588,000*

ALPHA ORDER

RANK	STATE	EXPENDITURES	% of USA
18	Alabama	$851,603,000	1.7%
42	Alaska	160,201,000	0.3%
17	Arizona	923,391,000	1.8%
34	Arkansas	316,228,000	0.6%
1	California	8,896,217,000	17.3%
27	Colorado	472,937,000	0.9%
28	Connecticut	450,221,000	0.9%
39	Delaware	215,588,000	0.4%
3	Florida	3,137,136,000	6.1%
12	Georgia	1,059,809,000	2.1%
30	Hawaii	408,479,000	0.8%
44	Idaho	139,240,000	0.3%
6	Illinois	2,424,891,000	4.7%
24	Indiana	572,475,000	1.1%
32	Iowa	373,966,000	0.7%
31	Kansas	408,358,000	0.8%
26	Kentucky	544,112,000	1.1%
25	Louisiana	552,240,000	1.1%
37	Maine	293,482,000	0.6%
16	Maryland	933,863,000	1.8%
11	Massachusetts	1,566,025,000	3.0%
5	Michigan	2,502,924,000	4.9%
22	Minnesota	715,323,000	1.4%
35	Mississippi	298,498,000	0.6%
21	Missouri	790,330,000	1.5%
38	Montana	246,150,000	0.5%
46	Nebraska	121,811,000	0.2%
41	Nevada	172,083,000	0.3%
45	New Hampshire	126,450,000	0.2%
14	New Jersey	1,017,852,000	2.0%
33	New Mexico	328,711,000	0.6%
2	New York	3,492,012,000	6.8%
9	North Carolina	1,713,098,000	3.3%
50	North Dakota	48,187,000	0.1%
4	Ohio	2,751,983,000	5.4%
29	Oklahoma	413,461,000	0.8%
23	Oregon	698,276,000	1.4%
7	Pennsylvania	2,392,413,000	4.7%
43	Rhode Island	156,085,000	0.3%
20	South Carolina	831,841,000	1.6%
48	South Dakota	78,428,000	0.2%
19	Tennessee	841,537,000	1.6%
8	Texas	2,317,786,000	4.5%
36	Utah	295,037,000	0.6%
49	Vermont	76,479,000	0.1%
15	Virginia	935,521,000	1.8%
10	Washington	1,702,867,000	3.3%
40	West Virginia	209,259,000	0.4%
13	Wisconsin	1,026,484,000	2.0%
47	Wyoming	90,075,000	0.2%

RANK ORDER

RANK	STATE	EXPENDITURES	% of USA
1	California	$8,896,217,000	17.3%
2	New York	3,492,012,000	6.8%
3	Florida	3,137,136,000	6.1%
4	Ohio	2,751,983,000	5.4%
5	Michigan	2,502,924,000	4.9%
6	Illinois	2,424,891,000	4.7%
7	Pennsylvania	2,392,413,000	4.7%
8	Texas	2,317,786,000	4.5%
9	North Carolina	1,713,098,000	3.3%
10	Washington	1,702,867,000	3.3%
11	Massachusetts	1,566,025,000	3.0%
12	Georgia	1,059,809,000	2.1%
13	Wisconsin	1,026,484,000	2.0%
14	New Jersey	1,017,852,000	2.0%
15	Virginia	935,521,000	1.8%
16	Maryland	933,863,000	1.8%
17	Arizona	923,391,000	1.8%
18	Alabama	851,603,000	1.7%
19	Tennessee	841,537,000	1.6%
20	South Carolina	831,841,000	1.6%
21	Missouri	790,330,000	1.5%
22	Minnesota	715,323,000	1.4%
23	Oregon	698,276,000	1.4%
24	Indiana	572,475,000	1.1%
25	Louisiana	552,240,000	1.1%
26	Kentucky	544,112,000	1.1%
27	Colorado	472,937,000	0.9%
28	Connecticut	450,221,000	0.9%
29	Oklahoma	413,461,000	0.8%
30	Hawaii	408,479,000	0.8%
31	Kansas	408,358,000	0.8%
32	Iowa	373,966,000	0.7%
33	New Mexico	328,711,000	0.6%
34	Arkansas	316,228,000	0.6%
35	Mississippi	298,498,000	0.6%
36	Utah	295,037,000	0.6%
37	Maine	293,482,000	0.6%
38	Montana	246,150,000	0.5%
39	Delaware	215,588,000	0.4%
40	West Virginia	209,259,000	0.4%
41	Nevada	172,083,000	0.3%
42	Alaska	160,201,000	0.3%
43	Rhode Island	156,085,000	0.3%
44	Idaho	139,240,000	0.3%
45	New Hampshire	126,450,000	0.2%
46	Nebraska	121,811,000	0.2%
47	Wyoming	90,075,000	0.2%
48	South Dakota	78,428,000	0.2%
49	Vermont	76,479,000	0.1%
50	North Dakota	48,187,000	0.1%
	District of Columbia	274,165,000	0.5%

Source: U.S. Bureau of the Census, Governments Division
"State and Local Government Finances: 1999-2000" (http://www.census.gov/govs/www/estimate00.html)
*Includes outpatient health services other than hospital care, research and education, categorical health programs, treatment and immunization clinics, nursing and environmental health activities. Includes capital expenditures.

Per Capita State and Local Government Expenditures for Health Programs in 2000
National Per Capita = $182*

ALPHA ORDER

RANK	STATE	PER CAPITA
17	Alabama	$191
6	Alaska	255
22	Arizona	179
39	Arkansas	118
5	California	262
42	Colorado	109
30	Connecticut	132
3	Delaware	274
14	Florida	195
33	Georgia	129
1	Hawaii	337
43	Idaho	107
14	Illinois	195
47	Indiana	94
34	Iowa	128
24	Kansas	152
29	Kentucky	134
36	Louisiana	124
10	Maine	230
23	Maryland	176
8	Massachusetts	246
7	Michigan	251
27	Minnesota	145
44	Mississippi	105
28	Missouri	141
4	Montana	272
50	Nebraska	71
48	Nevada	85
46	New Hampshire	102
37	New Jersey	121
21	New Mexico	180
19	New York	184
11	North Carolina	212
49	North Dakota	75
9	Ohio	242
38	Oklahoma	120
13	Oregon	204
14	Pennsylvania	195
25	Rhode Island	149
12	South Carolina	207
45	South Dakota	104
26	Tennessee	148
41	Texas	111
30	Utah	132
35	Vermont	125
30	Virginia	132
2	Washington	288
40	West Virginia	116
17	Wisconsin	191
20	Wyoming	182

RANK ORDER

RANK	STATE	PER CAPITA
1	Hawaii	$337
2	Washington	288
3	Delaware	274
4	Montana	272
5	California	262
6	Alaska	255
7	Michigan	251
8	Massachusetts	246
9	Ohio	242
10	Maine	230
11	North Carolina	212
12	South Carolina	207
13	Oregon	204
14	Florida	195
14	Illinois	195
14	Pennsylvania	195
17	Alabama	191
17	Wisconsin	191
19	New York	184
20	Wyoming	182
21	New Mexico	180
22	Arizona	179
23	Maryland	176
24	Kansas	152
25	Rhode Island	149
26	Tennessee	148
27	Minnesota	145
28	Missouri	141
29	Kentucky	134
30	Connecticut	132
30	Utah	132
30	Virginia	132
33	Georgia	129
34	Iowa	128
35	Vermont	125
36	Louisiana	124
37	New Jersey	121
38	Oklahoma	120
39	Arkansas	118
40	West Virginia	116
41	Texas	111
42	Colorado	109
43	Idaho	107
44	Mississippi	105
45	South Dakota	104
46	New Hampshire	102
47	Indiana	94
48	Nevada	85
49	North Dakota	75
50	Nebraska	71

District of Columbia   480

Source: Morgan Quitno Press using data from U.S. Bureau of the Census, Governments Division
   "State and Local Government Finances: 1999-2000" (http://www.census.gov/govs/www/estimate00.html)
*Includes outpatient health services other than hospital care, research and education, categorical health programs, treatment and immunization clinics, nursing and environmental health activities. Includes capital expenditures.

Percent of State and Local Government Expenditures
Used for Health Programs in 2000
National Percent = 3.4%*

ALPHA ORDER

RANK	STATE	PERCENT
14	Alabama	3.9
43	Alaska	2.1
13	Arizona	4.0
25	Arkansas	2.9
7	California	4.5
43	Colorado	2.1
43	Connecticut	2.1
5	Delaware	4.6
8	Florida	4.2
27	Georgia	2.8
1	Hawaii	5.6
34	Idaho	2.4
15	Illinois	3.8
47	Indiana	2.0
34	Iowa	2.4
22	Kansas	3.2
25	Kentucky	2.9
32	Louisiana	2.5
8	Maine	4.2
18	Maryland	3.4
11	Massachusetts	4.1
5	Michigan	4.6
38	Minnesota	2.3
43	Mississippi	2.1
22	Missouri	3.2
2	Montana	5.4
49	Nebraska	1.4
48	Nevada	1.8
40	New Hampshire	2.2
40	New Jersey	2.2
19	New Mexico	3.3
32	New York	2.5
8	North Carolina	4.2
50	North Dakota	1.3
4	Ohio	4.8
24	Oklahoma	3.0
17	Oregon	3.5
16	Pennsylvania	3.6
27	Rhode Island	2.8
11	South Carolina	4.1
38	South Dakota	2.3
19	Tennessee	3.3
34	Texas	2.4
29	Utah	2.7
40	Vermont	2.2
29	Virginia	2.7
3	Washington	5.1
34	West Virginia	2.4
19	Wisconsin	3.3
29	Wyoming	2.7

RANK ORDER

RANK	STATE	PERCENT
1	Hawaii	5.6
2	Montana	5.4
3	Washington	5.1
4	Ohio	4.8
5	Delaware	4.6
5	Michigan	4.6
7	California	4.5
8	Florida	4.2
8	Maine	4.2
8	North Carolina	4.2
11	Massachusetts	4.1
11	South Carolina	4.1
13	Arizona	4.0
14	Alabama	3.9
15	Illinois	3.8
16	Pennsylvania	3.6
17	Oregon	3.5
18	Maryland	3.4
19	New Mexico	3.3
19	Tennessee	3.3
19	Wisconsin	3.3
22	Kansas	3.2
22	Missouri	3.2
24	Oklahoma	3.0
25	Arkansas	2.9
25	Kentucky	2.9
27	Georgia	2.8
27	Rhode Island	2.8
29	Utah	2.7
29	Virginia	2.7
29	Wyoming	2.7
32	Louisiana	2.5
32	New York	2.5
34	Idaho	2.4
34	Iowa	2.4
34	Texas	2.4
34	West Virginia	2.4
38	Minnesota	2.3
38	South Dakota	2.3
40	New Hampshire	2.2
40	New Jersey	2.2
40	Vermont	2.2
43	Alaska	2.1
43	Colorado	2.1
43	Connecticut	2.1
43	Mississippi	2.1
47	Indiana	2.0
48	Nevada	1.8
49	Nebraska	1.4
50	North Dakota	1.3

District of Columbia   5.3

Source: Morgan Quitno Press using data from U.S. Bureau of the Census, Governments Division
"State and Local Government Finances: 1999-2000" (http://www.census.gov/govs/www/estimate00.html)
*Includes outpatient health services other than hospital care, research and education, categorical health programs, treatment and immunization clinics, nursing and environmental health activities. Includes capital expenditures.

Estimated State Funds from the Tobacco Settlement Through 2025

National Total = $195,918,675,920*

ALPHA ORDER

RANK	STATE	FUNDS	% of USA
21	Alabama	$3,166,302,119	1.6%
45	Alaska	668,903,057	0.3%
22	Arizona	2,887,614,909	1.5%
30	Arkansas	1,622,336,126	0.8%
1	California	25,006,972,511	12.8%
23	Colorado	2,685,773,549	1.4%
19	Connecticut	3,637,303,382	1.9%
41	Delaware	774,798,677	0.4%
NA	Florida**	NA	NA
9	Georgia	4,808,740,669	2.5%
35	Hawaii	1,179,165,923	0.6%
43	Idaho	711,700,479	0.4%
5	Illinois	9,118,539,559	4.7%
18	Indiana	3,996,355,551	2.0%
28	Iowa	1,703,839,986	0.9%
29	Kansas	1,633,317,646	0.8%
20	Kentucky	3,450,438,586	1.8%
14	Louisiana	4,418,657,915	2.3%
31	Maine	1,507,301,276	0.8%
13	Maryland	4,428,657,384	2.3%
7	Massachusetts	7,913,114,213	4.0%
6	Michigan	8,526,278,034	4.4%
NA	Minnesota**	NA	NA
NA	Mississippi**	NA	NA
12	Missouri	4,456,368,286	2.3%
39	Montana	832,182,431	0.4%
37	Nebraska	1,165,683,457	0.6%
34	Nevada	1,194,976,855	0.6%
33	New Hampshire	1,304,689,150	0.7%
8	New Jersey	7,576,167,918	3.9%
36	New Mexico	1,168,438,809	0.6%
2	New York	25,003,202,243	12.8%
11	North Carolina	4,569,381,898	2.3%
42	North Dakota	717,089,369	0.4%
4	Ohio	9,869,422,449	5.0%
26	Oklahoma	2,029,985,862	1.0%
25	Oregon	2,248,476,833	1.1%
3	Pennsylvania	11,259,169,603	5.7%
32	Rhode Island	1,408,469,747	0.7%
24	South Carolina	2,304,693,120	1.2%
44	South Dakota	683,650,009	0.3%
10	Tennessee	4,782,168,127	2.4%
NA	Texas**	NA	NA
38	Utah	871,616,513	0.4%
40	Vermont	805,588,329	0.4%
17	Virginia	4,006,037,550	2.0%
16	Washington	4,022,716,267	2.1%
27	West Virginia	1,736,741,427	0.9%
15	Wisconsin	4,059,511,421	2.1%
46	Wyoming	486,553,976	0.2%

RANK ORDER

RANK	STATE	FUNDS	% of USA
1	California	$25,006,972,511	12.8%
2	New York	25,003,202,243	12.8%
3	Pennsylvania	11,259,169,603	5.7%
4	Ohio	9,869,422,449	5.0%
5	Illinois	9,118,539,559	4.7%
6	Michigan	8,526,278,034	4.4%
7	Massachusetts	7,913,114,213	4.0%
8	New Jersey	7,576,167,918	3.9%
9	Georgia	4,808,740,669	2.5%
10	Tennessee	4,782,168,127	2.4%
11	North Carolina	4,569,381,898	2.3%
12	Missouri	4,456,368,286	2.3%
13	Maryland	4,428,657,384	2.3%
14	Louisiana	4,418,657,915	2.3%
15	Wisconsin	4,059,511,421	2.1%
16	Washington	4,022,716,267	2.1%
17	Virginia	4,006,037,550	2.0%
18	Indiana	3,996,355,551	2.0%
19	Connecticut	3,637,303,382	1.9%
20	Kentucky	3,450,438,586	1.8%
21	Alabama	3,166,302,119	1.6%
22	Arizona	2,887,614,909	1.5%
23	Colorado	2,685,773,549	1.4%
24	South Carolina	2,304,693,120	1.2%
25	Oregon	2,248,476,833	1.1%
26	Oklahoma	2,029,985,862	1.0%
27	West Virginia	1,736,741,427	0.9%
28	Iowa	1,703,839,986	0.9%
29	Kansas	1,633,317,646	0.8%
30	Arkansas	1,622,336,126	0.8%
31	Maine	1,507,301,276	0.8%
32	Rhode Island	1,408,469,747	0.7%
33	New Hampshire	1,304,689,150	0.7%
34	Nevada	1,194,976,855	0.6%
35	Hawaii	1,179,165,923	0.6%
36	New Mexico	1,168,438,809	0.6%
37	Nebraska	1,165,683,457	0.6%
38	Utah	871,616,513	0.4%
39	Montana	832,182,431	0.4%
40	Vermont	805,588,329	0.4%
41	Delaware	774,798,677	0.4%
42	North Dakota	717,089,369	0.4%
43	Idaho	711,700,479	0.4%
44	South Dakota	683,650,009	0.3%
45	Alaska	668,903,057	0.3%
46	Wyoming	486,553,976	0.2%
NA	Florida**	NA	NA
NA	Minnesota**	NA	NA
NA	Mississippi**	NA	NA
NA	Texas**	NA	NA
	District of Columbia	1,189,458,106	0.6%

Source: National Association of Attorneys General
"Attorneys General Announce Tobacco Settlement Proposal" (News release, http://www.naag.org/tob2.htm)
*This settlement was reached in November 1998. National total includes $4,640,249,229 for U.S. territories.
**Total does not include $40 billion in previous settlements with Florida, Minnesota, Mississippi and Texas.

State Health Care Costs Factors in 2003

National Factor = 1.0000*

ALPHA ORDER

RANK	STATE	FACTOR
27	Alabama	0.9659
11	Alaska	1.0375
8	Arizona	1.0593
38	Arkansas	0.9036
5	California	1.0972
14	Colorado	1.0199
6	Connecticut	1.0913
3	Delaware	1.1270
13	Florida	1.0211
21	Georgia	0.9995
2	Hawaii	1.1335
41	Idaho	0.8950
17	Illinois	1.0084
30	Indiana	0.9407
48	Iowa	0.8705
45	Kansas	0.8837
32	Kentucky	0.9366
46	Louisiana	0.8835
35	Maine	0.9232
10	Maryland	1.0394
9	Massachusetts	1.0587
15	Michigan	1.0132
16	Minnesota	1.0090
40	Mississippi	0.8956
34	Missouri	0.9300
49	Montana	0.8605
43	Nebraska	0.8888
1	Nevada	1.1640
19	New Hampshire	1.0011
4	New Jersey	1.1060
31	New Mexico	0.9390
7	New York	1.0633
22	North Carolina	0.9937
47	North Dakota	0.8730
29	Ohio	0.9589
50	Oklahoma	0.8578
12	Oregon	1.0217
23	Pennsylvania	0.9903
25	Rhode Island	0.9797
18	South Carolina	1.0068
44	South Dakota	0.8868
20	Tennessee	1.0002
33	Texas	0.9363
36	Utah	0.9164
42	Vermont	0.8914
24	Virginia	0.9802
28	Washington	0.9626
39	West Virginia	0.8991
26	Wisconsin	0.9687
37	Wyoming	0.9063

RANK ORDER

RANK	STATE	FACTOR
1	Nevada	1.1640
2	Hawaii	1.1335
3	Delaware	1.1270
4	New Jersey	1.1060
5	California	1.0972
6	Connecticut	1.0913
7	New York	1.0633
8	Arizona	1.0593
9	Massachusetts	1.0587
10	Maryland	1.0394
11	Alaska	1.0375
12	Oregon	1.0217
13	Florida	1.0211
14	Colorado	1.0199
15	Michigan	1.0132
16	Minnesota	1.0090
17	Illinois	1.0084
18	South Carolina	1.0068
19	New Hampshire	1.0011
20	Tennessee	1.0002
21	Georgia	0.9995
22	North Carolina	0.9937
23	Pennsylvania	0.9903
24	Virginia	0.9802
25	Rhode Island	0.9797
26	Wisconsin	0.9687
27	Alabama	0.9659
28	Washington	0.9626
29	Ohio	0.9589
30	Indiana	0.9407
31	New Mexico	0.9390
32	Kentucky	0.9366
33	Texas	0.9363
34	Missouri	0.9300
35	Maine	0.9232
36	Utah	0.9164
37	Wyoming	0.9063
38	Arkansas	0.9036
39	West Virginia	0.8991
40	Mississippi	0.8956
41	Idaho	0.8950
42	Vermont	0.8914
43	Nebraska	0.8888
44	South Dakota	0.8868
45	Kansas	0.8837
46	Louisiana	0.8835
47	North Dakota	0.8730
48	Iowa	0.8705
49	Montana	0.8605
50	Oklahoma	0.8578

	District of Columbia	1.2108

Source: U.S. Department of Health and Human Services, Centers for Medicare and Medicaid Services
   "SCHIP Allotments" (http://www.cms.gov/schip/regulations/allotments/)
*For fiscal year 2003. State cost factors are determined based on annual wages in the health care industry for each state.

Payroll of Health Care Establishments in 2001

National Total = $430,880,222,000*

ALPHA ORDER

RANK	STATE	PAYROLL	% of USA
25	Alabama	$6,055,366,000	1.4%
47	Alaska	1,139,280,000	0.3%
22	Arizona	6,225,741,000	1.4%
32	Arkansas	3,499,090,000	0.8%
1	California	43,661,974,000	10.1%
24	Colorado	6,079,877,000	1.4%
21	Connecticut	7,077,229,000	1.6%
44	Delaware	1,485,818,000	0.3%
4	Florida	23,841,810,000	5.5%
12	Georgia	11,030,202,000	2.6%
42	Hawaii	1,679,915,000	0.4%
43	Idaho	1,496,658,000	0.3%
6	Illinois	19,292,453,000	4.5%
16	Indiana	9,150,042,000	2.1%
29	Iowa	4,544,672,000	1.1%
31	Kansas	4,135,169,000	1.0%
26	Kentucky	5,841,722,000	1.4%
23	Louisiana	6,209,043,000	1.4%
38	Maine	2,257,114,000	0.5%
20	Maryland	8,151,517,000	1.9%
10	Massachusetts	14,095,510,000	3.3%
8	Michigan	15,300,909,000	3.6%
13	Minnesota	9,548,543,000	2.2%
33	Mississippi	3,457,436,000	0.8%
17	Missouri	8,961,779,000	2.1%
48	Montana	1,127,316,000	0.3%
34	Nebraska	2,823,516,000	0.7%
37	Nevada	2,483,034,000	0.6%
41	New Hampshire	2,011,957,000	0.5%
9	New Jersey	14,464,531,000	3.4%
39	New Mexico	2,226,295,000	0.5%
2	New York	36,995,350,000	8.6%
11	North Carolina	12,184,752,000	2.8%
46	North Dakota	1,170,786,000	0.3%
7	Ohio	19,106,613,000	4.4%
30	Oklahoma	4,486,771,000	1.0%
28	Oregon	4,792,224,000	1.1%
5	Pennsylvania	21,561,895,000	5.0%
40	Rhode Island	2,018,792,000	0.5%
27	South Carolina	5,516,993,000	1.3%
45	South Dakota	1,320,107,000	0.3%
18	Tennessee	8,880,749,000	2.1%
3	Texas	27,651,008,000	6.4%
36	Utah	2,496,563,000	0.6%
49	Vermont	901,977,000	0.2%
14	Virginia	9,310,880,000	2.2%
19	Washington	8,536,612,000	2.0%
35	West Virginia	2,645,760,000	0.6%
15	Wisconsin	9,167,175,000	2.1%
50	Wyoming	615,873,000	0.1%

RANK ORDER

RANK	STATE	PAYROLL	% of USA
1	California	$43,661,974,000	10.1%
2	New York	36,995,350,000	8.6%
3	Texas	27,651,008,000	6.4%
4	Florida	23,841,810,000	5.5%
5	Pennsylvania	21,561,895,000	5.0%
6	Illinois	19,292,453,000	4.5%
7	Ohio	19,106,613,000	4.4%
8	Michigan	15,300,909,000	3.6%
9	New Jersey	14,464,531,000	3.4%
10	Massachusetts	14,095,510,000	3.3%
11	North Carolina	12,184,752,000	2.8%
12	Georgia	11,030,202,000	2.6%
13	Minnesota	9,548,543,000	2.2%
14	Virginia	9,310,880,000	2.2%
15	Wisconsin	9,167,175,000	2.1%
16	Indiana	9,150,042,000	2.1%
17	Missouri	8,961,779,000	2.1%
18	Tennessee	8,880,749,000	2.1%
19	Washington	8,536,612,000	2.0%
20	Maryland	8,151,517,000	1.9%
21	Connecticut	7,077,229,000	1.6%
22	Arizona	6,225,741,000	1.4%
23	Louisiana	6,209,043,000	1.4%
24	Colorado	6,079,877,000	1.4%
25	Alabama	6,055,366,000	1.4%
26	Kentucky	5,841,722,000	1.4%
27	South Carolina	5,516,993,000	1.3%
28	Oregon	4,792,224,000	1.1%
29	Iowa	4,544,672,000	1.1%
30	Oklahoma	4,486,771,000	1.0%
31	Kansas	4,135,169,000	1.0%
32	Arkansas	3,499,090,000	0.8%
33	Mississippi	3,457,436,000	0.8%
34	Nebraska	2,823,516,000	0.7%
35	West Virginia	2,645,760,000	0.6%
36	Utah	2,496,563,000	0.6%
37	Nevada	2,483,034,000	0.6%
38	Maine	2,257,114,000	0.5%
39	New Mexico	2,226,295,000	0.5%
40	Rhode Island	2,018,792,000	0.5%
41	New Hampshire	2,011,957,000	0.5%
42	Hawaii	1,679,915,000	0.4%
43	Idaho	1,496,658,000	0.3%
44	Delaware	1,485,818,000	0.3%
45	South Dakota	1,320,107,000	0.3%
46	North Dakota	1,170,786,000	0.3%
47	Alaska	1,139,280,000	0.3%
48	Montana	1,127,316,000	0.3%
49	Vermont	901,977,000	0.2%
50	Wyoming	615,873,000	0.1%
	District of Columbia	2,163,824,000	0.5%

Source: U.S. Bureau of the Census
   "County Business Patterns 2001 (NAICS)" (http://censtats.census.gov/cbpnaic/cbpnaic.shtml)
*Includes establishments exempt from as well as subject to the federal income tax. Includes those establishments
within the North American Industry Classification System (NAICS) classifications 621 (ambulatory health care
services), 622 (hospitals) and 623 (nursing and residential care facilities). See Facilities Chapter for establishments.

Average Pay per Health Care Establishment Employee in 2001

National Average = $34,498 per Employee*

ALPHA ORDER

RANK	STATE	AVERAGE PAY
31	Alabama	$32,721
1	Alaska	46,339
9	Arizona	36,656
39	Arkansas	30,642
7	California	37,255
10	Colorado	36,627
6	Connecticut	37,796
5	Delaware	38,519
17	Florida	35,238
16	Georgia	35,293
3	Hawaii	39,615
40	Idaho	30,527
14	Illinois	35,306
33	Indiana	32,040
49	Iowa	28,999
41	Kansas	30,397
34	Kentucky	31,690
43	Louisiana	30,207
37	Maine	31,289
12	Maryland	35,823
8	Massachusetts	36,795
20	Michigan	34,383
24	Minnesota	34,020
38	Mississippi	31,054
35	Missouri	31,487
50	Montana	26,675
36	Nebraska	31,451
2	Nevada	39,859
19	New Hampshire	34,952
4	New Jersey	38,672
32	New Mexico	32,539
11	New York	36,412
26	North Carolina	33,859
48	North Dakota	29,638
30	Ohio	32,871
42	Oklahoma	30,246
18	Oregon	34,996
29	Pennsylvania	32,906
23	Rhode Island	34,087
27	South Carolina	33,793
45	South Dakota	29,827
22	Tennessee	34,245
28	Texas	33,140
44	Utah	30,088
46	Vermont	29,767
15	Virginia	35,304
13	Washington	35,683
47	West Virginia	29,646
21	Wisconsin	34,342
25	Wyoming	33,998

RANK ORDER

RANK	STATE	AVERAGE PAY
1	Alaska	$46,339
2	Nevada	39,859
3	Hawaii	39,615
4	New Jersey	38,672
5	Delaware	38,519
6	Connecticut	37,796
7	California	37,255
8	Massachusetts	36,795
9	Arizona	36,656
10	Colorado	36,627
11	New York	36,412
12	Maryland	35,823
13	Washington	35,683
14	Illinois	35,306
15	Virginia	35,304
16	Georgia	35,293
17	Florida	35,238
18	Oregon	34,996
19	New Hampshire	34,952
20	Michigan	34,383
21	Wisconsin	34,342
22	Tennessee	34,245
23	Rhode Island	34,087
24	Minnesota	34,020
25	Wyoming	33,998
26	North Carolina	33,859
27	South Carolina	33,793
28	Texas	33,140
29	Pennsylvania	32,906
30	Ohio	32,871
31	Alabama	32,721
32	New Mexico	32,539
33	Indiana	32,040
34	Kentucky	31,690
35	Missouri	31,487
36	Nebraska	31,451
37	Maine	31,289
38	Mississippi	31,054
39	Arkansas	30,642
40	Idaho	30,527
41	Kansas	30,397
42	Oklahoma	30,246
43	Louisiana	30,207
44	Utah	30,088
45	South Dakota	29,827
46	Vermont	29,767
47	West Virginia	29,646
48	North Dakota	29,638
49	Iowa	28,999
50	Montana	26,675

District of Columbia   42,856

Source: Morgan Quitno Press using data from U.S. Bureau of the Census
"County Business Patterns 2001 (NAICS)" (http://censtats.census.gov/cbpnaic/cbpnaic.shtml)
*Includes establishments exempt from as well as subject to the federal income tax. Includes those establishments within the North American Industry Classification System (NAICS) classifications 621 (ambulatory health care services), 622 (hospitals) and 623 (nursing and residential care facilities). See Facilities Chapter for establishments.

V. INCIDENCE OF DISEASE

V. INCIDENCE OF DISEASE (Continued)

Estimated New Cancer Cases in 2004

National Estimated Total = 1,368,030 New Cases*

ALPHA ORDER

RANK	STATE	CASES	% of USA
20	Alabama	24,270	1.8%
50	Alaska	1,890	0.1%
21	Arizona	23,560	1.7%
32	Arkansas	14,800	1.1%
1	California	134,300	9.8%
30	Colorado	15,510	1.1%
28	Connecticut	17,010	1.2%
45	Delaware	4,390	0.3%
2	Florida	97,290	7.1%
11	Georgia	35,430	2.6%
43	Hawaii	5,070	0.4%
42	Idaho	5,460	0.4%
6	Illinois	60,280	4.4%
13	Indiana	32,160	2.4%
29	Iowa	15,940	1.2%
33	Kansas	12,940	0.9%
23	Kentucky	22,720	1.7%
22	Louisiana	23,540	1.7%
38	Maine	7,520	0.5%
19	Maryland	25,310	1.9%
12	Massachusetts	33,050	2.4%
8	Michigan	48,220	3.5%
23	Minnesota	22,720	1.7%
31	Mississippi	15,120	1.1%
16	Missouri	30,290	2.2%
44	Montana	5,000	0.4%
36	Nebraska	8,280	0.6%
35	Nevada	10,990	0.8%
40	New Hampshire	6,290	0.5%
9	New Jersey	43,830	3.2%
37	New Mexico	7,550	0.6%
3	New York	88,190	6.4%
10	North Carolina	40,240	2.9%
47	North Dakota	3,250	0.2%
7	Ohio	59,410	4.3%
26	Oklahoma	18,540	1.4%
27	Oregon	17,280	1.3%
5	Pennsylvania	72,590	5.3%
41	Rhode Island	5,950	0.4%
25	South Carolina	21,500	1.6%
46	South Dakota	4,000	0.3%
15	Tennessee	30,850	2.3%
4	Texas	84,530	6.2%
39	Utah	6,360	0.5%
48	Vermont	3,150	0.2%
14	Virginia	31,190	2.3%
17	Washington	27,380	2.0%
34	West Virginia	11,430	0.8%
18	Wisconsin	26,160	1.9%
49	Wyoming	2,430	0.2%

RANK ORDER

RANK	STATE	CASES	% of USA
1	California	134,300	9.8%
2	Florida	97,290	7.1%
3	New York	88,190	6.4%
4	Texas	84,530	6.2%
5	Pennsylvania	72,590	5.3%
6	Illinois	60,280	4.4%
7	Ohio	59,410	4.3%
8	Michigan	48,220	3.5%
9	New Jersey	43,830	3.2%
10	North Carolina	40,240	2.9%
11	Georgia	35,430	2.6%
12	Massachusetts	33,050	2.4%
13	Indiana	32,160	2.4%
14	Virginia	31,190	2.3%
15	Tennessee	30,850	2.3%
16	Missouri	30,290	2.2%
17	Washington	27,380	2.0%
18	Wisconsin	26,160	1.9%
19	Maryland	25,310	1.9%
20	Alabama	24,270	1.8%
21	Arizona	23,560	1.7%
22	Louisiana	23,540	1.7%
23	Kentucky	22,720	1.7%
23	Minnesota	22,720	1.7%
25	South Carolina	21,500	1.6%
26	Oklahoma	18,540	1.4%
27	Oregon	17,280	1.3%
28	Connecticut	17,010	1.2%
29	Iowa	15,940	1.2%
30	Colorado	15,510	1.1%
31	Mississippi	15,120	1.1%
32	Arkansas	14,800	1.1%
33	Kansas	12,940	0.9%
34	West Virginia	11,430	0.8%
35	Nevada	10,990	0.8%
36	Nebraska	8,280	0.6%
37	New Mexico	7,550	0.6%
38	Maine	7,520	0.5%
39	Utah	6,360	0.5%
40	New Hampshire	6,290	0.5%
41	Rhode Island	5,950	0.4%
42	Idaho	5,460	0.4%
43	Hawaii	5,070	0.4%
44	Montana	5,000	0.4%
45	Delaware	4,390	0.3%
46	South Dakota	4,000	0.3%
47	North Dakota	3,250	0.2%
48	Vermont	3,150	0.2%
49	Wyoming	2,430	0.2%
50	Alaska	1,890	0.1%
	District of Columbia	2,860	0.2%

Source: American Cancer Society
"Cancer Facts & Figures 2004" (Copyright 2004, Reprinted with permission from the American Cancer Society)
*These estimates are offered as a rough guide and should not be regarded as definitive. They are calculated according to the distribution of estimated 2004 cancer deaths by state. Totals do not include basal and squamous cell skin cancers or in situ carcinomas except urinary bladder.

Estimated Rate of New Cancer Cases in 2004

National Estimated Rate = 470.4 New Cases per 100,000 Population*

ALPHA ORDER			RANK ORDER		
RANK	STATE	RATE	RANK	STATE	RATE
10	Alabama	539.2	1	West Virginia	631.4
49	Alaska	291.3	2	Pennsylvania	587.0
41	Arizona	422.2	3	Maine	575.9
8	Arkansas	543.0	4	Florida	571.7
47	California	378.5	5	Rhode Island	552.9
48	Colorado	340.8	6	Kentucky	551.7
27	Connecticut	488.3	7	Montana	544.9
11	Delaware	537.0	8	Arkansas	543.0
4	Florida	571.7	9	Iowa	541.4
42	Georgia	408.0	10	Alabama	539.2
43	Hawaii	403.1	11	Delaware	537.0
45	Idaho	399.6	12	Missouri	531.0
33	Illinois	476.4	13	Tennessee	528.1
19	Indiana	519.1	14	Oklahoma	528.0
9	Iowa	541.4	15	Mississippi	524.8
35	Kansas	475.1	16	Louisiana	523.5
6	Kentucky	551.7	17	South Dakota	523.3
16	Louisiana	523.5	18	Ohio	519.5
3	Maine	575.9	19	Indiana	519.1
37	Maryland	459.4	20	South Carolina	518.4
21	Massachusetts	513.7	21	Massachusetts	513.7
31	Michigan	478.4	22	North Dakota	512.8
38	Minnesota	449.1	23	Vermont	508.8
15	Mississippi	524.8	24	New Jersey	507.4
12	Missouri	531.0	25	Nevada	490.4
7	Montana	544.9	26	New Hampshire	488.5
34	Nebraska	476.1	27	Connecticut	488.3
25	Nevada	490.4	28	Oregon	485.4
26	New Hampshire	488.5	29	Wyoming	484.8
24	New Jersey	507.4	30	North Carolina	478.6
44	New Mexico	402.7	31	Michigan	478.4
36	New York	459.6	32	Wisconsin	478.0
30	North Carolina	478.6	33	Illinois	476.4
22	North Dakota	512.8	34	Nebraska	476.1
18	Ohio	519.5	35	Kansas	475.1
14	Oklahoma	528.0	36	New York	459.6
28	Oregon	485.4	37	Maryland	459.4
2	Pennsylvania	587.0	38	Minnesota	449.1
5	Rhode Island	552.9	39	Washington	446.6
20	South Carolina	518.4	40	Virginia	422.3
17	South Dakota	523.3	41	Arizona	422.2
13	Tennessee	528.1	42	Georgia	408.0
46	Texas	382.2	43	Hawaii	403.1
50	Utah	270.5	44	New Mexico	402.7
23	Vermont	508.8	45	Idaho	399.6
40	Virginia	422.3	46	Texas	382.2
39	Washington	446.6	47	California	378.5
1	West Virginia	631.4	48	Colorado	340.8
32	Wisconsin	478.0	49	Alaska	291.3
29	Wyoming	484.8	50	Utah	270.5
				District of Columbia	507.6

Source: Morgan Quitno Press using data from American Cancer Society
"Cancer Facts & Figures 2004" (Copyright 2004, Reprinted with permission from the American Cancer Society)
*These estimates are offered as a rough guide and should not be regarded as definitive. They are calculated according to the distribution of estimated 2004 cancer deaths by state. Totals do not include basal and squamous cell skin cancers or in situ carcinomas except urinary bladder.

Age-Adjusted Cancer Incidence Rates for Males in 2000

National Rate = 560.0 New Cases per 100,000 Male Population*

ALPHA ORDER

RANK	STATE	RATE
34	Alabama	512.9
18	Alaska	553.5
42	Arizona	472.1
37	Arkansas	499.1
28	California	532.1
32	Colorado	517.3
7	Connecticut	595.0
NA	Delaware**	NA
10	Florida	586.8
41	Georgia	473.4
39	Hawaii	484.2
33	Idaho	516.0
14	Illinois	570.0
35	Indiana	507.5
17	Iowa	555.3
NA	Kansas**	NA
5	Kentucky	597.7
6	Louisiana	597.3
11	Maine	585.4
8	Maryland	589.2
4	Massachusetts	599.4
3	Michigan	611.8
20	Minnesota	547.9
38	Mississippi	484.5
27	Missouri	533.4
22	Montana	543.4
21	Nebraska	543.7
40	Nevada	475.5
25	New Hampshire	539.4
2	New Jersey	626.7
44	New Mexico	462.8
16	New York	561.6
31	North Carolina	520.2
30	North Dakota	521.9
23	Ohio	541.0
45	Oklahoma	451.5
24	Oregon	539.9
9	Pennsylvania	588.0
1	Rhode Island	635.3
13	South Carolina	573.5
NA	South Dakota**	NA
NA	Tennessee**	NA
29	Texas	532.0
43	Utah	471.3
NA	Vermont**	NA
36	Virginia	501.4
15	Washington	569.7
12	West Virginia	576.6
19	Wisconsin	549.1
26	Wyoming	539.0

RANK ORDER

RANK	STATE	RATE
1	Rhode Island	635.3
2	New Jersey	626.7
3	Michigan	611.8
4	Massachusetts	599.4
5	Kentucky	597.7
6	Louisiana	597.3
7	Connecticut	595.0
8	Maryland	589.2
9	Pennsylvania	588.0
10	Florida	586.8
11	Maine	585.4
12	West Virginia	576.6
13	South Carolina	573.5
14	Illinois	570.0
15	Washington	569.7
16	New York	561.6
17	Iowa	555.3
18	Alaska	553.5
19	Wisconsin	549.1
20	Minnesota	547.9
21	Nebraska	543.7
22	Montana	543.4
23	Ohio	541.0
24	Oregon	539.9
25	New Hampshire	539.4
26	Wyoming	539.0
27	Missouri	533.4
28	California	532.1
29	Texas	532.0
30	North Dakota	521.9
31	North Carolina	520.2
32	Colorado	517.3
33	Idaho	516.0
34	Alabama	512.9
35	Indiana	507.5
36	Virginia	501.4
37	Arkansas	499.1
38	Mississippi	484.5
39	Hawaii	484.2
40	Nevada	475.5
41	Georgia	473.4
42	Arizona	472.1
43	Utah	471.3
44	New Mexico	462.8
45	Oklahoma	451.5
NA	Delaware**	NA
NA	Kansas**	NA
NA	South Dakota**	NA
NA	Tennessee**	NA
NA	Vermont**	NA

District of Columbia   685.9

Source: American Cancer Society
    "Cancer Facts & Figures 2004" (Copyright 2004, Reprinted with permission from the American Cancer Society)
*For 1996 to 2000. Age-adjusted to the 2000 U.S. standard population.
**Not available.

Age-Adjusted Cancer Incidence Rates for Females in 2000

National Rate = 419.9 New Cases per 100,000 Female Population*

ALPHA ORDER

RANK	STATE	RATE
39	Alabama	357.8
4	Alaska	447.1
35	Arizona	369.6
40	Arkansas	353.8
22	California	412.0
26	Colorado	399.2
3	Connecticut	450.2
NA	Delaware**	NA
7	Florida	439.3
44	Georgia	336.3
32	Hawaii	384.2
28	Idaho	395.0
15	Illinois	427.4
27	Indiana	396.8
17	Iowa	421.7
NA	Kansas**	NA
12	Kentucky	430.0
29	Louisiana	393.7
9	Maine	433.3
16	Maryland	425.7
5	Massachusetts	445.2
8	Michigan	434.9
24	Minnesota	410.5
45	Mississippi	327.5
18	Missouri	417.1
21	Montana	412.8
25	Nebraska	408.7
31	Nevada	387.6
20	New Hampshire	413.6
2	New Jersey	452.3
41	New Mexico	353.1
11	New York	430.6
36	North Carolina	368.8
37	North Dakota	368.5
19	Ohio	415.2
42	Oklahoma	349.9
13	Oregon	429.5
14	Pennsylvania	428.5
1	Rhode Island	458.4
33	South Carolina	379.9
NA	South Dakota**	NA
NA	Tennessee**	NA
34	Texas	378.2
43	Utah	343.0
NA	Vermont**	NA
38	Virginia	367.7
6	Washington	444.5
10	West Virginia	431.0
23	Wisconsin	411.8
29	Wyoming	393.7

RANK ORDER

RANK	STATE	RATE
1	Rhode Island	458.4
2	New Jersey	452.3
3	Connecticut	450.2
4	Alaska	447.1
5	Massachusetts	445.2
6	Washington	444.5
7	Florida	439.3
8	Michigan	434.9
9	Maine	433.3
10	West Virginia	431.0
11	New York	430.6
12	Kentucky	430.0
13	Oregon	429.5
14	Pennsylvania	428.5
15	Illinois	427.4
16	Maryland	425.7
17	Iowa	421.7
18	Missouri	417.1
19	Ohio	415.2
20	New Hampshire	413.6
21	Montana	412.8
22	California	412.0
23	Wisconsin	411.8
24	Minnesota	410.5
25	Nebraska	408.7
26	Colorado	399.2
27	Indiana	396.8
28	Idaho	395.0
29	Louisiana	393.7
29	Wyoming	393.7
31	Nevada	387.6
32	Hawaii	384.2
33	South Carolina	379.9
34	Texas	378.2
35	Arizona	369.6
36	North Carolina	368.8
37	North Dakota	368.5
38	Virginia	367.7
39	Alabama	357.8
40	Arkansas	353.8
41	New Mexico	353.1
42	Oklahoma	349.9
43	Utah	343.0
44	Georgia	336.3
45	Mississippi	327.5
NA	Delaware**	NA
NA	Kansas**	NA
NA	South Dakota**	NA
NA	Tennessee**	NA
NA	Vermont**	NA

District of Columbia 439.7

Source: American Cancer Society
 "Cancer Facts & Figures 2004" (Copyright 2004, Reprinted with permission from the American Cancer Society)
For 1996 to 2000. Age-adjusted to the 2000 U.S. standard population.
**Not available.*

Estimated New Cases of Bladder Cancer in 2004

National Estimated Total = 60,240 New Cases*

ALPHA ORDER

RANK	STATE	CASES	% of USA
24	Alabama	810	1.3%
48	Alaska	90	0.1%
17	Arizona	1,140	1.9%
32	Arkansas	570	0.9%
1	California	5,730	9.5%
30	Colorado	620	1.0%
28	Connecticut	660	1.1%
NA	Delaware**	NA	NA
2	Florida	4,550	7.6%
11	Georgia	1,520	2.5%
44	Hawaii	190	0.3%
38	Idaho	330	0.5%
7	Illinois	2,610	4.3%
16	Indiana	1,230	2.0%
30	Iowa	620	1.0%
28	Kansas	660	1.1%
23	Kentucky	850	1.4%
26	Louisiana	760	1.3%
35	Maine	470	0.8%
17	Maryland	1,140	1.9%
10	Massachusetts	1,800	3.0%
8	Michigan	2,370	3.9%
21	Minnesota	1,040	1.7%
35	Mississippi	470	0.8%
17	Missouri	1,140	1.9%
38	Montana	330	0.5%
38	Nebraska	330	0.5%
34	Nevada	520	0.9%
37	New Hampshire	380	0.6%
9	New Jersey	2,040	3.4%
38	New Mexico	330	0.5%
3	New York	4,410	7.3%
12	North Carolina	1,470	2.4%
44	North Dakota	190	0.3%
6	Ohio	2,940	4.9%
26	Oklahoma	760	1.3%
22	Oregon	900	1.5%
4	Pennsylvania	3,510	5.8%
38	Rhode Island	330	0.5%
24	South Carolina	810	1.3%
46	South Dakota	140	0.2%
20	Tennessee	1,090	1.8%
5	Texas	3,270	5.4%
43	Utah	280	0.5%
46	Vermont	140	0.2%
13	Virginia	1,330	2.2%
13	Washington	1,330	2.2%
32	West Virginia	570	0.9%
15	Wisconsin	1,280	2.1%
48	Wyoming	90	0.1%

RANK ORDER

RANK	STATE	CASES	% of USA
1	California	5,730	9.5%
2	Florida	4,550	7.6%
3	New York	4,410	7.3%
4	Pennsylvania	3,510	5.8%
5	Texas	3,270	5.4%
6	Ohio	2,940	4.9%
7	Illinois	2,610	4.3%
8	Michigan	2,370	3.9%
9	New Jersey	2,040	3.4%
10	Massachusetts	1,800	3.0%
11	Georgia	1,520	2.5%
12	North Carolina	1,470	2.4%
13	Virginia	1,330	2.2%
13	Washington	1,330	2.2%
15	Wisconsin	1,280	2.1%
16	Indiana	1,230	2.0%
17	Arizona	1,140	1.9%
17	Maryland	1,140	1.9%
17	Missouri	1,140	1.9%
20	Tennessee	1,090	1.8%
21	Minnesota	1,040	1.7%
22	Oregon	900	1.5%
23	Kentucky	850	1.4%
24	Alabama	810	1.3%
24	South Carolina	810	1.3%
26	Louisiana	760	1.3%
26	Oklahoma	760	1.3%
28	Connecticut	660	1.1%
28	Kansas	660	1.1%
30	Colorado	620	1.0%
30	Iowa	620	1.0%
32	Arkansas	570	0.9%
32	West Virginia	570	0.9%
34	Nevada	520	0.9%
35	Maine	470	0.8%
35	Mississippi	470	0.8%
37	New Hampshire	380	0.6%
38	Idaho	330	0.5%
38	Montana	330	0.5%
38	Nebraska	330	0.5%
38	New Mexico	330	0.5%
38	Rhode Island	330	0.5%
43	Utah	280	0.5%
44	Hawaii	190	0.3%
44	North Dakota	190	0.3%
46	South Dakota	140	0.2%
46	Vermont	140	0.2%
48	Alaska	90	0.1%
48	Wyoming	90	0.1%
NA	Delaware**	NA	NA
	District of Columbia	90	0.1%

Source: American Cancer Society
   "Cancer Facts & Figures 2004" (Copyright 2004, Reprinted with permission from the American Cancer Society)
*These estimates are offered as a rough guide and should be interpreted with caution. They are calculated
according to the distribution of estimated 2004 cancer deaths by state.
**Not available.

Estimated Rate of New Bladder Cancer Cases in 2004

National Estimated Rate = 20.7 New Cases per 100,000 Population*

ALPHA ORDER

RANK	STATE	RATE
36	Alabama	18.0
47	Alaska	13.9
28	Arizona	20.4
23	Arkansas	20.9
44	California	16.1
48	Colorado	13.6
33	Connecticut	18.9
NA	Delaware**	NA
9	Florida	26.7
40	Georgia	17.5
45	Hawaii	15.1
12	Idaho	24.2
25	Illinois	20.6
30	Indiana	19.9
22	Iowa	21.1
12	Kansas	24.2
25	Kentucky	20.6
42	Louisiana	16.9
1	Maine	36.0
24	Maryland	20.7
8	Massachusetts	28.0
15	Michigan	23.5
25	Minnesota	20.6
43	Mississippi	16.3
29	Missouri	20.0
1	Montana	36.0
32	Nebraska	19.0
17	Nevada	23.2
6	New Hampshire	29.5
14	New Jersey	23.6
39	New Mexico	17.6
18	New York	23.0
40	North Carolina	17.5
5	North Dakota	30.0
10	Ohio	25.7
21	Oklahoma	21.6
11	Oregon	25.3
7	Pennsylvania	28.4
4	Rhode Island	30.7
31	South Carolina	19.5
35	South Dakota	18.3
34	Tennessee	18.7
46	Texas	14.8
49	Utah	11.9
19	Vermont	22.6
36	Virginia	18.0
20	Washington	21.7
3	West Virginia	31.5
16	Wisconsin	23.4
36	Wyoming	18.0

RANK ORDER

RANK	STATE	RATE
1	Maine	36.0
1	Montana	36.0
3	West Virginia	31.5
4	Rhode Island	30.7
5	North Dakota	30.0
6	New Hampshire	29.5
7	Pennsylvania	28.4
8	Massachusetts	28.0
9	Florida	26.7
10	Ohio	25.7
11	Oregon	25.3
12	Idaho	24.2
12	Kansas	24.2
14	New Jersey	23.6
15	Michigan	23.5
16	Wisconsin	23.4
17	Nevada	23.2
18	New York	23.0
19	Vermont	22.6
20	Washington	21.7
21	Oklahoma	21.6
22	Iowa	21.1
23	Arkansas	20.9
24	Maryland	20.7
25	Illinois	20.6
25	Kentucky	20.6
25	Minnesota	20.6
28	Arizona	20.4
29	Missouri	20.0
30	Indiana	19.9
31	South Carolina	19.5
32	Nebraska	19.0
33	Connecticut	18.9
34	Tennessee	18.7
35	South Dakota	18.3
36	Alabama	18.0
36	Virginia	18.0
36	Wyoming	18.0
39	New Mexico	17.6
40	Georgia	17.5
40	North Carolina	17.5
42	Louisiana	16.9
43	Mississippi	16.3
44	California	16.1
45	Hawaii	15.1
46	Texas	14.8
47	Alaska	13.9
48	Colorado	13.6
49	Utah	11.9
NA	Delaware**	NA

	District of Columbia	16.0

Source: Morgan Quitno Press using data from American Cancer Society
 "Cancer Facts & Figures 2004" (Copyright 2004, Reprinted with permission from the American Cancer Society)
*These estimates are offered as a rough guide and should be interpreted with caution. They are calculated according to the distribution of estimated 2004 cancer deaths by state. Rates calculated using 2003 Census resident population estimates.
**Not available.

Estimated New Female Breast Cancer Cases in 2004

National Estimated Total = 215,990 New Cases*

ALPHA ORDER

RANK	STATE	CASES	% of USA
20	Alabama	3,980	1.8%
49	Alaska	270	0.1%
20	Arizona	3,980	1.8%
32	Arkansas	2,050	0.9%
1	California	21,860	10.1%
29	Colorado	2,580	1.2%
27	Connecticut	2,850	1.3%
44	Delaware	700	0.3%
3	Florida	13,350	6.2%
11	Georgia	6,080	2.8%
43	Hawaii	750	0.3%
39	Idaho	920	0.4%
7	Illinois	9,640	4.5%
14	Indiana	4,790	2.2%
31	Iowa	2,320	1.1%
33	Kansas	1,880	0.9%
24	Kentucky	3,340	1.5%
22	Louisiana	3,930	1.8%
39	Maine	920	0.4%
17	Maryland	4,090	1.9%
13	Massachusetts	5,170	2.4%
9	Michigan	7,270	3.4%
23	Minnesota	3,610	1.7%
30	Mississippi	2,480	1.1%
15	Missouri	4,680	2.2%
45	Montana	590	0.3%
36	Nebraska	1,290	0.6%
34	Nevada	1,620	0.8%
39	New Hampshire	920	0.4%
8	New Jersey	7,970	3.7%
38	New Mexico	1,020	0.5%
2	New York	15,190	7.0%
12	North Carolina	5,870	2.7%
47	North Dakota	540	0.3%
6	Ohio	10,070	4.7%
26	Oklahoma	2,910	1.3%
28	Oregon	2,750	1.3%
5	Pennsylvania	11,200	5.2%
42	Rhode Island	860	0.4%
25	South Carolina	3,280	1.5%
47	South Dakota	540	0.3%
16	Tennessee	4,310	2.0%
4	Texas	12,980	6.0%
37	Utah	1,080	0.5%
45	Vermont	590	0.3%
10	Virginia	6,350	2.9%
18	Washington	4,040	1.9%
34	West Virginia	1,620	0.8%
18	Wisconsin	4,040	1.9%
49	Wyoming	270	0.1%

RANK ORDER

RANK	STATE	CASES	% of USA
1	California	21,860	10.1%
2	New York	15,190	7.0%
3	Florida	13,350	6.2%
4	Texas	12,980	6.0%
5	Pennsylvania	11,200	5.2%
6	Ohio	10,070	4.7%
7	Illinois	9,640	4.5%
8	New Jersey	7,970	3.7%
9	Michigan	7,270	3.4%
10	Virginia	6,350	2.9%
11	Georgia	6,080	2.8%
12	North Carolina	5,870	2.7%
13	Massachusetts	5,170	2.4%
14	Indiana	4,790	2.2%
15	Missouri	4,680	2.2%
16	Tennessee	4,310	2.0%
17	Maryland	4,090	1.9%
18	Washington	4,040	1.9%
18	Wisconsin	4,040	1.9%
20	Alabama	3,980	1.8%
20	Arizona	3,980	1.8%
22	Louisiana	3,930	1.8%
23	Minnesota	3,610	1.7%
24	Kentucky	3,340	1.5%
25	South Carolina	3,280	1.5%
26	Oklahoma	2,910	1.3%
27	Connecticut	2,850	1.3%
28	Oregon	2,750	1.3%
29	Colorado	2,580	1.2%
30	Mississippi	2,480	1.1%
31	Iowa	2,320	1.1%
32	Arkansas	2,050	0.9%
33	Kansas	1,880	0.9%
34	Nevada	1,620	0.8%
34	West Virginia	1,620	0.8%
36	Nebraska	1,290	0.6%
37	Utah	1,080	0.5%
38	New Mexico	1,020	0.5%
39	Idaho	920	0.4%
39	Maine	920	0.4%
39	New Hampshire	920	0.4%
42	Rhode Island	860	0.4%
43	Hawaii	750	0.3%
44	Delaware	700	0.3%
45	Montana	590	0.3%
45	Vermont	590	0.3%
47	North Dakota	540	0.3%
47	South Dakota	540	0.3%
49	Alaska	270	0.1%
49	Wyoming	270	0.1%
	District of Columbia	590	0.3%

Source: American Cancer Society
    "Cancer Facts & Figures 2004" (Copyright 2004, Reprinted with permission from the American Cancer Society)
*These estimates are offered as a rough guide and should be interpreted with caution. They are calculated
according to the distribution of estimated 2004 cancer deaths by state.

Age-Adjusted Incidence Rate of Female Breast Cancer Cases in 2000

National Rate = 131.7 New Cases per 100,000 Female Population*

<u>ALPHA ORDER</u>

RANK	STATE	RATE
42	Alabama	113.6
5	Alaska	138.4
35	Arizona	120.9
41	Arkansas	114.9
11	California	133.8
9	Colorado	135.4
4	Connecticut	143.1
NA	Delaware**	NA
18	Florida	131.1
43	Georgia	110.5
18	Hawaii	131.1
24	Idaho	129.2
12	Illinois	133.3
28	Indiana	124.8
21	Iowa	130.4
NA	Kansas**	NA
31	Kentucky	123.8
34	Louisiana	121.6
26	Maine	127.0
8	Maryland	137.0
3	Massachusetts	143.3
15	Michigan	132.0
7	Minnesota	137.3
45	Mississippi	104.5
25	Missouri	127.6
10	Montana	135.1
22	Nebraska	130.2
44	Nevada	106.3
13	New Hampshire	133.0
6	New Jersey	138.2
38	New Mexico	116.9
17	New York	131.2
33	North Carolina	122.0
28	North Dakota	124.8
23	Ohio	130.0
40	Oklahoma	115.5
2	Oregon	143.4
20	Pennsylvania	130.6
14	Rhode Island	132.5
32	South Carolina	123.0
NA	South Dakota**	NA
NA	Tennessee**	NA
37	Texas	118.6
39	Utah	116.8
NA	Vermont**	NA
30	Virginia	124.2
1	Washington	145.2
36	West Virginia	119.8
16	Wisconsin	131.8
27	Wyoming	125.4

<u>RANK ORDER</u>

RANK	STATE	RATE
1	Washington	145.2
2	Oregon	143.4
3	Massachusetts	143.3
4	Connecticut	143.1
5	Alaska	138.4
6	New Jersey	138.2
7	Minnesota	137.3
8	Maryland	137.0
9	Colorado	135.4
10	Montana	135.1
11	California	133.8
12	Illinois	133.3
13	New Hampshire	133.0
14	Rhode Island	132.5
15	Michigan	132.0
16	Wisconsin	131.8
17	New York	131.2
18	Florida	131.1
18	Hawaii	131.1
20	Pennsylvania	130.6
21	Iowa	130.4
22	Nebraska	130.2
23	Ohio	130.0
24	Idaho	129.2
25	Missouri	127.6
26	Maine	127.0
27	Wyoming	125.4
28	Indiana	124.8
28	North Dakota	124.8
30	Virginia	124.2
31	Kentucky	123.8
32	South Carolina	123.0
33	North Carolina	122.0
34	Louisiana	121.6
35	Arizona	120.9
36	West Virginia	119.8
37	Texas	118.6
38	New Mexico	116.9
39	Utah	116.8
40	Oklahoma	115.5
41	Arkansas	114.9
42	Alabama	113.6
43	Georgia	110.5
44	Nevada	106.3
45	Mississippi	104.5
NA	Delaware**	NA
NA	Kansas**	NA
NA	South Dakota**	NA
NA	Tennessee**	NA
NA	Vermont**	NA
	District of Columbia	142.9

Source: American Cancer Society

"Cancer Facts & Figures 2004" (Copyright 2004, Reprinted with permission from the American Cancer Society)
*For 1996 to 2000. Age-adjusted to the 2000 U.S. standard population.
**Not available.

Percent of Women Who Have Ever Had a Mammogram: 2002

National Median = 63.4% of Women*

<table>
<tr><td colspan="3">ALPHA ORDER</td><td colspan="3">RANK ORDER</td></tr>
<tr><td>RANK</td><td>STATE</td><td>PERCENT</td><td>RANK</td><td>STATE</td><td>PERCENT</td></tr>
<tr><td>9</td><td>Alabama</td><td>66.6</td><td>1</td><td>Florida</td><td>69.5</td></tr>
<tr><td>48</td><td>Alaska</td><td>58.5</td><td>2</td><td>Delaware</td><td>69.1</td></tr>
<tr><td>12</td><td>Arizona</td><td>66.1</td><td>3</td><td>Connecticut</td><td>67.7</td></tr>
<tr><td>41</td><td>Arkansas</td><td>62.0</td><td>4</td><td>Maine</td><td>67.4</td></tr>
<tr><td>47</td><td>California</td><td>59.1</td><td>5</td><td>South Carolina</td><td>67.3</td></tr>
<tr><td>42</td><td>Colorado</td><td>61.3</td><td>5</td><td>West Virginia</td><td>67.3</td></tr>
<tr><td>3</td><td>Connecticut</td><td>67.7</td><td>7</td><td>Pennsylvania</td><td>66.9</td></tr>
<tr><td>2</td><td>Delaware</td><td>69.1</td><td>8</td><td>Rhode Island</td><td>66.8</td></tr>
<tr><td>1</td><td>Florida</td><td>69.5</td><td>9</td><td>Alabama</td><td>66.6</td></tr>
<tr><td>32</td><td>Georgia</td><td>62.9</td><td>10</td><td>Ohio</td><td>66.4</td></tr>
<tr><td>46</td><td>Hawaii</td><td>60.1</td><td>11</td><td>Michigan</td><td>66.2</td></tr>
<tr><td>49</td><td>Idaho</td><td>57.8</td><td>12</td><td>Arizona</td><td>66.1</td></tr>
<tr><td>32</td><td>Illinois</td><td>62.9</td><td>13</td><td>Maryland</td><td>65.5</td></tr>
<tr><td>30</td><td>Indiana</td><td>63.3</td><td>14</td><td>Oregon</td><td>65.1</td></tr>
<tr><td>15</td><td>Iowa</td><td>64.9</td><td>15</td><td>Iowa</td><td>64.9</td></tr>
<tr><td>38</td><td>Kansas</td><td>62.2</td><td>15</td><td>New Hampshire</td><td>64.9</td></tr>
<tr><td>18</td><td>Kentucky</td><td>64.8</td><td>15</td><td>North Carolina</td><td>64.9</td></tr>
<tr><td>21</td><td>Louisiana</td><td>64.1</td><td>18</td><td>Kentucky</td><td>64.8</td></tr>
<tr><td>4</td><td>Maine</td><td>67.4</td><td>19</td><td>North Dakota</td><td>64.5</td></tr>
<tr><td>13</td><td>Maryland</td><td>65.5</td><td>20</td><td>Massachusetts</td><td>64.4</td></tr>
<tr><td>20</td><td>Massachusetts</td><td>64.4</td><td>21</td><td>Louisiana</td><td>64.1</td></tr>
<tr><td>11</td><td>Michigan</td><td>66.2</td><td>22</td><td>Missouri</td><td>64.0</td></tr>
<tr><td>28</td><td>Minnesota</td><td>63.4</td><td>23</td><td>New Jersey</td><td>63.9</td></tr>
<tr><td>28</td><td>Mississippi</td><td>63.4</td><td>24</td><td>Montana</td><td>63.8</td></tr>
<tr><td>22</td><td>Missouri</td><td>64.0</td><td>25</td><td>Virginia</td><td>63.7</td></tr>
<tr><td>24</td><td>Montana</td><td>63.8</td><td>26</td><td>New York</td><td>63.5</td></tr>
<tr><td>38</td><td>Nebraska</td><td>62.2</td><td>26</td><td>Tennessee</td><td>63.5</td></tr>
<tr><td>31</td><td>Nevada</td><td>63.0</td><td>28</td><td>Minnesota</td><td>63.4</td></tr>
<tr><td>15</td><td>New Hampshire</td><td>64.9</td><td>28</td><td>Mississippi</td><td>63.4</td></tr>
<tr><td>23</td><td>New Jersey</td><td>63.9</td><td>30</td><td>Indiana</td><td>63.3</td></tr>
<tr><td>44</td><td>New Mexico</td><td>60.4</td><td>31</td><td>Nevada</td><td>63.0</td></tr>
<tr><td>26</td><td>New York</td><td>63.5</td><td>32</td><td>Georgia</td><td>62.9</td></tr>
<tr><td>15</td><td>North Carolina</td><td>64.9</td><td>32</td><td>Illinois</td><td>62.9</td></tr>
<tr><td>19</td><td>North Dakota</td><td>64.5</td><td>34</td><td>Vermont</td><td>62.7</td></tr>
<tr><td>10</td><td>Ohio</td><td>66.4</td><td>34</td><td>Wisconsin</td><td>62.7</td></tr>
<tr><td>38</td><td>Oklahoma</td><td>62.2</td><td>36</td><td>Washington</td><td>62.6</td></tr>
<tr><td>14</td><td>Oregon</td><td>65.1</td><td>37</td><td>South Dakota</td><td>62.4</td></tr>
<tr><td>7</td><td>Pennsylvania</td><td>66.9</td><td>38</td><td>Kansas</td><td>62.2</td></tr>
<tr><td>8</td><td>Rhode Island</td><td>66.8</td><td>38</td><td>Nebraska</td><td>62.2</td></tr>
<tr><td>5</td><td>South Carolina</td><td>67.3</td><td>38</td><td>Oklahoma</td><td>62.2</td></tr>
<tr><td>37</td><td>South Dakota</td><td>62.4</td><td>41</td><td>Arkansas</td><td>62.0</td></tr>
<tr><td>26</td><td>Tennessee</td><td>63.5</td><td>42</td><td>Colorado</td><td>61.3</td></tr>
<tr><td>45</td><td>Texas</td><td>60.2</td><td>43</td><td>Wyoming</td><td>60.5</td></tr>
<tr><td>50</td><td>Utah</td><td>51.4</td><td>44</td><td>New Mexico</td><td>60.4</td></tr>
<tr><td>34</td><td>Vermont</td><td>62.7</td><td>45</td><td>Texas</td><td>60.2</td></tr>
<tr><td>25</td><td>Virginia</td><td>63.7</td><td>46</td><td>Hawaii</td><td>60.1</td></tr>
<tr><td>36</td><td>Washington</td><td>62.6</td><td>47</td><td>California</td><td>59.1</td></tr>
<tr><td>5</td><td>West Virginia</td><td>67.3</td><td>48</td><td>Alaska</td><td>58.5</td></tr>
<tr><td>34</td><td>Wisconsin</td><td>62.7</td><td>49</td><td>Idaho</td><td>57.8</td></tr>
<tr><td>43</td><td>Wyoming</td><td>60.5</td><td>50</td><td>Utah</td><td>51.4</td></tr>
<tr><td></td><td></td><td></td><td></td><td>District of Columbia</td><td>61.4</td></tr>
</table>

Source: U.S. Department of Health and Human Services, Centers for Disease Control and Prevention
"2002 Behavioral Risk Factor Surveillance Summary Prevalence Data" (http://apps.nccd.cdc.gov/brfss/)
*Percent of women 18 years and older.

Estimated New Colon and Rectum Cancer Cases in 2004

National Estimated Total = 146,940 New Cases*

<table>
<tr><td colspan="4">ALPHA ORDER</td><td colspan="4">RANK ORDER</td></tr>
<tr><td>RANK</td><td>STATE</td><td>CASES</td><td>% of USA</td><td>RANK</td><td>STATE</td><td>CASES</td><td>% of USA</td></tr>
<tr><td>22</td><td>Alabama</td><td>2,330</td><td>1.6%</td><td>1</td><td>California</td><td>13,880</td><td>9.4%</td></tr>
<tr><td>50</td><td>Alaska</td><td>210</td><td>0.1%</td><td>2</td><td>Florida</td><td>9,950</td><td>6.8%</td></tr>
<tr><td>21</td><td>Arizona</td><td>2,490</td><td>1.7%</td><td>3</td><td>New York</td><td>9,890</td><td>6.7%</td></tr>
<tr><td>30</td><td>Arkansas</td><td>1,630</td><td>1.1%</td><td>4</td><td>Texas</td><td>9,220</td><td>6.3%</td></tr>
<tr><td>1</td><td>California</td><td>13,880</td><td>9.4%</td><td>5</td><td>Pennsylvania</td><td>8,570</td><td>5.8%</td></tr>
<tr><td>31</td><td>Colorado</td><td>1,610</td><td>1.1%</td><td>6</td><td>Ohio</td><td>6,760</td><td>4.6%</td></tr>
<tr><td>29</td><td>Connecticut</td><td>1,710</td><td>1.2%</td><td>7</td><td>Illinois</td><td>6,680</td><td>4.5%</td></tr>
<tr><td>46</td><td>Delaware</td><td>410</td><td>0.3%</td><td>8</td><td>Michigan</td><td>4,920</td><td>3.3%</td></tr>
<tr><td>2</td><td>Florida</td><td>9,950</td><td>6.8%</td><td>9</td><td>New Jersey</td><td>4,770</td><td>3.2%</td></tr>
<tr><td>15</td><td>Georgia</td><td>3,420</td><td>2.3%</td><td>10</td><td>North Carolina</td><td>4,120</td><td>2.8%</td></tr>
<tr><td>43</td><td>Hawaii</td><td>520</td><td>0.4%</td><td>11</td><td>Virginia</td><td>3,550</td><td>2.4%</td></tr>
<tr><td>42</td><td>Idaho</td><td>540</td><td>0.4%</td><td>12</td><td>Indiana</td><td>3,520</td><td>2.4%</td></tr>
<tr><td>7</td><td>Illinois</td><td>6,680</td><td>4.5%</td><td>12</td><td>Massachusetts</td><td>3,520</td><td>2.4%</td></tr>
<tr><td>12</td><td>Indiana</td><td>3,520</td><td>2.4%</td><td>14</td><td>Tennessee</td><td>3,470</td><td>2.4%</td></tr>
<tr><td>27</td><td>Iowa</td><td>1,840</td><td>1.3%</td><td>15</td><td>Georgia</td><td>3,420</td><td>2.3%</td></tr>
<tr><td>33</td><td>Kansas</td><td>1,480</td><td>1.0%</td><td>16</td><td>Missouri</td><td>3,240</td><td>2.2%</td></tr>
<tr><td>23</td><td>Kentucky</td><td>2,310</td><td>1.6%</td><td>17</td><td>Wisconsin</td><td>2,900</td><td>2.0%</td></tr>
<tr><td>20</td><td>Louisiana</td><td>2,560</td><td>1.7%</td><td>18</td><td>Maryland</td><td>2,820</td><td>1.9%</td></tr>
<tr><td>38</td><td>Maine</td><td>800</td><td>0.5%</td><td>19</td><td>Washington</td><td>2,720</td><td>1.9%</td></tr>
<tr><td>18</td><td>Maryland</td><td>2,820</td><td>1.9%</td><td>20</td><td>Louisiana</td><td>2,560</td><td>1.7%</td></tr>
<tr><td>12</td><td>Massachusetts</td><td>3,520</td><td>2.4%</td><td>21</td><td>Arizona</td><td>2,490</td><td>1.7%</td></tr>
<tr><td>8</td><td>Michigan</td><td>4,920</td><td>3.3%</td><td>22</td><td>Alabama</td><td>2,330</td><td>1.6%</td></tr>
<tr><td>25</td><td>Minnesota</td><td>2,200</td><td>1.5%</td><td>23</td><td>Kentucky</td><td>2,310</td><td>1.6%</td></tr>
<tr><td>31</td><td>Mississippi</td><td>1,610</td><td>1.1%</td><td>24</td><td>South Carolina</td><td>2,280</td><td>1.6%</td></tr>
<tr><td>16</td><td>Missouri</td><td>3,240</td><td>2.2%</td><td>25</td><td>Minnesota</td><td>2,200</td><td>1.5%</td></tr>
<tr><td>45</td><td>Montana</td><td>470</td><td>0.3%</td><td>26</td><td>Oklahoma</td><td>2,070</td><td>1.4%</td></tr>
<tr><td>36</td><td>Nebraska</td><td>1,010</td><td>0.7%</td><td>27</td><td>Iowa</td><td>1,840</td><td>1.3%</td></tr>
<tr><td>35</td><td>Nevada</td><td>1,240</td><td>0.8%</td><td>28</td><td>Oregon</td><td>1,790</td><td>1.2%</td></tr>
<tr><td>39</td><td>New Hampshire</td><td>670</td><td>0.5%</td><td>29</td><td>Connecticut</td><td>1,710</td><td>1.2%</td></tr>
<tr><td>9</td><td>New Jersey</td><td>4,770</td><td>3.2%</td><td>30</td><td>Arkansas</td><td>1,630</td><td>1.1%</td></tr>
<tr><td>37</td><td>New Mexico</td><td>830</td><td>0.6%</td><td>31</td><td>Colorado</td><td>1,610</td><td>1.1%</td></tr>
<tr><td>3</td><td>New York</td><td>9,890</td><td>6.7%</td><td>31</td><td>Mississippi</td><td>1,610</td><td>1.1%</td></tr>
<tr><td>10</td><td>North Carolina</td><td>4,120</td><td>2.8%</td><td>33</td><td>Kansas</td><td>1,480</td><td>1.0%</td></tr>
<tr><td>47</td><td>North Dakota</td><td>360</td><td>0.2%</td><td>34</td><td>West Virginia</td><td>1,270</td><td>0.9%</td></tr>
<tr><td>6</td><td>Ohio</td><td>6,760</td><td>4.6%</td><td>35</td><td>Nevada</td><td>1,240</td><td>0.8%</td></tr>
<tr><td>26</td><td>Oklahoma</td><td>2,070</td><td>1.4%</td><td>36</td><td>Nebraska</td><td>1,010</td><td>0.7%</td></tr>
<tr><td>28</td><td>Oregon</td><td>1,790</td><td>1.2%</td><td>37</td><td>New Mexico</td><td>830</td><td>0.6%</td></tr>
<tr><td>5</td><td>Pennsylvania</td><td>8,570</td><td>5.8%</td><td>38</td><td>Maine</td><td>800</td><td>0.5%</td></tr>
<tr><td>41</td><td>Rhode Island</td><td>650</td><td>0.4%</td><td>39</td><td>New Hampshire</td><td>670</td><td>0.5%</td></tr>
<tr><td>24</td><td>South Carolina</td><td>2,280</td><td>1.6%</td><td>39</td><td>Utah</td><td>670</td><td>0.5%</td></tr>
<tr><td>44</td><td>South Dakota</td><td>490</td><td>0.3%</td><td>41</td><td>Rhode Island</td><td>650</td><td>0.4%</td></tr>
<tr><td>14</td><td>Tennessee</td><td>3,470</td><td>2.4%</td><td>42</td><td>Idaho</td><td>540</td><td>0.4%</td></tr>
<tr><td>4</td><td>Texas</td><td>9,220</td><td>6.3%</td><td>43</td><td>Hawaii</td><td>520</td><td>0.4%</td></tr>
<tr><td>39</td><td>Utah</td><td>670</td><td>0.5%</td><td>44</td><td>South Dakota</td><td>490</td><td>0.3%</td></tr>
<tr><td>48</td><td>Vermont</td><td>340</td><td>0.2%</td><td>45</td><td>Montana</td><td>470</td><td>0.3%</td></tr>
<tr><td>11</td><td>Virginia</td><td>3,550</td><td>2.4%</td><td>46</td><td>Delaware</td><td>410</td><td>0.3%</td></tr>
<tr><td>19</td><td>Washington</td><td>2,720</td><td>1.9%</td><td>47</td><td>North Dakota</td><td>360</td><td>0.2%</td></tr>
<tr><td>34</td><td>West Virginia</td><td>1,270</td><td>0.9%</td><td>48</td><td>Vermont</td><td>340</td><td>0.2%</td></tr>
<tr><td>17</td><td>Wisconsin</td><td>2,900</td><td>2.0%</td><td>49</td><td>Wyoming</td><td>280</td><td>0.2%</td></tr>
<tr><td>49</td><td>Wyoming</td><td>280</td><td>0.2%</td><td>50</td><td>Alaska</td><td>210</td><td>0.1%</td></tr>
<tr><td></td><td></td><td></td><td></td><td></td><td>District of Columbia</td><td>340</td><td>0.2%</td></tr>
</table>

Source: American Cancer Society

"Cancer Facts & Figures 2004" (Copyright 2004, Reprinted with permission from the American Cancer Society)
*These estimates are offered as a rough guide and should be interpreted with caution. They are calculated according to the distribution of estimated 2004 cancer deaths by state.

Estimated Rate of New Colon and Rectum Cancer Cases in 2004

National Estimated Rate = 50.5 New Cases per 100,000 Population*

ALPHA ORDER

RANK	STATE	RATE
29	Alabama	51.8
49	Alaska	32.4
39	Arizona	44.6
7	Arkansas	59.8
47	California	39.1
48	Colorado	35.4
35	Connecticut	49.1
34	Delaware	50.2
11	Florida	58.5
46	Georgia	39.4
44	Hawaii	41.3
45	Idaho	39.5
27	Illinois	52.8
14	Indiana	56.8
4	Iowa	62.5
25	Kansas	54.3
17	Kentucky	56.1
13	Louisiana	56.9
5	Maine	61.3
31	Maryland	51.2
24	Massachusetts	54.7
37	Michigan	48.8
42	Minnesota	43.5
18	Mississippi	55.9
14	Missouri	56.8
31	Montana	51.2
12	Nebraska	58.1
20	Nevada	55.3
28	New Hampshire	52.0
21	New Jersey	55.2
41	New Mexico	44.3
30	New York	51.5
36	North Carolina	49.0
14	North Dakota	56.8
9	Ohio	59.1
10	Oklahoma	58.9
33	Oregon	50.3
2	Pennsylvania	69.3
6	Rhode Island	60.4
22	South Carolina	55.0
3	South Dakota	64.1
8	Tennessee	59.4
43	Texas	41.7
50	Utah	28.5
23	Vermont	54.9
38	Virginia	48.1
40	Washington	44.4
1	West Virginia	70.2
26	Wisconsin	53.0
18	Wyoming	55.9

RANK ORDER

RANK	STATE	RATE
1	West Virginia	70.2
2	Pennsylvania	69.3
3	South Dakota	64.1
4	Iowa	62.5
5	Maine	61.3
6	Rhode Island	60.4
7	Arkansas	59.8
8	Tennessee	59.4
9	Ohio	59.1
10	Oklahoma	58.9
11	Florida	58.5
12	Nebraska	58.1
13	Louisiana	56.9
14	Indiana	56.8
14	Missouri	56.8
14	North Dakota	56.8
17	Kentucky	56.1
18	Mississippi	55.9
18	Wyoming	55.9
20	Nevada	55.3
21	New Jersey	55.2
22	South Carolina	55.0
23	Vermont	54.9
24	Massachusetts	54.7
25	Kansas	54.3
26	Wisconsin	53.0
27	Illinois	52.8
28	New Hampshire	52.0
29	Alabama	51.8
30	New York	51.5
31	Maryland	51.2
31	Montana	51.2
33	Oregon	50.3
34	Delaware	50.2
35	Connecticut	49.1
36	North Carolina	49.0
37	Michigan	48.8
38	Virginia	48.1
39	Arizona	44.6
40	Washington	44.4
41	New Mexico	44.3
42	Minnesota	43.5
43	Texas	41.7
44	Hawaii	41.3
45	Idaho	39.5
46	Georgia	39.4
47	California	39.1
48	Colorado	35.4
49	Alaska	32.4
50	Utah	28.5
	District of Columbia	60.3

Source: Morgan Quitno Press using data from American Cancer Society
   "Cancer Facts & Figures 2004" (Copyright 2004, Reprinted with permission from the American Cancer Society)
*These estimates are offered as a rough guide and should be interpreted with caution. They are calculated
according to the distribution of estimated 2004 cancer deaths by state. Rates calculated using 2003 Census
resident population estimates.

Percent of Adults Receiving Recent Sigmoidoscopy or Colonoscopy Exam: 2002
National Median = 48.1% of Adults*

ALPHA ORDER

RANK	STATE	PERCENT
23	Alabama	48.7
15	Alaska	51.4
12	Arizona	51.8
42	Arkansas	42.9
16	California	50.7
23	Colorado	48.7
3	Connecticut	56.4
2	Delaware	57.4
13	Florida	51.5
21	Georgia	49.2
50	Hawaii	39.2
32	Idaho	46.3
37	Illinois	45.1
40	Indiana	44.1
25	Iowa	48.6
29	Kansas	47.7
41	Kentucky	43.9
48	Louisiana	40.6
30	Maine	47.3
6	Maryland	54.8
9	Massachusetts	53.4
5	Michigan	55.1
1	Minnesota	64.8
42	Mississippi	42.9
38	Missouri	44.2
30	Montana	47.3
44	Nebraska	42.2
36	Nevada	45.4
19	New Hampshire	50.1
26	New Jersey	48.2
38	New Mexico	44.2
13	New York	51.5
28	North Carolina	47.8
18	North Dakota	50.2
34	Ohio	46.0
47	Oklahoma	40.7
11	Oregon	52.7
27	Pennsylvania	48.0
8	Rhode Island	54.6
21	South Carolina	49.2
46	South Dakota	41.8
33	Tennessee	46.1
35	Texas	45.5
17	Utah	50.5
10	Vermont	52.9
19	Virginia	50.1
7	Washington	54.7
49	West Virginia	40.4
3	Wisconsin	56.4
45	Wyoming	42.1

RANK ORDER

RANK	STATE	PERCENT
1	Minnesota	64.8
2	Delaware	57.4
3	Connecticut	56.4
3	Wisconsin	56.4
5	Michigan	55.1
6	Maryland	54.8
7	Washington	54.7
8	Rhode Island	54.6
9	Massachusetts	53.4
10	Vermont	52.9
11	Oregon	52.7
12	Arizona	51.8
13	Florida	51.5
13	New York	51.5
15	Alaska	51.4
16	California	50.7
17	Utah	50.5
18	North Dakota	50.2
19	New Hampshire	50.1
19	Virginia	50.1
21	Georgia	49.2
21	South Carolina	49.2
23	Alabama	48.7
23	Colorado	48.7
25	Iowa	48.6
26	New Jersey	48.2
27	Pennsylvania	48.0
28	North Carolina	47.8
29	Kansas	47.7
30	Maine	47.3
30	Montana	47.3
32	Idaho	46.3
33	Tennessee	46.1
34	Ohio	46.0
35	Texas	45.5
36	Nevada	45.4
37	Illinois	45.1
38	Missouri	44.2
38	New Mexico	44.2
40	Indiana	44.1
41	Kentucky	43.9
42	Arkansas	42.9
42	Mississippi	42.9
44	Nebraska	42.2
45	Wyoming	42.1
46	South Dakota	41.8
47	Oklahoma	40.7
48	Louisiana	40.6
49	West Virginia	40.4
50	Hawaii	39.2

	District of Columbia	61.4

Source: U.S. Department of Health and Human Services, Centers for Disease Control and Prevention
   "2002 Behavioral Risk Factor Surveillance Summary Prevalence Data" (http://apps.nccd.cdc.gov/brfss/)
*Persons 50 and older.

Estimated New Leukemia Cases in 2004

National Estimated Total = 33,440 New Cases*

ALPHA ORDER

RANK	STATE	CASES	% of USA
23	Alabama	530	1.6%
NA	Alaska**	NA	NA
21	Arizona	590	1.8%
31	Arkansas	370	1.1%
1	California	3,240	9.7%
27	Colorado	440	1.3%
29	Connecticut	400	1.2%
44	Delaware	110	0.3%
2	Florida	2,500	7.5%
11	Georgia	790	2.4%
44	Hawaii	110	0.3%
39	Idaho	140	0.4%
6	Illinois	1,550	4.6%
11	Indiana	790	2.4%
26	Iowa	460	1.4%
32	Kansas	340	1.0%
25	Kentucky	470	1.4%
22	Louisiana	550	1.6%
39	Maine	140	0.4%
19	Maryland	650	1.9%
14	Massachusetts	760	2.3%
8	Michigan	1,210	3.6%
20	Minnesota	630	1.9%
33	Mississippi	300	0.9%
13	Missouri	780	2.3%
39	Montana	140	0.4%
36	Nebraska	230	0.7%
35	Nevada	260	0.8%
39	New Hampshire	140	0.4%
9	New Jersey	1,030	3.1%
38	New Mexico	170	0.5%
4	New York	2,110	6.3%
10	North Carolina	930	2.8%
47	North Dakota	100	0.3%
7	Ohio	1,450	4.3%
27	Oklahoma	440	1.3%
29	Oregon	400	1.2%
5	Pennsylvania	1,620	4.8%
43	Rhode Island	130	0.4%
24	South Carolina	490	1.5%
44	South Dakota	110	0.3%
17	Tennessee	730	2.2%
3	Texas	2,140	6.4%
37	Utah	220	0.7%
48	Vermont	70	0.2%
14	Virginia	760	2.3%
18	Washington	720	2.2%
34	West Virginia	270	0.8%
16	Wisconsin	750	2.2%
49	Wyoming	60	0.2%

RANK ORDER

RANK	STATE	CASES	% of USA
1	California	3,240	9.7%
2	Florida	2,500	7.5%
3	Texas	2,140	6.4%
4	New York	2,110	6.3%
5	Pennsylvania	1,620	4.8%
6	Illinois	1,550	4.6%
7	Ohio	1,450	4.3%
8	Michigan	1,210	3.6%
9	New Jersey	1,030	3.1%
10	North Carolina	930	2.8%
11	Georgia	790	2.4%
11	Indiana	790	2.4%
13	Missouri	780	2.3%
14	Massachusetts	760	2.3%
14	Virginia	760	2.3%
16	Wisconsin	750	2.2%
17	Tennessee	730	2.2%
18	Washington	720	2.2%
19	Maryland	650	1.9%
20	Minnesota	630	1.9%
21	Arizona	590	1.8%
22	Louisiana	550	1.6%
23	Alabama	530	1.6%
24	South Carolina	490	1.5%
25	Kentucky	470	1.4%
26	Iowa	460	1.4%
27	Colorado	440	1.3%
27	Oklahoma	440	1.3%
29	Connecticut	400	1.2%
29	Oregon	400	1.2%
31	Arkansas	370	1.1%
32	Kansas	340	1.0%
33	Mississippi	300	0.9%
34	West Virginia	270	0.8%
35	Nevada	260	0.8%
36	Nebraska	230	0.7%
37	Utah	220	0.7%
38	New Mexico	170	0.5%
39	Idaho	140	0.4%
39	Maine	140	0.4%
39	Montana	140	0.4%
39	New Hampshire	140	0.4%
43	Rhode Island	130	0.4%
44	Delaware	110	0.3%
44	Hawaii	110	0.3%
44	South Dakota	110	0.3%
47	North Dakota	100	0.3%
48	Vermont	70	0.2%
49	Wyoming	60	0.2%
NA	Alaska**	NA	NA
	District of Columbia**	NA	NA

Source: American Cancer Society
   "Cancer Facts & Figures 2004" (Copyright 2004, Reprinted with permission from the American Cancer Society)
*These estimates are offered as a rough guide and should be interpreted with caution. They are calculated
according to the distribution of estimated 2004 cancer deaths by state.
**Not available.

Estimated Rate of New Leukemia Cases in 2004

National Estimated Rate = 11.5 New Cases per 100,000 Population*

ALPHA ORDER

RANK	STATE	RATE
25	Alabama	11.8
NA	Alaska**	NA
39	Arizona	10.6
9	Arkansas	13.6
46	California	9.1
43	Colorado	9.7
31	Connecticut	11.5
10	Delaware	13.5
5	Florida	14.7
46	Georgia	9.1
49	Hawaii	8.7
42	Idaho	10.2
19	Illinois	12.2
13	Indiana	12.8
2	Iowa	15.6
15	Kansas	12.5
32	Kentucky	11.4
19	Louisiana	12.2
38	Maine	10.7
25	Maryland	11.8
25	Massachusetts	11.8
22	Michigan	12.0
15	Minnesota	12.5
40	Mississippi	10.4
7	Missouri	13.7
3	Montana	15.3
11	Nebraska	13.2
30	Nevada	11.6
37	New Hampshire	10.9
24	New Jersey	11.9
46	New Mexico	9.1
36	New York	11.0
35	North Carolina	11.1
1	North Dakota	15.8
14	Ohio	12.7
15	Oklahoma	12.5
34	Oregon	11.2
12	Pennsylvania	13.1
21	Rhode Island	12.1
25	South Carolina	11.8
6	South Dakota	14.4
15	Tennessee	12.5
43	Texas	9.7
45	Utah	9.4
33	Vermont	11.3
41	Virginia	10.3
29	Washington	11.7
4	West Virginia	14.9
7	Wisconsin	13.7
22	Wyoming	12.0

RANK ORDER

RANK	STATE	RATE
1	North Dakota	15.8
2	Iowa	15.6
3	Montana	15.3
4	West Virginia	14.9
5	Florida	14.7
6	South Dakota	14.4
7	Missouri	13.7
7	Wisconsin	13.7
9	Arkansas	13.6
10	Delaware	13.5
11	Nebraska	13.2
12	Pennsylvania	13.1
13	Indiana	12.8
14	Ohio	12.7
15	Kansas	12.5
15	Minnesota	12.5
15	Oklahoma	12.5
15	Tennessee	12.5
19	Illinois	12.2
19	Louisiana	12.2
21	Rhode Island	12.1
22	Michigan	12.0
22	Wyoming	12.0
24	New Jersey	11.9
25	Alabama	11.8
25	Maryland	11.8
25	Massachusetts	11.8
25	South Carolina	11.8
29	Washington	11.7
30	Nevada	11.6
31	Connecticut	11.5
32	Kentucky	11.4
33	Vermont	11.3
34	Oregon	11.2
35	North Carolina	11.1
36	New York	11.0
37	New Hampshire	10.9
38	Maine	10.7
39	Arizona	10.6
40	Mississippi	10.4
41	Virginia	10.3
42	Idaho	10.2
43	Colorado	9.7
43	Texas	9.7
45	Utah	9.4
46	California	9.1
46	Georgia	9.1
46	New Mexico	9.1
49	Hawaii	8.7
NA	Alaska**	NA
	District of Columbia**	NA

Source: Morgan Quitno Press using data from American Cancer Society
"Cancer Facts & Figures 2004" (Copyright 2004, Reprinted with permission from the American Cancer Society)
*These estimates are offered as a rough guide and should be interpreted with caution. They are calculated according to the distribution of estimated 2004 cancer deaths by state. Rates calculated using 2003 Census resident population estimates.
**Not available.

Estimated New Lung Cancer Cases in 2004

National Estimated Total = 173,770 New Cases*

ALPHA ORDER

RANK	STATE	CASES	% of USA
19	Alabama	3,350	1.9%
50	Alaska	240	0.1%
24	Arizona	2,760	1.6%
27	Arkansas	2,230	1.3%
1	California	15,650	9.0%
33	Colorado	1,740	1.0%
30	Connecticut	2,000	1.2%
44	Delaware	550	0.3%
2	Florida	13,390	7.7%
11	Georgia	5,050	2.9%
43	Hawaii	570	0.3%
41	Idaho	660	0.4%
7	Illinois	7,320	4.2%
13	Indiana	4,490	2.6%
31	Iowa	1,820	1.0%
34	Kansas	1,690	1.0%
17	Kentucky	3,660	2.1%
21	Louisiana	3,160	1.8%
37	Maine	950	0.5%
20	Maryland	3,180	1.8%
15	Massachusetts	4,050	2.3%
8	Michigan	6,160	3.5%
25	Minnesota	2,580	1.5%
27	Mississippi	2,230	1.3%
14	Missouri	4,090	2.4%
42	Montana	650	0.4%
36	Nebraska	1,040	0.6%
35	Nevada	1,570	0.9%
38	New Hampshire	800	0.5%
10	New Jersey	5,110	2.9%
40	New Mexico	750	0.4%
4	New York	10,020	5.8%
9	North Carolina	5,710	3.3%
48	North Dakota	360	0.2%
6	Ohio	7,720	4.4%
26	Oklahoma	2,570	1.5%
29	Oregon	2,140	1.2%
5	Pennsylvania	8,560	4.9%
39	Rhode Island	760	0.4%
23	South Carolina	2,950	1.7%
46	South Dakota	450	0.3%
12	Tennessee	4,680	2.7%
3	Texas	10,470	6.0%
45	Utah	480	0.3%
47	Vermont	400	0.2%
15	Virginia	4,050	2.3%
18	Washington	3,520	2.0%
32	West Virginia	1,780	1.0%
22	Wisconsin	3,050	1.8%
49	Wyoming	280	0.2%

RANK ORDER

RANK	STATE	CASES	% of USA
1	California	15,650	9.0%
2	Florida	13,390	7.7%
3	Texas	10,470	6.0%
4	New York	10,020	5.8%
5	Pennsylvania	8,560	4.9%
6	Ohio	7,720	4.4%
7	Illinois	7,320	4.2%
8	Michigan	6,160	3.5%
9	North Carolina	5,710	3.3%
10	New Jersey	5,110	2.9%
11	Georgia	5,050	2.9%
12	Tennessee	4,680	2.7%
13	Indiana	4,490	2.6%
14	Missouri	4,090	2.4%
15	Massachusetts	4,050	2.3%
15	Virginia	4,050	2.3%
17	Kentucky	3,660	2.1%
18	Washington	3,520	2.0%
19	Alabama	3,350	1.9%
20	Maryland	3,180	1.8%
21	Louisiana	3,160	1.8%
22	Wisconsin	3,050	1.8%
23	South Carolina	2,950	1.7%
24	Arizona	2,760	1.6%
25	Minnesota	2,580	1.5%
26	Oklahoma	2,570	1.5%
27	Arkansas	2,230	1.3%
27	Mississippi	2,230	1.3%
29	Oregon	2,140	1.2%
30	Connecticut	2,000	1.2%
31	Iowa	1,820	1.0%
32	West Virginia	1,780	1.0%
33	Colorado	1,740	1.0%
34	Kansas	1,690	1.0%
35	Nevada	1,570	0.9%
36	Nebraska	1,040	0.6%
37	Maine	950	0.5%
38	New Hampshire	800	0.5%
39	Rhode Island	760	0.4%
40	New Mexico	750	0.4%
41	Idaho	660	0.4%
42	Montana	650	0.4%
43	Hawaii	570	0.3%
44	Delaware	550	0.3%
45	Utah	480	0.3%
46	South Dakota	450	0.3%
47	Vermont	400	0.2%
48	North Dakota	360	0.2%
49	Wyoming	280	0.2%
50	Alaska	240	0.1%
	District of Columbia	300	0.2%

Source: American Cancer Society
"Cancer Facts & Figures 2004" (Copyright 2004, Reprinted with permission from the American Cancer Society)
*These estimates are offered as a rough guide and should be interpreted with caution. They are calculated according to the distribution of estimated 2004 cancer deaths by state.

Estimated Rate of New Lung Cancer Cases in 2004

National Estimated Rate = 59.8 New Cases per 100,000 Population*

ALPHA ORDER

RANK	STATE	RATE
7	Alabama	74.4
49	Alaska	37.0
42	Arizona	49.5
3	Arkansas	81.8
46	California	44.1
48	Colorado	38.2
34	Connecticut	57.4
20	Delaware	67.3
5	Florida	78.7
31	Georgia	58.1
45	Hawaii	45.3
43	Idaho	48.3
32	Illinois	57.8
10	Indiana	72.5
25	Iowa	61.8
23	Kansas	62.1
2	Kentucky	88.9
15	Louisiana	70.3
9	Maine	72.8
33	Maryland	57.7
22	Massachusetts	63.0
26	Michigan	61.1
41	Minnesota	51.0
6	Mississippi	77.4
11	Missouri	71.7
13	Montana	70.8
28	Nebraska	59.8
16	Nevada	70.1
23	New Hampshire	62.1
29	New Jersey	59.2
47	New Mexico	40.0
40	New York	52.2
18	North Carolina	67.9
36	North Dakota	56.8
19	Ohio	67.5
8	Oklahoma	73.2
27	Oregon	60.1
17	Pennsylvania	69.2
14	Rhode Island	70.6
12	South Carolina	71.1
30	South Dakota	58.9
4	Tennessee	80.1
44	Texas	47.3
50	Utah	20.4
21	Vermont	64.6
39	Virginia	54.8
34	Washington	57.4
1	West Virginia	98.3
38	Wisconsin	55.7
37	Wyoming	55.9

RANK ORDER

RANK	STATE	RATE
1	West Virginia	98.3
2	Kentucky	88.9
3	Arkansas	81.8
4	Tennessee	80.1
5	Florida	78.7
6	Mississippi	77.4
7	Alabama	74.4
8	Oklahoma	73.2
9	Maine	72.8
10	Indiana	72.5
11	Missouri	71.7
12	South Carolina	71.1
13	Montana	70.8
14	Rhode Island	70.6
15	Louisiana	70.3
16	Nevada	70.1
17	Pennsylvania	69.2
18	North Carolina	67.9
19	Ohio	67.5
20	Delaware	67.3
21	Vermont	64.6
22	Massachusetts	63.0
23	Kansas	62.1
23	New Hampshire	62.1
25	Iowa	61.8
26	Michigan	61.1
27	Oregon	60.1
28	Nebraska	59.8
29	New Jersey	59.2
30	South Dakota	58.9
31	Georgia	58.1
32	Illinois	57.8
33	Maryland	57.7
34	Connecticut	57.4
34	Washington	57.4
36	North Dakota	56.8
37	Wyoming	55.9
38	Wisconsin	55.7
39	Virginia	54.8
40	New York	52.2
41	Minnesota	51.0
42	Arizona	49.5
43	Idaho	48.3
44	Texas	47.3
45	Hawaii	45.3
46	California	44.1
47	New Mexico	40.0
48	Colorado	38.2
49	Alaska	37.0
50	Utah	20.4

District of Columbia	53.2

Source: Morgan Quitno Press using data from American Cancer Society
    "Cancer Facts & Figures 2004" (Copyright 2004, Reprinted with permission from the American Cancer Society)
*These estimates are offered as a rough guide and should be interpreted with caution. They are calculated according to the distribution of estimated 2004 cancer deaths by state. Rates calculated using 2003 Census resident population estimates.

Estimated New Non-Hodgkin's Lymphoma Cases in 2004

National Estimated Total = 54,370 New Cases*

ALPHA ORDER

RANK	STATE	CASES	% of USA
26	Alabama	840	1.5%
49	Alaska	80	0.1%
23	Arizona	950	1.7%
30	Arkansas	640	1.2%
1	California	5,550	10.2%
27	Colorado	810	1.5%
28	Connecticut	760	1.4%
44	Delaware	200	0.4%
5	Florida	2,690	4.9%
14	Georgia	1,320	2.4%
40	Hawaii	250	0.5%
40	Idaho	250	0.5%
7	Illinois	2,270	4.2%
11	Indiana	1,430	2.6%
30	Iowa	640	1.2%
30	Kansas	640	1.2%
21	Kentucky	980	1.8%
21	Louisiana	980	1.8%
40	Maine	250	0.5%
20	Maryland	1,040	1.9%
19	Massachusetts	1,150	2.1%
8	Michigan	2,040	3.8%
15	Minnesota	1,290	2.4%
35	Mississippi	390	0.7%
12	Missouri	1,400	2.6%
44	Montana	200	0.4%
37	Nebraska	360	0.7%
34	Nevada	420	0.8%
47	New Hampshire	140	0.3%
9	New Jersey	1,820	3.3%
38	New Mexico	310	0.6%
4	New York	2,770	5.1%
10	North Carolina	1,480	2.7%
47	North Dakota	140	0.3%
6	Ohio	2,410	4.4%
28	Oklahoma	760	1.4%
24	Oregon	920	1.7%
2	Pennsylvania	3,030	5.6%
39	Rhode Island	280	0.5%
25	South Carolina	870	1.6%
43	South Dakota	220	0.4%
12	Tennessee	1,400	2.6%
3	Texas	2,970	5.5%
35	Utah	390	0.7%
46	Vermont	170	0.3%
18	Virginia	1,230	2.3%
15	Washington	1,290	2.4%
33	West Virginia	500	0.9%
15	Wisconsin	1,290	2.4%
49	Wyoming	80	0.1%

RANK ORDER

RANK	STATE	CASES	% of USA
1	California	5,550	10.2%
2	Pennsylvania	3,030	5.6%
3	Texas	2,970	5.5%
4	New York	2,770	5.1%
5	Florida	2,690	4.9%
6	Ohio	2,410	4.4%
7	Illinois	2,270	4.2%
8	Michigan	2,040	3.8%
9	New Jersey	1,820	3.3%
10	North Carolina	1,480	2.7%
11	Indiana	1,430	2.6%
12	Missouri	1,400	2.6%
12	Tennessee	1,400	2.6%
14	Georgia	1,320	2.4%
15	Minnesota	1,290	2.4%
15	Washington	1,290	2.4%
15	Wisconsin	1,290	2.4%
18	Virginia	1,230	2.3%
19	Massachusetts	1,150	2.1%
20	Maryland	1,040	1.9%
21	Kentucky	980	1.8%
21	Louisiana	980	1.8%
23	Arizona	950	1.7%
24	Oregon	920	1.7%
25	South Carolina	870	1.6%
26	Alabama	840	1.5%
27	Colorado	810	1.5%
28	Connecticut	760	1.4%
28	Oklahoma	760	1.4%
30	Arkansas	640	1.2%
30	Iowa	640	1.2%
30	Kansas	640	1.2%
33	West Virginia	500	0.9%
34	Nevada	420	0.8%
35	Mississippi	390	0.7%
35	Utah	390	0.7%
37	Nebraska	360	0.7%
38	New Mexico	310	0.6%
39	Rhode Island	280	0.5%
40	Hawaii	250	0.5%
40	Idaho	250	0.5%
40	Maine	250	0.5%
43	South Dakota	220	0.4%
44	Delaware	200	0.4%
44	Montana	200	0.4%
46	Vermont	170	0.3%
47	New Hampshire	140	0.3%
47	North Dakota	140	0.3%
49	Alaska	80	0.1%
49	Wyoming	80	0.1%
	District of Columbia	60	0.1%

Source: American Cancer Society
   "Cancer Facts & Figures 2004" (Copyright 2004, Reprinted with permission from the American Cancer Society)
These estimates are offered as a rough guide and should be interpreted with caution. They are calculated according to the distribution of estimated 2004 cancer deaths by state.

Estimated Rate of New Non-Hodgkin's Lymphoma Cases in 2004

National Estimated Rate = 18.7 New Cases per 100,000 Population*

ALPHA ORDER

RANK	STATE	RATE
31	Alabama	18.7
49	Alaska	12.3
38	Arizona	17.0
13	Arkansas	23.5
44	California	15.6
36	Colorado	17.8
17	Connecticut	21.8
7	Delaware	24.5
43	Florida	15.8
45	Georgia	15.2
28	Hawaii	19.9
33	Idaho	18.3
34	Illinois	17.9
15	Indiana	23.1
20	Iowa	21.7
13	Kansas	23.5
11	Kentucky	23.8
17	Louisiana	21.8
29	Maine	19.1
30	Maryland	18.9
34	Massachusetts	17.9
27	Michigan	20.2
6	Minnesota	25.5
47	Mississippi	13.5
7	Missouri	24.5
17	Montana	21.8
26	Nebraska	20.7
31	Nevada	18.7
50	New Hampshire	10.9
22	New Jersey	21.1
41	New Mexico	16.5
46	New York	14.4
37	North Carolina	17.6
16	North Dakota	22.1
22	Ohio	21.1
21	Oklahoma	21.6
5	Oregon	25.8
7	Pennsylvania	24.5
4	Rhode Island	26.0
24	South Carolina	21.0
1	South Dakota	28.8
10	Tennessee	24.0
48	Texas	13.4
40	Utah	16.6
3	Vermont	27.5
39	Virginia	16.7
24	Washington	21.0
2	West Virginia	27.6
12	Wisconsin	23.6
42	Wyoming	16.0

RANK ORDER

RANK	STATE	RATE
1	South Dakota	28.8
2	West Virginia	27.6
3	Vermont	27.5
4	Rhode Island	26.0
5	Oregon	25.8
6	Minnesota	25.5
7	Delaware	24.5
7	Missouri	24.5
7	Pennsylvania	24.5
10	Tennessee	24.0
11	Kentucky	23.8
12	Wisconsin	23.6
13	Arkansas	23.5
13	Kansas	23.5
15	Indiana	23.1
16	North Dakota	22.1
17	Connecticut	21.8
17	Louisiana	21.8
17	Montana	21.8
20	Iowa	21.7
21	Oklahoma	21.6
22	New Jersey	21.1
22	Ohio	21.1
24	South Carolina	21.0
24	Washington	21.0
26	Nebraska	20.7
27	Michigan	20.2
28	Hawaii	19.9
29	Maine	19.1
30	Maryland	18.9
31	Alabama	18.7
31	Nevada	18.7
33	Idaho	18.3
34	Illinois	17.9
34	Massachusetts	17.9
36	Colorado	17.8
37	North Carolina	17.6
38	Arizona	17.0
39	Virginia	16.7
40	Utah	16.6
41	New Mexico	16.5
42	Wyoming	16.0
43	Florida	15.8
44	California	15.6
45	Georgia	15.2
46	New York	14.4
47	Mississippi	13.5
48	Texas	13.4
49	Alaska	12.3
50	New Hampshire	10.9

District of Columbia   10.6

Source: Morgan Quitno Press using data from American Cancer Society
    "Cancer Facts & Figures 2004" (Copyright 2004, Reprinted with permission from the American Cancer Society)
*These estimates are offered as a rough guide and should be interpreted with caution. They are calculated
according to the distribution of estimated 2004 cancer deaths by state. Rates calculated using 2003 Census
resident population estimates.

Estimated New Prostate Cancer Cases in 2004

National Estimated Total = 230,110 New Cases*

ALPHA ORDER

RANK	STATE	CASES	% of USA
15	Alabama	4,850	2.1%
50	Alaska	230	0.1%
21	Arizona	3,920	1.7%
33	Arkansas	2,150	0.9%
1	California	23,160	10.1%
32	Colorado	2,540	1.1%
26	Connecticut	3,310	1.4%
46	Delaware	690	0.3%
2	Florida	17,090	7.4%
11	Georgia	5,700	2.5%
42	Hawaii	1,000	0.4%
39	Idaho	1,080	0.5%
6	Illinois	9,930	4.3%
13	Indiana	5,390	2.3%
27	Iowa	3,160	1.4%
29	Kansas	2,690	1.2%
30	Kentucky	2,620	1.1%
23	Louisiana	3,690	1.6%
38	Maine	1,150	0.5%
20	Maryland	4,080	1.8%
11	Massachusetts	5,700	2.5%
8	Michigan	8,540	3.7%
19	Minnesota	4,230	1.8%
25	Mississippi	3,390	1.5%
24	Missouri	3,460	1.5%
39	Montana	1,080	0.5%
37	Nebraska	1,460	0.6%
34	Nevada	2,000	0.9%
42	New Hampshire	1,000	0.4%
9	New Jersey	7,930	3.4%
35	New Mexico	1,690	0.7%
3	New York	14,470	6.3%
10	North Carolina	7,160	3.1%
48	North Dakota	540	0.2%
7	Ohio	8,620	3.7%
30	Oklahoma	2,620	1.1%
28	Oregon	2,920	1.3%
5	Pennsylvania	12,010	5.2%
42	Rhode Island	1,000	0.4%
17	South Carolina	4,770	2.1%
45	South Dakota	920	0.4%
18	Tennessee	4,540	2.0%
4	Texas	13,540	5.9%
39	Utah	1,080	0.5%
49	Vermont	460	0.2%
14	Virginia	5,080	2.2%
15	Washington	4,850	2.1%
36	West Virginia	1,540	0.7%
22	Wisconsin	3,850	1.7%
47	Wyoming	620	0.3%

RANK ORDER

RANK	STATE	CASES	% of USA
1	California	23,160	10.1%
2	Florida	17,090	7.4%
3	New York	14,470	6.3%
4	Texas	13,540	5.9%
5	Pennsylvania	12,010	5.2%
6	Illinois	9,930	4.3%
7	Ohio	8,620	3.7%
8	Michigan	8,540	3.7%
9	New Jersey	7,930	3.4%
10	North Carolina	7,160	3.1%
11	Georgia	5,700	2.5%
11	Massachusetts	5,700	2.5%
13	Indiana	5,390	2.3%
14	Virginia	5,080	2.2%
15	Alabama	4,850	2.1%
15	Washington	4,850	2.1%
17	South Carolina	4,770	2.1%
18	Tennessee	4,540	2.0%
19	Minnesota	4,230	1.8%
20	Maryland	4,080	1.8%
21	Arizona	3,920	1.7%
22	Wisconsin	3,850	1.7%
23	Louisiana	3,690	1.6%
24	Missouri	3,460	1.5%
25	Mississippi	3,390	1.5%
26	Connecticut	3,310	1.4%
27	Iowa	3,160	1.4%
28	Oregon	2,920	1.3%
29	Kansas	2,690	1.2%
30	Kentucky	2,620	1.1%
30	Oklahoma	2,620	1.1%
32	Colorado	2,540	1.1%
33	Arkansas	2,150	0.9%
34	Nevada	2,000	0.9%
35	New Mexico	1,690	0.7%
36	West Virginia	1,540	0.7%
37	Nebraska	1,460	0.6%
38	Maine	1,150	0.5%
39	Idaho	1,080	0.5%
39	Montana	1,080	0.5%
39	Utah	1,080	0.5%
42	Hawaii	1,000	0.4%
42	New Hampshire	1,000	0.4%
42	Rhode Island	1,000	0.4%
45	South Dakota	920	0.4%
46	Delaware	690	0.3%
47	Wyoming	620	0.3%
48	North Dakota	540	0.2%
49	Vermont	460	0.2%
50	Alaska	230	0.1%
	District of Columbia	620	0.3%

Source: American Cancer Society
"Cancer Facts & Figures 2004" (Copyright 2004, Reprinted with permission from the American Cancer Society)
These estimates are offered as a rough guide and should be interpreted with caution. They are calculated according to the distribution of estimated 2004 cancer deaths by state.

Age-Adjusted Incidence Rate of Prostate Cancer Cases in 2000

National Rate = 160.4 New Cases per 100,000 Male Population*

ALPHA ORDER

RANK	STATE	RATE
39	Alabama	134.9
17	Alaska	161.9
41	Arizona	130.0
40	Arkansas	134.6
22	California	158.1
19	Colorado	160.8
13	Connecticut	170.2
NA	Delaware**	NA
25	Florida	153.0
38	Georgia	138.9
42	Hawaii	129.8
20	Idaho	160.4
23	Illinois	156.7
43	Indiana	124.3
27	Iowa	151.2
NA	Kansas**	NA
31	Kentucky	145.5
12	Louisiana	170.3
26	Maine	152.1
3	Maryland	182.2
4	Massachusetts	179.2
2	Michigan	192.6
5	Minnesota	178.8
36	Mississippi	140.5
37	Missouri	139.2
14	Montana	167.3
16	Nebraska	162.8
45	Nevada	110.7
32	New Hampshire	145.2
1	New Jersey	193.9
35	New Mexico	143.2
24	New York	156.1
30	North Carolina	147.6
6	North Dakota	177.7
34	Ohio	143.4
44	Oklahoma	120.5
21	Oregon	159.0
15	Pennsylvania	167.0
10	Rhode Island	174.0
9	South Carolina	174.4
NA	South Dakota**	NA
NA	Tennessee**	NA
29	Texas	148.5
7	Utah	176.4
NA	Vermont**	NA
28	Virginia	149.4
11	Washington	170.5
33	West Virginia	144.7
18	Wisconsin	161.3
8	Wyoming	175.7

RANK ORDER

RANK	STATE	RATE
1	New Jersey	193.9
2	Michigan	192.6
3	Maryland	182.2
4	Massachusetts	179.2
5	Minnesota	178.8
6	North Dakota	177.7
7	Utah	176.4
8	Wyoming	175.7
9	South Carolina	174.4
10	Rhode Island	174.0
11	Washington	170.5
12	Louisiana	170.3
13	Connecticut	170.2
14	Montana	167.3
15	Pennsylvania	167.0
16	Nebraska	162.8
17	Alaska	161.9
18	Wisconsin	161.3
19	Colorado	160.8
20	Idaho	160.4
21	Oregon	159.0
22	California	158.1
23	Illinois	156.7
24	New York	156.1
25	Florida	153.0
26	Maine	152.1
27	Iowa	151.2
28	Virginia	149.4
29	Texas	148.5
30	North Carolina	147.6
31	Kentucky	145.5
32	New Hampshire	145.2
33	West Virginia	144.7
34	Ohio	143.4
35	New Mexico	143.2
36	Mississippi	140.5
37	Missouri	139.2
38	Georgia	138.9
39	Alabama	134.9
40	Arkansas	134.6
41	Arizona	130.0
42	Hawaii	129.8
43	Indiana	124.3
44	Oklahoma	120.5
45	Nevada	110.7
NA	Delaware**	NA
NA	Kansas**	NA
NA	South Dakota**	NA
NA	Tennessee**	NA
NA	Vermont**	NA

District of Columbia 251.6

Source: American Cancer Society
    "Cancer Facts & Figures 2004" (Copyright 2004, Reprinted with permission from the American Cancer Society)
*For 1996 to 2000. Age-adjusted to the 2000 U.S. standard population.
**Not available.

Percent of Males Receiving Recent PSA Test for Prostate Cancer: 2001

National Median = 56.7% of Men 50 and Older*

ALPHA ORDER

RANK	STATE	PERCENT
26	Alabama	55.9
14	Alaska	60.5
11	Arizona	61.4
38	Arkansas	54.2
42	California	53.8
24	Colorado	56.8
17	Connecticut	58.7
4	Delaware	64.1
1	Florida	66.2
12	Georgia	60.9
48	Hawaii	49.5
32	Idaho	54.9
35	Illinois	54.6
33	Indiana	54.8
35	Iowa	54.6
19	Kansas	57.7
40	Kentucky	54.0
28	Louisiana	55.8
48	Maine	49.5
14	Maryland	60.5
6	Massachusetts	63.8
10	Michigan	61.9
44	Minnesota	52.3
30	Mississippi	55.4
7	Missouri	63.4
22	Montana	56.9
50	Nebraska	49.2
26	Nevada	55.9
20	New Hampshire	57.6
3	New Jersey	64.9
45	New Mexico	51.9
16	New York	60.0
37	North Carolina	54.4
22	North Dakota	56.9
9	Ohio	62.8
47	Oklahoma	50.7
33	Oregon	54.8
4	Pennsylvania	64.1
8	Rhode Island	63.2
13	South Carolina	60.6
29	South Dakota	55.6
46	Tennessee	51.8
21	Texas	57.1
42	Utah	53.8
39	Vermont	54.1
25	Virginia	56.7
40	Washington	54.0
18	West Virginia	58.5
31	Wisconsin	55.1
2	Wyoming	65.4

RANK ORDER

RANK	STATE	PERCENT
1	Florida	66.2
2	Wyoming	65.4
3	New Jersey	64.9
4	Delaware	64.1
4	Pennsylvania	64.1
6	Massachusetts	63.8
7	Missouri	63.4
8	Rhode Island	63.2
9	Ohio	62.8
10	Michigan	61.9
11	Arizona	61.4
12	Georgia	60.9
13	South Carolina	60.6
14	Alaska	60.5
14	Maryland	60.5
16	New York	60.0
17	Connecticut	58.7
18	West Virginia	58.5
19	Kansas	57.7
20	New Hampshire	57.6
21	Texas	57.1
22	Montana	56.9
22	North Dakota	56.9
24	Colorado	56.8
25	Virginia	56.7
26	Alabama	55.9
26	Nevada	55.9
28	Louisiana	55.8
29	South Dakota	55.6
30	Mississippi	55.4
31	Wisconsin	55.1
32	Idaho	54.9
33	Indiana	54.8
33	Oregon	54.8
35	Illinois	54.6
35	Iowa	54.6
37	North Carolina	54.4
38	Arkansas	54.2
39	Vermont	54.1
40	Kentucky	54.0
40	Washington	54.0
42	California	53.8
42	Utah	53.8
44	Minnesota	52.3
45	New Mexico	51.9
46	Tennessee	51.8
47	Oklahoma	50.7
48	Hawaii	49.5
48	Maine	49.5
50	Nebraska	49.2
	District of Columbia	63.8

Source: U.S. Department of Health and Human Services, Centers for Disease Control and Prevention
"2001 Behavioral Risk Factor Surveillance System Public Use Data Tape"
Men 50 and older receiving prostate-specific antigen (PSA) test within the past year.

Estimated New Skin Melanoma Cases in 2004

National Estimated Total = 55,100 New Cases*

RANK	STATE	CASES	% of USA
26	Alabama	840	1.5%
49	Alaska	70	0.1%
18	Arizona	1,180	2.1%
31	Arkansas	560	1.0%
1	California	5,020	9.1%
23	Colorado	910	1.7%
27	Connecticut	700	1.3%
43	Delaware	210	0.4%
2	Florida	4,250	7.7%
11	Georgia	1,460	2.6%
46	Hawaii	140	0.3%
38	Idaho	280	0.5%
7	Illinois	2,020	3.7%
14	Indiana	1,320	2.4%
31	Iowa	560	1.0%
30	Kansas	630	1.1%
20	Kentucky	1,040	1.9%
27	Louisiana	700	1.3%
38	Maine	280	0.5%
21	Maryland	980	1.8%
11	Massachusetts	1,460	2.6%
10	Michigan	1,670	3.0%
21	Minnesota	980	1.8%
34	Mississippi	420	0.8%
14	Missouri	1,320	2.4%
43	Montana	210	0.4%
37	Nebraska	350	0.6%
33	Nevada	490	0.9%
38	New Hampshire	280	0.5%
8	New Jersey	1,810	3.3%
38	New Mexico	280	0.5%
4	New York	3,060	5.6%
9	North Carolina	1,740	3.2%
49	North Dakota	70	0.1%
6	Ohio	2,300	4.2%
23	Oklahoma	910	1.7%
23	Oregon	910	1.7%
5	Pennsylvania	2,720	4.9%
38	Rhode Island	280	0.5%
27	South Carolina	700	1.3%
43	South Dakota	210	0.4%
17	Tennessee	1,250	2.3%
3	Texas	3,550	6.4%
34	Utah	420	0.8%
46	Vermont	140	0.3%
13	Virginia	1,390	2.5%
14	Washington	1,320	2.4%
34	West Virginia	420	0.8%
19	Wisconsin	1,110	2.0%
46	Wyoming	140	0.3%

RANK	STATE	CASES	% of USA
1	California	5,020	9.1%
2	Florida	4,250	7.7%
3	Texas	3,550	6.4%
4	New York	3,060	5.6%
5	Pennsylvania	2,720	4.9%
6	Ohio	2,300	4.2%
7	Illinois	2,020	3.7%
8	New Jersey	1,810	3.3%
9	North Carolina	1,740	3.2%
10	Michigan	1,670	3.0%
11	Georgia	1,460	2.6%
11	Massachusetts	1,460	2.6%
13	Virginia	1,390	2.5%
14	Indiana	1,320	2.4%
14	Missouri	1,320	2.4%
14	Washington	1,320	2.4%
17	Tennessee	1,250	2.3%
18	Arizona	1,180	2.1%
19	Wisconsin	1,110	2.0%
20	Kentucky	1,040	1.9%
21	Maryland	980	1.8%
21	Minnesota	980	1.8%
23	Colorado	910	1.7%
23	Oklahoma	910	1.7%
23	Oregon	910	1.7%
26	Alabama	840	1.5%
27	Connecticut	700	1.3%
27	Louisiana	700	1.3%
27	South Carolina	700	1.3%
30	Kansas	630	1.1%
31	Arkansas	560	1.0%
31	Iowa	560	1.0%
33	Nevada	490	0.9%
34	Mississippi	420	0.8%
34	Utah	420	0.8%
34	West Virginia	420	0.8%
37	Nebraska	350	0.6%
38	Idaho	280	0.5%
38	Maine	280	0.5%
38	New Hampshire	280	0.5%
38	New Mexico	280	0.5%
38	Rhode Island	280	0.5%
43	Delaware	210	0.4%
43	Montana	210	0.4%
43	South Dakota	210	0.4%
46	Hawaii	140	0.3%
46	Vermont	140	0.3%
46	Wyoming	140	0.3%
49	Alaska	70	0.1%
49	North Dakota	70	0.1%
	District of Columbia	70	0.1%

Source: American Cancer Society
"Cancer Facts & Figures 2004" (Copyright 2004, Reprinted with permission from the American Cancer Society)
*These estimates are offered as a rough guide and should be interpreted with caution. They are calculated according to the distribution of estimated 2004 cancer deaths by state.

Estimated Rate of New Skin Melanoma Cases in 2004

National Estimated Rate = 18.9 New Cases per 100,000 Population*

ALPHA ORDER

RANK	STATE	RATE
35	Alabama	18.7
50	Alaska	10.8
22	Arizona	21.1
25	Arkansas	20.5
47	California	14.1
31	Colorado	20.0
28	Connecticut	20.1
5	Delaware	25.7
8	Florida	25.0
39	Georgia	16.8
48	Hawaii	11.1
25	Idaho	20.5
41	Illinois	16.0
21	Indiana	21.3
33	Iowa	19.0
10	Kansas	23.1
7	Kentucky	25.3
44	Louisiana	15.6
19	Maine	21.4
37	Maryland	17.8
13	Massachusetts	22.7
40	Michigan	16.6
32	Minnesota	19.4
46	Mississippi	14.6
10	Missouri	23.1
12	Montana	22.9
28	Nebraska	20.1
16	Nevada	21.9
17	New Hampshire	21.7
23	New Jersey	21.0
45	New Mexico	14.9
43	New York	15.9
24	North Carolina	20.7
49	North Dakota	11.0
28	Ohio	20.1
4	Oklahoma	25.9
6	Oregon	25.6
15	Pennsylvania	22.0
3	Rhode Island	26.0
38	South Carolina	16.9
2	South Dakota	27.5
19	Tennessee	21.4
41	Texas	16.0
36	Utah	17.9
14	Vermont	22.6
34	Virginia	18.8
18	Washington	21.5
9	West Virginia	23.2
27	Wisconsin	20.3
1	Wyoming	27.9

RANK ORDER

RANK	STATE	RATE
1	Wyoming	27.9
2	South Dakota	27.5
3	Rhode Island	26.0
4	Oklahoma	25.9
5	Delaware	25.7
6	Oregon	25.6
7	Kentucky	25.3
8	Florida	25.0
9	West Virginia	23.2
10	Kansas	23.1
10	Missouri	23.1
12	Montana	22.9
13	Massachusetts	22.7
14	Vermont	22.6
15	Pennsylvania	22.0
16	Nevada	21.9
17	New Hampshire	21.7
18	Washington	21.5
19	Maine	21.4
19	Tennessee	21.4
21	Indiana	21.3
22	Arizona	21.1
23	New Jersey	21.0
24	North Carolina	20.7
25	Arkansas	20.5
25	Idaho	20.5
27	Wisconsin	20.3
28	Connecticut	20.1
28	Nebraska	20.1
28	Ohio	20.1
31	Colorado	20.0
32	Minnesota	19.4
33	Iowa	19.0
34	Virginia	18.8
35	Alabama	18.7
36	Utah	17.9
37	Maryland	17.8
38	South Carolina	16.9
39	Georgia	16.8
40	Michigan	16.6
41	Illinois	16.0
41	Texas	16.0
43	New York	15.9
44	Louisiana	15.6
45	New Mexico	14.9
46	Mississippi	14.6
47	California	14.1
48	Hawaii	11.1
49	North Dakota	11.0
50	Alaska	10.8

District of Columbia 12.4

Source: Morgan Quitno Press using data from American Cancer Society
    "Cancer Facts & Figures 2004" (Copyright 2004, Reprinted with permission from the American Cancer Society)
*These estimates are offered as a rough guide and should be interpreted with caution. They are calculated
according to the distribution of estimated 2004 cancer deaths by state. Rates calculated using 2003 Census
resident population estimates.

Estimated New Cervical Cancer Cases in 2004

National Estimated Total = 10,520 New Cases*

ALPHA ORDER

RANK	STATE	CASES	% of USA
16	Alabama	190	1.8%
NA	Alaska**	NA	NA
16	Arizona	190	1.8%
20	Arkansas	160	1.5%
1	California	1,210	11.5%
26	Colorado	110	1.0%
33	Connecticut	80	0.8%
NA	Delaware**	NA	NA
4	Florida	730	6.9%
8	Georgia	350	3.3%
NA	Hawaii**	NA	NA
NA	Idaho**	NA	NA
5	Illinois	490	4.7%
22	Indiana	130	1.2%
26	Iowa	110	1.0%
33	Kansas	80	0.8%
16	Kentucky	190	1.8%
16	Louisiana	190	1.8%
NA	Maine**	NA	NA
14	Maryland	220	2.1%
22	Massachusetts	130	1.2%
8	Michigan	350	3.3%
26	Minnesota	110	1.0%
26	Mississippi	110	1.0%
13	Missouri	240	2.3%
NA	Montana**	NA	NA
NA	Nebraska**	NA	NA
33	Nevada	80	0.8%
36	New Hampshire	30	0.3%
7	New Jersey	380	3.6%
NA	New Mexico**	NA	NA
3	New York	840	8.0%
10	North Carolina	320	3.0%
NA	North Dakota**	NA	NA
10	Ohio	320	3.0%
22	Oklahoma	130	1.2%
26	Oregon	110	1.0%
6	Pennsylvania	400	3.8%
NA	Rhode Island**	NA	NA
20	South Carolina	160	1.5%
NA	South Dakota**	NA	NA
12	Tennessee	300	2.9%
2	Texas	1,030	9.8%
NA	Utah**	NA	NA
NA	Vermont**	NA	NA
14	Virginia	220	2.1%
22	Washington	130	1.2%
26	West Virginia	110	1.0%
26	Wisconsin	110	1.0%
NA	Wyoming**	NA	NA

RANK ORDER

RANK	STATE	CASES	% of USA
1	California	1,210	11.5%
2	Texas	1,030	9.8%
3	New York	840	8.0%
4	Florida	730	6.9%
5	Illinois	490	4.7%
6	Pennsylvania	400	3.8%
7	New Jersey	380	3.6%
8	Georgia	350	3.3%
8	Michigan	350	3.3%
10	North Carolina	320	3.0%
10	Ohio	320	3.0%
12	Tennessee	300	2.9%
13	Missouri	240	2.3%
14	Maryland	220	2.1%
14	Virginia	220	2.1%
16	Alabama	190	1.8%
16	Arizona	190	1.8%
16	Kentucky	190	1.8%
16	Louisiana	190	1.8%
20	Arkansas	160	1.5%
20	South Carolina	160	1.5%
22	Indiana	130	1.2%
22	Massachusetts	130	1.2%
22	Oklahoma	130	1.2%
22	Washington	130	1.2%
26	Colorado	110	1.0%
26	Iowa	110	1.0%
26	Minnesota	110	1.0%
26	Mississippi	110	1.0%
26	Oregon	110	1.0%
26	West Virginia	110	1.0%
26	Wisconsin	110	1.0%
33	Connecticut	80	0.8%
33	Kansas	80	0.8%
33	Nevada	80	0.8%
36	New Hampshire	30	0.3%
NA	Alaska**	NA	NA
NA	Delaware**	NA	NA
NA	Hawaii**	NA	NA
NA	Idaho**	NA	NA
NA	Maine**	NA	NA
NA	Montana**	NA	NA
NA	Nebraska**	NA	NA
NA	New Mexico**	NA	NA
NA	North Dakota**	NA	NA
NA	Rhode Island**	NA	NA
NA	South Dakota**	NA	NA
NA	Utah**	NA	NA
NA	Vermont**	NA	NA
NA	Wyoming**	NA	NA

District of Columbia**   NA   NA

Source: Morgan Quitno Press using data from American Cancer Society
"Cancer Facts & Figures 2004" (Copyright 2004, Reprinted with permission from the American Cancer Society)
These estimates are offered as a rough guide and should be interpreted with caution. They are calculated according to the distribution of estimated 2004 cancer deaths by state. Rates calculated using 2003 Census resident population estimates.
***Not available.*

Estimated Rate of New Cervical Cancer Cases in 2004

National Estimated Rate = 7.2 New Cases per 100,000 Female Population*

ALPHA ORDER

RANK	STATE	RATE
9	Alabama	8.2
NA	Alaska**	NA
21	Arizona	7.0
2	Arkansas	11.5
22	California	6.9
29	Colorado	4.9
31	Connecticut	4.5
NA	Delaware**	NA
7	Florida	8.5
12	Georgia	8.1
NA	Hawaii**	NA
NA	Idaho**	NA
14	Illinois	7.6
34	Indiana	4.1
18	Iowa	7.4
27	Kansas	5.8
5	Kentucky	9.1
9	Louisiana	8.2
NA	Maine**	NA
13	Maryland	7.8
36	Massachusetts	3.9
23	Michigan	6.8
32	Minnesota	4.3
18	Mississippi	7.4
9	Missouri	8.2
NA	Montana**	NA
NA	Nebraska**	NA
16	Nevada	7.5
30	New Hampshire	4.6
6	New Jersey	8.6
NA	New Mexico**	NA
7	New York	8.5
16	North Carolina	7.5
NA	North Dakota**	NA
28	Ohio	5.5
20	Oklahoma	7.3
25	Oregon	6.2
24	Pennsylvania	6.3
NA	Rhode Island**	NA
14	South Carolina	7.6
NA	South Dakota**	NA
3	Tennessee	10.1
4	Texas	9.4
NA	Utah**	NA
NA	Vermont**	NA
26	Virginia	5.9
32	Washington	4.3
1	West Virginia	11.9
35	Wisconsin	4.0
NA	Wyoming**	NA

RANK ORDER

RANK	STATE	RATE
1	West Virginia	11.9
2	Arkansas	11.5
3	Tennessee	10.1
4	Texas	9.4
5	Kentucky	9.1
6	New Jersey	8.6
7	Florida	8.5
7	New York	8.5
9	Alabama	8.2
9	Louisiana	8.2
9	Missouri	8.2
12	Georgia	8.1
13	Maryland	7.8
14	Illinois	7.6
14	South Carolina	7.6
16	Nevada	7.5
16	North Carolina	7.5
18	Iowa	7.4
18	Mississippi	7.4
20	Oklahoma	7.3
21	Arizona	7.0
22	California	6.9
23	Michigan	6.8
24	Pennsylvania	6.3
25	Oregon	6.2
26	Virginia	5.9
27	Kansas	5.8
28	Ohio	5.5
29	Colorado	4.9
30	New Hampshire	4.6
31	Connecticut	4.5
32	Minnesota	4.3
32	Washington	4.3
34	Indiana	4.1
35	Wisconsin	4.0
36	Massachusetts	3.9
NA	Alaska**	NA
NA	Delaware**	NA
NA	Hawaii**	NA
NA	Idaho**	NA
NA	Maine**	NA
NA	Montana**	NA
NA	Nebraska**	NA
NA	New Mexico**	NA
NA	North Dakota**	NA
NA	Rhode Island**	NA
NA	South Dakota**	NA
NA	Utah**	NA
NA	Vermont**	NA
NA	Wyoming**	NA
	District of Columbia**	NA

Source: Morgan Quitno Press using data from American Cancer Society
"Cancer Facts & Figures 2004" (Copyright 2004, Reprinted with permission from the American Cancer Society)
*These estimates are offered as a rough guide and should be interpreted with caution. They are calculated according to the distribution of estimated 2004 cancer deaths by state. Rates calculated using 2002 Census female population estimates.
**Not available.

Percent of Women 18 Years Old and Older
Who Had a Pap Smear Within the Past Three Years: 2002
National Median = 87.5% of Women 18 Years and Older*

ALPHA ORDER

RANK	STATE	PERCENT
28	Alabama	88.0
11	Alaska	90.1
39	Arizona	85.7
50	Arkansas	80.5
31	California	87.2
19	Colorado	88.7
5	Connecticut	91.1
3	Delaware	91.6
19	Florida	88.7
7	Georgia	90.8
14	Hawaii	89.8
48	Idaho	82.8
33	Illinois	86.7
43	Indiana	84.7
25	Iowa	88.1
18	Kansas	89.2
14	Kentucky	89.8
11	Louisiana	90.1
19	Maine	88.7
1	Maryland	93.3
7	Massachusetts	90.8
19	Michigan	88.7
25	Minnesota	88.1
42	Mississippi	85.2
40	Missouri	85.5
46	Montana	84.3
29	Nebraska	87.8
36	Nevada	86.3
16	New Hampshire	89.7
7	New Jersey	90.8
38	New Mexico	86.2
6	New York	90.9
4	North Carolina	91.2
36	North Dakota	86.3
24	Ohio	88.2
49	Oklahoma	82.0
47	Oregon	82.9
32	Pennsylvania	87.1
7	Rhode Island	90.8
25	South Carolina	88.1
23	South Dakota	88.4
2	Tennessee	91.7
29	Texas	87.8
44	Utah	84.6
17	Vermont	89.3
13	Virginia	90.0
35	Washington	86.4
41	West Virginia	85.4
33	Wisconsin	86.7
45	Wyoming	84.4

RANK ORDER

RANK	STATE	PERCENT
1	Maryland	93.3
2	Tennessee	91.7
3	Delaware	91.6
4	North Carolina	91.2
5	Connecticut	91.1
6	New York	90.9
7	Georgia	90.8
7	Massachusetts	90.8
7	New Jersey	90.8
7	Rhode Island	90.8
11	Alaska	90.1
11	Louisiana	90.1
13	Virginia	90.0
14	Hawaii	89.8
14	Kentucky	89.8
16	New Hampshire	89.7
17	Vermont	89.3
18	Kansas	89.2
19	Colorado	88.7
19	Florida	88.7
19	Maine	88.7
19	Michigan	88.7
23	South Dakota	88.4
24	Ohio	88.2
25	Iowa	88.1
25	Minnesota	88.1
25	South Carolina	88.1
28	Alabama	88.0
29	Nebraska	87.8
29	Texas	87.8
31	California	87.2
32	Pennsylvania	87.1
33	Illinois	86.7
33	Wisconsin	86.7
35	Washington	86.4
36	Nevada	86.3
36	North Dakota	86.3
38	New Mexico	86.2
39	Arizona	85.7
40	Missouri	85.5
41	West Virginia	85.4
42	Mississippi	85.2
43	Indiana	84.7
44	Utah	84.6
45	Wyoming	84.4
46	Montana	84.3
47	Oregon	82.9
48	Idaho	82.8
49	Oklahoma	82.0
50	Arkansas	80.5

District of Columbia   93.4

Source: Morgan Quitno Press using data from U.S. Dept of HHS, Centers for Disease Control and Prevention
"2002 Behavioral Risk Factor Surveillance Summary Prevalence Data" (http://apps.nccd.cdc.gov/brfss/)
*Of women with intact cervix. Pap smear is a test for cancer, especially of the female genital tract. Named after George Papanicolaou (1883-1962), American anatomist.

Estimated New Uterine Cancer Cases in 2004

National Estimated Total = 40,320 New Cases*

ALPHA ORDER

RANK	STATE	CASES	% of USA
20	Alabama	680	1.7%
48	Alaska	60	0.1%
22	Arizona	510	1.3%
32	Arkansas	340	0.8%
1	California	3,920	9.7%
29	Colorado	400	1.0%
27	Connecticut	450	1.1%
43	Delaware	110	0.3%
4	Florida	2,450	6.1%
12	Georgia	970	2.4%
39	Hawaii	170	0.4%
39	Idaho	170	0.4%
6	Illinois	2,050	5.1%
14	Indiana	910	2.3%
22	Iowa	510	1.3%
29	Kansas	400	1.0%
22	Kentucky	510	1.3%
22	Louisiana	510	1.3%
36	Maine	230	0.6%
18	Maryland	740	1.8%
12	Massachusetts	970	2.4%
9	Michigan	1,420	3.5%
20	Minnesota	680	1.7%
34	Mississippi	280	0.7%
16	Missouri	850	2.1%
43	Montana	110	0.3%
34	Nebraska	280	0.7%
39	Nevada	170	0.4%
39	New Hampshire	170	0.4%
8	New Jersey	1,760	4.4%
36	New Mexico	230	0.6%
2	New York	3,180	7.9%
10	North Carolina	1,190	3.0%
48	North Dakota	60	0.1%
7	Ohio	1,880	4.7%
29	Oklahoma	400	1.0%
27	Oregon	450	1.1%
3	Pennsylvania	2,500	6.2%
43	Rhode Island	110	0.3%
22	South Carolina	510	1.3%
43	South Dakota	110	0.3%
18	Tennessee	740	1.8%
5	Texas	2,390	5.9%
36	Utah	230	0.6%
43	Vermont	110	0.3%
11	Virginia	1,080	2.7%
14	Washington	910	2.3%
32	West Virginia	340	0.8%
16	Wisconsin	850	2.1%
48	Wyoming	60	0.1%

RANK ORDER

RANK	STATE	CASES	% of USA
1	California	3,920	9.7%
2	New York	3,180	7.9%
3	Pennsylvania	2,500	6.2%
4	Florida	2,450	6.1%
5	Texas	2,390	5.9%
6	Illinois	2,050	5.1%
7	Ohio	1,880	4.7%
8	New Jersey	1,760	4.4%
9	Michigan	1,420	3.5%
10	North Carolina	1,190	3.0%
11	Virginia	1,080	2.7%
12	Georgia	970	2.4%
12	Massachusetts	970	2.4%
14	Indiana	910	2.3%
14	Washington	910	2.3%
16	Missouri	850	2.1%
16	Wisconsin	850	2.1%
18	Maryland	740	1.8%
18	Tennessee	740	1.8%
20	Alabama	680	1.7%
20	Minnesota	680	1.7%
22	Arizona	510	1.3%
22	Iowa	510	1.3%
22	Kentucky	510	1.3%
22	Louisiana	510	1.3%
22	South Carolina	510	1.3%
27	Connecticut	450	1.1%
27	Oregon	450	1.1%
29	Colorado	400	1.0%
29	Kansas	400	1.0%
29	Oklahoma	400	1.0%
32	Arkansas	340	0.8%
32	West Virginia	340	0.8%
34	Mississippi	280	0.7%
34	Nebraska	280	0.7%
36	Maine	230	0.6%
36	New Mexico	230	0.6%
36	Utah	230	0.6%
39	Hawaii	170	0.4%
39	Idaho	170	0.4%
39	Nevada	170	0.4%
39	New Hampshire	170	0.4%
43	Delaware	110	0.3%
43	Montana	110	0.3%
43	Rhode Island	110	0.3%
43	South Dakota	110	0.3%
43	Vermont	110	0.3%
48	Alaska	60	0.1%
48	North Dakota	60	0.1%
48	Wyoming	60	0.1%
	District of Columbia	170	0.4%

Source: American Cancer Society
    "Cancer Facts & Figures 2004" (Copyright 2004, Reprinted with permission from the American Cancer Society)
*These estimates are offered as a rough guide and should be interpreted with caution. They are calculated
according to the distribution of estimated 2004 cancer deaths by state.

Estimated Rate of New Uterine Cancer Cases in 2004

National Estimated Rate = 27.5 New Cases per 100,000 Female Population*

ALPHA ORDER

RANK	STATE	RATE
13	Alabama	29.3
45	Alaska	19.3
48	Arizona	18.7
32	Arkansas	24.5
39	California	22.3
49	Colorado	17.9
30	Connecticut	25.3
25	Delaware	26.5
19	Florida	28.7
39	Georgia	22.3
23	Hawaii	27.4
28	Idaho	25.4
10	Illinois	31.9
18	Indiana	29.0
6	Iowa	34.1
14	Kansas	29.2
33	Kentucky	24.4
41	Louisiana	22.1
5	Maine	34.6
27	Maryland	26.2
14	Massachusetts	29.2
22	Michigan	27.8
24	Minnesota	26.9
46	Mississippi	18.9
14	Missouri	29.2
36	Montana	24.1
8	Nebraska	32.0
50	Nevada	15.9
26	New Hampshire	26.3
1	New Jersey	39.9
33	New Mexico	24.4
7	New York	32.1
21	North Carolina	28.1
46	North Dakota	18.9
8	Ohio	32.0
38	Oklahoma	22.5
28	Oregon	25.4
2	Pennsylvania	39.3
44	Rhode Island	19.8
36	South Carolina	24.1
19	South Dakota	28.7
31	Tennessee	24.9
42	Texas	21.8
43	Utah	19.9
4	Vermont	35.0
17	Virginia	29.1
12	Washington	29.9
3	West Virginia	36.8
11	Wisconsin	30.9
35	Wyoming	24.2

RANK ORDER

RANK	STATE	RATE
1	New Jersey	39.9
2	Pennsylvania	39.3
3	West Virginia	36.8
4	Vermont	35.0
5	Maine	34.6
6	Iowa	34.1
7	New York	32.1
8	Nebraska	32.0
8	Ohio	32.0
10	Illinois	31.9
11	Wisconsin	30.9
12	Washington	29.9
13	Alabama	29.3
14	Kansas	29.2
14	Massachusetts	29.2
14	Missouri	29.2
17	Virginia	29.1
18	Indiana	29.0
19	Florida	28.7
19	South Dakota	28.7
21	North Carolina	28.1
22	Michigan	27.8
23	Hawaii	27.4
24	Minnesota	26.9
25	Delaware	26.5
26	New Hampshire	26.3
27	Maryland	26.2
28	Idaho	25.4
28	Oregon	25.4
30	Connecticut	25.3
31	Tennessee	24.9
32	Arkansas	24.5
33	Kentucky	24.4
33	New Mexico	24.4
35	Wyoming	24.2
36	Montana	24.1
36	South Carolina	24.1
38	Oklahoma	22.5
39	California	22.3
39	Georgia	22.3
41	Louisiana	22.1
42	Texas	21.8
43	Utah	19.9
44	Rhode Island	19.8
45	Alaska	19.3
46	Mississippi	18.9
46	North Dakota	18.9
48	Arizona	18.7
49	Colorado	17.9
50	Nevada	15.9

District of Columbia	56.4

Source: Morgan Quitno Press using data from American Cancer Society
"Cancer Facts & Figures 2004" (Copyright 2004, Reprinted with permission from the American Cancer Society)
*These estimates are offered as a rough guide and should be interpreted with caution. They are calculated according to the distribution of estimated 2004 cancer deaths by state. Rates calculated using 2002 Census female population estimates.

Percent of Women Who Have Had a Hysterectomy: 2002

National Median = 20.8% of Women*

ALPHA ORDER

RANK	STATE	PERCENT
4	Alabama	30.0
43	Alaska	16.6
11	Arizona	25.6
2	Arkansas	30.5
39	California	18.7
25	Colorado	21.1
46	Connecticut	15.6
1	Delaware	32.6
13	Florida	25.1
18	Georgia	23.8
50	Hawaii	14.6
16	Idaho	24.3
35	Illinois	19.4
21	Indiana	22.8
29	Iowa	20.7
14	Kansas	25.0
9	Kentucky	26.4
3	Louisiana	30.1
37	Maine	19.1
41	Maryland	17.3
46	Massachusetts	15.6
25	Michigan	21.1
42	Minnesota	17.0
6	Mississippi	29.1
27	Missouri	20.8
20	Montana	23.2
23	Nebraska	22.4
22	Nevada	22.7
44	New Hampshire	16.3
45	New Jersey	15.7
37	New Mexico	19.1
49	New York	14.7
19	North Carolina	23.5
27	North Dakota	20.8
29	Ohio	20.7
5	Oklahoma	29.6
12	Oregon	25.4
34	Pennsylvania	19.6
31	Rhode Island	20.3
7	South Carolina	26.5
33	South Dakota	19.8
7	Tennessee	26.5
17	Texas	23.9
24	Utah	21.5
48	Vermont	15.2
36	Virginia	19.3
32	Washington	20.2
14	West Virginia	25.0
40	Wisconsin	18.2
10	Wyoming	26.1

RANK ORDER

RANK	STATE	PERCENT
1	Delaware	32.6
2	Arkansas	30.5
3	Louisiana	30.1
4	Alabama	30.0
5	Oklahoma	29.6
6	Mississippi	29.1
7	South Carolina	26.5
7	Tennessee	26.5
9	Kentucky	26.4
10	Wyoming	26.1
11	Arizona	25.6
12	Oregon	25.4
13	Florida	25.1
14	Kansas	25.0
14	West Virginia	25.0
16	Idaho	24.3
17	Texas	23.9
18	Georgia	23.8
19	North Carolina	23.5
20	Montana	23.2
21	Indiana	22.8
22	Nevada	22.7
23	Nebraska	22.4
24	Utah	21.5
25	Colorado	21.1
25	Michigan	21.1
27	Missouri	20.8
27	North Dakota	20.8
29	Iowa	20.7
29	Ohio	20.7
31	Rhode Island	20.3
32	Washington	20.2
33	South Dakota	19.8
34	Pennsylvania	19.6
35	Illinois	19.4
36	Virginia	19.3
37	Maine	19.1
37	New Mexico	19.1
39	California	18.7
40	Wisconsin	18.2
41	Maryland	17.3
42	Minnesota	17.0
43	Alaska	16.6
44	New Hampshire	16.3
45	New Jersey	15.7
46	Connecticut	15.6
46	Massachusetts	15.6
48	Vermont	15.2
49	New York	14.7
50	Hawaii	14.6
	District of Columbia	16.5

Source: U.S. Department of Health and Human Services, Centers for Disease Control and Prevention
"2002 Behavioral Risk Factor Surveillance Summary Prevalence Data" (http://apps.nccd.cdc.gov/brfss/)
*Of women 18 years old and older.

AIDS Cases Reported in 2003

National Total = 41,832 New AIDS Cases*

ALPHA ORDER

RANK	STATE	CASES	% of USA
22	Alabama	441	1.1%
46	Alaska	15	0.0%
16	Arizona	646	1.5%
31	Arkansas	172	0.4%
2	California	5,802	13.9%
25	Colorado	343	0.8%
17	Connecticut	631	1.5%
28	Delaware	202	0.5%
3	Florida	4,409	10.5%
6	Georgia	1,825	4.4%
36	Hawaii	97	0.2%
44	Idaho	24	0.1%
7	Illinois	1,718	4.1%
20	Indiana	514	1.2%
39	Iowa	82	0.2%
37	Kansas	91	0.2%
30	Kentucky	200	0.5%
18	Louisiana	610	1.5%
41	Maine	52	0.1%
9	Maryland	1,441	3.4%
19	Massachusetts	599	1.4%
15	Michigan	703	1.7%
33	Minnesota	162	0.4%
23	Mississippi	438	1.0%
24	Missouri	365	0.9%
48	Montana	13	0.0%
41	Nebraska	52	0.1%
26	Nevada	254	0.6%
43	New Hampshire	36	0.1%
8	New Jersey	1,448	3.5%
34	New Mexico	102	0.2%
1	New York	6,208	14.8%
10	North Carolina	1,060	2.5%
50	North Dakota	2	0.0%
13	Ohio	757	1.8%
28	Oklahoma	202	0.5%
27	Oregon	242	0.6%
5	Pennsylvania	2,058	4.9%
34	Rhode Island	102	0.2%
14	South Carolina	756	1.8%
47	South Dakota	14	0.0%
12	Tennessee	800	1.9%
4	Texas	3,582	8.6%
40	Utah	72	0.2%
45	Vermont	16	0.0%
11	Virginia	856	2.0%
21	Washington	491	1.2%
38	West Virginia	86	0.2%
32	Wisconsin	171	0.4%
49	Wyoming	7	0.0%

RANK ORDER

RANK	STATE	CASES	% of USA
1	New York	6,208	14.8%
2	California	5,802	13.9%
3	Florida	4,409	10.5%
4	Texas	3,582	8.6%
5	Pennsylvania	2,058	4.9%
6	Georgia	1,825	4.4%
7	Illinois	1,718	4.1%
8	New Jersey	1,448	3.5%
9	Maryland	1,441	3.4%
10	North Carolina	1,060	2.5%
11	Virginia	856	2.0%
12	Tennessee	800	1.9%
13	Ohio	757	1.8%
14	South Carolina	756	1.8%
15	Michigan	703	1.7%
16	Arizona	646	1.5%
17	Connecticut	631	1.5%
18	Louisiana	610	1.5%
19	Massachusetts	599	1.4%
20	Indiana	514	1.2%
21	Washington	491	1.2%
22	Alabama	441	1.1%
23	Mississippi	438	1.0%
24	Missouri	365	0.9%
25	Colorado	343	0.8%
26	Nevada	254	0.6%
27	Oregon	242	0.6%
28	Delaware	202	0.5%
28	Oklahoma	202	0.5%
30	Kentucky	200	0.5%
31	Arkansas	172	0.4%
32	Wisconsin	171	0.4%
33	Minnesota	162	0.4%
34	New Mexico	102	0.2%
34	Rhode Island	102	0.2%
36	Hawaii	97	0.2%
37	Kansas	91	0.2%
38	West Virginia	86	0.2%
39	Iowa	82	0.2%
40	Utah	72	0.2%
41	Maine	52	0.1%
41	Nebraska	52	0.1%
43	New Hampshire	36	0.1%
44	Idaho	24	0.1%
45	Vermont	16	0.0%
46	Alaska	15	0.0%
47	South Dakota	14	0.0%
48	Montana	13	0.0%
49	Wyoming	7	0.0%
50	North Dakota	2	0.0%

	District of Columbia	863	2.1%

Source: U.S. Department of Health and Human Services, National Center for Health Statistics
    "Morbidity and Mortality Weekly Report" (January 2, 2004, Vol. 52, Nos. 51 & 52)
*Provisional data. AIDS is Acquired Immunodeficiency Syndrome. It is a specific group of diseases or conditions which are indicative of severe immunosuppression related to infection with the Human Immunodeficiency Virus (HIV). National total does not include 1,025 new cases in Puerto Rico.

AIDS Rate in 2003

National Rate = 14.4 New AIDS Cases Reported per 100,000 Population*

ALPHA ORDER

RANK	STATE	RATE
20	Alabama	9.8
45	Alaska	2.3
17	Arizona	11.6
31	Arkansas	6.3
10	California	16.4
26	Colorado	7.5
7	Connecticut	18.1
4	Delaware	24.7
3	Florida	25.9
5	Georgia	21.0
25	Hawaii	7.7
46	Idaho	1.8
14	Illinois	13.6
23	Indiana	8.3
42	Iowa	2.8
37	Kansas	3.3
34	Kentucky	4.9
14	Louisiana	13.6
36	Maine	4.0
2	Maryland	26.2
22	Massachusetts	9.3
27	Michigan	7.0
38	Minnesota	3.2
12	Mississippi	15.2
30	Missouri	6.4
48	Montana	1.4
41	Nebraska	3.0
19	Nevada	11.3
42	New Hampshire	2.8
8	New Jersey	16.8
33	New Mexico	5.4
1	New York	32.3
16	North Carolina	12.6
50	North Dakota	0.3
29	Ohio	6.6
32	Oklahoma	5.8
28	Oregon	6.8
9	Pennsylvania	16.6
21	Rhode Island	9.5
6	South Carolina	18.2
46	South Dakota	1.8
13	Tennessee	13.7
11	Texas	16.2
39	Utah	3.1
44	Vermont	2.6
17	Virginia	11.6
24	Washington	8.0
35	West Virginia	4.8
39	Wisconsin	3.1
48	Wyoming	1.4

RANK ORDER

RANK	STATE	RATE
1	New York	32.3
2	Maryland	26.2
3	Florida	25.9
4	Delaware	24.7
5	Georgia	21.0
6	South Carolina	18.2
7	Connecticut	18.1
8	New Jersey	16.8
9	Pennsylvania	16.6
10	California	16.4
11	Texas	16.2
12	Mississippi	15.2
13	Tennessee	13.7
14	Illinois	13.6
14	Louisiana	13.6
16	North Carolina	12.6
17	Arizona	11.6
17	Virginia	11.6
19	Nevada	11.3
20	Alabama	9.8
21	Rhode Island	9.5
22	Massachusetts	9.3
23	Indiana	8.3
24	Washington	8.0
25	Hawaii	7.7
26	Colorado	7.5
27	Michigan	7.0
28	Oregon	6.8
29	Ohio	6.6
30	Missouri	6.4
31	Arkansas	6.3
32	Oklahoma	5.8
33	New Mexico	5.4
34	Kentucky	4.9
35	West Virginia	4.8
36	Maine	4.0
37	Kansas	3.3
38	Minnesota	3.2
39	Utah	3.1
39	Wisconsin	3.1
41	Nebraska	3.0
42	Iowa	2.8
42	New Hampshire	2.8
44	Vermont	2.6
45	Alaska	2.3
46	Idaho	1.8
46	South Dakota	1.8
48	Montana	1.4
48	Wyoming	1.4
50	North Dakota	0.3

District of Columbia	153.2

Source: Morgan Quitno Press using data from U.S. Dept. of Health & Human Serv's, National Center for Health Statistics "Morbidity and Mortality Weekly Report" (January 2, 2004, Vol. 52, Nos. 51 & 52)
Provisional data. AIDS is Acquired Immunodeficiency Syndrome. It is a specific group of diseases or conditions which are indicative of severe immunosuppression related to infection with the Human Immunodeficiency Virus (HIV). National rate does not include cases or population in U.S. territories.

AIDS Cases Reported Through December 2002

National Total = 830,274 Reported AIDS Cases*

ALPHA ORDER

ALPHA ORDER

RANK	STATE	CASES	% of USA
23	Alabama	7,135	0.9%
45	Alaska	530	0.1%
21	Arizona	8,570	1.0%
32	Arkansas	3,393	0.4%
2	California	128,064	15.4%
22	Colorado	7,713	0.9%
13	Connecticut	12,765	1.5%
33	Delaware	3,019	0.4%
3	Florida	90,233	10.9%
8	Georgia	26,008	3.1%
34	Hawaii	2,720	0.3%
44	Idaho	547	0.1%
6	Illinois	28,426	3.4%
24	Indiana	7,003	0.8%
39	Iowa	1,498	0.2%
35	Kansas	2,540	0.3%
30	Kentucky	3,976	0.5%
12	Louisiana	14,624	1.8%
42	Maine	1,032	0.1%
9	Maryland	25,358	3.1%
10	Massachusetts	17,774	2.1%
15	Michigan	12,645	1.5%
29	Minnesota	4,076	0.5%
26	Mississippi	5,293	0.6%
19	Missouri	10,006	1.2%
47	Montana	359	0.0%
41	Nebraska	1,237	0.1%
27	Nevada	4,972	0.6%
43	New Hampshire	960	0.1%
5	New Jersey	45,237	5.4%
36	New Mexico	2,277	0.3%
1	New York	155,755	18.8%
16	North Carolina	12,384	1.5%
50	North Dakota	112	0.0%
14	Ohio	12,733	1.5%
28	Oklahoma	4,229	0.5%
25	Oregon	5,357	0.6%
7	Pennsylvania	28,136	3.4%
37	Rhode Island	2,261	0.3%
17	South Carolina	11,055	1.3%
49	South Dakota	203	0.0%
20	Tennessee	9,924	1.2%
4	Texas	59,772	7.2%
38	Utah	2,189	0.3%
46	Vermont	442	0.1%
11	Virginia	14,959	1.8%
18	Washington	10,473	1.3%
40	West Virginia	1,262	0.2%
31	Wisconsin	3,952	0.5%
48	Wyoming	204	0.0%

RANK ORDER

RANK	STATE	CASES	% of USA
1	New York	155,755	18.8%
2	California	128,064	15.4%
3	Florida	90,233	10.9%
4	Texas	59,772	7.2%
5	New Jersey	45,237	5.4%
6	Illinois	28,426	3.4%
7	Pennsylvania	28,136	3.4%
8	Georgia	26,008	3.1%
9	Maryland	25,358	3.1%
10	Massachusetts	17,774	2.1%
11	Virginia	14,959	1.8%
12	Louisiana	14,624	1.8%
13	Connecticut	12,765	1.5%
14	Ohio	12,733	1.5%
15	Michigan	12,645	1.5%
16	North Carolina	12,384	1.5%
17	South Carolina	11,055	1.3%
18	Washington	10,473	1.3%
19	Missouri	10,006	1.2%
20	Tennessee	9,924	1.2%
21	Arizona	8,570	1.0%
22	Colorado	7,713	0.9%
23	Alabama	7,135	0.9%
24	Indiana	7,003	0.8%
25	Oregon	5,357	0.6%
26	Mississippi	5,293	0.6%
27	Nevada	4,972	0.6%
28	Oklahoma	4,229	0.5%
29	Minnesota	4,076	0.5%
30	Kentucky	3,976	0.5%
31	Wisconsin	3,952	0.5%
32	Arkansas	3,393	0.4%
33	Delaware	3,019	0.4%
34	Hawaii	2,720	0.3%
35	Kansas	2,540	0.3%
36	New Mexico	2,277	0.3%
37	Rhode Island	2,261	0.3%
38	Utah	2,189	0.3%
39	Iowa	1,498	0.2%
40	West Virginia	1,262	0.2%
41	Nebraska	1,237	0.1%
42	Maine	1,032	0.1%
43	New Hampshire	960	0.1%
44	Idaho	547	0.1%
45	Alaska	530	0.1%
46	Vermont	442	0.1%
47	Montana	359	0.0%
48	Wyoming	204	0.0%
49	South Dakota	203	0.0%
50	North Dakota	112	0.0%
	District of Columbia	14,882	1.8%

Source: U.S. Department of Health and Human Services, Centers for Disease Control and Prevention "HIV/AIDS Surveillance Report, 2002" (Year-end Edition, Vol. 14, No. 2)

Cumulative through December 2002. AIDS is Acquired Immunodeficiency Syndrome. It is a specific group of diseases or conditions which are indicative of severe immunosuppression related to infection with the Human Immunodeficiency Virus (HIV). National total does not include 27,242 cases in Puerto Rico, 575 cases in the Virgin Islands and 68 cases in other U.S. territories.

AIDS Cases in Children 12 Years and Younger Through December 2002

National Total = 8,804 Juvenile AIDS Cases*

ALPHA ORDER

RANK	STATE	CASES	% of USA
18	Alabama	76	0.9%
45	Alaska	5	0.1%
23	Arizona	41	0.5%
24	Arkansas	38	0.4%
4	California	630	7.2%
27	Colorado	31	0.4%
12	Connecticut	177	2.0%
33	Delaware	24	0.3%
2	Florida	1,473	16.7%
9	Georgia	213	2.4%
36	Hawaii	16	0.2%
47	Idaho	3	0.0%
8	Illinois	277	3.1%
21	Indiana	53	0.6%
38	Iowa	11	0.1%
37	Kansas	12	0.1%
28	Kentucky	30	0.3%
13	Louisiana	130	1.5%
41	Maine	9	0.1%
7	Maryland	313	3.6%
9	Massachusetts	213	2.4%
16	Michigan	110	1.2%
30	Minnesota	27	0.3%
20	Mississippi	57	0.6%
19	Missouri	60	0.7%
47	Montana	3	0.0%
39	Nebraska	10	0.1%
29	Nevada	28	0.3%
41	New Hampshire	9	0.1%
3	New Jersey	764	8.7%
43	New Mexico	8	0.1%
1	New York	2,298	26.1%
15	North Carolina	120	1.4%
50	North Dakota	1	0.0%
14	Ohio	127	1.4%
30	Oklahoma	27	0.3%
35	Oregon	18	0.2%
6	Pennsylvania	340	3.9%
32	Rhode Island	25	0.3%
17	South Carolina	88	1.0%
46	South Dakota	4	0.0%
22	Tennessee	52	0.6%
5	Texas	392	4.5%
34	Utah	21	0.2%
44	Vermont	6	0.1%
11	Virginia	179	2.0%
25	Washington	34	0.4%
39	West Virginia	10	0.1%
26	Wisconsin	33	0.4%
47	Wyoming	3	0.0%

RANK ORDER

RANK	STATE	CASES	% of USA
1	New York	2,298	26.1%
2	Florida	1,473	16.7%
3	New Jersey	764	8.7%
4	California	630	7.2%
5	Texas	392	4.5%
6	Pennsylvania	340	3.9%
7	Maryland	313	3.6%
8	Illinois	277	3.1%
9	Georgia	213	2.4%
9	Massachusetts	213	2.4%
11	Virginia	179	2.0%
12	Connecticut	177	2.0%
13	Louisiana	130	1.5%
14	Ohio	127	1.4%
15	North Carolina	120	1.4%
16	Michigan	110	1.2%
17	South Carolina	88	1.0%
18	Alabama	76	0.9%
19	Missouri	60	0.7%
20	Mississippi	57	0.6%
21	Indiana	53	0.6%
22	Tennessee	52	0.6%
23	Arizona	41	0.5%
24	Arkansas	38	0.4%
25	Washington	34	0.4%
26	Wisconsin	33	0.4%
27	Colorado	31	0.4%
28	Kentucky	30	0.3%
29	Nevada	28	0.3%
30	Minnesota	27	0.3%
30	Oklahoma	27	0.3%
32	Rhode Island	25	0.3%
33	Delaware	24	0.3%
34	Utah	21	0.2%
35	Oregon	18	0.2%
36	Hawaii	16	0.2%
37	Kansas	12	0.1%
38	Iowa	11	0.1%
39	Nebraska	10	0.1%
39	West Virginia	10	0.1%
41	Maine	9	0.1%
41	New Hampshire	9	0.1%
43	New Mexico	8	0.1%
44	Vermont	6	0.1%
45	Alaska	5	0.1%
46	South Dakota	4	0.0%
47	Idaho	3	0.0%
47	Montana	3	0.0%
47	Wyoming	3	0.0%
50	North Dakota	1	0.0%
	District of Columbia	175	2.0%

Source: U.S. Department of Health and Human Services, Centers for Disease Control and Prevention "HIV/AIDS Surveillance Report, 2002" (Year-end Edition, Vol. 14, No. 2)

Cumulative through December 2002. AIDS is Acquired Immunodeficiency Syndrome. It is a specific group of diseases or conditions which are indicative of severe immunosuppression related to infection with the Human Immunodeficiency Virus (HIV). National total does not include 395 cases in Puerto Rico and 18 cases in the Virgin Islands.

Chickenpox (Varicella) Cases Reported in 2003

National Total = 13,246 Cases*

ALPHA ORDER

RANK	STATE	CASES	% of USA
21	Alabama	0	0.0%
21	Alaska	0	0.0%
18	Arizona	4	0.0%
21	Arkansas	0	0.0%
21	California	0	0.0%
21	Colorado	0	0.0%
21	Connecticut	0	0.0%
15	Delaware	28	0.2%
NA	Florida**	NA	NA
21	Georgia	0	0.0%
21	Hawaii	0	0.0%
NA	Idaho**	NA	NA
21	Illinois	0	0.0%
21	Indiana	0	0.0%
NA	Iowa**	NA	NA
21	Kansas	0	0.0%
NA	Kentucky**	NA	NA
16	Louisiana	14	0.1%
7	Maine	780	5.9%
21	Maryland	0	0.0%
11	Massachusetts	151	1.1%
1	Michigan	4,084	30.8%
NA	Minnesota**	NA	NA
20	Mississippi	2	0.0%
21	Missouri	0	0.0%
NA	Montana**	NA	NA
21	Nebraska	0	0.0%
21	Nevada	0	0.0%
21	New Hampshire	0	0.0%
21	New Jersey	0	0.0%
18	New Mexico	4	0.0%
21	New York	0	0.0%
NA	North Carolina**	NA	NA
13	North Dakota	78	0.6%
4	Ohio	1,228	9.3%
NA	Oklahoma**	NA	NA
21	Oregon	0	0.0%
14	Pennsylvania	39	0.3%
17	Rhode Island	5	0.0%
10	South Carolina	267	2.0%
21	South Dakota	0	0.0%
NA	Tennessee**	NA	NA
2	Texas	2,275	17.2%
8	Utah	629	4.7%
5	Vermont	907	6.8%
9	Virginia	503	3.8%
21	Washington	0	0.0%
3	West Virginia	1,262	9.5%
6	Wisconsin	849	6.4%
12	Wyoming	106	0.8%

RANK ORDER

RANK	STATE	CASES	% of USA
1	Michigan	4,084	30.8%
2	Texas	2,275	17.2%
3	West Virginia	1,262	9.5%
4	Ohio	1,228	9.3%
5	Vermont	907	6.8%
6	Wisconsin	849	6.4%
7	Maine	780	5.9%
8	Utah	629	4.7%
9	Virginia	503	3.8%
10	South Carolina	267	2.0%
11	Massachusetts	151	1.1%
12	Wyoming	106	0.8%
13	North Dakota	78	0.6%
14	Pennsylvania	39	0.3%
15	Delaware	28	0.2%
16	Louisiana	14	0.1%
17	Rhode Island	5	0.0%
18	Arizona	4	0.0%
18	New Mexico	4	0.0%
20	Mississippi	2	0.0%
21	Alabama	0	0.0%
21	Alaska	0	0.0%
21	Arkansas	0	0.0%
21	California	0	0.0%
21	Colorado	0	0.0%
21	Connecticut	0	0.0%
21	Georgia	0	0.0%
21	Hawaii	0	0.0%
21	Illinois	0	0.0%
21	Indiana	0	0.0%
21	Kansas	0	0.0%
21	Maryland	0	0.0%
21	Missouri	0	0.0%
21	Nebraska	0	0.0%
21	Nevada	0	0.0%
21	New Hampshire	0	0.0%
21	New Jersey	0	0.0%
21	New York	0	0.0%
21	Oregon	0	0.0%
21	South Dakota	0	30.0%
21	Washington	0	0.0%
NA	Florida**	NA	NA
NA	Idaho**	NA	NA
NA	Iowa**	NA	NA
NA	Kentucky**	NA	NA
NA	Minnesota**	NA	NA
NA	Montana**	NA	NA
NA	North Carolina**	NA	NA
NA	Oklahoma**	NA	NA
NA	Tennessee**	NA	NA

| | District of Columbia | 31 | 0.2% |

Source: U.S. Department of Health and Human Services, National Center for Health Statistics
   "Morbidity and Mortality Weekly Report" (January 2, 2004, Vol. 52, Nos. 51 & 52)
*Provisional data. An illness with acute onset of generalized maculo-papulovesicular rash without other apparent cause.
**Not notifiable.

Chickenpox (Varicella) Rate in 2003

National Rate = 4.6 Cases per 100,000 Population*

ALPHA ORDER

RANK	STATE	RATE
21	Alabama	0.0
21	Alaska	0.0
19	Arizona	0.1
21	Arkansas	0.0
21	California	0.0
21	Colorado	0.0
21	Connecticut	0.0
13	Delaware	3.4
NA	Florida**	NA
21	Georgia	0.0
21	Hawaii	0.0
NA	Idaho**	NA
21	Illinois	0.0
21	Indiana	0.0
NA	Iowa**	NA
21	Kansas	0.0
NA	Kentucky**	NA
16	Louisiana	0.3
3	Maine	59.7
21	Maryland	0.0
14	Massachusetts	2.3
4	Michigan	40.5
NA	Minnesota**	NA
19	Mississippi	0.1
21	Missouri	0.0
NA	Montana**	NA
21	Nebraska	0.0
21	Nevada	0.0
21	New Hampshire	0.0
21	New Jersey	0.0
18	New Mexico	0.2
21	New York	0.0
NA	North Carolina**	NA
8	North Dakota	12.3
9	Ohio	10.7
NA	Oklahoma**	NA
21	Oregon	0.0
16	Pennsylvania	0.3
15	Rhode Island	0.5
12	South Carolina	6.4
21	South Dakota	0.0
NA	Tennessee**	NA
10	Texas	10.3
5	Utah	26.7
1	Vermont	146.5
11	Virginia	6.8
21	Washington	0.0
2	West Virginia	69.7
7	Wisconsin	15.5
6	Wyoming	21.1

RANK ORDER

RANK	STATE	RATE
1	Vermont	146.5
2	West Virginia	69.7
3	Maine	59.7
4	Michigan	40.5
5	Utah	26.7
6	Wyoming	21.1
7	Wisconsin	15.5
8	North Dakota	12.3
9	Ohio	10.7
10	Texas	10.3
11	Virginia	6.8
12	South Carolina	6.4
13	Delaware	3.4
14	Massachusetts	2.3
15	Rhode Island	0.5
16	Louisiana	0.3
16	Pennsylvania	0.3
18	New Mexico	0.2
19	Arizona	0.1
19	Mississippi	0.1
21	Alabama	0.0
21	Alaska	0.0
21	Arkansas	0.0
21	California	0.0
21	Colorado	0.0
21	Connecticut	0.0
21	Georgia	0.0
21	Hawaii	0.0
21	Illinois	0.0
21	Indiana	0.0
21	Kansas	0.0
21	Maryland	0.0
21	Missouri	0.0
21	Nebraska	0.0
21	Nevada	0.0
21	New Hampshire	0.0
21	New Jersey	0.0
21	New York	0.0
21	Oregon	0.0
21	South Dakota	0.0
21	Washington	0.0
NA	Florida**	NA
NA	Idaho**	NA
NA	Iowa**	NA
NA	Kentucky**	NA
NA	Minnesota**	NA
NA	Montana**	NA
NA	North Carolina**	NA
NA	Oklahoma**	NA
NA	Tennessee**	NA

	District of Columbia	5.5

Source: Morgan Quitno Press using data from U.S. Dept. of Health & Human Serv's, National Center for Health Statistics
   "Morbidity and Mortality Weekly Report" (January 2, 2004, Vol. 52, Nos. 51 & 52)
*Provisional data. An illness with acute onset of generalized maculo-papulovesicular rash without other apparent cause.
**Not notifiable.

E-Coli Cases Reported in 2003

National Total = 2,944 Cases*

ALPHA ORDER

RANK ORDER

RANK	STATE	CASES	% of USA
38	Alabama	14	0.5%
47	Alaska	4	0.1%
24	Arizona	40	1.4%
41	Arkansas	12	0.4%
1	California	254	8.6%
18	Colorado	79	2.7%
15	Connecticut	91	3.1%
42	Delaware	11	0.4%
17	Florida	83	2.8%
25	Georgia	37	1.3%
43	Hawaii	9	0.3%
12	Idaho	102	3.5%
8	Illinois	114	3.9%
16	Indiana	89	3.0%
11	Iowa	104	3.5%
23	Kansas	42	1.4%
25	Kentucky	37	1.3%
50	Louisiana	3	0.1%
37	Maine	15	0.5%
38	Maryland	14	0.5%
13	Massachusetts	93	3.2%
14	Michigan	92	3.1%
3	Minnesota	157	5.3%
44	Mississippi	6	0.2%
9	Missouri	110	3.7%
35	Montana	17	0.6%
22	Nebraska	43	1.5%
32	Nevada	24	0.8%
38	New Hampshire	14	0.5%
33	New Jersey	23	0.8%
36	New Mexico	16	0.5%
6	New York	139	4.7%
27	North Carolina	35	1.2%
31	North Dakota	25	0.8%
2	Ohio	171	5.8%
30	Oklahoma	29	1.0%
10	Oregon	106	3.6%
5	Pennsylvania	140	4.8%
47	Rhode Island	4	0.1%
47	South Carolina	4	0.1%
29	South Dakota	32	1.1%
27	Tennessee	35	1.2%
20	Texas	63	2.1%
19	Utah	76	2.6%
34	Vermont	18	0.6%
21	Virginia	49	1.7%
7	Washington	116	3.9%
44	West Virginia	6	0.2%
4	Wisconsin	141	4.8%
46	Wyoming	5	0.2%

RANK	STATE	CASES	% of USA
1	California	254	8.6%
2	Ohio	171	5.8%
3	Minnesota	157	5.3%
4	Wisconsin	141	4.8%
5	Pennsylvania	140	4.8%
6	New York	139	4.7%
7	Washington	116	3.9%
8	Illinois	114	3.9%
9	Missouri	110	3.7%
10	Oregon	106	3.6%
11	Iowa	104	3.5%
12	Idaho	102	3.5%
13	Massachusetts	93	3.2%
14	Michigan	92	3.1%
15	Connecticut	91	3.1%
16	Indiana	89	3.0%
17	Florida	83	2.8%
18	Colorado	79	2.7%
19	Utah	76	2.6%
20	Texas	63	2.1%
21	Virginia	49	1.7%
22	Nebraska	43	1.5%
23	Kansas	42	1.4%
24	Arizona	40	1.4%
25	Georgia	37	1.3%
25	Kentucky	37	1.3%
27	North Carolina	35	1.2%
27	Tennessee	35	1.2%
29	South Dakota	32	1.1%
30	Oklahoma	29	1.0%
31	North Dakota	25	0.8%
32	Nevada	24	0.8%
33	New Jersey	23	0.8%
34	Vermont	18	0.6%
35	Montana	17	0.6%
36	New Mexico	16	0.5%
37	Maine	15	0.5%
38	Alabama	14	0.5%
38	Maryland	14	0.5%
38	New Hampshire	14	0.5%
41	Arkansas	12	0.4%
42	Delaware	11	0.4%
43	Hawaii	9	0.3%
44	Mississippi	6	0.2%
44	West Virginia	6	0.2%
46	Wyoming	5	0.2%
47	Alaska	4	0.1%
47	Rhode Island	4	0.1%
47	South Carolina	4	0.1%
50	Louisiana	3	0.1%
	District of Columbia	1	0.0%

Source: U.S. Department of Health and Human Services, National Center for Health Statistics
   "Morbidity and Mortality Weekly Report" (January 2, 2004, Vol. 52, Nos. 51 & 52)
*Escherichia Coli is a common bacterium that normally inhabits the intestinal tracts of humans and animals but can cause infection in other parts of the body, especially the urinary tract. One strain, sometimes transmitted in hamburger meat, can cause serious infection resulting in sickness and death.

E-Coli Rate in 2003

National Rate = 1.0 Cases per 100,000 Population*

ALPHA ORDER

RANK	STATE	RATE
43	Alabama	0.3
36	Alaska	0.6
31	Arizona	0.7
39	Arkansas	0.4
31	California	0.7
15	Colorado	1.7
9	Connecticut	2.6
20	Delaware	1.3
38	Florida	0.5
39	Georgia	0.4
31	Hawaii	0.7
1	Idaho	7.5
26	Illinois	0.9
18	Indiana	1.4
4	Iowa	3.5
16	Kansas	1.5
26	Kentucky	0.9
49	Louisiana	0.1
21	Maine	1.1
43	Maryland	0.3
18	Massachusetts	1.4
26	Michigan	0.9
6	Minnesota	3.1
48	Mississippi	0.2
12	Missouri	1.9
12	Montana	1.9
11	Nebraska	2.5
21	Nevada	1.1
21	New Hampshire	1.1
43	New Jersey	0.3
26	New Mexico	0.9
31	New York	0.7
39	North Carolina	0.4
3	North Dakota	3.9
16	Ohio	1.5
30	Oklahoma	0.8
7	Oregon	3.0
21	Pennsylvania	1.1
39	Rhode Island	0.4
49	South Carolina	0.1
2	South Dakota	4.2
36	Tennessee	0.6
43	Texas	0.3
5	Utah	3.2
8	Vermont	2.9
31	Virginia	0.7
12	Washington	1.9
43	West Virginia	0.3
9	Wisconsin	2.6
25	Wyoming	1.0

RANK ORDER

RANK	STATE	RATE
1	Idaho	7.5
2	South Dakota	4.2
3	North Dakota	3.9
4	Iowa	3.5
5	Utah	3.2
6	Minnesota	3.1
7	Oregon	3.0
8	Vermont	2.9
9	Connecticut	2.6
9	Wisconsin	2.6
11	Nebraska	2.5
12	Missouri	1.9
12	Montana	1.9
12	Washington	1.9
15	Colorado	1.7
16	Kansas	1.5
16	Ohio	1.5
18	Indiana	1.4
18	Massachusetts	1.4
20	Delaware	1.3
21	Maine	1.1
21	Nevada	1.1
21	New Hampshire	1.1
21	Pennsylvania	1.1
25	Wyoming	1.0
26	Illinois	0.9
26	Kentucky	0.9
26	Michigan	0.9
26	New Mexico	0.9
30	Oklahoma	0.8
31	Arizona	0.7
31	California	0.7
31	Hawaii	0.7
31	New York	0.7
31	Virginia	0.7
36	Alaska	0.6
36	Tennessee	0.6
38	Florida	0.5
39	Arkansas	0.4
39	Georgia	0.4
39	North Carolina	0.4
39	Rhode Island	0.4
43	Alabama	0.3
43	Maryland	0.3
43	New Jersey	0.3
43	Texas	0.3
43	West Virginia	0.3
48	Mississippi	0.2
49	Louisiana	0.1
49	South Carolina	0.1
	District of Columbia	0.2

Source: Morgan Quitno Press using data from U.S. Dept. of Health & Human Serv's, National Center for Health Statistics "Morbidity and Mortality Weekly Report" (January 2, 2004, Vol. 52, Nos. 51 & 52)

*Escherichia Coli is a common bacterium that normally inhabits the intestinal tracts of humans and animals but can cause infection in other parts of the body, especially the urinary tract. One strain, sometimes transmitted in hamburger meat, can cause serious infection resulting in sickness and death.

Hepatitis A and B Cases Reported in 2003

National Total = 13,871 Cases*

ALPHA ORDER

RANK	STATE	CASES	% of USA
31	Alabama	76	0.5%
46	Alaska	20	0.1%
7	Arizona	545	3.9%
30	Arkansas	78	0.6%
1	California	1,737	12.5%
21	Colorado	147	1.1%
27	Connecticut	104	0.7%
47	Delaware	19	0.1%
4	Florida	1,046	7.5%
2	Georgia	1,643	11.8%
39	Hawaii	36	0.3%
42	Idaho	26	0.2%
17	Illinois	202	1.5%
25	Indiana	113	0.8%
36	Iowa	52	0.4%
37	Kansas	47	0.3%
26	Kentucky	105	0.8%
20	Louisiana	171	1.2%
44	Maine	22	0.2%
14	Maryland	312	2.2%
10	Massachusetts	392	2.8%
9	Michigan	396	2.9%
29	Minnesota	84	0.6%
27	Mississippi	104	0.7%
13	Missouri	325	2.3%
43	Montana	24	0.2%
38	Nebraska	41	0.3%
23	Nevada	135	1.0%
44	New Hampshire	22	0.2%
11	New Jersey	339	2.4%
34	New Mexico	57	0.4%
5	New York	999	7.2%
16	North Carolina	284	2.0%
49	North Dakota	3	0.0%
12	Ohio	327	2.4%
33	Oklahoma	64	0.5%
19	Oregon	174	1.3%
3·	Pennsylvania	1,293	9.3%
40	Rhode Island	33	0.2%
18	South Carolina	195	1.4%
50	South Dakota	2	0.0%
8	Tennessee	397	2.9%
6	Texas	899	6.5%
24	Utah	114	0.8%
48	Vermont	10	0.1%
15	Virginia	297	2.1%
22	Washington	142	1.0%
35	West Virginia	54	0.4%
31	Wisconsin	76	0.5%
40	Wyoming	33	0.2%

RANK ORDER

RANK	STATE	CASES	% of USA
1	California	1,737	12.5%
2	Georgia	1,643	11.8%
3	Pennsylvania	1,293	9.3%
4	Florida	1,046	7.5%
5	New York	999	7.2%
6	Texas	899	6.5%
7	Arizona	545	3.9%
8	Tennessee	397	2.9%
9	Michigan	396	2.9%
10	Massachusetts	392	2.8%
11	New Jersey	339	2.4%
12	Ohio	327	2.4%
13	Missouri	325	2.3%
14	Maryland	312	2.2%
15	Virginia	297	2.1%
16	North Carolina	284	2.0%
17	Illinois	202	1.5%
18	South Carolina	195	1.4%
19	Oregon	174	1.3%
20	Louisiana	171	1.2%
21	Colorado	147	1.1%
22	Washington	142	1.0%
23	Nevada	135	1.0%
24	Utah	114	0.8%
25	Indiana	113	0.8%
26	Kentucky	105	0.8%
27	Connecticut	104	0.7%
27	Mississippi	104	0.7%
29	Minnesota	84	0.6%
30	Arkansas	78	0.6%
31	Alabama	76	0.5%
31	Wisconsin	76	0.5%
33	Oklahoma	64	0.5%
34	New Mexico	57	0.4%
35	West Virginia	54	0.4%
36	Iowa	52	0.4%
37	Kansas	47	0.3%
38	Nebraska	41	0.3%
39	Hawaii	36	0.3%
40	Rhode Island	33	0.2%
40	Wyoming	33	0.2%
42	Idaho	26	0.2%
43	Montana	24	0.2%
44	Maine	22	0.2%
44	New Hampshire	22	0.2%
46	Alaska	20	0.1%
47	Delaware	19	0.1%
48	Vermont	10	0.1%
49	North Dakota	3	0.0%
50	South Dakota	2	0.0%
	District of Columbia	55	0.4%

Source: U.S. Department of Health and Human Services, National Center for Health Statistics
    "Morbidity and Mortality Weekly Report" (January 2, 2004, Vol. 52, Nos. 51 & 52)
*Provisional data. An inflammation of the liver.

Hepatitis A and B Rate in 2003

National Rate = 4.8 Cases per 100,000 Population*

ALPHA ORDER

RANK	STATE	RATE
41	Alabama	1.7
24	Alaska	3.1
3	Arizona	9.8
29	Arkansas	2.9
12	California	4.9
23	Colorado	3.2
26	Connecticut	3.0
35	Delaware	2.3
6	Florida	6.1
1	Georgia	18.9
29	Hawaii	2.9
37	Idaho	1.9
46	Illinois	1.6
38	Indiana	1.8
38	Iowa	1.8
41	Kansas	1.7
33	Kentucky	2.5
20	Louisiana	3.8
41	Maine	1.7
9	Maryland	5.7
6	Massachusetts	6.1
18	Michigan	3.9
41	Minnesota	1.7
21	Mississippi	3.6
9	Missouri	5.7
32	Montana	2.6
34	Nebraska	2.4
8	Nevada	6.0
41	New Hampshire	1.7
18	New Jersey	3.9
26	New Mexico	3.0
11	New York	5.2
22	North Carolina	3.4
49	North Dakota	0.5
29	Ohio	2.9
38	Oklahoma	1.8
12	Oregon	4.9
2	Pennsylvania	10.5
24	Rhode Island	3.1
15	South Carolina	4.7
50	South Dakota	0.3
4	Tennessee	6.8
16	Texas	4.1
14	Utah	4.8
46	Vermont	1.6
17	Virginia	4.0
35	Washington	2.3
26	West Virginia	3.0
48	Wisconsin	1.4
5	Wyoming	6.6

RANK ORDER

RANK	STATE	RATE
1	Georgia	18.9
2	Pennsylvania	10.5
3	Arizona	9.8
4	Tennessee	6.8
5	Wyoming	6.6
6	Florida	6.1
6	Massachusetts	6.1
8	Nevada	6.0
9	Maryland	5.7
9	Missouri	5.7
11	New York	5.2
12	California	4.9
12	Oregon	4.9
14	Utah	4.8
15	South Carolina	4.7
16	Texas	4.1
17	Virginia	4.0
18	Michigan	3.9
18	New Jersey	3.9
20	Louisiana	3.8
21	Mississippi	3.6
22	North Carolina	3.4
23	Colorado	3.2
24	Alaska	3.1
24	Rhode Island	3.1
26	Connecticut	3.0
26	New Mexico	3.0
26	West Virginia	3.0
29	Arkansas	2.9
29	Hawaii	2.9
29	Ohio	2.9
32	Montana	2.6
33	Kentucky	2.5
34	Nebraska	2.4
35	Delaware	2.3
35	Washington	2.3
37	Idaho	1.9
38	Indiana	1.8
38	Iowa	1.8
38	Oklahoma	1.8
41	Alabama	1.7
41	Kansas	1.7
41	Maine	1.7
41	Minnesota	1.7
41	New Hampshire	1.7
46	Illinois	1.6
46	Vermont	1.6
48	Wisconsin	1.4
49	North Dakota	0.5
50	South Dakota	0.3

	District of Columbia	9.8

Source: Morgan Quitno Press using data from U.S. Dept. of Health & Human Serv's, National Center for Health Statistics
"Morbidity and Mortality Weekly Report" (January 2, 2004, Vol. 52, Nos. 51 & 52)
*Provisional data. An inflammation of the liver.

Hepatitis C Cases Reported in 2003

National Total = 1,805 Cases*

ALPHA ORDER

RANK	STATE	CASES	% of USA
28	Alabama	7	0.4%
35	Alaska	1	0.1%
28	Arizona	7	0.4%
31	Arkansas	3	0.2%
6	California	85	4.7%
16	Colorado	17	0.9%
NA	Connecticut**	NA	NA
38	Delaware	0	0.0%
7	Florida	81	4.5%
23	Georgia	10	0.6%
23	Hawaii	10	0.6%
35	Idaho	1	0.1%
14	Illinois	18	1.0%
25	Indiana	9	0.5%
35	Iowa	1	0.1%
38	Kansas	0	0.0%
12	Kentucky	20	1.1%
4	Louisiana	116	6.4%
33	Maine	2	0.1%
14	Maryland	18	1.0%
38	Massachusetts	0	0.0%
4	Michigan	116	6.4%
21	Minnesota	11	0.6%
9	Mississippi	39	2.2%
2	Missouri	258	14.3%
30	Montana	4	0.2%
31	Nebraska	3	0.2%
10	Nevada	27	1.5%
38	New Hampshire	0	0.0%
38	New Jersey	0	0.0%
38	New Mexico	0	0.0%
8	New York	41	2.3%
19	North Carolina	13	0.7%
38	North Dakota	0	0.0%
20	Ohio	12	0.7%
33	Oklahoma	2	0.1%
17	Oregon	16	0.9%
3	Pennsylvania	123	6.8%
38	Rhode Island	0	0.0%
11	South Carolina	24	1.3%
38	South Dakota	0	0.0%
13	Tennessee	19	1.1%
1	Texas	646	35.8%
38	Utah	0	0.0%
25	Vermont	9	0.5%
21	Virginia	11	0.6%
17	Washington	16	0.9%
25	West Virginia	9	0.5%
38	Wisconsin	0	0.0%
38	Wyoming	0	0.0%

RANK ORDER

RANK	STATE	CASES	% of USA
1	Texas	646	35.8%
2	Missouri	258	14.3%
3	Pennsylvania	123	6.8%
4	Louisiana	116	6.4%
4	Michigan	116	6.4%
6	California	85	4.7%
7	Florida	81	4.5%
8	New York	41	2.3%
9	Mississippi	39	2.2%
10	Nevada	27	1.5%
11	South Carolina	24	1.3%
12	Kentucky	20	1.1%
13	Tennessee	19	1.1%
14	Illinois	18	1.0%
14	Maryland	18	1.0%
16	Colorado	17	0.9%
17	Oregon	16	0.9%
17	Washington	16	0.9%
19	North Carolina	13	0.7%
20	Ohio	12	0.7%
21	Minnesota	11	0.6%
21	Virginia	11	0.6%
23	Georgia	10	0.6%
23	Hawaii	10	0.6%
25	Indiana	9	0.5%
25	Vermont	9	0.5%
25	West Virginia	9	0.5%
28	Alabama	7	0.4%
28	Arizona	7	0.4%
30	Montana	4	0.2%
31	Arkansas	3	0.2%
31	Nebraska	3	0.2%
33	Maine	2	0.1%
33	Oklahoma	2	0.1%
35	Alaska	1	0.1%
35	Idaho	1	0.1%
35	Iowa	1	0.1%
38	Delaware	0	0.0%
38	Kansas	0	0.0%
38	Massachusetts	0	0.0%
38	New Hampshire	0	0.0%
38	New Jersey	0	0.0%
38	New Mexico	0	0.0%
38	North Dakota	0	0.0%
38	Rhode Island	0	0.0%
38	South Dakota	0	0.0%
38	Utah	0	0.0%
38	Wisconsin	0	0.0%
38	Wyoming	0	0.0%
NA	Connecticut**	NA	NA
	District of Columbia	0	0.0%

*Source: U.S. Department of Health and Human Services, National Center for Health Statistics
"Morbidity and Mortality Weekly Report" (January 2, 2004, Vol. 52, Nos. 51 & 52)*
*Provisional data. An inflammation of the liver. It is the leading cause for liver transplantation and is transmitted by blood-to-blood contact. Most new cases of C are caused by high-risk drug behaviors.
**Not available.

Hepatitis C Rate in 2003

National Rate = 0.6 Cases per 100,000 Population*

ALPHA ORDER

RANK	STATE	RATE
20	Alabama	0.2
20	Alaska	0.2
28	Arizona	0.1
28	Arkansas	0.1
20	California	0.2
14	Colorado	0.4
NA	Connecticut**	NA
37	Delaware	0.0
11	Florida	0.5
28	Georgia	0.1
9	Hawaii	0.8
28	Idaho	0.1
28	Illinois	0.1
28	Indiana	0.1
37	Iowa	0.0
37	Kansas	0.0
11	Kentucky	0.5
3	Louisiana	2.6
20	Maine	0.2
17	Maryland	0.3
37	Massachusetts	0.0
6	Michigan	1.2
20	Minnesota	0.2
5	Mississippi	1.4
1	Missouri	4.5
14	Montana	0.4
20	Nebraska	0.2
6	Nevada	1.2
37	New Hampshire	0.0
37	New Jersey	0.0
37	New Mexico	0.0
20	New York	0.2
20	North Carolina	0.2
37	North Dakota	0.0
28	Ohio	0.1
28	Oklahoma	0.1
14	Oregon	0.4
8	Pennsylvania	1.0
37	Rhode Island	0.0
10	South Carolina	0.6
37	South Dakota	0.0
17	Tennessee	0.3
2	Texas	2.9
37	Utah	0.0
4	Vermont	1.5
28	Virginia	0.1
17	Washington	0.3
11	West Virginia	0.5
37	Wisconsin	0.0
37	Wyoming	0.0

RANK ORDER

RANK	STATE	RATE
1	Missouri	4.5
2	Texas	2.9
3	Louisiana	2.6
4	Vermont	1.5
5	Mississippi	1.4
6	Michigan	1.2
6	Nevada	1.2
8	Pennsylvania	1.0
9	Hawaii	0.8
10	South Carolina	0.6
11	Florida	0.5
11	Kentucky	0.5
11	West Virginia	0.5
14	Colorado	0.4
14	Montana	0.4
14	Oregon	0.4
17	Maryland	0.3
17	Tennessee	0.3
17	Washington	0.3
20	Alabama	0.2
20	Alaska	0.2
20	California	0.2
20	Maine	0.2
20	Minnesota	0.2
20	Nebraska	0.2
20	New York	0.2
20	North Carolina	0.2
28	Arizona	0.1
28	Arkansas	0.1
28	Georgia	0.1
28	Idaho	0.1
28	Illinois	0.1
28	Indiana	0.1
28	Ohio	0.1
28	Oklahoma	0.1
28	Virginia	0.1
37	Delaware	0.0
37	Iowa	0.0
37	Kansas	0.0
37	Massachusetts	0.0
37	New Hampshire	0.0
37	New Jersey	0.0
37	New Mexico	0.0
37	North Dakota	0.0
37	Rhode Island	0.0
37	South Dakota	0.0
37	Utah	0.0
37	Wisconsin	0.0
37	Wyoming	0.0
NA	Connecticut**	NA

District of Columbia   0.0

Source: Morgan Quitno Press using data from U.S. Dept. of Health & Human Serv's, National Center for Health Statistics
"Morbidity and Mortality Weekly Report" (January 2, 2004, Vol. 52, Nos. 51 & 52)
*Provisional data. An inflammation of the liver. It is the leading cause for liver transplantation and is transmitted
by blood-to-blood contact. Most new cases of C are caused by high-risk drug behaviors.
**Not available.

Legionellosis Cases Reported in 2003

National Total = 1,987 Cases*

RANK	STATE	CASES	% of USA
25	Alabama	13	0.7%
49	Alaska	0	0.0%
26	Arizona	11	0.6%
42	Arkansas	2	0.1%
8	California	83	4.2%
24	Colorado	15	0.8%
18	Connecticut	28	1.4%
18	Delaware	28	1.4%
4	Florida	147	7.4%
16	Georgia	32	1.6%
46	Hawaii	1	0.1%
31	Idaho	7	0.4%
40	Illinois	3	0.2%
17	Indiana	29	1.5%
29	Iowa	10	0.5%
26	Kansas	11	0.6%
12	Kentucky	43	2.2%
46	Louisiana	1	0.1%
42	Maine	2	0.1%
5	Maryland	133	6.7%
11	Massachusetts	44	2.2%
6	Michigan	120	6.0%
36	Minnesota	5	0.3%
36	Mississippi	5	0.3%
14	Missouri	34	1.7%
39	Montana	4	0.2%
36	Nebraska	5	0.3%
26	Nevada	11	0.6%
34	New Hampshire	6	0.3%
9	New Jersey	73	3.7%
40	New Mexico	3	0.2%
3	New York	220	11.1%
13	North Carolina	39	2.0%
46	North Dakota	1	0.1%
2	Ohio	226	11.4%
31	Oklahoma	7	0.4%
NA	Oregon**	NA	NA
1	Pennsylvania	276	13.9%
23	Rhode Island	17	0.9%
31	South Carolina	7	0.4%
42	South Dakota	2	0.1%
14	Tennessee	34	1.7%
10	Texas	53	2.7%
20	Utah	27	1.4%
34	Vermont	6	0.3%
7	Virginia	93	4.7%
29	Washington	10	0.5%
21	West Virginia	21	1.1%
22	Wisconsin	18	0.9%
42	Wyoming	2	0.1%

RANK	STATE	CASES	% of USA
1	Pennsylvania	276	13.9%
2	Ohio	226	11.4%
3	New York	220	11.1%
4	Florida	147	7.4%
5	Maryland	133	6.7%
6	Michigan	120	6.0%
7	Virginia	93	4.7%
8	California	83	4.2%
9	New Jersey	73	3.7%
10	Texas	53	2.7%
11	Massachusetts	44	2.2%
12	Kentucky	43	2.2%
13	North Carolina	39	2.0%
14	Missouri	34	1.7%
14	Tennessee	34	1.7%
16	Georgia	32	1.6%
17	Indiana	29	1.5%
18	Connecticut	28	1.4%
18	Delaware	28	1.4%
20	Utah	27	1.4%
21	West Virginia	21	1.1%
22	Wisconsin	18	0.9%
23	Rhode Island	17	0.9%
24	Colorado	15	0.8%
25	Alabama	13	0.7%
26	Arizona	11	0.6%
26	Kansas	11	0.6%
26	Nevada	11	0.6%
29	Iowa	10	0.5%
29	Washington	10	0.5%
31	Idaho	7	0.4%
31	Oklahoma	7	0.4%
31	South Carolina	7	0.4%
34	New Hampshire	6	0.3%
34	Vermont	6	0.3%
36	Minnesota	5	0.3%
36	Mississippi	5	0.3%
36	Nebraska	5	0.3%
39	Montana	4	0.2%
40	Illinois	3	0.2%
40	New Mexico	3	0.2%
42	Arkansas	2	0.1%
42	Maine	2	0.1%
42	South Dakota	2	0.1%
42	Wyoming	2	0.1%
46	Hawaii	1	0.1%
46	Louisiana	1	0.1%
46	North Dakota	1	0.1%
49	Alaska	0	0.0%
NA	Oregon**	NA	NA

| | District of Columbia | 19 | 1.0% |

Source: U.S. Department of Health and Human Services, National Center for Health Statistics
    "Morbidity and Mortality Weekly Report" (January 2, 2004, Vol. 52, Nos. 51 & 52)
*Provisional data. A pneumonia-like disease (Legionnaire's Disease).
**Not notifiable.

Legionellosis Rate in 2003

National Rate = 0.7 Cases per 100,000 Population*

ALPHA ORDER

RANK	STATE	RATE
28	Alabama	0.3
47	Alaska	0.0
34	Arizona	0.2
44	Arkansas	0.1
34	California	0.2
28	Colorado	0.3
14	Connecticut	0.8
1	Delaware	3.4
13	Florida	0.9
24	Georgia	0.4
44	Hawaii	0.1
19	Idaho	0.5
47	Illinois	0.0
19	Indiana	0.5
28	Iowa	0.3
24	Kansas	0.4
11	Kentucky	1.0
47	Louisiana	0.0
34	Maine	0.2
2	Maryland	2.4
16	Massachusetts	0.7
7	Michigan	1.2
44	Minnesota	0.1
34	Mississippi	0.2
17	Missouri	0.6
24	Montana	0.4
28	Nebraska	0.3
19	Nevada	0.5
19	New Hampshire	0.5
14	New Jersey	0.8
34	New Mexico	0.2
9	New York	1.1
19	North Carolina	0.5
34	North Dakota	0.2
4	Ohio	2.0
34	Oklahoma	0.2
NA	Oregon**	NA
3	Pennsylvania	2.2
5	Rhode Island	1.6
34	South Carolina	0.2
28	South Dakota	0.3
17	Tennessee	0.6
34	Texas	0.2
9	Utah	1.1
11	Vermont	1.0
6	Virginia	1.3
34	Washington	0.2
7	West Virginia	1.2
28	Wisconsin	0.3
24	Wyoming	0.4

RANK ORDER

RANK	STATE	RATE
1	Delaware	3.4
2	Maryland	2.4
3	Pennsylvania	2.2
4	Ohio	2.0
5	Rhode Island	1.6
6	Virginia	1.3
7	Michigan	1.2
7	West Virginia	1.2
9	New York	1.1
9	Utah	1.1
11	Kentucky	1.0
11	Vermont	1.0
13	Florida	0.9
14	Connecticut	0.8
14	New Jersey	0.8
16	Massachusetts	0.7
17	Missouri	0.6
17	Tennessee	0.6
19	Idaho	0.5
19	Indiana	0.5
19	Nevada	0.5
19	New Hampshire	0.5
19	North Carolina	0.5
24	Georgia	0.4
24	Kansas	0.4
24	Montana	0.4
24	Wyoming	0.4
28	Alabama	0.3
28	Colorado	0.3
28	Iowa	0.3
28	Nebraska	0.3
28	South Dakota	0.3
28	Wisconsin	0.3
34	Arizona	0.2
34	California	0.2
34	Maine	0.2
34	Mississippi	0.2
34	New Mexico	0.2
34	North Dakota	0.2
34	Oklahoma	0.2
34	South Carolina	0.2
34	Texas	0.2
34	Washington	0.2
44	Arkansas	0.1
44	Hawaii	0.1
44	Minnesota	0.1
47	Alaska	0.0
47	Illinois	0.0
47	Louisiana	0.0
NA	Oregon**	NA

District of Columbia 3.4

Source: Morgan Quitno Press using data from U.S. Dept. of Health & Human Serv's, National Center for Health Statistics "Morbidity and Mortality Weekly Report" (January 2, 2004, Vol. 52, Nos. 51 & 52)

*Provisional data. A pneumonia-like disease (Legionnaire's Disease).

**Not notifiable.

Lyme Disease Cases in 2003

National Total = 17,970 Cases*

ALPHA ORDER

RANK	STATE	CASES	% of USA
34	Alabama	5	0.0%
36	Alaska	3	0.0%
36	Arizona	3	0.0%
46	Arkansas	0	0.0%
14	California	101	0.6%
35	Colorado	4	0.0%
4	Connecticut	1,307	7.3%
11	Delaware	191	1.1%
17	Florida	71	0.4%
27	Georgia	17	0.1%
NA	Hawaii**	NA	NA
36	Idaho	3	0.0%
22	Illinois	33	0.2%
25	Indiana	23	0.1%
20	Iowa	53	0.3%
32	Kansas	8	0.0%
29	Kentucky	15	0.1%
33	Louisiana	6	0.0%
10	Maine	227	1.3%
7	Maryland	649	3.6%
5	Massachusetts	1,171	6.5%
31	Michigan	12	0.1%
9	Minnesota	346	1.9%
24	Mississippi	24	0.1%
19	Missouri	65	0.4%
46	Montana	0	0.0%
42	Nebraska	2	0.0%
36	Nevada	3	0.0%
15	New Hampshire	95	0.5%
3	New Jersey	2,049	11.4%
44	New Mexico	1	0.0%
2	New York	4,555	25.3%
13	North Carolina	147	0.8%
46	North Dakota	0	0.0%
17	Ohio	71	0.4%
46	Oklahoma	0	0.0%
26	Oregon	18	0.1%
1	Pennsylvania	5,096	28.4%
8	Rhode Island	581	3.2%
29	South Carolina	15	0.1%
44	South Dakota	1	0.0%
27	Tennessee	17	0.1%
16	Texas	74	0.4%
36	Utah	3	0.0%
21	Vermont	43	0.2%
12	Virginia	159	0.9%
36	Washington	3	0.0%
23	West Virginia	27	0.2%
6	Wisconsin	658	3.7%
42	Wyoming	2	0.0%

RANK ORDER

RANK	STATE	CASES	% of USA
1	Pennsylvania	5,096	28.4%
2	New York	4,555	25.3%
3	New Jersey	2,049	11.4%
4	Connecticut	1,307	7.3%
5	Massachusetts	1,171	6.5%
6	Wisconsin	658	3.7%
7	Maryland	649	3.6%
8	Rhode Island	581	3.2%
9	Minnesota	346	1.9%
10	Maine	227	1.3%
11	Delaware	191	1.1%
12	Virginia	159	0.9%
13	North Carolina	147	0.8%
14	California	101	0.6%
15	New Hampshire	95	0.5%
16	Texas	74	0.4%
17	Florida	71	0.4%
17	Ohio	71	0.4%
19	Missouri	65	0.4%
20	Iowa	53	0.3%
21	Vermont	43	0.2%
22	Illinois	33	0.2%
23	West Virginia	27	0.2%
24	Mississippi	24	0.1%
25	Indiana	23	0.1%
26	Oregon	18	0.1%
27	Georgia	17	0.1%
27	Tennessee	17	0.1%
29	Kentucky	15	0.1%
29	South Carolina	15	0.1%
31	Michigan	12	0.1%
32	Kansas	8	0.0%
33	Louisiana	6	0.0%
34	Alabama	5	0.0%
35	Colorado	4	0.0%
36	Alaska	3	0.0%
36	Arizona	3	0.0%
36	Idaho	3	0.0%
36	Nevada	3	0.0%
36	Utah	3	0.0%
36	Washington	3	0.0%
42	Nebraska	2	0.0%
42	Wyoming	2	0.0%
44	New Mexico	1	0.0%
44	South Dakota	1	0.0%
46	Arkansas	0	0.0%
46	Montana	0	0.0%
46	North Dakota	0	0.0%
46	Oklahoma	0	0.0%
NA	Hawaii**	NA	NA
	District of Columbia	13	0.1%

Source: U.S. Department of Health and Human Services, National Center for Health Statistics
    "Morbidity and Mortality Weekly Report" (January 2, 2004, Vol. 52, Nos. 51 & 52)
*Provisional data. Caused by ticks-lesions, followed by arthritis of large joints, myalgia, malaise and neurologic
and cardiac manifestations. Named after Old Lyme, CT, where the disease was first reported.
**Not notifiable.

Lyme Disease Rate in 2003

National Rate = 6.2 Cases per 100,000 Population*

ALPHA ORDER

RANK	STATE	RATE
35	Alabama	0.1
21	Alaska	0.5
35	Arizona	0.1
45	Arkansas	0.0
28	California	0.3
35	Colorado	0.1
3	Connecticut	37.5
6	Delaware	23.4
23	Florida	0.4
33	Georgia	0.2
NA	Hawaii**	NA
33	Idaho	0.2
28	Illinois	0.3
23	Indiana	0.4
15	Iowa	1.8
28	Kansas	0.3
23	Kentucky	0.4
35	Louisiana	0.1
8	Maine	17.4
10	Maryland	11.8
7	Massachusetts	18.2
35	Michigan	0.1
13	Minnesota	6.8
19	Mississippi	0.8
18	Missouri	1.1
45	Montana	0.0
35	Nebraska	0.1
35	Nevada	0.1
11	New Hampshire	7.4
4	New Jersey	23.7
35	New Mexico	0.1
4	New York	23.7
16	North Carolina	1.7
45	North Dakota	0.0
20	Ohio	0.6
45	Oklahoma	0.0
21	Oregon	0.5
2	Pennsylvania	41.2
1	Rhode Island	54.0
23	South Carolina	0.4
35	South Dakota	0.1
28	Tennessee	0.3
28	Texas	0.3
35	Utah	0.1
12	Vermont	6.9
14	Virginia	2.2
45	Washington	0.0
17	West Virginia	1.5
9	Wisconsin	12.0
23	Wyoming	0.4

RANK ORDER

RANK	STATE	RATE
1	Rhode Island	54.0
2	Pennsylvania	41.2
3	Connecticut	37.5
4	New Jersey	23.7
4	New York	23.7
6	Delaware	23.4
7	Massachusetts	18.2
8	Maine	17.4
9	Wisconsin	12.0
10	Maryland	11.8
11	New Hampshire	7.4
12	Vermont	6.9
13	Minnesota	6.8
14	Virginia	2.2
15	Iowa	1.8
16	North Carolina	1.7
17	West Virginia	1.5
18	Missouri	1.1
19	Mississippi	0.8
20	Ohio	0.6
21	Alaska	0.5
21	Oregon	0.5
23	Florida	0.4
23	Indiana	0.4
23	Kentucky	0.4
23	South Carolina	0.4
23	Wyoming	0.4
28	California	0.3
28	Illinois	0.3
28	Kansas	0.3
28	Tennessee	0.3
28	Texas	0.3
33	Georgia	0.2
33	Idaho	0.2
35	Alabama	0.1
35	Arizona	0.1
35	Colorado	0.1
35	Louisiana	0.1
35	Michigan	0.1
35	Nebraska	0.1
35	Nevada	0.1
35	New Mexico	0.1
35	South Dakota	0.1
35	Utah	0.1
45	Arkansas	0.0
45	Montana	0.0
45	North Dakota	0.0
45	Oklahoma	0.0
45	Washington	0.0
NA	Hawaii**	NA

District of Columbia 2.3

Source: Morgan Quitno Press using data from U.S. Dept. of Health & Human Serv's, National Center for Health Statistics
    "Morbidity and Mortality Weekly Report" (January 2, 2004, Vol. 52, Nos. 51 & 52)
*Provisional data. Caused by ticks-lesions, followed by arthritis of large joints, myalgia, malaise and neurologic
and cardiac manifestations. Named after Old Lyme, CT, where the disease was first reported.
**Not notifiable.

Malaria Cases Reported in 2003

National Total = 1,155 Cases*

ALPHA ORDER

RANK ORDER

RANK	STATE	CASES	% of USA		RANK	STATE	CASES	% of USA
36	Alabama	3	0.3%		1	New York	203	17.6%
46	Alaska	1	0.1%		2	California	157	13.6%
18	Arizona	17	1.5%		3	Florida	90	7.8%
29	Arkansas	4	0.3%		4	Maryland	76	6.6%
2	California	157	13.6%		5	Georgia	67	5.8%
16	Colorado	22	1.9%		6	Texas	65	5.6%
17	Connecticut	19	1.6%		7	Pennsylvania	44	3.8%
36	Delaware	3	0.3%		8	New Jersey	42	3.6%
3	Florida	90	7.8%		9	Virginia	40	3.5%
5	Georgia	67	5.8%		10	Washington	30	2.6%
24	Hawaii	7	0.6%		11	Illinois	27	2.3%
46	Idaho	1	0.1%		12	Michigan	25	2.2%
11	Illinois	27	2.3%		12	Minnesota	25	2.2%
36	Indiana	3	0.3%		12	North Carolina	25	2.2%
26	Iowa	6	0.5%		15	Ohio	23	2.0%
20	Kansas	11	1.0%		16	Colorado	22	1.9%
23	Kentucky	9	0.8%		17	Connecticut	19	1.6%
29	Louisiana	4	0.3%		18	Arizona	17	1.5%
29	Maine	4	0.3%		19	Oregon	12	1.0%
4	Maryland	76	6.6%		20	Kansas	11	1.0%
20	Massachusetts	11	1.0%		20	Massachusetts	11	1.0%
12	Michigan	25	2.2%		22	Wisconsin	10	0.9%
12	Minnesota	25	2.2%		23	Kentucky	9	0.8%
36	Mississippi	3	0.3%		24	Hawaii	7	0.6%
26	Missouri	6	0.5%		24	Tennessee	7	0.6%
49	Montana	0	0.0%		26	Iowa	6	0.5%
49	Nebraska	0	0.0%		26	Missouri	6	0.5%
43	Nevada	2	0.2%		26	Utah	6	0.5%
29	New Hampshire	4	0.3%		29	Arkansas	4	0.3%
8	New Jersey	42	3.6%		29	Louisiana	4	0.3%
36	New Mexico	3	0.3%		29	Maine	4	0.3%
1	New York	203	17.6%		29	New Hampshire	4	0.3%
12	North Carolina	25	2.2%		29	Oklahoma	4	0.3%
46	North Dakota	1	0.1%		29	South Carolina	4	0.3%
15	Ohio	23	2.0%		29	West Virginia	4	0.3%
29	Oklahoma	4	0.3%		36	Alabama	3	0.3%
19	Oregon	12	1.0%		36	Delaware	3	0.3%
7	Pennsylvania	44	3.8%		36	Indiana	3	0.3%
36	Rhode Island	3	0.3%		36	Mississippi	3	0.3%
29	South Carolina	4	0.3%		36	New Mexico	3	0.3%
36	South Dakota	3	0.3%		36	Rhode Island	3	0.3%
24	Tennessee	7	0.6%		36	South Dakota	3	0.3%
6	Texas	65	5.6%		43	Nevada	2	0.2%
26	Utah	6	0.5%		43	Vermont	2	0.2%
43	Vermont	2	0.2%		43	Wyoming	2	0.2%
9	Virginia	40	3.5%		46	Alaska	1	0.1%
10	Washington	30	2.6%		46	Idaho	1	0.1%
29	West Virginia	4	0.3%		46	North Dakota	1	0.1%
22	Wisconsin	10	0.9%		49	Montana	0	0.0%
43	Wyoming	2	0.2%		49	Nebraska	0	0.0%
						District of Columbia	15	1.3%

Source: U.S. Department of Health and Human Services, National Center for Health Statistics
"Morbidity and Mortality Weekly Report" (January 2, 2004, Vol. 52, Nos. 51 & 52)
Provisional data. Infectious disease usually transmitted by bites of infected mosquitoes. Symptoms include high fever, shaking chills, sweating and anemia.

Malaria Rate in 2003

National Rate = 0.4 Cases per 100,000 Population*

ALPHA ORDER

RANK	STATE	RATE
38	Alabama	0.1
27	Alaska	0.2
18	Arizona	0.3
38	Arkansas	0.1
12	California	0.4
5	Colorado	0.5
5	Connecticut	0.5
12	Delaware	0.4
5	Florida	0.5
3	Georgia	0.8
4	Hawaii	0.6
38	Idaho	0.1
27	Illinois	0.2
48	Indiana	0.0
27	Iowa	0.2
12	Kansas	0.4
27	Kentucky	0.2
38	Louisiana	0.1
18	Maine	0.3
1	Maryland	1.4
27	Massachusetts	0.2
27	Michigan	0.2
5	Minnesota	0.5
38	Mississippi	0.1
38	Missouri	0.1
48	Montana	0.0
48	Nebraska	0.0
38	Nevada	0.1
18	New Hampshire	0.3
5	New Jersey	0.5
27	New Mexico	0.2
2	New York	1.1
18	North Carolina	0.3
27	North Dakota	0.2
27	Ohio	0.2
38	Oklahoma	0.1
18	Oregon	0.3
12	Pennsylvania	0.4
18	Rhode Island	0.3
38	South Carolina	0.1
12	South Dakota	0.4
38	Tennessee	0.1
18	Texas	0.3
18	Utah	0.3
18	Vermont	0.3
5	Virginia	0.5
5	Washington	0.5
27	West Virginia	0.2
27	Wisconsin	0.2
12	Wyoming	0.4

RANK ORDER

RANK	STATE	RATE
1	Maryland	1.4
2	New York	1.1
3	Georgia	0.8
4	Hawaii	0.6
5	Colorado	0.5
5	Connecticut	0.5
5	Florida	0.5
5	Minnesota	0.5
5	New Jersey	0.5
5	Virginia	0.5
5	Washington	0.5
12	California	0.4
12	Delaware	0.4
12	Kansas	0.4
12	Pennsylvania	0.4
12	South Dakota	0.4
12	Wyoming	0.4
18	Arizona	0.3
18	Maine	0.3
18	New Hampshire	0.3
18	North Carolina	0.3
18	Oregon	0.3
18	Rhode Island	0.3
18	Texas	0.3
18	Utah	0.3
18	Vermont	0.3
27	Alaska	0.2
27	Illinois	0.2
27	Iowa	0.2
27	Kentucky	0.2
27	Massachusetts	0.2
27	Michigan	0.2
27	New Mexico	0.2
27	North Dakota	0.2
27	Ohio	0.2
27	West Virginia	0.2
27	Wisconsin	0.2
38	Alabama	0.1
38	Arkansas	0.1
38	Idaho	0.1
38	Louisiana	0.1
38	Mississippi	0.1
38	Missouri	0.1
38	Nevada	0.1
38	Oklahoma	0.1
38	South Carolina	0.1
38	Tennessee	0.1
48	Indiana	0.0
48	Montana	0.0
48	Nebraska	0.0

District of Columbia 2.7

Source: Morgan Quitno Press using data from U.S. Dept. of Health & Human Serv's, National Center for Health Statistics
"Morbidity and Mortality Weekly Report" (January 2, 2004, Vol. 52, Nos. 51 & 52)
*Provisional data. Infectious disease usually transmitted by bites of infected mosquitoes. Symptoms include high
fever, shaking chills, sweating and anemia.

Meningococcal Infections Reported in 2003

National Total = 1,550 Cases*

ALPHA ORDER

RANK	STATE	CASES	% of USA
30	Alabama	15	1.0%
44	Alaska	3	0.2%
30	Arizona	15	1.0%
29	Arkansas	17	1.1%
1	California	219	14.1%
23	Colorado	22	1.4%
33	Connecticut	13	0.8%
36	Delaware	9	0.6%
3	Florida	106	6.8%
16	Georgia	30	1.9%
35	Hawaii	10	0.6%
36	Idaho	9	0.6%
11	Illinois	43	2.8%
11	Indiana	43	2.8%
18	Iowa	27	1.7%
32	Kansas	14	0.9%
28	Kentucky	20	1.3%
15	Louisiana	35	2.3%
40	Maine	6	0.4%
18	Maryland	27	1.7%
10	Massachusetts	44	2.8%
9	Michigan	46	3.0%
21	Minnesota	26	1.7%
23	Mississippi	22	1.4%
8	Missouri	55	3.5%
40	Montana	6	0.4%
39	Nebraska	7	0.5%
38	Nevada	8	0.5%
44	New Hampshire	3	0.2%
18	New Jersey	27	1.7%
34	New Mexico	11	0.7%
4	New York	91	5.9%
14	North Carolina	36	2.3%
49	North Dakota	1	0.1%
7	Ohio	57	3.7%
26	Oklahoma	21	1.4%
6	Oregon	62	4.0%
5	Pennsylvania	75	4.8%
47	Rhode Island	2	0.1%
23	South Carolina	22	1.4%
49	South Dakota	1	0.1%
16	Tennessee	30	1.9%
2	Texas	112	7.2%
40	Utah	6	0.4%
44	Vermont	3	0.2%
22	Virginia	24	1.5%
13	Washington	40	2.6%
40	West Virginia	6	0.4%
26	Wisconsin	21	1.4%
47	Wyoming	2	0.1%

RANK ORDER

RANK	STATE	CASES	% of USA
1	California	219	14.1%
2	Texas	112	7.2%
3	Florida	106	6.8%
4	New York	91	5.9%
5	Pennsylvania	75	4.8%
6	Oregon	62	4.0%
7	Ohio	57	3.7%
8	Missouri	55	3.5%
9	Michigan	46	3.0%
10	Massachusetts	44	2.8%
11	Illinois	43	2.8%
11	Indiana	43	2.8%
13	Washington	40	2.6%
14	North Carolina	36	2.3%
15	Louisiana	35	2.3%
16	Georgia	30	1.9%
16	Tennessee	30	1.9%
18	Iowa	27	1.7%
18	Maryland	27	1.7%
18	New Jersey	27	1.7%
21	Minnesota	26	1.7%
22	Virginia	24	1.5%
23	Colorado	22	1.4%
23	Mississippi	22	1.4%
23	South Carolina	22	1.4%
26	Oklahoma	21	1.4%
26	Wisconsin	21	1.4%
28	Kentucky	20	1.3%
29	Arkansas	17	1.1%
30	Alabama	15	1.0%
30	Arizona	15	1.0%
32	Kansas	14	0.9%
33	Connecticut	13	0.8%
34	New Mexico	11	0.7%
35	Hawaii	10	0.6%
36	Delaware	9	0.6%
36	Idaho	9	0.6%
38	Nevada	8	0.5%
39	Nebraska	7	0.5%
40	Maine	6	0.4%
40	Montana	6	0.4%
40	Utah	6	0.4%
40	West Virginia	6	0.4%
44	Alaska	3	0.2%
44	New Hampshire	3	0.2%
44	Vermont	3	0.2%
47	Rhode Island	2	0.1%
47	Wyoming	2	0.1%
49	North Dakota	1	0.1%
49	South Dakota	1	0.1%
	District of Columbia	0	0.0%

Source: U.S. Department of Health and Human Services, National Center for Health Statistics
"Morbidity and Mortality Weekly Report" (January 2, 2004, Vol. 52, Nos. 51 & 52)
*Provisional data. A bacterium (Neisseria meningitidis) that causes cerebrospinal meningitis.

Meningococcal Infection Rate in 2003

National Rate = 0.5 Cases per 100,000 Population*

ALPHA ORDER

RANK	STATE	RATE
39	Alabama	0.3
19	Alaska	0.5
39	Arizona	0.3
13	Arkansas	0.6
13	California	0.6
19	Colorado	0.5
33	Connecticut	0.4
2	Delaware	1.1
13	Florida	0.6
39	Georgia	0.3
5	Hawaii	0.8
8	Idaho	0.7
39	Illinois	0.3
8	Indiana	0.7
4	Iowa	0.9
19	Kansas	0.5
19	Kentucky	0.5
5	Louisiana	0.8
19	Maine	0.5
19	Maryland	0.5
8	Massachusetts	0.7
19	Michigan	0.5
19	Minnesota	0.5
5	Mississippi	0.8
3	Missouri	1.0
8	Montana	0.7
33	Nebraska	0.4
33	Nevada	0.4
47	New Hampshire	0.2
39	New Jersey	0.3
13	New Mexico	0.6
19	New York	0.5
33	North Carolina	0.4
47	North Dakota	0.2
19	Ohio	0.5
13	Oklahoma	0.6
1	Oregon	1.7
13	Pennsylvania	0.6
47	Rhode Island	0.2
19	South Carolina	0.5
50	South Dakota	0.1
19	Tennessee	0.5
19	Texas	0.5
39	Utah	0.3
19	Vermont	0.5
39	Virginia	0.3
8	Washington	0.7
39	West Virginia	0.3
33	Wisconsin	0.4
33	Wyoming	0.4

RANK ORDER

RANK	STATE	RATE
1	Oregon	1.7
2	Delaware	1.1
3	Missouri	1.0
4	Iowa	0.9
5	Hawaii	0.8
5	Louisiana	0.8
5	Mississippi	0.8
8	Idaho	0.7
8	Indiana	0.7
8	Massachusetts	0.7
8	Montana	0.7
8	Washington	0.7
13	Arkansas	0.6
13	California	0.6
13	Florida	0.6
13	New Mexico	0.6
13	Oklahoma	0.6
13	Pennsylvania	0.6
19	Alaska	0.5
19	Colorado	0.5
19	Kansas	0.5
19	Kentucky	0.5
19	Maine	0.5
19	Maryland	0.5
19	Michigan	0.5
19	Minnesota	0.5
19	New York	0.5
19	Ohio	0.5
19	South Carolina	0.5
19	Tennessee	0.5
19	Texas	0.5
19	Vermont	0.5
33	Connecticut	0.4
33	Nebraska	0.4
33	Nevada	0.4
33	North Carolina	0.4
33	Wisconsin	0.4
33	Wyoming	0.4
39	Alabama	0.3
39	Arizona	0.3
39	Georgia	0.3
39	Illinois	0.3
39	New Jersey	0.3
39	Utah	0.3
39	Virginia	0.3
39	West Virginia	0.3
47	New Hampshire	0.2
47	North Dakota	0.2
47	Rhode Island	0.2
50	South Dakota	0.1
	District of Columbia	0.0

Source: Morgan Quitno Press using data from U.S. Dept. of Health & Human Serv's, National Center for Health Statistics
    "Morbidity and Mortality Weekly Report" (January 2, 2004, Vol. 52, Nos. 51 & 52)
*Provisional data. A bacterium (Neisseria meningitidis) that causes cerebrospinal meningitis.

Rabies (Animal) Cases Reported in 2003

National Total = 5,451 Cases*

RANK	STATE	CASES	% of USA
32	Alabama	33	0.6%
40	Alaska	8	0.1%
20	Arizona	65	1.2%
34	Arkansas	25	0.5%
10	California	190	3.5%
30	Colorado	38	0.7%
12	Connecticut	169	3.1%
21	Delaware	64	1.2%
11	Florida	189	3.5%
5	Georgia	388	7.1%
47	Hawaii	0	0.0%
37	Idaho	15	0.3%
35	Illinois	24	0.4%
33	Indiana	32	0.6%
14	Iowa	104	1.9%
13	Kansas	155	2.8%
29	Kentucky	39	0.7%
47	Louisiana	0	0.0%
18	Maine	68	1.2%
6	Maryland	256	4.7%
8	Massachusetts	211	3.9%
27	Michigan	48	0.9%
28	Minnesota	41	0.8%
46	Mississippi	1	0.0%
24	Missouri	55	1.0%
36	Montana	21	0.4%
15	Nebraska	100	1.8%
44	Nevada	5	0.1%
39	New Hampshire	13	0.2%
22	New Jersey	62	1.1%
44	New Mexico	5	0.1%
4	New York	431	7.9%
1	North Carolina	751	13.8%
25	North Dakota	54	1.0%
26	Ohio	53	1.0%
9	Oklahoma	197	3.6%
41	Oregon	7	0.1%
3	Pennsylvania	438	8.0%
23	Rhode Island	60	1.1%
7	South Carolina	246	4.5%
19	South Dakota	67	1.2%
15	Tennessee	100	1.8%
47	Texas	0	0.0%
38	Utah	14	0.3%
30	Vermont	38	0.7%
2	Virginia	477	8.8%
47	Washington	0	0.0%
17	West Virginia	81	1.5%
41	Wisconsin	7	0.1%
43	Wyoming	6	0.1%

RANK	STATE	CASES	% of USA
1	North Carolina	751	13.8%
2	Virginia	477	8.8%
3	Pennsylvania	438	8.0%
4	New York	431	7.9%
5	Georgia	388	7.1%
6	Maryland	256	4.7%
7	South Carolina	246	4.5%
8	Massachusetts	211	3.9%
9	Oklahoma	197	3.6%
10	California	190	3.5%
11	Florida	189	3.5%
12	Connecticut	169	3.1%
13	Kansas	155	2.8%
14	Iowa	104	1.9%
15	Nebraska	100	1.8%
15	Tennessee	100	1.8%
17	West Virginia	81	1.5%
18	Maine	68	1.2%
19	South Dakota	67	1.2%
20	Arizona	65	1.2%
21	Delaware	64	1.2%
22	New Jersey	62	1.1%
23	Rhode Island	60	1.1%
24	Missouri	55	1.0%
25	North Dakota	54	1.0%
26	Ohio	53	1.0%
27	Michigan	48	0.9%
28	Minnesota	41	0.8%
29	Kentucky	39	0.7%
30	Colorado	38	0.7%
30	Vermont	38	0.7%
32	Alabama	33	0.6%
33	Indiana	32	0.6%
34	Arkansas	25	0.5%
35	Illinois	24	0.4%
36	Montana	21	0.4%
37	Idaho	15	0.3%
38	Utah	14	0.3%
39	New Hampshire	13	0.2%
40	Alaska	8	0.1%
41	Oregon	7	0.1%
41	Wisconsin	7	0.1%
43	Wyoming	6	0.1%
44	Nevada	5	0.1%
44	New Mexico	5	0.1%
46	Mississippi	1	0.0%
47	Hawaii	0	0.0%
47	Louisiana	0	0.0%
47	Texas	0	0.0%
47	Washington	0	0.0%
	District of Columbia	0	0.0%

Source: U.S. Department of Health and Human Services, National Center for Health Statistics
    "Morbidity and Mortality Weekly Report" (January 2, 2004, Vol. 52, Nos. 51 & 52)
*Provisional data. An acute, infectious, often fatal viral disease of most warm-blooded animals, especially wolves,
cats, and dogs, that attacks the central nervous system and is transmitted by the bite of infected animals.

Rabies (Animal) Rate in 2003

National Rate = 1.9 Cases per 100,000 Human Population*

ALPHA ORDER

RANK	STATE	RATE
34	Alabama	0.7
23	Alaska	1.2
23	Arizona	1.2
30	Arkansas	0.9
37	California	0.5
32	Colorado	0.8
13	Connecticut	4.9
4	Delaware	7.8
26	Florida	1.1
15	Georgia	4.5
46	Hawaii	0.0
26	Idaho	1.1
42	Illinois	0.2
37	Indiana	0.5
17	Iowa	3.5
8	Kansas	5.7
30	Kentucky	0.9
46	Louisiana	0.0
12	Maine	5.2
14	Maryland	4.6
19	Massachusetts	3.3
37	Michigan	0.5
32	Minnesota	0.8
46	Mississippi	0.0
28	Missouri	1.0
20	Montana	2.3
8	Nebraska	5.7
42	Nevada	0.2
28	New Hampshire	1.0
34	New Jersey	0.7
41	New Mexico	0.3
21	New York	2.2
1	North Carolina	8.9
3	North Dakota	8.5
37	Ohio	0.5
10	Oklahoma	5.6
42	Oregon	0.2
17	Pennsylvania	3.5
10	Rhode Island	5.6
7	South Carolina	5.9
2	South Dakota	8.8
22	Tennessee	1.7
46	Texas	0.0
36	Utah	0.6
6	Vermont	6.1
5	Virginia	6.5
46	Washington	0.0
15	West Virginia	4.5
45	Wisconsin	0.1
23	Wyoming	1.2

RANK ORDER

RANK	STATE	RATE
1	North Carolina	8.9
2	South Dakota	8.8
3	North Dakota	8.5
4	Delaware	7.8
5	Virginia	6.5
6	Vermont	6.1
7	South Carolina	5.9
8	Kansas	5.7
8	Nebraska	5.7
10	Oklahoma	5.6
10	Rhode Island	5.6
12	Maine	5.2
13	Connecticut	4.9
14	Maryland	4.6
15	Georgia	4.5
15	West Virginia	4.5
17	Iowa	3.5
17	Pennsylvania	3.5
19	Massachusetts	3.3
20	Montana	2.3
21	New York	2.2
22	Tennessee	1.7
23	Alaska	1.2
23	Arizona	1.2
23	Wyoming	1.2
26	Florida	1.1
26	Idaho	1.1
28	Missouri	1.0
28	New Hampshire	1.0
30	Arkansas	0.9
30	Kentucky	0.9
32	Colorado	0.8
32	Minnesota	0.8
34	Alabama	0.7
34	New Jersey	0.7
36	Utah	0.6
37	California	0.5
37	Indiana	0.5
37	Michigan	0.5
37	Ohio	0.5
41	New Mexico	0.3
42	Illinois	0.2
42	Nevada	0.2
42	Oregon	0.2
45	Wisconsin	0.1
46	Hawaii	0.0
46	Louisiana	0.0
46	Mississippi	0.0
46	Texas	0.0
46	Washington	0.0
	District of Columbia	0.0

Source: Morgan Quitno Press using data from U.S. Dept. of Health & Human Serv's, National Center for Health Statistics "Morbidity and Mortality Weekly Report" (January 2, 2004, Vol. 52, Nos. 51 & 52)
*Provisional data. An acute, infectious, often fatal viral disease of most warm-blooded animals, especially wolves, cats, and dogs, that attacks the central nervous system and is transmitted by the bite of infected animals.

Rocky Mountain Spotted Fever Cases Reported in 2003

National Total = 957 Cases*

ALPHA ORDER

RANK	STATE	CASES	% of USA
13	Alabama	12	1.3%
36	Alaska	0	0.0%
36	Arizona	0	0.0%
6	Arkansas	44	4.6%
21	California	4	0.4%
25	Colorado	2	0.2%
36	Connecticut	0	0.0%
31	Delaware	1	0.1%
11	Florida	18	1.9%
3	Georgia	82	8.6%
36	Hawaii	0	0.0%
25	Idaho	2	0.2%
36	Illinois	0	0.0%
31	Indiana	1	0.1%
25	Iowa	2	0.2%
23	Kansas	3	0.3%
23	Kentucky	3	0.3%
36	Louisiana	0	0.0%
36	Maine	0	0.0%
2	Maryland	106	11.1%
31	Massachusetts	1	0.1%
18	Michigan	5	0.5%
25	Minnesota	2	0.2%
10	Mississippi	29	3.0%
5	Missouri	55	5.7%
31	Montana	1	0.1%
21	Nebraska	4	0.4%
36	Nevada	0	0.0%
36	New Hampshire	0	0.0%
13	New Jersey	12	1.3%
31	New Mexico	1	0.1%
12	New York	16	1.7%
1	North Carolina	321	33.5%
36	North Dakota	0	0.0%
15	Ohio	11	1.1%
8	Oklahoma	42	4.4%
36	Oregon	0	0.0%
15	Pennsylvania	11	1.1%
36	Rhode Island	0	0.0%
6	South Carolina	44	4.6%
18	South Dakota	5	0.5%
4	Tennessee	66	6.9%
15	Texas	11	1.1%
25	Utah	2	0.2%
36	Vermont	0	0.0%
9	Virginia	30	3.1%
36	Washington	0	0.0%
18	West Virginia	5	0.5%
36	Wisconsin	0	0.0%
25	Wyoming	2	0.2%

RANK ORDER

RANK	STATE	CASES	% of USA
1	North Carolina	321	33.5%
2	Maryland	106	11.1%
3	Georgia	82	8.6%
4	Tennessee	66	6.9%
5	Missouri	55	5.7%
6	Arkansas	44	4.6%
6	South Carolina	44	4.6%
8	Oklahoma	42	4.4%
9	Virginia	30	3.1%
10	Mississippi	29	3.0%
11	Florida	18	1.9%
12	New York	16	1.7%
13	Alabama	12	1.3%
13	New Jersey	12	1.3%
15	Ohio	11	1.1%
15	Pennsylvania	11	1.1%
15	Texas	11	1.1%
18	Michigan	5	0.5%
18	South Dakota	5	0.5%
18	West Virginia	5	0.5%
21	California	4	0.4%
21	Nebraska	4	0.4%
23	Kansas	3	0.3%
23	Kentucky	3	0.3%
25	Colorado	2	0.2%
25	Idaho	2	0.2%
25	Iowa	2	0.2%
25	Minnesota	2	0.2%
25	Utah	2	0.2%
25	Wyoming	2	0.2%
31	Delaware	1	0.1%
31	Indiana	1	0.1%
31	Massachusetts	1	0.1%
31	Montana	1	0.1%
31	New Mexico	1	0.1%
36	Alaska	0	0.0%
36	Arizona	0	0.0%
36	Connecticut	0	0.0%
36	Hawaii	0	0.0%
36	Illinois	0	0.0%
36	Louisiana	0	0.0%
36	Maine	0	0.0%
36	Nevada	0	0.0%
36	New Hampshire	0	0.0%
36	North Dakota	0	0.0%
36	Oregon	0	0.0%
36	Rhode Island	0	0.0%
36	Vermont	0	0.0%
36	Washington	0	0.0%
36	Wisconsin	0	0.0%
	District of Columbia	1	0.1%

Source: U.S. Department of Health and Human Services, National Center for Health Statistics "Morbidity and Mortality Weekly Report" (January 2, 2004, Vol. 52, Nos. 51 & 52)
Provisional data. An illness caused by Rickettsia rickettsii, a bacterial pathogen transmitted to humans through contact with ticks. Characterized by acute onset of fever, and may be accompanied by headache, malaise, myalgia, nausea/vomiting, or neurologic signs. A rash is often present on the palms and soles.

Rocky Mountain Spotted Fever Rate in 2003

National Rate = 0.3 Cases per 100,000 Population*

ALPHA ORDER

RANK	STATE	RATE
13	Alabama	0.3
29	Alaska	0.0
29	Arizona	0.0
3	Arkansas	1.6
29	California	0.0
29	Colorado	0.0
29	Connecticut	0.0
16	Delaware	0.1
16	Florida	0.1
9	Georgia	0.9
29	Hawaii	0.0
16	Idaho	0.1
29	Illinois	0.0
29	Indiana	0.0
16	Iowa	0.1
16	Kansas	0.1
16	Kentucky	0.1
29	Louisiana	0.0
29	Maine	0.0
2	Maryland	1.9
29	Massachusetts	0.0
29	Michigan	0.0
29	Minnesota	0.0
7	Mississippi	1.0
7	Missouri	1.0
16	Montana	0.1
15	Nebraska	0.2
29	Nevada	0.0
29	New Hampshire	0.0
16	New Jersey	0.1
16	New Mexico	0.1
16	New York	0.1
1	North Carolina	3.8
29	North Dakota	0.0
16	Ohio	0.1
4	Oklahoma	1.2
29	Oregon	0.0
16	Pennsylvania	0.1
29	Rhode Island	0.0
5	South Carolina	1.1
10	South Dakota	0.7
5	Tennessee	1.1
29	Texas	0.0
16	Utah	0.1
29	Vermont	0.0
11	Virginia	0.4
29	Washington	0.0
13	West Virginia	0.3
29	Wisconsin	0.0
11	Wyoming	0.4

RANK ORDER

RANK	STATE	RATE
1	North Carolina	3.8
2	Maryland	1.9
3	Arkansas	1.6
4	Oklahoma	1.2
5	South Carolina	1.1
5	Tennessee	1.1
7	Mississippi	1.0
7	Missouri	1.0
9	Georgia	0.9
10	South Dakota	0.7
11	Virginia	0.4
11	Wyoming	0.4
13	Alabama	0.3
13	West Virginia	0.3
15	Nebraska	0.2
16	Delaware	0.1
16	Florida	0.1
16	Idaho	0.1
16	Iowa	0.1
16	Kansas	0.1
16	Kentucky	0.1
16	Montana	0.1
16	New Jersey	0.1
16	New Mexico	0.1
16	New York	0.1
16	Ohio	0.1
16	Pennsylvania	0.1
16	Utah	0.1
29	Alaska	0.0
29	Arizona	0.0
29	California	0.0
29	Colorado	0.0
29	Connecticut	0.0
29	Hawaii	0.0
29	Illinois	0.0
29	Indiana	0.0
29	Louisiana	0.0
29	Maine	0.0
29	Massachusetts	0.0
29	Michigan	0.0
29	Minnesota	0.0
29	Nevada	0.0
29	New Hampshire	0.0
29	North Dakota	0.0
29	Oregon	0.0
29	Rhode Island	0.0
29	Texas	0.0
29	Vermont	0.0
29	Washington	0.0
29	Wisconsin	0.0
	District of Columbia	0.2

Source: Morgan Quitno Press using data from U.S. Dept. of Health & Human Serv's, National Center for Health Statistics
"Morbidity and Mortality Weekly Report" (January 2, 2004, Vol. 52, Nos. 51 & 52)
*Provisional data. An illness caused by Rickettsia rickettsii, a bacterial pathogen transmitted to humans through
contact with ticks. Characterized by acute onset of fever, and may be accompanied by headache, malaise, myalgia,
nausea/vomiting, or neurologic signs. A rash is often present on the palms and soles.

Salmonellosis Cases Reported in 2003

National Total = 40,369 Cases*

<table>
<tr><td colspan="4">ALPHA ORDER</td><td colspan="4">RANK ORDER</td></tr>
<tr><td>RANK</td><td>STATE</td><td>CASES</td><td>% of USA</td><td>RANK</td><td>STATE</td><td>CASES</td><td>% of USA</td></tr>
<tr><td>26</td><td>Alabama</td><td>531</td><td>1.3%</td><td>1</td><td>Florida</td><td>4,567</td><td>11.3%</td></tr>
<tr><td>47</td><td>Alaska</td><td>97</td><td>0.2%</td><td>2</td><td>California</td><td>3,921</td><td>9.7%</td></tr>
<tr><td>19</td><td>Arizona</td><td>764</td><td>1.9%</td><td>3</td><td>Texas</td><td>2,925</td><td>7.2%</td></tr>
<tr><td>18</td><td>Arkansas</td><td>782</td><td>1.9%</td><td>4</td><td>New York</td><td>2,437</td><td>6.0%</td></tr>
<tr><td>2</td><td>California</td><td>3,921</td><td>9.7%</td><td>5</td><td>Georgia</td><td>2,186</td><td>5.4%</td></tr>
<tr><td>28</td><td>Colorado</td><td>443</td><td>1.1%</td><td>6</td><td>Illinois</td><td>1,665</td><td>4.1%</td></tr>
<tr><td>32</td><td>Connecticut</td><td>389</td><td>1.0%</td><td>7</td><td>Pennsylvania</td><td>1,529</td><td>3.8%</td></tr>
<tr><td>46</td><td>Delaware</td><td>99</td><td>0.2%</td><td>8</td><td>North Carolina</td><td>1,392</td><td>3.4%</td></tr>
<tr><td>1</td><td>Florida</td><td>4,567</td><td>11.3%</td><td>9</td><td>Ohio</td><td>1,324</td><td>3.3%</td></tr>
<tr><td>5</td><td>Georgia</td><td>2,186</td><td>5.4%</td><td>10</td><td>Massachusetts</td><td>1,217</td><td>3.0%</td></tr>
<tr><td>36</td><td>Hawaii</td><td>223</td><td>0.6%</td><td>11</td><td>Virginia</td><td>1,068</td><td>2.6%</td></tr>
<tr><td>37</td><td>Idaho</td><td>180</td><td>0.4%</td><td>12</td><td>Mississippi</td><td>986</td><td>2.4%</td></tr>
<tr><td>6</td><td>Illinois</td><td>1,665</td><td>4.1%</td><td>13</td><td>Missouri</td><td>978</td><td>2.4%</td></tr>
<tr><td>24</td><td>Indiana</td><td>565</td><td>1.4%</td><td>14</td><td>Maryland</td><td>858</td><td>2.1%</td></tr>
<tr><td>31</td><td>Iowa</td><td>396</td><td>1.0%</td><td>15</td><td>Wisconsin</td><td>856</td><td>2.1%</td></tr>
<tr><td>33</td><td>Kansas</td><td>289</td><td>0.7%</td><td>16</td><td>South Carolina</td><td>822</td><td>2.0%</td></tr>
<tr><td>30</td><td>Kentucky</td><td>397</td><td>1.0%</td><td>17</td><td>Michigan</td><td>792</td><td>2.0%</td></tr>
<tr><td>25</td><td>Louisiana</td><td>538</td><td>1.3%</td><td>18</td><td>Arkansas</td><td>782</td><td>1.9%</td></tr>
<tr><td>40</td><td>Maine</td><td>137</td><td>0.3%</td><td>19</td><td>Arizona</td><td>764</td><td>1.9%</td></tr>
<tr><td>14</td><td>Maryland</td><td>858</td><td>2.1%</td><td>20</td><td>Tennessee</td><td>744</td><td>1.8%</td></tr>
<tr><td>10</td><td>Massachusetts</td><td>1,217</td><td>3.0%</td><td>21</td><td>New Jersey</td><td>573</td><td>1.4%</td></tr>
<tr><td>17</td><td>Michigan</td><td>792</td><td>2.0%</td><td>22</td><td>Minnesota</td><td>571</td><td>1.4%</td></tr>
<tr><td>22</td><td>Minnesota</td><td>571</td><td>1.4%</td><td>23</td><td>Washington</td><td>569</td><td>1.4%</td></tr>
<tr><td>12</td><td>Mississippi</td><td>986</td><td>2.4%</td><td>24</td><td>Indiana</td><td>565</td><td>1.4%</td></tr>
<tr><td>13</td><td>Missouri</td><td>978</td><td>2.4%</td><td>25</td><td>Louisiana</td><td>538</td><td>1.3%</td></tr>
<tr><td>44</td><td>Montana</td><td>112</td><td>0.3%</td><td>26</td><td>Alabama</td><td>531</td><td>1.3%</td></tr>
<tr><td>39</td><td>Nebraska</td><td>147</td><td>0.4%</td><td>27</td><td>Oklahoma</td><td>471</td><td>1.2%</td></tr>
<tr><td>38</td><td>Nevada</td><td>176</td><td>0.4%</td><td>28</td><td>Colorado</td><td>443</td><td>1.1%</td></tr>
<tr><td>45</td><td>New Hampshire</td><td>100</td><td>0.2%</td><td>29</td><td>Oregon</td><td>423</td><td>1.0%</td></tr>
<tr><td>21</td><td>New Jersey</td><td>573</td><td>1.4%</td><td>30</td><td>Kentucky</td><td>397</td><td>1.0%</td></tr>
<tr><td>34</td><td>New Mexico</td><td>274</td><td>0.7%</td><td>31</td><td>Iowa</td><td>396</td><td>1.0%</td></tr>
<tr><td>4</td><td>New York</td><td>2,437</td><td>6.0%</td><td>32</td><td>Connecticut</td><td>389</td><td>1.0%</td></tr>
<tr><td>8</td><td>North Carolina</td><td>1,392</td><td>3.4%</td><td>33</td><td>Kansas</td><td>289</td><td>0.7%</td></tr>
<tr><td>50</td><td>North Dakota</td><td>43</td><td>0.1%</td><td>34</td><td>New Mexico</td><td>274</td><td>0.7%</td></tr>
<tr><td>9</td><td>Ohio</td><td>1,324</td><td>3.3%</td><td>35</td><td>Utah</td><td>230</td><td>0.6%</td></tr>
<tr><td>27</td><td>Oklahoma</td><td>471</td><td>1.2%</td><td>36</td><td>Hawaii</td><td>223</td><td>0.6%</td></tr>
<tr><td>29</td><td>Oregon</td><td>423</td><td>1.0%</td><td>37</td><td>Idaho</td><td>180</td><td>0.4%</td></tr>
<tr><td>7</td><td>Pennsylvania</td><td>1,529</td><td>3.8%</td><td>38</td><td>Nevada</td><td>176</td><td>0.4%</td></tr>
<tr><td>42</td><td>Rhode Island</td><td>129</td><td>0.3%</td><td>39</td><td>Nebraska</td><td>147</td><td>0.4%</td></tr>
<tr><td>16</td><td>South Carolina</td><td>822</td><td>2.0%</td><td>40</td><td>Maine</td><td>137</td><td>0.3%</td></tr>
<tr><td>43</td><td>South Dakota</td><td>118</td><td>0.3%</td><td>41</td><td>West Virginia</td><td>134</td><td>0.3%</td></tr>
<tr><td>20</td><td>Tennessee</td><td>744</td><td>1.8%</td><td>42</td><td>Rhode Island</td><td>129</td><td>0.3%</td></tr>
<tr><td>3</td><td>Texas</td><td>2,925</td><td>7.2%</td><td>43</td><td>South Dakota</td><td>118</td><td>0.3%</td></tr>
<tr><td>35</td><td>Utah</td><td>230</td><td>0.6%</td><td>44</td><td>Montana</td><td>112</td><td>0.3%</td></tr>
<tr><td>49</td><td>Vermont</td><td>73</td><td>0.2%</td><td>45</td><td>New Hampshire</td><td>100</td><td>0.2%</td></tr>
<tr><td>11</td><td>Virginia</td><td>1,068</td><td>2.6%</td><td>46</td><td>Delaware</td><td>99</td><td>0.2%</td></tr>
<tr><td>23</td><td>Washington</td><td>569</td><td>1.4%</td><td>47</td><td>Alaska</td><td>97</td><td>0.2%</td></tr>
<tr><td>41</td><td>West Virginia</td><td>134</td><td>0.3%</td><td>48</td><td>Wyoming</td><td>77</td><td>0.2%</td></tr>
<tr><td>15</td><td>Wisconsin</td><td>856</td><td>2.1%</td><td>49</td><td>Vermont</td><td>73</td><td>0.2%</td></tr>
<tr><td>48</td><td>Wyoming</td><td>77</td><td>0.2%</td><td>50</td><td>North Dakota</td><td>43</td><td>0.1%</td></tr>
<tr><td></td><td></td><td></td><td></td><td></td><td>District of Columbia</td><td>52</td><td>0.1%</td></tr>
</table>

Source: U.S. Department of Health and Human Services, National Center for Health Statistics
   "Morbidity and Mortality Weekly Report" (January 2, 2004, Vol. 52, Nos. 51 & 52)
*Provisional data. Any disease caused by a salmonella infection, which may be manifested as food poisoning with acute gastroenteritis, vomiting and diarrhea.

Salmonellosis Rate in 2003

National Rate = 13.9 Cases per 100,000 Population*

ALPHA ORDER

RANK	STATE	RATE
31	Alabama	11.8
14	Alaska	15.0
17	Arizona	13.7
2	Arkansas	28.7
36	California	11.0
40	Colorado	9.7
35	Connecticut	11.2
27	Delaware	12.1
3	Florida	26.8
4	Georgia	25.2
7	Hawaii	17.7
20	Idaho	13.2
20	Illinois	13.2
43	Indiana	9.1
18	Iowa	13.5
37	Kansas	10.6
41	Kentucky	9.6
28	Louisiana	12.0
38	Maine	10.5
10	Maryland	15.6
6	Massachusetts	18.9
45	Michigan	7.9
34	Minnesota	11.3
1	Mississippi	34.2
8	Missouri	17.1
26	Montana	12.2
44	Nebraska	8.5
45	Nevada	7.9
47	New Hampshire	7.8
50	New Jersey	6.6
15	New Mexico	14.6
23	New York	12.7
9	North Carolina	16.6
49	North Dakota	6.8
33	Ohio	11.6
19	Oklahoma	13.4
30	Oregon	11.9
25	Pennsylvania	12.4
28	Rhode Island	12.0
5	South Carolina	19.8
12	South Dakota	15.4
23	Tennessee	12.7
20	Texas	13.2
39	Utah	9.8
31	Vermont	11.8
16	Virginia	14.5
42	Washington	9.3
48	West Virginia	7.4
10	Wisconsin	15.6
12	Wyoming	15.4

RANK ORDER

RANK	STATE	RATE
1	Mississippi	34.2
2	Arkansas	28.7
3	Florida	26.8
4	Georgia	25.2
5	South Carolina	19.8
6	Massachusetts	18.9
7	Hawaii	17.7
8	Missouri	17.1
9	North Carolina	16.6
10	Maryland	15.6
10	Wisconsin	15.6
12	South Dakota	15.4
12	Wyoming	15.4
14	Alaska	15.0
15	New Mexico	14.6
16	Virginia	14.5
17	Arizona	13.7
18	Iowa	13.5
19	Oklahoma	13.4
20	Idaho	13.2
20	Illinois	13.2
20	Texas	13.2
23	New York	12.7
23	Tennessee	12.7
25	Pennsylvania	12.4
26	Montana	12.2
27	Delaware	12.1
28	Louisiana	12.0
28	Rhode Island	12.0
30	Oregon	11.9
31	Alabama	11.8
31	Vermont	11.8
33	Ohio	11.6
34	Minnesota	11.3
35	Connecticut	11.2
36	California	11.0
37	Kansas	10.6
38	Maine	10.5
39	Utah	9.8
40	Colorado	9.7
41	Kentucky	9.6
42	Washington	9.3
43	Indiana	9.1
44	Nebraska	8.5
45	Michigan	7.9
45	Nevada	7.9
47	New Hampshire	7.8
48	West Virginia	7.4
49	North Dakota	6.8
50	New Jersey	6.6

District of Columbia 9.2

Source: Morgan Quitno Press using data from U.S. Dept. of Health & Human Serv's, National Center for Health Statistics "Morbidity and Mortality Weekly Report" (January 2, 2004, Vol. 52, Nos. 51 & 52)

*Provisional data. Any disease caused by a salmonella infection, which may be manifested as food poisoning with acute gastroenteritis, vomiting and diarrhea.

Shigellosis Cases Reported in 2003

National Total = 21,475 Cases*

ALPHA ORDER

RANK	STATE	CASES	% of USA
21	Alabama	249	1.2%
43	Alaska	10	0.0%
11	Arizona	563	2.6%
33	Arkansas	99	0.5%
3	California	2,116	9.9%
19	Colorado	277	1.3%
36	Connecticut	66	0.3%
27	Delaware	157	0.7%
2	Florida	2,811	13.1%
4	Georgia	1,598	7.4%
39	Hawaii	45	0.2%
40	Idaho	36	0.2%
8	Illinois	881	4.1%
25	Indiana	179	0.8%
34	Iowa	93	0.4%
31	Kansas	118	0.5%
29	Kentucky	128	0.6%
16	Louisiana	303	1.4%
46	Maine	7	0.0%
10	Maryland	583	2.7%
23	Massachusetts	224	1.0%
22	Michigan	234	1.1%
32	Minnesota	108	0.5%
26	Mississippi	167	0.8%
15	Missouri	372	1.7%
49	Montana	2	0.0%
35	Nebraska	86	0.4%
36	Nevada	66	0.3%
48	New Hampshire	5	0.0%
18	New Jersey	280	1.3%
20	New Mexico	252	1.2%
5	New York	1,001	4.7%
6	North Carolina	985	4.6%
47	North Dakota	6	0.0%
17	Ohio	300	1.4%
9	Oklahoma	840	3.9%
24	Oregon	213	1.0%
7	Pennsylvania	983	4.6%
41	Rhode Island	21	0.1%
12	South Carolina	514	2.4%
42	South Dakota	17	0.1%
14	Tennessee	392	1.8%
1	Texas	3,242	15.1%
38	Utah	53	0.2%
44	Vermont	8	0.0%
13	Virginia	426	2.0%
27	Washington	157	0.7%
50	West Virginia	1	0.0%
30	Wisconsin	120	0.6%
44	Wyoming	8	0.0%

RANK ORDER

RANK	STATE	CASES	% of USA
1	Texas	3,242	15.1%
2	Florida	2,811	13.1%
3	California	2,116	9.9%
4	Georgia	1,598	7.4%
5	New York	1,001	4.7%
6	North Carolina	985	4.6%
7	Pennsylvania	983	4.6%
8	Illinois	881	4.1%
9	Oklahoma	840	3.9%
10	Maryland	583	2.7%
11	Arizona	563	2.6%
12	South Carolina	514	2.4%
13	Virginia	426	2.0%
14	Tennessee	392	1.8%
15	Missouri	372	1.7%
16	Louisiana	303	1.4%
17	Ohio	300	1.4%
18	New Jersey	280	1.3%
19	Colorado	277	1.3%
20	New Mexico	252	1.2%
21	Alabama	249	1.2%
22	Michigan	234	1.1%
23	Massachusetts	224	1.0%
24	Oregon	213	1.0%
25	Indiana	179	0.8%
26	Mississippi	167	0.8%
27	Delaware	157	0.7%
27	Washington	157	0.7%
29	Kentucky	128	0.6%
30	Wisconsin	120	0.6%
31	Kansas	118	0.5%
32	Minnesota	108	0.5%
33	Arkansas	99	0.5%
34	Iowa	93	0.4%
35	Nebraska	86	0.4%
36	Connecticut	66	0.3%
36	Nevada	66	0.3%
38	Utah	53	0.2%
39	Hawaii	45	0.2%
40	Idaho	36	0.2%
41	Rhode Island	21	0.1%
42	South Dakota	17	0.1%
43	Alaska	10	0.0%
44	Vermont	8	0.0%
44	Wyoming	8	0.0%
46	Maine	7	0.0%
47	North Dakota	6	0.0%
48	New Hampshire	5	0.0%
49	Montana	2	0.0%
50	West Virginia	1	0.0%

| | District of Columbia | 73 | 0.3% |

Source: U.S. Department of Health and Human Services, National Center for Health Statistics
   "Morbidity and Mortality Weekly Report" (January 2, 2004, Vol. 52, Nos. 51 & 52)
*Provisional data. Dysentery caused by any of various species of shigellae, occurring most frequently in areas where poor sanitation and malnutrition are prevalent and commonly affecting children and infants.

Shigellosis Rate in 2003

National Rate = 7.4 Cases per 100,000 Population*

ALPHA ORDER

RANK	STATE	RATE
21	Alabama	5.5
44	Alaska	1.5
10	Arizona	10.1
25	Arkansas	3.6
17	California	6.0
16	Colorado	6.1
42	Connecticut	1.9
2	Delaware	19.2
4	Florida	16.5
3	Georgia	18.4
25	Hawaii	3.6
33	Idaho	2.6
12	Illinois	7.0
31	Indiana	2.9
28	Iowa	3.2
24	Kansas	4.3
30	Kentucky	3.1
13	Louisiana	6.7
47	Maine	0.5
9	Maryland	10.6
27	Massachusetts	3.5
36	Michigan	2.3
40	Minnesota	2.1
19	Mississippi	5.8
15	Missouri	6.5
49	Montana	0.2
23	Nebraska	4.9
31	Nevada	2.9
48	New Hampshire	0.4
28	New Jersey	3.2
6	New Mexico	13.4
22	New York	5.2
8	North Carolina	11.7
46	North Dakota	0.9
33	Ohio	2.6
1	Oklahoma	23.9
17	Oregon	6.0
11	Pennsylvania	7.9
41	Rhode Island	2.0
7	South Carolina	12.4
38	South Dakota	2.2
13	Tennessee	6.7
5	Texas	14.7
36	Utah	2.3
45	Vermont	1.3
19	Virginia	5.8
33	Washington	2.6
50	West Virginia	0.1
38	Wisconsin	2.2
43	Wyoming	1.6

RANK ORDER

RANK	STATE	RATE
1	Oklahoma	23.9
2	Delaware	19.2
3	Georgia	18.4
4	Florida	16.5
5	Texas	14.7
6	New Mexico	13.4
7	South Carolina	12.4
8	North Carolina	11.7
9	Maryland	10.6
10	Arizona	10.1
11	Pennsylvania	7.9
12	Illinois	7.0
13	Louisiana	6.7
13	Tennessee	6.7
15	Missouri	6.5
16	Colorado	6.1
17	California	6.0
17	Oregon	6.0
19	Mississippi	5.8
19	Virginia	5.8
21	Alabama	5.5
22	New York	5.2
23	Nebraska	4.9
24	Kansas	4.3
25	Arkansas	3.6
25	Hawaii	3.6
27	Massachusetts	3.5
28	Iowa	3.2
28	New Jersey	3.2
30	Kentucky	3.1
31	Indiana	2.9
31	Nevada	2.9
33	Idaho	2.6
33	Ohio	2.6
33	Washington	2.6
36	Michigan	2.3
36	Utah	2.3
38	South Dakota	2.2
38	Wisconsin	2.2
40	Minnesota	2.1
41	Rhode Island	2.0
42	Connecticut	1.9
43	Wyoming	1.6
44	Alaska	1.5
45	Vermont	1.3
46	North Dakota	0.9
47	Maine	0.5
48	New Hampshire	0.4
49	Montana	0.2
50	West Virginia	0.1

District of Columbia   13.0

Source: Morgan Quitno Press using data from U.S. Dept. of Health & Human Serv's, National Center for Health Statistics
"Morbidity and Mortality Weekly Report" (January 2, 2004, Vol. 52, Nos. 51 & 52)
*Provisional data. Dysentery caused by any of various species of shigellae, occurring most frequently in areas
where poor sanitation and malnutrition are prevalent and commonly affecting children and infants.

Tuberculosis Cases Reported in 2003

National Total = 11,339 Cases*

ALPHA ORDER

RANK ORDER

RANK	STATE	CASES	% of USA
13	Alabama	238	2.1%
31	Alaska	55	0.5%
17	Arizona	206	1.8%
24	Arkansas	110	1.0%
1	California	1,909	16.8%
30	Colorado	64	0.6%
33	Connecticut	50	0.4%
38	Delaware	23	0.2%
4	Florida	889	7.8%
7	Georgia	375	3.3%
29	Hawaii	69	0.6%
42	Idaho	8	0.1%
5	Illinois	557	4.9%
23	Indiana	129	1.1%
37	Iowa	25	0.2%
28	Kansas	95	0.8%
22	Kentucky	130	1.1%
50	Louisiana	0	0.0%
46	Maine	5	0.0%
12	Maryland	239	2.1%
14	Massachusetts	228	2.0%
15	Michigan	220	1.9%
19	Minnesota	197	1.7%
26	Mississippi	101	0.9%
25	Missouri	109	1.0%
46	Montana	5	0.0%
36	Nebraska	27	0.2%
39	Nevada	22	0.2%
43	New Hampshire	7	0.1%
6	New Jersey	426	3.8%
45	New Mexico	6	0.1%
2	New York	1,381	12.2%
8	North Carolina	354	3.1%
48	North Dakota	4	0.0%
16	Ohio	208	1.8%
21	Oklahoma	145	1.3%
26	Oregon	101	0.9%
9	Pennsylvania	331	2.9%
35	Rhode Island	32	0.3%
20	South Carolina	170	1.5%
41	South Dakota	20	0.2%
18	Tennessee	201	1.8%
3	Texas	1,250	11.0%
34	Utah	39	0.3%
43	Vermont	7	0.1%
10	Virginia	255	2.2%
11	Washington	240	2.1%
40	West Virginia	21	0.2%
32	Wisconsin	52	0.5%
48	Wyoming	4	0.0%

RANK	STATE	CASES	% of USA
1	California	1,909	16.8%
2	New York	1,381	12.2%
3	Texas	1,250	11.0%
4	Florida	889	7.8%
5	Illinois	557	4.9%
6	New Jersey	426	3.8%
7	Georgia	375	3.3%
8	North Carolina	354	3.1%
9	Pennsylvania	331	2.9%
10	Virginia	255	2.2%
11	Washington	240	2.1%
12	Maryland	239	2.1%
13	Alabama	238	2.1%
14	Massachusetts	228	2.0%
15	Michigan	220	1.9%
16	Ohio	208	1.8%
17	Arizona	206	1.8%
18	Tennessee	201	1.8%
19	Minnesota	197	1.7%
20	South Carolina	170	1.5%
21	Oklahoma	145	1.3%
22	Kentucky	130	1.1%
23	Indiana	129	1.1%
24	Arkansas	110	1.0%
25	Missouri	109	1.0%
26	Mississippi	101	0.9%
26	Oregon	101	0.9%
28	Kansas	95	0.8%
29	Hawaii	69	0.6%
30	Colorado	64	0.6%
31	Alaska	55	0.5%
32	Wisconsin	52	0.5%
33	Connecticut	50	0.4%
34	Utah	39	0.3%
35	Rhode Island	32	0.3%
36	Nebraska	27	0.2%
37	Iowa	25	0.2%
38	Delaware	23	0.2%
39	Nevada	22	0.2%
40	West Virginia	21	0.2%
41	South Dakota	20	0.2%
42	Idaho	8	0.1%
43	New Hampshire	7	0.1%
43	Vermont	7	0.1%
45	New Mexico	6	0.1%
46	Maine	5	0.0%
46	Montana	5	0.0%
48	North Dakota	4	0.0%
48	Wyoming	4	0.0%
50	Louisiana	0	0.0%
	District of Columbia	0	0.0%

Source: U.S. Department of Health and Human Services, National Center for Health Statistics
    "Morbidity and Mortality Weekly Report" (January 2, 2004, Vol. 52, Nos. 51 & 52)
*Provisional data. An infectious disease caused by the tubercle bacillus and causing the formation of tubercles on the lungs and other tissues of the body, often developing long after the initial infection. Characterized by the coughing up of mucus and sputum, fever, weight loss, and chest pain.

Tuberculosis Rate in 2003

National Rate = 3.9 Cases per 100,000 Population*

ALPHA ORDER

RANK	STATE	RATE
6	Alabama	5.3
1	Alaska	8.5
18	Arizona	3.7
15	Arkansas	4.0
5	California	5.4
36	Colorado	1.4
36	Connecticut	1.4
26	Delaware	2.8
7	Florida	5.2
10	Georgia	4.3
4	Hawaii	5.5
44	Idaho	0.6
9	Illinois	4.4
31	Indiana	2.1
42	Iowa	0.8
19	Kansas	3.5
24	Kentucky	3.2
50	Louisiana	0.0
48	Maine	0.4
10	Maryland	4.3
19	Massachusetts	3.5
30	Michigan	2.2
16	Minnesota	3.9
19	Mississippi	3.5
32	Missouri	1.9
46	Montana	0.5
35	Nebraska	1.6
40	Nevada	1.0
46	New Hampshire	0.5
8	New Jersey	4.9
49	New Mexico	0.3
2	New York	7.2
12	North Carolina	4.2
44	North Dakota	0.6
33	Ohio	1.8
13	Oklahoma	4.1
26	Oregon	2.8
28	Pennsylvania	2.7
25	Rhode Island	3.0
13	South Carolina	4.1
29	South Dakota	2.6
23	Tennessee	3.4
3	Texas	5.7
34	Utah	1.7
39	Vermont	1.1
19	Virginia	3.5
16	Washington	3.9
38	West Virginia	1.2
40	Wisconsin	1.0
42	Wyoming	0.8

RANK ORDER

RANK	STATE	RATE
1	Alaska	8.5
2	New York	7.2
3	Texas	5.7
4	Hawaii	5.5
5	California	5.4
6	Alabama	5.3
7	Florida	5.2
8	New Jersey	4.9
9	Illinois	4.4
10	Georgia	4.3
10	Maryland	4.3
12	North Carolina	4.2
13	Oklahoma	4.1
13	South Carolina	4.1
15	Arkansas	4.0
16	Minnesota	3.9
16	Washington	3.9
18	Arizona	3.7
19	Kansas	3.5
19	Massachusetts	3.5
19	Mississippi	3.5
19	Virginia	3.5
23	Tennessee	3.4
24	Kentucky	3.2
25	Rhode Island	3.0
26	Delaware	2.8
26	Oregon	2.8
28	Pennsylvania	2.7
29	South Dakota	2.6
30	Michigan	2.2
31	Indiana	2.1
32	Missouri	1.9
33	Ohio	1.8
34	Utah	1.7
35	Nebraska	1.6
36	Colorado	1.4
36	Connecticut	1.4
38	West Virginia	1.2
39	Vermont	1.1
40	Nevada	1.0
40	Wisconsin	1.0
42	Iowa	0.8
42	Wyoming	0.8
44	Idaho	0.6
44	North Dakota	0.6
46	Montana	0.5
46	New Hampshire	0.5
48	Maine	0.4
49	New Mexico	0.3
50	Louisiana	0.0

District of Columbia   0.0

Source: Morgan Quitno Press using data from U.S. Dept. of Health & Human Serv's, National Center for Health Statistics
"Morbidity and Mortality Weekly Report" (January 2, 2004, Vol. 52, Nos. 51 & 52)

*Provisional data. An infectious disease caused by the tubercle bacillus and causing the formation of tubercles on the lungs and other tissues of the body, often developing long after the initial infection. Characterized by the coughing up of mucus and sputum, fever, weight loss, and chest pain.

West Nile Encephalitis and Meningitis Cases Reported in 2003

National Total = 2,677 Cases*

ALPHA ORDER

RANK	STATE	CASES	% of USA
24	Alabama	22	0.8%
43	Alaska	0	0.0%
35	Arizona	7	0.3%
23	Arkansas	23	0.9%
39	California	2	0.1%
1	Colorado	539	20.1%
31	Connecticut	12	0.4%
31	Delaware	12	0.4%
15	Florida	53	2.0%
21	Georgia	27	1.0%
43	Hawaii	0	0.0%
43	Idaho	0	0.0%
20	Illinois	28	1.0%
29	Indiana	15	0.6%
11	Iowa	78	2.9%
8	Kansas	88	3.3%
33	Kentucky	11	0.4%
7	Louisiana	91	3.4%
43	Maine	0	0.0%
17	Maryland	49	1.8%
34	Massachusetts	10	0.4%
30	Michigan	13	0.5%
18	Minnesota	48	1.8%
21	Mississippi	27	1.0%
19	Missouri	37	1.4%
12	Montana	75	2.8%
3	Nebraska	193	7.2%
39	Nevada	2	0.1%
39	New Hampshire	2	0.1%
25	New Jersey	21	0.8%
13	New Mexico	70	2.6%
16	New York	50	1.9%
28	North Carolina	16	0.6%
10	North Dakota	79	3.0%
9	Ohio	83	3.1%
14	Oklahoma	54	2.0%
43	Oregon	0	0.0%
5	Pennsylvania	142	5.3%
36	Rhode Island	5	0.2%
38	South Carolina	3	0.1%
4	South Dakota	151	5.6%
25	Tennessee	21	0.8%
2	Texas	400	14.9%
43	Utah	0	0.0%
43	Vermont	0	0.0%
27	Virginia	18	0.7%
43	Washington	0	0.0%
42	West Virginia	1	0.0%
37	Wisconsin	4	0.1%
6	Wyoming	92	3.4%

RANK ORDER

RANK	STATE	CASES	% of USA
1	Colorado	539	20.1%
2	Texas	400	14.9%
3	Nebraska	193	7.2%
4	South Dakota	151	5.6%
5	Pennsylvania	142	5.3%
6	Wyoming	92	3.4%
7	Louisiana	91	3.4%
8	Kansas	88	3.3%
9	Ohio	83	3.1%
10	North Dakota	79	3.0%
11	Iowa	78	2.9%
12	Montana	75	2.8%
13	New Mexico	70	2.6%
14	Oklahoma	54	2.0%
15	Florida	53	2.0%
16	New York	50	1.9%
17	Maryland	49	1.8%
18	Minnesota	48	1.8%
19	Missouri	37	1.4%
20	Illinois	28	1.0%
21	Georgia	27	1.0%
21	Mississippi	27	1.0%
23	Arkansas	23	0.9%
24	Alabama	22	0.8%
25	New Jersey	21	0.8%
25	Tennessee	21	0.8%
27	Virginia	18	0.7%
28	North Carolina	16	0.6%
29	Indiana	15	0.6%
30	Michigan	13	0.5%
31	Connecticut	12	0.4%
31	Delaware	12	0.4%
33	Kentucky	11	0.4%
34	Massachusetts	10	0.4%
35	Arizona	7	0.3%
36	Rhode Island	5	0.2%
37	Wisconsin	4	0.1%
38	South Carolina	3	0.1%
39	California	2	0.1%
39	Nevada	2	0.1%
39	New Hampshire	2	0.1%
42	West Virginia	1	0.0%
43	Alaska	0	0.0%
43	Hawaii	0	0.0%
43	Idaho	0	0.0%
43	Maine	0	0.0%
43	Oregon	0	0.0%
43	Utah	0	0.0%
43	Vermont	0	0.0%
43	Washington	0	0.0%
	District of Columbia	3	0.1%

Source: U.S. Department of Health and Human Services, Centers for Disease Control and Prevention
"West Nile Virus 2003 Human Cases" (January 14, 2004, http://www.cdc.gov/ncidod/dvbid/westnile/index.htm)
Provisional data. A flavivirus typically carried by mosquitoes. Figures do not include 6,162 West Nile Fever cases caused by the West Nile virus that result in mild, flu-like symptoms. Encephalitis refers to an inflammation of the brain, meningitis is an inflammation of the membrane around the brain and the spinal cord, and meningoencephalitis refers to inflammation of the brain and the membrane surrounding it.

West Nile Encephalitis and Meningitis Rate in 2003

National Rate = 0.9 Cases per 100,000 Population

ALPHA ORDER

RANK	STATE	RATE
21	Alabama	0.5
42	Alaska	0.0
36	Arizona	0.1
18	Arkansas	0.8
42	California	0.0
4	Colorado	11.8
24	Connecticut	0.3
12	Delaware	1.5
24	Florida	0.3
24	Georgia	0.3
42	Hawaii	0.0
42	Idaho	0.0
29	Illinois	0.2
29	Indiana	0.2
9	Iowa	2.6
8	Kansas	3.2
24	Kentucky	0.3
10	Louisiana	2.0
42	Maine	0.0
15	Maryland	0.9
29	Massachusetts	0.2
36	Michigan	0.1
15	Minnesota	0.9
15	Mississippi	0.9
20	Missouri	0.6
6	Montana	8.2
5	Nebraska	11.1
36	Nevada	0.1
29	New Hampshire	0.2
29	New Jersey	0.2
7	New Mexico	3.7
24	New York	0.3
29	North Carolina	0.2
3	North Dakota	12.5
19	Ohio	0.7
12	Oklahoma	1.5
42	Oregon	0.0
14	Pennsylvania	1.1
21	Rhode Island	0.5
36	South Carolina	0.1
1	South Dakota	19.8
23	Tennessee	0.4
11	Texas	1.8
42	Utah	0.0
42	Vermont	0.0
29	Virginia	0.2
42	Washington	0.0
36	West Virginia	0.1
36	Wisconsin	0.1
2	Wyoming	18.4

RANK ORDER

RANK	STATE	RATE
1	South Dakota	19.8
2	Wyoming	18.4
3	North Dakota	12.5
4	Colorado	11.8
5	Nebraska	11.1
6	Montana	8.2
7	New Mexico	3.7
8	Kansas	3.2
9	Iowa	2.6
10	Louisiana	2.0
11	Texas	1.8
12	Delaware	1.5
12	Oklahoma	1.5
14	Pennsylvania	1.1
15	Maryland	0.9
15	Minnesota	0.9
15	Mississippi	0.9
18	Arkansas	0.8
19	Ohio	0.7
20	Missouri	0.6
21	Alabama	0.5
21	Rhode Island	0.5
23	Tennessee	0.4
24	Connecticut	0.3
24	Florida	0.3
24	Georgia	0.3
24	Kentucky	0.3
24	New York	0.3
29	Illinois	0.2
29	Indiana	0.2
29	Massachusetts	0.2
29	New Hampshire	0.2
29	New Jersey	0.2
29	North Carolina	0.2
29	Virginia	0.2
36	Arizona	0.1
36	Michigan	0.1
36	Nevada	0.1
36	South Carolina	0.1
36	West Virginia	0.1
36	Wisconsin	0.1
42	Alaska	0.0
42	California	0.0
42	Hawaii	0.0
42	Idaho	0.0
42	Maine	0.0
42	Oregon	0.0
42	Utah	0.0
42	Vermont	0.0
42	Washington	0.0

District of Columbia 0.5

Source: Morgan Quitno Press using data from U.S. Dept. of Health & Human Serv's, CDC
"West Nile Virus 2003 Human Cases" (January 14, 2004, http://www.cdc.gov/ncidod/dvbid/westnile/index.htm)
*Provisional data. A flavivirus typically carried by mosquitoes. Figures do not include 6,162 West Nile Fever cases caused by the West Nile virus that result in mild, flu-like symptoms. Encephalitis refers to an inflammation of the brain, meningitis is an inflammation of the membrane around the brain and the spinal cord, and meningoencephalitis refers to inflammation of the brain and the membrane surrounding it.

Whooping Cough (Pertussis) Cases Reported in 2003

National Total = 8,067 Cases*

<table>
<tr><td colspan="4">ALPHA ORDER</td><td colspan="4">RANK ORDER</td></tr>
<tr><td>RANK</td><td>STATE</td><td>CASES</td><td>% of USA</td><td>RANK</td><td>STATE</td><td>CASES</td><td>% of USA</td></tr>
<tr><td>39</td><td>Alabama</td><td>17</td><td>0.2%</td><td>1</td><td>Massachusetts</td><td>1,017</td><td>12.6%</td></tr>
<tr><td>44</td><td>Alaska</td><td>7</td><td>0.1%</td><td>2</td><td>New York</td><td>811</td><td>10.1%</td></tr>
<tr><td>19</td><td>Arizona</td><td>126</td><td>1.6%</td><td>3</td><td>California</td><td>735</td><td>9.1%</td></tr>
<tr><td>33</td><td>Arkansas</td><td>37</td><td>0.5%</td><td>4</td><td>Washington</td><td>703</td><td>8.7%</td></tr>
<tr><td>3</td><td>California</td><td>735</td><td>9.1%</td><td>5</td><td>Texas</td><td>561</td><td>7.0%</td></tr>
<tr><td>7</td><td>Colorado</td><td>340</td><td>4.2%</td><td>6</td><td>Oregon</td><td>439</td><td>5.4%</td></tr>
<tr><td>37</td><td>Connecticut</td><td>25</td><td>0.3%</td><td>7</td><td>Colorado</td><td>340</td><td>4.2%</td></tr>
<tr><td>43</td><td>Delaware</td><td>8</td><td>0.1%</td><td>8</td><td>Pennsylvania</td><td>327</td><td>4.1%</td></tr>
<tr><td>20</td><td>Florida</td><td>119</td><td>1.5%</td><td>9</td><td>Ohio</td><td>317</td><td>3.9%</td></tr>
<tr><td>35</td><td>Georgia</td><td>32</td><td>0.4%</td><td>10</td><td>Wisconsin</td><td>215</td><td>2.7%</td></tr>
<tr><td>42</td><td>Hawaii</td><td>11</td><td>0.1%</td><td>11</td><td>South Carolina</td><td>192</td><td>2.4%</td></tr>
<tr><td>25</td><td>Idaho</td><td>82</td><td>1.0%</td><td>12</td><td>Missouri</td><td>173</td><td>2.1%</td></tr>
<tr><td>50</td><td>Illinois</td><td>0</td><td>0.0%</td><td>13</td><td>Iowa</td><td>151</td><td>1.9%</td></tr>
<tr><td>28</td><td>Indiana</td><td>70</td><td>0.9%</td><td>14</td><td>Minnesota</td><td>146</td><td>1.8%</td></tr>
<tr><td>13</td><td>Iowa</td><td>151</td><td>1.9%</td><td>15</td><td>North Carolina</td><td>137</td><td>1.7%</td></tr>
<tr><td>31</td><td>Kansas</td><td>45</td><td>0.6%</td><td>16</td><td>Michigan</td><td>130</td><td>1.6%</td></tr>
<tr><td>31</td><td>Kentucky</td><td>45</td><td>0.6%</td><td>16</td><td>Wyoming</td><td>130</td><td>1.6%</td></tr>
<tr><td>45</td><td>Louisiana</td><td>6</td><td>0.1%</td><td>18</td><td>Utah</td><td>128</td><td>1.6%</td></tr>
<tr><td>41</td><td>Maine</td><td>12</td><td>0.1%</td><td>19</td><td>Arizona</td><td>126</td><td>1.6%</td></tr>
<tr><td>24</td><td>Maryland</td><td>86</td><td>1.1%</td><td>20</td><td>Florida</td><td>119</td><td>1.5%</td></tr>
<tr><td>1</td><td>Massachusetts</td><td>1,017</td><td>12.6%</td><td>21</td><td>New Jersey</td><td>107</td><td>1.3%</td></tr>
<tr><td>16</td><td>Michigan</td><td>130</td><td>1.6%</td><td>22</td><td>Oklahoma</td><td>92</td><td>1.1%</td></tr>
<tr><td>14</td><td>Minnesota</td><td>146</td><td>1.8%</td><td>23</td><td>Virginia</td><td>90</td><td>1.1%</td></tr>
<tr><td>45</td><td>Mississippi</td><td>6</td><td>0.1%</td><td>24</td><td>Maryland</td><td>86</td><td>1.1%</td></tr>
<tr><td>12</td><td>Missouri</td><td>173</td><td>2.1%</td><td>25</td><td>Idaho</td><td>82</td><td>1.0%</td></tr>
<tr><td>48</td><td>Montana</td><td>5</td><td>0.1%</td><td>26</td><td>Tennessee</td><td>76</td><td>0.9%</td></tr>
<tr><td>40</td><td>Nebraska</td><td>15</td><td>0.2%</td><td>27</td><td>Vermont</td><td>71</td><td>0.9%</td></tr>
<tr><td>34</td><td>Nevada</td><td>35</td><td>0.4%</td><td>28</td><td>Indiana</td><td>70</td><td>0.9%</td></tr>
<tr><td>30</td><td>New Hampshire</td><td>60</td><td>0.7%</td><td>29</td><td>New Mexico</td><td>69</td><td>0.9%</td></tr>
<tr><td>21</td><td>New Jersey</td><td>107</td><td>1.3%</td><td>30</td><td>New Hampshire</td><td>60</td><td>0.7%</td></tr>
<tr><td>29</td><td>New Mexico</td><td>69</td><td>0.9%</td><td>31</td><td>Kansas</td><td>45</td><td>0.6%</td></tr>
<tr><td>2</td><td>New York</td><td>811</td><td>10.1%</td><td>31</td><td>Kentucky</td><td>45</td><td>0.6%</td></tr>
<tr><td>15</td><td>North Carolina</td><td>137</td><td>1.7%</td><td>33</td><td>Arkansas</td><td>37</td><td>0.5%</td></tr>
<tr><td>45</td><td>North Dakota</td><td>6</td><td>0.1%</td><td>34</td><td>Nevada</td><td>35</td><td>0.4%</td></tr>
<tr><td>9</td><td>Ohio</td><td>317</td><td>3.9%</td><td>35</td><td>Georgia</td><td>32</td><td>0.4%</td></tr>
<tr><td>22</td><td>Oklahoma</td><td>92</td><td>1.1%</td><td>36</td><td>West Virginia</td><td>27</td><td>0.3%</td></tr>
<tr><td>6</td><td>Oregon</td><td>439</td><td>5.4%</td><td>37</td><td>Connecticut</td><td>25</td><td>0.3%</td></tr>
<tr><td>8</td><td>Pennsylvania</td><td>327</td><td>4.1%</td><td>38</td><td>Rhode Island</td><td>20</td><td>0.2%</td></tr>
<tr><td>38</td><td>Rhode Island</td><td>20</td><td>0.2%</td><td>39</td><td>Alabama</td><td>17</td><td>0.2%</td></tr>
<tr><td>11</td><td>South Carolina</td><td>192</td><td>2.4%</td><td>40</td><td>Nebraska</td><td>15</td><td>0.2%</td></tr>
<tr><td>48</td><td>South Dakota</td><td>5</td><td>0.1%</td><td>41</td><td>Maine</td><td>12</td><td>0.1%</td></tr>
<tr><td>26</td><td>Tennessee</td><td>76</td><td>0.9%</td><td>42</td><td>Hawaii</td><td>11</td><td>0.1%</td></tr>
<tr><td>5</td><td>Texas</td><td>561</td><td>7.0%</td><td>43</td><td>Delaware</td><td>8</td><td>0.1%</td></tr>
<tr><td>18</td><td>Utah</td><td>128</td><td>1.6%</td><td>44</td><td>Alaska</td><td>7</td><td>0.1%</td></tr>
<tr><td>27</td><td>Vermont</td><td>71</td><td>0.9%</td><td>45</td><td>Louisiana</td><td>6</td><td>0.1%</td></tr>
<tr><td>23</td><td>Virginia</td><td>90</td><td>1.1%</td><td>45</td><td>Mississippi</td><td>6</td><td>0.1%</td></tr>
<tr><td>4</td><td>Washington</td><td>703</td><td>8.7%</td><td>45</td><td>North Dakota</td><td>6</td><td>0.1%</td></tr>
<tr><td>36</td><td>West Virginia</td><td>27</td><td>0.3%</td><td>48</td><td>Montana</td><td>5</td><td>0.1%</td></tr>
<tr><td>10</td><td>Wisconsin</td><td>215</td><td>2.7%</td><td>48</td><td>South Dakota</td><td>5</td><td>0.1%</td></tr>
<tr><td>16</td><td>Wyoming</td><td>130</td><td>1.6%</td><td>50</td><td>Illinois</td><td>0</td><td>0.0%</td></tr>
<tr><td></td><td></td><td></td><td></td><td></td><td>District of Columbia</td><td>3</td><td>0.0%</td></tr>
</table>

Source: U.S. Department of Health and Human Services, National Center for Health Statistics
"Morbidity and Mortality Weekly Report" (January 2, 2004, Vol. 52, Nos. 51 & 52)
*Provisional data. Acute, highly contagious infection of respiratory tract.

Whooping Cough (Pertussis) Rate in 2003

National Rate = 2.8 Cases per 100,000 Population*

<table>
<tr><td colspan="3"><u>ALPHA ORDER</u></td><td colspan="3"><u>RANK ORDER</u></td></tr>
<tr><td>RANK</td><td>STATE</td><td>RATE</td><td>RANK</td><td>STATE</td><td>RATE</td></tr>
<tr><td>46</td><td>Alabama</td><td>0.4</td><td>1</td><td>Wyoming</td><td>25.9</td></tr>
<tr><td>34</td><td>Alaska</td><td>1.1</td><td>2</td><td>Massachusetts</td><td>15.8</td></tr>
<tr><td>21</td><td>Arizona</td><td>2.3</td><td>3</td><td>Oregon</td><td>12.3</td></tr>
<tr><td>29</td><td>Arkansas</td><td>1.4</td><td>4</td><td>Vermont</td><td>11.5</td></tr>
<tr><td>22</td><td>California</td><td>2.1</td><td>4</td><td>Washington</td><td>11.5</td></tr>
<tr><td>6</td><td>Colorado</td><td>7.5</td><td>6</td><td>Colorado</td><td>7.5</td></tr>
<tr><td>42</td><td>Connecticut</td><td>0.7</td><td>7</td><td>Idaho</td><td>6.0</td></tr>
<tr><td>37</td><td>Delaware</td><td>1.0</td><td>8</td><td>Utah</td><td>5.4</td></tr>
<tr><td>42</td><td>Florida</td><td>0.7</td><td>9</td><td>Iowa</td><td>5.1</td></tr>
<tr><td>46</td><td>Georgia</td><td>0.4</td><td>10</td><td>New Hampshire</td><td>4.7</td></tr>
<tr><td>38</td><td>Hawaii</td><td>0.9</td><td>11</td><td>South Carolina</td><td>4.6</td></tr>
<tr><td>7</td><td>Idaho</td><td>6.0</td><td>12</td><td>New York</td><td>4.2</td></tr>
<tr><td>50</td><td>Illinois</td><td>0.0</td><td>13</td><td>Wisconsin</td><td>3.9</td></tr>
<tr><td>34</td><td>Indiana</td><td>1.1</td><td>14</td><td>New Mexico</td><td>3.7</td></tr>
<tr><td>9</td><td>Iowa</td><td>5.1</td><td>15</td><td>Missouri</td><td>3.0</td></tr>
<tr><td>24</td><td>Kansas</td><td>1.7</td><td>16</td><td>Minnesota</td><td>2.9</td></tr>
<tr><td>34</td><td>Kentucky</td><td>1.1</td><td>17</td><td>Ohio</td><td>2.8</td></tr>
<tr><td>49</td><td>Louisiana</td><td>0.1</td><td>18</td><td>Oklahoma</td><td>2.6</td></tr>
<tr><td>38</td><td>Maine</td><td>0.9</td><td>18</td><td>Pennsylvania</td><td>2.6</td></tr>
<tr><td>25</td><td>Maryland</td><td>1.6</td><td>20</td><td>Texas</td><td>2.5</td></tr>
<tr><td>2</td><td>Massachusetts</td><td>15.8</td><td>21</td><td>Arizona</td><td>2.3</td></tr>
<tr><td>30</td><td>Michigan</td><td>1.3</td><td>22</td><td>California</td><td>2.1</td></tr>
<tr><td>16</td><td>Minnesota</td><td>2.9</td><td>23</td><td>Rhode Island</td><td>1.9</td></tr>
<tr><td>48</td><td>Mississippi</td><td>0.2</td><td>24</td><td>Kansas</td><td>1.7</td></tr>
<tr><td>15</td><td>Missouri</td><td>3.0</td><td>25</td><td>Maryland</td><td>1.6</td></tr>
<tr><td>45</td><td>Montana</td><td>0.5</td><td>25</td><td>Nevada</td><td>1.6</td></tr>
<tr><td>38</td><td>Nebraska</td><td>0.9</td><td>25</td><td>North Carolina</td><td>1.6</td></tr>
<tr><td>25</td><td>Nevada</td><td>1.6</td><td>28</td><td>West Virginia</td><td>1.5</td></tr>
<tr><td>10</td><td>New Hampshire</td><td>4.7</td><td>29</td><td>Arkansas</td><td>1.4</td></tr>
<tr><td>32</td><td>New Jersey</td><td>1.2</td><td>30</td><td>Michigan</td><td>1.3</td></tr>
<tr><td>14</td><td>New Mexico</td><td>3.7</td><td>30</td><td>Tennessee</td><td>1.3</td></tr>
<tr><td>12</td><td>New York</td><td>4.2</td><td>32</td><td>New Jersey</td><td>1.2</td></tr>
<tr><td>25</td><td>North Carolina</td><td>1.6</td><td>32</td><td>Virginia</td><td>1.2</td></tr>
<tr><td>38</td><td>North Dakota</td><td>0.9</td><td>34</td><td>Alaska</td><td>1.1</td></tr>
<tr><td>17</td><td>Ohio</td><td>2.8</td><td>34</td><td>Indiana</td><td>1.1</td></tr>
<tr><td>18</td><td>Oklahoma</td><td>2.6</td><td>34</td><td>Kentucky</td><td>1.1</td></tr>
<tr><td>3</td><td>Oregon</td><td>12.3</td><td>37</td><td>Delaware</td><td>1.0</td></tr>
<tr><td>18</td><td>Pennsylvania</td><td>2.6</td><td>38</td><td>Hawaii</td><td>0.9</td></tr>
<tr><td>23</td><td>Rhode Island</td><td>1.9</td><td>38</td><td>Maine</td><td>0.9</td></tr>
<tr><td>11</td><td>South Carolina</td><td>4.6</td><td>38</td><td>Nebraska</td><td>0.9</td></tr>
<tr><td>42</td><td>South Dakota</td><td>0.7</td><td>38</td><td>North Dakota</td><td>0.9</td></tr>
<tr><td>30</td><td>Tennessee</td><td>1.3</td><td>42</td><td>Connecticut</td><td>0.7</td></tr>
<tr><td>20</td><td>Texas</td><td>2.5</td><td>42</td><td>Florida</td><td>0.7</td></tr>
<tr><td>8</td><td>Utah</td><td>5.4</td><td>42</td><td>South Dakota</td><td>0.7</td></tr>
<tr><td>4</td><td>Vermont</td><td>11.5</td><td>45</td><td>Montana</td><td>0.5</td></tr>
<tr><td>32</td><td>Virginia</td><td>1.2</td><td>46</td><td>Alabama</td><td>0.4</td></tr>
<tr><td>4</td><td>Washington</td><td>11.5</td><td>46</td><td>Georgia</td><td>0.4</td></tr>
<tr><td>28</td><td>West Virginia</td><td>1.5</td><td>48</td><td>Mississippi</td><td>0.2</td></tr>
<tr><td>13</td><td>Wisconsin</td><td>3.9</td><td>49</td><td>Louisiana</td><td>0.1</td></tr>
<tr><td>1</td><td>Wyoming</td><td>25.9</td><td>50</td><td>Illinois</td><td>0.0</td></tr>
<tr><td></td><td></td><td></td><td></td><td>District of Columbia</td><td>0.5</td></tr>
</table>

Source: Morgan Quitno Press using data from U.S. Dept. of Health & Human Serv's, National Center for Health Statistics
    "Morbidity and Mortality Weekly Report" (January 2, 2004, Vol. 52, Nos. 51 & 52)
*Provisional data. Acute, highly contagious infection of respiratory tract.

Percent of Children Aged 19 to 35 Months Immunized in 2002

National Percent = 77.5%*

RANK	STATE	PERCENT
21	Alabama	79.5
27	Alaska	78.3
46	Arizona	69.5
39	Arkansas	74.4
37	California	75.8
50	Colorado	64.3
6	Connecticut	85.7
13	Delaware	81.1
32	Florida	77.2
9	Georgia	82.0
14	Hawaii	80.9
41	Idaho	73.3
20	Illinois	79.6
28	Indiana	77.9
18	Iowa	79.7
43	Kansas	72.9
39	Kentucky	74.4
47	Louisiana	69.3
8	Maine	82.8
15	Maryland	80.8
1	Massachusetts	89.2
7	Michigan	83.8
24	Minnesota	78.9
29	Mississippi	77.8
31	Missouri	77.3
44	Montana	70.9
22	Nebraska	79.2
29	Nevada	77.8
2	New Hampshire	87.3
16	New Jersey	80.4
48	New Mexico	67.4
11	New York	81.3
4	North Carolina	86.5
25	North Dakota	78.8
33	Ohio	77.1
49	Oklahoma	66.7
38	Oregon	74.5
33	Pennsylvania	77.1
5	Rhode Island	85.8
17	South Carolina	80.2
12	South Dakota	81.2
18	Tennessee	79.7
44	Texas	70.9
23	Utah	79.1
3	Vermont	87.0
35	Virginia	76.6
42	Washington	73.1
26	West Virginia	78.5
10	Wisconsin	81.8
36	Wyoming	76.5

RANK	STATE	PERCENT
1	Massachusetts	89.2
2	New Hampshire	87.3
3	Vermont	87.0
4	North Carolina	86.5
5	Rhode Island	85.8
6	Connecticut	85.7
7	Michigan	83.8
8	Maine	82.8
9	Georgia	82.0
10	Wisconsin	81.8
11	New York	81.3
12	South Dakota	81.2
13	Delaware	81.1
14	Hawaii	80.9
15	Maryland	80.8
16	New Jersey	80.4
17	South Carolina	80.2
18	Iowa	79.7
18	Tennessee	79.7
20	Illinois	79.6
21	Alabama	79.5
22	Nebraska	79.2
23	Utah	79.1
24	Minnesota	78.9
25	North Dakota	78.8
26	West Virginia	78.5
27	Alaska	78.3
28	Indiana	77.9
29	Mississippi	77.8
29	Nevada	77.8
31	Missouri	77.3
32	Florida	77.2
33	Ohio	77.1
33	Pennsylvania	77.1
35	Virginia	76.6
36	Wyoming	76.5
37	California	75.8
38	Oregon	74.5
39	Arkansas	74.4
39	Kentucky	74.4
41	Idaho	73.3
42	Washington	73.1
43	Kansas	72.9
44	Montana	70.9
44	Texas	70.9
46	Arizona	69.5
47	Louisiana	69.3
48	New Mexico	67.4
49	Oklahoma	66.7
50	Colorado	64.3

	District of Columbia	72.2

Source: U.S. Department of Health and Human Services, Centers for Disease Control and Prevention
"State Vaccination Coverage Levels" (Morbidity and Mortality Weekly Report, Vol. 52, No. 31, August 8, 2003)
This table is consistent with previous tables showing "fully" immunized children. Figures here are for the 4:3:1:3 series. Children received four doses of DTP/DT/DTaP (Diphtheria, Tetanus, Pertussis (Whooping Cough), Acellular Pertussis), three doses of OPV (Oral Poliovirus Vaccine), one dose of MCV (Measles-Containing Vaccine) and three doses of Hib (Haemophilus influenzae type b). Hepatitis B and Varicella vaccines are not included in this series.

Percent of Children Aged 19 to 35 Months Fully Immunized in 2002

National Percent = 65.5%*

ALPHA ORDER

RANK	STATE	PERCENT
5	Alabama	73.3
44	Alaska	56.2
39	Arizona	59.0
12	Arkansas	68.3
17	California	67.1
45	Colorado	56.1
6	Connecticut	72.8
9	Delaware	69.7
18	Florida	66.4
3	Georgia	76.5
11	Hawaii	69.1
48	Idaho	52.6
41	Illinois	58.1
37	Indiana	59.4
40	Iowa	58.2
46	Kansas	55.1
27	Kentucky	63.6
31	Louisiana	61.9
29	Maine	62.1
8	Maryland	70.7
2	Massachusetts	78.0
7	Michigan	71.7
32	Minnesota	61.5
26	Mississippi	63.9
36	Missouri	60.1
50	Montana	49.4
25	Nebraska	64.3
22	Nevada	65.3
19	New Hampshire	66.2
21	New Jersey	65.5
38	New Mexico	59.1
15	New York	67.3
9	North Carolina	69.7
43	North Dakota	56.3
28	Ohio	63.5
34	Oklahoma	60.3
34	Oregon	60.3
13	Pennsylvania	67.6
1	Rhode Island	80.7
4	South Carolina	73.8
30	South Dakota	62.0
15	Tennessee	67.3
23	Texas	65.0
33	Utah	61.4
42	Vermont	57.7
24	Virginia	64.8
49	Washington	51.9
20	West Virginia	65.8
14	Wisconsin	67.5
47	Wyoming	54.1

RANK ORDER

RANK	STATE	PERCENT
1	Rhode Island	80.7
2	Massachusetts	78.0
3	Georgia	76.5
4	South Carolina	73.8
5	Alabama	73.3
6	Connecticut	72.8
7	Michigan	71.7
8	Maryland	70.7
9	Delaware	69.7
9	North Carolina	69.7
11	Hawaii	69.1
12	Arkansas	68.3
13	Pennsylvania	67.6
14	Wisconsin	67.5
15	New York	67.3
15	Tennessee	67.3
17	California	67.1
18	Florida	66.4
19	New Hampshire	66.2
20	West Virginia	65.8
21	New Jersey	65.5
22	Nevada	65.3
23	Texas	65.0
24	Virginia	64.8
25	Nebraska	64.3
26	Mississippi	63.9
27	Kentucky	63.6
28	Ohio	63.5
29	Maine	62.1
30	South Dakota	62.0
31	Louisiana	61.9
32	Minnesota	61.5
33	Utah	61.4
34	Oklahoma	60.3
34	Oregon	60.3
36	Missouri	60.1
37	Indiana	59.4
38	New Mexico	59.1
39	Arizona	59.0
40	Iowa	58.2
41	Illinois	58.1
42	Vermont	57.7
43	North Dakota	56.3
44	Alaska	56.2
45	Colorado	56.1
46	Kansas	55.1
47	Wyoming	54.1
48	Idaho	52.6
49	Washington	51.9
50	Montana	49.4

| | District of Columbia | 68.3 |

Source: U.S. Department of Health and Human Services, Centers for Disease Control and Prevention
"State Vaccination Coverage Levels" (Morbidity and Mortality Weekly Report, Vol. 52, No. 31, August 8, 2003)
*Fully immunized (4:3:1:3:3:1 series) children received four doses of DTP/DT/DTaP (Diphtheria, Tetanus, Pertussis (Whooping Cough), Acellular Pertussis), three doses of OPV (Oral Poliovirus Vaccine), one dose of MCV (Measles-Containing Vaccine), three doses of Hib (Haemophilus influenzae type b), three doses of Hepatitis B vaccine and one dose of Varicella (chickenpox) vaccine. This differs from previous "fully" immunized tables.

Percent of Adults Aged 65 Years and Older Who Received Flu Shots in 2002

National Median = 68.4%*

ALPHA ORDER

RANK	STATE	PERCENT
42	Alabama	64.8
22	Alaska	69.5
21	Arizona	69.7
25	Arkansas	69.0
15	California	71.5
10	Colorado	73.3
17	Connecticut	71.4
15	Delaware	71.5
50	Florida	57.0
48	Georgia	59.3
4	Hawaii	73.9
40	Idaho	65.1
45	Illinois	61.1
35	Indiana	66.3
9	Iowa	73.5
27	Kansas	68.6
38	Kentucky	65.7
49	Louisiana	57.3
6	Maine	73.8
36	Maryland	65.9
12	Massachusetts	72.6
31	Michigan	67.7
1	Minnesota	76.6
44	Mississippi	63.0
26	Missouri	68.7
32	Montana	67.6
28	Nebraska	68.2
47	Nevada	60.3
13	New Hampshire	72.3
24	New Jersey	69.1
33	New Mexico	66.6
43	New York	64.7
29	North Carolina	68.1
4	North Dakota	73.9
33	Ohio	66.6
11	Oklahoma	72.7
30	Oregon	68.0
20	Pennsylvania	70.5
7	Rhode Island	73.7
23	South Carolina	69.4
2	South Dakota	74.2
14	Tennessee	71.6
46	Texas	61.0
18	Utah	71.1
8	Vermont	73.6
39	Virginia	65.3
40	Washington	65.1
37	West Virginia	65.8
3	Wisconsin	74.0
19	Wyoming	70.6

RANK ORDER

RANK	STATE	PERCENT
1	Minnesota	76.6
2	South Dakota	74.2
3	Wisconsin	74.0
4	Hawaii	73.9
4	North Dakota	73.9
6	Maine	73.8
7	Rhode Island	73.7
8	Vermont	73.6
9	Iowa	73.5
10	Colorado	73.3
11	Oklahoma	72.7
12	Massachusetts	72.6
13	New Hampshire	72.3
14	Tennessee	71.6
15	California	71.5
15	Delaware	71.5
17	Connecticut	71.4
18	Utah	71.1
19	Wyoming	70.6
20	Pennsylvania	70.5
21	Arizona	69.7
22	Alaska	69.5
23	South Carolina	69.4
24	New Jersey	69.1
25	Arkansas	69.0
26	Missouri	68.7
27	Kansas	68.6
28	Nebraska	68.2
29	North Carolina	68.1
30	Oregon	68.0
31	Michigan	67.7
32	Montana	67.6
33	New Mexico	66.6
33	Ohio	66.6
35	Indiana	66.3
36	Maryland	65.9
37	West Virginia	65.8
38	Kentucky	65.7
39	Virginia	65.3
40	Idaho	65.1
40	Washington	65.1
42	Alabama	64.8
43	New York	64.7
44	Mississippi	63.0
45	Illinois	61.1
46	Texas	61.0
47	Nevada	60.3
48	Georgia	59.3
49	Louisiana	57.3
50	Florida	57.0

District of Columbia	58.7

Source: U.S. Department of Health and Human Services, National Center for Health Statistics
"Morbidity and Mortality Weekly Report" (October 17, 2003, Vol. 52, No. 41)
*Percent of adults 65 years old and older who reported receiving influenza vaccine during the preceding 12 months.

Sexually Transmitted Diseases in 2002

National Total = 1,193,336 Cases*

ALPHA ORDER

RANK	STATE	CASES	% of USA
14	Alabama	25,878	2.2%
38	Alaska	4,447	0.4%
21	Arizona	18,968	1.6%
30	Arkansas	11,930	1.0%
1	California	135,929	11.4%
24	Colorado	17,603	1.5%
28	Connecticut	13,077	1.1%
39	Delaware	4,236	0.4%
5	Florida	64,030	5.4%
7	Georgia	52,820	4.4%
37	Hawaii	5,272	0.4%
43	Idaho	2,605	0.2%
4	Illinois	72,606	6.1%
17	Indiana	24,557	2.1%
35	Iowa	7,683	0.6%
31	Kansas	9,548	0.8%
29	Kentucky	12,616	1.1%
11	Louisiana	29,983	2.5%
46	Maine	1,949	0.2%
13	Maryland	26,474	2.2%
26	Massachusetts	14,258	1.2%
8	Michigan	47,528	4.0%
27	Minnesota	13,215	1.1%
22	Mississippi	18,724	1.6%
16	Missouri	25,167	2.1%
44	Montana	2,598	0.2%
36	Nebraska	6,349	0.5%
34	Nevada	7,939	0.7%
47	New Hampshire	1,685	0.1%
20	New Jersey	22,227	1.9%
32	New Mexico	8,918	0.7%
3	New York	73,444	6.2%
10	North Carolina	40,536	3.4%
48	North Dakota	1,328	0.1%
6	Ohio	60,199	5.0%
25	Oklahoma	15,537	1.3%
33	Oregon	7,946	0.7%
9	Pennsylvania	45,190	3.8%
41	Rhode Island	3,745	0.3%
18	South Carolina	23,643	2.0%
45	South Dakota	2,478	0.2%
15	Tennessee	25,558	2.1%
2	Texas	97,103	8.1%
40	Utah	3,921	0.3%
49	Vermont	1,054	0.1%
12	Virginia	29,052	2.4%
23	Washington	17,930	1.5%
42	West Virginia	3,440	0.3%
19	Wisconsin	23,372	2.0%
50	Wyoming	1,009	0.1%

RANK ORDER

RANK	STATE	CASES	% of USA
1	California	135,929	11.4%
2	Texas	97,103	8.1%
3	New York	73,444	6.2%
4	Illinois	72,606	6.1%
5	Florida	64,030	5.4%
6	Ohio	60,199	5.0%
7	Georgia	52,820	4.4%
8	Michigan	47,528	4.0%
9	Pennsylvania	45,190	3.8%
10	North Carolina	40,536	3.4%
11	Louisiana	29,983	2.5%
12	Virginia	29,052	2.4%
13	Maryland	26,474	2.2%
14	Alabama	25,878	2.2%
15	Tennessee	25,558	2.1%
16	Missouri	25,167	2.1%
17	Indiana	24,557	2.1%
18	South Carolina	23,643	2.0%
19	Wisconsin	23,372	2.0%
20	New Jersey	22,227	1.9%
21	Arizona	18,968	1.6%
22	Mississippi	18,724	1.6%
23	Washington	17,930	1.5%
24	Colorado	17,603	1.5%
25	Oklahoma	15,537	1.3%
26	Massachusetts	14,258	1.2%
27	Minnesota	13,215	1.1%
28	Connecticut	13,077	1.1%
29	Kentucky	12,616	1.1%
30	Arkansas	11,930	1.0%
31	Kansas	9,548	0.8%
32	New Mexico	8,918	0.7%
33	Oregon	7,946	0.7%
34	Nevada	7,939	0.7%
35	Iowa	7,683	0.6%
36	Nebraska	6,349	0.5%
37	Hawaii	5,272	0.4%
38	Alaska	4,447	0.4%
39	Delaware	4,236	0.4%
40	Utah	3,921	0.3%
41	Rhode Island	3,745	0.3%
42	West Virginia	3,440	0.3%
43	Idaho	2,605	0.2%
44	Montana	2,598	0.2%
45	South Dakota	2,478	0.2%
46	Maine	1,949	0.2%
47	New Hampshire	1,685	0.1%
48	North Dakota	1,328	0.1%
49	Vermont	1,054	0.1%
50	Wyoming	1,009	0.1%
	District of Columbia	6,032	0.5%

Source: Morgan Quitno Press using data from U.S. Dept. of Health and Human Services, Nat'l Center for Health Statistics "Sexually Transmitted Disease Surveillance 2002" (http://www.cdc.gov/std/stats/TOC2002.htm)
*Includes chancroid, chlamydia, gonorrhea and primary and secondary syphilis.

Sexually Transmitted Disease Rate in 2002

National Rate = 423.9 Cases per 100,000 Population*

ALPHA ORDER

RANK	STATE	RATE
7	Alabama	581.9
1	Alaska	709.3
30	Arizona	369.7
18	Arkansas	446.3
24	California	401.2
22	Colorado	409.2
28	Connecticut	384.0
8	Delaware	540.6
25	Florida	400.7
4	Georgia	645.3
20	Hawaii	435.2
45	Idaho	201.3
6	Illinois	584.7
23	Indiana	403.8
40	Iowa	262.6
33	Kansas	355.1
35	Kentucky	312.1
2	Louisiana	670.9
49	Maine	152.9
11	Maryland	499.8
42	Massachusetts	224.6
13	Michigan	478.2
38	Minnesota	268.6
3	Mississippi	658.2
16	Missouri	449.8
37	Montana	287.9
29	Nebraska	371.1
26	Nevada	397.4
50	New Hampshire	136.3
39	New Jersey	264.1
12	New Mexico	490.2
27	New York	387.0
10	North Carolina	503.6
43	North Dakota	206.8
9	Ohio	530.2
15	Oklahoma	450.3
41	Oregon	232.3
31	Pennsylvania	368.0
32	Rhode Island	357.2
5	South Carolina	589.3
34	South Dakota	328.2
17	Tennessee	449.3
14	Texas	465.6
47	Utah	175.5
48	Vermont	173.1
21	Virginia	410.4
36	Washington	304.2
46	West Virginia	190.3
19	Wisconsin	435.7
44	Wyoming	204.4

RANK ORDER

RANK	STATE	RATE
1	Alaska	709.3
2	Louisiana	670.9
3	Mississippi	658.2
4	Georgia	645.3
5	South Carolina	589.3
6	Illinois	584.7
7	Alabama	581.9
8	Delaware	540.6
9	Ohio	530.2
10	North Carolina	503.6
11	Maryland	499.8
12	New Mexico	490.2
13	Michigan	478.2
14	Texas	465.6
15	Oklahoma	450.3
16	Missouri	449.8
17	Tennessee	449.3
18	Arkansas	446.3
19	Wisconsin	435.7
20	Hawaii	435.2
21	Virginia	410.4
22	Colorado	409.2
23	Indiana	403.8
24	California	401.2
25	Florida	400.7
26	Nevada	397.4
27	New York	387.0
28	Connecticut	384.0
29	Nebraska	371.1
30	Arizona	369.7
31	Pennsylvania	368.0
32	Rhode Island	357.2
33	Kansas	355.1
34	South Dakota	328.2
35	Kentucky	312.1
36	Washington	304.2
37	Montana	287.9
38	Minnesota	268.6
39	New Jersey	264.1
40	Iowa	262.6
41	Oregon	232.3
42	Massachusetts	224.6
43	North Dakota	206.8
44	Wyoming	204.4
45	Idaho	201.3
46	West Virginia	190.3
47	Utah	175.5
48	Vermont	173.1
49	Maine	152.9
50	New Hampshire	136.3

District of Columbia — 1,059.8

Source: Morgan Quitno Press using data from U.S. Dept. of Health and Human Services, Nat'l Center for Health Statistics
"Sexually Transmitted Disease Surveillance 2002" (http://www.cdc.gov/std/stats/TOC2002.htm)
*Includes chancroid, chlamydia, gonorrhea and primary and secondary syphilis.

Chlamydia Cases Reported in 2002

National Total = 834,555 Cases*

ALPHA ORDER

RANK	STATE	CASES	% of USA
18	Alabama	15,611	1.9%
38	Alaska	3,806	0.5%
19	Arizona	14,973	1.8%
31	Arkansas	7,312	0.9%
1	California	110,288	13.2%
23	Colorado	14,028	1.7%
28	Connecticut	9,808	1.2%
41	Delaware	2,649	0.3%
5	Florida	42,058	5.0%
7	Georgia	33,998	4.1%
37	Hawaii	4,521	0.5%
42	Idaho	2,503	0.3%
4	Illinois	48,101	5.8%
13	Indiana	17,100	2.0%
34	Iowa	6,195	0.7%
33	Kansas	6,784	0.8%
29	Kentucky	8,756	1.0%
12	Louisiana	18,442	2.2%
46	Maine	1,805	0.2%
15	Maryland	16,891	2.0%
25	Massachusetts	10,914	1.3%
8	Michigan	32,272	3.9%
27	Minnesota	10,107	1.2%
24	Mississippi	11,800	1.4%
16	Missouri	16,181	1.9%
43	Montana	2,475	0.3%
36	Nebraska	4,779	0.6%
35	Nevada	5,936	0.7%
47	New Hampshire	1,557	0.2%
22	New Jersey	14,164	1.7%
30	New Mexico	7,417	0.9%
3	New York	51,123	6.1%
10	North Carolina	24,726	3.0%
48	North Dakota	1,256	0.2%
6	Ohio	38,032	4.6%
26	Oklahoma	10,804	1.3%
32	Oregon	7,009	0.8%
9	Pennsylvania	31,791	3.8%
40	Rhode Island	2,832	0.3%
21	South Carolina	14,314	1.7%
45	South Dakota	2,215	0.3%
17	Tennessee	16,042	1.9%
2	Texas	69,521	8.3%
39	Utah	3,540	0.4%
49	Vermont	954	0.1%
11	Virginia	18,518	2.2%
20	Washington	14,934	1.8%
44	West Virginia	2,464	0.3%
14	Wisconsin	17,000	2.0%
50	Wyoming	944	0.1%

RANK ORDER

RANK	STATE	CASES	% of USA
1	California	110,288	13.2%
2	Texas	69,521	8.3%
3	New York	51,123	6.1%
4	Illinois	48,101	5.8%
5	Florida	42,058	5.0%
6	Ohio	38,032	4.6%
7	Georgia	33,998	4.1%
8	Michigan	32,272	3.9%
9	Pennsylvania	31,791	3.8%
10	North Carolina	24,726	3.0%
11	Virginia	18,518	2.2%
12	Louisiana	18,442	2.2%
13	Indiana	17,100	2.0%
14	Wisconsin	17,000	2.0%
15	Maryland	16,891	2.0%
16	Missouri	16,181	1.9%
17	Tennessee	16,042	1.9%
18	Alabama	15,611	1.9%
19	Arizona	14,973	1.8%
20	Washington	14,934	1.8%
21	South Carolina	14,314	1.7%
22	New Jersey	14,164	1.7%
23	Colorado	14,028	1.7%
24	Mississippi	11,800	1.4%
25	Massachusetts	10,914	1.3%
26	Oklahoma	10,804	1.3%
27	Minnesota	10,107	1.2%
28	Connecticut	9,808	1.2%
29	Kentucky	8,756	1.0%
30	New Mexico	7,417	0.9%
31	Arkansas	7,312	0.9%
32	Oregon	7,009	0.8%
33	Kansas	6,784	0.8%
34	Iowa	6,195	0.7%
35	Nevada	5,936	0.7%
36	Nebraska	4,779	0.6%
37	Hawaii	4,521	0.5%
38	Alaska	3,806	0.5%
39	Utah	3,540	0.4%
40	Rhode Island	2,832	0.3%
41	Delaware	2,649	0.3%
42	Idaho	2,503	0.3%
43	Montana	2,475	0.3%
44	West Virginia	2,464	0.3%
45	South Dakota	2,215	0.3%
46	Maine	1,805	0.2%
47	New Hampshire	1,557	0.2%
48	North Dakota	1,256	0.2%
49	Vermont	954	0.1%
50	Wyoming	944	0.1%
	District of Columbia	3,305	0.4%

Source: U.S. Department of Health and Human Services, National Center for Health Statistics
    "Sexually Transmitted Disease Surveillance 2002" (http://www.cdc.gov/std/stats/TOC2002.htm)
Any of several common, often asymptomatic, sexually transmitted diseases caused by the microorganism Chlamydia trachomatis, including nonspecific urethritis in men.

Chlamydia Rate in 2002

National Rate = 296.5 Cases per 100,000 Population*

ALPHA ORDER

RANK	STATE	RATE
9	Alabama	351.0
1	Alaska	607.1
22	Arizona	291.8
29	Arkansas	273.5
14	California	325.6
13	Colorado	326.1
24	Connecticut	288.0
10	Delaware	338.1
32	Florida	263.2
2	Georgia	415.3
7	Hawaii	373.2
42	Idaho	193.4
6	Illinois	387.3
26	Indiana	281.2
38	Iowa	211.7
36	Kansas	252.3
37	Kentucky	216.6
4	Louisiana	412.7
48	Maine	141.6
16	Maryland	318.9
44	Massachusetts	171.9
15	Michigan	324.7
39	Minnesota	205.4
3	Mississippi	414.8
23	Missouri	289.2
28	Montana	274.3
27	Nebraska	279.3
20	Nevada	297.1
50	New Hampshire	126.0
45	New Jersey	168.3
5	New Mexico	407.7
31	New York	269.4
19	North Carolina	307.2
41	North Dakota	195.6
11	Ohio	335.0
18	Oklahoma	313.1
40	Oregon	204.9
34	Pennsylvania	258.9
30	Rhode Island	270.1
8	South Carolina	356.8
21	South Dakota	293.4
25	Tennessee	282.0
12	Texas	333.4
46	Utah	158.5
47	Vermont	156.7
33	Virginia	261.6
35	Washington	253.4
49	West Virginia	136.3
17	Wisconsin	316.9
43	Wyoming	191.2

RANK ORDER

RANK	STATE	RATE
1	Alaska	607.1
2	Georgia	415.3
3	Mississippi	414.8
4	Louisiana	412.7
5	New Mexico	407.7
6	Illinois	387.3
7	Hawaii	373.2
8	South Carolina	356.8
9	Alabama	351.0
10	Delaware	338.1
11	Ohio	335.0
12	Texas	333.4
13	Colorado	326.1
14	California	325.6
15	Michigan	324.7
16	Maryland	318.9
17	Wisconsin	316.9
18	Oklahoma	313.1
19	North Carolina	307.2
20	Nevada	297.1
21	South Dakota	293.4
22	Arizona	291.8
23	Missouri	289.2
24	Connecticut	288.0
25	Tennessee	282.0
26	Indiana	281.2
27	Nebraska	279.3
28	Montana	274.3
29	Arkansas	273.5
30	Rhode Island	270.1
31	New York	269.4
32	Florida	263.2
33	Virginia	261.6
34	Pennsylvania	258.9
35	Washington	253.4
36	Kansas	252.3
37	Kentucky	216.6
38	Iowa	211.7
39	Minnesota	205.4
40	Oregon	204.9
41	North Dakota	195.6
42	Idaho	193.4
43	Wyoming	191.2
44	Massachusetts	171.9
45	New Jersey	168.3
46	Utah	158.5
47	Vermont	156.7
48	Maine	141.6
49	West Virginia	136.3
50	New Hampshire	126.0

District of Columbia 580.7

Source: U.S. Department of Health and Human Services, National Center for Health Statistics
   "Sexually Transmitted Disease Surveillance 2002" (http://www.cdc.gov/std/stats/TOC2002.htm)
Any of several common, often asymptomatic, sexually transmitted diseases caused by the microorganism Chlamydia trachomatis, including nonspecific urethritis in men.

Gonorrhea Cases Reported in 2002

National Total = 351,852 Cases*

ALPHA ORDER

RANK	STATE	CASES	% of USA
13	Alabama	10,118	2.9%
41	Alaska	641	0.2%
24	Arizona	3,795	1.1%
23	Arkansas	4,584	1.3%
2	California	24,606	7.0%
26	Colorado	3,511	1.0%
28	Connecticut	3,241	0.9%
33	Delaware	1,576	0.4%
6	Florida	21,348	6.1%
7	Georgia	18,383	5.2%
40	Hawaii	740	0.2%
48	Idaho	94	0.0%
3	Illinois	24,026	6.8%
19	Indiana	7,395	2.1%
35	Iowa	1,480	0.4%
31	Kansas	2,744	0.8%
25	Kentucky	3,772	1.1%
11	Louisiana	11,387	3.2%
44	Maine	142	0.0%
14	Maryland	9,355	2.7%
27	Massachusetts	3,242	0.9%
9	Michigan	14,770	4.2%
29	Minnesota	3,049	0.9%
20	Mississippi	6,875	2.0%
17	Missouri	8,952	2.5%
45	Montana	123	0.0%
34	Nebraska	1,564	0.4%
32	Nevada	1,988	0.6%
46	New Hampshire	120	0.0%
18	New Jersey	7,894	2.2%
36	New Mexico	1,462	0.4%
5	New York	21,841	6.2%
8	North Carolina	15,531	4.4%
49	North Dakota	72	0.0%
4	Ohio	22,008	6.3%
22	Oklahoma	4,661	1.3%
38	Oregon	909	0.3%
10	Pennsylvania	13,294	3.8%
39	Rhode Island	900	0.3%
16	South Carolina	9,152	2.6%
43	South Dakota	263	0.1%
15	Tennessee	9,348	2.7%
1	Texas	26,988	7.7%
42	Utah	374	0.1%
47	Vermont	98	0.0%
12	Virginia	10,462	3.0%
30	Washington	2,925	0.8%
37	West Virginia	974	0.3%
21	Wisconsin	6,341	1.8%
50	Wyoming	65	0.0%

RANK ORDER

RANK	STATE	CASES	% of USA
1	Texas	26,988	7.7%
2	California	24,606	7.0%
3	Illinois	24,026	6.8%
4	Ohio	22,008	6.3%
5	New York	21,841	6.2%
6	Florida	21,348	6.1%
7	Georgia	18,383	5.2%
8	North Carolina	15,531	4.4%
9	Michigan	14,770	4.2%
10	Pennsylvania	13,294	3.8%
11	Louisiana	11,387	3.2%
12	Virginia	10,462	3.0%
13	Alabama	10,118	2.9%
14	Maryland	9,355	2.7%
15	Tennessee	9,348	2.7%
16	South Carolina	9,152	2.6%
17	Missouri	8,952	2.5%
18	New Jersey	7,894	2.2%
19	Indiana	7,395	2.1%
20	Mississippi	6,875	2.0%
21	Wisconsin	6,341	1.8%
22	Oklahoma	4,661	1.3%
23	Arkansas	4,584	1.3%
24	Arizona	3,795	1.1%
25	Kentucky	3,772	1.1%
26	Colorado	3,511	1.0%
27	Massachusetts	3,242	0.9%
28	Connecticut	3,241	0.9%
29	Minnesota	3,049	0.9%
30	Washington	2,925	0.8%
31	Kansas	2,744	0.8%
32	Nevada	1,988	0.6%
33	Delaware	1,576	0.4%
34	Nebraska	1,564	0.4%
35	Iowa	1,480	0.4%
36	New Mexico	1,462	0.4%
37	West Virginia	974	0.3%
38	Oregon	909	0.3%
39	Rhode Island	900	0.3%
40	Hawaii	740	0.2%
41	Alaska	641	0.2%
42	Utah	374	0.1%
43	South Dakota	263	0.1%
44	Maine	142	0.0%
45	Montana	123	0.0%
46	New Hampshire	120	0.0%
47	Vermont	98	0.0%
48	Idaho	94	0.0%
49	North Dakota	72	0.0%
50	Wyoming	65	0.0%
	District of Columbia	2,669	0.8%

Source: U.S. Department of Health and Human Services, National Center for Health Statistics
"Sexually Transmitted Disease Surveillance 2002" (http://www.cdc.gov/std/stats/TOC2002.htm)
*Gonorrhea is a sexually transmitted disease caused by gonococcal bacteria that affects the mucous membrane chiefly of the genital and urinary tracts and is characterized by an acute purulent discharge and painful or difficult urination, though women often have no symptoms.

Gonorrhea Rate in 2002

National Rate = 125.0 Cases per 100,000 Population*

ALPHA ORDER

RANK	STATE	RATE
4	Alabama	227.5
23	Alaska	102.2
33	Arizona	74.0
11	Arkansas	171.5
34	California	72.6
31	Colorado	81.6
26	Connecticut	95.2
6	Delaware	201.1
17	Florida	133.6
5	Georgia	224.6
36	Hawaii	61.1
50	Idaho	7.3
8	Illinois	193.5
19	Indiana	121.6
39	Iowa	50.6
24	Kansas	102.1
28	Kentucky	93.3
1	Louisiana	254.8
48	Maine	11.1
10	Maryland	176.6
38	Massachusetts	51.1
14	Michigan	148.6
35	Minnesota	62.0
2	Mississippi	241.7
13	Missouri	160.0
45	Montana	13.6
29	Nebraska	91.4
25	Nevada	99.5
49	New Hampshire	9.7
27	New Jersey	93.8
32	New Mexico	80.4
21	New York	115.1
9	North Carolina	192.9
47	North Dakota	11.2
7	Ohio	193.8
16	Oklahoma	135.1
42	Oregon	26.6
22	Pennsylvania	108.2
30	Rhode Island	85.9
3	South Carolina	228.1
41	South Dakota	34.8
12	Tennessee	164.3
18	Texas	129.4
43	Utah	16.7
44	Vermont	16.1
15	Virginia	147.8
40	Washington	49.6
37	West Virginia	53.9
20	Wisconsin	118.2
46	Wyoming	13.2

RANK ORDER

RANK	STATE	RATE
1	Louisiana	254.8
2	Mississippi	241.7
3	South Carolina	228.1
4	Alabama	227.5
5	Georgia	224.6
6	Delaware	201.1
7	Ohio	193.8
8	Illinois	193.5
9	North Carolina	192.9
10	Maryland	176.6
11	Arkansas	171.5
12	Tennessee	164.3
13	Missouri	160.0
14	Michigan	148.6
15	Virginia	147.8
16	Oklahoma	135.1
17	Florida	133.6
18	Texas	129.4
19	Indiana	121.6
20	Wisconsin	118.2
21	New York	115.1
22	Pennsylvania	108.2
23	Alaska	102.2
24	Kansas	102.1
25	Nevada	99.5
26	Connecticut	95.2
27	New Jersey	93.8
28	Kentucky	93.3
29	Nebraska	91.4
30	Rhode Island	85.9
31	Colorado	81.6
32	New Mexico	80.4
33	Arizona	74.0
34	California	72.6
35	Minnesota	62.0
36	Hawaii	61.1
37	West Virginia	53.9
38	Massachusetts	51.1
39	Iowa	50.6
40	Washington	49.6
41	South Dakota	34.8
42	Oregon	26.6
43	Utah	16.7
44	Vermont	16.1
45	Montana	13.6
46	Wyoming	13.2
47	North Dakota	11.2
48	Maine	11.1
49	New Hampshire	9.7
50	Idaho	7.3

District of Columbia	468.9

Source: U.S. Department of Health and Human Services, National Center for Health Statistics
    "Sexually Transmitted Disease Surveillance 2002" (http://www.cdc.gov/std/stats/TOC2002.htm)
*Gonorrhea is a sexually transmitted disease caused by gonococcal bacteria that affects the mucous membrane
chiefly of the genital and urinary tracts and is characterized by an acute purulent discharge and painful or difficult
urination, though women often have no symptoms.*

Syphilis Cases Reported in 2002

National Total = 6,862 Cases*

ALPHA ORDER

RANK	STATE	CASES	% of USA
15	Alabama	149	2.2%
46	Alaska	0	0.0%
10	Arizona	200	2.9%
28	Arkansas	34	0.5%
1	California	1,033	15.1%
23	Colorado	64	0.9%
31	Connecticut	28	0.4%
36	Delaware	11	0.2%
2	Florida	617	9.0%
7	Georgia	439	6.4%
36	Hawaii	11	0.2%
38	Idaho	8	0.1%
5	Illinois	479	7.0%
24	Indiana	62	0.9%
38	Iowa	8	0.1%
33	Kansas	20	0.3%
19	Kentucky	88	1.3%
14	Louisiana	152	2.2%
43	Maine	2	0.0%
9	Maryland	228	3.3%
18	Massachusetts	99	1.4%
4	Michigan	486	7.1%
25	Minnesota	59	0.9%
26	Mississippi	49	0.7%
28	Missouri	34	0.5%
46	Montana	0	0.0%
42	Nebraska	6	0.1%
34	Nevada	15	0.2%
38	New Hampshire	8	0.1%
11	New Jersey	169	2.5%
27	New Mexico	39	0.6%
6	New York	478	7.0%
8	North Carolina	279	4.1%
46	North Dakota	0	0.0%
13	Ohio	159	2.3%
20	Oklahoma	72	1.0%
31	Oregon	28	0.4%
17	Pennsylvania	105	1.5%
35	Rhode Island	13	0.2%
16	South Carolina	134	2.0%
46	South Dakota	0	0.0%
12	Tennessee	168	2.4%
3	Texas	589	8.6%
41	Utah	7	0.1%
43	Vermont	2	0.0%
21	Virginia	71	1.0%
22	Washington	70	1.0%
43	West Virginia	2	0.0%
30	Wisconsin	30	0.4%
46	Wyoming	0	0.0%

RANK ORDER

RANK	STATE	CASES	% of USA
1	California	1,033	15.1%
2	Florida	617	9.0%
3	Texas	589	8.6%
4	Michigan	486	7.1%
5	Illinois	479	7.0%
6	New York	478	7.0%
7	Georgia	439	6.4%
8	North Carolina	279	4.1%
9	Maryland	228	3.3%
10	Arizona	200	2.9%
11	New Jersey	169	2.5%
12	Tennessee	168	2.4%
13	Ohio	159	2.3%
14	Louisiana	152	2.2%
15	Alabama	149	2.2%
16	South Carolina	134	2.0%
17	Pennsylvania	105	1.5%
18	Massachusetts	99	1.4%
19	Kentucky	88	1.3%
20	Oklahoma	72	1.0%
21	Virginia	71	1.0%
22	Washington	70	1.0%
23	Colorado	64	0.9%
24	Indiana	62	0.9%
25	Minnesota	59	0.9%
26	Mississippi	49	0.7%
27	New Mexico	39	0.6%
28	Arkansas	34	0.5%
28	Missouri	34	0.5%
30	Wisconsin	30	0.4%
31	Connecticut	28	0.4%
31	Oregon	28	0.4%
33	Kansas	20	0.3%
34	Nevada	15	0.2%
35	Rhode Island	13	0.2%
36	Delaware	11	0.2%
36	Hawaii	11	0.2%
38	Idaho	8	0.1%
38	Iowa	8	0.1%
38	New Hampshire	8	0.1%
41	Utah	7	0.1%
42	Nebraska	6	0.1%
43	Maine	2	0.0%
43	Vermont	2	0.0%
43	West Virginia	2	0.0%
46	Alaska	0	0.0%
46	Montana	0	0.0%
46	North Dakota	0	0.0%
46	South Dakota	0	0.0%
46	Wyoming	0	0.0%
	District of Columbia	58	0.8%

Source: U.S. Department of Health and Human Services, National Center for Health Statistics
     "Sexually Transmitted Disease Surveillance 2002" (http://www.cdc.gov/std/stats/TOC2002.htm)
*Includes only primary and secondary cases. Does not include 26,009 cases in other stages. A chronic infectious disease caused by a spirochete (Treponema pallidum), either transmitted by direct contact, usually in sexual intercourse, or passed from mother to child in utero, and progressing through three stages characterized respectively by local formation of chancres, ulcerous skin eruptions, and systemic infection leading to general paresis.

Syphilis Rate in 2002

National Rate = 2.4 Cases per 100,000 Population*

ALPHA ORDER

RANK	STATE	RATE
8	Alabama	3.4
46	Alaska	0.0
4	Arizona	3.9
24	Arkansas	1.3
11	California	3.0
21	Colorado	1.5
32	Connecticut	0.8
22	Delaware	1.4
4	Florida	3.9
1	Georgia	5.4
30	Hawaii	0.9
36	Idaho	0.6
4	Illinois	3.9
28	Indiana	1.0
41	Iowa	0.3
35	Kansas	0.7
15	Kentucky	2.2
8	Louisiana	3.4
44	Maine	0.2
3	Maryland	4.3
20	Massachusetts	1.6
2	Michigan	4.9
25	Minnesota	1.2
19	Mississippi	1.7
36	Missouri	0.6
46	Montana	0.0
40	Nebraska	0.4
32	Nevada	0.8
36	New Hampshire	0.6
18	New Jersey	2.0
16	New Mexico	2.1
14	New York	2.5
7	North Carolina	3.5
46	North Dakota	0.0
22	Ohio	1.4
16	Oklahoma	2.1
32	Oregon	0.8
30	Pennsylvania	0.9
25	Rhode Island	1.2
10	South Carolina	3.3
46	South Dakota	0.0
11	Tennessee	3.0
13	Texas	2.8
41	Utah	0.3
41	Vermont	0.3
28	Virginia	1.0
25	Washington	1.2
45	West Virginia	0.1
36	Wisconsin	0.6
46	Wyoming	0.0

RANK ORDER

RANK	STATE	RATE
1	Georgia	5.4
2	Michigan	4.9
3	Maryland	4.3
4	Arizona	3.9
4	Florida	3.9
4	Illinois	3.9
7	North Carolina	3.5
8	Alabama	3.4
8	Louisiana	3.4
10	South Carolina	3.3
11	California	3.0
11	Tennessee	3.0
13	Texas	2.8
14	New York	2.5
15	Kentucky	2.2
16	New Mexico	2.1
16	Oklahoma	2.1
18	New Jersey	2.0
19	Mississippi	1.7
20	Massachusetts	1.6
21	Colorado	1.5
22	Delaware	1.4
22	Ohio	1.4
24	Arkansas	1.3
25	Minnesota	1.2
25	Rhode Island	1.2
25	Washington	1.2
28	Indiana	1.0
28	Virginia	1.0
30	Hawaii	0.9
30	Pennsylvania	0.9
32	Connecticut	0.8
32	Nevada	0.8
32	Oregon	0.8
35	Kansas	0.7
36	Idaho	0.6
36	Missouri	0.6
36	New Hampshire	0.6
36	Wisconsin	0.6
40	Nebraska	0.4
41	Iowa	0.3
41	Utah	0.3
41	Vermont	0.3
44	Maine	0.2
45	West Virginia	0.1
46	Alaska	0.0
46	Montana	0.0
46	North Dakota	0.0
46	South Dakota	0.0
46	Wyoming	0.0

District of Columbia   10.2

Source: U.S. Department of Health and Human Services, National Center for Health Statistics
    "Sexually Transmitted Disease Surveillance 2002" (http://www.cdc.gov/std/stats/TOC2002.htm)
*Includes only primary and secondary cases. Does not include 26,009 cases in other stages. A chronic infectious disease caused by a spirochete (Treponema pallidum), either transmitted by direct contact, usually in sexual intercourse, or passed from mother to child in utero, and progressing through three stages characterized respectively by local formation of chancres, ulcerous skin eruptions, and systemic infection leading to general paresis.

Percent of Adults Who Have or Have Had Asthma: 2002

National Median = 11.8% of Adults*

<table>
<tr><td colspan="3">ALPHA ORDER</td><td colspan="3">RANK ORDER</td></tr>
<tr><th>RANK</th><th>STATE</th><th>PERCENT</th><th>RANK</th><th>STATE</th><th>PERCENT</th></tr>
<tr><td>39</td><td>Alabama</td><td>11.0</td><td>1</td><td>Montana</td><td>14.5</td></tr>
<tr><td>30</td><td>Alaska</td><td>11.6</td><td>2</td><td>Washington</td><td>14.3</td></tr>
<tr><td>4</td><td>Arizona</td><td>13.9</td><td>3</td><td>Oregon</td><td>14.0</td></tr>
<tr><td>21</td><td>Arkansas</td><td>12.1</td><td>4</td><td>Arizona</td><td>13.9</td></tr>
<tr><td>14</td><td>California</td><td>12.7</td><td>4</td><td>New Hampshire</td><td>13.9</td></tr>
<tr><td>21</td><td>Colorado</td><td>12.1</td><td>6</td><td>Maine</td><td>13.6</td></tr>
<tr><td>8</td><td>Connecticut</td><td>13.2</td><td>7</td><td>Hawaii</td><td>13.4</td></tr>
<tr><td>24</td><td>Delaware</td><td>11.8</td><td>8</td><td>Connecticut</td><td>13.2</td></tr>
<tr><td>44</td><td>Florida</td><td>10.5</td><td>9</td><td>Massachusetts</td><td>12.9</td></tr>
<tr><td>27</td><td>Georgia</td><td>11.7</td><td>10</td><td>Kentucky</td><td>12.8</td></tr>
<tr><td>7</td><td>Hawaii</td><td>13.4</td><td>10</td><td>Michigan</td><td>12.8</td></tr>
<tr><td>24</td><td>Idaho</td><td>11.8</td><td>10</td><td>Rhode Island</td><td>12.8</td></tr>
<tr><td>41</td><td>Illinois</td><td>10.7</td><td>10</td><td>West Virginia</td><td>12.8</td></tr>
<tr><td>34</td><td>Indiana</td><td>11.3</td><td>14</td><td>California</td><td>12.7</td></tr>
<tr><td>49</td><td>Iowa</td><td>9.0</td><td>14</td><td>Maryland</td><td>12.7</td></tr>
<tr><td>36</td><td>Kansas</td><td>11.2</td><td>14</td><td>Vermont</td><td>12.7</td></tr>
<tr><td>10</td><td>Kentucky</td><td>12.8</td><td>17</td><td>Missouri</td><td>12.5</td></tr>
<tr><td>45</td><td>Louisiana</td><td>10.4</td><td>18</td><td>Nevada</td><td>12.4</td></tr>
<tr><td>6</td><td>Maine</td><td>13.6</td><td>19</td><td>Utah</td><td>12.3</td></tr>
<tr><td>14</td><td>Maryland</td><td>12.7</td><td>20</td><td>Tennessee</td><td>12.2</td></tr>
<tr><td>9</td><td>Massachusetts</td><td>12.9</td><td>21</td><td>Arkansas</td><td>12.1</td></tr>
<tr><td>10</td><td>Michigan</td><td>12.8</td><td>21</td><td>Colorado</td><td>12.1</td></tr>
<tr><td>34</td><td>Minnesota</td><td>11.3</td><td>21</td><td>Virginia</td><td>12.1</td></tr>
<tr><td>42</td><td>Mississippi</td><td>10.6</td><td>24</td><td>Delaware</td><td>11.8</td></tr>
<tr><td>17</td><td>Missouri</td><td>12.5</td><td>24</td><td>Idaho</td><td>11.8</td></tr>
<tr><td>1</td><td>Montana</td><td>14.5</td><td>24</td><td>New Jersey</td><td>11.8</td></tr>
<tr><td>42</td><td>Nebraska</td><td>10.6</td><td>27</td><td>Georgia</td><td>11.7</td></tr>
<tr><td>18</td><td>Nevada</td><td>12.4</td><td>27</td><td>New Mexico</td><td>11.7</td></tr>
<tr><td>4</td><td>New Hampshire</td><td>13.9</td><td>27</td><td>Wisconsin</td><td>11.7</td></tr>
<tr><td>24</td><td>New Jersey</td><td>11.8</td><td>30</td><td>Alaska</td><td>11.6</td></tr>
<tr><td>27</td><td>New Mexico</td><td>11.7</td><td>30</td><td>Texas</td><td>11.6</td></tr>
<tr><td>32</td><td>New York</td><td>11.5</td><td>32</td><td>New York</td><td>11.5</td></tr>
<tr><td>40</td><td>North Carolina</td><td>10.9</td><td>32</td><td>Pennsylvania</td><td>11.5</td></tr>
<tr><td>46</td><td>North Dakota</td><td>10.3</td><td>34</td><td>Indiana</td><td>11.3</td></tr>
<tr><td>46</td><td>Ohio</td><td>10.3</td><td>34</td><td>Minnesota</td><td>11.3</td></tr>
<tr><td>36</td><td>Oklahoma</td><td>11.2</td><td>36</td><td>Kansas</td><td>11.2</td></tr>
<tr><td>3</td><td>Oregon</td><td>14.0</td><td>36</td><td>Oklahoma</td><td>11.2</td></tr>
<tr><td>32</td><td>Pennsylvania</td><td>11.5</td><td>38</td><td>Wyoming</td><td>11.1</td></tr>
<tr><td>10</td><td>Rhode Island</td><td>12.8</td><td>39</td><td>Alabama</td><td>11.0</td></tr>
<tr><td>48</td><td>South Carolina</td><td>10.0</td><td>40</td><td>North Carolina</td><td>10.9</td></tr>
<tr><td>50</td><td>South Dakota</td><td>8.6</td><td>41</td><td>Illinois</td><td>10.7</td></tr>
<tr><td>20</td><td>Tennessee</td><td>12.2</td><td>42</td><td>Mississippi</td><td>10.6</td></tr>
<tr><td>30</td><td>Texas</td><td>11.6</td><td>42</td><td>Nebraska</td><td>10.6</td></tr>
<tr><td>19</td><td>Utah</td><td>12.3</td><td>44</td><td>Florida</td><td>10.5</td></tr>
<tr><td>14</td><td>Vermont</td><td>12.7</td><td>45</td><td>Louisiana</td><td>10.4</td></tr>
<tr><td>21</td><td>Virginia</td><td>12.1</td><td>46</td><td>North Dakota</td><td>10.3</td></tr>
<tr><td>2</td><td>Washington</td><td>14.3</td><td>46</td><td>Ohio</td><td>10.3</td></tr>
<tr><td>10</td><td>West Virginia</td><td>12.8</td><td>48</td><td>South Carolina</td><td>10.0</td></tr>
<tr><td>27</td><td>Wisconsin</td><td>11.7</td><td>49</td><td>Iowa</td><td>9.0</td></tr>
<tr><td>38</td><td>Wyoming</td><td>11.1</td><td>50</td><td>South Dakota</td><td>8.6</td></tr>
<tr><td></td><td></td><td></td><td></td><td>District of Columbia</td><td>14.2</td></tr>
</table>

Source: U.S. Department of Health and Human Services, Centers for Disease Control and Prevention
"2002 Behavioral Risk Factor Surveillance Summary Prevalence Data" (http://apps.nccd.cdc.gov/brfss/)
*Percent of adults who answered yes to the question "Has a doctor ever told you that you have asthma?"

Percent of Adults Who Have Been Told They Have Diabetes: 2002

National Median = 6.7% of Adults*

ALPHA ORDER

RANK	STATE	PERCENT
3	Alabama	8.5
50	Alaska	3.5
26	Arizona	6.4
7	Arkansas	7.9
11	California	7.4
48	Colorado	4.4
37	Connecticut	5.9
17	Delaware	7.1
10	Florida	7.6
17	Georgia	7.1
39	Hawaii	5.8
34	Idaho	6.1
23	Illinois	6.8
11	Indiana	7.4
25	Iowa	6.5
26	Kansas	6.4
20	Kentucky	7.0
17	Louisiana	7.1
13	Maine	7.3
22	Maryland	6.9
39	Massachusetts	5.8
7	Michigan	7.9
47	Minnesota	4.9
2	Mississippi	8.6
13	Missouri	7.3
45	Montana	5.5
39	Nebraska	5.8
29	Nevada	6.2
29	New Hampshire	6.2
34	New Jersey	6.1
29	New Mexico	6.2
15	New York	7.2
15	North Carolina	7.2
34	North Dakota	6.1
9	Ohio	7.7
24	Oklahoma	6.7
29	Oregon	6.2
6	Pennsylvania	8.1
43	Rhode Island	5.6
5	South Carolina	8.4
28	South Dakota	6.3
3	Tennessee	8.5
20	Texas	7.0
48	Utah	4.4
37	Vermont	5.9
29	Virginia	6.2
39	Washington	5.8
1	West Virginia	10.2
46	Wisconsin	5.1
43	Wyoming	5.6

RANK ORDER

RANK	STATE	PERCENT
1	West Virginia	10.2
2	Mississippi	8.6
3	Alabama	8.5
3	Tennessee	8.5
5	South Carolina	8.4
6	Pennsylvania	8.1
7	Arkansas	7.9
7	Michigan	7.9
9	Ohio	7.7
10	Florida	7.6
11	California	7.4
11	Indiana	7.4
13	Maine	7.3
13	Missouri	7.3
15	New York	7.2
15	North Carolina	7.2
17	Delaware	7.1
17	Georgia	7.1
17	Louisiana	7.1
20	Kentucky	7.0
20	Texas	7.0
22	Maryland	6.9
23	Illinois	6.8
24	Oklahoma	6.7
25	Iowa	6.5
26	Arizona	6.4
26	Kansas	6.4
28	South Dakota	6.3
29	Nevada	6.2
29	New Hampshire	6.2
29	New Mexico	6.2
29	Oregon	6.2
29	Virginia	6.2
34	Idaho	6.1
34	New Jersey	6.1
34	North Dakota	6.1
37	Connecticut	5.9
37	Vermont	5.9
39	Hawaii	5.8
39	Massachusetts	5.8
39	Nebraska	5.8
39	Washington	5.8
43	Rhode Island	5.6
43	Wyoming	5.6
45	Montana	5.5
46	Wisconsin	5.1
47	Minnesota	4.9
48	Colorado	4.4
48	Utah	4.4
50	Alaska	3.5

District of Columbia	7.6

Source: U.S. Department of Health and Human Services, Centers for Disease Control and Prevention
   "2002 Behavioral Risk Factor Surveillance Summary Prevalence Data" (http://apps.nccd.cdc.gov/brfss/)
Of population 18 years old and older.

Percent of Adult Population with Serious Mental Illness in 2001

National Percent = 6.9% of Population 18 Years Old and Older*

ALPHA ORDER

RANK	STATE	PERCENT
20	Alabama	7.2
41	Alaska	6.4
18	Arizona	7.3
6	Arkansas	7.7
28	California	6.8
41	Colorado	6.4
49	Connecticut	5.6
45	Delaware	6.3
47	Florida	6.2
5	Georgia	7.9
50	Hawaii	4.5
11	Idaho	7.6
33	Illinois	6.6
33	Indiana	6.6
40	Iowa	6.5
14	Kansas	7.5
2	Kentucky	8.4
6	Louisiana	7.7
6	Maine	7.7
41	Maryland	6.4
33	Massachusetts	6.6
4	Michigan	8.0
6	Minnesota	7.7
11	Mississippi	7.6
24	Missouri	7.0
11	Montana	7.6
24	Nebraska	7.0
41	Nevada	6.4
45	New Hampshire	6.3
48	New Jersey	6.0
30	New Mexico	6.7
27	New York	6.9
30	North Carolina	6.7
24	North Dakota	7.0
17	Ohio	7.4
1	Oklahoma	9.7
20	Oregon	7.2
33	Pennsylvania	6.6
20	Rhode Island	7.2
28	South Carolina	6.8
30	South Dakota	6.7
14	Tennessee	7.5
33	Texas	6.6
14	Utah	7.5
18	Vermont	7.3
23	Virginia	7.1
6	Washington	7.7
3	West Virginia	8.1
33	Wisconsin	6.6
33	Wyoming	6.6

RANK ORDER

RANK	STATE	PERCENT
1	Oklahoma	9.7
2	Kentucky	8.4
3	West Virginia	8.1
4	Michigan	8.0
5	Georgia	7.9
6	Arkansas	7.7
6	Louisiana	7.7
6	Maine	7.7
6	Minnesota	7.7
6	Washington	7.7
11	Idaho	7.6
11	Mississippi	7.6
11	Montana	7.6
14	Kansas	7.5
14	Tennessee	7.5
14	Utah	7.5
17	Ohio	7.4
18	Arizona	7.3
18	Vermont	7.3
20	Alabama	7.2
20	Oregon	7.2
20	Rhode Island	7.2
23	Virginia	7.1
24	Missouri	7.0
24	Nebraska	7.0
24	North Dakota	7.0
27	New York	6.9
28	California	6.8
28	South Carolina	6.8
30	New Mexico	6.7
30	North Carolina	6.7
30	South Dakota	6.7
33	Illinois	6.6
33	Indiana	6.6
33	Massachusetts	6.6
33	Pennsylvania	6.6
33	Texas	6.6
33	Wisconsin	6.6
33	Wyoming	6.6
40	Iowa	6.5
41	Alaska	6.4
41	Colorado	6.4
41	Maryland	6.4
41	Nevada	6.4
45	Delaware	6.3
45	New Hampshire	6.3
47	Florida	6.2
48	New Jersey	6.0
49	Connecticut	5.6
50	Hawaii	4.5

District of Columbia 6.1

Source: Morgan Quitno Press using data from U.S. Dept of HHS, Substance Abuse and Mental Health Services Admin.
"2001 National Household Survey on Drug Abuse" (September 2003)

*Percent of population 18 years old and over estimated to have a diagnosable mental, behavioral or emotional disorder that met the DSM-IV criteria and resulted in functional impairment that substantially interfered with, or limited one or more life activities. Calculated using July 1, 2002 population estimates.

VI. PROVIDERS

VI. PROVIDERS (continued)

Health Care Practitioners and Technicians in 2002

National Total = 6,185,020 Practitioners and Technicians*

ALPHA ORDER

RANK	STATE	PRACTITIONERS	% of USA
22	Alabama	98,150	1.6%
49	Alaska	12,100	0.2%
24	Arizona	93,300	1.5%
32	Arkansas	59,210	1.0%
1	California	586,380	9.5%
26	Colorado	86,450	1.4%
27	Connecticut	85,730	1.4%
46	Delaware	18,760	0.3%
4	Florida	357,530	5.8%
12	Georgia	161,690	2.6%
43	Hawaii	22,400	0.4%
42	Idaho	26,880	0.4%
7	Illinois	275,610	4.5%
13	Indiana	146,910	2.4%
29	Iowa	67,370	1.1%
31	Kansas	64,150	1.0%
23	Kentucky	93,530	1.5%
21	Louisiana	102,840	1.7%
39	Maine	33,460	0.5%
19	Maryland	123,130	2.0%
10	Massachusetts	179,620	2.9%
8	Michigan	217,070	3.5%
17	Minnesota	132,710	2.1%
33	Mississippi	58,330	0.9%
16	Missouri	144,400	2.3%
45	Montana	20,140	0.3%
34	Nebraska	44,920	0.7%
37	Nevada	36,230	0.6%
40	New Hampshire	29,300	0.5%
11	New Jersey	176,770	2.9%
38	New Mexico	35,310	0.6%
2	New York	432,460	7.0%
9	North Carolina	180,730	2.9%
47	North Dakota	17,290	0.3%
6	Ohio	286,680	4.6%
28	Oklahoma	74,480	1.2%
30	Oregon	65,840	1.1%
5	Pennsylvania	314,860	5.1%
41	Rhode Island	28,710	0.5%
25	South Carolina	87,310	1.4%
44	South Dakota	20,380	0.3%
15	Tennessee	144,950	2.3%
3	Texas	408,740	6.6%
36	Utah	42,070	0.7%
48	Vermont	15,580	0.3%
14	Virginia	146,650	2.4%
20	Washington	119,810	1.9%
35	West Virginia	43,820	0.7%
18	Wisconsin	128,140	2.1%
50	Wyoming	10,470	0.2%

RANK ORDER

RANK	STATE	PRACTITIONERS	% of USA
1	California	586,380	9.5%
2	New York	432,460	7.0%
3	Texas	408,740	6.6%
4	Florida	357,530	5.8%
5	Pennsylvania	314,860	5.1%
6	Ohio	286,680	4.6%
7	Illinois	275,610	4.5%
8	Michigan	217,070	3.5%
9	North Carolina	180,730	2.9%
10	Massachusetts	179,620	2.9%
11	New Jersey	176,770	2.9%
12	Georgia	161,690	2.6%
13	Indiana	146,910	2.4%
14	Virginia	146,650	2.4%
15	Tennessee	144,950	2.3%
16	Missouri	144,400	2.3%
17	Minnesota	132,710	2.1%
18	Wisconsin	128,140	2.1%
19	Maryland	123,130	2.0%
20	Washington	119,810	1.9%
21	Louisiana	102,840	1.7%
22	Alabama	98,150	1.6%
23	Kentucky	93,530	1.5%
24	Arizona	93,300	1.5%
25	South Carolina	87,310	1.4%
26	Colorado	86,450	1.4%
27	Connecticut	85,730	1.4%
28	Oklahoma	74,480	1.2%
29	Iowa	67,370	1.1%
30	Oregon	65,840	1.1%
31	Kansas	64,150	1.0%
32	Arkansas	59,210	1.0%
33	Mississippi	58,330	0.9%
34	Nebraska	44,920	0.7%
35	West Virginia	43,820	0.7%
36	Utah	42,070	0.7%
37	Nevada	36,230	0.6%
38	New Mexico	35,310	0.6%
39	Maine	33,460	0.5%
40	New Hampshire	29,300	0.5%
41	Rhode Island	28,710	0.5%
42	Idaho	26,880	0.4%
43	Hawaii	22,400	0.4%
44	South Dakota	20,380	0.3%
45	Montana	20,140	0.3%
46	Delaware	18,760	0.3%
47	North Dakota	17,290	0.3%
48	Vermont	15,580	0.3%
49	Alaska	12,100	0.2%
50	Wyoming	10,470	0.2%
	District of Columbia	25,700	0.4%

Source: U.S. Department of Labor, Bureau of Labor Statistics
"Occupational Employment and Wages, 2002" (http://www.bls.gov/oes/)
*Does not include self-employed. Includes various doctors, dentists, nurses, therapists, optometrists, paramedics and technicians. Does not include assistants and aides listed under health care support occupations.

Rate of Health Care Practitioners and Technicians in 2002

National Rate = 2,148 Practitioners and Technicians per 100,000 Population*

ALPHA ORDER

RANK	STATE	RATE
26	Alabama	2,191
43	Alaska	1,886
48	Arizona	1,715
28	Arkansas	2,188
49	California	1,675
40	Colorado	1,921
13	Connecticut	2,479
18	Delaware	2,328
31	Florida	2,142
42	Georgia	1,892
47	Hawaii	1,805
38	Idaho	2,001
27	Illinois	2,190
15	Indiana	2,386
21	Iowa	2,295
16	Kansas	2,366
22	Kentucky	2,287
20	Louisiana	2,297
7	Maine	2,584
24	Maryland	2,259
1	Massachusetts	2,797
30	Michigan	2,161
5	Minnesota	2,641
36	Mississippi	2,035
9	Missouri	2,547
25	Montana	2,212
6	Nebraska	2,600
50	Nevada	1,672
19	New Hampshire	2,299
35	New Jersey	2,061
41	New Mexico	1,907
23	New York	2,260
29	North Carolina	2,176
2	North Dakota	2,728
11	Ohio	2,513
32	Oklahoma	2,134
45	Oregon	1,870
8	Pennsylvania	2,554
3	Rhode Island	2,687
33	South Carolina	2,128
4	South Dakota	2,680
12	Tennessee	2,504
44	Texas	1,880
46	Utah	1,814
10	Vermont	2,528
37	Virginia	2,012
39	Washington	1,975
14	West Virginia	2,428
17	Wisconsin	2,356
34	Wyoming	2,099

RANK ORDER

RANK	STATE	RATE
1	Massachusetts	2,797
2	North Dakota	2,728
3	Rhode Island	2,687
4	South Dakota	2,680
5	Minnesota	2,641
6	Nebraska	2,600
7	Maine	2,584
8	Pennsylvania	2,554
9	Missouri	2,547
10	Vermont	2,528
11	Ohio	2,513
12	Tennessee	2,504
13	Connecticut	2,479
14	West Virginia	2,428
15	Indiana	2,386
16	Kansas	2,366
17	Wisconsin	2,356
18	Delaware	2,328
19	New Hampshire	2,299
20	Louisiana	2,297
21	Iowa	2,295
22	Kentucky	2,287
23	New York	2,260
24	Maryland	2,259
25	Montana	2,212
26	Alabama	2,191
27	Illinois	2,190
28	Arkansas	2,188
29	North Carolina	2,176
30	Michigan	2,161
31	Florida	2,142
32	Oklahoma	2,134
33	South Carolina	2,128
34	Wyoming	2,099
35	New Jersey	2,061
36	Mississippi	2,035
37	Virginia	2,012
38	Idaho	2,001
39	Washington	1,975
40	Colorado	1,921
41	New Mexico	1,907
42	Georgia	1,892
43	Alaska	1,886
44	Texas	1,880
45	Oregon	1,870
46	Utah	1,814
47	Hawaii	1,805
48	Arizona	1,715
49	California	1,675
50	Nevada	1,672

| | District of Columbia | 4,515 |

Source: Morgan Quitno Press using data from U.S. Department of Labor, Bureau of Labor Statistics
    "Occupational Employment and Wages, 2002" (http://www.bls.gov/oes/)
*Does not include self-employed. Includes various doctors, dentists, nurses, therapists, optometrists, paramedics
and technicians. Does not include assistants and aides listed under health care support occupations.

Physicians in 2002

National Total = 840,331 Physicians*

ALPHA ORDER

RANK	STATE	PHYSICIANS	% of USA
27	Alabama	10,116	1.2%
49	Alaska	1,495	0.2%
22	Arizona	12,989	1.5%
32	Arkansas	6,001	0.7%
1	California	101,940	12.1%
24	Colorado	12,404	1.5%
21	Connecticut	13,910	1.7%
46	Delaware	2,211	0.3%
4	Florida	48,706	5.8%
14	Georgia	20,472	2.4%
39	Hawaii	4,210	0.5%
43	Idaho	2,551	0.3%
6	Illinois	37,020	4.4%
20	Indiana	14,305	1.7%
31	Iowa	6,099	0.7%
29	Kansas	6,677	0.8%
28	Kentucky	9,991	1.2%
23	Louisiana	12,738	1.5%
41	Maine	3,825	0.5%
11	Maryland	24,396	2.9%
8	Massachusetts	29,915	3.6%
10	Michigan	25,787	3.1%
17	Minnesota	14,994	1.8%
33	Mississippi	5,680	0.7%
19	Missouri	14,567	1.7%
45	Montana	2,359	0.3%
37	Nebraska	4,489	0.5%
38	Nevada	4,417	0.5%
42	New Hampshire	3,741	0.4%
9	New Jersey	28,756	3.4%
35	New Mexico	4,799	0.6%
2	New York	80,865	9.6%
12	North Carolina	22,824	2.7%
48	North Dakota	1,653	0.2%
7	Ohio	31,751	3.8%
30	Oklahoma	6,676	0.8%
26	Oregon	10,168	1.2%
5	Pennsylvania	40,478	4.8%
40	Rhode Island	4,043	0.5%
25	South Carolina	10,195	1.2%
47	South Dakota	1,808	0.2%
16	Tennessee	16,223	1.9%
3	Texas	49,745	5.9%
34	Utah	5,283	0.6%
44	Vermont	2,497	0.3%
13	Virginia	21,594	2.6%
15	Washington	17,990	2.1%
36	West Virginia	4,562	0.5%
18	Wisconsin	14,852	1.8%
50	Wyoming	1,053	0.1%

RANK ORDER

RANK	STATE	PHYSICIANS	% of USA
1	California	101,940	12.1%
2	New York	80,865	9.6%
3	Texas	49,745	5.9%
4	Florida	48,706	5.8%
5	Pennsylvania	40,478	4.8%
6	Illinois	37,020	4.4%
7	Ohio	31,751	3.8%
8	Massachusetts	29,915	3.6%
9	New Jersey	28,756	3.4%
10	Michigan	25,787	3.1%
11	Maryland	24,396	2.9%
12	North Carolina	22,824	2.7%
13	Virginia	21,594	2.6%
14	Georgia	20,472	2.4%
15	Washington	17,990	2.1%
16	Tennessee	16,223	1.9%
17	Minnesota	14,994	1.8%
18	Wisconsin	14,852	1.8%
19	Missouri	14,567	1.7%
20	Indiana	14,305	1.7%
21	Connecticut	13,910	1.7%
22	Arizona	12,989	1.5%
23	Louisiana	12,738	1.5%
24	Colorado	12,404	1.5%
25	South Carolina	10,195	1.2%
26	Oregon	10,168	1.2%
27	Alabama	10,116	1.2%
28	Kentucky	9,991	1.2%
29	Kansas	6,677	0.8%
30	Oklahoma	6,676	0.8%
31	Iowa	6,099	0.7%
32	Arkansas	6,001	0.7%
33	Mississippi	5,680	0.7%
34	Utah	5,283	0.6%
35	New Mexico	4,799	0.6%
36	West Virginia	4,562	0.5%
37	Nebraska	4,489	0.5%
38	Nevada	4,417	0.5%
39	Hawaii	4,210	0.5%
40	Rhode Island	4,043	0.5%
41	Maine	3,825	0.5%
42	New Hampshire	3,741	0.4%
43	Idaho	2,551	0.3%
44	Vermont	2,497	0.3%
45	Montana	2,359	0.3%
46	Delaware	2,211	0.3%
47	South Dakota	1,808	0.2%
48	North Dakota	1,653	0.2%
49	Alaska	1,495	0.2%
50	Wyoming	1,053	0.1%
	District of Columbia	4,511	0.5%

Source: American Medical Association (Chicago, Illinois)
    "Physician Characteristics and Distribution in the U.S." (2004 Edition)
*As of December 31, 2002. Comprised of federal and nonfederal physicians. Total does not include 12,856 physicians in the U.S. territories and possessions, at APO's and FPO's and whose addresses are unknown.

Male Physicians in 2002

National Total = 628,845 Physicians*

ALPHA ORDER

RANK	STATE	PHYSICIANS	% of USA
25	Alabama	8,148	1.3%
49	Alaska	1,075	0.2%
22	Arizona	10,062	1.6%
32	Arkansas	4,848	0.8%
1	California	76,085	12.1%
24	Colorado	9,149	1.5%
21	Connecticut	10,222	1.6%
46	Delaware	1,608	0.3%
3	Florida	39,443	6.3%
14	Georgia	15,665	2.5%
39	Hawaii	3,195	0.5%
43	Idaho	2,150	0.3%
6	Illinois	26,241	4.2%
19	Indiana	11,115	1.8%
31	Iowa	4,851	0.8%
30	Kansas	5,170	0.8%
27	Kentucky	7,770	1.2%
23	Louisiana	9,862	1.6%
40	Maine	2,902	0.5%
12	Maryland	17,193	2.7%
8	Massachusetts	20,716	3.3%
10	Michigan	18,919	3.0%
18	Minnesota	11,125	1.8%
33	Mississippi	4,635	0.7%
20	Missouri	10,973	1.7%
44	Montana	1,929	0.3%
37	Nebraska	3,522	0.6%
36	Nevada	3,548	0.6%
42	New Hampshire	2,858	0.5%
9	New Jersey	20,443	3.3%
38	New Mexico	3,437	0.5%
2	New York	57,174	9.1%
11	North Carolina	17,353	2.8%
48	North Dakota	1,349	0.2%
7	Ohio	23,663	3.8%
29	Oklahoma	5,333	0.8%
28	Oregon	7,652	1.2%
5	Pennsylvania	29,958	4.8%
41	Rhode Island	2,859	0.5%
26	South Carolina	8,099	1.3%
47	South Dakota	1,483	0.2%
16	Tennessee	12,881	2.0%
4	Texas	37,848	6.0%
34	Utah	4,331	0.7%
45	Vermont	1,819	0.3%
13	Virginia	15,933	2.5%
15	Washington	13,425	2.1%
35	West Virginia	3,607	0.6%
17	Wisconsin	11,297	1.8%
50	Wyoming	879	0.1%

RANK ORDER

RANK	STATE	PHYSICIANS	% of USA
1	California	76,085	12.1%
2	New York	57,174	9.1%
3	Florida	39,443	6.3%
4	Texas	37,848	6.0%
5	Pennsylvania	29,958	4.8%
6	Illinois	26,241	4.2%
7	Ohio	23,663	3.8%
8	Massachusetts	20,716	3.3%
9	New Jersey	20,443	3.3%
10	Michigan	18,919	3.0%
11	North Carolina	17,353	2.8%
12	Maryland	17,193	2.7%
13	Virginia	15,933	2.5%
14	Georgia	15,665	2.5%
15	Washington	13,425	2.1%
16	Tennessee	12,881	2.0%
17	Wisconsin	11,297	1.8%
18	Minnesota	11,125	1.8%
19	Indiana	11,115	1.8%
20	Missouri	10,973	1.7%
21	Connecticut	10,222	1.6%
22	Arizona	10,062	1.6%
23	Louisiana	9,862	1.6%
24	Colorado	9,149	1.5%
25	Alabama	8,148	1.3%
26	South Carolina	8,099	1.3%
27	Kentucky	7,770	1.2%
28	Oregon	7,652	1.2%
29	Oklahoma	5,333	0.8%
30	Kansas	5,170	0.8%
31	Iowa	4,851	0.8%
32	Arkansas	4,848	0.8%
33	Mississippi	4,635	0.7%
34	Utah	4,331	0.7%
35	West Virginia	3,607	0.6%
36	Nevada	3,548	0.6%
37	Nebraska	3,522	0.6%
38	New Mexico	3,437	0.5%
39	Hawaii	3,195	0.5%
40	Maine	2,902	0.5%
41	Rhode Island	2,859	0.5%
42	New Hampshire	2,858	0.5%
43	Idaho	2,150	0.3%
44	Montana	1,929	0.3%
45	Vermont	1,819	0.3%
46	Delaware	1,608	0.3%
47	South Dakota	1,483	0.2%
48	North Dakota	1,349	0.2%
49	Alaska	1,075	0.2%
50	Wyoming	879	0.1%
	District of Columbia	3,043	0.5%

Source: American Medical Association (Chicago, Illinois)
"Physician Characteristics and Distribution in the U.S." (2004 Edition)
*As of December 31, 2002. Comprised of federal and nonfederal physicians. Total does not include 9,337 male physicians in the U.S. territories and possessions, at APO's and FPO's and whose addresses are unknown.

Female Physicians in 2002

National Total = 211,486 Physicians*

ALPHA ORDER

RANK	STATE	PHYSICIANS	% of USA
28	Alabama	1,968	0.9%
46	Alaska	420	0.2%
23	Arizona	2,927	1.4%
34	Arkansas	1,153	0.5%
1	California	25,855	12.2%
21	Colorado	3,255	1.5%
17	Connecticut	3,688	1.7%
44	Delaware	603	0.3%
6	Florida	9,263	4.4%
14	Georgia	4,807	2.3%
36	Hawaii	1,015	0.5%
47	Idaho	401	0.2%
4	Illinois	10,779	5.1%
22	Indiana	3,190	1.5%
32	Iowa	1,248	0.6%
29	Kansas	1,507	0.7%
26	Kentucky	2,221	1.1%
24	Louisiana	2,876	1.4%
40	Maine	923	0.4%
10	Maryland	7,203	3.4%
7	Massachusetts	9,199	4.3%
11	Michigan	6,868	3.2%
16	Minnesota	3,869	1.8%
35	Mississippi	1,045	0.5%
18	Missouri	3,594	1.7%
45	Montana	430	0.2%
37	Nebraska	967	0.5%
42	Nevada	869	0.4%
41	New Hampshire	883	0.4%
8	New Jersey	8,313	3.9%
30	New Mexico	1,362	0.6%
2	New York	23,691	11.2%
13	North Carolina	5,471	2.6%
49	North Dakota	304	0.1%
9	Ohio	8,088	3.8%
31	Oklahoma	1,343	0.6%
25	Oregon	2,516	1.2%
5	Pennsylvania	10,520	5.0%
33	Rhode Island	1,184	0.6%
27	South Carolina	2,096	1.0%
48	South Dakota	325	0.2%
20	Tennessee	3,342	1.6%
3	Texas	11,897	5.6%
39	Utah	952	0.5%
43	Vermont	678	0.3%
12	Virginia	5,661	2.7%
15	Washington	4,565	2.2%
38	West Virginia	955	0.5%
19	Wisconsin	3,555	1.7%
50	Wyoming	174	0.1%

RANK ORDER

RANK	STATE	PHYSICIANS	% of USA
1	California	25,855	12.2%
2	New York	23,691	11.2%
3	Texas	11,897	5.6%
4	Illinois	10,779	5.1%
5	Pennsylvania	10,520	5.0%
6	Florida	9,263	4.4%
7	Massachusetts	9,199	4.3%
8	New Jersey	8,313	3.9%
9	Ohio	8,088	3.8%
10	Maryland	7,203	3.4%
11	Michigan	6,868	3.2%
12	Virginia	5,661	2.7%
13	North Carolina	5,471	2.6%
14	Georgia	4,807	2.3%
15	Washington	4,565	2.2%
16	Minnesota	3,869	1.8%
17	Connecticut	3,688	1.7%
18	Missouri	3,594	1.7%
19	Wisconsin	3,555	1.7%
20	Tennessee	3,342	1.6%
21	Colorado	3,255	1.5%
22	Indiana	3,190	1.5%
23	Arizona	2,927	1.4%
24	Louisiana	2,876	1.4%
25	Oregon	2,516	1.2%
26	Kentucky	2,221	1.1%
27	South Carolina	2,096	1.0%
28	Alabama	1,968	0.9%
29	Kansas	1,507	0.7%
30	New Mexico	1,362	0.6%
31	Oklahoma	1,343	0.6%
32	Iowa	1,248	0.6%
33	Rhode Island	1,184	0.6%
34	Arkansas	1,153	0.5%
35	Mississippi	1,045	0.5%
36	Hawaii	1,015	0.5%
37	Nebraska	967	0.5%
38	West Virginia	955	0.5%
39	Utah	952	0.5%
40	Maine	923	0.4%
41	New Hampshire	883	0.4%
42	Nevada	869	0.4%
43	Vermont	678	0.3%
44	Delaware	603	0.3%
45	Montana	430	0.2%
46	Alaska	420	0.2%
47	Idaho	401	0.2%
48	South Dakota	325	0.2%
49	North Dakota	304	0.1%
50	Wyoming	174	0.1%
	District of Columbia	1,468	0.7%

Source: American Medical Association (Chicago, Illinois)
"Physician Characteristics and Distribution in the U.S." (2004 Edition)
*As of December 31, 2002. Comprised of federal and nonfederal physicians. Total does not include 3,519 female physicians in the U.S. territories and possessions, at APO's and FPO's and whose addresses are unknown.

Percent of Physicians Who Are Female: 2002

National Percent = 25.2% of Physicians*

ALPHA ORDER

RANK ORDER

RANK	STATE	PERCENT
41	Alabama	19.5
8	Alaska	28.1
31	Arizona	22.5
42	Arkansas	19.2
18	California	25.4
13	Colorado	26.2
12	Connecticut	26.5
9	Delaware	27.3
43	Florida	19.0
28	Georgia	23.5
22	Hawaii	24.1
50	Idaho	15.7
5	Illinois	29.1
32	Indiana	22.3
38	Iowa	20.5
29	Kansas	22.6
33	Kentucky	22.2
29	Louisiana	22.6
22	Maine	24.1
2	Maryland	29.5
1	Massachusetts	30.8
11	Michigan	26.6
16	Minnesota	25.8
44	Mississippi	18.4
20	Missouri	24.7
46	Montana	18.2
34	Nebraska	21.5
40	Nevada	19.7
27	New Hampshire	23.6
6	New Jersey	28.9
7	New Mexico	28.4
3	New York	29.3
24	North Carolina	24.0
44	North Dakota	18.4
17	Ohio	25.5
39	Oklahoma	20.1
20	Oregon	24.7
15	Pennsylvania	26.0
3	Rhode Island	29.3
36	South Carolina	20.6
47	South Dakota	18.0
36	Tennessee	20.6
25	Texas	23.9
47	Utah	18.0
10	Vermont	27.2
13	Virginia	26.2
18	Washington	25.4
35	West Virginia	20.9
25	Wisconsin	23.9
49	Wyoming	16.5

RANK	STATE	PERCENT
1	Massachusetts	30.8
2	Maryland	29.5
3	New York	29.3
3	Rhode Island	29.3
5	Illinois	29.1
6	New Jersey	28.9
7	New Mexico	28.4
8	Alaska	28.1
9	Delaware	27.3
10	Vermont	27.2
11	Michigan	26.6
12	Connecticut	26.5
13	Colorado	26.2
13	Virginia	26.2
15	Pennsylvania	26.0
16	Minnesota	25.8
17	Ohio	25.5
18	California	25.4
18	Washington	25.4
20	Missouri	24.7
20	Oregon	24.7
22	Hawaii	24.1
22	Maine	24.1
24	North Carolina	24.0
25	Texas	23.9
25	Wisconsin	23.9
27	New Hampshire	23.6
28	Georgia	23.5
29	Kansas	22.6
29	Louisiana	22.6
31	Arizona	22.5
32	Indiana	22.3
33	Kentucky	22.2
34	Nebraska	21.5
35	West Virginia	20.9
36	South Carolina	20.6
36	Tennessee	20.6
38	Iowa	20.5
39	Oklahoma	20.1
40	Nevada	19.7
41	Alabama	19.5
42	Arkansas	19.2
43	Florida	19.0
44	Mississippi	18.4
44	North Dakota	18.4
46	Montana	18.2
47	South Dakota	18.0
47	Utah	18.0
49	Wyoming	16.5
50	Idaho	15.7

District of Columbia   32.5

Source: Morgan Quitno Press using data from American Medical Association (Chicago, Illinois)
 "Physician Characteristics and Distribution in the U.S." (2004 Edition)
As of December 31, 2002. Comprised of federal and nonfederal physicians. National percent does not include physicians in the U.S. territories and possessions, at APO's and FPO's and whose addresses are unknown.

Physicians Under 35 Years Old in 2002

National Total = 137,453 Physicians*

ALPHA ORDER

RANK	STATE	PHYSICIANS	% of USA
26	Alabama	1,617	1.2%
48	Alaska	153	0.1%
24	Arizona	1,660	1.2%
31	Arkansas	981	0.7%
2	California	14,213	10.3%
23	Colorado	1,754	1.3%
19	Connecticut	2,301	1.7%
43	Delaware	372	0.3%
9	Florida	4,767	3.5%
14	Georgia	3,160	2.3%
39	Hawaii	551	0.4%
46	Idaho	193	0.1%
4	Illinois	7,736	5.6%
22	Indiana	2,193	1.6%
30	Iowa	1,028	0.7%
29	Kansas	1,033	0.8%
27	Kentucky	1,604	1.2%
18	Louisiana	2,531	1.8%
42	Maine	379	0.3%
12	Maryland	4,025	2.9%
7	Massachusetts	5,801	4.2%
8	Michigan	5,137	3.7%
17	Minnesota	2,654	1.9%
36	Mississippi	797	0.6%
15	Missouri	2,875	2.1%
48	Montana	153	0.1%
34	Nebraska	828	0.6%
41	Nevada	470	0.3%
40	New Hampshire	473	0.3%
10	New Jersey	4,206	3.1%
38	New Mexico	629	0.5%
1	New York	15,870	11.5%
11	North Carolina	4,137	3.0%
45	North Dakota	199	0.1%
6	Ohio	6,185	4.5%
32	Oklahoma	942	0.7%
28	Oregon	1,200	0.9%
5	Pennsylvania	7,217	5.3%
33	Rhode Island	844	0.6%
25	South Carolina	1,656	1.2%
47	South Dakota	167	0.1%
16	Tennessee	2,715	2.0%
3	Texas	8,897	6.5%
35	Utah	824	0.6%
43	Vermont	372	0.3%
13	Virginia	3,638	2.6%
21	Washington	2,230	1.6%
37	West Virginia	750	0.5%
20	Wisconsin	2,278	1.7%
50	Wyoming	88	0.1%

RANK ORDER

RANK	STATE	PHYSICIANS	% of USA
1	New York	15,870	11.5%
2	California	14,213	10.3%
3	Texas	8,897	6.5%
4	Illinois	7,736	5.6%
5	Pennsylvania	7,217	5.3%
6	Ohio	6,185	4.5%
7	Massachusetts	5,801	4.2%
8	Michigan	5,137	3.7%
9	Florida	4,767	3.5%
10	New Jersey	4,206	3.1%
11	North Carolina	4,137	3.0%
12	Maryland	4,025	2.9%
13	Virginia	3,638	2.6%
14	Georgia	3,160	2.3%
15	Missouri	2,875	2.1%
16	Tennessee	2,715	2.0%
17	Minnesota	2,654	1.9%
18	Louisiana	2,531	1.8%
19	Connecticut	2,301	1.7%
20	Wisconsin	2,278	1.7%
21	Washington	2,230	1.6%
22	Indiana	2,193	1.6%
23	Colorado	1,754	1.3%
24	Arizona	1,660	1.2%
25	South Carolina	1,656	1.2%
26	Alabama	1,617	1.2%
27	Kentucky	1,604	1.2%
28	Oregon	1,200	0.9%
29	Kansas	1,033	0.8%
30	Iowa	1,028	0.7%
31	Arkansas	981	0.7%
32	Oklahoma	942	0.7%
33	Rhode Island	844	0.6%
34	Nebraska	828	0.6%
35	Utah	824	0.6%
36	Mississippi	797	0.6%
37	West Virginia	750	0.5%
38	New Mexico	629	0.5%
39	Hawaii	551	0.4%
40	New Hampshire	473	0.3%
41	Nevada	470	0.3%
42	Maine	379	0.3%
43	Delaware	372	0.3%
43	Vermont	372	0.3%
45	North Dakota	199	0.1%
46	Idaho	193	0.1%
47	South Dakota	167	0.1%
48	Alaska	153	0.1%
48	Montana	153	0.1%
50	Wyoming	88	0.1%
	District of Columbia	970	0.7%

Source: American Medical Association (Chicago, Illinois)
"Physician Characteristics and Distribution in the U.S." (2004 Edition)
*As of December 31, 2002. Comprised of federal and nonfederal physicians. Total does not include 1,755 physicians in the U.S. territories and possessions, at APO's and FPO's and whose addresses are unknown.

Percent of Physicians Under 35 Years Old in 2002

National Percent = 16.4% of Physicians*

ALPHA ORDER				RANK ORDER		
RANK	STATE	PERCENT		RANK	STATE	PERCENT
24	Alabama	16.0		1	Illinois	20.9
44	Alaska	10.2		1	Rhode Island	20.9
38	Arizona	12.8		3	Louisiana	19.9
21	Arkansas	16.3		3	Michigan	19.9
35	California	13.9		5	Missouri	19.7
32	Colorado	14.1		6	New York	19.6
18	Connecticut	16.5		7	Ohio	19.5
15	Delaware	16.8		8	Massachusetts	19.4
46	Florida	9.8		9	Nebraska	18.4
27	Georgia	15.4		10	North Carolina	18.1
36	Hawaii	13.1		11	Texas	17.9
49	Idaho	7.6		12	Pennsylvania	17.8
1	Illinois	20.9		13	Minnesota	17.7
28	Indiana	15.3		14	Iowa	16.9
14	Iowa	16.9		15	Delaware	16.8
26	Kansas	15.5		15	Virginia	16.8
23	Kentucky	16.1		17	Tennessee	16.7
3	Louisiana	19.9		18	Connecticut	16.5
45	Maine	9.9		18	Maryland	16.5
18	Maryland	16.5		20	West Virginia	16.4
8	Massachusetts	19.4		21	Arkansas	16.3
3	Michigan	19.9		22	South Carolina	16.2
13	Minnesota	17.7		23	Kentucky	16.1
34	Mississippi	14.0		24	Alabama	16.0
5	Missouri	19.7		25	Utah	15.6
50	Montana	6.5		26	Kansas	15.5
9	Nebraska	18.4		27	Georgia	15.4
43	Nevada	10.6		28	Indiana	15.3
39	New Hampshire	12.6		28	Wisconsin	15.3
31	New Jersey	14.6		30	Vermont	14.9
36	New Mexico	13.1		31	New Jersey	14.6
6	New York	19.6		32	Colorado	14.1
10	North Carolina	18.1		32	Oklahoma	14.1
41	North Dakota	12.0		34	Mississippi	14.0
7	Ohio	19.5		35	California	13.9
32	Oklahoma	14.1		36	Hawaii	13.1
42	Oregon	11.8		36	New Mexico	13.1
12	Pennsylvania	17.8		38	Arizona	12.8
1	Rhode Island	20.9		39	New Hampshire	12.6
22	South Carolina	16.2		40	Washington	12.4
47	South Dakota	9.2		41	North Dakota	12.0
17	Tennessee	16.7		42	Oregon	11.8
11	Texas	17.9		43	Nevada	10.6
25	Utah	15.6		44	Alaska	10.2
30	Vermont	14.9		45	Maine	9.9
15	Virginia	16.8		46	Florida	9.8
40	Washington	12.4		47	South Dakota	9.2
20	West Virginia	16.4		48	Wyoming	8.4
28	Wisconsin	15.3		49	Idaho	7.6
48	Wyoming	8.4		50	Montana	6.5
					District of Columbia	21.5

Source: Morgan Quitno Press using data from American Medical Association (Chicago, Illinois)
"Physician Characteristics and Distribution in the U.S." (2004 Edition)
*As of December 31, 2002. Comprised of federal and nonfederal physicians. National percent does not include physicians in the U.S. territories and possessions, at APO's and FPO's and whose addresses are unknown.

Physicians 35 to 44 Years Old in 2002

National Total = 206,791 Physicians*

ALPHA ORDER

RANK	STATE	PHYSICIANS	% of USA
27	Alabama	2,595	1.3%
49	Alaska	435	0.2%
23	Arizona	3,122	1.5%
33	Arkansas	1,478	0.7%
1	California	21,779	10.5%
24	Colorado	3,108	1.5%
21	Connecticut	3,298	1.6%
45	Delaware	572	0.3%
4	Florida	11,092	5.4%
13	Georgia	5,602	2.7%
40	Hawaii	986	0.5%
43	Idaho	673	0.3%
6	Illinois	9,152	4.4%
20	Indiana	3,784	1.8%
32	Iowa	1,511	0.7%
29	Kansas	1,610	0.8%
26	Kentucky	2,689	1.3%
22	Louisiana	3,143	1.5%
42	Maine	888	0.4%
12	Maryland	6,043	2.9%
8	Massachusetts	7,850	3.8%
10	Michigan	6,400	3.1%
18	Minnesota	3,982	1.9%
31	Mississippi	1,519	0.7%
19	Missouri	3,794	1.8%
46	Montana	552	0.3%
36	Nebraska	1,177	0.6%
35	Nevada	1,208	0.6%
41	New Hampshire	900	0.4%
9	New Jersey	7,071	3.4%
37	New Mexico	1,082	0.5%
2	New York	19,406	9.4%
11	North Carolina	6,283	3.0%
48	North Dakota	441	0.2%
7	Ohio	8,209	4.0%
30	Oklahoma	1,578	0.8%
28	Oregon	2,389	1.2%
5	Pennsylvania	9,651	4.7%
39	Rhode Island	1,027	0.5%
25	South Carolina	2,833	1.4%
47	South Dakota	508	0.2%
16	Tennessee	4,205	2.0%
3	Texas	13,234	6.4%
34	Utah	1,428	0.7%
44	Vermont	607	0.3%
14	Virginia	5,266	2.5%
15	Washington	4,304	2.1%
38	West Virginia	1,048	0.5%
17	Wisconsin	4,092	2.0%
50	Wyoming	246	0.1%

RANK ORDER

RANK	STATE	PHYSICIANS	% of USA
1	California	21,779	10.5%
2	New York	19,406	9.4%
3	Texas	13,234	6.4%
4	Florida	11,092	5.4%
5	Pennsylvania	9,651	4.7%
6	Illinois	9,152	4.4%
7	Ohio	8,209	4.0%
8	Massachusetts	7,850	3.8%
9	New Jersey	7,071	3.4%
10	Michigan	6,400	3.1%
11	North Carolina	6,283	3.0%
12	Maryland	6,043	2.9%
13	Georgia	5,602	2.7%
14	Virginia	5,266	2.5%
15	Washington	4,304	2.1%
16	Tennessee	4,205	2.0%
17	Wisconsin	4,092	2.0%
18	Minnesota	3,982	1.9%
19	Missouri	3,794	1.8%
20	Indiana	3,784	1.8%
21	Connecticut	3,298	1.6%
22	Louisiana	3,143	1.5%
23	Arizona	3,122	1.5%
24	Colorado	3,108	1.5%
25	South Carolina	2,833	1.4%
26	Kentucky	2,689	1.3%
27	Alabama	2,595	1.3%
28	Oregon	2,389	1.2%
29	Kansas	1,610	0.8%
30	Oklahoma	1,578	0.8%
31	Mississippi	1,519	0.7%
32	Iowa	1,511	0.7%
33	Arkansas	1,478	0.7%
34	Utah	1,428	0.7%
35	Nevada	1,208	0.6%
36	Nebraska	1,177	0.6%
37	New Mexico	1,082	0.5%
38	West Virginia	1,048	0.5%
39	Rhode Island	1,027	0.5%
40	Hawaii	986	0.5%
41	New Hampshire	900	0.4%
42	Maine	888	0.4%
43	Idaho	673	0.3%
44	Vermont	607	0.3%
45	Delaware	572	0.3%
46	Montana	552	0.3%
47	South Dakota	508	0.2%
48	North Dakota	441	0.2%
49	Alaska	435	0.2%
50	Wyoming	246	0.1%
	District of Columbia	941	0.5%

Source: American Medical Association (Chicago, Illinois)
   "Physician Characteristics and Distribution in the U.S." (2004 Edition)
As of December 31, 2002. Comprised of federal and nonfederal physicians. Total does not include 3,261 physicians in the U.S. territories and possessions, at APO's and FPO's and whose addresses are unknown.

Physicians 45 to 54 Years Old in 2002

National Total = 209,548 Physicians*

ALPHA ORDER

RANK	STATE	PHYSICIANS	% of USA
25	Alabama	2,746	1.3%
49	Alaska	423	0.2%
23	Arizona	3,173	1.5%
31	Arkansas	1,611	0.8%
1	California	24,859	11.9%
22	Colorado	3,275	1.6%
20	Connecticut	3,565	1.7%
47	Delaware	500	0.2%
4	Florida	12,180	5.8%
13	Georgia	5,484	2.6%
37	Hawaii	1,119	0.5%
43	Idaho	700	0.3%
6	Illinois	8,565	4.1%
19	Indiana	3,815	1.8%
32	Iowa	1,602	0.8%
30	Kansas	1,677	0.8%
27	Kentucky	2,656	1.3%
24	Louisiana	3,115	1.5%
40	Maine	1,072	0.5%
10	Maryland	6,051	2.9%
9	Massachusetts	7,149	3.4%
11	Michigan	6,048	2.9%
17	Minnesota	3,920	1.9%
33	Mississippi	1,446	0.7%
21	Missouri	3,563	1.7%
44	Montana	688	0.3%
36	Nebraska	1,148	0.5%
38	Nevada	1,084	0.5%
41	New Hampshire	1,040	0.5%
7	New Jersey	7,543	3.6%
34	New Mexico	1,356	0.6%
2	New York	18,734	8.9%
12	North Carolina	5,749	2.7%
48	North Dakota	485	0.2%
8	Ohio	7,498	3.6%
29	Oklahoma	1,759	0.8%
26	Oregon	2,736	1.3%
5	Pennsylvania	10,281	4.9%
42	Rhode Island	908	0.4%
28	South Carolina	2,524	1.2%
46	South Dakota	561	0.3%
16	Tennessee	4,436	2.1%
3	Texas	12,196	5.8%
35	Utah	1,327	0.6%
45	Vermont	635	0.3%
14	Virginia	5,387	2.6%
15	Washington	4,982	2.4%
38	West Virginia	1,084	0.5%
18	Wisconsin	3,898	1.9%
50	Wyoming	290	0.1%

RANK ORDER

RANK	STATE	PHYSICIANS	% of USA
1	California	24,859	11.9%
2	New York	18,734	8.9%
3	Texas	12,196	5.8%
4	Florida	12,180	5.8%
5	Pennsylvania	10,281	4.9%
6	Illinois	8,565	4.1%
7	New Jersey	7,543	3.6%
8	Ohio	7,498	3.6%
9	Massachusetts	7,149	3.4%
10	Maryland	6,051	2.9%
11	Michigan	6,048	2.9%
12	North Carolina	5,749	2.7%
13	Georgia	5,484	2.6%
14	Virginia	5,387	2.6%
15	Washington	4,982	2.4%
16	Tennessee	4,436	2.1%
17	Minnesota	3,920	1.9%
18	Wisconsin	3,898	1.9%
19	Indiana	3,815	1.8%
20	Connecticut	3,565	1.7%
21	Missouri	3,563	1.7%
22	Colorado	3,275	1.6%
23	Arizona	3,173	1.5%
24	Louisiana	3,115	1.5%
25	Alabama	2,746	1.3%
26	Oregon	2,736	1.3%
27	Kentucky	2,656	1.3%
28	South Carolina	2,524	1.2%
29	Oklahoma	1,759	0.8%
30	Kansas	1,677	0.8%
31	Arkansas	1,611	0.8%
32	Iowa	1,602	0.8%
33	Mississippi	1,446	0.7%
34	New Mexico	1,356	0.6%
35	Utah	1,327	0.6%
36	Nebraska	1,148	0.5%
37	Hawaii	1,119	0.5%
38	Nevada	1,084	0.5%
38	West Virginia	1,084	0.5%
40	Maine	1,072	0.5%
41	New Hampshire	1,040	0.5%
42	Rhode Island	908	0.4%
43	Idaho	700	0.3%
44	Montana	688	0.3%
45	Vermont	635	0.3%
46	South Dakota	561	0.3%
47	Delaware	500	0.2%
48	North Dakota	485	0.2%
49	Alaska	423	0.2%
50	Wyoming	290	0.1%
	District of Columbia	905	0.4%

Source: American Medical Association (Chicago, Illinois)
    "Physician Characteristics and Distribution in the U.S." (2004 Edition)
*As of December 31, 2002. Comprised of federal and nonfederal physicians. Total does not include 3,296
physicians in the U.S. territories and possessions, at APO's and FPO's and whose addresses are unknown.

Physicians 55 to 64 Years Old in 2002

National Total = 132,891 Physicians*

ALPHA ORDER

RANK	STATE	PHYSICIANS	% of USA
26	Alabama	1,579	1.2%
47	Alaska	304	0.2%
20	Arizona	2,109	1.6%
31	Arkansas	913	0.7%
1	California	18,742	14.1%
22	Colorado	2,076	1.6%
18	Connecticut	2,131	1.6%
46	Delaware	358	0.3%
3	Florida	7,841	5.9%
14	Georgia	3,058	2.3%
37	Hawaii	730	0.5%
43	Idaho	462	0.3%
5	Illinois	6,012	4.5%
21	Indiana	2,079	1.6%
33	Iowa	891	0.7%
30	Kansas	1,071	0.8%
27	Kentucky	1,518	1.1%
24	Louisiana	1,920	1.4%
39	Maine	666	0.5%
10	Maryland	4,037	3.0%
9	Massachusetts	4,339	3.3%
11	Michigan	3,925	3.0%
23	Minnesota	2,059	1.5%
35	Mississippi	872	0.7%
17	Missouri	2,178	1.6%
44	Montana	460	0.3%
40	Nebraska	621	0.5%
38	Nevada	725	0.5%
41	New Hampshire	556	0.4%
7	New Jersey	4,903	3.7%
32	New Mexico	898	0.7%
2	New York	12,033	9.1%
15	North Carolina	3,003	2.3%
49	North Dakota	268	0.2%
8	Ohio	4,584	3.4%
29	Oklahoma	1,113	0.8%
25	Oregon	1,830	1.4%
6	Pennsylvania	5,981	4.5%
42	Rhode Island	539	0.4%
28	South Carolina	1,479	1.1%
48	South Dakota	275	0.2%
16	Tennessee	2,368	1.8%
4	Texas	7,561	5.7%
36	Utah	869	0.7%
45	Vermont	361	0.3%
12	Virginia	3,401	2.6%
13	Washington	3,103	2.3%
34	West Virginia	879	0.7%
19	Wisconsin	2,130	1.6%
50	Wyoming	219	0.2%

RANK ORDER

RANK	STATE	PHYSICIANS	% of USA
1	California	18,742	14.1%
2	New York	12,033	9.1%
3	Florida	7,841	5.9%
4	Texas	7,561	5.7%
5	Illinois	6,012	4.5%
6	Pennsylvania	5,981	4.5%
7	New Jersey	4,903	3.7%
8	Ohio	4,584	3.4%
9	Massachusetts	4,339	3.3%
10	Maryland	4,037	3.0%
11	Michigan	3,925	3.0%
12	Virginia	3,401	2.6%
13	Washington	3,103	2.3%
14	Georgia	3,058	2.3%
15	North Carolina	3,003	2.3%
16	Tennessee	2,368	1.8%
17	Missouri	2,178	1.6%
18	Connecticut	2,131	1.6%
19	Wisconsin	2,130	1.6%
20	Arizona	2,109	1.6%
21	Indiana	2,079	1.6%
22	Colorado	2,076	1.6%
23	Minnesota	2,059	1.5%
24	Louisiana	1,920	1.4%
25	Oregon	1,830	1.4%
26	Alabama	1,579	1.2%
27	Kentucky	1,518	1.1%
28	South Carolina	1,479	1.1%
29	Oklahoma	1,113	0.8%
30	Kansas	1,071	0.8%
31	Arkansas	913	0.7%
32	New Mexico	898	0.7%
33	Iowa	891	0.7%
34	West Virginia	879	0.7%
35	Mississippi	872	0.7%
36	Utah	869	0.7%
37	Hawaii	730	0.5%
38	Nevada	725	0.5%
39	Maine	666	0.5%
40	Nebraska	621	0.5%
41	New Hampshire	556	0.4%
42	Rhode Island	539	0.4%
43	Idaho	462	0.3%
44	Montana	460	0.3%
45	Vermont	361	0.3%
46	Delaware	358	0.3%
47	Alaska	304	0.2%
48	South Dakota	275	0.2%
49	North Dakota	268	0.2%
50	Wyoming	219	0.2%
	District of Columbia	862	0.6%

Source: American Medical Association (Chicago, Illinois)
"Physician Characteristics and Distribution in the U.S." (2004 Edition)
*As of December 31, 2002. Comprised of federal and nonfederal physicians. Total does not include 1,775 physicians in the U.S. territories and possessions, at APO's and FPO's and whose addresses are unknown.

Physicians 65 Years Old and Older in 2002

National Total = 153,648 Physicians*

ALPHA ORDER

RANK	STATE	PHYSICIANS	% of USA
27	Alabama	1,579	1.0%
50	Alaska	180	0.1%
16	Arizona	2,925	1.9%
33	Arkansas	1,018	0.7%
1	California	22,347	14.5%
22	Colorado	2,191	1.4%
17	Connecticut	2,615	1.7%
46	Delaware	409	0.3%
3	Florida	12,826	8.3%
15	Georgia	3,168	2.1%
37	Hawaii	824	0.5%
43	Idaho	523	0.3%
6	Illinois	5,555	3.6%
20	Indiana	2,434	1.6%
31	Iowa	1,067	0.7%
29	Kansas	1,286	0.8%
28	Kentucky	1,524	1.0%
24	Louisiana	2,029	1.3%
38	Maine	820	0.5%
11	Maryland	4,240	2.8%
9	Massachusetts	4,776	3.1%
10	Michigan	4,277	2.8%
21	Minnesota	2,379	1.5%
32	Mississippi	1,046	0.7%
23	Missouri	2,157	1.4%
45	Montana	506	0.3%
42	Nebraska	715	0.5%
34	Nevada	930	0.6%
40	New Hampshire	772	0.5%
8	New Jersey	5,033	3.3%
36	New Mexico	834	0.5%
2	New York	14,822	9.6%
13	North Carolina	3,652	2.4%
48	North Dakota	260	0.2%
7	Ohio	5,275	3.4%
30	Oklahoma	1,284	0.8%
25	Oregon	2,013	1.3%
5	Pennsylvania	7,348	4.8%
41	Rhode Island	725	0.5%
26	South Carolina	1,703	1.1%
47	South Dakota	297	0.2%
18	Tennessee	2,499	1.6%
4	Texas	7,857	5.1%
35	Utah	835	0.5%
44	Vermont	522	0.3%
12	Virginia	3,902	2.5%
14	Washington	3,371	2.2%
39	West Virginia	801	0.5%
19	Wisconsin	2,454	1.6%
49	Wyoming	210	0.1%

RANK ORDER

RANK	STATE	PHYSICIANS	% of USA
1	California	22,347	14.5%
2	New York	14,822	9.6%
3	Florida	12,826	8.3%
4	Texas	7,857	5.1%
5	Pennsylvania	7,348	4.8%
6	Illinois	5,555	3.6%
7	Ohio	5,275	3.4%
8	New Jersey	5,033	3.3%
9	Massachusetts	4,776	3.1%
10	Michigan	4,277	2.8%
11	Maryland	4,240	2.8%
12	Virginia	3,902	2.5%
13	North Carolina	3,652	2.4%
14	Washington	3,371	2.2%
15	Georgia	3,168	2.1%
16	Arizona	2,925	1.9%
17	Connecticut	2,615	1.7%
18	Tennessee	2,499	1.6%
19	Wisconsin	2,454	1.6%
20	Indiana	2,434	1.6%
21	Minnesota	2,379	1.5%
22	Colorado	2,191	1.4%
23	Missouri	2,157	1.4%
24	Louisiana	2,029	1.3%
25	Oregon	2,013	1.3%
26	South Carolina	1,703	1.1%
27	Alabama	1,579	1.0%
28	Kentucky	1,524	1.0%
29	Kansas	1,286	0.8%
30	Oklahoma	1,284	0.8%
31	Iowa	1,067	0.7%
32	Mississippi	1,046	0.7%
33	Arkansas	1,018	0.7%
34	Nevada	930	0.6%
35	Utah	835	0.5%
36	New Mexico	834	0.5%
37	Hawaii	824	0.5%
38	Maine	820	0.5%
39	West Virginia	801	0.5%
40	New Hampshire	772	0.5%
41	Rhode Island	725	0.5%
42	Nebraska	715	0.5%
43	Idaho	523	0.3%
44	Vermont	522	0.3%
45	Montana	506	0.3%
46	Delaware	409	0.3%
47	South Dakota	297	0.2%
48	North Dakota	260	0.2%
49	Wyoming	210	0.1%
50	Alaska	180	0.1%
	District of Columbia	833	0.5%

Source: American Medical Association (Chicago, Illinois)
   "Physician Characteristics and Distribution in the U.S." (2004 Edition)
*As of December 31, 2002. Comprised of federal and nonfederal physicians. Total does not include 2,769 physicians in the U.S. territories and possessions, at APO's and FPO's and whose addresses are unknown.

Percent of Physicians 65 Years Old and Older in 2002

National Percent = 18.3% of Physicians*

ALPHA ORDER

ALPHA ORDER

RANK	STATE	PERCENT
44	Alabama	15.6
50	Alaska	12.0
2	Arizona	22.5
29	Arkansas	17.0
3	California	21.9
23	Colorado	17.7
15	Connecticut	18.8
17	Delaware	18.5
1	Florida	26.3
45	Georgia	15.5
12	Hawaii	19.6
9	Idaho	20.5
48	Illinois	15.0
29	Indiana	17.0
25	Iowa	17.5
13	Kansas	19.3
47	Kentucky	15.3
38	Louisiana	15.9
4	Maine	21.4
27	Maryland	17.4
36	Massachusetts	16.0
32	Michigan	16.6
38	Minnesota	15.9
18	Mississippi	18.4
49	Missouri	14.8
4	Montana	21.4
38	Nebraska	15.9
6	Nevada	21.1
8	New Hampshire	20.6
25	New Jersey	17.5
27	New Mexico	17.4
19	New York	18.3
36	North Carolina	16.0
43	North Dakota	15.7
32	Ohio	16.6
14	Oklahoma	19.2
11	Oregon	19.8
20	Pennsylvania	18.2
22	Rhode Island	17.9
31	South Carolina	16.7
35	South Dakota	16.4
46	Tennessee	15.4
41	Texas	15.8
41	Utah	15.8
7	Vermont	20.9
21	Virginia	18.1
16	Washington	18.7
24	West Virginia	17.6
34	Wisconsin	16.5
10	Wyoming	19.9

RANK ORDER

RANK	STATE	PERCENT
1	Florida	26.3
2	Arizona	22.5
3	California	21.9
4	Maine	21.4
4	Montana	21.4
6	Nevada	21.1
7	Vermont	20.9
8	New Hampshire	20.6
9	Idaho	20.5
10	Wyoming	19.9
11	Oregon	19.8
12	Hawaii	19.6
13	Kansas	19.3
14	Oklahoma	19.2
15	Connecticut	18.8
16	Washington	18.7
17	Delaware	18.5
18	Mississippi	18.4
19	New York	18.3
20	Pennsylvania	18.2
21	Virginia	18.1
22	Rhode Island	17.9
23	Colorado	17.7
24	West Virginia	17.6
25	Iowa	17.5
25	New Jersey	17.5
27	Maryland	17.4
27	New Mexico	17.4
29	Arkansas	17.0
29	Indiana	17.0
31	South Carolina	16.7
32	Michigan	16.6
32	Ohio	16.6
34	Wisconsin	16.5
35	South Dakota	16.4
36	Massachusetts	16.0
36	North Carolina	16.0
38	Louisiana	15.9
38	Minnesota	15.9
38	Nebraska	15.9
41	Texas	15.8
41	Utah	15.8
43	North Dakota	15.7
44	Alabama	15.6
45	Georgia	15.5
46	Tennessee	15.4
47	Kentucky	15.3
48	Illinois	15.0
49	Missouri	14.8
50	Alaska	12.0

District of Columbia	18.5

Source: Morgan Quitno Press using data from American Medical Association (Chicago, Illinois)
    "Physician Characteristics and Distribution in the U.S." (2004 Edition)
*As of December 31, 2002. Comprised of federal and nonfederal physicians. National percent does not include
physicians in the U.S. territories and possessions, at APO's and FPO's and whose addresses are unknown.

Federal Physicians in 2002

National Total = 20,688 Physicians*

ALPHA ORDER

RANK	STATE	PHYSICIANS	% of USA
28	Alabama	211	1.0%
35	Alaska	149	0.7%
13	Arizona	446	2.2%
34	Arkansas	160	0.8%
1	California	2,220	10.7%
16	Colorado	377	1.8%
31	Connecticut	193	0.9%
47	Delaware	53	0.3%
4	Florida	1,303	6.3%
7	Georgia	887	4.3%
22	Hawaii	281	1.4%
42	Idaho	87	0.4%
11	Illinois	581	2.8%
29	Indiana	202	1.0%
39	Iowa	108	0.5%
33	Kansas	186	0.9%
32	Kentucky	192	0.9%
26	Louisiana	223	1.1%
45	Maine	77	0.4%
2	Maryland	1,883	9.1%
14	Massachusetts	441	2.1%
18	Michigan	312	1.5%
20	Minnesota	285	1.4%
24	Mississippi	247	1.2%
19	Missouri	290	1.4%
46	Montana	71	0.3%
42	Nebraska	87	0.4%
37	Nevada	132	0.6%
44	New Hampshire	80	0.4%
17	New Jersey	321	1.6%
25	New Mexico	237	1.1%
6	New York	976	4.7%
8	North Carolina	620	3.0%
48	North Dakota	50	0.2%
12	Ohio	519	2.5%
29	Oklahoma	202	1.0%
23	Oregon	276	1.3%
10	Pennsylvania	592	2.9%
41	Rhode Island	90	0.4%
21	South Carolina	283	1.4%
40	South Dakota	94	0.5%
15	Tennessee	428	2.1%
3	Texas	1,589	7.7%
38	Utah	127	0.6%
49	Vermont	46	0.2%
5	Virginia	1,095	5.3%
9	Washington	619	3.0%
36	West Virginia	147	0.7%
27	Wisconsin	216	1.0%
50	Wyoming	45	0.2%

RANK ORDER

RANK	STATE	PHYSICIANS	% of USA
1	California	2,220	10.7%
2	Maryland	1,883	9.1%
3	Texas	1,589	7.7%
4	Florida	1,303	6.3%
5	Virginia	1,095	5.3%
6	New York	976	4.7%
7	Georgia	887	4.3%
8	North Carolina	620	3.0%
9	Washington	619	3.0%
10	Pennsylvania	592	2.9%
11	Illinois	581	2.8%
12	Ohio	519	2.5%
13	Arizona	446	2.2%
14	Massachusetts	441	2.1%
15	Tennessee	428	2.1%
16	Colorado	377	1.8%
17	New Jersey	321	1.6%
18	Michigan	312	1.5%
19	Missouri	290	1.4%
20	Minnesota	285	1.4%
21	South Carolina	283	1.4%
22	Hawaii	281	1.4%
23	Oregon	276	1.3%
24	Mississippi	247	1.2%
25	New Mexico	237	1.1%
26	Louisiana	223	1.1%
27	Wisconsin	216	1.0%
28	Alabama	211	1.0%
29	Indiana	202	1.0%
29	Oklahoma	202	1.0%
31	Connecticut	193	0.9%
32	Kentucky	192	0.9%
33	Kansas	186	0.9%
34	Arkansas	160	0.8%
35	Alaska	149	0.7%
36	West Virginia	147	0.7%
37	Nevada	132	0.6%
38	Utah	127	0.6%
39	Iowa	108	0.5%
40	South Dakota	94	0.5%
41	Rhode Island	90	0.4%
42	Idaho	87	0.4%
42	Nebraska	87	0.4%
44	New Hampshire	80	0.4%
45	Maine	77	0.4%
46	Montana	71	0.3%
47	Delaware	53	0.3%
48	North Dakota	50	0.2%
49	Vermont	46	0.2%
50	Wyoming	45	0.2%
	District of Columbia	352	1.7%

Source: American Medical Association (Chicago, Illinois)
    "Physician Characteristics and Distribution in the U.S." (2004 Edition)
*As of December 31, 2002. Total does not include 854 physicians in U.S. territories and possessions, at APO's and FPO's and whose addresses are unknown.

Rate of Federal Physicians in 2002

National Rate = 7.2 Physicians per 100,000 Population*

<table>
<tr><td colspan="3">ALPHA ORDER</td><td colspan="3">RANK ORDER</td></tr>
<tr><td>RANK</td><td>STATE</td><td>PERCENT</td><td>RANK</td><td>STATE</td><td>PERCENT</td></tr>
<tr><td>42</td><td>Alabama</td><td>4.7</td><td>1</td><td>Maryland</td><td>34.5</td></tr>
<tr><td>2</td><td>Alaska</td><td>23.2</td><td>2</td><td>Alaska</td><td>23.2</td></tr>
<tr><td>13</td><td>Arizona</td><td>8.2</td><td>3</td><td>Hawaii</td><td>22.6</td></tr>
<tr><td>31</td><td>Arkansas</td><td>5.9</td><td>4</td><td>Virginia</td><td>15.0</td></tr>
<tr><td>28</td><td>California</td><td>6.3</td><td>5</td><td>New Mexico</td><td>12.8</td></tr>
<tr><td>11</td><td>Colorado</td><td>8.4</td><td>6</td><td>South Dakota</td><td>12.4</td></tr>
<tr><td>35</td><td>Connecticut</td><td>5.6</td><td>7</td><td>Georgia</td><td>10.4</td></tr>
<tr><td>26</td><td>Delaware</td><td>6.6</td><td>8</td><td>Washington</td><td>10.2</td></tr>
<tr><td>16</td><td>Florida</td><td>7.8</td><td>9</td><td>Wyoming</td><td>9.0</td></tr>
<tr><td>7</td><td>Georgia</td><td>10.4</td><td>10</td><td>Mississippi</td><td>8.6</td></tr>
<tr><td>3</td><td>Hawaii</td><td>22.6</td><td>11</td><td>Colorado</td><td>8.4</td></tr>
<tr><td>27</td><td>Idaho</td><td>6.5</td><td>11</td><td>Rhode Island</td><td>8.4</td></tr>
<tr><td>44</td><td>Illinois</td><td>4.6</td><td>13</td><td>Arizona</td><td>8.2</td></tr>
<tr><td>49</td><td>Indiana</td><td>3.3</td><td>14</td><td>West Virginia</td><td>8.1</td></tr>
<tr><td>47</td><td>Iowa</td><td>3.7</td><td>15</td><td>North Dakota</td><td>7.9</td></tr>
<tr><td>23</td><td>Kansas</td><td>6.9</td><td>16</td><td>Florida</td><td>7.8</td></tr>
<tr><td>42</td><td>Kentucky</td><td>4.7</td><td>16</td><td>Montana</td><td>7.8</td></tr>
<tr><td>39</td><td>Louisiana</td><td>5.0</td><td>16</td><td>Oregon</td><td>7.8</td></tr>
<tr><td>31</td><td>Maine</td><td>5.9</td><td>19</td><td>North Carolina</td><td>7.5</td></tr>
<tr><td>1</td><td>Maryland</td><td>34.5</td><td>19</td><td>Vermont</td><td>7.5</td></tr>
<tr><td>23</td><td>Massachusetts</td><td>6.9</td><td>21</td><td>Tennessee</td><td>7.4</td></tr>
<tr><td>50</td><td>Michigan</td><td>3.1</td><td>22</td><td>Texas</td><td>7.3</td></tr>
<tr><td>34</td><td>Minnesota</td><td>5.7</td><td>23</td><td>Kansas</td><td>6.9</td></tr>
<tr><td>10</td><td>Mississippi</td><td>8.6</td><td>23</td><td>Massachusetts</td><td>6.9</td></tr>
<tr><td>37</td><td>Missouri</td><td>5.1</td><td>23</td><td>South Carolina</td><td>6.9</td></tr>
<tr><td>16</td><td>Montana</td><td>7.8</td><td>26</td><td>Delaware</td><td>6.6</td></tr>
<tr><td>39</td><td>Nebraska</td><td>5.0</td><td>27</td><td>Idaho</td><td>6.5</td></tr>
<tr><td>30</td><td>Nevada</td><td>6.1</td><td>28</td><td>California</td><td>6.3</td></tr>
<tr><td>28</td><td>New Hampshire</td><td>6.3</td><td>28</td><td>New Hampshire</td><td>6.3</td></tr>
<tr><td>47</td><td>New Jersey</td><td>3.7</td><td>30</td><td>Nevada</td><td>6.1</td></tr>
<tr><td>5</td><td>New Mexico</td><td>12.8</td><td>31</td><td>Arkansas</td><td>5.9</td></tr>
<tr><td>37</td><td>New York</td><td>5.1</td><td>31</td><td>Maine</td><td>5.9</td></tr>
<tr><td>19</td><td>North Carolina</td><td>7.5</td><td>33</td><td>Oklahoma</td><td>5.8</td></tr>
<tr><td>15</td><td>North Dakota</td><td>7.9</td><td>34</td><td>Minnesota</td><td>5.7</td></tr>
<tr><td>45</td><td>Ohio</td><td>4.5</td><td>35</td><td>Connecticut</td><td>5.6</td></tr>
<tr><td>33</td><td>Oklahoma</td><td>5.8</td><td>36</td><td>Utah</td><td>5.5</td></tr>
<tr><td>16</td><td>Oregon</td><td>7.8</td><td>37</td><td>Missouri</td><td>5.1</td></tr>
<tr><td>41</td><td>Pennsylvania</td><td>4.8</td><td>37</td><td>New York</td><td>5.1</td></tr>
<tr><td>11</td><td>Rhode Island</td><td>8.4</td><td>39</td><td>Louisiana</td><td>5.0</td></tr>
<tr><td>23</td><td>South Carolina</td><td>6.9</td><td>39</td><td>Nebraska</td><td>5.0</td></tr>
<tr><td>6</td><td>South Dakota</td><td>12.4</td><td>41</td><td>Pennsylvania</td><td>4.8</td></tr>
<tr><td>21</td><td>Tennessee</td><td>7.4</td><td>42</td><td>Alabama</td><td>4.7</td></tr>
<tr><td>22</td><td>Texas</td><td>7.3</td><td>42</td><td>Kentucky</td><td>4.7</td></tr>
<tr><td>36</td><td>Utah</td><td>5.5</td><td>44</td><td>Illinois</td><td>4.6</td></tr>
<tr><td>19</td><td>Vermont</td><td>7.5</td><td>45</td><td>Ohio</td><td>4.5</td></tr>
<tr><td>4</td><td>Virginia</td><td>15.0</td><td>46</td><td>Wisconsin</td><td>4.0</td></tr>
<tr><td>8</td><td>Washington</td><td>10.2</td><td>47</td><td>Iowa</td><td>3.7</td></tr>
<tr><td>14</td><td>West Virginia</td><td>8.1</td><td>47</td><td>New Jersey</td><td>3.7</td></tr>
<tr><td>46</td><td>Wisconsin</td><td>4.0</td><td>49</td><td>Indiana</td><td>3.3</td></tr>
<tr><td>9</td><td>Wyoming</td><td>9.0</td><td>50</td><td>Michigan</td><td>3.1</td></tr>
</table>

District of Columbia   61.8

Source: Morgan Quitno Press using data from American Medical Association (Chicago, Illinois)
   "Physician Characteristics and Distribution in the U.S." (2004 Edition)
*As of December 31, 2002. National rate does not include physicians in U.S. territories and possessions, at APO's and FPO's and whose addresses are unknown.

Nonfederal Physicians in 2002

National Total = 819,643 Physicians*

ALPHA ORDER

RANK ORDER

RANK	STATE	PHYSICIANS	% of USA
26	Alabama	9,905	1.2%
49	Alaska	1,346	0.2%
22	Arizona	12,543	1.5%
32	Arkansas	5,841	0.7%
1	California	99,720	12.2%
24	Colorado	12,027	1.5%
21	Connecticut	13,717	1.7%
46	Delaware	2,158	0.3%
4	Florida	47,403	5.8%
14	Georgia	19,585	2.4%
40	Hawaii	3,929	0.5%
43	Idaho	2,464	0.3%
6	Illinois	36,439	4.4%
20	Indiana	14,103	1.7%
31	Iowa	5,991	0.7%
29	Kansas	6,491	0.8%
28	Kentucky	9,799	1.2%
23	Louisiana	12,515	1.5%
41	Maine	3,748	0.5%
11	Maryland	22,513	2.7%
8	Massachusetts	29,474	3.6%
10	Michigan	25,475	3.1%
17	Minnesota	14,709	1.8%
33	Mississippi	5,433	0.7%
19	Missouri	14,277	1.7%
45	Montana	2,288	0.3%
37	Nebraska	4,402	0.5%
38	Nevada	4,285	0.5%
42	New Hampshire	3,661	0.4%
9	New Jersey	28,435	3.5%
35	New Mexico	4,562	0.6%
2	New York	79,889	9.7%
12	North Carolina	22,204	2.7%
48	North Dakota	1,603	0.2%
7	Ohio	31,232	3.8%
30	Oklahoma	6,474	0.8%
27	Oregon	9,892	1.2%
5	Pennsylvania	39,886	4.9%
39	Rhode Island	3,953	0.5%
25	South Carolina	9,912	1.2%
47	South Dakota	1,714	0.2%
16	Tennessee	15,795	1.9%
3	Texas	48,156	5.9%
34	Utah	5,156	0.6%
44	Vermont	2,451	0.3%
13	Virginia	20,499	2.5%
15	Washington	17,371	2.1%
36	West Virginia	4,415	0.5%
18	Wisconsin	14,636	1.8%
50	Wyoming	1,008	0.1%

RANK	STATE	PHYSICIANS	% of USA
1	California	99,720	12.2%
2	New York	79,889	9.7%
3	Texas	48,156	5.9%
4	Florida	47,403	5.8%
5	Pennsylvania	39,886	4.9%
6	Illinois	36,439	4.4%
7	Ohio	31,232	3.8%
8	Massachusetts	29,474	3.6%
9	New Jersey	28,435	3.5%
10	Michigan	25,475	3.1%
11	Maryland	22,513	2.7%
12	North Carolina	22,204	2.7%
13	Virginia	20,499	2.5%
14	Georgia	19,585	2.4%
15	Washington	17,371	2.1%
16	Tennessee	15,795	1.9%
17	Minnesota	14,709	1.8%
18	Wisconsin	14,636	1.8%
19	Missouri	14,277	1.7%
20	Indiana	14,103	1.7%
21	Connecticut	13,717	1.7%
22	Arizona	12,543	1.5%
23	Louisiana	12,515	1.5%
24	Colorado	12,027	1.5%
25	South Carolina	9,912	1.2%
26	Alabama	9,905	1.2%
27	Oregon	9,892	1.2%
28	Kentucky	9,799	1.2%
29	Kansas	6,491	0.8%
30	Oklahoma	6,474	0.8%
31	Iowa	5,991	0.7%
32	Arkansas	5,841	0.7%
33	Mississippi	5,433	0.7%
34	Utah	5,156	0.6%
35	New Mexico	4,562	0.6%
36	West Virginia	4,415	0.5%
37	Nebraska	4,402	0.5%
38	Nevada	4,285	0.5%
39	Rhode Island	3,953	0.5%
40	Hawaii	3,929	0.5%
41	Maine	3,748	0.5%
42	New Hampshire	3,661	0.4%
43	Idaho	2,464	0.3%
44	Vermont	2,451	0.3%
45	Montana	2,288	0.3%
46	Delaware	2,158	0.3%
47	South Dakota	1,714	0.2%
48	North Dakota	1,603	0.2%
49	Alaska	1,346	0.2%
50	Wyoming	1,008	0.1%
	District of Columbia	4,159	0.5%

Source: American Medical Association (Chicago, Illinois)
"Physician Characteristics and Distribution in the U.S." (2004 Edition)
As of December 31, 2002. Total does not include 12,002 physicians in U.S. territories and possessions, at APO's and FPO's and whose addresses are unknown.

Rate of Nonfederal Physicians in 2002

National Rate = 285 Physicians per 100,000 Population*

ALPHA ORDER

RANK	STATE	RATE
42	Alabama	221
44	Alaska	210
36	Arizona	231
43	Arkansas	216
15	California	285
24	Colorado	267
5	Connecticut	397
23	Delaware	268
16	Florida	284
37	Georgia	229
9	Hawaii	317
50	Idaho	183
11	Illinois	290
37	Indiana	229
45	Iowa	204
35	Kansas	239
34	Kentucky	240
19	Louisiana	280
12	Maine	289
3	Maryland	413
1	Massachusetts	459
27	Michigan	254
10	Minnesota	293
48	Mississippi	190
29	Missouri	252
30	Montana	251
26	Nebraska	255
47	Nevada	198
13	New Hampshire	287
7	New Jersey	332
31	New Mexico	246
2	New York	418
24	North Carolina	267
28	North Dakota	253
20	Ohio	274
49	Oklahoma	186
17	Oregon	281
8	Pennsylvania	324
6	Rhode Island	370
33	South Carolina	242
39	South Dakota	225
21	Tennessee	273
40	Texas	222
40	Utah	222
4	Vermont	398
17	Virginia	281
14	Washington	286
32	West Virginia	245
22	Wisconsin	269
46	Wyoming	202

RANK ORDER

RANK	STATE	RATE
1	Massachusetts	459
2	New York	418
3	Maryland	413
4	Vermont	398
5	Connecticut	397
6	Rhode Island	370
7	New Jersey	332
8	Pennsylvania	324
9	Hawaii	317
10	Minnesota	293
11	Illinois	290
12	Maine	289
13	New Hampshire	287
14	Washington	286
15	California	285
16	Florida	284
17	Oregon	281
17	Virginia	281
19	Louisiana	280
20	Ohio	274
21	Tennessee	273
22	Wisconsin	269
23	Delaware	268
24	Colorado	267
24	North Carolina	267
26	Nebraska	255
27	Michigan	254
28	North Dakota	253
29	Missouri	252
30	Montana	251
31	New Mexico	246
32	West Virginia	245
33	South Carolina	242
34	Kentucky	240
35	Kansas	239
36	Arizona	231
37	Georgia	229
37	Indiana	229
39	South Dakota	225
40	Texas	222
40	Utah	222
42	Alabama	221
43	Arkansas	216
44	Alaska	210
45	Iowa	204
46	Wyoming	202
47	Nevada	198
48	Mississippi	190
49	Oklahoma	186
50	Idaho	183

District of Columbia — 731

Source: Morgan Quitno Press using data from American Medical Association (Chicago, Illinois)
"Physician Characteristics and Distribution in the U.S." (2004 Edition)
*As of December 31, 2002. National rate does not include physicians in U.S. territories and possessions, at APO's and FPO's and whose addresses are unknown.

Nonfederal Physicians in Patient Care in 2002

National Total = 649,332 Physicians*

ALPHA ORDER

RANK	STATE	PHYSICIANS	% of USA
25	Alabama	8,226	1.3%
49	Alaska	1,140	0.2%
23	Arizona	9,604	1.5%
31	Arkansas	4,814	0.7%
1	California	76,743	11.8%
24	Colorado	9,538	1.5%
21	Connecticut	10,695	1.6%
46	Delaware	1,741	0.3%
4	Florida	35,752	5.5%
14	Georgia	16,086	2.5%
40	Hawaii	3,146	0.5%
43	Idaho	2,044	0.3%
6	Illinois	29,135	4.5%
20	Indiana	11,657	1.8%
32	Iowa	4,616	0.7%
30	Kansas	5,100	0.8%
27	Kentucky	8,096	1.2%
22	Louisiana	10,336	1.6%
42	Maine	2,924	0.5%
12	Maryland	17,032	2.6%
9	Massachusetts	22,564	3.5%
10	Michigan	20,246	3.1%
18	Minnesota	11,700	1.8%
33	Mississippi	4,488	0.7%
19	Missouri	11,692	1.8%
45	Montana	1,842	0.3%
35	Nebraska	3,603	0.6%
38	Nevada	3,494	0.5%
41	New Hampshire	2,930	0.5%
8	New Jersey	23,025	3.5%
37	New Mexico	3,527	0.5%
2	New York	62,431	9.6%
11	North Carolina	17,850	2.7%
48	North Dakota	1,318	0.2%
7	Ohio	25,136	3.9%
29	Oklahoma	5,167	0.8%
28	Oregon	7,637	1.2%
5	Pennsylvania	31,496	4.9%
39	Rhode Island	3,177	0.5%
26	South Carolina	8,182	1.3%
47	South Dakota	1,418	0.2%
16	Tennessee	13,024	2.0%
3	Texas	39,528	6.1%
34	Utah	4,147	0.6%
44	Vermont	1,889	0.3%
13	Virginia	16,437	2.5%
15	Washington	13,523	2.1%
36	West Virginia	3,565	0.5%
17	Wisconsin	11,961	1.8%
50	Wyoming	827	0.1%

RANK ORDER

RANK	STATE	PHYSICIANS	% of USA
1	California	76,743	11.8%
2	New York	62,431	9.6%
3	Texas	39,528	6.1%
4	Florida	35,752	5.5%
5	Pennsylvania	31,496	4.9%
6	Illinois	29,135	4.5%
7	Ohio	25,136	3.9%
8	New Jersey	23,025	3.5%
9	Massachusetts	22,564	3.5%
10	Michigan	20,246	3.1%
11	North Carolina	17,850	2.7%
12	Maryland	17,032	2.6%
13	Virginia	16,437	2.5%
14	Georgia	16,086	2.5%
15	Washington	13,523	2.1%
16	Tennessee	13,024	2.0%
17	Wisconsin	11,961	1.8%
18	Minnesota	11,700	1.8%
19	Missouri	11,692	1.8%
20	Indiana	11,657	1.8%
21	Connecticut	10,695	1.6%
22	Louisiana	10,336	1.6%
23	Arizona	9,604	1.5%
24	Colorado	9,538	1.5%
25	Alabama	8,226	1.3%
26	South Carolina	8,182	1.3%
27	Kentucky	8,096	1.2%
28	Oregon	7,637	1.2%
29	Oklahoma	5,167	0.8%
30	Kansas	5,100	0.8%
31	Arkansas	4,814	0.7%
32	Iowa	4,616	0.7%
33	Mississippi	4,488	0.7%
34	Utah	4,147	0.6%
35	Nebraska	3,603	0.6%
36	West Virginia	3,565	0.5%
37	New Mexico	3,527	0.5%
38	Nevada	3,494	0.5%
39	Rhode Island	3,177	0.5%
40	Hawaii	3,146	0.5%
41	New Hampshire	2,930	0.5%
42	Maine	2,924	0.5%
43	Idaho	2,044	0.3%
44	Vermont	1,889	0.3%
45	Montana	1,842	0.3%
46	Delaware	1,741	0.3%
47	South Dakota	1,418	0.2%
48	North Dakota	1,318	0.2%
49	Alaska	1,140	0.2%
50	Wyoming	827	0.1%
	District of Columbia	3,083	0.5%

Source: American Medical Association (Chicago, Illinois)
    "Physician Characteristics and Distribution in the U.S." (2004 Edition)
*As of December 31, 2002. Total does not include 8,791 physicians in U.S. territories and possessions.

Rate of Nonfederal Physicians in Patient Care in 2002

National Rate = 225 Physicians per 100,000 Population*

ALPHA ORDER

ALPHA ORDER

RANK	STATE	RATE
39	Alabama	183
43	Alaska	177
44	Arizona	176
42	Arkansas	178
20	California	219
25	Colorado	212
4	Connecticut	309
22	Delaware	216
24	Florida	214
36	Georgia	188
9	Hawaii	253
49	Idaho	152
11	Illinois	231
35	Indiana	189
47	Iowa	157
36	Kansas	188
32	Kentucky	198
11	Louisiana	231
14	Maine	226
3	Maryland	312
1	Massachusetts	351
30	Michigan	201
10	Minnesota	233
48	Mississippi	156
28	Missouri	206
29	Montana	203
26	Nebraska	208
46	Nevada	161
13	New Hampshire	230
7	New Jersey	268
34	New Mexico	190
2	New York	326
23	North Carolina	215
26	North Dakota	208
18	Ohio	220
50	Oklahoma	148
21	Oregon	217
8	Pennsylvania	255
6	Rhode Island	297
31	South Carolina	199
38	South Dakota	186
15	Tennessee	225
40	Texas	181
41	Utah	179
5	Vermont	306
15	Virginia	225
17	Washington	223
32	West Virginia	198
18	Wisconsin	220
45	Wyoming	166

RANK ORDER

RANK	STATE	RATE
1	Massachusetts	351
2	New York	326
3	Maryland	312
4	Connecticut	309
5	Vermont	306
6	Rhode Island	297
7	New Jersey	268
8	Pennsylvania	255
9	Hawaii	253
10	Minnesota	233
11	Illinois	231
11	Louisiana	231
13	New Hampshire	230
14	Maine	226
15	Tennessee	225
15	Virginia	225
17	Washington	223
18	Ohio	220
18	Wisconsin	220
20	California	219
21	Oregon	217
22	Delaware	216
23	North Carolina	215
24	Florida	214
25	Colorado	212
26	Nebraska	208
26	North Dakota	208
28	Missouri	206
29	Montana	203
30	Michigan	201
31	South Carolina	199
32	Kentucky	198
32	West Virginia	198
34	New Mexico	190
35	Indiana	189
36	Georgia	188
36	Kansas	188
38	South Dakota	186
39	Alabama	183
40	Texas	181
41	Utah	179
42	Arkansas	178
43	Alaska	177
44	Arizona	176
45	Wyoming	166
46	Nevada	161
47	Iowa	157
48	Mississippi	156
49	Idaho	152
50	Oklahoma	148

District of Columbia   540

Source: Morgan Quitno Press using data from American Medical Association (Chicago, Illinois)
"Physician Characteristics and Distribution in the U.S." (2004 Edition)
*As of December 31, 2002. National rate does not include physicians in U.S. territories and possessions.

Physicians in Primary Care in 2002

National Total = 281,086 Physicians*

ALPHA ORDER

RANK	STATE	PHYSICIANS	% of USA
25	Alabama	3,699	1.3%
49	Alaska	643	0.2%
24	Arizona	4,104	1.5%
31	Arkansas	2,209	0.8%
1	California	33,774	12.0%
22	Colorado	4,207	1.5%
21	Connecticut	4,377	1.6%
46	Delaware	739	0.3%
4	Florida	14,515	5.2%
14	Georgia	7,329	2.6%
39	Hawaii	1,501	0.5%
43	Idaho	919	0.3%
5	Illinois	13,223	4.7%
19	Indiana	5,057	1.8%
32	Iowa	2,078	0.7%
30	Kansas	2,303	0.8%
27	Kentucky	3,494	1.2%
23	Louisiana	4,204	1.5%
41	Maine	1,342	0.5%
13	Maryland	7,440	2.6%
9	Massachusetts	8,884	3.2%
10	Michigan	8,809	3.1%
17	Minnesota	5,430	1.9%
33	Mississippi	1,979	0.7%
20	Missouri	4,830	1.7%
45	Montana	832	0.3%
35	Nebraska	1,696	0.6%
38	Nevada	1,533	0.5%
42	New Hampshire	1,283	0.5%
8	New Jersey	9,873	3.5%
36	New Mexico	1,687	0.6%
2	New York	26,199	9.3%
11	North Carolina	7,783	2.8%
48	North Dakota	646	0.2%
7	Ohio	10,855	3.9%
29	Oklahoma	2,336	0.8%
28	Oregon	3,486	1.2%
6	Pennsylvania	12,736	4.5%
40	Rhode Island	1,347	0.5%
26	South Carolina	3,679	1.3%
47	South Dakota	686	0.2%
16	Tennessee	5,540	2.0%
3	Texas	16,783	6.0%
34	Utah	1,740	0.6%
44	Vermont	888	0.3%
12	Virginia	7,524	2.7%
15	Washington	6,194	2.2%
37	West Virginia	1,611	0.6%
18	Wisconsin	5,350	1.9%
50	Wyoming	415	0.1%

RANK ORDER

RANK	STATE	PHYSICIANS	% of USA
1	California	33,774	12.0%
2	New York	26,199	9.3%
3	Texas	16,783	6.0%
4	Florida	14,515	5.2%
5	Illinois	13,223	4.7%
6	Pennsylvania	12,736	4.5%
7	Ohio	10,855	3.9%
8	New Jersey	9,873	3.5%
9	Massachusetts	8,884	3.2%
10	Michigan	8,809	3.1%
11	North Carolina	7,783	2.8%
12	Virginia	7,524	2.7%
13	Maryland	7,440	2.6%
14	Georgia	7,329	2.6%
15	Washington	6,194	2.2%
16	Tennessee	5,540	2.0%
17	Minnesota	5,430	1.9%
18	Wisconsin	5,350	1.9%
19	Indiana	5,057	1.8%
20	Missouri	4,830	1.7%
21	Connecticut	4,377	1.6%
22	Colorado	4,207	1.5%
23	Louisiana	4,204	1.5%
24	Arizona	4,104	1.5%
25	Alabama	3,699	1.3%
26	South Carolina	3,679	1.3%
27	Kentucky	3,494	1.2%
28	Oregon	3,486	1.2%
29	Oklahoma	2,336	0.8%
30	Kansas	2,303	0.8%
31	Arkansas	2,209	0.8%
32	Iowa	2,078	0.7%
33	Mississippi	1,979	0.7%
34	Utah	1,740	0.6%
35	Nebraska	1,696	0.6%
36	New Mexico	1,687	0.6%
37	West Virginia	1,611	0.6%
38	Nevada	1,533	0.5%
39	Hawaii	1,501	0.5%
40	Rhode Island	1,347	0.5%
41	Maine	1,342	0.5%
42	New Hampshire	1,283	0.5%
43	Idaho	919	0.3%
44	Vermont	888	0.3%
45	Montana	832	0.3%
46	Delaware	739	0.3%
47	South Dakota	686	0.2%
48	North Dakota	646	0.2%
49	Alaska	643	0.2%
50	Wyoming	415	0.1%
	District of Columbia	1,295	0.5%

Source: American Medical Association (Chicago, Illinois)
"Physician Characteristics and Distribution in the U.S." (2004 Edition)
*Federal and nonfederal physicians as of December 31, 2002. National total does not include 5,208 physicians in U.S. territories and possessions. Primary Care Specialties include Family Practice, General Practice, Internal Medicine, Obstetrics/Gynecology and Pediatrics excluding subspecialties within each category.

Rate of Physicians in Primary Care in 2002

National Rate = 98 Physicians per 100,000 Population*

ALPHA ORDER

RANK	STATE	RATE
39	Alabama	83
17	Alaska	100
44	Arizona	75
41	Arkansas	82
21	California	96
26	Colorado	93
5	Connecticut	127
27	Delaware	92
34	Florida	87
35	Georgia	86
7	Hawaii	121
49	Idaho	68
10	Illinois	105
41	Indiana	82
46	Iowa	71
36	Kansas	85
36	Kentucky	85
24	Louisiana	94
11	Maine	104
3	Maryland	137
2	Massachusetts	138
33	Michigan	88
9	Minnesota	108
48	Mississippi	69
36	Missouri	85
28	Montana	91
19	Nebraska	98
46	Nevada	71
16	New Hampshire	101
8	New Jersey	115
28	New Mexico	91
3	New York	137
24	North Carolina	94
14	North Dakota	102
23	Ohio	95
50	Oklahoma	67
18	Oregon	99
12	Pennsylvania	103
6	Rhode Island	126
30	South Carolina	90
30	South Dakota	90
21	Tennessee	96
43	Texas	77
44	Utah	75
1	Vermont	144
12	Virginia	103
14	Washington	102
32	West Virginia	89
19	Wisconsin	98
39	Wyoming	83

RANK ORDER

RANK	STATE	RATE
1	Vermont	144
2	Massachusetts	138
3	Maryland	137
3	New York	137
5	Connecticut	127
6	Rhode Island	126
7	Hawaii	121
8	New Jersey	115
9	Minnesota	108
10	Illinois	105
11	Maine	104
12	Pennsylvania	103
12	Virginia	103
14	North Dakota	102
14	Washington	102
16	New Hampshire	101
17	Alaska	100
18	Oregon	99
19	Nebraska	98
19	Wisconsin	98
21	California	96
21	Tennessee	96
23	Ohio	95
24	Louisiana	94
24	North Carolina	94
26	Colorado	93
27	Delaware	92
28	Montana	91
28	New Mexico	91
30	South Carolina	90
30	South Dakota	90
32	West Virginia	89
33	Michigan	88
34	Florida	87
35	Georgia	86
36	Kansas	85
36	Kentucky	85
36	Missouri	85
39	Alabama	83
39	Wyoming	83
41	Arkansas	82
41	Indiana	82
43	Texas	77
44	Arizona	75
44	Utah	75
46	Iowa	71
46	Nevada	71
48	Mississippi	69
49	Idaho	68
50	Oklahoma	67

District of Columbia	228

Source: Morgan Quitno Press using data from American Medical Association (Chicago, Illinois)
"Physician Characteristics and Distribution in the U.S." (2004 Edition)
*Federal and nonfederal physicians as of December 31, 2002. National rate does not include physicians in U.S. territories and possessions. Primary Care Specialties include Family Practice, General Practice, Internal Medicine, Obstetrics/Gynecology and Pediatrics excluding subspecialties within each category.

Percent of Physicians in Primary Care in 2002

National Percent = 33.4% of Physicians*

ALPHA ORDER			RANK ORDER		
RANK	STATE	PERCENT	RANK	STATE	PERCENT
7	Alabama	36.6	1	Alaska	43.0
1	Alaska	43.0	2	Wyoming	39.4
45	Arizona	31.6	3	North Dakota	39.1
6	Arkansas	36.8	4	South Dakota	37.9
41	California	33.1	5	Nebraska	37.8
36	Colorado	33.9	6	Arkansas	36.8
46	Connecticut	31.5	7	Alabama	36.6
38	Delaware	33.4	8	Minnesota	36.2
49	Florida	29.8	9	South Carolina	36.1
12	Georgia	35.8	10	Idaho	36.0
13	Hawaii	35.7	10	Wisconsin	36.0
10	Idaho	36.0	12	Georgia	35.8
13	Illinois	35.7	13	Hawaii	35.7
16	Indiana	35.4	13	Illinois	35.7
33	Iowa	34.1	15	Vermont	35.6
26	Kansas	34.5	16	Indiana	35.4
21	Kentucky	35.0	17	Montana	35.3
42	Louisiana	33.0	17	West Virginia	35.3
20	Maine	35.1	19	New Mexico	35.2
48	Maryland	30.5	20	Maine	35.1
50	Massachusetts	29.7	21	Kentucky	35.0
31	Michigan	34.2	21	Oklahoma	35.0
8	Minnesota	36.2	23	Mississippi	34.8
23	Mississippi	34.8	23	Virginia	34.8
40	Missouri	33.2	25	Nevada	34.7
17	Montana	35.3	26	Kansas	34.5
5	Nebraska	37.8	27	Washington	34.4
25	Nevada	34.7	28	New Hampshire	34.3
28	New Hampshire	34.3	28	New Jersey	34.3
28	New Jersey	34.3	28	Oregon	34.3
19	New Mexico	35.2	31	Michigan	34.2
44	New York	32.4	31	Ohio	34.2
33	North Carolina	34.1	33	Iowa	34.1
3	North Dakota	39.1	33	North Carolina	34.1
31	Ohio	34.2	33	Tennessee	34.1
21	Oklahoma	35.0	36	Colorado	33.9
28	Oregon	34.3	37	Texas	33.7
46	Pennsylvania	31.5	38	Delaware	33.4
39	Rhode Island	33.3	39	Rhode Island	33.3
9	South Carolina	36.1	40	Missouri	33.2
4	South Dakota	37.9	41	California	33.1
33	Tennessee	34.1	42	Louisiana	33.0
37	Texas	33.7	43	Utah	32.9
43	Utah	32.9	44	New York	32.4
15	Vermont	35.6	45	Arizona	31.6
23	Virginia	34.8	46	Connecticut	31.5
27	Washington	34.4	46	Pennsylvania	31.5
17	West Virginia	35.3	48	Maryland	30.5
10	Wisconsin	36.0	49	Florida	29.8
2	Wyoming	39.4	50	Massachusetts	29.7
				District of Columbia	28.7

Source: Morgan Quitno Press using data from American Medical Association (Chicago, Illinois)
    "Physician Characteristics and Distribution in the U.S." (2004 Edition)
*Federal and nonfederal physicians as of December 31, 2002. National percent does not include physicians in U.S. territories and possessions. Primary Care Specialties include Family Practice, General Practice, Internal Medicine, Obstetrics/Gynecology and Pediatrics excluding subspecialties within each category.

Percent of Population Lacking Access to Primary Care in 2003

National Percent = 11.5% of Population*

ALPHA ORDER

RANK	STATE	PERCENT
2	Alabama	26.4
19	Alaska	13.4
18	Arizona	13.6
29	Arkansas	9.9
31	California	9.3
30	Colorado	9.7
43	Connecticut	6.5
35	Delaware	8.2
13	Florida	15.6
12	Georgia	16.4
48	Hawaii	4.4
7	Idaho	19.0
22	Illinois	12.7
35	Indiana	8.2
34	Iowa	8.8
14	Kansas	15.5
16	Kentucky	14.7
8	Louisiana	18.5
35	Maine	8.2
40	Maryland	7.6
47	Massachusetts	5.4
26	Michigan	10.9
25	Minnesota	11.5
1	Mississippi	28.2
3	Missouri	24.7
9	Montana	17.6
46	Nebraska	5.5
21	Nevada	12.8
45	New Hampshire	5.9
50	New Jersey	2.9
4	New Mexico	23.0
28	New York	10.1
35	North Carolina	8.2
6	North Dakota	19.4
42	Ohio	7.2
32	Oklahoma	9.2
39	Oregon	7.7
44	Pennsylvania	6.3
32	Rhode Island	9.2
11	South Carolina	17.0
5	South Dakota	19.5
23	Tennessee	11.8
17	Texas	14.4
15	Utah	15.4
49	Vermont	3.3
40	Virginia	7.6
23	Washington	11.8
20	West Virginia	13.2
27	Wisconsin	10.3
10	Wyoming	17.1

RANK ORDER

RANK	STATE	PERCENT
1	Mississippi	28.2
2	Alabama	26.4
3	Missouri	24.7
4	New Mexico	23.0
5	South Dakota	19.5
6	North Dakota	19.4
7	Idaho	19.0
8	Louisiana	18.5
9	Montana	17.6
10	Wyoming	17.1
11	South Carolina	17.0
12	Georgia	16.4
13	Florida	15.6
14	Kansas	15.5
15	Utah	15.4
16	Kentucky	14.7
17	Texas	14.4
18	Arizona	13.6
19	Alaska	13.4
20	West Virginia	13.2
21	Nevada	12.8
22	Illinois	12.7
23	Tennessee	11.8
23	Washington	11.8
25	Minnesota	11.5
26	Michigan	10.9
27	Wisconsin	10.3
28	New York	10.1
29	Arkansas	9.9
30	Colorado	9.7
31	California	9.3
32	Oklahoma	9.2
32	Rhode Island	9.2
34	Iowa	8.8
35	Delaware	8.2
35	Indiana	8.2
35	Maine	8.2
35	North Carolina	8.2
39	Oregon	7.7
40	Maryland	7.6
40	Virginia	7.6
42	Ohio	7.2
43	Connecticut	6.5
44	Pennsylvania	6.3
45	New Hampshire	5.9
46	Nebraska	5.5
47	Massachusetts	5.4
48	Hawaii	4.4
49	Vermont	3.3
50	New Jersey	2.9

District of Columbia	26.5

Source: Morgan Quitno Press using data from U.S. Dept. of Health and Human Services, Div. of Shortage Designation "Selected Statistics on Health Professional Shortage Areas"

*Percent of population considered under-served by primary medical practitioners (Family & General Practice doctors, Internists, Ob/Gyns and Pediatricians). An under-served population does not have primary medical care within reasonable economic and geographic bounds.

Nonfederal Physicians in General/Family Practice in 2002

National Total = 85,641 Physicians*

RANK	STATE	PHYSICIANS	% of USA
24	Alabama	1,250	1.5%
46	Alaska	316	0.4%
20	Arizona	1,369	1.6%
28	Arkansas	1,161	1.4%
1	California	10,297	12.0%
18	Colorado	1,617	1.9%
37	Connecticut	608	0.7%
50	Delaware	219	0.3%
3	Florida	4,617	5.4%
15	Georgia	2,073	2.4%
43	Hawaii	362	0.4%
39	Idaho	509	0.6%
6	Illinois	3,721	4.3%
13	Indiana	2,387	2.8%
29	Iowa	1,141	1.3%
30	Kansas	1,047	1.2%
21	Kentucky	1,306	1.5%
23	Louisiana	1,301	1.5%
38	Maine	567	0.7%
25	Maryland	1,240	1.4%
26	Massachusetts	1,209	1.4%
10	Michigan	2,608	3.0%
11	Minnesota	2,606	3.0%
33	Mississippi	762	0.9%
22	Missouri	1,302	1.5%
42	Montana	403	0.5%
32	Nebraska	866	1.0%
40	Nevada	484	0.6%
41	New Hampshire	441	0.5%
17	New Jersey	1,643	1.9%
34	New Mexico	662	0.8%
5	New York	3,804	4.4%
9	North Carolina	2,683	3.1%
44	North Dakota	359	0.4%
7	Ohio	3,394	4.0%
31	Oklahoma	991	1.2%
26	Oregon	1,209	1.4%
4	Pennsylvania	3,838	4.5%
49	Rhode Island	220	0.3%
19	South Carolina	1,479	1.7%
45	South Dakota	355	0.4%
16	Tennessee	1,823	2.1%
2	Texas	5,962	7.0%
36	Utah	640	0.7%
47	Vermont	303	0.4%
12	Virginia	2,433	2.8%
8	Washington	2,749	3.2%
35	West Virginia	646	0.8%
14	Wisconsin	2,280	2.7%
48	Wyoming	233	0.3%

RANK	STATE	PHYSICIANS	% of USA
1	California	10,297	12.0%
2	Texas	5,962	7.0%
3	Florida	4,617	5.4%
4	Pennsylvania	3,838	4.5%
5	New York	3,804	4.4%
6	Illinois	3,721	4.3%
7	Ohio	3,394	4.0%
8	Washington	2,749	3.2%
9	North Carolina	2,683	3.1%
10	Michigan	2,608	3.0%
11	Minnesota	2,606	3.0%
12	Virginia	2,433	2.8%
13	Indiana	2,387	2.8%
14	Wisconsin	2,280	2.7%
15	Georgia	2,073	2.4%
16	Tennessee	1,823	2.1%
17	New Jersey	1,643	1.9%
18	Colorado	1,617	1.9%
19	South Carolina	1,479	1.7%
20	Arizona	1,369	1.6%
21	Kentucky	1,306	1.5%
22	Missouri	1,302	1.5%
23	Louisiana	1,301	1.5%
24	Alabama	1,250	1.5%
25	Maryland	1,240	1.4%
26	Massachusetts	1,209	1.4%
26	Oregon	1,209	1.4%
28	Arkansas	1,161	1.4%
29	Iowa	1,141	1.3%
30	Kansas	1,047	1.2%
31	Oklahoma	991	1.2%
32	Nebraska	866	1.0%
33	Mississippi	762	0.9%
34	New Mexico	662	0.8%
35	West Virginia	646	0.8%
36	Utah	640	0.7%
37	Connecticut	608	0.7%
38	Maine	567	0.7%
39	Idaho	509	0.6%
40	Nevada	484	0.6%
41	New Hampshire	441	0.5%
42	Montana	403	0.5%
43	Hawaii	362	0.4%
44	North Dakota	359	0.4%
45	South Dakota	355	0.4%
46	Alaska	316	0.4%
47	Vermont	303	0.4%
48	Wyoming	233	0.3%
49	Rhode Island	220	0.3%
50	Delaware	219	0.3%
	District of Columbia	146	0.2%

Source: American Medical Association (Chicago, Illinois)
  "Physician Characteristics and Distribution in the U.S." (2004 Edition)
*As of December 31, 2002. Total does not include 2,259 physicians in U.S. territories and possessions.

Rate of Nonfederal Physicians in General/Family Practice in 2002

National Rate = 30 Physicians per 100,000 Population*

ALPHA ORDER

RANK	STATE	RATE
33	Alabama	28
4	Alaska	49
41	Arizona	25
11	Arkansas	43
30	California	29
17	Colorado	36
50	Connecticut	18
37	Delaware	27
33	Florida	28
42	Georgia	24
30	Hawaii	29
16	Idaho	38
28	Illinois	30
13	Indiana	39
13	Iowa	39
13	Kansas	39
24	Kentucky	32
30	Louisiana	29
9	Maine	44
43	Maryland	23
48	Massachusetts	19
40	Michigan	26
2	Minnesota	52
37	Mississippi	27
43	Missouri	23
9	Montana	44
3	Nebraska	50
45	Nevada	22
21	New Hampshire	35
48	New Jersey	19
17	New Mexico	36
47	New York	20
24	North Carolina	32
1	North Dakota	57
28	Ohio	30
33	Oklahoma	28
22	Oregon	34
26	Pennsylvania	31
46	Rhode Island	21
17	South Carolina	36
6	South Dakota	47
26	Tennessee	31
37	Texas	27
33	Utah	28
4	Vermont	49
23	Virginia	33
8	Washington	45
17	West Virginia	36
12	Wisconsin	42
6	Wyoming	47

RANK ORDER

RANK	STATE	RATE
1	North Dakota	57
2	Minnesota	52
3	Nebraska	50
4	Alaska	49
4	Vermont	49
6	South Dakota	47
6	Wyoming	47
8	Washington	45
9	Maine	44
9	Montana	44
11	Arkansas	43
12	Wisconsin	42
13	Indiana	39
13	Iowa	39
13	Kansas	39
16	Idaho	38
17	Colorado	36
17	New Mexico	36
17	South Carolina	36
17	West Virginia	36
21	New Hampshire	35
22	Oregon	34
23	Virginia	33
24	Kentucky	32
24	North Carolina	32
26	Pennsylvania	31
26	Tennessee	31
28	Illinois	30
28	Ohio	30
30	California	29
30	Hawaii	29
30	Louisiana	29
33	Alabama	28
33	Florida	28
33	Oklahoma	28
33	Utah	28
37	Delaware	27
37	Mississippi	27
37	Texas	27
40	Michigan	26
41	Arizona	25
42	Georgia	24
43	Maryland	23
43	Missouri	23
45	Nevada	22
46	Rhode Island	21
47	New York	20
48	Massachusetts	19
48	New Jersey	19
50	Connecticut	18

	District of Columbia	26

Source: Morgan Quitno Press using data from American Medical Association (Chicago, Illinois)
    "Physician Characteristics and Distribution in the U.S." (2004 Edition)
*As of December 31, 2002. National rate does not include physicians in U.S. territories and possessions.

Percent of Nonfederal Physicians Who Are Specialists in 2002

National Percent = 74.6% of Physicians*

<table>
<tr><td colspan="3">ALPHA ORDER</td><td colspan="3">RANK ORDER</td></tr>
<tr><th>RANK</th><th>STATE</th><th>PERCENT</th><th>RANK</th><th>STATE</th><th>PERCENT</th></tr>
<tr><td>14</td><td>Alabama</td><td>74.6</td><td>1</td><td>Connecticut</td><td>80.4</td></tr>
<tr><td>45</td><td>Alaska</td><td>65.2</td><td>2</td><td>New Jersey</td><td>80.3</td></tr>
<tr><td>33</td><td>Arizona</td><td>69.8</td><td>2</td><td>Rhode Island</td><td>80.3</td></tr>
<tr><td>43</td><td>Arkansas</td><td>66.0</td><td>4</td><td>Massachusetts</td><td>80.1</td></tr>
<tr><td>27</td><td>California</td><td>71.6</td><td>5</td><td>New York</td><td>79.1</td></tr>
<tr><td>28</td><td>Colorado</td><td>70.9</td><td>6</td><td>Maryland</td><td>78.0</td></tr>
<tr><td>1</td><td>Connecticut</td><td>80.4</td><td>7</td><td>Missouri</td><td>77.9</td></tr>
<tr><td>13</td><td>Delaware</td><td>74.9</td><td>8</td><td>Louisiana</td><td>76.3</td></tr>
<tr><td>35</td><td>Florida</td><td>69.2</td><td>9</td><td>Georgia</td><td>75.7</td></tr>
<tr><td>9</td><td>Georgia</td><td>75.7</td><td>10</td><td>Pennsylvania</td><td>75.4</td></tr>
<tr><td>12</td><td>Hawaii</td><td>75.1</td><td>11</td><td>Tennessee</td><td>75.2</td></tr>
<tr><td>47</td><td>Idaho</td><td>64.4</td><td>12</td><td>Hawaii</td><td>75.1</td></tr>
<tr><td>15</td><td>Illinois</td><td>74.5</td><td>13</td><td>Delaware</td><td>74.9</td></tr>
<tr><td>32</td><td>Indiana</td><td>70.0</td><td>14</td><td>Alabama</td><td>74.6</td></tr>
<tr><td>49</td><td>Iowa</td><td>62.8</td><td>15</td><td>Illinois</td><td>74.5</td></tr>
<tr><td>41</td><td>Kansas</td><td>66.5</td><td>16</td><td>Texas</td><td>74.1</td></tr>
<tr><td>22</td><td>Kentucky</td><td>72.9</td><td>17</td><td>Michigan</td><td>74.0</td></tr>
<tr><td>8</td><td>Louisiana</td><td>76.3</td><td>18</td><td>Ohio</td><td>73.9</td></tr>
<tr><td>38</td><td>Maine</td><td>67.7</td><td>19</td><td>North Carolina</td><td>73.4</td></tr>
<tr><td>6</td><td>Maryland</td><td>78.0</td><td>20</td><td>Utah</td><td>73.2</td></tr>
<tr><td>4</td><td>Massachusetts</td><td>80.1</td><td>21</td><td>Nevada</td><td>73.0</td></tr>
<tr><td>17</td><td>Michigan</td><td>74.0</td><td>22</td><td>Kentucky</td><td>72.9</td></tr>
<tr><td>40</td><td>Minnesota</td><td>66.8</td><td>23</td><td>Virginia</td><td>72.6</td></tr>
<tr><td>24</td><td>Mississippi</td><td>71.9</td><td>24</td><td>Mississippi</td><td>71.9</td></tr>
<tr><td>7</td><td>Missouri</td><td>77.9</td><td>24</td><td>New Hampshire</td><td>71.9</td></tr>
<tr><td>44</td><td>Montana</td><td>65.6</td><td>26</td><td>South Carolina</td><td>71.7</td></tr>
<tr><td>41</td><td>Nebraska</td><td>66.5</td><td>27</td><td>California</td><td>71.6</td></tr>
<tr><td>21</td><td>Nevada</td><td>73.0</td><td>28</td><td>Colorado</td><td>70.9</td></tr>
<tr><td>24</td><td>New Hampshire</td><td>71.9</td><td>29</td><td>Wisconsin</td><td>70.6</td></tr>
<tr><td>2</td><td>New Jersey</td><td>80.3</td><td>30</td><td>Vermont</td><td>70.5</td></tr>
<tr><td>37</td><td>New Mexico</td><td>68.1</td><td>31</td><td>West Virginia</td><td>70.2</td></tr>
<tr><td>5</td><td>New York</td><td>79.1</td><td>32</td><td>Indiana</td><td>70.0</td></tr>
<tr><td>19</td><td>North Carolina</td><td>73.4</td><td>33</td><td>Arizona</td><td>69.8</td></tr>
<tr><td>48</td><td>North Dakota</td><td>62.9</td><td>34</td><td>Oregon</td><td>69.4</td></tr>
<tr><td>18</td><td>Ohio</td><td>73.9</td><td>35</td><td>Florida</td><td>69.2</td></tr>
<tr><td>36</td><td>Oklahoma</td><td>68.5</td><td>36</td><td>Oklahoma</td><td>68.5</td></tr>
<tr><td>34</td><td>Oregon</td><td>69.4</td><td>37</td><td>New Mexico</td><td>68.1</td></tr>
<tr><td>10</td><td>Pennsylvania</td><td>75.4</td><td>38</td><td>Maine</td><td>67.7</td></tr>
<tr><td>2</td><td>Rhode Island</td><td>80.3</td><td>39</td><td>Washington</td><td>67.3</td></tr>
<tr><td>26</td><td>South Carolina</td><td>71.7</td><td>40</td><td>Minnesota</td><td>66.8</td></tr>
<tr><td>46</td><td>South Dakota</td><td>64.6</td><td>41</td><td>Kansas</td><td>66.5</td></tr>
<tr><td>11</td><td>Tennessee</td><td>75.2</td><td>41</td><td>Nebraska</td><td>66.5</td></tr>
<tr><td>16</td><td>Texas</td><td>74.1</td><td>43</td><td>Arkansas</td><td>66.0</td></tr>
<tr><td>20</td><td>Utah</td><td>73.2</td><td>44</td><td>Montana</td><td>65.6</td></tr>
<tr><td>30</td><td>Vermont</td><td>70.5</td><td>45</td><td>Alaska</td><td>65.2</td></tr>
<tr><td>23</td><td>Virginia</td><td>72.6</td><td>46</td><td>South Dakota</td><td>64.6</td></tr>
<tr><td>39</td><td>Washington</td><td>67.3</td><td>47</td><td>Idaho</td><td>64.4</td></tr>
<tr><td>31</td><td>West Virginia</td><td>70.2</td><td>48</td><td>North Dakota</td><td>62.9</td></tr>
<tr><td>29</td><td>Wisconsin</td><td>70.6</td><td>49</td><td>Iowa</td><td>62.8</td></tr>
<tr><td>50</td><td>Wyoming</td><td>62.4</td><td>50</td><td>Wyoming</td><td>62.4</td></tr>
<tr><td></td><td></td><td></td><td></td><td>District of Columbia</td><td>80.6</td></tr>
</table>

Source: Morgan Quitno Press using data from American Medical Association (Chicago, Illinois)
    "Physician Characteristics and Distribution in the U.S." (2004 Edition)
*As of December 31, 2002. National percent does not include physicians in U.S. territories and possessions.
Includes physicians in medical, surgical and other specialties.

Nonfederal Physicians in Medical Specialties in 2002

National Total = 257,618 Physicians*

<table>
<tr><td colspan="4">ALPHA ORDER</td><td colspan="4">RANK ORDER</td></tr>
<tr><th>RANK</th><th>STATE</th><th>PHYSICIANS</th><th>% of USA</th><th>RANK</th><th>STATE</th><th>PHYSICIANS</th><th>% of USA</th></tr>
<tr><td>25</td><td>Alabama</td><td>3,103</td><td>1.2%</td><td>1</td><td>California</td><td>30,007</td><td>11.6%</td></tr>
<tr><td>49</td><td>Alaska</td><td>283</td><td>0.1%</td><td>2</td><td>New York</td><td>29,822</td><td>11.6%</td></tr>
<tr><td>23</td><td>Arizona</td><td>3,437</td><td>1.3%</td><td>3</td><td>Texas</td><td>14,173</td><td>5.5%</td></tr>
<tr><td>32</td><td>Arkansas</td><td>1,501</td><td>0.6%</td><td>4</td><td>Florida</td><td>14,004</td><td>5.4%</td></tr>
<tr><td>1</td><td>California</td><td>30,007</td><td>11.6%</td><td>5</td><td>Pennsylvania</td><td>12,794</td><td>5.0%</td></tr>
<tr><td>24</td><td>Colorado</td><td>3,323</td><td>1.3%</td><td>6</td><td>Illinois</td><td>12,277</td><td>4.8%</td></tr>
<tr><td>15</td><td>Connecticut</td><td>5,068</td><td>2.0%</td><td>7</td><td>Massachusetts</td><td>11,106</td><td>4.3%</td></tr>
<tr><td>43</td><td>Delaware</td><td>715</td><td>0.3%</td><td>8</td><td>New Jersey</td><td>10,952</td><td>4.3%</td></tr>
<tr><td>4</td><td>Florida</td><td>14,004</td><td>5.4%</td><td>9</td><td>Ohio</td><td>9,898</td><td>3.8%</td></tr>
<tr><td>14</td><td>Georgia</td><td>6,079</td><td>2.4%</td><td>10</td><td>Michigan</td><td>8,117</td><td>3.2%</td></tr>
<tr><td>38</td><td>Hawaii</td><td>1,233</td><td>0.5%</td><td>11</td><td>Maryland</td><td>7,996</td><td>3.1%</td></tr>
<tr><td>46</td><td>Idaho</td><td>503</td><td>0.2%</td><td>12</td><td>North Carolina</td><td>6,785</td><td>2.6%</td></tr>
<tr><td>6</td><td>Illinois</td><td>12,277</td><td>4.8%</td><td>13</td><td>Virginia</td><td>6,098</td><td>2.4%</td></tr>
<tr><td>22</td><td>Indiana</td><td>3,791</td><td>1.5%</td><td>14</td><td>Georgia</td><td>6,079</td><td>2.4%</td></tr>
<tr><td>35</td><td>Iowa</td><td>1,403</td><td>0.5%</td><td>15</td><td>Connecticut</td><td>5,068</td><td>2.0%</td></tr>
<tr><td>30</td><td>Kansas</td><td>1,638</td><td>0.6%</td><td>16</td><td>Tennessee</td><td>5,008</td><td>1.9%</td></tr>
<tr><td>26</td><td>Kentucky</td><td>2,882</td><td>1.1%</td><td>17</td><td>Missouri</td><td>4,856</td><td>1.9%</td></tr>
<tr><td>21</td><td>Louisiana</td><td>3,893</td><td>1.5%</td><td>18</td><td>Washington</td><td>4,522</td><td>1.8%</td></tr>
<tr><td>42</td><td>Maine</td><td>981</td><td>0.4%</td><td>19</td><td>Minnesota</td><td>4,192</td><td>1.6%</td></tr>
<tr><td>11</td><td>Maryland</td><td>7,996</td><td>3.1%</td><td>20</td><td>Wisconsin</td><td>4,126</td><td>1.6%</td></tr>
<tr><td>7</td><td>Massachusetts</td><td>11,106</td><td>4.3%</td><td>21</td><td>Louisiana</td><td>3,893</td><td>1.5%</td></tr>
<tr><td>10</td><td>Michigan</td><td>8,117</td><td>3.2%</td><td>22</td><td>Indiana</td><td>3,791</td><td>1.5%</td></tr>
<tr><td>19</td><td>Minnesota</td><td>4,192</td><td>1.6%</td><td>23</td><td>Arizona</td><td>3,437</td><td>1.3%</td></tr>
<tr><td>33</td><td>Mississippi</td><td>1,464</td><td>0.6%</td><td>24</td><td>Colorado</td><td>3,323</td><td>1.3%</td></tr>
<tr><td>17</td><td>Missouri</td><td>4,856</td><td>1.9%</td><td>25</td><td>Alabama</td><td>3,103</td><td>1.2%</td></tr>
<tr><td>45</td><td>Montana</td><td>511</td><td>0.2%</td><td>26</td><td>Kentucky</td><td>2,882</td><td>1.1%</td></tr>
<tr><td>40</td><td>Nebraska</td><td>1,095</td><td>0.4%</td><td>27</td><td>Oregon</td><td>2,720</td><td>1.1%</td></tr>
<tr><td>36</td><td>Nevada</td><td>1,264</td><td>0.5%</td><td>28</td><td>South Carolina</td><td>2,671</td><td>1.0%</td></tr>
<tr><td>41</td><td>New Hampshire</td><td>1,033</td><td>0.4%</td><td>29</td><td>Oklahoma</td><td>1,726</td><td>0.7%</td></tr>
<tr><td>8</td><td>New Jersey</td><td>10,952</td><td>4.3%</td><td>30</td><td>Kansas</td><td>1,638</td><td>0.6%</td></tr>
<tr><td>37</td><td>New Mexico</td><td>1,248</td><td>0.5%</td><td>31</td><td>Rhode Island</td><td>1,519</td><td>0.6%</td></tr>
<tr><td>2</td><td>New York</td><td>29,822</td><td>11.6%</td><td>32</td><td>Arkansas</td><td>1,501</td><td>0.6%</td></tr>
<tr><td>12</td><td>North Carolina</td><td>6,785</td><td>2.6%</td><td>33</td><td>Mississippi</td><td>1,464</td><td>0.6%</td></tr>
<tr><td>48</td><td>North Dakota</td><td>375</td><td>0.1%</td><td>34</td><td>Utah</td><td>1,440</td><td>0.6%</td></tr>
<tr><td>9</td><td>Ohio</td><td>9,898</td><td>3.8%</td><td>35</td><td>Iowa</td><td>1,403</td><td>0.5%</td></tr>
<tr><td>29</td><td>Oklahoma</td><td>1,726</td><td>0.7%</td><td>36</td><td>Nevada</td><td>1,264</td><td>0.5%</td></tr>
<tr><td>27</td><td>Oregon</td><td>2,720</td><td>1.1%</td><td>37</td><td>New Mexico</td><td>1,248</td><td>0.5%</td></tr>
<tr><td>5</td><td>Pennsylvania</td><td>12,794</td><td>5.0%</td><td>38</td><td>Hawaii</td><td>1,233</td><td>0.5%</td></tr>
<tr><td>31</td><td>Rhode Island</td><td>1,519</td><td>0.6%</td><td>39</td><td>West Virginia</td><td>1,228</td><td>0.5%</td></tr>
<tr><td>28</td><td>South Carolina</td><td>2,671</td><td>1.0%</td><td>40</td><td>Nebraska</td><td>1,095</td><td>0.4%</td></tr>
<tr><td>47</td><td>South Dakota</td><td>408</td><td>0.2%</td><td>41</td><td>New Hampshire</td><td>1,033</td><td>0.4%</td></tr>
<tr><td>16</td><td>Tennessee</td><td>5,008</td><td>1.9%</td><td>42</td><td>Maine</td><td>981</td><td>0.4%</td></tr>
<tr><td>3</td><td>Texas</td><td>14,173</td><td>5.5%</td><td>43</td><td>Delaware</td><td>715</td><td>0.3%</td></tr>
<tr><td>34</td><td>Utah</td><td>1,440</td><td>0.6%</td><td>44</td><td>Vermont</td><td>706</td><td>0.3%</td></tr>
<tr><td>44</td><td>Vermont</td><td>706</td><td>0.3%</td><td>45</td><td>Montana</td><td>511</td><td>0.2%</td></tr>
<tr><td>13</td><td>Virginia</td><td>6,098</td><td>2.4%</td><td>46</td><td>Idaho</td><td>503</td><td>0.2%</td></tr>
<tr><td>18</td><td>Washington</td><td>4,522</td><td>1.8%</td><td>47</td><td>South Dakota</td><td>408</td><td>0.2%</td></tr>
<tr><td>39</td><td>West Virginia</td><td>1,228</td><td>0.5%</td><td>48</td><td>North Dakota</td><td>375</td><td>0.1%</td></tr>
<tr><td>20</td><td>Wisconsin</td><td>4,126</td><td>1.6%</td><td>49</td><td>Alaska</td><td>283</td><td>0.1%</td></tr>
<tr><td>50</td><td>Wyoming</td><td>179</td><td>0.1%</td><td>50</td><td>Wyoming</td><td>179</td><td>0.1%</td></tr>
<tr><td></td><td></td><td></td><td></td><td></td><td>District of Columbia</td><td>1,465</td><td>0.6%</td></tr>
</table>

Source: American Medical Association (Chicago, Illinois)
    "Physician Characteristics and Distribution in the U.S." (2004 Edition)
*As of December 31, 2002. Total does not include 2,979 physicians in U.S. territories and possessions. Medical Specialties are Allergy/Immunology, Cardiovascular Diseases, Dermatology, Gastroenterology, Internal Medicine, Pediatrics, Pediatric Cardiology and Pulmonary Diseases.

Rate of Nonfederal Physicians in Medical Specialties in 2002

National Rate = 89 Physicians per 100,000 Population*

ALPHA ORDER

RANK	STATE	RATE
30	Alabama	69
48	Alaska	44
35	Arizona	63
43	Arkansas	55
16	California	85
27	Colorado	74
3	Connecticut	146
11	Delaware	89
17	Florida	84
28	Georgia	71
9	Hawaii	99
49	Idaho	38
10	Illinois	97
37	Indiana	62
47	Iowa	48
39	Kansas	60
29	Kentucky	70
12	Louisiana	87
24	Maine	76
3	Maryland	146
1	Massachusetts	173
21	Michigan	81
17	Minnesota	84
45	Mississippi	51
14	Missouri	86
42	Montana	56
35	Nebraska	63
41	Nevada	58
21	New Hampshire	81
6	New Jersey	127
32	New Mexico	67
2	New York	156
20	North Carolina	82
40	North Dakota	59
12	Ohio	87
46	Oklahoma	49
23	Oregon	77
8	Pennsylvania	104
5	Rhode Island	142
33	South Carolina	65
44	South Dakota	54
14	Tennessee	86
33	Texas	65
37	Utah	62
7	Vermont	115
17	Virginia	84
26	Washington	75
31	West Virginia	68
24	Wisconsin	76
50	Wyoming	36

RANK ORDER

RANK	STATE	RATE
1	Massachusetts	173
2	New York	156
3	Connecticut	146
3	Maryland	146
5	Rhode Island	142
6	New Jersey	127
7	Vermont	115
8	Pennsylvania	104
9	Hawaii	99
10	Illinois	97
11	Delaware	89
12	Louisiana	87
12	Ohio	87
14	Missouri	86
14	Tennessee	86
16	California	85
17	Florida	84
17	Minnesota	84
17	Virginia	84
20	North Carolina	82
21	Michigan	81
21	New Hampshire	81
23	Oregon	77
24	Maine	76
24	Wisconsin	76
26	Washington	75
27	Colorado	74
28	Georgia	71
29	Kentucky	70
30	Alabama	69
31	West Virginia	68
32	New Mexico	67
33	South Carolina	65
33	Texas	65
35	Arizona	63
35	Nebraska	63
37	Indiana	62
37	Utah	62
39	Kansas	60
40	North Dakota	59
41	Nevada	58
42	Montana	56
43	Arkansas	55
44	South Dakota	54
45	Mississippi	51
46	Oklahoma	49
47	Iowa	48
48	Alaska	44
49	Idaho	38
50	Wyoming	36

	District of Columbia	257

Source: Morgan Quitno Press using data from American Medical Association (Chicago, Illinois)
    "Physician Characteristics and Distribution in the U.S." (2004 Edition)
*As of December 31, 2002. National rate does not include physicians in U.S. territories and possessions. Medical Specialties are Allergy/Immunology, Cardiovascular Diseases, Dermatology, Gastroenterology, Internal Medicine, Pediatrics, Pediatric Cardiology and Pulmonary Diseases.

Nonfederal Physicians in Internal Medicine in 2002

National Total = 136,908 Physicians*

ALPHA ORDER

RANK	STATE	PHYSICIANS	% of USA
25	Alabama	1,674	1.2%
49	Alaska	136	0.1%
24	Arizona	1,685	1.2%
37	Arkansas	656	0.5%
2	California	15,725	11.5%
23	Colorado	1,723	1.3%
15	Connecticut	2,943	2.1%
44	Delaware	339	0.2%
5	Florida	6,873	5.0%
13	Georgia	3,192	2.3%
34	Hawaii	691	0.5%
46	Idaho	261	0.2%
4	Illinois	6,939	5.1%
22	Indiana	1,885	1.4%
38	Iowa	646	0.5%
30	Kansas	845	0.6%
27	Kentucky	1,433	1.0%
21	Louisiana	1,939	1.4%
40	Maine	541	0.4%
11	Maryland	4,448	3.2%
7	Massachusetts	6,435	4.7%
10	Michigan	4,498	3.3%
19	Minnesota	2,257	1.6%
32	Mississippi	725	0.5%
16	Missouri	2,540	1.9%
45	Montana	274	0.2%
42	Nebraska	532	0.4%
33	Nevada	698	0.5%
41	New Hampshire	537	0.4%
8	New Jersey	5,834	4.3%
35	New Mexico	669	0.5%
1	New York	16,953	12.4%
12	North Carolina	3,417	2.5%
47	North Dakota	231	0.2%
9	Ohio	5,077	3.7%
29	Oklahoma	878	0.6%
26	Oregon	1,605	1.2%
3	Pennsylvania	7,044	5.1%
31	Rhode Island	826	0.6%
28	South Carolina	1,311	1.0%
48	South Dakota	227	0.2%
17	Tennessee	2,523	1.8%
6	Texas	6,854	5.0%
39	Utah	642	0.5%
43	Vermont	403	0.3%
14	Virginia	3,147	2.3%
18	Washington	2,437	1.8%
36	West Virginia	664	0.5%
20	Wisconsin	2,227	1.6%
50	Wyoming	94	0.1%

RANK ORDER

RANK	STATE	PHYSICIANS	% of USA
1	New York	16,953	12.4%
2	California	15,725	11.5%
3	Pennsylvania	7,044	5.1%
4	Illinois	6,939	5.1%
5	Florida	6,873	5.0%
6	Texas	6,854	5.0%
7	Massachusetts	6,435	4.7%
8	New Jersey	5,834	4.3%
9	Ohio	5,077	3.7%
10	Michigan	4,498	3.3%
11	Maryland	4,448	3.2%
12	North Carolina	3,417	2.5%
13	Georgia	3,192	2.3%
14	Virginia	3,147	2.3%
15	Connecticut	2,943	2.1%
16	Missouri	2,540	1.9%
17	Tennessee	2,523	1.8%
18	Washington	2,437	1.8%
19	Minnesota	2,257	1.6%
20	Wisconsin	2,227	1.6%
21	Louisiana	1,939	1.4%
22	Indiana	1,885	1.4%
23	Colorado	1,723	1.3%
24	Arizona	1,685	1.2%
25	Alabama	1,674	1.2%
26	Oregon	1,605	1.2%
27	Kentucky	1,433	1.0%
28	South Carolina	1,311	1.0%
29	Oklahoma	878	0.6%
30	Kansas	845	0.6%
31	Rhode Island	826	0.6%
32	Mississippi	725	0.5%
33	Nevada	698	0.5%
34	Hawaii	691	0.5%
35	New Mexico	669	0.5%
36	West Virginia	664	0.5%
37	Arkansas	656	0.5%
38	Iowa	646	0.5%
39	Utah	642	0.5%
40	Maine	541	0.4%
41	New Hampshire	537	0.4%
42	Nebraska	532	0.4%
43	Vermont	403	0.3%
44	Delaware	339	0.2%
45	Montana	274	0.2%
46	Idaho	261	0.2%
47	North Dakota	231	0.2%
48	South Dakota	227	0.2%
49	Alaska	136	0.1%
50	Wyoming	94	0.1%
	District of Columbia	775	0.6%

Source: American Medical Association (Chicago, Illinois)
   "Physician Characteristics and Distribution in the U.S." (2004 Edition)
As of December 31, 2002. Total does not include 1,370 physicians in U.S. territories and possessions. Internal Medicine includes Diabetes, Endocrinology, Geriatrics, Hematology, Infectious Diseases, Nephrology, Nutrition, Medical Oncology and Rheumatology.

Rate of Nonfederal Physicians in Internal Medicine in 2002

National Rate = 47 Physicians per 100,000 Population*

RANK	STATE	RATE
28	Alabama	37
48	Alaska	21
36	Arizona	31
46	Arkansas	24
12	California	45
27	Colorado	38
3	Connecticut	85
20	Delaware	42
23	Florida	41
28	Georgia	37
9	Hawaii	56
49	Idaho	19
10	Illinois	55
36	Indiana	31
47	Iowa	22
36	Kansas	31
33	Kentucky	35
18	Louisiana	43
20	Maine	42
4	Maryland	81
1	Massachusetts	100
12	Michigan	45
12	Minnesota	45
44	Mississippi	25
12	Missouri	45
41	Montana	30
36	Nebraska	31
34	Nevada	32
20	New Hampshire	42
6	New Jersey	68
31	New Mexico	36
2	New York	88
23	North Carolina	41
31	North Dakota	36
16	Ohio	44
44	Oklahoma	25
11	Oregon	46
8	Pennsylvania	57
5	Rhode Island	77
34	South Carolina	32
41	South Dakota	30
16	Tennessee	44
36	Texas	31
43	Utah	28
7	Vermont	65
18	Virginia	43
26	Washington	40
28	West Virginia	37
23	Wisconsin	41
49	Wyoming	19

RANK	STATE	RATE
1	Massachusetts	100
2	New York	88
3	Connecticut	85
4	Maryland	81
5	Rhode Island	77
6	New Jersey	68
7	Vermont	65
8	Pennsylvania	57
9	Hawaii	56
10	Illinois	55
11	Oregon	46
12	California	45
12	Michigan	45
12	Minnesota	45
12	Missouri	45
16	Ohio	44
16	Tennessee	44
18	Louisiana	43
18	Virginia	43
20	Delaware	42
20	Maine	42
20	New Hampshire	42
23	Florida	41
23	North Carolina	41
23	Wisconsin	41
26	Washington	40
27	Colorado	38
28	Alabama	37
28	Georgia	37
28	West Virginia	37
31	New Mexico	36
31	North Dakota	36
33	Kentucky	35
34	Nevada	32
34	South Carolina	32
36	Arizona	31
36	Indiana	31
36	Kansas	31
36	Nebraska	31
36	Texas	31
41	Montana	30
41	South Dakota	30
43	Utah	28
44	Mississippi	25
44	Oklahoma	25
46	Arkansas	24
47	Iowa	22
48	Alaska	21
49	Idaho	19
49	Wyoming	19
	District of Columbia	136

Source: Morgan Quitno Press using data from American Medical Association (Chicago, Illinois)
    "Physician Characteristics and Distribution in the U.S." (2004 Edition)
*As of December 31, 2002. National rate does not include physicians in U.S. territories and possessions. Internal Medicine includes Diabetes, Endocrinology, Geriatrics, Hematology, Infectious Diseases, Nephrology, Nutrition, Medical Oncology and Rheumatology.

Nonfederal Physicians in Pediatrics in 2002

National Total = 64,270 Physicians*

ALPHA ORDER

RANK	STATE	PHYSICIANS	% of USA
26	Alabama	742	1.2%
46	Alaska	102	0.2%
23	Arizona	894	1.4%
30	Arkansas	451	0.7%
1	California	7,761	12.1%
24	Colorado	850	1.3%
18	Connecticut	1,082	1.7%
43	Delaware	232	0.4%
4	Florida	3,339	5.2%
14	Georgia	1,593	2.5%
36	Hawaii	344	0.5%
47	Idaho	101	0.2%
5	Illinois	2,883	4.5%
21	Indiana	963	1.5%
35	Iowa	347	0.5%
32	Kansas	403	0.6%
25	Kentucky	782	1.2%
19	Louisiana	1,039	1.6%
42	Maine	238	0.4%
11	Maryland	1,966	3.1%
9	Massachusetts	2,444	3.8%
10	Michigan	1,976	3.1%
22	Minnesota	936	1.5%
33	Mississippi	387	0.6%
16	Missouri	1,203	1.9%
45	Montana	109	0.2%
39	Nebraska	304	0.5%
40	Nevada	268	0.4%
40	New Hampshire	268	0.4%
6	New Jersey	2,777	4.3%
37	New Mexico	326	0.5%
2	New York	7,122	11.1%
12	North Carolina	1,780	2.8%
49	North Dakota	72	0.1%
7	Ohio	2,750	4.3%
31	Oklahoma	417	0.6%
28	Oregon	583	0.9%
8	Pennsylvania	2,720	4.2%
33	Rhode Island	387	0.6%
27	South Carolina	720	1.1%
48	South Dakota	78	0.1%
15	Tennessee	1,369	2.1%
3	Texas	3,971	6.2%
29	Utah	453	0.7%
44	Vermont	184	0.3%
13	Virginia	1,646	2.6%
17	Washington	1,121	1.7%
38	West Virginia	312	0.5%
20	Wisconsin	1,023	1.6%
50	Wyoming	44	0.1%

RANK ORDER

RANK	STATE	PHYSICIANS	% of USA
1	California	7,761	12.1%
2	New York	7,122	11.1%
3	Texas	3,971	6.2%
4	Florida	3,339	5.2%
5	Illinois	2,883	4.5%
6	New Jersey	2,777	4.3%
7	Ohio	2,750	4.3%
8	Pennsylvania	2,720	4.2%
9	Massachusetts	2,444	3.8%
10	Michigan	1,976	3.1%
11	Maryland	1,966	3.1%
12	North Carolina	1,780	2.8%
13	Virginia	1,646	2.6%
14	Georgia	1,593	2.5%
15	Tennessee	1,369	2.1%
16	Missouri	1,203	1.9%
17	Washington	1,121	1.7%
18	Connecticut	1,082	1.7%
19	Louisiana	1,039	1.6%
20	Wisconsin	1,023	1.6%
21	Indiana	963	1.5%
22	Minnesota	936	1.5%
23	Arizona	894	1.4%
24	Colorado	850	1.3%
25	Kentucky	782	1.2%
26	Alabama	742	1.2%
27	South Carolina	720	1.1%
28	Oregon	583	0.9%
29	Utah	453	0.7%
30	Arkansas	451	0.7%
31	Oklahoma	417	0.6%
32	Kansas	403	0.6%
33	Mississippi	387	0.6%
33	Rhode Island	387	0.6%
35	Iowa	347	0.5%
36	Hawaii	344	0.5%
37	New Mexico	326	0.5%
38	West Virginia	312	0.5%
39	Nebraska	304	0.5%
40	Nevada	268	0.4%
40	New Hampshire	268	0.4%
42	Maine	238	0.4%
43	Delaware	232	0.4%
44	Vermont	184	0.3%
45	Montana	109	0.2%
46	Alaska	102	0.2%
47	Idaho	101	0.2%
48	South Dakota	78	0.1%
49	North Dakota	72	0.1%
50	Wyoming	44	0.1%
	District of Columbia	408	0.6%

Source: American Medical Association (Chicago, Illinois)
"Physician Characteristics and Distribution in the U.S." (2004 Edition)

As of December 31, 2002. Total does not include 1,076 physicians in U.S. territories and possessions. Pediatrics includes Adolescent Medicine, Neonatal-Perinatal, Pediatric Allergy, Pediatric Endocrinology, Pediatric Pulmonology, Pediatric Hematology-Oncology and Pediatric Nephrology.

Rate of Nonfederal Physicians in Pediatrics in 2002

National Rate = 88 Physicians per 100,000 Population 17 Years and Younger*

ALPHA ORDER

RANK	STATE	RATE
33	Alabama	67
41	Alaska	53
38	Arizona	61
33	Arkansas	67
22	California	82
27	Colorado	74
7	Connecticut	124
8	Delaware	122
17	Florida	86
30	Georgia	70
9	Hawaii	116
50	Idaho	27
14	Illinois	89
39	Indiana	60
43	Iowa	50
40	Kansas	58
21	Kentucky	84
15	Louisiana	88
20	Maine	85
4	Maryland	142
1	Massachusetts	167
24	Michigan	77
26	Minnesota	75
42	Mississippi	51
17	Missouri	86
43	Montana	50
31	Nebraska	69
47	Nevada	47
16	New Hampshire	87
6	New Jersey	131
35	New Mexico	65
3	New York	154
17	North Carolina	86
45	North Dakota	49
11	Ohio	95
46	Oklahoma	48
32	Oregon	68
11	Pennsylvania	95
2	Rhode Island	162
27	South Carolina	74
48	South Dakota	40
10	Tennessee	97
35	Texas	65
37	Utah	64
5	Vermont	132
13	Virginia	93
27	Washington	74
23	West Virginia	80
25	Wisconsin	76
49	Wyoming	36

RANK ORDER

RANK	STATE	RATE
1	Massachusetts	167
2	Rhode Island	162
3	New York	154
4	Maryland	142
5	Vermont	132
6	New Jersey	131
7	Connecticut	124
8	Delaware	122
9	Hawaii	116
10	Tennessee	97
11	Ohio	95
11	Pennsylvania	95
13	Virginia	93
14	Illinois	89
15	Louisiana	88
16	New Hampshire	87
17	Florida	86
17	Missouri	86
17	North Carolina	86
20	Maine	85
21	Kentucky	84
22	California	82
23	West Virginia	80
24	Michigan	77
25	Wisconsin	76
26	Minnesota	75
27	Colorado	74
27	South Carolina	74
27	Washington	74
30	Georgia	70
31	Nebraska	69
32	Oregon	68
33	Alabama	67
33	Arkansas	67
35	New Mexico	65
35	Texas	65
37	Utah	64
38	Arizona	61
39	Indiana	60
40	Kansas	58
41	Alaska	53
42	Mississippi	51
43	Iowa	50
43	Montana	50
45	North Dakota	49
46	Oklahoma	48
47	Nevada	47
48	South Dakota	40
49	Wyoming	36
50	Idaho	27
	District of Columbia	364

Source: Morgan Quitno Press using data from American Medical Association (Chicago, Illinois)
"Physician Characteristics and Distribution in the U.S." (2004 Edition)

*As of December 31, 2002. National rate does not include physicians in U.S. territories and possessions. Pediatrics includes Adolescent Medicine, Neonatal-Perinatal, Pediatric Allergy, Pediatric Endocrinology, Pediatric Pulmonology, Pediatric Hematology-Oncology and Pediatric Nephrology.

Nonfederal Physicians in Surgical Specialties in 2002

National Total = 153,268 Physicians*

ALPHA ORDER

ALPHA ORDER

RANK	STATE	PHYSICIANS	% of USA
25	Alabama	2,186	1.4%
49	Alaska	267	0.2%
23	Arizona	2,298	1.5%
32	Arkansas	1,105	0.7%
1	California	17,690	11.5%
24	Colorado	2,241	1.5%
21	Connecticut	2,531	1.7%
46	Delaware	403	0.3%
4	Florida	8,733	5.7%
12	Georgia	4,217	2.8%
38	Hawaii	760	0.5%
43	Idaho	561	0.4%
6	Illinois	6,351	4.1%
20	Indiana	2,622	1.7%
33	Iowa	1,079	0.7%
31	Kansas	1,217	0.8%
27	Kentucky	1,981	1.3%
18	Louisiana	2,829	1.8%
42	Maine	652	0.4%
14	Maryland	3,936	2.6%
10	Massachusetts	4,584	3.0%
9	Michigan	4,817	3.1%
22	Minnesota	2,441	1.6%
30	Mississippi	1,269	0.8%
17	Missouri	2,905	1.9%
44	Montana	466	0.3%
36	Nebraska	875	0.6%
37	Nevada	833	0.5%
41	New Hampshire	712	0.5%
8	New Jersey	5,353	3.5%
40	New Mexico	736	0.5%
2	New York	13,965	9.1%
11	North Carolina	4,398	2.9%
48	North Dakota	292	0.2%
7	Ohio	5,995	3.9%
29	Oklahoma	1,271	0.8%
28	Oregon	1,811	1.2%
5	Pennsylvania	7,407	4.8%
39	Rhode Island	738	0.5%
26	South Carolina	2,145	1.4%
47	South Dakota	342	0.2%
15	Tennessee	3,378	2.2%
3	Texas	9,888	6.5%
34	Utah	1,058	0.7%
45	Vermont	421	0.3%
13	Virginia	4,026	2.6%
16	Washington	2,956	1.9%
35	West Virginia	886	0.6%
19	Wisconsin	2,625	1.7%
50	Wyoming	217	0.1%

RANK ORDER

RANK	STATE	PHYSICIANS	% of USA
1	California	17,690	11.5%
2	New York	13,965	9.1%
3	Texas	9,888	6.5%
4	Florida	8,733	5.7%
5	Pennsylvania	7,407	4.8%
6	Illinois	6,351	4.1%
7	Ohio	5,995	3.9%
8	New Jersey	5,353	3.5%
9	Michigan	4,817	3.1%
10	Massachusetts	4,584	3.0%
11	North Carolina	4,398	2.9%
12	Georgia	4,217	2.8%
13	Virginia	4,026	2.6%
14	Maryland	3,936	2.6%
15	Tennessee	3,378	2.2%
16	Washington	2,956	1.9%
17	Missouri	2,905	1.9%
18	Louisiana	2,829	1.8%
19	Wisconsin	2,625	1.7%
20	Indiana	2,622	1.7%
21	Connecticut	2,531	1.7%
22	Minnesota	2,441	1.6%
23	Arizona	2,298	1.5%
24	Colorado	2,241	1.5%
25	Alabama	2,186	1.4%
26	South Carolina	2,145	1.4%
27	Kentucky	1,981	1.3%
28	Oregon	1,811	1.2%
29	Oklahoma	1,271	0.8%
30	Mississippi	1,269	0.8%
31	Kansas	1,217	0.8%
32	Arkansas	1,105	0.7%
33	Iowa	1,079	0.7%
34	Utah	1,058	0.7%
35	West Virginia	886	0.6%
36	Nebraska	875	0.6%
37	Nevada	833	0.5%
38	Hawaii	760	0.5%
39	Rhode Island	738	0.5%
40	New Mexico	736	0.5%
41	New Hampshire	712	0.5%
42	Maine	652	0.4%
43	Idaho	561	0.4%
44	Montana	466	0.3%
45	Vermont	421	0.3%
46	Delaware	403	0.3%
47	South Dakota	342	0.2%
48	North Dakota	292	0.2%
49	Alaska	267	0.2%
50	Wyoming	217	0.1%
	District of Columbia	799	0.5%

Source: American Medical Association (Chicago, Illinois)
    "Physician Characteristics and Distribution in the U.S." (2004 Edition)
*As of December 31, 2002. Total does not include 1,705 physicians in U.S. territories and possessions. Surgical Specialties include Colon and Rectal, General, Neurological, Obstetrics & Gynecology, Ophthalmology, Orthopedic, Otolaryngology, Plastic, Thoracic and Urological Surgeries.

Rate of Nonfederal Physicians in Surgical Specialties in 2002

National Rate = 53 Physicians per 100,000 Population*

ALPHA ORDER

RANK	STATE	RATE
27	Alabama	49
45	Alaska	41
43	Arizona	42
45	Arkansas	41
22	California	50
22	Colorado	50
1	Connecticut	73
22	Delaware	50
15	Florida	52
27	Georgia	49
9	Hawaii	61
43	Idaho	42
22	Illinois	50
42	Indiana	43
49	Iowa	37
37	Kansas	45
32	Kentucky	48
7	Louisiana	63
22	Maine	50
3	Maryland	72
4	Massachusetts	71
32	Michigan	48
27	Minnesota	49
40	Mississippi	44
18	Missouri	51
18	Montana	51
18	Nebraska	51
48	Nevada	38
12	New Hampshire	56
8	New Jersey	62
47	New Mexico	40
1	New York	73
14	North Carolina	53
35	North Dakota	46
15	Ohio	52
50	Oklahoma	36
18	Oregon	51
10	Pennsylvania	60
5	Rhode Island	69
15	South Carolina	52
37	South Dakota	45
11	Tennessee	58
37	Texas	45
35	Utah	46
6	Vermont	68
13	Virginia	55
27	Washington	49
27	West Virginia	49
32	Wisconsin	48
40	Wyoming	44

RANK ORDER

RANK	STATE	RATE
1	Connecticut	73
1	New York	73
3	Maryland	72
4	Massachusetts	71
5	Rhode Island	69
6	Vermont	68
7	Louisiana	63
8	New Jersey	62
9	Hawaii	61
10	Pennsylvania	60
11	Tennessee	58
12	New Hampshire	56
13	Virginia	55
14	North Carolina	53
15	Florida	52
15	Ohio	52
15	South Carolina	52
18	Missouri	51
18	Montana	51
18	Nebraska	51
18	Oregon	51
22	California	50
22	Colorado	50
22	Delaware	50
22	Illinois	50
22	Maine	50
27	Alabama	49
27	Georgia	49
27	Minnesota	49
27	Washington	49
27	West Virginia	49
32	Kentucky	48
32	Michigan	48
32	Wisconsin	48
35	North Dakota	46
35	Utah	46
37	Kansas	45
37	South Dakota	45
37	Texas	45
40	Mississippi	44
40	Wyoming	44
42	Indiana	43
43	Arizona	42
43	Idaho	42
45	Alaska	41
45	Arkansas	41
47	New Mexico	40
48	Nevada	38
49	Iowa	37
50	Oklahoma	36
	District of Columbia	140

Source: Morgan Quitno Press using data from American Medical Association (Chicago, Illinois)
     "Physician Characteristics and Distribution in the U.S." (2004 Edition)
*As of December 31, 2002. National rate does not include physicians in U.S. territories and possessions. Surgical Specialties include Colon and Rectal, General, Neurological, Obstetrics & Gynecology, Ophthalmology, Orthopedic, Otolaryngology, Plastic, Thoracic and Urological Surgeries.

Nonfederal Physicians in General Surgery in 2002

National Total = 35,761 Physicians*

<table>
<tr><td colspan="4">ALPHA ORDER</td><td colspan="4">RANK ORDER</td></tr>
<tr><td>RANK</td><td>STATE</td><td>PHYSICIANS</td><td>% of USA</td><td>RANK</td><td>STATE</td><td>PHYSICIANS</td><td>% of USA</td></tr>
<tr><td>24</td><td>Alabama</td><td>520</td><td>1.5%</td><td>1</td><td>California</td><td>3,721</td><td>10.4%</td></tr>
<tr><td>49</td><td>Alaska</td><td>58</td><td>0.2%</td><td>2</td><td>New York</td><td>3,496</td><td>9.8%</td></tr>
<tr><td>23</td><td>Arizona</td><td>522</td><td>1.5%</td><td>3</td><td>Texas</td><td>2,128</td><td>6.0%</td></tr>
<tr><td>33</td><td>Arkansas</td><td>264</td><td>0.7%</td><td>4</td><td>Pennsylvania</td><td>1,914</td><td>5.4%</td></tr>
<tr><td>1</td><td>California</td><td>3,721</td><td>10.4%</td><td>5</td><td>Florida</td><td>1,752</td><td>4.9%</td></tr>
<tr><td>27</td><td>Colorado</td><td>492</td><td>1.4%</td><td>6</td><td>Ohio</td><td>1,524</td><td>4.3%</td></tr>
<tr><td>20</td><td>Connecticut</td><td>598</td><td>1.7%</td><td>7</td><td>Illinois</td><td>1,497</td><td>4.2%</td></tr>
<tr><td>46</td><td>Delaware</td><td>100</td><td>0.3%</td><td>8</td><td>New Jersey</td><td>1,272</td><td>3.6%</td></tr>
<tr><td>5</td><td>Florida</td><td>1,752</td><td>4.9%</td><td>9</td><td>Michigan</td><td>1,240</td><td>3.5%</td></tr>
<tr><td>12</td><td>Georgia</td><td>972</td><td>2.7%</td><td>10</td><td>Massachusetts</td><td>1,182</td><td>3.3%</td></tr>
<tr><td>42</td><td>Hawaii</td><td>173</td><td>0.5%</td><td>11</td><td>North Carolina</td><td>1,014</td><td>2.8%</td></tr>
<tr><td>43</td><td>Idaho</td><td>132</td><td>0.4%</td><td>12</td><td>Georgia</td><td>972</td><td>2.7%</td></tr>
<tr><td>7</td><td>Illinois</td><td>1,497</td><td>4.2%</td><td>13</td><td>Maryland</td><td>903</td><td>2.5%</td></tr>
<tr><td>21</td><td>Indiana</td><td>565</td><td>1.6%</td><td>14</td><td>Virginia</td><td>901</td><td>2.5%</td></tr>
<tr><td>32</td><td>Iowa</td><td>276</td><td>0.8%</td><td>15</td><td>Tennessee</td><td>842</td><td>2.4%</td></tr>
<tr><td>29</td><td>Kansas</td><td>300</td><td>0.8%</td><td>16</td><td>Missouri</td><td>669</td><td>1.9%</td></tr>
<tr><td>25</td><td>Kentucky</td><td>519</td><td>1.5%</td><td>17</td><td>Washington</td><td>659</td><td>1.8%</td></tr>
<tr><td>18</td><td>Louisiana</td><td>631</td><td>1.8%</td><td>18</td><td>Louisiana</td><td>631</td><td>1.8%</td></tr>
<tr><td>40</td><td>Maine</td><td>176</td><td>0.5%</td><td>19</td><td>Wisconsin</td><td>629</td><td>1.8%</td></tr>
<tr><td>13</td><td>Maryland</td><td>903</td><td>2.5%</td><td>20</td><td>Connecticut</td><td>598</td><td>1.7%</td></tr>
<tr><td>10</td><td>Massachusetts</td><td>1,182</td><td>3.3%</td><td>21</td><td>Indiana</td><td>565</td><td>1.6%</td></tr>
<tr><td>9</td><td>Michigan</td><td>1,240</td><td>3.5%</td><td>22</td><td>Minnesota</td><td>556</td><td>1.6%</td></tr>
<tr><td>22</td><td>Minnesota</td><td>556</td><td>1.6%</td><td>23</td><td>Arizona</td><td>522</td><td>1.5%</td></tr>
<tr><td>31</td><td>Mississippi</td><td>294</td><td>0.8%</td><td>24</td><td>Alabama</td><td>520</td><td>1.5%</td></tr>
<tr><td>16</td><td>Missouri</td><td>669</td><td>1.9%</td><td>25</td><td>Kentucky</td><td>519</td><td>1.5%</td></tr>
<tr><td>45</td><td>Montana</td><td>102</td><td>0.3%</td><td>26</td><td>South Carolina</td><td>516</td><td>1.4%</td></tr>
<tr><td>35</td><td>Nebraska</td><td>232</td><td>0.6%</td><td>27</td><td>Colorado</td><td>492</td><td>1.4%</td></tr>
<tr><td>37</td><td>Nevada</td><td>184</td><td>0.5%</td><td>28</td><td>Oregon</td><td>420</td><td>1.2%</td></tr>
<tr><td>41</td><td>New Hampshire</td><td>175</td><td>0.5%</td><td>29</td><td>Kansas</td><td>300</td><td>0.8%</td></tr>
<tr><td>8</td><td>New Jersey</td><td>1,272</td><td>3.6%</td><td>30</td><td>Oklahoma</td><td>295</td><td>0.8%</td></tr>
<tr><td>38</td><td>New Mexico</td><td>183</td><td>0.5%</td><td>31</td><td>Mississippi</td><td>294</td><td>0.8%</td></tr>
<tr><td>2</td><td>New York</td><td>3,496</td><td>9.8%</td><td>32</td><td>Iowa</td><td>276</td><td>0.8%</td></tr>
<tr><td>11</td><td>North Carolina</td><td>1,014</td><td>2.8%</td><td>33</td><td>Arkansas</td><td>264</td><td>0.7%</td></tr>
<tr><td>48</td><td>North Dakota</td><td>80</td><td>0.2%</td><td>34</td><td>West Virginia</td><td>245</td><td>0.7%</td></tr>
<tr><td>6</td><td>Ohio</td><td>1,524</td><td>4.3%</td><td>35</td><td>Nebraska</td><td>232</td><td>0.6%</td></tr>
<tr><td>30</td><td>Oklahoma</td><td>295</td><td>0.8%</td><td>36</td><td>Utah</td><td>203</td><td>0.6%</td></tr>
<tr><td>28</td><td>Oregon</td><td>420</td><td>1.2%</td><td>37</td><td>Nevada</td><td>184</td><td>0.5%</td></tr>
<tr><td>4</td><td>Pennsylvania</td><td>1,914</td><td>5.4%</td><td>38</td><td>New Mexico</td><td>183</td><td>0.5%</td></tr>
<tr><td>39</td><td>Rhode Island</td><td>181</td><td>0.5%</td><td>39</td><td>Rhode Island</td><td>181</td><td>0.5%</td></tr>
<tr><td>26</td><td>South Carolina</td><td>516</td><td>1.4%</td><td>40</td><td>Maine</td><td>176</td><td>0.5%</td></tr>
<tr><td>47</td><td>South Dakota</td><td>84</td><td>0.2%</td><td>41</td><td>New Hampshire</td><td>175</td><td>0.5%</td></tr>
<tr><td>15</td><td>Tennessee</td><td>842</td><td>2.4%</td><td>42</td><td>Hawaii</td><td>173</td><td>0.5%</td></tr>
<tr><td>3</td><td>Texas</td><td>2,128</td><td>6.0%</td><td>43</td><td>Idaho</td><td>132</td><td>0.4%</td></tr>
<tr><td>36</td><td>Utah</td><td>203</td><td>0.6%</td><td>44</td><td>Vermont</td><td>114</td><td>0.3%</td></tr>
<tr><td>44</td><td>Vermont</td><td>114</td><td>0.3%</td><td>45</td><td>Montana</td><td>102</td><td>0.3%</td></tr>
<tr><td>14</td><td>Virginia</td><td>901</td><td>2.5%</td><td>46</td><td>Delaware</td><td>100</td><td>0.3%</td></tr>
<tr><td>17</td><td>Washington</td><td>659</td><td>1.8%</td><td>47</td><td>South Dakota</td><td>84</td><td>0.2%</td></tr>
<tr><td>34</td><td>West Virginia</td><td>245</td><td>0.7%</td><td>48</td><td>North Dakota</td><td>80</td><td>0.2%</td></tr>
<tr><td>19</td><td>Wisconsin</td><td>629</td><td>1.8%</td><td>49</td><td>Alaska</td><td>58</td><td>0.2%</td></tr>
<tr><td>50</td><td>Wyoming</td><td>50</td><td>0.1%</td><td>50</td><td>Wyoming</td><td>50</td><td>0.1%</td></tr>
<tr><td></td><td></td><td></td><td></td><td></td><td>District of Columbia</td><td>206</td><td>0.6%</td></tr>
</table>

Source: American Medical Association (Chicago, Illinois)
    "Physician Characteristics and Distribution in the U.S." (2004 Edition)
*As of December 31, 2002. Total does not include 473 physicians in U.S. territories and possessions. General Surgery includes Abdominal, Cardiovascular, Hand, Head and Neck, Pediatric, Traumatic and Vascular Surgeries.

Rate of Nonfederal Physicians in General Surgery in 2002

National Rate = 12.4 Physicians per 100,000 Population*

<table>
<tr><td colspan="3">ALPHA ORDER</td><td colspan="3">RANK ORDER</td></tr>
<tr><td colspan="2">RANK STATE</td><td>RATE</td><td colspan="2">RANK STATE</td><td>RATE</td></tr>
<tr><td>27</td><td>Alabama</td><td>11.6</td><td>1</td><td>Vermont</td><td>18.5</td></tr>
<tr><td>47</td><td>Alaska</td><td>9.0</td><td>2</td><td>Massachusetts</td><td>18.4</td></tr>
<tr><td>44</td><td>Arizona</td><td>9.6</td><td>3</td><td>New York</td><td>18.2</td></tr>
<tr><td>43</td><td>Arkansas</td><td>9.7</td><td>4</td><td>Connecticut</td><td>17.3</td></tr>
<tr><td>36</td><td>California</td><td>10.6</td><td>5</td><td>Rhode Island</td><td>16.9</td></tr>
<tr><td>34</td><td>Colorado</td><td>10.9</td><td>6</td><td>Maryland</td><td>16.5</td></tr>
<tr><td>4</td><td>Connecticut</td><td>17.3</td><td>7</td><td>Pennsylvania</td><td>15.5</td></tr>
<tr><td>20</td><td>Delaware</td><td>12.4</td><td>8</td><td>New Jersey</td><td>14.8</td></tr>
<tr><td>37</td><td>Florida</td><td>10.5</td><td>9</td><td>Tennessee</td><td>14.5</td></tr>
<tr><td>29</td><td>Georgia</td><td>11.4</td><td>10</td><td>Louisiana</td><td>14.1</td></tr>
<tr><td>11</td><td>Hawaii</td><td>13.9</td><td>11</td><td>Hawaii</td><td>13.9</td></tr>
<tr><td>41</td><td>Idaho</td><td>9.8</td><td>12</td><td>New Hampshire</td><td>13.7</td></tr>
<tr><td>24</td><td>Illinois</td><td>11.9</td><td>13</td><td>Maine</td><td>13.6</td></tr>
<tr><td>46</td><td>Indiana</td><td>9.2</td><td>13</td><td>West Virginia</td><td>13.6</td></tr>
<tr><td>45</td><td>Iowa</td><td>9.4</td><td>15</td><td>Nebraska</td><td>13.4</td></tr>
<tr><td>32</td><td>Kansas</td><td>11.0</td><td>16</td><td>Ohio</td><td>13.3</td></tr>
<tr><td>17</td><td>Kentucky</td><td>12.7</td><td>17</td><td>Kentucky</td><td>12.7</td></tr>
<tr><td>10</td><td>Louisiana</td><td>14.1</td><td>18</td><td>North Dakota</td><td>12.6</td></tr>
<tr><td>13</td><td>Maine</td><td>13.6</td><td>18</td><td>South Carolina</td><td>12.6</td></tr>
<tr><td>6</td><td>Maryland</td><td>16.5</td><td>20</td><td>Delaware</td><td>12.4</td></tr>
<tr><td>2</td><td>Massachusetts</td><td>18.4</td><td>20</td><td>Virginia</td><td>12.4</td></tr>
<tr><td>22</td><td>Michigan</td><td>12.3</td><td>22</td><td>Michigan</td><td>12.3</td></tr>
<tr><td>31</td><td>Minnesota</td><td>11.1</td><td>23</td><td>North Carolina</td><td>12.2</td></tr>
<tr><td>38</td><td>Mississippi</td><td>10.2</td><td>24</td><td>Illinois</td><td>11.9</td></tr>
<tr><td>26</td><td>Missouri</td><td>11.8</td><td>24</td><td>Oregon</td><td>11.9</td></tr>
<tr><td>30</td><td>Montana</td><td>11.2</td><td>26</td><td>Missouri</td><td>11.8</td></tr>
<tr><td>15</td><td>Nebraska</td><td>13.4</td><td>27</td><td>Alabama</td><td>11.6</td></tr>
<tr><td>49</td><td>Nevada</td><td>8.5</td><td>27</td><td>Wisconsin</td><td>11.6</td></tr>
<tr><td>12</td><td>New Hampshire</td><td>13.7</td><td>29</td><td>Georgia</td><td>11.4</td></tr>
<tr><td>8</td><td>New Jersey</td><td>14.8</td><td>30</td><td>Montana</td><td>11.2</td></tr>
<tr><td>40</td><td>New Mexico</td><td>9.9</td><td>31</td><td>Minnesota</td><td>11.1</td></tr>
<tr><td>3</td><td>New York</td><td>18.2</td><td>32</td><td>Kansas</td><td>11.0</td></tr>
<tr><td>23</td><td>North Carolina</td><td>12.2</td><td>32</td><td>South Dakota</td><td>11.0</td></tr>
<tr><td>18</td><td>North Dakota</td><td>12.6</td><td>34</td><td>Colorado</td><td>10.9</td></tr>
<tr><td>16</td><td>Ohio</td><td>13.3</td><td>34</td><td>Washington</td><td>10.9</td></tr>
<tr><td>50</td><td>Oklahoma</td><td>8.4</td><td>36</td><td>California</td><td>10.6</td></tr>
<tr><td>24</td><td>Oregon</td><td>11.9</td><td>37</td><td>Florida</td><td>10.5</td></tr>
<tr><td>7</td><td>Pennsylvania</td><td>15.5</td><td>38</td><td>Mississippi</td><td>10.2</td></tr>
<tr><td>5</td><td>Rhode Island</td><td>16.9</td><td>39</td><td>Wyoming</td><td>10.0</td></tr>
<tr><td>18</td><td>South Carolina</td><td>12.6</td><td>40</td><td>New Mexico</td><td>9.9</td></tr>
<tr><td>32</td><td>South Dakota</td><td>11.0</td><td>41</td><td>Idaho</td><td>9.8</td></tr>
<tr><td>9</td><td>Tennessee</td><td>14.5</td><td>41</td><td>Texas</td><td>9.8</td></tr>
<tr><td>41</td><td>Texas</td><td>9.8</td><td>43</td><td>Arkansas</td><td>9.7</td></tr>
<tr><td>48</td><td>Utah</td><td>8.8</td><td>44</td><td>Arizona</td><td>9.6</td></tr>
<tr><td>1</td><td>Vermont</td><td>18.5</td><td>45</td><td>Iowa</td><td>9.4</td></tr>
<tr><td>20</td><td>Virginia</td><td>12.4</td><td>46</td><td>Indiana</td><td>9.2</td></tr>
<tr><td>34</td><td>Washington</td><td>10.9</td><td>47</td><td>Alaska</td><td>9.0</td></tr>
<tr><td>13</td><td>West Virginia</td><td>13.6</td><td>48</td><td>Utah</td><td>8.8</td></tr>
<tr><td>27</td><td>Wisconsin</td><td>11.6</td><td>49</td><td>Nevada</td><td>8.5</td></tr>
<tr><td>39</td><td>Wyoming</td><td>10.0</td><td>50</td><td>Oklahoma</td><td>8.4</td></tr>
<tr><td colspan="3"></td><td colspan="2">District of Columbia</td><td>36.1</td></tr>
</table>

Source: Morgan Quitno Press using data from American Medical Association (Chicago, Illinois)
"Physician Characteristics and Distribution in the U.S." (2004 Edition)
*As of December 31, 2002. National rate does not include physicians in U.S. territories and possessions. General Surgery includes Abdominal, Cardiovascular, Hand, Head and Neck, Pediatric, Traumatic and Vascular Surgeries.

Nonfederal Physicians in Obstetrics and Gynecology in 2002

National Total = 39,855 Physicians*

ALPHA ORDER

RANK	STATE	PHYSICIANS	% of USA
25	Alabama	559	1.4%
47	Alaska	71	0.2%
21	Arizona	621	1.6%
34	Arkansas	250	0.6%
1	California	4,702	11.8%
22	Colorado	592	1.5%
19	Connecticut	687	1.7%
44	Delaware	110	0.3%
4	Florida	2,087	5.2%
10	Georgia	1,312	3.3%
35	Hawaii	229	0.6%
43	Idaho	119	0.3%
5	Illinois	1,805	4.5%
20	Indiana	672	1.7%
36	Iowa	212	0.5%
31	Kansas	280	0.7%
27	Kentucky	477	1.2%
16	Louisiana	731	1.8%
42	Maine	149	0.4%
14	Maryland	1,078	2.7%
12	Massachusetts	1,132	2.8%
9	Michigan	1,323	3.3%
26	Minnesota	537	1.3%
29	Mississippi	321	0.8%
17	Missouri	724	1.8%
46	Montana	97	0.2%
41	Nebraska	177	0.4%
33	Nevada	252	0.6%
39	New Hampshire	197	0.5%
7	New Jersey	1,534	3.8%
40	New Mexico	186	0.5%
2	New York	3,712	9.3%
11	North Carolina	1,207	3.0%
50	North Dakota	51	0.1%
8	Ohio	1,530	3.8%
30	Oklahoma	301	0.8%
28	Oregon	453	1.1%
6	Pennsylvania	1,744	4.4%
38	Rhode Island	204	0.5%
23	South Carolina	584	1.5%
48	South Dakota	64	0.2%
15	Tennessee	834	2.1%
3	Texas	2,731	6.9%
32	Utah	255	0.6%
45	Vermont	100	0.3%
13	Virginia	1,123	2.8%
18	Washington	695	1.7%
37	West Virginia	205	0.5%
24	Wisconsin	566	1.4%
49	Wyoming	52	0.1%

RANK ORDER

RANK	STATE	PHYSICIANS	% of USA
1	California	4,702	11.8%
2	New York	3,712	9.3%
3	Texas	2,731	6.9%
4	Florida	2,087	5.2%
5	Illinois	1,805	4.5%
6	Pennsylvania	1,744	4.4%
7	New Jersey	1,534	3.8%
8	Ohio	1,530	3.8%
9	Michigan	1,323	3.3%
10	Georgia	1,312	3.3%
11	North Carolina	1,207	3.0%
12	Massachusetts	1,132	2.8%
13	Virginia	1,123	2.8%
14	Maryland	1,078	2.7%
15	Tennessee	834	2.1%
16	Louisiana	731	1.8%
17	Missouri	724	1.8%
18	Washington	695	1.7%
19	Connecticut	687	1.7%
20	Indiana	672	1.7%
21	Arizona	621	1.6%
22	Colorado	592	1.5%
23	South Carolina	584	1.5%
24	Wisconsin	566	1.4%
25	Alabama	559	1.4%
26	Minnesota	537	1.3%
27	Kentucky	477	1.2%
28	Oregon	453	1.1%
29	Mississippi	321	0.8%
30	Oklahoma	301	0.8%
31	Kansas	280	0.7%
32	Utah	255	0.6%
33	Nevada	252	0.6%
34	Arkansas	250	0.6%
35	Hawaii	229	0.6%
36	Iowa	212	0.5%
37	West Virginia	205	0.5%
38	Rhode Island	204	0.5%
39	New Hampshire	197	0.5%
40	New Mexico	186	0.5%
41	Nebraska	177	0.4%
42	Maine	149	0.4%
43	Idaho	119	0.3%
44	Delaware	110	0.3%
45	Vermont	100	0.3%
46	Montana	97	0.2%
47	Alaska	71	0.2%
48	South Dakota	64	0.2%
49	Wyoming	52	0.1%
50	North Dakota	51	0.1%
	District of Columbia	221	0.6%

Source: American Medical Association (Chicago, Illinois)
"Physician Characteristics and Distribution in the U.S." (2004 Edition)
*As of December 31, 2002. Total does not include 593 physicians in U.S. territories and possessions. Obstetrics and Gynecology includes Gynecology and Oncology, Maternal and Fetal Medicine and Reproductive Endocrinology.

Rate of Nonfederal Physicians in Obstetrics and Gynecology in 2002

National Rate = 27 Physicians per 100,000 Female Population*

ALPHA ORDER

RANK	STATE	RATE
26	Alabama	24
29	Alaska	23
29	Arizona	23
45	Arkansas	18
17	California	27
20	Colorado	26
1	Connecticut	39
17	Delaware	27
26	Florida	24
10	Georgia	30
3	Hawaii	37
45	Idaho	18
13	Illinois	28
37	Indiana	21
50	Iowa	14
42	Kansas	20
29	Kentucky	23
8	Louisiana	32
33	Maine	22
2	Maryland	38
7	Massachusetts	34
20	Michigan	26
37	Minnesota	21
33	Mississippi	22
24	Missouri	25
37	Montana	21
42	Nebraska	20
26	Nevada	24
10	New Hampshire	30
6	New Jersey	35
42	New Mexico	20
3	New York	37
13	North Carolina	28
49	North Dakota	16
20	Ohio	26
47	Oklahoma	17
20	Oregon	26
17	Pennsylvania	27
3	Rhode Island	37
13	South Carolina	28
47	South Dakota	17
13	Tennessee	28
24	Texas	25
33	Utah	22
8	Vermont	32
10	Virginia	30
29	Washington	23
33	West Virginia	22
37	Wisconsin	21
37	Wyoming	21

RANK ORDER

RANK	STATE	RATE
1	Connecticut	39
2	Maryland	38
3	Hawaii	37
3	New York	37
3	Rhode Island	37
6	New Jersey	35
7	Massachusetts	34
8	Louisiana	32
8	Vermont	32
10	Georgia	30
10	New Hampshire	30
10	Virginia	30
13	Illinois	28
13	North Carolina	28
13	South Carolina	28
13	Tennessee	28
17	California	27
17	Delaware	27
17	Pennsylvania	27
20	Colorado	26
20	Michigan	26
20	Ohio	26
20	Oregon	26
24	Missouri	25
24	Texas	25
26	Alabama	24
26	Florida	24
26	Nevada	24
29	Alaska	23
29	Arizona	23
29	Kentucky	23
29	Washington	23
33	Maine	22
33	Mississippi	22
33	Utah	22
33	West Virginia	22
37	Indiana	21
37	Minnesota	21
37	Montana	21
37	Wisconsin	21
37	Wyoming	21
42	Kansas	20
42	Nebraska	20
42	New Mexico	20
45	Arkansas	18
45	Idaho	18
47	Oklahoma	17
47	South Dakota	17
49	North Dakota	16
50	Iowa	14
	District of Columbia	73

Source: Morgan Quitno Press using data from American Medical Association (Chicago, Illinois)
"Physician Characteristics and Distribution in the U.S." (2004 Edition)
*As of December 31, 2002. National rate does not include physicians in U.S. territories and possessions. Obstetrics and Gynecology includes Gynecology and Oncology, Maternal and Fetal Medicine and Reproductive Endocrinology.

Nonfederal Physicians in Ophthalmology in 2002

National Total = 18,101 Physicians*

ALPHA ORDER

RANK	STATE	PHYSICIANS	% of USA
27	Alabama	216	1.2%
49	Alaska	26	0.1%
23	Arizona	271	1.5%
33	Arkansas	136	0.8%
1	California	2,203	12.2%
24	Colorado	264	1.5%
20	Connecticut	314	1.7%
46	Delaware	41	0.2%
3	Florida	1,159	6.4%
14	Georgia	422	2.3%
37	Hawaii	95	0.5%
43	Idaho	62	0.3%
6	Illinois	720	4.0%
22	Indiana	288	1.6%
29	Iowa	157	0.9%
30	Kansas	151	0.8%
28	Kentucky	193	1.1%
18	Louisiana	337	1.9%
41	Maine	77	0.4%
11	Maryland	503	2.8%
10	Massachusetts	546	3.0%
9	Michigan	570	3.1%
21	Minnesota	311	1.7%
32	Mississippi	139	0.8%
16	Missouri	352	1.9%
45	Montana	51	0.3%
35	Nebraska	100	0.6%
38	Nevada	88	0.5%
42	New Hampshire	73	0.4%
7	New Jersey	648	3.6%
40	New Mexico	78	0.4%
2	New York	1,785	9.9%
12	North Carolina	448	2.5%
48	North Dakota	37	0.2%
8	Ohio	645	3.6%
31	Oklahoma	150	0.8%
26	Oregon	223	1.2%
5	Pennsylvania	912	5.0%
39	Rhode Island	82	0.5%
25	South Carolina	249	1.4%
47	South Dakota	39	0.2%
17	Tennessee	351	1.9%
4	Texas	1,066	5.9%
34	Utah	122	0.7%
44	Vermont	54	0.3%
13	Virginia	441	2.4%
15	Washington	360	2.0%
36	West Virginia	99	0.5%
19	Wisconsin	324	1.8%
50	Wyoming	17	0.1%

RANK ORDER

RANK	STATE	PHYSICIANS	% of USA
1	California	2,203	12.2%
2	New York	1,785	9.9%
3	Florida	1,159	6.4%
4	Texas	1,066	5.9%
5	Pennsylvania	912	5.0%
6	Illinois	720	4.0%
7	New Jersey	648	3.6%
8	Ohio	645	3.6%
9	Michigan	570	3.1%
10	Massachusetts	546	3.0%
11	Maryland	503	2.8%
12	North Carolina	448	2.5%
13	Virginia	441	2.4%
14	Georgia	422	2.3%
15	Washington	360	2.0%
16	Missouri	352	1.9%
17	Tennessee	351	1.9%
18	Louisiana	337	1.9%
19	Wisconsin	324	1.8%
20	Connecticut	314	1.7%
21	Minnesota	311	1.7%
22	Indiana	288	1.6%
23	Arizona	271	1.5%
24	Colorado	264	1.5%
25	South Carolina	249	1.4%
26	Oregon	223	1.2%
27	Alabama	216	1.2%
28	Kentucky	193	1.1%
29	Iowa	157	0.9%
30	Kansas	151	0.8%
31	Oklahoma	150	0.8%
32	Mississippi	139	0.8%
33	Arkansas	136	0.8%
34	Utah	122	0.7%
35	Nebraska	100	0.6%
36	West Virginia	99	0.5%
37	Hawaii	95	0.5%
38	Nevada	88	0.5%
39	Rhode Island	82	0.5%
40	New Mexico	78	0.4%
41	Maine	77	0.4%
42	New Hampshire	73	0.4%
43	Idaho	62	0.3%
44	Vermont	54	0.3%
45	Montana	51	0.3%
46	Delaware	41	0.2%
47	South Dakota	39	0.2%
48	North Dakota	37	0.2%
49	Alaska	26	0.1%
50	Wyoming	17	0.1%
	District of Columbia	106	0.6%

Source: American Medical Association (Chicago, Illinois)
    "Physician Characteristics and Distribution in the U.S." (2004 Edition)
*As of December 31, 2002. Total does not include 182 physicians in U.S. territories and possessions.
Ophthalmology is the branch of medicine dealing with the anatomy, functions and diseases of the eye.

Rate of Nonfederal Physicians in Ophthalmology in 2002

National Rate = 6.3 Physicians per 100,000 Population*

ALPHA ORDER

RANK	STATE	RATE
41	Alabama	4.8
48	Alaska	4.0
37	Arizona	5.0
37	Arkansas	5.0
12	California	6.3
20	Colorado	5.9
3	Connecticut	9.1
35	Delaware	5.1
11	Florida	6.9
39	Georgia	4.9
7	Hawaii	7.6
45	Idaho	4.6
25	Illinois	5.7
43	Indiana	4.7
33	Iowa	5.3
28	Kansas	5.6
43	Kentucky	4.7
8	Louisiana	7.5
20	Maine	5.9
2	Maryland	9.2
5	Massachusetts	8.5
25	Michigan	5.7
14	Minnesota	6.2
41	Mississippi	4.8
14	Missouri	6.2
28	Montana	5.6
23	Nebraska	5.8
48	Nevada	4.0
25	New Hampshire	5.7
8	New Jersey	7.5
47	New Mexico	4.2
1	New York	9.3
32	North Carolina	5.4
23	North Dakota	5.8
28	Ohio	5.6
46	Oklahoma	4.3
12	Oregon	6.3
10	Pennsylvania	7.4
6	Rhode Island	7.7
16	South Carolina	6.1
35	South Dakota	5.1
16	Tennessee	6.1
39	Texas	4.9
33	Utah	5.3
4	Vermont	8.8
18	Virginia	6.0
20	Washington	5.9
31	West Virginia	5.5
18	Wisconsin	6.0
50	Wyoming	3.4

RANK ORDER

RANK	STATE	RATE
1	New York	9.3
2	Maryland	9.2
3	Connecticut	9.1
4	Vermont	8.8
5	Massachusetts	8.5
6	Rhode Island	7.7
7	Hawaii	7.6
8	Louisiana	7.5
8	New Jersey	7.5
10	Pennsylvania	7.4
11	Florida	6.9
12	California	6.3
12	Oregon	6.3
14	Minnesota	6.2
14	Missouri	6.2
16	South Carolina	6.1
16	Tennessee	6.1
18	Virginia	6.0
18	Wisconsin	6.0
20	Colorado	5.9
20	Maine	5.9
20	Washington	5.9
23	Nebraska	5.8
23	North Dakota	5.8
25	Illinois	5.7
25	Michigan	5.7
25	New Hampshire	5.7
28	Kansas	5.6
28	Montana	5.6
28	Ohio	5.6
31	West Virginia	5.5
32	North Carolina	5.4
33	Iowa	5.3
33	Utah	5.3
35	Delaware	5.1
35	South Dakota	5.1
37	Arizona	5.0
37	Arkansas	5.0
39	Georgia	4.9
39	Texas	4.9
41	Alabama	4.8
41	Mississippi	4.8
43	Indiana	4.7
43	Kentucky	4.7
45	Idaho	4.6
46	Oklahoma	4.3
47	New Mexico	4.2
48	Alaska	4.0
48	Nevada	4.0
50	Wyoming	3.4

District of Columbia   18.6

Source: Morgan Quitno Press using data from American Medical Association (Chicago, Illinois)
"Physician Characteristics and Distribution in the U.S." (2004 Edition)
*As of December 31, 2002. National rate does not include physicians in U.S. territories and possessions.
Ophthalmology is the branch of medicine dealing with the anatomy, functions and diseases of the eye.

Nonfederal Physicians in Orthopedic Surgery in 2002

National Total = 22,558 Physicians*

RANK	STATE	PHYSICIANS	% of USA
25	Alabama	332	1.5%
49	Alaska	52	0.2%
24	Arizona	339	1.5%
32	Arkansas	180	0.8%
1	California	2,724	12.1%
22	Colorado	400	1.8%
23	Connecticut	371	1.6%
47	Delaware	60	0.3%
4	Florida	1,255	5.6%
13	Georgia	555	2.5%
42	Hawaii	110	0.5%
41	Idaho	111	0.5%
7	Illinois	836	3.7%
19	Indiana	427	1.9%
34	Iowa	177	0.8%
29	Kansas	203	0.9%
28	Kentucky	274	1.2%
20	Louisiana	409	1.8%
38	Maine	115	0.5%
14	Maryland	547	2.4%
9	Massachusetts	697	3.1%
11	Michigan	590	2.6%
18	Minnesota	430	1.9%
33	Mississippi	179	0.8%
21	Missouri	408	1.8%
44	Montana	103	0.5%
35	Nebraska	153	0.7%
40	Nevada	112	0.5%
37	New Hampshire	120	0.5%
8	New Jersey	704	3.1%
36	New Mexico	132	0.6%
2	New York	1,793	7.9%
10	North Carolina	659	2.9%
50	North Dakota	47	0.2%
6	Ohio	872	3.9%
30	Oklahoma	201	0.9%
27	Oregon	300	1.3%
5	Pennsylvania	1,052	4.7%
38	Rhode Island	115	0.5%
26	South Carolina	330	1.5%
46	South Dakota	61	0.3%
16	Tennessee	515	2.3%
3	Texas	1,438	6.4%
31	Utah	190	0.8%
45	Vermont	74	0.3%
12	Virginia	572	2.5%
15	Washington	526	2.3%
42	West Virginia	110	0.5%
17	Wisconsin	454	2.0%
48	Wyoming	53	0.2%

RANK	STATE	PHYSICIANS	% of USA
1	California	2,724	12.1%
2	New York	1,793	7.9%
3	Texas	1,438	6.4%
4	Florida	1,255	5.6%
5	Pennsylvania	1,052	4.7%
6	Ohio	872	3.9%
7	Illinois	836	3.7%
8	New Jersey	704	3.1%
9	Massachusetts	697	3.1%
10	North Carolina	659	2.9%
11	Michigan	590	2.6%
12	Virginia	572	2.5%
13	Georgia	555	2.5%
14	Maryland	547	2.4%
15	Washington	526	2.3%
16	Tennessee	515	2.3%
17	Wisconsin	454	2.0%
18	Minnesota	430	1.9%
19	Indiana	427	1.9%
20	Louisiana	409	1.8%
21	Missouri	408	1.8%
22	Colorado	400	1.8%
23	Connecticut	371	1.6%
24	Arizona	339	1.5%
25	Alabama	332	1.5%
26	South Carolina	330	1.5%
27	Oregon	300	1.3%
28	Kentucky	274	1.2%
29	Kansas	203	0.9%
30	Oklahoma	201	0.9%
31	Utah	190	0.8%
32	Arkansas	180	0.8%
33	Mississippi	179	0.8%
34	Iowa	177	0.8%
35	Nebraska	153	0.7%
36	New Mexico	132	0.6%
37	New Hampshire	120	0.5%
38	Maine	115	0.5%
38	Rhode Island	115	0.5%
40	Nevada	112	0.5%
41	Idaho	111	0.5%
42	Hawaii	110	0.5%
42	West Virginia	110	0.5%
44	Montana	103	0.5%
45	Vermont	74	0.3%
46	South Dakota	61	0.3%
47	Delaware	60	0.3%
48	Wyoming	53	0.2%
49	Alaska	52	0.2%
50	North Dakota	47	0.2%
	District of Columbia	91	0.4%

Source: American Medical Association (Chicago, Illinois)
    "Physician Characteristics and Distribution in the U.S." (2004 Edition)
*As of December 31, 2002. Total does not include 167 physicians in U.S. territories and possessions.
Orthopedics is the branch of medicine dealing with the skeletal system.

Rate of Nonfederal Physicians in Orthopedic Surgery in 2002

National Rate = 7.8 Physicians per 100,000 Population*

ALPHA ORDER

RANK	STATE	RATE
33	Alabama	7.4
24	Alaska	8.1
44	Arizona	6.2
40	Arkansas	6.6
28	California	7.8
11	Colorado	8.9
5	Connecticut	10.7
33	Delaware	7.4
31	Florida	7.5
43	Georgia	6.5
14	Hawaii	8.8
20	Idaho	8.3
40	Illinois	6.6
38	Indiana	6.9
47	Iowa	6.0
31	Kansas	7.5
39	Kentucky	6.7
10	Louisiana	9.1
11	Maine	8.9
7	Maryland	10.0
3	Massachusetts	10.8
48	Michigan	5.9
17	Minnesota	8.6
44	Mississippi	6.2
36	Missouri	7.2
2	Montana	11.3
14	Nebraska	8.8
50	Nevada	5.2
8	New Hampshire	9.4
22	New Jersey	8.2
37	New Mexico	7.1
8	New York	9.4
27	North Carolina	7.9
33	North Dakota	7.4
30	Ohio	7.6
49	Oklahoma	5.8
18	Oregon	8.5
18	Pennsylvania	8.5
3	Rhode Island	10.8
25	South Carolina	8.0
25	South Dakota	8.0
11	Tennessee	8.9
40	Texas	6.6
22	Utah	8.2
1	Vermont	12.0
28	Virginia	7.8
16	Washington	8.7
46	West Virginia	6.1
20	Wisconsin	8.3
6	Wyoming	10.6

RANK ORDER

RANK	STATE	RATE
1	Vermont	12.0
2	Montana	11.3
3	Massachusetts	10.8
3	Rhode Island	10.8
5	Connecticut	10.7
6	Wyoming	10.6
7	Maryland	10.0
8	New Hampshire	9.4
8	New York	9.4
10	Louisiana	9.1
11	Colorado	8.9
11	Maine	8.9
11	Tennessee	8.9
14	Hawaii	8.8
14	Nebraska	8.8
16	Washington	8.7
17	Minnesota	8.6
18	Oregon	8.5
18	Pennsylvania	8.5
20	Idaho	8.3
20	Wisconsin	8.3
22	New Jersey	8.2
22	Utah	8.2
24	Alaska	8.1
25	South Carolina	8.0
25	South Dakota	8.0
27	North Carolina	7.9
28	California	7.8
28	Virginia	7.8
30	Ohio	7.6
31	Florida	7.5
31	Kansas	7.5
33	Alabama	7.4
33	Delaware	7.4
33	North Dakota	7.4
36	Missouri	7.2
37	New Mexico	7.1
38	Indiana	6.9
39	Kentucky	6.7
40	Arkansas	6.6
40	Illinois	6.6
40	Texas	6.6
43	Georgia	6.5
44	Arizona	6.2
44	Mississippi	6.2
46	West Virginia	6.1
47	Iowa	6.0
48	Michigan	5.9
49	Oklahoma	5.8
50	Nevada	5.2

District of Columbia — 15.9

Source: Morgan Quitno Press using data from American Medical Association (Chicago, Illinois)
    "Physician Characteristics and Distribution in the U.S." (2004 Edition)
*As of December 31, 2002. National rate does not include physicians in U.S. territories and possessions.
Orthopedics is the branch of medicine dealing with the skeletal system.

Nonfederal Physicians in Plastic Surgery in 2002

National Total = 6,430 Physicians*

ALPHA ORDER

RANK	STATE	PHYSICIANS	% of USA
26	Alabama	78	1.2%
49	Alaska	8	0.1%
17	Arizona	126	2.0%
35	Arkansas	32	0.5%
1	California	961	14.9%
21	Colorado	90	1.4%
20	Connecticut	94	1.5%
43	Delaware	17	0.3%
3	Florida	509	7.9%
12	Georgia	162	2.5%
34	Hawaii	34	0.5%
38	Idaho	25	0.4%
6	Illinois	242	3.8%
19	Indiana	98	1.5%
40	Iowa	24	0.4%
30	Kansas	51	0.8%
21	Kentucky	90	1.4%
21	Louisiana	90	1.4%
46	Maine	11	0.2%
15	Maryland	144	2.2%
10	Massachusetts	183	2.8%
9	Michigan	198	3.1%
24	Minnesota	84	1.3%
31	Mississippi	41	0.6%
16	Missouri	130	2.0%
44	Montana	14	0.2%
38	Nebraska	25	0.4%
32	Nevada	40	0.6%
42	New Hampshire	21	0.3%
7	New Jersey	215	3.3%
41	New Mexico	23	0.4%
2	New York	608	9.5%
13	North Carolina	157	2.4%
47	North Dakota	10	0.2%
8	Ohio	204	3.2%
32	Oklahoma	40	0.6%
29	Oregon	52	0.8%
5	Pennsylvania	248	3.9%
37	Rhode Island	28	0.4%
28	South Carolina	62	1.0%
48	South Dakota	9	0.1%
14	Tennessee	145	2.3%
4	Texas	495	7.7%
27	Utah	67	1.0%
45	Vermont	12	0.2%
11	Virginia	168	2.6%
18	Washington	118	1.8%
36	West Virginia	29	0.5%
25	Wisconsin	83	1.3%
50	Wyoming	3	0.0%

RANK ORDER

RANK	STATE	PHYSICIANS	% of USA
1	California	961	14.9%
2	New York	608	9.5%
3	Florida	509	7.9%
4	Texas	495	7.7%
5	Pennsylvania	248	3.9%
6	Illinois	242	3.8%
7	New Jersey	215	3.3%
8	Ohio	204	3.2%
9	Michigan	198	3.1%
10	Massachusetts	183	2.8%
11	Virginia	168	2.6%
12	Georgia	162	2.5%
13	North Carolina	157	2.4%
14	Tennessee	145	2.3%
15	Maryland	144	2.2%
16	Missouri	130	2.0%
17	Arizona	126	2.0%
18	Washington	118	1.8%
19	Indiana	98	1.5%
20	Connecticut	94	1.5%
21	Colorado	90	1.4%
21	Kentucky	90	1.4%
21	Louisiana	90	1.4%
24	Minnesota	84	1.3%
25	Wisconsin	83	1.3%
26	Alabama	78	1.2%
27	Utah	67	1.0%
28	South Carolina	62	1.0%
29	Oregon	52	0.8%
30	Kansas	51	0.8%
31	Mississippi	41	0.6%
32	Nevada	40	0.6%
32	Oklahoma	40	0.6%
34	Hawaii	34	0.5%
35	Arkansas	32	0.5%
36	West Virginia	29	0.5%
37	Rhode Island	28	0.4%
38	Idaho	25	0.4%
38	Nebraska	25	0.4%
40	Iowa	24	0.4%
41	New Mexico	23	0.4%
42	New Hampshire	21	0.3%
43	Delaware	17	0.3%
44	Montana	14	0.2%
45	Vermont	12	0.2%
46	Maine	11	0.2%
47	North Dakota	10	0.2%
48	South Dakota	9	0.1%
49	Alaska	8	0.1%
50	Wyoming	3	0.0%
	District of Columbia	32	0.5%

Source: American Medical Association (Chicago, Illinois)
   "Physician Characteristics and Distribution in the U.S." (2004 Edition)
*As of December 31, 2002. Total does not include 40 physicians in U.S. territories and possessions.

Rate of Nonfederal Physicians in Plastic Surgery in 2002

National Rate = 2.2 Physicians per 100,000 Population*

ALPHA ORDER

RANK	STATE	RATE
31	Alabama	1.7
43	Alaska	1.2
12	Arizona	2.3
43	Arkansas	1.2
5	California	2.7
18	Colorado	2.0
5	Connecticut	2.7
17	Delaware	2.1
2	Florida	3.0
22	Georgia	1.9
5	Hawaii	2.7
22	Idaho	1.9
22	Illinois	1.9
33	Indiana	1.6
48	Iowa	0.8
22	Kansas	1.9
16	Kentucky	2.2
18	Louisiana	2.0
48	Maine	0.8
8	Maryland	2.6
4	Massachusetts	2.8
18	Michigan	2.0
31	Minnesota	1.7
41	Mississippi	1.4
12	Missouri	2.3
37	Montana	1.5
41	Nebraska	1.4
29	Nevada	1.8
33	New Hampshire	1.6
10	New Jersey	2.5
43	New Mexico	1.2
1	New York	3.2
22	North Carolina	1.9
33	North Dakota	1.6
29	Ohio	1.8
47	Oklahoma	1.1
37	Oregon	1.5
18	Pennsylvania	2.0
8	Rhode Island	2.6
37	South Carolina	1.5
43	South Dakota	1.2
10	Tennessee	2.5
12	Texas	2.3
3	Utah	2.9
22	Vermont	1.9
12	Virginia	2.3
22	Washington	1.9
33	West Virginia	1.6
37	Wisconsin	1.5
50	Wyoming	0.6

RANK ORDER

RANK	STATE	RATE
1	New York	3.2
2	Florida	3.0
3	Utah	2.9
4	Massachusetts	2.8
5	California	2.7
5	Connecticut	2.7
5	Hawaii	2.7
8	Maryland	2.6
8	Rhode Island	2.6
10	New Jersey	2.5
10	Tennessee	2.5
12	Arizona	2.3
12	Missouri	2.3
12	Texas	2.3
12	Virginia	2.3
16	Kentucky	2.2
17	Delaware	2.1
18	Colorado	2.0
18	Louisiana	2.0
18	Michigan	2.0
18	Pennsylvania	2.0
22	Georgia	1.9
22	Idaho	1.9
22	Illinois	1.9
22	Kansas	1.9
22	North Carolina	1.9
22	Vermont	1.9
22	Washington	1.9
29	Nevada	1.8
29	Ohio	1.8
31	Alabama	1.7
31	Minnesota	1.7
33	Indiana	1.6
33	New Hampshire	1.6
33	North Dakota	1.6
33	West Virginia	1.6
37	Montana	1.5
37	Oregon	1.5
37	South Carolina	1.5
37	Wisconsin	1.5
41	Mississippi	1.4
41	Nebraska	1.4
43	Alaska	1.2
43	Arkansas	1.2
43	New Mexico	1.2
43	South Dakota	1.2
47	Oklahoma	1.1
48	Iowa	0.8
48	Maine	0.8
50	Wyoming	0.6

District of Columbia   5.6

Source: Morgan Quitno Press using data from American Medical Association (Chicago, Illinois)
        "Physician Characteristics and Distribution in the U.S." (2004 Edition)
*As of December 31, 2002. National rate does not include physicians in U.S. territories and possessions.

Nonfederal Physicians in Other Specialties in 2002

National Total = 193,497 Physicians*

ALPHA ORDER

RANK	STATE	PHYSICIANS	% of USA
28	Alabama	2,096	1.1%
49	Alaska	328	0.2%
22	Arizona	3,020	1.6%
33	Arkansas	1,250	0.6%
1	California	23,735	12.3%
23	Colorado	2,966	1.5%
19	Connecticut	3,434	1.8%
46	Delaware	499	0.3%
4	Florida	10,085	5.2%
14	Georgia	4,530	2.3%
38	Hawaii	958	0.5%
45	Idaho	522	0.3%
6	Illinois	8,519	4.4%
18	Indiana	3,462	1.8%
31	Iowa	1,281	0.7%
29	Kansas	1,460	0.8%
27	Kentucky	2,284	1.2%
24	Louisiana	2,823	1.5%
41	Maine	905	0.5%
11	Maryland	5,622	2.9%
7	Massachusetts	7,919	4.1%
10	Michigan	5,928	3.1%
21	Minnesota	3,195	1.7%
34	Mississippi	1,171	0.6%
20	Missouri	3,357	1.7%
44	Montana	525	0.3%
39	Nebraska	956	0.5%
36	Nevada	1,029	0.5%
42	New Hampshire	887	0.5%
9	New Jersey	6,539	3.4%
35	New Mexico	1,122	0.6%
2	New York	19,423	10.0%
12	North Carolina	5,123	2.6%
48	North Dakota	342	0.2%
8	Ohio	7,179	3.7%
30	Oklahoma	1,438	0.7%
25	Oregon	2,333	1.2%
5	Pennsylvania	9,856	5.1%
40	Rhode Island	918	0.5%
26	South Carolina	2,291	1.2%
47	South Dakota	358	0.2%
17	Tennessee	3,487	1.8%
3	Texas	11,600	6.0%
32	Utah	1,278	0.7%
43	Vermont	601	0.3%
13	Virginia	4,761	2.5%
15	Washington	4,212	2.2%
37	West Virginia	985	0.5%
16	Wisconsin	3,585	1.9%
50	Wyoming	233	0.1%

RANK ORDER

RANK	STATE	PHYSICIANS	% of USA
1	California	23,735	12.3%
2	New York	19,423	10.0%
3	Texas	11,600	6.0%
4	Florida	10,085	5.2%
5	Pennsylvania	9,856	5.1%
6	Illinois	8,519	4.4%
7	Massachusetts	7,919	4.1%
8	Ohio	7,179	3.7%
9	New Jersey	6,539	3.4%
10	Michigan	5,928	3.1%
11	Maryland	5,622	2.9%
12	North Carolina	5,123	2.6%
13	Virginia	4,761	2.5%
14	Georgia	4,530	2.3%
15	Washington	4,212	2.2%
16	Wisconsin	3,585	1.9%
17	Tennessee	3,487	1.8%
18	Indiana	3,462	1.8%
19	Connecticut	3,434	1.8%
20	Missouri	3,357	1.7%
21	Minnesota	3,195	1.7%
22	Arizona	3,020	1.6%
23	Colorado	2,966	1.5%
24	Louisiana	2,823	1.5%
25	Oregon	2,333	1.2%
26	South Carolina	2,291	1.2%
27	Kentucky	2,284	1.2%
28	Alabama	2,096	1.1%
29	Kansas	1,460	0.8%
30	Oklahoma	1,438	0.7%
31	Iowa	1,281	0.7%
32	Utah	1,278	0.7%
33	Arkansas	1,250	0.6%
34	Mississippi	1,171	0.6%
35	New Mexico	1,122	0.6%
36	Nevada	1,029	0.5%
37	West Virginia	985	0.5%
38	Hawaii	958	0.5%
39	Nebraska	956	0.5%
40	Rhode Island	918	0.5%
41	Maine	905	0.5%
42	New Hampshire	887	0.5%
43	Vermont	601	0.3%
44	Montana	525	0.3%
45	Idaho	522	0.3%
46	Delaware	499	0.3%
47	South Dakota	358	0.2%
48	North Dakota	342	0.2%
49	Alaska	328	0.2%
50	Wyoming	233	0.1%
	District of Columbia	1,087	0.6%

Source: American Medical Association (Chicago, Illinois)
   "Physician Characteristics and Distribution in the U.S." (2004 Edition)
*As of December 31, 2002. Total does not include 2,282 physicians in U.S. territories and possessions. Other Specialties include Aerospace Medicine, Anesthesiology, Child Psychiatry, Diagnostic Radiology, Emergency Medicine, Forensic Pathology, Nuclear Medicine, Occupational Medicine, Neurology, Psychiatry, Public Health, Anatomic/Clinical Pathology, Radiology, Radiation Oncology and other specialties.

Rate of Nonfederal Physicians in Other Specialties in 2002

National Rate = 67 Physicians per 100,000 Population*

<table>
<tr><td colspan="3">ALPHA ORDER</td><td colspan="3">RANK ORDER</td></tr>
<tr><td>RANK</td><td>STATE</td><td>RATE</td><td>RANK</td><td>STATE</td><td>RATE</td></tr>
<tr><td>42</td><td>Alabama</td><td>47</td><td>1</td><td>Massachusetts</td><td>123</td></tr>
<tr><td>41</td><td>Alaska</td><td>51</td><td>2</td><td>Maryland</td><td>103</td></tr>
<tr><td>33</td><td>Arizona</td><td>55</td><td>3</td><td>New York</td><td>101</td></tr>
<tr><td>46</td><td>Arkansas</td><td>46</td><td>4</td><td>Connecticut</td><td>99</td></tr>
<tr><td>13</td><td>California</td><td>68</td><td>5</td><td>Vermont</td><td>97</td></tr>
<tr><td>15</td><td>Colorado</td><td>66</td><td>6</td><td>Rhode Island</td><td>86</td></tr>
<tr><td>4</td><td>Connecticut</td><td>99</td><td>7</td><td>Pennsylvania</td><td>80</td></tr>
<tr><td>22</td><td>Delaware</td><td>62</td><td>8</td><td>Hawaii</td><td>77</td></tr>
<tr><td>24</td><td>Florida</td><td>60</td><td>9</td><td>New Jersey</td><td>76</td></tr>
<tr><td>39</td><td>Georgia</td><td>53</td><td>10</td><td>Maine</td><td>70</td></tr>
<tr><td>8</td><td>Hawaii</td><td>77</td><td>10</td><td>New Hampshire</td><td>70</td></tr>
<tr><td>50</td><td>Idaho</td><td>39</td><td>12</td><td>Washington</td><td>69</td></tr>
<tr><td>13</td><td>Illinois</td><td>68</td><td>13</td><td>California</td><td>68</td></tr>
<tr><td>30</td><td>Indiana</td><td>56</td><td>13</td><td>Illinois</td><td>68</td></tr>
<tr><td>47</td><td>Iowa</td><td>44</td><td>15</td><td>Colorado</td><td>66</td></tr>
<tr><td>37</td><td>Kansas</td><td>54</td><td>15</td><td>Oregon</td><td>66</td></tr>
<tr><td>30</td><td>Kentucky</td><td>56</td><td>15</td><td>Wisconsin</td><td>66</td></tr>
<tr><td>20</td><td>Louisiana</td><td>63</td><td>18</td><td>Virginia</td><td>65</td></tr>
<tr><td>10</td><td>Maine</td><td>70</td><td>19</td><td>Minnesota</td><td>64</td></tr>
<tr><td>2</td><td>Maryland</td><td>103</td><td>20</td><td>Louisiana</td><td>63</td></tr>
<tr><td>1</td><td>Massachusetts</td><td>123</td><td>20</td><td>Ohio</td><td>63</td></tr>
<tr><td>27</td><td>Michigan</td><td>59</td><td>22</td><td>Delaware</td><td>62</td></tr>
<tr><td>19</td><td>Minnesota</td><td>64</td><td>22</td><td>North Carolina</td><td>62</td></tr>
<tr><td>48</td><td>Mississippi</td><td>41</td><td>24</td><td>Florida</td><td>60</td></tr>
<tr><td>27</td><td>Missouri</td><td>59</td><td>24</td><td>New Mexico</td><td>60</td></tr>
<tr><td>29</td><td>Montana</td><td>58</td><td>24</td><td>Tennessee</td><td>60</td></tr>
<tr><td>33</td><td>Nebraska</td><td>55</td><td>27</td><td>Michigan</td><td>59</td></tr>
<tr><td>42</td><td>Nevada</td><td>47</td><td>27</td><td>Missouri</td><td>59</td></tr>
<tr><td>10</td><td>New Hampshire</td><td>70</td><td>29</td><td>Montana</td><td>58</td></tr>
<tr><td>9</td><td>New Jersey</td><td>76</td><td>30</td><td>Indiana</td><td>56</td></tr>
<tr><td>24</td><td>New Mexico</td><td>60</td><td>30</td><td>Kentucky</td><td>56</td></tr>
<tr><td>3</td><td>New York</td><td>101</td><td>30</td><td>South Carolina</td><td>56</td></tr>
<tr><td>22</td><td>North Carolina</td><td>62</td><td>33</td><td>Arizona</td><td>55</td></tr>
<tr><td>37</td><td>North Dakota</td><td>54</td><td>33</td><td>Nebraska</td><td>55</td></tr>
<tr><td>20</td><td>Ohio</td><td>63</td><td>33</td><td>Utah</td><td>55</td></tr>
<tr><td>48</td><td>Oklahoma</td><td>41</td><td>33</td><td>West Virginia</td><td>55</td></tr>
<tr><td>15</td><td>Oregon</td><td>66</td><td>37</td><td>Kansas</td><td>54</td></tr>
<tr><td>7</td><td>Pennsylvania</td><td>80</td><td>37</td><td>North Dakota</td><td>54</td></tr>
<tr><td>6</td><td>Rhode Island</td><td>86</td><td>39</td><td>Georgia</td><td>53</td></tr>
<tr><td>30</td><td>South Carolina</td><td>56</td><td>39</td><td>Texas</td><td>53</td></tr>
<tr><td>42</td><td>South Dakota</td><td>47</td><td>41</td><td>Alaska</td><td>51</td></tr>
<tr><td>24</td><td>Tennessee</td><td>60</td><td>42</td><td>Alabama</td><td>47</td></tr>
<tr><td>39</td><td>Texas</td><td>53</td><td>42</td><td>Nevada</td><td>47</td></tr>
<tr><td>33</td><td>Utah</td><td>55</td><td>42</td><td>South Dakota</td><td>47</td></tr>
<tr><td>5</td><td>Vermont</td><td>97</td><td>42</td><td>Wyoming</td><td>47</td></tr>
<tr><td>18</td><td>Virginia</td><td>65</td><td>46</td><td>Arkansas</td><td>46</td></tr>
<tr><td>12</td><td>Washington</td><td>69</td><td>47</td><td>Iowa</td><td>44</td></tr>
<tr><td>33</td><td>West Virginia</td><td>55</td><td>48</td><td>Mississippi</td><td>41</td></tr>
<tr><td>15</td><td>Wisconsin</td><td>66</td><td>48</td><td>Oklahoma</td><td>41</td></tr>
<tr><td>42</td><td>Wyoming</td><td>47</td><td>50</td><td>Idaho</td><td>39</td></tr>
<tr><td></td><td></td><td></td><td></td><td>District of Columbia</td><td>190</td></tr>
</table>

Source: Morgan Quitno Press using data from American Medical Association (Chicago, Illinois)
   "Physician Characteristics and Distribution in the U.S." (2004 Edition)
*As of December 31, 2002. National rate does not include physicians in U.S. territories and possessions. Other Specialties include Aerospace Medicine, Anesthesiology, Child Psychiatry, Diagnostic Radiology, Emergency Medicine, Forensic Pathology, Nuclear Medicine, Occupational Medicine, Neurology, Psychiatry, Public Health, Anatomic/Clinical Pathology, Radiology, Radiation Oncology and other specialties.

Nonfederal Physicians in Anesthesiology in 2002

National Total = 36,636 Physicians*

ALPHA ORDER

RANK	STATE	PHYSICIANS	% of USA
27	Alabama	422	1.2%
47	Alaska	68	0.2%
19	Arizona	694	1.9%
34	Arkansas	266	0.7%
1	California	4,521	12.3%
21	Colorado	602	1.6%
22	Connecticut	531	1.4%
46	Delaware	73	0.2%
4	Florida	2,242	6.1%
14	Georgia	856	2.3%
41	Hawaii	139	0.4%
44	Idaho	95	0.3%
5	Illinois	1,701	4.6%
15	Indiana	843	2.3%
30	Iowa	301	0.8%
32	Kansas	279	0.8%
26	Kentucky	474	1.3%
24	Louisiana	491	1.3%
40	Maine	145	0.4%
10	Maryland	948	2.6%
9	Massachusetts	1,278	3.5%
12	Michigan	892	2.4%
23	Minnesota	508	1.4%
35	Mississippi	243	0.7%
20	Missouri	623	1.7%
42	Montana	116	0.3%
36	Nebraska	200	0.5%
33	Nevada	275	0.8%
39	New Hampshire	165	0.5%
7	New Jersey	1,372	3.7%
37	New Mexico	193	0.5%
2	New York	3,163	8.6%
13	North Carolina	874	2.4%
49	North Dakota	53	0.1%
8	Ohio	1,356	3.7%
29	Oklahoma	322	0.9%
25	Oregon	476	1.3%
6	Pennsylvania	1,635	4.5%
43	Rhode Island	101	0.3%
28	South Carolina	420	1.1%
48	South Dakota	56	0.2%
18	Tennessee	721	2.0%
3	Texas	2,732	7.5%
31	Utah	294	0.8%
45	Vermont	91	0.2%
16	Virginia	821	2.2%
11	Washington	896	2.4%
38	West Virginia	167	0.5%
17	Wisconsin	741	2.0%
50	Wyoming	51	0.1%

RANK ORDER

RANK	STATE	PHYSICIANS	% of USA
1	California	4,521	12.3%
2	New York	3,163	8.6%
3	Texas	2,732	7.5%
4	Florida	2,242	6.1%
5	Illinois	1,701	4.6%
6	Pennsylvania	1,635	4.5%
7	New Jersey	1,372	3.7%
8	Ohio	1,356	3.7%
9	Massachusetts	1,278	3.5%
10	Maryland	948	2.6%
11	Washington	896	2.4%
12	Michigan	892	2.4%
13	North Carolina	874	2.4%
14	Georgia	856	2.3%
15	Indiana	843	2.3%
16	Virginia	821	2.2%
17	Wisconsin	741	2.0%
18	Tennessee	721	2.0%
19	Arizona	694	1.9%
20	Missouri	623	1.7%
21	Colorado	602	1.6%
22	Connecticut	531	1.4%
23	Minnesota	508	1.4%
24	Louisiana	491	1.3%
25	Oregon	476	1.3%
26	Kentucky	474	1.3%
27	Alabama	422	1.2%
28	South Carolina	420	1.1%
29	Oklahoma	322	0.9%
30	Iowa	301	0.8%
31	Utah	294	0.8%
32	Kansas	279	0.8%
33	Nevada	275	0.8%
34	Arkansas	266	0.7%
35	Mississippi	243	0.7%
36	Nebraska	200	0.5%
37	New Mexico	193	0.5%
38	West Virginia	167	0.5%
39	New Hampshire	165	0.5%
40	Maine	145	0.4%
41	Hawaii	139	0.4%
42	Montana	116	0.3%
43	Rhode Island	101	0.3%
44	Idaho	95	0.3%
45	Vermont	91	0.2%
46	Delaware	73	0.2%
47	Alaska	68	0.2%
48	South Dakota	56	0.2%
49	North Dakota	53	0.1%
50	Wyoming	51	0.1%
	District of Columbia	110	0.3%

Source: American Medical Association (Chicago, Illinois)
"Physician Characteristics and Distribution in the U.S." (2004 Edition)

As of December 31, 2002. Total does not include 235 physicians in U.S. territories and possessions.

Rate of Nonfederal Physicians in Anesthesiology in 2002

National Rate = 12.7 Physicians per 100,000 Population*

ALPHA ORDER

RANK	STATE	RATE
41	Alabama	9.4
31	Alaska	10.6
18	Arizona	12.7
40	Arkansas	9.8
15	California	12.9
12	Colorado	13.4
5	Connecticut	15.3
45	Delaware	9.0
12	Florida	13.4
39	Georgia	10.0
27	Hawaii	11.2
50	Idaho	7.1
10	Illinois	13.5
8	Indiana	13.7
35	Iowa	10.2
34	Kansas	10.3
24	Kentucky	11.6
29	Louisiana	11.0
27	Maine	11.2
2	Maryland	17.4
1	Massachusetts	19.9
46	Michigan	8.9
38	Minnesota	10.1
47	Mississippi	8.5
29	Missouri	11.0
17	Montana	12.8
24	Nebraska	11.6
18	Nevada	12.7
15	New Hampshire	12.9
4	New Jersey	16.0
33	New Mexico	10.4
3	New York	16.5
32	North Carolina	10.5
48	North Dakota	8.4
23	Ohio	11.9
44	Oklahoma	9.2
10	Oregon	13.5
14	Pennsylvania	13.3
41	Rhode Island	9.4
35	South Carolina	10.2
49	South Dakota	7.4
22	Tennessee	12.4
21	Texas	12.5
18	Utah	12.7
6	Vermont	14.8
26	Virginia	11.3
6	Washington	14.8
43	West Virginia	9.3
9	Wisconsin	13.6
35	Wyoming	10.2

RANK ORDER

RANK	STATE	RATE
1	Massachusetts	19.9
2	Maryland	17.4
3	New York	16.5
4	New Jersey	16.0
5	Connecticut	15.3
6	Vermont	14.8
6	Washington	14.8
8	Indiana	13.7
9	Wisconsin	13.6
10	Illinois	13.5
10	Oregon	13.5
12	Colorado	13.4
12	Florida	13.4
14	Pennsylvania	13.3
15	California	12.9
15	New Hampshire	12.9
17	Montana	12.8
18	Arizona	12.7
18	Nevada	12.7
18	Utah	12.7
21	Texas	12.5
22	Tennessee	12.4
23	Ohio	11.9
24	Kentucky	11.6
24	Nebraska	11.6
26	Virginia	11.3
27	Hawaii	11.2
27	Maine	11.2
29	Louisiana	11.0
29	Missouri	11.0
31	Alaska	10.6
32	North Carolina	10.5
33	New Mexico	10.4
34	Kansas	10.3
35	Iowa	10.2
35	South Carolina	10.2
35	Wyoming	10.2
38	Minnesota	10.1
39	Georgia	10.0
40	Arkansas	9.8
41	Alabama	9.4
41	Rhode Island	9.4
43	West Virginia	9.3
44	Oklahoma	9.2
45	Delaware	9.0
46	Michigan	8.9
47	Mississippi	8.5
48	North Dakota	8.4
49	South Dakota	7.4
50	Idaho	7.1

| | District of Columbia | 19.3 |

Source: Morgan Quitno Press using data from American Medical Association (Chicago, Illinois)
"Physician Characteristics and Distribution in the U.S." (2004 Edition)
*As of December 31, 2002. National rate does not include physicians in U.S. territories and possessions.

Nonfederal Physicians in Psychiatry in 2002

National Total = 37,487 Physicians*

ALPHA ORDER

RANK	STATE	PHYSICIANS	% of USA
28	Alabama	298	0.8%
46	Alaska	69	0.2%
22	Arizona	504	1.3%
37	Arkansas	180	0.5%
2	California	5,097	13.6%
18	Colorado	519	1.4%
14	Connecticut	892	2.4%
44	Delaware	79	0.2%
6	Florida	1,584	4.2%
15	Georgia	815	2.2%
34	Hawaii	203	0.5%
47	Idaho	63	0.2%
7	Illinois	1,510	4.0%
23	Indiana	470	1.3%
36	Iowa	191	0.5%
29	Kansas	281	0.7%
27	Kentucky	379	1.0%
19	Louisiana	513	1.4%
33	Maine	214	0.6%
9	Maryland	1,228	3.3%
3	Massachusetts	2,021	5.4%
11	Michigan	1,000	2.7%
24	Minnesota	464	1.2%
39	Mississippi	173	0.5%
20	Missouri	512	1.4%
45	Montana	75	0.2%
42	Nebraska	145	0.4%
43	Nevada	136	0.4%
35	New Hampshire	193	0.5%
8	New Jersey	1,358	3.6%
31	New Mexico	243	0.6%
1	New York	5,447	14.5%
13	North Carolina	934	2.5%
49	North Dakota	57	0.2%
10	Ohio	1,141	3.0%
30	Oklahoma	247	0.7%
26	Oregon	401	1.1%
4	Pennsylvania	1,883	5.0%
32	Rhode Island	239	0.6%
25	South Carolina	424	1.1%
47	South Dakota	63	0.2%
20	Tennessee	512	1.4%
5	Texas	1,684	4.5%
38	Utah	175	0.5%
41	Vermont	157	0.4%
12	Virginia	940	2.5%
16	Washington	706	1.9%
40	West Virginia	162	0.4%
17	Wisconsin	565	1.5%
50	Wyoming	31	0.1%

RANK ORDER

RANK	STATE	PHYSICIANS	% of USA
1	New York	5,447	14.5%
2	California	5,097	13.6%
3	Massachusetts	2,021	5.4%
4	Pennsylvania	1,883	5.0%
5	Texas	1,684	4.5%
6	Florida	1,584	4.2%
7	Illinois	1,510	4.0%
8	New Jersey	1,358	3.6%
9	Maryland	1,228	3.3%
10	Ohio	1,141	3.0%
11	Michigan	1,000	2.7%
12	Virginia	940	2.5%
13	North Carolina	934	2.5%
14	Connecticut	892	2.4%
15	Georgia	815	2.2%
16	Washington	706	1.9%
17	Wisconsin	565	1.5%
18	Colorado	519	1.4%
19	Louisiana	513	1.4%
20	Missouri	512	1.4%
20	Tennessee	512	1.4%
22	Arizona	504	1.3%
23	Indiana	470	1.3%
24	Minnesota	464	1.2%
25	South Carolina	424	1.1%
26	Oregon	401	1.1%
27	Kentucky	379	1.0%
28	Alabama	298	0.8%
29	Kansas	281	0.7%
30	Oklahoma	247	0.7%
31	New Mexico	243	0.6%
32	Rhode Island	239	0.6%
33	Maine	214	0.6%
34	Hawaii	203	0.5%
35	New Hampshire	193	0.5%
36	Iowa	191	0.5%
37	Arkansas	180	0.5%
38	Utah	175	0.5%
39	Mississippi	173	0.5%
40	West Virginia	162	0.4%
41	Vermont	157	0.4%
42	Nebraska	145	0.4%
43	Nevada	136	0.4%
44	Delaware	79	0.2%
45	Montana	75	0.2%
46	Alaska	69	0.2%
47	Idaho	63	0.2%
47	South Dakota	63	0.2%
49	North Dakota	57	0.2%
50	Wyoming	31	0.1%
	District of Columbia	310	0.8%

Source: American Medical Association (Chicago, Illinois)
    "Physician Characteristics and Distribution in the U.S." (2004 Edition)
*As of December 31, 2002. Total does not include 403 physicians in U.S. territories and possessions. Psychiatry includes psychoanalysis.

Rate of Nonfederal Physicians in Psychiatry in 2002

National Rate = 13.0 Physicians per 100,000 Population*

ALPHA ORDER

RANK	STATE	RATE
44	Alabama	6.6
21	Alaska	10.7
31	Arizona	9.2
44	Arkansas	6.6
12	California	14.5
17	Colorado	11.5
3	Connecticut	25.8
27	Delaware	9.8
28	Florida	9.5
28	Georgia	9.5
8	Hawaii	16.3
50	Idaho	4.7
15	Illinois	12.0
41	Indiana	7.6
46	Iowa	6.5
23	Kansas	10.3
30	Kentucky	9.3
18	Louisiana	11.4
7	Maine	16.5
5	Maryland	22.5
1	Massachusetts	31.4
26	Michigan	9.9
31	Minnesota	9.2
49	Mississippi	6.0
33	Missouri	9.0
39	Montana	8.2
37	Nebraska	8.4
47	Nevada	6.3
11	New Hampshire	15.1
9	New Jersey	15.8
13	New Mexico	13.1
2	New York	28.4
20	North Carolina	11.2
33	North Dakota	9.0
25	Ohio	10.0
43	Oklahoma	7.1
18	Oregon	11.4
10	Pennsylvania	15.3
6	Rhode Island	22.3
23	South Carolina	10.3
38	South Dakota	8.3
36	Tennessee	8.8
40	Texas	7.7
41	Utah	7.6
4	Vermont	25.5
14	Virginia	12.9
16	Washington	11.6
33	West Virginia	9.0
22	Wisconsin	10.4
48	Wyoming	6.2

RANK ORDER

RANK	STATE	RATE
1	Massachusetts	31.4
2	New York	28.4
3	Connecticut	25.8
4	Vermont	25.5
5	Maryland	22.5
6	Rhode Island	22.3
7	Maine	16.5
8	Hawaii	16.3
9	New Jersey	15.8
10	Pennsylvania	15.3
11	New Hampshire	15.1
12	California	14.5
13	New Mexico	13.1
14	Virginia	12.9
15	Illinois	12.0
16	Washington	11.6
17	Colorado	11.5
18	Louisiana	11.4
18	Oregon	11.4
20	North Carolina	11.2
21	Alaska	10.7
22	Wisconsin	10.4
23	Kansas	10.3
23	South Carolina	10.3
25	Ohio	10.0
26	Michigan	9.9
27	Delaware	9.8
28	Florida	9.5
28	Georgia	9.5
30	Kentucky	9.3
31	Arizona	9.2
31	Minnesota	9.2
33	Missouri	9.0
33	North Dakota	9.0
33	West Virginia	9.0
36	Tennessee	8.8
37	Nebraska	8.4
38	South Dakota	8.3
39	Montana	8.2
40	Texas	7.7
41	Indiana	7.6
41	Utah	7.6
43	Oklahoma	7.1
44	Alabama	6.6
44	Arkansas	6.6
46	Iowa	6.5
47	Nevada	6.3
48	Wyoming	6.2
49	Mississippi	6.0
50	Idaho	4.7

	District of Columbia	54.3

Source: Morgan Quitno Press using data from American Medical Association (Chicago, Illinois)
    "Physician Characteristics and Distribution in the U.S." (2004 Edition)
As of December 31, 2002. National rate does not include physicians in U.S. territories and possessions.
Psychiatry includes psychoanalysis.

Percent of Population Lacking Access to Mental Health Care in 2003

National Percent = 14.9% of Population*

ALPHA ORDER

RANK	STATE	PERCENT
3	Alabama	52.1
14	Alaska	31.9
31	Arizona	10.3
5	Arkansas	43.5
38	California	7.7
46	Colorado	2.7
48	Connecticut	1.5
50	Delaware	0.0
38	Florida	7.7
19	Georgia	22.3
36	Hawaii	8.0
2	Idaho	64.5
27	Illinois	16.0
42	Indiana	5.2
11	Iowa	35.0
14	Kansas	31.9
17	Kentucky	26.7
44	Louisiana	3.3
30	Maine	11.9
46	Maryland	2.7
49	Massachusetts	1.2
26	Michigan	17.4
23	Minnesota	19.0
23	Mississippi	19.0
25	Missouri	18.8
7	Montana	41.6
6	Nebraska	41.8
34	Nevada	8.8
40	New Hampshire	7.6
43	New Jersey	4.6
4	New Mexico	48.5
41	New York	5.7
32	North Carolina	9.5
8	North Dakota	37.9
35	Ohio	8.3
9	Oklahoma	36.7
22	Oregon	19.8
33	Pennsylvania	8.9
20	Rhode Island	21.5
13	South Carolina	34.1
10	South Dakota	36.4
12	Tennessee	34.4
18	Texas	24.8
16	Utah	27.0
29	Vermont	12.5
45	Virginia	3.1
28	Washington	12.8
37	West Virginia	7.8
21	Wisconsin	21.0
1	Wyoming	75.0

RANK ORDER

RANK	STATE	PERCENT
1	Wyoming	75.0
2	Idaho	64.5
3	Alabama	52.1
4	New Mexico	48.5
5	Arkansas	43.5
6	Nebraska	41.8
7	Montana	41.6
8	North Dakota	37.9
9	Oklahoma	36.7
10	South Dakota	36.4
11	Iowa	35.0
12	Tennessee	34.4
13	South Carolina	34.1
14	Alaska	31.9
14	Kansas	31.9
16	Utah	27.0
17	Kentucky	26.7
18	Texas	24.8
19	Georgia	22.3
20	Rhode Island	21.5
21	Wisconsin	21.0
22	Oregon	19.8
23	Minnesota	19.0
23	Mississippi	19.0
25	Missouri	18.8
26	Michigan	17.4
27	Illinois	16.0
28	Washington	12.8
29	Vermont	12.5
30	Maine	11.9
31	Arizona	10.3
32	North Carolina	9.5
33	Pennsylvania	8.9
34	Nevada	8.8
35	Ohio	8.3
36	Hawaii	8.0
37	West Virginia	7.8
38	California	7.7
38	Florida	7.7
40	New Hampshire	7.6
41	New York	5.7
42	Indiana	5.2
43	New Jersey	4.6
44	Louisiana	3.3
45	Virginia	3.1
46	Colorado	2.7
46	Maryland	2.7
48	Connecticut	1.5
49	Massachusetts	1.2
50	Delaware	0.0

	District of Columbia	0.7

Source: Morgan Quitno Press using data from U.S. Dept. of Health and Human Services, Div. of Shortage Designation "Selected Statistics on Health Professional Shortage Areas"

*Percent of population considered under-served by mental health practitioners. An under-served population does not have primary medical care within reasonable economic and geographic bounds.

International Medical School Graduates Practicing in the U.S. in 2002

National Total = 204,545 Nonfederal Physicians*

ALPHA ORDER

RANK	STATE	PHYSICIANS	% of USA
26	Alabama	1,508	0.7%
48	Alaska	92	0.0%
20	Arizona	2,317	1.1%
33	Arkansas	807	0.4%
2	California	22,452	11.0%
34	Colorado	800	0.4%
13	Connecticut	3,861	1.9%
38	Delaware	657	0.3%
3	Florida	17,012	8.3%
14	Georgia	3,587	1.8%
39	Hawaii	630	0.3%
49	Idaho	74	0.0%
4	Illinois	12,803	6.3%
16	Indiana	2,749	1.3%
31	Iowa	1,045	0.5%
27	Kansas	1,183	0.6%
22	Kentucky	2,042	1.0%
21	Louisiana	2,191	1.1%
42	Maine	453	0.2%
10	Maryland	6,581	3.2%
11	Massachusetts	6,274	3.1%
9	Michigan	8,402	4.1%
23	Minnesota	1,982	1.0%
37	Mississippi	664	0.3%
15	Missouri	3,122	1.5%
47	Montana	103	0.1%
40	Nebraska	536	0.3%
30	Nevada	1,083	0.5%
41	New Hampshire	497	0.2%
5	New Jersey	12,786	6.3%
36	New Mexico	685	0.3%
1	New York	33,985	16.6%
17	North Carolina	2,628	1.3%
43	North Dakota	377	0.2%
8	Ohio	8,724	4.3%
29	Oklahoma	1,152	0.6%
35	Oregon	771	0.4%
7	Pennsylvania	9,822	4.8%
32	Rhode Island	1,042	0.5%
28	South Carolina	1,176	0.6%
45	South Dakota	232	0.1%
19	Tennessee	2,380	1.2%
6	Texas	11,331	5.5%
44	Utah	365	0.2%
46	Vermont	188	0.1%
12	Virginia	4,412	2.2%
24	Washington	1,919	0.9%
25	West Virginia	1,614	0.8%
18	Wisconsin	2,512	1.2%
50	Wyoming	64	0.0%

RANK ORDER

RANK	STATE	PHYSICIANS	% of USA
1	New York	33,985	16.6%
2	California	22,452	11.0%
3	Florida	17,012	8.3%
4	Illinois	12,803	6.3%
5	New Jersey	12,786	6.3%
6	Texas	11,331	5.5%
7	Pennsylvania	9,822	4.8%
8	Ohio	8,724	4.3%
9	Michigan	8,402	4.1%
10	Maryland	6,581	3.2%
11	Massachusetts	6,274	3.1%
12	Virginia	4,412	2.2%
13	Connecticut	3,861	1.9%
14	Georgia	3,587	1.8%
15	Missouri	3,122	1.5%
16	Indiana	2,749	1.3%
17	North Carolina	2,628	1.3%
18	Wisconsin	2,512	1.2%
19	Tennessee	2,380	1.2%
20	Arizona	2,317	1.1%
21	Louisiana	2,191	1.1%
22	Kentucky	2,042	1.0%
23	Minnesota	1,982	1.0%
24	Washington	1,919	0.9%
25	West Virginia	1,614	0.8%
26	Alabama	1,508	0.7%
27	Kansas	1,183	0.6%
28	South Carolina	1,176	0.6%
29	Oklahoma	1,152	0.6%
30	Nevada	1,083	0.5%
31	Iowa	1,045	0.5%
32	Rhode Island	1,042	0.5%
33	Arkansas	807	0.4%
34	Colorado	800	0.4%
35	Oregon	771	0.4%
36	New Mexico	685	0.3%
37	Mississippi	664	0.3%
38	Delaware	657	0.3%
39	Hawaii	630	0.3%
40	Nebraska	536	0.3%
41	New Hampshire	497	0.2%
42	Maine	453	0.2%
43	North Dakota	377	0.2%
44	Utah	365	0.2%
45	South Dakota	232	0.1%
46	Vermont	188	0.1%
47	Montana	103	0.1%
48	Alaska	92	0.0%
49	Idaho	74	0.0%
50	Wyoming	64	0.0%
	District of Columbia	873	0.4%

Source: American Medical Association (Chicago, Illinois)
   "Physician Characteristics and Distribution in the U.S." (2004 Edition)
*Nonfederal physicians as of December 31, 2002. Total does not include 5,810 physicians in U.S. territories and possessions.

Rate of International Medical School Graduates Practicing in the U.S. in 2002

National Rate = 71 Nonfederal Physicians per 100,000 Population*

ALPHA ORDER

RANK	STATE	RATE
34	Alabama	34
47	Alaska	14
26	Arizona	43
40	Arkansas	30
14	California	64
45	Colorado	18
4	Connecticut	112
11	Delaware	82
5	Florida	102
27	Georgia	42
19	Hawaii	51
50	Idaho	6
5	Illinois	102
24	Indiana	45
32	Iowa	36
25	Kansas	44
20	Kentucky	50
22	Louisiana	49
33	Maine	35
3	Maryland	121
7	Massachusetts	98
10	Michigan	84
29	Minnesota	39
43	Mississippi	23
17	Missouri	55
49	Montana	11
38	Nebraska	31
20	Nevada	50
29	New Hampshire	39
2	New Jersey	149
31	New Mexico	37
1	New York	178
36	North Carolina	32
16	North Dakota	59
13	Ohio	76
35	Oklahoma	33
44	Oregon	22
12	Pennsylvania	80
7	Rhode Island	98
42	South Carolina	29
38	South Dakota	31
28	Tennessee	41
18	Texas	52
46	Utah	16
40	Vermont	30
15	Virginia	61
36	Washington	32
9	West Virginia	89
23	Wisconsin	46
48	Wyoming	13

RANK ORDER

RANK	STATE	RATE
1	New York	178
2	New Jersey	149
3	Maryland	121
4	Connecticut	112
5	Florida	102
5	Illinois	102
7	Massachusetts	98
7	Rhode Island	98
9	West Virginia	89
10	Michigan	84
11	Delaware	82
12	Pennsylvania	80
13	Ohio	76
14	California	64
15	Virginia	61
16	North Dakota	59
17	Missouri	55
18	Texas	52
19	Hawaii	51
20	Kentucky	50
20	Nevada	50
22	Louisiana	49
23	Wisconsin	46
24	Indiana	45
25	Kansas	44
26	Arizona	43
27	Georgia	42
28	Tennessee	41
29	Minnesota	39
29	New Hampshire	39
31	New Mexico	37
32	Iowa	36
33	Maine	35
34	Alabama	34
35	Oklahoma	33
36	North Carolina	32
36	Washington	32
38	Nebraska	31
38	South Dakota	31
40	Arkansas	30
40	Vermont	30
42	South Carolina	29
43	Mississippi	23
44	Oregon	22
45	Colorado	18
46	Utah	16
47	Alaska	14
48	Wyoming	13
49	Montana	11
50	Idaho	6

District of Columbia	153

Source: Morgan Quitno Press using data from American Medical Association (Chicago, Illinois)
"Physician Characteristics and Distribution in the U.S." (2004 Edition)
As of December 31, 2002. National rate does not include physicians in U.S. territories and possessions.

International Medical School Graduates
As a Percent of Nonfederal Physicians in 2002
National Percent = 25.0% of Nonfederal Physicians*

ALPHA ORDER

RANK	STATE	PERCENT
30	Alabama	15.2
46	Alaska	6.8
22	Arizona	18.5
33	Arkansas	13.8
16	California	22.5
47	Colorado	6.7
9	Connecticut	28.1
7	Delaware	30.4
4	Florida	35.9
23	Georgia	18.3
29	Hawaii	16.0
50	Idaho	3.0
5	Illinois	35.1
21	Indiana	19.5
27	Iowa	17.4
24	Kansas	18.2
20	Kentucky	20.8
26	Louisiana	17.5
39	Maine	12.1
8	Maryland	29.2
19	Massachusetts	21.3
6	Michigan	33.0
35	Minnesota	13.5
37	Mississippi	12.2
17	Missouri	21.9
49	Montana	4.5
37	Nebraska	12.2
12	Nevada	25.3
34	New Hampshire	13.6
1	New Jersey	45.0
32	New Mexico	15.0
2	New York	42.5
41	North Carolina	11.8
14	North Dakota	23.5
10	Ohio	27.9
25	Oklahoma	17.8
43	Oregon	7.8
13	Pennsylvania	24.6
11	Rhode Island	26.4
40	South Carolina	11.9
35	South Dakota	13.5
31	Tennessee	15.1
14	Texas	23.5
45	Utah	7.1
44	Vermont	7.7
18	Virginia	21.5
42	Washington	11.0
3	West Virginia	36.6
28	Wisconsin	17.2
48	Wyoming	6.3

RANK ORDER

RANK	STATE	PERCENT
1	New Jersey	45.0
2	New York	42.5
3	West Virginia	36.6
4	Florida	35.9
5	Illinois	35.1
6	Michigan	33.0
7	Delaware	30.4
8	Maryland	29.2
9	Connecticut	28.1
10	Ohio	27.9
11	Rhode Island	26.4
12	Nevada	25.3
13	Pennsylvania	24.6
14	North Dakota	23.5
14	Texas	23.5
16	California	22.5
17	Missouri	21.9
18	Virginia	21.5
19	Massachusetts	21.3
20	Kentucky	20.8
21	Indiana	19.5
22	Arizona	18.5
23	Georgia	18.3
24	Kansas	18.2
25	Oklahoma	17.8
26	Louisiana	17.5
27	Iowa	17.4
28	Wisconsin	17.2
29	Hawaii	16.0
30	Alabama	15.2
31	Tennessee	15.1
32	New Mexico	15.0
33	Arkansas	13.8
34	New Hampshire	13.6
35	Minnesota	13.5
35	South Dakota	13.5
37	Mississippi	12.2
37	Nebraska	12.2
39	Maine	12.1
40	South Carolina	11.9
41	North Carolina	11.8
42	Washington	11.0
43	Oregon	7.8
44	Vermont	7.7
45	Utah	7.1
46	Alaska	6.8
47	Colorado	6.7
48	Wyoming	6.3
49	Montana	4.5
50	Idaho	3.0

	District of Columbia	21.0

Source: Morgan Quitno Press using data from American Medical Association (Chicago, Illinois)
   "Physician Characteristics and Distribution in the U.S." (2004 Edition)
*As of December 31, 2002. National percent does not include physicians in U.S. territories and possessions.

Osteopathic Physicians in 2002

National Total = 43,910 Osteopathic Physicians*

ALPHA ORDER

RANK	STATE	OSTEOPATHS	% of USA
29	Alabama	304	0.7%
44	Alaska	92	0.2%
12	Arizona	1,143	2.6%
38	Arkansas	173	0.4%
7	California	2,532	5.8%
14	Colorado	690	1.6%
33	Connecticut	261	0.6%
36	Delaware	194	0.4%
4	Florida	2,865	6.5%
16	Georgia	590	1.3%
40	Hawaii	137	0.3%
42	Idaho	132	0.3%
9	Illinois	1,908	4.3%
15	Indiana	631	1.4%
13	Iowa	930	2.1%
18	Kansas	523	1.2%
32	Kentucky	266	0.6%
46	Louisiana	84	0.2%
22	Maine	498	1.1%
23	Maryland	475	1.1%
24	Massachusetts	405	0.9%
2	Michigan	4,443	10.1%
31	Minnesota	274	0.6%
35	Mississippi	246	0.6%
10	Missouri	1,650	3.8%
45	Montana	88	0.2%
43	Nebraska	112	0.3%
30	Nevada	279	0.6%
41	New Hampshire	135	0.3%
8	New Jersey	2,509	5.7%
28	New Mexico	308	0.7%
5	New York	2,817	6.4%
26	North Carolina	400	0.9%
48	North Dakota	57	0.1%
3	Ohio	3,197	7.3%
11	Oklahoma	1,266	2.9%
25	Oregon	403	0.9%
1	Pennsylvania	4,900	11.2%
37	Rhode Island	176	0.4%
34	South Carolina	256	0.6%
47	South Dakota	64	0.1%
27	Tennessee	355	0.8%
6	Texas	2,691	6.1%
39	Utah	160	0.4%
49	Vermont	48	0.1%
20	Virginia	517	1.2%
17	Washington	536	1.2%
19	West Virginia	522	1.2%
21	Wisconsin	501	1.1%
50	Wyoming	45	0.1%

RANK ORDER

RANK	STATE	OSTEOPATHS	% of USA
1	Pennsylvania	4,900	11.2%
2	Michigan	4,443	10.1%
3	Ohio	3,197	7.3%
4	Florida	2,865	6.5%
5	New York	2,817	6.4%
6	Texas	2,691	6.1%
7	California	2,532	5.8%
8	New Jersey	2,509	5.7%
9	Illinois	1,908	4.3%
10	Missouri	1,650	3.8%
11	Oklahoma	1,266	2.9%
12	Arizona	1,143	2.6%
13	Iowa	930	2.1%
14	Colorado	690	1.6%
15	Indiana	631	1.4%
16	Georgia	590	1.3%
17	Washington	536	1.2%
18	Kansas	523	1.2%
19	West Virginia	522	1.2%
20	Virginia	517	1.2%
21	Wisconsin	501	1.1%
22	Maine	498	1.1%
23	Maryland	475	1.1%
24	Massachusetts	405	0.9%
25	Oregon	403	0.9%
26	North Carolina	400	0.9%
27	Tennessee	355	0.8%
28	New Mexico	308	0.7%
29	Alabama	304	0.7%
30	Nevada	279	0.6%
31	Minnesota	274	0.6%
32	Kentucky	266	0.6%
33	Connecticut	261	0.6%
34	South Carolina	256	0.6%
35	Mississippi	246	0.6%
36	Delaware	194	0.4%
37	Rhode Island	176	0.4%
38	Arkansas	173	0.4%
39	Utah	160	0.4%
40	Hawaii	137	0.3%
41	New Hampshire	135	0.3%
42	Idaho	132	0.3%
43	Nebraska	112	0.3%
44	Alaska	92	0.2%
45	Montana	88	0.2%
46	Louisiana	84	0.2%
47	South Dakota	64	0.1%
48	North Dakota	57	0.1%
49	Vermont	48	0.1%
50	Wyoming	45	0.1%
	District of Columbia	34	0.1%

Source: American Osteopathic Association
   "Fact Sheet: Active D.O.'s by State" (November 2002, http://www.aoa.net/AOAGeneral/AOAFactsnov02.pdf)
*Excludes retired, disabled, foreign and federal osteopaths. Osteopaths practice a system of medicine based on the theory that disturbances in the musculoskeletal system affect other body parts, causing many disorders that can be corrected by various manipulative techniques in conjunction with conventional medical, surgical, pharmacological, and other therapeutic procedures.

Rate of Osteopathic Physicians in 2002

National Rate = 15 Osteopaths per 100,000 Population*

ALPHA ORDER

RANK ORDER

RANK	STATE	RATE
37	Alabama	7
19	Alaska	14
11	Arizona	21
42	Arkansas	6
37	California	7
16	Colorado	15
34	Connecticut	8
10	Delaware	24
13	Florida	17
37	Georgia	7
22	Hawaii	11
25	Idaho	10
16	Illinois	15
25	Indiana	10
5	Iowa	32
12	Kansas	19
42	Kentucky	6
50	Louisiana	2
3	Maine	38
28	Maryland	9
42	Massachusetts	6
1	Michigan	44
48	Minnesota	5
28	Mississippi	9
6	Missouri	29
25	Montana	10
42	Nebraska	6
20	Nevada	13
22	New Hampshire	11
6	New Jersey	29
13	New Mexico	17
16	New York	15
48	North Carolina	5
28	North Dakota	9
9	Ohio	28
4	Oklahoma	36
22	Oregon	11
2	Pennsylvania	40
15	Rhode Island	16
42	South Carolina	6
34	South Dakota	8
42	Tennessee	6
21	Texas	12
37	Utah	7
34	Vermont	8
37	Virginia	7
28	Washington	9
6	West Virginia	29
28	Wisconsin	9
28	Wyoming	9

RANK	STATE	RATE
1	Michigan	44
2	Pennsylvania	40
3	Maine	38
4	Oklahoma	36
5	Iowa	32
6	Missouri	29
6	New Jersey	29
6	West Virginia	29
9	Ohio	28
10	Delaware	24
11	Arizona	21
12	Kansas	19
13	Florida	17
13	New Mexico	17
15	Rhode Island	16
16	Colorado	15
16	Illinois	15
16	New York	15
19	Alaska	14
20	Nevada	13
21	Texas	12
22	Hawaii	11
22	New Hampshire	11
22	Oregon	11
25	Idaho	10
25	Indiana	10
25	Montana	10
28	Maryland	9
28	Mississippi	9
28	North Dakota	9
28	Washington	9
28	Wisconsin	9
28	Wyoming	9
34	Connecticut	8
34	South Dakota	8
34	Vermont	8
37	Alabama	7
37	California	7
37	Georgia	7
37	Utah	7
37	Virginia	7
42	Arkansas	6
42	Kentucky	6
42	Massachusetts	6
42	Nebraska	6
42	South Carolina	6
42	Tennessee	6
48	Minnesota	5
48	North Carolina	5
50	Louisiana	2
	District of Columbia	6

Source: Morgan Quitno Press using data from American Osteopathic Association
"Fact Sheet: Active D.O.'s by State" (November 2002, http://www.aoa.net/AOAGeneral/AOAFactsnov02.pdf)
*Calculated using 2002 population estimates. Excludes retired, disabled, foreign and federal osteopaths.
Osteopaths practice a system of medicine based on the theory that disturbances in the musculoskeletal system affect other body parts, causing many disorders that can be corrected by various manipulative techniques in conjunction with conventional medical, surgical, pharmacological, and other therapeutic procedures.

Podiatric Physicians in 2002

National Total = 14,850 Podiatric Physicians*

ALPHA ORDER

RANK	STATE	PODIATRISTS	% of USA
25	Alabama	128	0.9%
49	Alaska	15	0.1%
18	Arizona	230	1.5%
36	Arkansas	68	0.5%
2	California	1,545	10.4%
23	Colorado	148	1.0%
14	Connecticut	248	1.7%
41	Delaware	49	0.3%
3	Florida	1,152	7.8%
13	Georgia	287	1.9%
50	Hawaii	8	0.1%
44	Idaho	41	0.3%
5	Illinois	882	5.9%
15	Indiana	240	1.6%
20	Iowa	174	1.2%
31	Kansas	93	0.6%
29	Kentucky	104	0.7%
27	Louisiana	120	0.8%
35	Maine	73	0.5%
11	Maryland	357	2.4%
10	Massachusetts	403	2.7%
9	Michigan	612	4.1%
24	Minnesota	140	0.9%
41	Mississippi	49	0.3%
21	Missouri	172	1.2%
43	Montana	42	0.3%
40	Nebraska	55	0.4%
34	Nevada	83	0.6%
39	New Hampshire	61	0.4%
6	New Jersey	823	5.5%
37	New Mexico	64	0.4%
1	New York	1,941	13.1%
16	North Carolina	238	1.6%
47	North Dakota	21	0.1%
7	Ohio	805	5.4%
32	Oklahoma	92	0.6%
26	Oregon	126	0.8%
4	Pennsylvania	1,069	7.2%
33	Rhode Island	84	0.6%
30	South Carolina	97	0.7%
45	South Dakota	33	0.2%
22	Tennessee	170	1.1%
8	Texas	695	4.7%
28	Utah	105	0.7%
46	Vermont	23	0.2%
12	Virginia	322	2.2%
17	Washington	233	1.6%
37	West Virginia	64	0.4%
19	Wisconsin	202	1.4%
48	Wyoming	16	0.1%

RANK ORDER

RANK	STATE	PODIATRISTS	% of USA
1	New York	1,941	13.1%
2	California	1,545	10.4%
3	Florida	1,152	7.8%
4	Pennsylvania	1,069	7.2%
5	Illinois	882	5.9%
6	New Jersey	823	5.5%
7	Ohio	805	5.4%
8	Texas	695	4.7%
9	Michigan	612	4.1%
10	Massachusetts	403	2.7%
11	Maryland	357	2.4%
12	Virginia	322	2.2%
13	Georgia	287	1.9%
14	Connecticut	248	1.7%
15	Indiana	240	1.6%
16	North Carolina	238	1.6%
17	Washington	233	1.6%
18	Arizona	230	1.5%
19	Wisconsin	202	1.4%
20	Iowa	174	1.2%
21	Missouri	172	1.2%
22	Tennessee	170	1.1%
23	Colorado	148	1.0%
24	Minnesota	140	0.9%
25	Alabama	128	0.9%
26	Oregon	126	0.8%
27	Louisiana	120	0.8%
28	Utah	105	0.7%
29	Kentucky	104	0.7%
30	South Carolina	97	0.7%
31	Kansas	93	0.6%
32	Oklahoma	92	0.6%
33	Rhode Island	84	0.6%
34	Nevada	83	0.6%
35	Maine	73	0.5%
36	Arkansas	68	0.5%
37	New Mexico	64	0.4%
37	West Virginia	64	0.4%
39	New Hampshire	61	0.4%
40	Nebraska	55	0.4%
41	Delaware	49	0.3%
41	Mississippi	49	0.3%
43	Montana	42	0.3%
44	Idaho	41	0.3%
45	South Dakota	33	0.2%
46	Vermont	23	0.2%
47	North Dakota	21	0.1%
48	Wyoming	16	0.1%
49	Alaska	15	0.1%
50	Hawaii	8	0.1%
	District of Columbia	48	0.3%

Source: American Podiatric Medical Association, Inc.
"Podiatric Physicians in Active Practice"
*Podiatry deals with the diagnosis, treatment, and prevention of diseases of the human foot. National total does not include 49 podiatrists in Puerto Rico, Virgin Islands and U.S. Armed Services.

Rate of Podiatric Physicians in 2002

National Rate = 5.1 Podiatrists per 100,000 Population*

ALPHA ORDER

RANK	STATE	RATE
39	Alabama	2.9
48	Alaska	2.3
21	Arizona	4.2
45	Arkansas	2.5
18	California	4.4
32	Colorado	3.3
5	Connecticut	7.2
11	Delaware	6.1
8	Florida	6.9
30	Georgia	3.4
50	Hawaii	0.6
37	Idaho	3.1
6	Illinois	7.0
22	Indiana	3.9
13	Iowa	5.9
30	Kansas	3.4
45	Kentucky	2.5
43	Louisiana	2.7
14	Maine	5.6
9	Maryland	6.5
10	Massachusetts	6.3
11	Michigan	6.1
42	Minnesota	2.8
49	Mississippi	1.7
38	Missouri	3.0
16	Montana	4.6
34	Nebraska	3.2
23	Nevada	3.8
15	New Hampshire	4.8
2	New Jersey	9.6
29	New Mexico	3.5
1	New York	10.1
39	North Carolina	2.9
32	North Dakota	3.3
6	Ohio	7.0
44	Oklahoma	2.6
27	Oregon	3.6
3	Pennsylvania	8.7
4	Rhode Island	7.9
47	South Carolina	2.4
20	South Dakota	4.3
39	Tennessee	2.9
34	Texas	3.2
17	Utah	4.5
25	Vermont	3.7
18	Virginia	4.4
23	Washington	3.8
27	West Virginia	3.6
25	Wisconsin	3.7
34	Wyoming	3.2

RANK ORDER

RANK	STATE	RATE
1	New York	10.1
2	New Jersey	9.6
3	Pennsylvania	8.7
4	Rhode Island	7.9
5	Connecticut	7.2
6	Illinois	7.0
6	Ohio	7.0
8	Florida	6.9
9	Maryland	6.5
10	Massachusetts	6.3
11	Delaware	6.1
11	Michigan	6.1
13	Iowa	5.9
14	Maine	5.6
15	New Hampshire	4.8
16	Montana	4.6
17	Utah	4.5
18	California	4.4
18	Virginia	4.4
20	South Dakota	4.3
21	Arizona	4.2
22	Indiana	3.9
23	Nevada	3.8
23	Washington	3.8
25	Vermont	3.7
25	Wisconsin	3.7
27	Oregon	3.6
27	West Virginia	3.6
29	New Mexico	3.5
30	Georgia	3.4
30	Kansas	3.4
32	Colorado	3.3
32	North Dakota	3.3
34	Nebraska	3.2
34	Texas	3.2
34	Wyoming	3.2
37	Idaho	3.1
38	Missouri	3.0
39	Alabama	2.9
39	North Carolina	2.9
39	Tennessee	2.9
42	Minnesota	2.8
43	Louisiana	2.7
44	Oklahoma	2.6
45	Arkansas	2.5
45	Kentucky	2.5
47	South Carolina	2.4
48	Alaska	2.3
49	Mississippi	1.7
50	Hawaii	0.6

	District of Columbia	8.4

Source: Morgan Quitno Press using data from American Podiatric Medical Association, Inc.
   "Podiatric Physicians in Active Practice"
*Podiatry deals with the diagnosis, treatment, and prevention of diseases of the human foot. National rate does
not include podiatrists in Puerto Rico, Virgin Islands and U.S. Armed Services.

Doctors of Chiropractic in 2002

National Total = 84,825 Chiropractors*

ALPHA ORDER

RANK	STATE	CHIROPRACTOR	% of USA
30	Alabama	757	0.9%
49	Alaska	200	0.2%
10	Arizona	2,576	3.0%
33	Arkansas	563	0.7%
1	California	13,231	15.6%
12	Colorado	2,093	2.5%
26	Connecticut	951	1.1%
47	Delaware	227	0.3%
4	Florida	4,437	5.2%
3	Georgia	5,253	6.2%
34	Hawaii	527	0.6%
36	Idaho	485	0.6%
7	Illinois	3,761	4.4%
27	Indiana	943	1.1%
20	Iowa	1,316	1.6%
25	Kansas	980	1.2%
24	Kentucky	1,074	1.3%
32	Louisiana	582	0.7%
40	Maine	361	0.4%
31	Maryland	677	0.8%
15	Massachusetts	1,866	2.2%
9	Michigan	2,806	3.3%
11	Minnesota	2,157	2.5%
41	Mississippi	335	0.4%
22	Missouri	1,211	1.4%
42	Montana	327	0.4%
39	Nebraska	369	0.4%
35	Nevada	509	0.6%
38	New Hampshire	454	0.5%
8	New Jersey	3,369	4.0%
37	New Mexico	472	0.6%
2	New York	6,220	7.3%
16	North Carolina	1,726	2.0%
46	North Dakota	239	0.3%
14	Ohio	2,028	2.4%
29	Oklahoma	768	0.9%
23	Oregon	1,094	1.3%
6	Pennsylvania	3,775	4.5%
45	Rhode Island	245	0.3%
19	South Carolina	1,323	1.6%
44	South Dakota	269	0.3%
18	Tennessee	1,672	2.0%
5	Texas	3,994	4.7%
28	Utah	797	0.9%
48	Vermont	214	0.3%
21	Virginia	1,306	1.5%
13	Washington	2,042	2.4%
43	West Virginia	297	0.4%
17	Wisconsin	1,707	2.0%
50	Wyoming	180	0.2%

RANK ORDER

RANK	STATE	CHIROPRACTOR	% of USA
1	California	13,231	15.6%
2	New York	6,220	7.3%
3	Georgia	5,253	6.2%
4	Florida	4,437	5.2%
5	Texas	3,994	4.7%
6	Pennsylvania	3,775	4.5%
7	Illinois	3,761	4.4%
8	New Jersey	3,369	4.0%
9	Michigan	2,806	3.3%
10	Arizona	2,576	3.0%
11	Minnesota	2,157	2.5%
12	Colorado	2,093	2.5%
13	Washington	2,042	2.4%
14	Ohio	2,028	2.4%
15	Massachusetts	1,866	2.2%
16	North Carolina	1,726	2.0%
17	Wisconsin	1,707	2.0%
18	Tennessee	1,672	2.0%
19	South Carolina	1,323	1.6%
20	Iowa	1,316	1.6%
21	Virginia	1,306	1.5%
22	Missouri	1,211	1.4%
23	Oregon	1,094	1.3%
24	Kentucky	1,074	1.3%
25	Kansas	980	1.2%
26	Connecticut	951	1.1%
27	Indiana	943	1.1%
28	Utah	797	0.9%
29	Oklahoma	768	0.9%
30	Alabama	757	0.9%
31	Maryland	677	0.8%
32	Louisiana	582	0.7%
33	Arkansas	563	0.7%
34	Hawaii	527	0.6%
35	Nevada	509	0.6%
36	Idaho	485	0.6%
37	New Mexico	472	0.6%
38	New Hampshire	454	0.5%
39	Nebraska	369	0.4%
40	Maine	361	0.4%
41	Mississippi	335	0.4%
42	Montana	327	0.4%
43	West Virginia	297	0.4%
44	South Dakota	269	0.3%
45	Rhode Island	245	0.3%
46	North Dakota	239	0.3%
47	Delaware	227	0.3%
48	Vermont	214	0.3%
49	Alaska	200	0.2%
50	Wyoming	180	0.2%
	District of Columbia	60	0.1%

Source: Federation of Chiropractic Licensing Boards
"Official Directory" (http://www.fclb.org/directory/index.htm)
As of December 2002. Licensed active doctors. There is some duplication as some doctors are licensed in more than one state.

Rate of Doctors of Chiropractic in 2002

National Rate = 29 Chiropractors per 100,000 Population*

ALPHA ORDER

RANK	STATE	RATE
45	Alabama	17
21	Alaska	31
2	Arizona	47
38	Arkansas	21
8	California	38
2	Colorado	47
31	Connecticut	27
28	Delaware	28
31	Florida	27
1	Georgia	61
6	Hawaii	42
10	Idaho	36
25	Illinois	30
47	Indiana	15
4	Iowa	45
10	Kansas	36
33	Kentucky	26
48	Louisiana	13
28	Maine	28
49	Maryland	12
26	Massachusetts	29
28	Michigan	28
5	Minnesota	43
49	Mississippi	12
38	Missouri	21
10	Montana	36
38	Nebraska	21
35	Nevada	23
10	New Hampshire	36
7	New Jersey	39
34	New Mexico	25
19	New York	33
38	North Carolina	21
8	North Dakota	38
42	Ohio	18
37	Oklahoma	22
21	Oregon	31
21	Pennsylvania	31
35	Rhode Island	23
20	South Carolina	32
15	South Dakota	35
26	Tennessee	29
42	Texas	18
17	Utah	34
15	Vermont	35
42	Virginia	18
17	Washington	34
46	West Virginia	16
21	Wisconsin	31
10	Wyoming	36

RANK ORDER

RANK	STATE	RATE
1	Georgia	61
2	Arizona	47
2	Colorado	47
4	Iowa	45
5	Minnesota	43
6	Hawaii	42
7	New Jersey	39
8	California	38
8	North Dakota	38
10	Idaho	36
10	Kansas	36
10	Montana	36
10	New Hampshire	36
10	Wyoming	36
15	South Dakota	35
15	Vermont	35
17	Utah	34
17	Washington	34
19	New York	33
20	South Carolina	32
21	Alaska	31
21	Oregon	31
21	Pennsylvania	31
21	Wisconsin	31
25	Illinois	30
26	Massachusetts	29
26	Tennessee	29
28	Delaware	28
28	Maine	28
28	Michigan	28
31	Connecticut	27
31	Florida	27
33	Kentucky	26
34	New Mexico	25
35	Nevada	23
35	Rhode Island	23
37	Oklahoma	22
38	Arkansas	21
38	Missouri	21
38	Nebraska	21
38	North Carolina	21
42	Ohio	18
42	Texas	18
42	Virginia	18
45	Alabama	17
46	West Virginia	16
47	Indiana	15
48	Louisiana	13
49	Maryland	12
49	Mississippi	12
	District of Columbia	11

Source: Morgan Quitno Press using data from Federation of Chiropractic Licensing Boards
  "Official Directory" (http://www.fclb.org/directory/index.htm)
*As of December 2002. Licensed active doctors. There is some duplication as some doctors are licensed in more than one state.

Physician Assistants in Clinical Practice in 2004

National Total = 49,542 Physician Assistants*

ALPHA ORDER

RANK	STATE	PAs	% of USA
38	Alabama	294	0.6%
40	Alaska	278	0.6%
16	Arizona	1,010	2.0%
49	Arkansas	65	0.1%
2	California	4,873	9.8%
13	Colorado	1,181	2.4%
17	Connecticut	981	2.0%
46	Delaware	147	0.3%
5	Florida	2,771	5.6%
8	Georgia	1,615	3.3%
48	Hawaii	114	0.2%
36	Idaho	309	0.6%
12	Illinois	1,273	2.6%
34	Indiana	390	0.8%
25	Iowa	586	1.2%
23	Kansas	592	1.2%
24	Kentucky	588	1.2%
35	Louisiana	354	0.7%
31	Maine	438	0.9%
10	Maryland	1,368	2.8%
14	Massachusetts	1,108	2.2%
7	Michigan	2,082	4.2%
20	Minnesota	727	1.5%
49	Mississippi	65	0.1%
32	Missouri	408	0.8%
42	Montana	242	0.5%
26	Nebraska	552	1.1%
41	Nevada	276	0.6%
39	New Hampshire	283	0.6%
19	New Jersey	751	1.5%
33	New Mexico	398	0.8%
1	New York	5,944	12.0%
6	North Carolina	2,429	4.9%
43	North Dakota	218	0.4%
11	Ohio	1,365	2.8%
21	Oklahoma	724	1.5%
27	Oregon	502	1.0%
4	Pennsylvania	2,873	5.8%
44	Rhode Island	184	0.4%
30	South Carolina	447	0.9%
36	South Dakota	309	0.6%
22	Tennessee	614	1.2%
3	Texas	3,058	6.2%
29	Utah	458	0.9%
45	Vermont	171	0.3%
18	Virginia	914	1.8%
9	Washington	1,369	2.8%
28	West Virginia	485	1.0%
15	Wisconsin	1,037	2.1%
47	Wyoming	132	0.3%

RANK ORDER

RANK	STATE	PAs	% of USA
1	New York	5,944	12.0%
2	California	4,873	9.8%
3	Texas	3,058	6.2%
4	Pennsylvania	2,873	5.8%
5	Florida	2,771	5.6%
6	North Carolina	2,429	4.9%
7	Michigan	2,082	4.2%
8	Georgia	1,615	3.3%
9	Washington	1,369	2.8%
10	Maryland	1,368	2.8%
11	Ohio	1,365	2.8%
12	Illinois	1,273	2.6%
13	Colorado	1,181	2.4%
14	Massachusetts	1,108	2.2%
15	Wisconsin	1,037	2.1%
16	Arizona	1,010	2.0%
17	Connecticut	981	2.0%
18	Virginia	914	1.8%
19	New Jersey	751	1.5%
20	Minnesota	727	1.5%
21	Oklahoma	724	1.5%
22	Tennessee	614	1.2%
23	Kansas	592	1.2%
24	Kentucky	588	1.2%
25	Iowa	586	1.2%
26	Nebraska	552	1.1%
27	Oregon	502	1.0%
28	West Virginia	485	1.0%
29	Utah	458	0.9%
30	South Carolina	447	0.9%
31	Maine	438	0.9%
32	Missouri	408	0.8%
33	New Mexico	398	0.8%
34	Indiana	390	0.8%
35	Louisiana	354	0.7%
36	Idaho	309	0.6%
36	South Dakota	309	0.6%
38	Alabama	294	0.6%
39	New Hampshire	283	0.6%
40	Alaska	278	0.6%
41	Nevada	276	0.6%
42	Montana	242	0.5%
43	North Dakota	218	0.4%
44	Rhode Island	184	0.4%
45	Vermont	171	0.3%
46	Delaware	147	0.3%
47	Wyoming	132	0.3%
48	Hawaii	114	0.2%
49	Arkansas	65	0.1%
49	Mississippi	65	0.1%
	District of Columbia	190	0.4%

Source: The American Academy of Physician Assistants
  "Projected Number of PAs in Clinical Practice as of January 1, 2004"
    (http://www.aapa.org/research/03-04num-clin-prac.pdf)
*Projected. National total does not include 236 physician assistants who work outside the United States or whose location is unknown.

Rate of Physician Assistants in Clinical Practice in 2004

National Rate = 17 PAs per 100,000 Population*

ALPHA ORDER

RANK	STATE	RATE
46	Alabama	7
1	Alaska	43
27	Arizona	18
49	Arkansas	2
32	California	14
11	Colorado	26
8	Connecticut	28
27	Delaware	18
31	Florida	16
24	Georgia	19
43	Hawaii	9
15	Idaho	23
42	Illinois	10
48	Indiana	6
23	Iowa	20
17	Kansas	22
32	Kentucky	14
45	Louisiana	8
3	Maine	34
14	Maryland	25
29	Massachusetts	17
20	Michigan	21
32	Minnesota	14
49	Mississippi	2
46	Missouri	7
11	Montana	26
5	Nebraska	32
37	Nevada	12
17	New Hampshire	22
43	New Jersey	9
20	New Mexico	21
6	New York	31
7	North Carolina	29
3	North Dakota	34
37	Ohio	12
20	Oklahoma	21
32	Oregon	14
15	Pennsylvania	23
29	Rhode Island	17
40	South Carolina	11
2	South Dakota	40
40	Tennessee	11
32	Texas	14
24	Utah	19
8	Vermont	28
37	Virginia	12
17	Washington	22
10	West Virginia	27
24	Wisconsin	19
11	Wyoming	26

RANK ORDER

RANK	STATE	RATE
1	Alaska	43
2	South Dakota	40
3	Maine	34
3	North Dakota	34
5	Nebraska	32
6	New York	31
7	North Carolina	29
8	Connecticut	28
8	Vermont	28
10	West Virginia	27
11	Colorado	26
11	Montana	26
11	Wyoming	26
14	Maryland	25
15	Idaho	23
15	Pennsylvania	23
17	Kansas	22
17	New Hampshire	22
17	Washington	22
20	Michigan	21
20	New Mexico	21
20	Oklahoma	21
23	Iowa	20
24	Georgia	19
24	Utah	19
24	Wisconsin	19
27	Arizona	18
27	Delaware	18
29	Massachusetts	17
29	Rhode Island	17
31	Florida	16
32	California	14
32	Kentucky	14
32	Minnesota	14
32	Oregon	14
32	Texas	14
37	Nevada	12
37	Ohio	12
37	Virginia	12
40	South Carolina	11
40	Tennessee	11
42	Illinois	10
43	Hawaii	9
43	New Jersey	9
45	Louisiana	8
46	Alabama	7
46	Missouri	7
48	Indiana	6
49	Arkansas	2
49	Mississippi	2
	District of Columbia	34

Source: Morgan Quitno Press using data from The American Academy of Physician Assistants
"Projected Number of PAs in Clinical Practice as of January 1, 2004"
(http://www.aapa.org/research/03-04num-clin-prac.pdf)
*Projected. Rates calculated using 2003 Census population figures.

Registered Nurses in 2002

National Total = 2,239,530 Registered Nurses*

ALPHA ORDER

RANK	STATE	NURSES	% of USA
23	Alabama	34,970	1.6%
49	Alaska	5,190	0.2%
24	Arizona	32,450	1.4%
33	Arkansas	18,660	0.8%
1	California	206,140	9.2%
26	Colorado	29,210	1.3%
25	Connecticut	31,330	1.4%
46	Delaware	6,470	0.3%
4	Florida	130,000	5.8%
12	Georgia	55,290	2.5%
44	Hawaii	7,680	0.3%
42	Idaho	10,050	0.4%
7	Illinois	98,270	4.4%
17	Indiana	49,840	2.2%
28	Iowa	27,690	1.2%
30	Kansas	24,900	1.1%
22	Kentucky	35,230	1.6%
21	Louisiana	36,530	1.6%
38	Maine	12,100	0.5%
18	Maryland	47,030	2.1%
10	Massachusetts	71,750	3.2%
8	Michigan	77,660	3.5%
14	Minnesota	51,310	2.3%
31	Mississippi	23,180	1.0%
15	Missouri	50,790	2.3%
45	Montana	7,650	0.3%
34	Nebraska	16,320	0.7%
37	Nevada	12,740	0.6%
39	New Hampshire	11,870	0.5%
9	New Jersey	73,530	3.3%
40	New Mexico	11,660	0.5%
2	New York	163,600	7.3%
11	North Carolina	66,290	3.0%
47	North Dakota	6,180	0.3%
6	Ohio	104,810	4.7%
32	Oklahoma	21,610	1.0%
29	Oregon	26,370	1.2%
5	Pennsylvania	117,470	5.2%
41	Rhode Island	11,220	0.5%
27	South Carolina	28,610	1.3%
43	South Dakota	8,410	0.4%
13	Tennessee	53,020	2.4%
3	Texas	136,420	6.1%
36	Utah	13,820	0.6%
48	Vermont	5,440	0.2%
16	Virginia	50,780	2.3%
20	Washington	44,150	2.0%
35	West Virginia	15,720	0.7%
19	Wisconsin	46,560	2.1%
50	Wyoming	3,530	0.2%

RANK ORDER

RANK	STATE	NURSES	% of USA
1	California	206,140	9.2%
2	New York	163,600	7.3%
3	Texas	136,420	6.1%
4	Florida	130,000	5.8%
5	Pennsylvania	117,470	5.2%
6	Ohio	104,810	4.7%
7	Illinois	98,270	4.4%
8	Michigan	77,660	3.5%
9	New Jersey	73,530	3.3%
10	Massachusetts	71,750	3.2%
11	North Carolina	66,290	3.0%
12	Georgia	55,290	2.5%
13	Tennessee	53,020	2.4%
14	Minnesota	51,310	2.3%
15	Missouri	50,790	2.3%
16	Virginia	50,780	2.3%
17	Indiana	49,840	2.2%
18	Maryland	47,030	2.1%
19	Wisconsin	46,560	2.1%
20	Washington	44,150	2.0%
21	Louisiana	36,530	1.6%
22	Kentucky	35,230	1.6%
23	Alabama	34,970	1.6%
24	Arizona	32,450	1.4%
25	Connecticut	31,330	1.4%
26	Colorado	29,210	1.3%
27	South Carolina	28,610	1.3%
28	Iowa	27,690	1.2%
29	Oregon	26,370	1.2%
30	Kansas	24,900	1.1%
31	Mississippi	23,180	1.0%
32	Oklahoma	21,610	1.0%
33	Arkansas	18,660	0.8%
34	Nebraska	16,320	0.7%
35	West Virginia	15,720	0.7%
36	Utah	13,820	0.6%
37	Nevada	12,740	0.6%
38	Maine	12,100	0.5%
39	New Hampshire	11,870	0.5%
40	New Mexico	11,660	0.5%
41	Rhode Island	11,220	0.5%
42	Idaho	10,050	0.4%
43	South Dakota	8,410	0.4%
44	Hawaii	7,680	0.3%
45	Montana	7,650	0.3%
46	Delaware	6,470	0.3%
47	North Dakota	6,180	0.3%
48	Vermont	5,440	0.2%
49	Alaska	5,190	0.2%
50	Wyoming	3,530	0.2%
	District of Columbia	8,070	0.4%

Source: U.S. Department of Labor, Bureau of Labor Statistics
"Occupational Employment and Wages, 2002" (http://www.bls.gov/oes/)
Does not include self-employed.

Rate of Registered Nurses in 2002

National Rate = 778 Nurses per 100,000 Population*

ALPHA ORDER

ALPHA ORDER

RANK	STATE	RATE
30	Alabama	781
25	Alaska	809
47	Arizona	596
40	Arkansas	690
49	California	589
41	Colorado	649
14	Connecticut	906
28	Delaware	803
32	Florida	779
42	Georgia	647
45	Hawaii	619
35	Idaho	748
30	Illinois	781
25	Indiana	809
8	Iowa	943
12	Kansas	918
19	Kentucky	861
24	Louisiana	816
9	Maine	934
18	Maryland	863
1	Massachusetts	1,117
33	Michigan	773
4	Minnesota	1,021
25	Mississippi	809
15	Missouri	896
23	Montana	840
7	Nebraska	945
50	Nevada	588
10	New Hampshire	931
20	New Jersey	857
43	New Mexico	630
22	New York	855
29	North Carolina	798
5	North Dakota	975
11	Ohio	919
45	Oklahoma	619
34	Oregon	749
6	Pennsylvania	953
3	Rhode Island	1,050
38	South Carolina	697
2	South Dakota	1,106
13	Tennessee	916
44	Texas	628
47	Utah	596
16	Vermont	883
38	Virginia	697
36	Washington	728
17	West Virginia	871
21	Wisconsin	856
37	Wyoming	708

RANK ORDER

RANK	STATE	RATE
1	Massachusetts	1,117
2	South Dakota	1,106
3	Rhode Island	1,050
4	Minnesota	1,021
5	North Dakota	975
6	Pennsylvania	953
7	Nebraska	945
8	Iowa	943
9	Maine	934
10	New Hampshire	931
11	Ohio	919
12	Kansas	918
13	Tennessee	916
14	Connecticut	906
15	Missouri	896
16	Vermont	883
17	West Virginia	871
18	Maryland	863
19	Kentucky	861
20	New Jersey	857
21	Wisconsin	856
22	New York	855
23	Montana	840
24	Louisiana	816
25	Alaska	809
25	Indiana	809
25	Mississippi	809
28	Delaware	803
29	North Carolina	798
30	Alabama	781
30	Illinois	781
32	Florida	779
33	Michigan	773
34	Oregon	749
35	Idaho	748
36	Washington	728
37	Wyoming	708
38	South Carolina	697
38	Virginia	697
40	Arkansas	690
41	Colorado	649
42	Georgia	647
43	New Mexico	630
44	Texas	628
45	Hawaii	619
45	Oklahoma	619
47	Arizona	596
47	Utah	596
49	California	589
50	Nevada	588
	District of Columbia	1,418

Source: Morgan Quitno Press using data from U.S. Department of Labor, Bureau of Labor Statistics
    "Occupational Employment and Wages, 2002" (http://www.bls.gov/oes/)
*Does not include self-employed.

Licensed Practical and Licensed Vocational Nurses in 2002

National Total = 692,290 LPN/LVNs*

ALPHA ORDER

RANK	STATE	LPN/LVN	% of USA
19	Alabama	15,380	2.2%
49	Alaska	470	0.1%
27	Arizona	8,420	1.2%
21	Arkansas	12,700	1.8%
2	California	54,990	7.9%
33	Colorado	6,300	0.9%
29	Connecticut	7,110	1.0%
43	Delaware	2,190	0.3%
4	Florida	43,120	6.2%
7	Georgia	22,460	3.2%
40	Hawaii	2,450	0.4%
37	Idaho	2,930	0.4%
9	Illinois	20,600	3.0%
10	Indiana	19,220	2.8%
30	Iowa	7,080	1.0%
31	Kansas	6,890	1.0%
23	Kentucky	12,000	1.7%
14	Louisiana	17,740	2.6%
NA	Maine**	NA	NA
28	Maryland	7,890	1.1%
18	Massachusetts	16,210	2.3%
13	Michigan	17,870	2.6%
15	Minnesota	17,690	2.6%
26	Mississippi	8,850	1.3%
12	Missouri	18,120	2.6%
41	Montana	2,350	0.3%
34	Nebraska	6,130	0.9%
42	Nevada	2,310	0.3%
44	New Hampshire	2,000	0.3%
16	New Jersey	17,610	2.5%
35	New Mexico	3,140	0.5%
3	New York	48,560	7.0%
17	North Carolina	17,560	2.5%
39	North Dakota	2,670	0.4%
5	Ohio	35,930	5.2%
20	Oklahoma	13,590	2.0%
36	Oregon	2,990	0.4%
6	Pennsylvania	35,720	5.2%
45	Rhode Island	1,950	0.3%
24	South Carolina	10,820	1.6%
46	South Dakota	1,940	0.3%
8	Tennessee	21,890	3.2%
1	Texas	59,240	8.6%
38	Utah	2,830	0.4%
47	Vermont	1,620	0.2%
11	Virginia	18,140	2.6%
25	Washington	9,890	1.4%
32	West Virginia	6,730	1.0%
22	Wisconsin	12,300	1.8%
48	Wyoming	850	0.1%

RANK ORDER

RANK	STATE	LPN/LVN	% of USA
1	Texas	59,240	8.6%
2	California	54,990	7.9%
3	New York	48,560	7.0%
4	Florida	43,120	6.2%
5	Ohio	35,930	5.2%
6	Pennsylvania	35,720	5.2%
7	Georgia	22,460	3.2%
8	Tennessee	21,890	3.2%
9	Illinois	20,600	3.0%
10	Indiana	19,220	2.8%
11	Virginia	18,140	2.6%
12	Missouri	18,120	2.6%
13	Michigan	17,870	2.6%
14	Louisiana	17,740	2.6%
15	Minnesota	17,690	2.6%
16	New Jersey	17,610	2.5%
17	North Carolina	17,560	2.5%
18	Massachusetts	16,210	2.3%
19	Alabama	15,380	2.2%
20	Oklahoma	13,590	2.0%
21	Arkansas	12,700	1.8%
22	Wisconsin	12,300	1.8%
23	Kentucky	12,000	1.7%
24	South Carolina	10,820	1.6%
25	Washington	9,890	1.4%
26	Mississippi	8,850	1.3%
27	Arizona	8,420	1.2%
28	Maryland	7,890	1.1%
29	Connecticut	7,110	1.0%
30	Iowa	7,080	1.0%
31	Kansas	6,890	1.0%
32	West Virginia	6,730	1.0%
33	Colorado	6,300	0.9%
34	Nebraska	6,130	0.9%
35	New Mexico	3,140	0.5%
36	Oregon	2,990	0.4%
37	Idaho	2,930	0.4%
38	Utah	2,830	0.4%
39	North Dakota	2,670	0.4%
40	Hawaii	2,450	0.4%
41	Montana	2,350	0.3%
42	Nevada	2,310	0.3%
43	Delaware	2,190	0.3%
44	New Hampshire	2,000	0.3%
45	Rhode Island	1,950	0.3%
46	South Dakota	1,940	0.3%
47	Vermont	1,620	0.2%
48	Wyoming	850	0.1%
49	Alaska	470	0.1%
NA	Maine**	NA	NA
	District of Columbia	1,770	0.3%

Source: U.S. Department of Labor, Bureau of Labor Statistics
    "Occupational Employment and Wages, 2002" (http://www.bls.gov/oes/)
*Does not include self-employed.
**Not available.

Rate of Licensed Practical and Licensed Vocational Nurses in 2002

National Rate = 240 LPN/LVNs per 100,000 Population*

ALPHA ORDER

RANK ORDER

RANK	STATE	RATE	RANK	STATE	RATE
9	Alabama	343	1	Arkansas	469
49	Alaska	73	2	North Dakota	421
43	Arizona	155	3	Louisiana	396
1	Arkansas	469	4	Oklahoma	389
41	California	157	5	Tennessee	378
45	Colorado	140	6	West Virginia	373
32	Connecticut	206	7	Nebraska	355
17	Delaware	272	8	Minnesota	352
21	Florida	258	9	Alabama	343
19	Georgia	263	10	Missouri	320
34	Hawaii	197	11	Ohio	315
30	Idaho	218	12	Indiana	312
39	Illinois	164	13	Mississippi	309
12	Indiana	312	14	Kentucky	293
28	Iowa	241	15	Pennsylvania	290
24	Kansas	254	16	Texas	273
14	Kentucky	293	17	Delaware	272
3	Louisiana	396	18	South Carolina	264
NA	Maine**	NA	19	Georgia	263
44	Maryland	145	19	Vermont	263
26	Massachusetts	252	21	Florida	258
36	Michigan	178	21	Montana	258
8	Minnesota	352	23	South Dakota	255
13	Mississippi	309	24	Kansas	254
10	Missouri	320	24	New York	254
21	Montana	258	26	Massachusetts	252
7	Nebraska	355	27	Virginia	249
47	Nevada	107	28	Iowa	241
41	New Hampshire	157	29	Wisconsin	226
33	New Jersey	205	30	Idaho	218
37	New Mexico	170	31	North Carolina	211
24	New York	254	32	Connecticut	206
31	North Carolina	211	33	New Jersey	205
2	North Dakota	421	34	Hawaii	197
11	Ohio	315	35	Rhode Island	183
4	Oklahoma	389	36	Michigan	178
48	Oregon	85	37	New Mexico	170
15	Pennsylvania	290	37	Wyoming	170
35	Rhode Island	183	39	Illinois	164
18	South Carolina	264	40	Washington	163
23	South Dakota	255	41	California	157
5	Tennessee	378	41	New Hampshire	157
16	Texas	273	43	Arizona	155
46	Utah	122	44	Maryland	145
19	Vermont	263	45	Colorado	140
27	Virginia	249	46	Utah	122
40	Washington	163	47	Nevada	107
6	West Virginia	373	48	Oregon	85
29	Wisconsin	226	49	Alaska	73
37	Wyoming	170	NA	Maine**	NA
				District of Columbia	311

Source: Morgan Quitno Press using data from U.S. Department of Labor, Bureau of Labor Statistics
    "Occupational Employment and Wages, 2002" (http://www.bls.gov/oes/)
*Does not include self-employed.
**Not available.

Dentists in 2001

National Total = 168,556 Dentists*

ALPHA ORDER

RANK	STATE	DENTISTS	% of USA
27	Alabama	1,904	1.1%
45	Alaska	458	0.3%
23	Arizona	2,421	1.4%
35	Arkansas	1,083	0.6%
1	California	23,536	14.0%
20	Colorado	2,839	1.7%
22	Connecticut	2,666	1.6%
48	Delaware	345	0.2%
4	Florida	8,424	5.0%
14	Georgia	3,681	2.2%
36	Hawaii	991	0.6%
41	Idaho	706	0.4%
5	Illinois	8,196	4.9%
19	Indiana	2,921	1.7%
30	Iowa	1,558	0.9%
32	Kansas	1,380	0.8%
25	Kentucky	2,274	1.3%
26	Louisiana	2,078	1.2%
42	Maine	605	0.4%
12	Maryland	4,057	2.4%
10	Massachusetts	5,207	3.1%
9	Michigan	5,952	3.5%
18	Minnesota	2,986	1.8%
33	Mississippi	1,119	0.7%
21	Missouri	2,758	1.6%
44	Montana	507	0.3%
34	Nebraska	1,098	0.7%
39	Nevada	781	0.5%
40	New Hampshire	727	0.4%
7	New Jersey	6,632	3.9%
38	New Mexico	810	0.5%
2	New York	15,244	9.0%
15	North Carolina	3,459	2.1%
49	North Dakota	306	0.2%
8	Ohio	6,060	3.6%
29	Oklahoma	1,693	1.0%
24	Oregon	2,323	1.4%
6	Pennsylvania	8,050	4.8%
43	Rhode Island	592	0.4%
28	South Carolina	1,833	1.1%
46	South Dakota	366	0.2%
17	Tennessee	3,003	1.8%
3	Texas	9,989	5.9%
31	Utah	1,441	0.9%
47	Vermont	357	0.2%
11	Virginia	4,128	2.4%
13	Washington	3,962	2.4%
37	West Virginia	839	0.5%
16	Wisconsin	3,163	1.9%
50	Wyoming	261	0.2%

RANK ORDER

RANK	STATE	DENTISTS	% of USA
1	California	23,536	14.0%
2	New York	15,244	9.0%
3	Texas	9,989	5.9%
4	Florida	8,424	5.0%
5	Illinois	8,196	4.9%
6	Pennsylvania	8,050	4.8%
7	New Jersey	6,632	3.9%
8	Ohio	6,060	3.6%
9	Michigan	5,952	3.5%
10	Massachusetts	5,207	3.1%
11	Virginia	4,128	2.4%
12	Maryland	4,057	2.4%
13	Washington	3,962	2.4%
14	Georgia	3,681	2.2%
15	North Carolina	3,459	2.1%
16	Wisconsin	3,163	1.9%
17	Tennessee	3,003	1.8%
18	Minnesota	2,986	1.8%
19	Indiana	2,921	1.7%
20	Colorado	2,839	1.7%
21	Missouri	2,758	1.6%
22	Connecticut	2,666	1.6%
23	Arizona	2,421	1.4%
24	Oregon	2,323	1.4%
25	Kentucky	2,274	1.3%
26	Louisiana	2,078	1.2%
27	Alabama	1,904	1.1%
28	South Carolina	1,833	1.1%
29	Oklahoma	1,693	1.0%
30	Iowa	1,558	0.9%
31	Utah	1,441	0.9%
32	Kansas	1,380	0.8%
33	Mississippi	1,119	0.7%
34	Nebraska	1,098	0.7%
35	Arkansas	1,083	0.6%
36	Hawaii	991	0.6%
37	West Virginia	839	0.5%
38	New Mexico	810	0.5%
39	Nevada	781	0.5%
40	New Hampshire	727	0.4%
41	Idaho	706	0.4%
42	Maine	605	0.4%
43	Rhode Island	592	0.4%
44	Montana	507	0.3%
45	Alaska	458	0.3%
46	South Dakota	366	0.2%
47	Vermont	357	0.2%
48	Delaware	345	0.2%
49	North Dakota	306	0.2%
50	Wyoming	261	0.2%
	District of Columbia	721	0.4%

Source: American Dental Association
  "Distribution of Dentists, by Region and State, 2001"
*Professionally active dentists. Total includes 66 dentists for whom state is not known. Total does not include
2,233 dentists in territories nor dentists in the Armed Forces stationed overseas.

Rate of Dentists in 2001

National Rate = 59 Dentists per 100,000 Population*

RANK	STATE	RATE
45	Alabama	43
7	Alaska	72
41	Arizona	46
48	Arkansas	40
8	California	68
13	Colorado	64
4	Connecticut	78
45	Delaware	43
29	Florida	52
43	Georgia	44
1	Hawaii	81
25	Idaho	53
11	Illinois	65
34	Indiana	48
25	Iowa	53
31	Kansas	51
22	Kentucky	56
37	Louisiana	47
37	Maine	47
6	Maryland	75
1	Massachusetts	81
17	Michigan	59
16	Minnesota	60
49	Mississippi	39
32	Missouri	49
22	Montana	56
13	Nebraska	64
50	Nevada	37
19	New Hampshire	58
4	New Jersey	78
43	New Mexico	44
3	New York	80
47	North Carolina	42
34	North Dakota	48
25	Ohio	53
32	Oklahoma	49
9	Oregon	67
11	Pennsylvania	65
22	Rhode Island	56
42	South Carolina	45
34	South Dakota	48
29	Tennessee	52
37	Texas	47
15	Utah	63
19	Vermont	58
21	Virginia	57
10	Washington	66
37	West Virginia	47
17	Wisconsin	59
25	Wyoming	53

RANK	STATE	RATE
1	Hawaii	81
1	Massachusetts	81
3	New York	80
4	Connecticut	78
4	New Jersey	78
6	Maryland	75
7	Alaska	72
8	California	68
9	Oregon	67
10	Washington	66
11	Illinois	65
11	Pennsylvania	65
13	Colorado	64
13	Nebraska	64
15	Utah	63
16	Minnesota	60
17	Michigan	59
17	Wisconsin	59
19	New Hampshire	58
19	Vermont	58
21	Virginia	57
22	Kentucky	56
22	Montana	56
22	Rhode Island	56
25	Idaho	53
25	Iowa	53
25	Ohio	53
25	Wyoming	53
29	Florida	52
29	Tennessee	52
31	Kansas	51
32	Missouri	49
32	Oklahoma	49
34	Indiana	48
34	North Dakota	48
34	South Dakota	48
37	Louisiana	47
37	Maine	47
37	Texas	47
37	West Virginia	47
41	Arizona	46
42	South Carolina	45
43	Georgia	44
43	New Mexico	44
45	Alabama	43
45	Delaware	43
47	North Carolina	42
48	Arkansas	40
49	Mississippi	39
50	Nevada	37
	District of Columbia	126

Source: Morgan Quitno Press using data from American Dental Association
    "Distribution of Dentists, by Region and State, 2001"
*Professionally active dentists. National rate includes dentists for whom state is not known. National rate does not
include dentists in territories nor dentists in the Armed Forces stationed overseas.

Percent of Population Lacking Access to Dental Care in 2003

National Percent = 9.3% of Population*

ALPHA ORDER

RANK	STATE	PERCENT
1	Alabama	32.5
14	Alaska	13.8
29	Arizona	8.5
42	Arkansas	5.0
48	California	2.9
44	Colorado	4.2
40	Connecticut	5.1
12	Delaware	16.0
18	Florida	11.7
26	Georgia	9.3
28	Hawaii	8.7
9	Idaho	18.1
30	Illinois	8.3
46	Indiana	4.0
11	Iowa	16.9
8	Kansas	19.5
36	Kentucky	6.3
35	Louisiana	6.5
6	Maine	21.1
37	Maryland	5.5
43	Massachusetts	4.5
20	Michigan	11.4
44	Minnesota	4.2
22	Mississippi	10.5
5	Missouri	22.3
4	Montana	23.2
50	Nebraska	1.2
16	Nevada	12.3
39	New Hampshire	5.3
49	New Jersey	1.8
2	New Mexico	25.7
40	New York	5.1
15	North Carolina	13.1
33	North Dakota	7.1
32	Ohio	7.4
38	Oklahoma	5.4
13	Oregon	14.6
22	Pennsylvania	10.5
27	Rhode Island	8.8
3	South Carolina	23.5
24	South Dakota	10.4
7	Tennessee	20.4
18	Texas	11.7
10	Utah	17.3
47	Vermont	3.3
34	Virginia	6.8
25	Washington	9.9
31	West Virginia	7.7
21	Wisconsin	10.8
17	Wyoming	11.9

RANK ORDER

RANK	STATE	PERCENT
1	Alabama	32.5
2	New Mexico	25.7
3	South Carolina	23.5
4	Montana	23.2
5	Missouri	22.3
6	Maine	21.1
7	Tennessee	20.4
8	Kansas	19.5
9	Idaho	18.1
10	Utah	17.3
11	Iowa	16.9
12	Delaware	16.0
13	Oregon	14.6
14	Alaska	13.8
15	North Carolina	13.1
16	Nevada	12.3
17	Wyoming	11.9
18	Florida	11.7
18	Texas	11.7
20	Michigan	11.4
21	Wisconsin	10.8
22	Mississippi	10.5
22	Pennsylvania	10.5
24	South Dakota	10.4
25	Washington	9.9
26	Georgia	9.3
27	Rhode Island	8.8
28	Hawaii	8.7
29	Arizona	8.5
30	Illinois	8.3
31	West Virginia	7.7
32	Ohio	7.4
33	North Dakota	7.1
34	Virginia	6.8
35	Louisiana	6.5
36	Kentucky	6.3
37	Maryland	5.5
38	Oklahoma	5.4
39	New Hampshire	5.3
40	Connecticut	5.1
40	New York	5.1
42	Arkansas	5.0
43	Massachusetts	4.5
44	Colorado	4.2
44	Minnesota	4.2
46	Indiana	4.0
47	Vermont	3.3
48	California	2.9
49	New Jersey	1.8
50	Nebraska	1.2

District of Columbia   7.7

Source: Morgan Quitno Press using data from U.S. Dept. of Health and Human Services, Div. of Shortage Designation
    "Selected Statistics on Health Professional Shortage Areas"
*Percent of population considered under-served by dental practitioners. An under-served population does not have primary medical care within reasonable economic and geographic bounds.

Pharmacists in 2002

National Total = 219,390 Pharmacists*

RANK	STATE	PHARMACISTS	% of USA
22	Alabama	3,930	1.8%
49	Alaska	370	0.2%
25	Arizona	3,040	1.4%
31	Arkansas	2,360	1.1%
1	California	21,720	9.9%
25	Colorado	3,040	1.4%
30	Connecticut	2,570	1.2%
45	Delaware	560	0.3%
4	Florida	12,720	5.8%
10	Georgia	6,470	2.9%
40	Hawaii	1,080	0.5%
39	Idaho	1,200	0.5%
5	Illinois	10,970	5.0%
13	Indiana	5,170	2.4%
28	Iowa	2,840	1.3%
32	Kansas	2,220	1.0%
23	Kentucky	3,740	1.7%
19	Louisiana	4,230	1.9%
42	Maine	850	0.4%
17	Maryland	4,650	2.1%
16	Massachusetts	4,670	2.1%
8	Michigan	7,360	3.4%
21	Minnesota	3,960	1.8%
33	Mississippi	2,110	1.0%
15	Missouri	4,760	2.2%
43	Montana	780	0.4%
34	Nebraska	1,850	0.8%
37	Nevada	1,560	0.7%
41	New Hampshire	860	0.4%
9	New Jersey	6,650	3.0%
38	New Mexico	1,410	0.6%
3	New York	13,730	6.3%
11	North Carolina	5,790	2.6%
46	North Dakota	510	0.2%
6	Ohio	10,240	4.7%
27	Oklahoma	2,850	1.3%
24	Oregon	3,150	1.4%
7	Pennsylvania	9,830	4.5%
NA	Rhode Island**	NA	NA
29	South Carolina	2,740	1.2%
44	South Dakota	660	0.3%
12	Tennessee	5,210	2.4%
2	Texas	16,470	7.5%
35	Utah	1,800	0.8%
48	Vermont	440	0.2%
14	Virginia	4,770	2.2%
18	Washington	4,270	1.9%
36	West Virginia	1,650	0.8%
20	Wisconsin	4,030	1.8%
46	Wyoming	510	0.2%

RANK	STATE	PHARMACISTS	% of USA
1	California	21,720	9.9%
2	Texas	16,470	7.5%
3	New York	13,730	6.3%
4	Florida	12,720	5.8%
5	Illinois	10,970	5.0%
6	Ohio	10,240	4.7%
7	Pennsylvania	9,830	4.5%
8	Michigan	7,360	3.4%
9	New Jersey	6,650	3.0%
10	Georgia	6,470	2.9%
11	North Carolina	5,790	2.6%
12	Tennessee	5,210	2.4%
13	Indiana	5,170	2.4%
14	Virginia	4,770	2.2%
15	Missouri	4,760	2.2%
16	Massachusetts	4,670	2.1%
17	Maryland	4,650	2.1%
18	Washington	4,270	1.9%
19	Louisiana	4,230	1.9%
20	Wisconsin	4,030	1.8%
21	Minnesota	3,960	1.8%
22	Alabama	3,930	1.8%
23	Kentucky	3,740	1.7%
24	Oregon	3,150	1.4%
25	Arizona	3,040	1.4%
25	Colorado	3,040	1.4%
27	Oklahoma	2,850	1.3%
28	Iowa	2,840	1.3%
29	South Carolina	2,740	1.2%
30	Connecticut	2,570	1.2%
31	Arkansas	2,360	1.1%
32	Kansas	2,220	1.0%
33	Mississippi	2,110	1.0%
34	Nebraska	1,850	0.8%
35	Utah	1,800	0.8%
36	West Virginia	1,650	0.8%
37	Nevada	1,560	0.7%
38	New Mexico	1,410	0.6%
39	Idaho	1,200	0.5%
40	Hawaii	1,080	0.5%
41	New Hampshire	860	0.4%
42	Maine	850	0.4%
43	Montana	780	0.4%
44	South Dakota	660	0.3%
45	Delaware	560	0.3%
46	North Dakota	510	0.2%
46	Wyoming	510	0.2%
48	Vermont	440	0.2%
49	Alaska	370	0.2%
NA	Rhode Island**	NA	NA
	District of Columbia	440	0.2%

Source: U.S. Department of Labor, Bureau of Labor Statistics
   "Occupational Employment and Wages, 2002" (http://www.bls.gov/oes/)
*Does not include self-employed.
**Not available.

Rate of Pharmacists in 2002

National Rate = 76 Pharmacists per 100,000 Population*

ALPHA ORDER

RANK	STATE	RATE
11	Alabama	88
48	Alaska	58
49	Arizona	56
12	Arkansas	87
47	California	62
42	Colorado	68
31	Connecticut	74
41	Delaware	69
27	Florida	76
27	Georgia	76
12	Hawaii	87
9	Idaho	89
12	Illinois	87
18	Indiana	84
3	Iowa	97
20	Kansas	82
5	Kentucky	91
4	Louisiana	94
45	Maine	66
17	Maryland	85
34	Massachusetts	73
34	Michigan	73
24	Minnesota	79
31	Mississippi	74
18	Missouri	84
16	Montana	86
1	Nebraska	107
36	Nevada	72
43	New Hampshire	67
25	New Jersey	78
27	New Mexico	76
36	New York	72
39	North Carolina	70
22	North Dakota	80
7	Ohio	90
20	Oklahoma	82
9	Oregon	89
22	Pennsylvania	80
NA	Rhode Island**	NA
43	South Carolina	67
12	South Dakota	87
7	Tennessee	90
27	Texas	76
25	Utah	78
38	Vermont	71
46	Virginia	65
39	Washington	70
5	West Virginia	91
31	Wisconsin	74
2	Wyoming	102

RANK ORDER

RANK	STATE	RATE
1	Nebraska	107
2	Wyoming	102
3	Iowa	97
4	Louisiana	94
5	Kentucky	91
5	West Virginia	91
7	Ohio	90
7	Tennessee	90
9	Idaho	89
9	Oregon	89
11	Alabama	88
12	Arkansas	87
12	Hawaii	87
12	Illinois	87
12	South Dakota	87
16	Montana	86
17	Maryland	85
18	Indiana	84
18	Missouri	84
20	Kansas	82
20	Oklahoma	82
22	North Dakota	80
22	Pennsylvania	80
24	Minnesota	79
25	New Jersey	78
25	Utah	78
27	Florida	76
27	Georgia	76
27	New Mexico	76
27	Texas	76
31	Connecticut	74
31	Mississippi	74
31	Wisconsin	74
34	Massachusetts	73
34	Michigan	73
36	Nevada	72
36	New York	72
38	Vermont	71
39	North Carolina	70
39	Washington	70
41	Delaware	69
42	Colorado	68
43	New Hampshire	67
43	South Carolina	67
45	Maine	66
46	Virginia	65
47	California	62
48	Alaska	58
49	Arizona	56
NA	Rhode Island**	NA

District of Columbia	77

Source: Morgan Quitno Press using data from U.S. Department of Labor, Bureau of Labor Statistics
    "Occupational Employment and Wages, 2002" (http://www.bls.gov/oes/)
*Does not include self-employed.
**Not available.

Optometrists in 2002

National Total = 23,040 Optometrists*

ALPHA ORDER

RANK	STATE	OPTOMETRISTS	% of USA
20	Alabama	350	1.5%
45	Alaska	70	0.3%
30	Arizona	260	1.1%
32	Arkansas	190	0.8%
1	California	2,360	10.2%
17	Colorado	380	1.6%
22	Connecticut	340	1.5%
NA	Delaware**	NA	NA
5	Florida	950	4.1%
14	Georgia	450	2.0%
33	Hawaii	180	0.8%
38	Idaho	130	0.6%
3	Illinois	1,180	5.1%
12	Indiana	520	2.3%
27	Iowa	280	1.2%
24	Kansas	330	1.4%
22	Kentucky	340	1.5%
25	Louisiana	310	1.3%
NA	Maine**	NA	NA
29	Maryland	270	1.2%
7	Massachusetts	920	4.0%
8	Michigan	850	3.7%
19	Minnesota	370	1.6%
38	Mississippi	130	0.6%
14	Missouri	450	2.0%
41	Montana	80	0.3%
20	Nebraska	350	1.5%
31	Nevada	200	0.9%
41	New Hampshire	80	0.3%
11	New Jersey	590	2.6%
41	New Mexico	80	0.3%
NA	New York**	NA	NA
10	North Carolina	630	2.7%
41	North Dakota	80	0.3%
9	Ohio	830	3.6%
26	Oklahoma	290	1.3%
27	Oregon	280	1.2%
4	Pennsylvania	970	4.2%
36	Rhode Island	150	0.7%
36	South Carolina	150	0.7%
NA	South Dakota**	NA	NA
17	Tennessee	380	1.6%
2	Texas	1,870	8.1%
33	Utah	180	0.8%
46	Vermont	50	0.2%
6	Virginia	930	4.0%
13	Washington	470	2.0%
33	West Virginia	180	0.8%
16	Wisconsin	410	1.8%
40	Wyoming	100	0.4%

RANK ORDER

RANK	STATE	OPTOMETRISTS	% of USA
1	California	2,360	10.2%
2	Texas	1,870	8.1%
3	Illinois	1,180	5.1%
4	Pennsylvania	970	4.2%
5	Florida	950	4.1%
6	Virginia	930	4.0%
7	Massachusetts	920	4.0%
8	Michigan	850	3.7%
9	Ohio	830	3.6%
10	North Carolina	630	2.7%
11	New Jersey	590	2.6%
12	Indiana	520	2.3%
13	Washington	470	2.0%
14	Georgia	450	2.0%
14	Missouri	450	2.0%
16	Wisconsin	410	1.8%
17	Colorado	380	1.6%
17	Tennessee	380	1.6%
19	Minnesota	370	1.6%
20	Alabama	350	1.5%
20	Nebraska	350	1.5%
22	Connecticut	340	1.5%
22	Kentucky	340	1.5%
24	Kansas	330	1.4%
25	Louisiana	310	1.3%
26	Oklahoma	290	1.3%
27	Iowa	280	1.2%
27	Oregon	280	1.2%
29	Maryland	270	1.2%
30	Arizona	260	1.1%
31	Nevada	200	0.9%
32	Arkansas	190	0.8%
33	Hawaii	180	0.8%
33	Utah	180	0.8%
33	West Virginia	180	0.8%
36	Rhode Island	150	0.7%
36	South Carolina	150	0.7%
38	Idaho	130	0.6%
38	Mississippi	130	0.6%
40	Wyoming	100	0.4%
41	Montana	80	0.3%
41	New Hampshire	80	0.3%
41	New Mexico	80	0.3%
41	North Dakota	80	0.3%
45	Alaska	70	0.3%
46	Vermont	50	0.2%
NA	Delaware**	NA	NA
NA	Maine**	NA	NA
NA	New York**	NA	NA
NA	South Dakota**	NA	NA
	District of Columbia	150	0.7%

Source: U.S. Department of Labor, Bureau of Labor Statistics
"Occupational Employment and Wages, 2002" (http://www.bls.gov/oes/)
*Does not include self-employed.
**Not available.

Rate of Optometrists in 2002

National Rate = 8 Optometrists per 100,000 Population*

<table>
<tr><td colspan="3">ALPHA ORDER</td><td colspan="3">RANK ORDER</td></tr>
<tr><td>RANK</td><td>STATE</td><td>RATE</td><td>RANK</td><td>STATE</td><td>RATE</td></tr>
<tr><td>18</td><td>Alabama</td><td>8</td><td>1</td><td>Nebraska</td><td>20</td></tr>
<tr><td>9</td><td>Alaska</td><td>11</td><td>1</td><td>Wyoming</td><td>20</td></tr>
<tr><td>41</td><td>Arizona</td><td>5</td><td>3</td><td>Hawaii</td><td>15</td></tr>
<tr><td>32</td><td>Arkansas</td><td>7</td><td>4</td><td>Massachusetts</td><td>14</td></tr>
<tr><td>32</td><td>California</td><td>7</td><td>4</td><td>Rhode Island</td><td>14</td></tr>
<tr><td>18</td><td>Colorado</td><td>8</td><td>6</td><td>North Dakota</td><td>13</td></tr>
<tr><td>10</td><td>Connecticut</td><td>10</td><td>6</td><td>Virginia</td><td>13</td></tr>
<tr><td>NA</td><td>Delaware**</td><td>NA</td><td>8</td><td>Kansas</td><td>12</td></tr>
<tr><td>39</td><td>Florida</td><td>6</td><td>9</td><td>Alaska</td><td>11</td></tr>
<tr><td>41</td><td>Georgia</td><td>5</td><td>10</td><td>Connecticut</td><td>10</td></tr>
<tr><td>3</td><td>Hawaii</td><td>15</td><td>10</td><td>Idaho</td><td>10</td></tr>
<tr><td>10</td><td>Idaho</td><td>10</td><td>10</td><td>Iowa</td><td>10</td></tr>
<tr><td>14</td><td>Illinois</td><td>9</td><td>10</td><td>West Virginia</td><td>10</td></tr>
<tr><td>18</td><td>Indiana</td><td>8</td><td>14</td><td>Illinois</td><td>9</td></tr>
<tr><td>10</td><td>Iowa</td><td>10</td><td>14</td><td>Montana</td><td>9</td></tr>
<tr><td>8</td><td>Kansas</td><td>12</td><td>14</td><td>Nevada</td><td>9</td></tr>
<tr><td>18</td><td>Kentucky</td><td>8</td><td>14</td><td>Texas</td><td>9</td></tr>
<tr><td>32</td><td>Louisiana</td><td>7</td><td>18</td><td>Alabama</td><td>8</td></tr>
<tr><td>NA</td><td>Maine**</td><td>NA</td><td>18</td><td>Colorado</td><td>8</td></tr>
<tr><td>41</td><td>Maryland</td><td>5</td><td>18</td><td>Indiana</td><td>8</td></tr>
<tr><td>4</td><td>Massachusetts</td><td>14</td><td>18</td><td>Kentucky</td><td>8</td></tr>
<tr><td>18</td><td>Michigan</td><td>8</td><td>18</td><td>Michigan</td><td>8</td></tr>
<tr><td>32</td><td>Minnesota</td><td>7</td><td>18</td><td>Missouri</td><td>8</td></tr>
<tr><td>41</td><td>Mississippi</td><td>5</td><td>18</td><td>North Carolina</td><td>8</td></tr>
<tr><td>18</td><td>Missouri</td><td>8</td><td>18</td><td>Oklahoma</td><td>8</td></tr>
<tr><td>14</td><td>Montana</td><td>9</td><td>18</td><td>Oregon</td><td>8</td></tr>
<tr><td>1</td><td>Nebraska</td><td>20</td><td>18</td><td>Pennsylvania</td><td>8</td></tr>
<tr><td>14</td><td>Nevada</td><td>9</td><td>18</td><td>Utah</td><td>8</td></tr>
<tr><td>39</td><td>New Hampshire</td><td>6</td><td>18</td><td>Vermont</td><td>8</td></tr>
<tr><td>32</td><td>New Jersey</td><td>7</td><td>18</td><td>Washington</td><td>8</td></tr>
<tr><td>45</td><td>New Mexico</td><td>4</td><td>18</td><td>Wisconsin</td><td>8</td></tr>
<tr><td>NA</td><td>New York**</td><td>NA</td><td>32</td><td>Arkansas</td><td>7</td></tr>
<tr><td>18</td><td>North Carolina</td><td>8</td><td>32</td><td>California</td><td>7</td></tr>
<tr><td>6</td><td>North Dakota</td><td>13</td><td>32</td><td>Louisiana</td><td>7</td></tr>
<tr><td>32</td><td>Ohio</td><td>7</td><td>32</td><td>Minnesota</td><td>7</td></tr>
<tr><td>18</td><td>Oklahoma</td><td>8</td><td>32</td><td>New Jersey</td><td>7</td></tr>
<tr><td>18</td><td>Oregon</td><td>8</td><td>32</td><td>Ohio</td><td>7</td></tr>
<tr><td>18</td><td>Pennsylvania</td><td>8</td><td>32</td><td>Tennessee</td><td>7</td></tr>
<tr><td>4</td><td>Rhode Island</td><td>14</td><td>39</td><td>Florida</td><td>6</td></tr>
<tr><td>45</td><td>South Carolina</td><td>4</td><td>39</td><td>New Hampshire</td><td>6</td></tr>
<tr><td>NA</td><td>South Dakota**</td><td>NA</td><td>41</td><td>Arizona</td><td>5</td></tr>
<tr><td>32</td><td>Tennessee</td><td>7</td><td>41</td><td>Georgia</td><td>5</td></tr>
<tr><td>14</td><td>Texas</td><td>9</td><td>41</td><td>Maryland</td><td>5</td></tr>
<tr><td>18</td><td>Utah</td><td>8</td><td>41</td><td>Mississippi</td><td>5</td></tr>
<tr><td>18</td><td>Vermont</td><td>8</td><td>45</td><td>New Mexico</td><td>4</td></tr>
<tr><td>6</td><td>Virginia</td><td>13</td><td>45</td><td>South Carolina</td><td>4</td></tr>
<tr><td>18</td><td>Washington</td><td>8</td><td>NA</td><td>Delaware**</td><td>NA</td></tr>
<tr><td>10</td><td>West Virginia</td><td>10</td><td>NA</td><td>Maine**</td><td>NA</td></tr>
<tr><td>18</td><td>Wisconsin</td><td>8</td><td>NA</td><td>New York**</td><td>NA</td></tr>
<tr><td>1</td><td>Wyoming</td><td>20</td><td>NA</td><td>South Dakota**</td><td>NA</td></tr>
<tr><td></td><td></td><td></td><td></td><td>District of Columbia</td><td>26</td></tr>
</table>

*Source: Morgan Quitno Press using data from U.S. Department of Labor, Bureau of Labor Statistics
"Occupational Employment and Wages, 2002" (http://www.bls.gov/oes/)*
Does not include self-employed.
**Not available.*

Employment in Health Care Industries in 2001

National Total = 12,490,106 Employees*

ALPHA ORDER

RANK	STATE	EMPLOYEES	% of USA
23	Alabama	185,063	1.5%
49	Alaska	24,586	0.2%
25	Arizona	169,842	1.4%
32	Arkansas	114,194	0.9%
1	California	1,171,961	9.4%
26	Colorado	165,996	1.3%
22	Connecticut	187,249	1.5%
47	Delaware	38,574	0.3%
4	Florida	676,599	5.4%
12	Georgia	312,528	2.5%
44	Hawaii	42,406	0.3%
42	Idaho	49,027	0.4%
7	Illinois	546,439	4.4%
13	Indiana	285,579	2.3%
28	Iowa	156,716	1.3%
31	Kansas	136,037	1.1%
24	Kentucky	184,341	1.5%
21	Louisiana	205,551	1.6%
37	Maine	72,137	0.6%
20	Maryland	227,550	1.8%
9	Massachusetts	383,078	3.1%
8	Michigan	445,017	3.6%
15	Minnesota	280,671	2.2%
33	Mississippi	111,338	0.9%
14	Missouri	284,621	2.3%
45	Montana	42,261	0.3%
34	Nebraska	89,774	0.7%
39	Nevada	62,296	0.5%
41	New Hampshire	57,563	0.5%
10	New Jersey	374,033	3.0%
38	New Mexico	68,420	0.5%
2	New York	1,016,030	8.1%
11	North Carolina	359,864	2.9%
46	North Dakota	39,503	0.3%
6	Ohio	581,253	4.7%
29	Oklahoma	148,342	1.2%
30	Oregon	136,936	1.1%
5	Pennsylvania	655,265	5.2%
40	Rhode Island	59,225	0.5%
27	South Carolina	163,258	1.3%
43	South Dakota	44,259	0.4%
18	Tennessee	259,328	2.1%
3	Texas	834,361	6.7%
36	Utah	82,974	0.7%
48	Vermont	30,301	0.2%
17	Virginia	263,734	2.1%
19	Washington	239,237	1.9%
35	West Virginia	89,244	0.7%
16	Wisconsin	266,940	2.1%
50	Wyoming	18,115	0.1%

RANK ORDER

RANK	STATE	EMPLOYEES	% of USA
1	California	1,171,961	9.4%
2	New York	1,016,030	8.1%
3	Texas	834,361	6.7%
4	Florida	676,599	5.4%
5	Pennsylvania	655,265	5.2%
6	Ohio	581,253	4.7%
7	Illinois	546,439	4.4%
8	Michigan	445,017	3.6%
9	Massachusetts	383,078	3.1%
10	New Jersey	374,033	3.0%
11	North Carolina	359,864	2.9%
12	Georgia	312,528	2.5%
13	Indiana	285,579	2.3%
14	Missouri	284,621	2.3%
15	Minnesota	280,671	2.2%
16	Wisconsin	266,940	2.1%
17	Virginia	263,734	2.1%
18	Tennessee	259,328	2.1%
19	Washington	239,237	1.9%
20	Maryland	227,550	1.8%
21	Louisiana	205,551	1.6%
22	Connecticut	187,249	1.5%
23	Alabama	185,063	1.5%
24	Kentucky	184,341	1.5%
25	Arizona	169,842	1.4%
26	Colorado	165,996	1.3%
27	South Carolina	163,258	1.3%
28	Iowa	156,716	1.3%
29	Oklahoma	148,342	1.2%
30	Oregon	136,936	1.1%
31	Kansas	136,037	1.1%
32	Arkansas	114,194	0.9%
33	Mississippi	111,338	0.9%
34	Nebraska	89,774	0.7%
35	West Virginia	89,244	0.7%
36	Utah	82,974	0.7%
37	Maine	72,137	0.6%
38	New Mexico	68,420	0.5%
39	Nevada	62,296	0.5%
40	Rhode Island	59,225	0.5%
41	New Hampshire	57,563	0.5%
42	Idaho	49,027	0.4%
43	South Dakota	44,259	0.4%
44	Hawaii	42,406	0.3%
45	Montana	42,261	0.3%
46	North Dakota	39,503	0.3%
47	Delaware	38,574	0.3%
48	Vermont	30,301	0.2%
49	Alaska	24,586	0.2%
50	Wyoming	18,115	0.1%
	District of Columbia	50,490	0.4%

Source: U.S. Bureau of the Census
   "County Business Patterns 2001 (NAICS)" (http://censtats.census.gov/cbpnaic/cbpnaic.shtml)
Includes employees at establishments exempt from as well as subject to the federal income tax. Includes employees at those establishments within the North American Industry Classification System (NAICS) classifications 621 (ambulatory health care services), 622 (hospitals) and 623 (nursing and residential care facilities). See Facilities Chapter for establishments.

Percent of Total Employment in Health Care Industries in 2001

National Percent = 10.9%*

RANK	STATE	PERCENT
25	Alabama	11.4
23	Alaska	11.5
48	Arizona	8.7
23	Arkansas	11.5
46	California	8.9
49	Colorado	8.4
16	Connecticut	12.0
42	Delaware	9.9
31	Florida	10.5
46	Georgia	8.9
43	Hawaii	9.6
31	Idaho	10.5
40	Illinois	10.0
28	Indiana	11.0
10	Iowa	12.5
13	Kansas	12.2
12	Kentucky	12.3
8	Louisiana	12.9
3	Maine	14.4
29	Maryland	10.9
13	Massachusetts	12.2
26	Michigan	11.1
21	Minnesota	11.6
16	Mississippi	12.0
19	Missouri	11.8
6	Montana	14.0
16	Nebraska	12.0
50	Nevada	6.8
35	New Hampshire	10.3
35	New Jersey	10.3
11	New Mexico	12.4
7	New York	13.7
31	North Carolina	10.5
2	North Dakota	15.4
19	Ohio	11.8
13	Oklahoma	12.2
40	Oregon	10.0
9	Pennsylvania	12.8
4	Rhode Island	14.3
37	South Carolina	10.2
4	South Dakota	14.3
29	Tennessee	10.9
37	Texas	10.2
44	Utah	9.1
21	Vermont	11.6
45	Virginia	9.0
34	Washington	10.4
1	West Virginia	16.1
26	Wisconsin	11.1
37	Wyoming	10.2

RANK	STATE	PERCENT
1	West Virginia	16.1
2	North Dakota	15.4
3	Maine	14.4
4	Rhode Island	14.3
4	South Dakota	14.3
6	Montana	14.0
7	New York	13.7
8	Louisiana	12.9
9	Pennsylvania	12.8
10	Iowa	12.5
11	New Mexico	12.4
12	Kentucky	12.3
13	Kansas	12.2
13	Massachusetts	12.2
13	Oklahoma	12.2
16	Connecticut	12.0
16	Mississippi	12.0
16	Nebraska	12.0
19	Missouri	11.8
19	Ohio	11.8
21	Minnesota	11.6
21	Vermont	11.6
23	Alaska	11.5
23	Arkansas	11.5
25	Alabama	11.4
26	Michigan	11.1
26	Wisconsin	11.1
28	Indiana	11.0
29	Maryland	10.9
29	Tennessee	10.9
31	Florida	10.5
31	Idaho	10.5
31	North Carolina	10.5
34	Washington	10.4
35	New Hampshire	10.3
35	New Jersey	10.3
37	South Carolina	10.2
37	Texas	10.2
37	Wyoming	10.2
40	Illinois	10.0
40	Oregon	10.0
42	Delaware	9.9
43	Hawaii	9.6
44	Utah	9.1
45	Virginia	9.0
46	California	8.9
46	Georgia	8.9
48	Arizona	8.7
49	Colorado	8.4
50	Nevada	6.8

District of Columbia	11.9

Source: Morgan Quitno Press using data from U.S. Bureau of the Census
   "County Business Patterns 2001 (NAICS)" (http://censtats.census.gov/cbpnaic/cbpnaic.shtml)
*Includes employees at establishments exempt from as well as subject to the federal income tax. Includes employees at those establishments within the North American Industry Classification System (NAICS) classifications 621 (ambulatory health care services), 622 (hospitals) and 623 (nursing and residential care facilities). See Facilities Chapter for establishments.

VII. PHYSICAL FITNESS

Users of Exercise Equipment in 2002

National Total = 50,227,000 Users

RANK	STATE	USERS	% of USA
30	Alabama	426,000	0.8%
NA	Alaska*	NA	NA
19	Arizona	939,000	1.9%
40	Arkansas	197,000	0.4%
1	California	5,250,000	10.5%
20	Colorado	904,000	1.8%
22	Connecticut	796,000	1.6%
42	Delaware	174,000	0.3%
4	Florida	3,468,000	6.9%
10	Georgia	1,404,000	2.8%
NA	Hawaii*	NA	NA
37	Idaho	241,000	0.5%
5	Illinois	2,801,000	5.6%
15	Indiana	1,170,000	2.3%
34	Iowa	306,000	0.6%
24	Kansas	695,000	1.4%
25	Kentucky	650,000	1.3%
28	Louisiana	506,000	1.0%
44	Maine	136,000	0.3%
17	Maryland	979,000	1.9%
14	Massachusetts	1,181,000	2.4%
8	Michigan	1,984,000	4.0%
18	Minnesota	962,000	1.9%
33	Mississippi	314,000	0.6%
13	Missouri	1,268,000	2.5%
41	Montana	179,000	0.4%
30	Nebraska	426,000	0.8%
35	Nevada	286,000	0.6%
36	New Hampshire	254,000	0.5%
9	New Jersey	1,445,000	2.9%
39	New Mexico	220,000	0.4%
3	New York	3,681,000	7.3%
12	North Carolina	1,345,000	2.7%
48	North Dakota	92,000	0.2%
7	Ohio	2,061,000	4.1%
32	Oklahoma	357,000	0.7%
29	Oregon	472,000	0.9%
6	Pennsylvania	2,526,000	5.0%
43	Rhode Island	167,000	0.3%
23	South Carolina	742,000	1.5%
45	South Dakota	128,000	0.3%
21	Tennessee	877,000	1.7%
2	Texas	4,168,000	8.3%
27	Utah	553,000	1.1%
47	Vermont	93,000	0.2%
11	Virginia	1,398,000	2.8%
26	Washington	606,000	1.2%
38	West Virginia	231,000	0.5%
16	Wisconsin	1,057,000	2.1%
46	Wyoming	99,000	0.2%

RANK	STATE	USERS	% of USA
1	California	5,250,000	10.5%
2	Texas	4,168,000	8.3%
3	New York	3,681,000	7.3%
4	Florida	3,468,000	6.9%
5	Illinois	2,801,000	5.6%
6	Pennsylvania	2,526,000	5.0%
7	Ohio	2,061,000	4.1%
8	Michigan	1,984,000	4.0%
9	New Jersey	1,445,000	2.9%
10	Georgia	1,404,000	2.8%
11	Virginia	1,398,000	2.8%
12	North Carolina	1,345,000	2.7%
13	Missouri	1,268,000	2.5%
14	Massachusetts	1,181,000	2.4%
15	Indiana	1,170,000	2.3%
16	Wisconsin	1,057,000	2.1%
17	Maryland	979,000	1.9%
18	Minnesota	962,000	1.9%
19	Arizona	939,000	1.9%
20	Colorado	904,000	1.8%
21	Tennessee	877,000	1.7%
22	Connecticut	796,000	1.6%
23	South Carolina	742,000	1.5%
24	Kansas	695,000	1.4%
25	Kentucky	650,000	1.3%
26	Washington	606,000	1.2%
27	Utah	553,000	1.1%
28	Louisiana	506,000	1.0%
29	Oregon	472,000	0.9%
30	Alabama	426,000	0.8%
30	Nebraska	426,000	0.8%
32	Oklahoma	357,000	0.7%
33	Mississippi	314,000	0.6%
34	Iowa	306,000	0.6%
35	Nevada	286,000	0.6%
36	New Hampshire	254,000	0.5%
37	Idaho	241,000	0.5%
38	West Virginia	231,000	0.5%
39	New Mexico	220,000	0.4%
40	Arkansas	197,000	0.4%
41	Montana	179,000	0.4%
42	Delaware	174,000	0.3%
43	Rhode Island	167,000	0.3%
44	Maine	136,000	0.3%
45	South Dakota	128,000	0.3%
46	Wyoming	99,000	0.2%
47	Vermont	93,000	0.2%
48	North Dakota	92,000	0.2%
NA	Alaska*	NA	NA
NA	Hawaii*	NA	NA
	District of Columbia*	NA	NA

Source: The National Sporting Goods Association
"NSGA Sports Participation Survey, January-December 2002 (Copyright 2003, reprinted with permission)
*Not available.

Participants in Golf in 2002

National Total = 28,257,000 Golfers

ALPHA ORDER

RANK	STATE	GOLFERS	% of USA
47	Alabama	40,000	0.1%
NA	Alaska*	NA	NA
19	Arizona	578,000	2.0%
42	Arkansas	87,000	0.3%
1	California	2,666,000	9.4%
21	Colorado	476,000	1.7%
23	Connecticut	456,000	1.6%
45	Delaware	74,000	0.3%
4	Florida	1,666,000	5.9%
13	Georgia	722,000	2.6%
NA	Hawaii*	NA	NA
44	Idaho	80,000	0.3%
8	Illinois	1,378,000	4.9%
14	Indiana	683,000	2.4%
26	Iowa	417,000	1.5%
31	Kansas	243,000	0.9%
29	Kentucky	292,000	1.0%
30	Louisiana	244,000	0.9%
41	Maine	88,000	0.3%
17	Maryland	645,000	2.3%
24	Massachusetts	449,000	1.6%
7	Michigan	1,420,000	5.0%
15	Minnesota	681,000	2.4%
34	Mississippi	189,000	0.7%
16	Missouri	659,000	2.3%
43	Montana	86,000	0.3%
33	Nebraska	191,000	0.7%
32	Nevada	194,000	0.7%
36	New Hampshire	128,000	0.5%
11	New Jersey	868,000	3.1%
37	New Mexico	107,000	0.4%
3	New York	1,722,000	6.1%
10	North Carolina	885,000	3.1%
38	North Dakota	104,000	0.4%
5	Ohio	1,642,000	5.8%
28	Oklahoma	296,000	1.0%
25	Oregon	422,000	1.5%
6	Pennsylvania	1,485,000	5.3%
48	Rhode Island	23,000	0.1%
18	South Carolina	617,000	2.2%
35	South Dakota	183,000	0.6%
20	Tennessee	536,000	1.9%
2	Texas	1,753,000	6.2%
27	Utah	389,000	1.4%
39	Vermont	96,000	0.3%
12	Virginia	734,000	2.6%
22	Washington	463,000	1.6%
40	West Virginia	95,000	0.3%
9	Wisconsin	937,000	3.3%
46	Wyoming	66,000	0.2%

RANK ORDER

RANK	STATE	GOLFERS	% of USA
1	California	2,666,000	9.4%
2	Texas	1,753,000	6.2%
3	New York	1,722,000	6.1%
4	Florida	1,666,000	5.9%
5	Ohio	1,642,000	5.8%
6	Pennsylvania	1,485,000	5.3%
7	Michigan	1,420,000	5.0%
8	Illinois	1,378,000	4.9%
9	Wisconsin	937,000	3.3%
10	North Carolina	885,000	3.1%
11	New Jersey	868,000	3.1%
12	Virginia	734,000	2.6%
13	Georgia	722,000	2.6%
14	Indiana	683,000	2.4%
15	Minnesota	681,000	2.4%
16	Missouri	659,000	2.3%
17	Maryland	645,000	2.3%
18	South Carolina	617,000	2.2%
19	Arizona	578,000	2.0%
20	Tennessee	536,000	1.9%
21	Colorado	476,000	1.7%
22	Washington	463,000	1.6%
23	Connecticut	456,000	1.6%
24	Massachusetts	449,000	1.6%
25	Oregon	422,000	1.5%
26	Iowa	417,000	1.5%
27	Utah	389,000	1.4%
28	Oklahoma	296,000	1.0%
29	Kentucky	292,000	1.0%
30	Louisiana	244,000	0.9%
31	Kansas	243,000	0.9%
32	Nevada	194,000	0.7%
33	Nebraska	191,000	0.7%
34	Mississippi	189,000	0.7%
35	South Dakota	183,000	0.6%
36	New Hampshire	128,000	0.5%
37	New Mexico	107,000	0.4%
38	North Dakota	104,000	0.4%
39	Vermont	96,000	0.3%
40	West Virginia	95,000	0.3%
41	Maine	88,000	0.3%
42	Arkansas	87,000	0.3%
43	Montana	86,000	0.3%
44	Idaho	80,000	0.3%
45	Delaware	74,000	0.3%
46	Wyoming	66,000	0.2%
47	Alabama	40,000	0.1%
48	Rhode Island	23,000	0.1%
NA	Alaska*	NA	NA
NA	Hawaii*	NA	NA
	District of Columbia*	NA	NA

Source: The National Sporting Goods Association
   "NSGA Sports Participation Survey, January-December 2002 (Copyright 2003, reprinted with permission)
*Not available.

Participants in Running/Jogging in 2002

National Total = 24,748,000 Runners/Joggers

ALPHA ORDER

RANK	STATE	RUNNERS	% of USA
38	Alabama	132,000	0.5%
NA	Alaska*	NA	NA
16	Arizona	491,000	2.0%
28	Arkansas	250,000	1.0%
1	California	2,811,000	11.4%
22	Colorado	428,000	1.7%
18	Connecticut	487,000	2.0%
47	Delaware	24,000	0.1%
6	Florida	1,168,000	4.7%
9	Georgia	863,000	3.5%
NA	Hawaii*	NA	NA
33	Idaho	175,000	0.7%
3	Illinois	1,504,000	6.1%
10	Indiana	809,000	3.3%
36	Iowa	158,000	0.6%
30	Kansas	233,000	0.9%
27	Kentucky	274,000	1.1%
26	Louisiana	285,000	1.2%
42	Maine	56,000	0.2%
21	Maryland	433,000	1.7%
17	Massachusetts	489,000	2.0%
8	Michigan	1,137,000	4.6%
14	Minnesota	507,000	2.0%
29	Mississippi	245,000	1.0%
13	Missouri	607,000	2.5%
43	Montana	54,000	0.2%
34	Nebraska	172,000	0.7%
40	Nevada	98,000	0.4%
35	New Hampshire	171,000	0.7%
12	New Jersey	636,000	2.6%
39	New Mexico	116,000	0.5%
5	New York	1,300,000	5.3%
19	North Carolina	472,000	1.9%
48	North Dakota	21,000	0.1%
7	Ohio	1,142,000	4.6%
32	Oklahoma	194,000	0.8%
23	Oregon	397,000	1.6%
4	Pennsylvania	1,363,000	5.5%
44	Rhode Island	42,000	0.2%
31	South Carolina	208,000	0.8%
44	South Dakota	42,000	0.2%
15	Tennessee	503,000	2.0%
2	Texas	2,085,000	8.4%
24	Utah	374,000	1.5%
37	Vermont	149,000	0.6%
11	Virginia	787,000	3.2%
25	Washington	300,000	1.2%
46	West Virginia	38,000	0.2%
20	Wisconsin	449,000	1.8%
41	Wyoming	71,000	0.3%

RANK ORDER

RANK	STATE	RUNNERS	% of USA
1	California	2,811,000	11.4%
2	Texas	2,085,000	8.4%
3	Illinois	1,504,000	6.1%
4	Pennsylvania	1,363,000	5.5%
5	New York	1,300,000	5.3%
6	Florida	1,168,000	4.7%
7	Ohio	1,142,000	4.6%
8	Michigan	1,137,000	4.6%
9	Georgia	863,000	3.5%
10	Indiana	809,000	3.3%
11	Virginia	787,000	3.2%
12	New Jersey	636,000	2.6%
13	Missouri	607,000	2.5%
14	Minnesota	507,000	2.0%
15	Tennessee	503,000	2.0%
16	Arizona	491,000	2.0%
17	Massachusetts	489,000	2.0%
18	Connecticut	487,000	2.0%
19	North Carolina	472,000	1.9%
20	Wisconsin	449,000	1.8%
21	Maryland	433,000	1.7%
22	Colorado	428,000	1.7%
23	Oregon	397,000	1.6%
24	Utah	374,000	1.5%
25	Washington	300,000	1.2%
26	Louisiana	285,000	1.2%
27	Kentucky	274,000	1.1%
28	Arkansas	250,000	1.0%
29	Mississippi	245,000	1.0%
30	Kansas	233,000	0.9%
31	South Carolina	208,000	0.8%
32	Oklahoma	194,000	0.8%
33	Idaho	175,000	0.7%
34	Nebraska	172,000	0.7%
35	New Hampshire	171,000	0.7%
36	Iowa	158,000	0.6%
37	Vermont	149,000	0.6%
38	Alabama	132,000	0.5%
39	New Mexico	116,000	0.5%
40	Nevada	98,000	0.4%
41	Wyoming	71,000	0.3%
42	Maine	56,000	0.2%
43	Montana	54,000	0.2%
44	Rhode Island	42,000	0.2%
44	South Dakota	42,000	0.2%
46	West Virginia	38,000	0.2%
47	Delaware	24,000	0.1%
48	North Dakota	21,000	0.1%
NA	Alaska*	NA	NA
NA	Hawaii*	NA	NA
	District of Columbia*	NA	NA

Source: The National Sporting Goods Association
"NSGA Sports Participation Survey, January-December 2002 (Copyright 2003, reprinted with permission)
*Not available.

Participants in Swimming in 2002

National Total = 54,657,000 Swimmers

ALPHA ORDER

RANK	STATE	SWIMMERS	% of USA
29	Alabama	455,000	0.8%
NA	Alaska*	NA	NA
14	Arizona	1,392,000	2.5%
31	Arkansas	436,000	0.8%
1	California	6,131,000	11.2%
25	Colorado	717,000	1.3%
22	Connecticut	868,000	1.6%
46	Delaware	35,000	0.1%
2	Florida	4,126,000	7.5%
12	Georgia	1,425,000	2.6%
NA	Hawaii*	NA	NA
43	Idaho	101,000	0.2%
8	Illinois	2,208,000	4.0%
19	Indiana	1,067,000	2.0%
30	Iowa	453,000	0.8%
26	Kansas	621,000	1.1%
32	Kentucky	429,000	0.8%
28	Louisiana	531,000	1.0%
39	Maine	219,000	0.4%
20	Maryland	974,000	1.8%
10	Massachusetts	1,565,000	2.9%
6	Michigan	3,080,000	5.6%
21	Minnesota	959,000	1.8%
37	Mississippi	281,000	0.5%
15	Missouri	1,232,000	2.3%
47	Montana	30,000	0.1%
34	Nebraska	374,000	0.7%
35	Nevada	346,000	0.6%
36	New Hampshire	287,000	0.5%
9	New Jersey	1,664,000	3.0%
40	New Mexico	199,000	0.4%
3	New York	3,731,000	6.8%
16	North Carolina	1,221,000	2.2%
48	North Dakota	21,000	0.0%
7	Ohio	2,535,000	4.6%
23	Oklahoma	805,000	1.5%
27	Oregon	591,000	1.1%
4	Pennsylvania	3,315,000	6.1%
43	Rhode Island	101,000	0.2%
24	South Carolina	767,000	1.4%
42	South Dakota	124,000	0.2%
13	Tennessee	1,405,000	2.6%
5	Texas	3,298,000	6.0%
33	Utah	404,000	0.7%
38	Vermont	268,000	0.5%
11	Virginia	1,456,000	2.7%
18	Washington	1,072,000	2.0%
41	West Virginia	134,000	0.2%
17	Wisconsin	1,101,000	2.0%
45	Wyoming	82,000	0.2%

RANK ORDER

RANK	STATE	SWIMMERS	% of USA
1	California	6,131,000	11.2%
2	Florida	4,126,000	7.5%
3	New York	3,731,000	6.8%
4	Pennsylvania	3,315,000	6.1%
5	Texas	3,298,000	6.0%
6	Michigan	3,080,000	5.6%
7	Ohio	2,535,000	4.6%
8	Illinois	2,208,000	4.0%
9	New Jersey	1,664,000	3.0%
10	Massachusetts	1,565,000	2.9%
11	Virginia	1,456,000	2.7%
12	Georgia	1,425,000	2.6%
13	Tennessee	1,405,000	2.6%
14	Arizona	1,392,000	2.5%
15	Missouri	1,232,000	2.3%
16	North Carolina	1,221,000	2.2%
17	Wisconsin	1,101,000	2.0%
18	Washington	1,072,000	2.0%
19	Indiana	1,067,000	2.0%
20	Maryland	974,000	1.8%
21	Minnesota	959,000	1.8%
22	Connecticut	868,000	1.6%
23	Oklahoma	805,000	1.5%
24	South Carolina	767,000	1.4%
25	Colorado	717,000	1.3%
26	Kansas	621,000	1.1%
27	Oregon	591,000	1.1%
28	Louisiana	531,000	1.0%
29	Alabama	455,000	0.8%
30	Iowa	453,000	0.8%
31	Arkansas	436,000	0.8%
32	Kentucky	429,000	0.8%
33	Utah	404,000	0.7%
34	Nebraska	374,000	0.7%
35	Nevada	346,000	0.6%
36	New Hampshire	287,000	0.5%
37	Mississippi	281,000	0.5%
38	Vermont	268,000	0.5%
39	Maine	219,000	0.4%
40	New Mexico	199,000	0.4%
41	West Virginia	134,000	0.2%
42	South Dakota	124,000	0.2%
43	Idaho	101,000	0.2%
43	Rhode Island	101,000	0.2%
45	Wyoming	82,000	0.2%
46	Delaware	35,000	0.1%
47	Montana	30,000	0.1%
48	North Dakota	21,000	0.0%
NA	Alaska*	NA	NA
NA	Hawaii*	NA	NA
	District of Columbia*	NA	NA

Source: The National Sporting Goods Association
"NSGA Sports Participation Survey, January-December 2002 (Copyright 2003, reprinted with permission)
*Not available.

Participants in Tennis in 2002

National Total = 10,970,000 Tennis Players

RANK	STATE	PLAYERS	% of USA
NA	Alabama*	NA	NA
NA	Alaska*	NA	NA
32	Arizona	90,000	0.8%
NA	Arkansas*	NA	NA
1	California	1,389,000	12.7%
18	Colorado	222,000	2.0%
9	Connecticut	391,000	3.6%
37	Delaware	71,000	0.6%
2	Florida	1,020,000	9.3%
12	Georgia	277,000	2.5%
NA	Hawaii*	NA	NA
41	Idaho	13,000	0.1%
22	Illinois	188,000	1.7%
30	Indiana	104,000	0.9%
36	Iowa	75,000	0.7%
33	Kansas	83,000	0.8%
24	Kentucky	161,000	1.5%
10	Louisiana	312,000	2.8%
NA	Maine*	NA	NA
16	Maryland	232,000	2.1%
7	Massachusetts	418,000	3.8%
11	Michigan	281,000	2.6%
17	Minnesota	230,000	2.1%
25	Mississippi	137,000	1.2%
31	Missouri	97,000	0.9%
40	Montana	16,000	0.1%
34	Nebraska	80,000	0.7%
NA	Nevada*	NA	NA
NA	New Hampshire*	NA	NA
6	New Jersey	475,000	4.3%
27	New Mexico	134,000	1.2%
4	New York	576,000	5.3%
29	North Carolina	111,000	1.0%
NA	North Dakota*	NA	NA
5	Ohio	487,000	4.4%
20	Oklahoma	209,000	1.9%
28	Oregon	117,000	1.1%
8	Pennsylvania	406,000	3.7%
26	Rhode Island	135,000	1.2%
19	South Carolina	221,000	2.0%
38	South Dakota	60,000	0.5%
20	Tennessee	209,000	1.9%
3	Texas	895,000	8.2%
14	Utah	241,000	2.2%
39	Vermont	58,000	0.5%
23	Virginia	182,000	1.7%
13	Washington	249,000	2.3%
35	West Virginia	77,000	0.7%
14	Wisconsin	241,000	2.2%
NA	Wyoming*	NA	NA

RANK	STATE	PLAYERS	% of USA
1	California	1,389,000	12.7%
2	Florida	1,020,000	9.3%
3	Texas	895,000	8.2%
4	New York	576,000	5.3%
5	Ohio	487,000	4.4%
6	New Jersey	475,000	4.3%
7	Massachusetts	418,000	3.8%
8	Pennsylvania	406,000	3.7%
9	Connecticut	391,000	3.6%
10	Louisiana	312,000	2.8%
11	Michigan	281,000	2.6%
12	Georgia	277,000	2.5%
13	Washington	249,000	2.3%
14	Utah	241,000	2.2%
14	Wisconsin	241,000	2.2%
16	Maryland	232,000	2.1%
17	Minnesota	230,000	2.1%
18	Colorado	222,000	2.0%
19	South Carolina	221,000	2.0%
20	Oklahoma	209,000	1.9%
20	Tennessee	209,000	1.9%
22	Illinois	188,000	1.7%
23	Virginia	182,000	1.7%
24	Kentucky	161,000	1.5%
25	Mississippi	137,000	1.2%
26	Rhode Island	135,000	1.2%
27	New Mexico	134,000	1.2%
28	Oregon	117,000	1.1%
29	North Carolina	111,000	1.0%
30	Indiana	104,000	0.9%
31	Missouri	97,000	0.9%
32	Arizona	90,000	0.8%
33	Kansas	83,000	0.8%
34	Nebraska	80,000	0.7%
35	West Virginia	77,000	0.7%
36	Iowa	75,000	0.7%
37	Delaware	71,000	0.6%
38	South Dakota	60,000	0.5%
39	Vermont	58,000	0.5%
40	Montana	16,000	0.1%
41	Idaho	13,000	0.1%
NA	Alabama*	NA	NA
NA	Alaska*	NA	NA
NA	Arkansas*	NA	NA
NA	Hawaii*	NA	NA
NA	Maine*	NA	NA
NA	Nevada*	NA	NA
NA	New Hampshire*	NA	NA
NA	North Dakota*	NA	NA
NA	Wyoming*	NA	NA
	District of Columbia*	NA	NA

Source: The National Sporting Goods Association
"NSGA Sports Participation Survey, January-December 2002 (Copyright 2003, reprinted with permission)
*Not available.

Alcohol Consumption in 2000

National Total = 492,521,000 Gallons*

ALPHA ORDER

RANK ORDER

RANK	STATE	GALLONS	% of USA
25	Alabama	6,734,000	1.4%
47	Alaska	1,267,000	0.3%
16	Arizona	10,218,000	2.1%
35	Arkansas	3,749,000	0.8%
1	California	58,545,000	11.9%
20	Colorado	9,022,000	1.8%
27	Connecticut	5,982,000	1.2%
45	Delaware	1,836,000	0.4%
3	Florida	33,694,000	6.8%
10	Georgia	14,153,000	2.9%
41	Hawaii	2,285,000	0.5%
40	Idaho	2,360,000	0.5%
5	Illinois	22,161,000	4.5%
18	Indiana	9,629,000	2.0%
32	Iowa	4,690,000	1.0%
34	Kansas	3,898,000	0.8%
29	Kentucky	5,717,000	1.2%
22	Louisiana	8,585,000	1.7%
39	Maine	2,406,000	0.5%
21	Maryland	8,869,000	1.8%
11	Massachusetts	13,225,000	2.7%
8	Michigan	16,827,000	3.4%
19	Minnesota	9,338,000	1.9%
30	Mississippi	4,791,000	1.0%
17	Missouri	10,138,000	2.1%
44	Montana	1,851,000	0.4%
37	Nebraska	3,055,000	0.6%
28	Nevada	5,901,000	1.2%
33	New Hampshire	4,007,000	0.8%
9	New Jersey	14,888,000	3.0%
36	New Mexico	3,414,000	0.7%
4	New York	28,777,000	5.8%
12	North Carolina	12,651,000	2.6%
48	North Dakota	1,254,000	0.3%
7	Ohio	18,173,000	3.7%
31	Oklahoma	4,698,000	1.0%
26	Oregon	6,329,000	1.3%
6	Pennsylvania	19,043,000	3.9%
43	Rhode Island	1,981,000	0.4%
24	South Carolina	7,688,000	1.6%
46	South Dakota	1,368,000	0.3%
23	Tennessee	8,584,000	1.7%
2	Texas	36,767,000	7.5%
42	Utah	2,148,000	0.4%
49	Vermont	1,165,000	0.2%
14	Virginia	11,330,000	2.3%
15	Washington	10,256,000	2.1%
38	West Virginia	2,457,000	0.5%
13	Wisconsin	11,941,000	2.4%
50	Wyoming	981,000	0.2%

RANK	STATE	GALLONS	% of USA
1	California	58,545,000	11.9%
2	Texas	36,767,000	7.5%
3	Florida	33,694,000	6.8%
4	New York	28,777,000	5.8%
5	Illinois	22,161,000	4.5%
6	Pennsylvania	19,043,000	3.9%
7	Ohio	18,173,000	3.7%
8	Michigan	16,827,000	3.4%
9	New Jersey	14,888,000	3.0%
10	Georgia	14,153,000	2.9%
11	Massachusetts	13,225,000	2.7%
12	North Carolina	12,651,000	2.6%
13	Wisconsin	11,941,000	2.4%
14	Virginia	11,330,000	2.3%
15	Washington	10,256,000	2.1%
16	Arizona	10,218,000	2.1%
17	Missouri	10,138,000	2.1%
18	Indiana	9,629,000	2.0%
19	Minnesota	9,338,000	1.9%
20	Colorado	9,022,000	1.8%
21	Maryland	8,869,000	1.8%
22	Louisiana	8,585,000	1.7%
23	Tennessee	8,584,000	1.7%
24	South Carolina	7,688,000	1.6%
25	Alabama	6,734,000	1.4%
26	Oregon	6,329,000	1.3%
27	Connecticut	5,982,000	1.2%
28	Nevada	5,901,000	1.2%
29	Kentucky	5,717,000	1.2%
30	Mississippi	4,791,000	1.0%
31	Oklahoma	4,698,000	1.0%
32	Iowa	4,690,000	1.0%
33	New Hampshire	4,007,000	0.8%
34	Kansas	3,898,000	0.8%
35	Arkansas	3,749,000	0.8%
36	New Mexico	3,414,000	0.7%
37	Nebraska	3,055,000	0.6%
38	West Virginia	2,457,000	0.5%
39	Maine	2,406,000	0.5%
40	Idaho	2,360,000	0.5%
41	Hawaii	2,285,000	0.5%
42	Utah	2,148,000	0.4%
43	Rhode Island	1,981,000	0.4%
44	Montana	1,851,000	0.4%
45	Delaware	1,836,000	0.4%
46	South Dakota	1,368,000	0.3%
47	Alaska	1,267,000	0.3%
48	North Dakota	1,254,000	0.3%
49	Vermont	1,165,000	0.2%
50	Wyoming	981,000	0.2%
	District of Columbia	1,693,000	0.3%

Source: U.S. Department of Health and Human Services, National Institute on Alcohol Abuse and Alcoholism
"Volume Beverage and Ethanol Consumption for States" (http://www.niaaa.nih.gov/databases/consum02.txt)
*This is apparent consumption of actual alcohol, not entire volume of an alcoholic beverage (e.g. wine is roughly 11% absolute alcohol content). Apparent consumption is based on several sources which together approximate sales but do not actually measure consumption. Accordingly, figures for some states may be skewed by purchases by nonresidents.

Adult Per Capita Alcohol Consumption in 2000

National Per Capita = 2.5 Gallons Consumed per Adult 21 Years and Older*

ALPHA ORDER

RANK	STATE	PER CAPITA
39	Alabama	2.2
5	Alaska	3.1
7	Arizona	2.9
46	Arkansas	2.0
28	California	2.5
6	Colorado	3.0
28	Connecticut	2.5
3	Delaware	3.3
7	Florida	2.9
28	Georgia	2.5
20	Hawaii	2.6
15	Idaho	2.7
20	Illinois	2.6
36	Indiana	2.3
36	Iowa	2.3
43	Kansas	2.1
46	Kentucky	2.0
12	Louisiana	2.8
20	Maine	2.6
34	Maryland	2.4
7	Massachusetts	2.9
34	Michigan	2.4
15	Minnesota	2.7
28	Mississippi	2.5
20	Missouri	2.6
7	Montana	2.9
20	Nebraska	2.6
2	Nevada	4.2
1	New Hampshire	4.6
28	New Jersey	2.5
12	New Mexico	2.8
43	New York	2.1
39	North Carolina	2.2
12	North Dakota	2.8
36	Ohio	2.3
46	Oklahoma	2.0
20	Oregon	2.6
39	Pennsylvania	2.2
20	Rhode Island	2.6
15	South Carolina	2.7
15	South Dakota	2.7
43	Tennessee	2.1
20	Texas	2.6
50	Utah	1.6
15	Vermont	2.7
39	Virginia	2.2
28	Washington	2.5
49	West Virginia	1.9
4	Wisconsin	3.2
7	Wyoming	2.9

RANK ORDER

RANK	STATE	PER CAPITA
1	New Hampshire	4.6
2	Nevada	4.2
3	Delaware	3.3
4	Wisconsin	3.2
5	Alaska	3.1
6	Colorado	3.0
7	Arizona	2.9
7	Florida	2.9
7	Massachusetts	2.9
7	Montana	2.9
7	Wyoming	2.9
12	Louisiana	2.8
12	New Mexico	2.8
12	North Dakota	2.8
15	Idaho	2.7
15	Minnesota	2.7
15	South Carolina	2.7
15	South Dakota	2.7
15	Vermont	2.7
20	Hawaii	2.6
20	Illinois	2.6
20	Maine	2.6
20	Missouri	2.6
20	Nebraska	2.6
20	Oregon	2.6
20	Rhode Island	2.6
20	Texas	2.6
28	California	2.5
28	Connecticut	2.5
28	Georgia	2.5
28	Mississippi	2.5
28	New Jersey	2.5
28	Washington	2.5
34	Maryland	2.4
34	Michigan	2.4
36	Indiana	2.3
36	Iowa	2.3
36	Ohio	2.3
39	Alabama	2.2
39	North Carolina	2.2
39	Pennsylvania	2.2
39	Virginia	2.2
43	Kansas	2.1
43	New York	2.1
43	Tennessee	2.1
46	Arkansas	2.0
46	Kentucky	2.0
46	Oklahoma	2.0
49	West Virginia	1.9
50	Utah	1.6

| | District of Columbia | 4.0 |

Source: Morgan Quitno Press using data from U.S. Dept. of HHS, National Institute on Alcohol Abuse and Alcoholism
"Volume Beverage and Ethanol Consumption for States" (http://www.niaaa.nih.gov/databases/consum02.txt)
*This is apparent consumption of actual alcohol, not entire volume of an alcoholic beverage (e.g. wine is roughly
11% absolute alcohol content). Apparent consumption is based on several sources which together approximate
sales but do not actually measure consumption. Accordingly, figures for some states may be skewed by purchases
by nonresidents.

Apparent Beer Consumption in 2000

National Total = 6,139,957,000 Gallons of Beer Consumed*

RANK	STATE	GALLONS	% of USA		RANK	STATE	GALLONS	% of USA
25	Alabama	94,530,000	1.5%		1	California	637,080,000	10.4%
48	Alaska	14,373,000	0.2%		2	Texas	556,051,000	9.1%
15	Arizona	134,336,000	2.2%		3	Florida	388,796,000	6.3%
34	Arkansas	52,053,000	0.8%		4	New York	313,158,000	5.1%
1	California	637,080,000	10.4%		5	Illinois	282,189,000	4.6%
23	Colorado	103,734,000	1.7%		6	Pennsylvania	270,006,000	4.4%
32	Connecticut	57,491,000	0.9%		7	Ohio	263,287,000	4.3%
46	Delaware	19,156,000	0.3%		8	Michigan	209,608,000	3.4%
3	Florida	388,796,000	6.3%		9	Georgia	177,061,000	2.9%
9	Georgia	177,061,000	2.9%		10	North Carolina	173,293,000	2.8%
39	Hawaii	29,065,000	0.5%		11	Virginia	148,362,000	2.4%
42	Idaho	26,257,000	0.4%		12	Wisconsin	147,700,000	2.4%
5	Illinois	282,189,000	4.6%		13	New Jersey	144,883,000	2.4%
17	Indiana	125,490,000	2.0%		14	Missouri	135,246,000	2.2%
29	Iowa	71,323,000	1.2%		15	Arizona	134,336,000	2.2%
33	Kansas	54,832,000	0.9%		16	Massachusetts	133,990,000	2.2%
26	Kentucky	78,055,000	1.3%		17	Indiana	125,490,000	2.0%
19	Louisiana	117,937,000	1.9%		18	Tennessee	124,041,000	2.0%
41	Maine	27,370,000	0.4%		19	Louisiana	117,937,000	1.9%
24	Maryland	97,754,000	1.6%		20	Washington	115,148,000	1.9%
16	Massachusetts	133,990,000	2.2%		21	Minnesota	108,478,000	1.8%
8	Michigan	209,608,000	3.4%		22	South Carolina	104,116,000	1.7%
21	Minnesota	108,478,000	1.8%		23	Colorado	103,734,000	1.7%
28	Mississippi	71,823,000	1.2%		24	Maryland	97,754,000	1.6%
14	Missouri	135,246,000	2.2%		25	Alabama	94,530,000	1.5%
43	Montana	25,257,000	0.4%		26	Kentucky	78,055,000	1.3%
36	Nebraska	43,943,000	0.7%		27	Oregon	74,313,000	1.2%
31	Nevada	64,055,000	1.0%		28	Mississippi	71,823,000	1.2%
38	New Hampshire	39,001,000	0.6%		29	Iowa	71,323,000	1.2%
13	New Jersey	144,883,000	2.4%		30	Oklahoma	69,346,000	1.1%
35	New Mexico	48,624,000	0.8%		31	Nevada	64,055,000	1.0%
4	New York	313,158,000	5.1%		32	Connecticut	57,491,000	0.9%
10	North Carolina	173,293,000	2.8%		33	Kansas	54,832,000	0.9%
47	North Dakota	17,018,000	0.3%		34	Arkansas	52,053,000	0.8%
7	Ohio	263,287,000	4.3%		35	New Mexico	48,624,000	0.8%
30	Oklahoma	69,346,000	1.1%		36	Nebraska	43,943,000	0.7%
27	Oregon	74,313,000	1.2%		37	West Virginia	39,513,000	0.6%
6	Pennsylvania	270,006,000	4.4%		38	New Hampshire	39,001,000	0.6%
44	Rhode Island	21,988,000	0.4%		39	Hawaii	29,065,000	0.5%
22	South Carolina	104,116,000	1.7%		40	Utah	28,797,000	0.5%
45	South Dakota	19,349,000	0.3%		41	Maine	27,370,000	0.4%
18	Tennessee	124,041,000	2.0%		42	Idaho	26,257,000	0.4%
2	Texas	556,051,000	9.1%		43	Montana	25,257,000	0.4%
40	Utah	28,797,000	0.5%		44	Rhode Island	21,988,000	0.4%
49	Vermont	13,656,000	0.2%		45	South Dakota	19,349,000	0.3%
11	Virginia	148,362,000	2.4%		46	Delaware	19,156,000	0.3%
20	Washington	115,148,000	1.9%		47	North Dakota	17,018,000	0.3%
37	West Virginia	39,513,000	0.6%		48	Alaska	14,373,000	0.2%
12	Wisconsin	147,700,000	2.4%		49	Vermont	13,656,000	0.2%
50	Wyoming	12,595,000	0.2%		50	Wyoming	12,595,000	0.2%
						District of Columbia	14,428,000	0.2%

ALPHA ORDER — RANK ORDER

Source: U.S. Department of Health and Human Services, National Institute on Alcohol Abuse and Alcoholism "Volume Beverage and Ethanol Consumption for States" (http://www.niaaa.nih.gov/databases/consum02.txt)
This is apparent consumption and is based on several sources which together approximate sales but do not actually measure consumption. Reported state volumes reflect only in-state purchases. Accordingly, figures for some states may be skewed by purchases by nonresidents.

Adult Per Capita Beer Consumption in 2000

National Per Capita = 31.2 Gallons Consumed per Adult 21 Years and Older*

ALPHA ORDER

RANK	STATE	PER CAPITA
31	Alabama	30.3
15	Alaska	35.0
9	Arizona	38.0
43	Arkansas	27.8
44	California	27.5
19	Colorado	34.4
48	Connecticut	23.6
17	Delaware	34.6
21	Florida	33.1
26	Georgia	31.4
20	Hawaii	33.5
29	Idaho	30.5
23	Illinois	32.7
35	Indiana	29.7
16	Iowa	34.8
35	Kansas	29.7
45	Kentucky	27.2
7	Louisiana	38.9
37	Maine	29.6
46	Maryland	26.2
40	Massachusetts	29.2
31	Michigan	30.3
24	Minnesota	31.8
11	Mississippi	37.3
18	Missouri	34.5
3	Montana	40.0
12	Nebraska	37.2
1	Nevada	45.4
2	New Hampshire	44.5
47	New Jersey	24.0
5	New Mexico	39.6
49	New York	23.2
33	North Carolina	30.2
8	North Dakota	38.1
22	Ohio	33.0
41	Oklahoma	29.0
28	Oregon	30.6
29	Pennsylvania	30.5
38	Rhode Island	29.4
13	South Carolina	37.0
10	South Dakota	37.6
27	Tennessee	30.7
4	Texas	39.8
50	Utah	20.9
25	Vermont	31.5
38	Virginia	29.4
42	Washington	27.9
34	West Virginia	29.8
6	Wisconsin	39.4
13	Wyoming	37.0

RANK ORDER

RANK	STATE	PER CAPITA
1	Nevada	45.4
2	New Hampshire	44.5
3	Montana	40.0
4	Texas	39.8
5	New Mexico	39.6
6	Wisconsin	39.4
7	Louisiana	38.9
8	North Dakota	38.1
9	Arizona	38.0
10	South Dakota	37.6
11	Mississippi	37.3
12	Nebraska	37.2
13	South Carolina	37.0
13	Wyoming	37.0
15	Alaska	35.0
16	Iowa	34.8
17	Delaware	34.6
18	Missouri	34.5
19	Colorado	34.4
20	Hawaii	33.5
21	Florida	33.1
22	Ohio	33.0
23	Illinois	32.7
24	Minnesota	31.8
25	Vermont	31.5
26	Georgia	31.4
27	Tennessee	30.7
28	Oregon	30.6
29	Idaho	30.5
29	Pennsylvania	30.5
31	Alabama	30.3
31	Michigan	30.3
33	North Carolina	30.2
34	West Virginia	29.8
35	Indiana	29.7
35	Kansas	29.7
37	Maine	29.6
38	Rhode Island	29.4
38	Virginia	29.4
40	Massachusetts	29.2
41	Oklahoma	29.0
42	Washington	27.9
43	Arkansas	27.8
44	California	27.5
45	Kentucky	27.2
46	Maryland	26.2
47	New Jersey	24.0
48	Connecticut	23.6
49	New York	23.2
50	Utah	20.9
	District of Columbia	33.9

*Source: Morgan Quitno Press using data from U.S. Dept. of HHS, National Institute on Alcohol Abuse and Alcoholism
"Volume Beverage and Ethanol Consumption for States" (http://www.niaaa.nih.gov/databases/consum02.txt)
*This is apparent consumption and is based on several sources which together approximate sales but do not
actually measure consumption. Reported state volumes reflect only in-state purchases. Accordingly, figures for
some states may be skewed by purchases by nonresidents.*

Wine Consumption in 2000

National Total = 546,540,000 Gallons of Wine Consumed*

ALPHA ORDER

RANK	STATE	GALLONS	% of USA
29	Alabama	4,934,000	0.9%
46	Alaska	1,379,000	0.3%
17	Arizona	9,869,000	1.8%
40	Arkansas	1,993,000	0.4%
1	California	99,930,000	18.3%
18	Colorado	9,845,000	1.8%
15	Connecticut	10,521,000	1.9%
38	Delaware	2,382,000	0.4%
3	Florida	41,383,000	7.6%
13	Georgia	12,902,000	2.4%
34	Hawaii	3,002,000	0.5%
28	Idaho	5,142,000	0.9%
5	Illinois	24,663,000	4.5%
24	Indiana	7,738,000	1.4%
39	Iowa	2,353,000	0.4%
37	Kansas	2,516,000	0.5%
31	Kentucky	3,460,000	0.6%
25	Louisiana	6,159,000	1.1%
32	Maine	3,179,000	0.6%
16	Maryland	10,009,000	1.8%
7	Massachusetts	20,635,000	3.8%
10	Michigan	14,757,000	2.7%
22	Minnesota	7,918,000	1.4%
44	Mississippi	1,657,000	0.3%
21	Missouri	8,144,000	1.5%
43	Montana	1,671,000	0.3%
42	Nebraska	1,791,000	0.3%
23	Nevada	7,745,000	1.4%
30	New Hampshire	4,373,000	0.8%
6	New Jersey	24,472,000	4.5%
35	New Mexico	2,771,000	0.5%
2	New York	44,840,000	8.2%
14	North Carolina	11,486,000	2.1%
49	North Dakota	591,000	0.1%
12	Ohio	13,693,000	2.5%
36	Oklahoma	2,672,000	0.5%
19	Oregon	9,409,000	1.7%
8	Pennsylvania	16,553,000	3.0%
33	Rhode Island	3,033,000	0.6%
26	South Carolina	5,611,000	1.0%
48	South Dakota	680,000	0.1%
27	Tennessee	5,290,000	1.0%
4	Texas	27,653,000	5.1%
45	Utah	1,416,000	0.3%
41	Vermont	1,824,000	0.3%
11	Virginia	14,010,000	2.6%
9	Washington	15,125,000	2.8%
47	West Virginia	1,135,000	0.2%
20	Wisconsin	9,085,000	1.7%
50	Wyoming	547,000	0.1%

RANK ORDER

RANK	STATE	GALLONS	% of USA
1	California	99,930,000	18.3%
2	New York	44,840,000	8.2%
3	Florida	41,383,000	7.6%
4	Texas	27,653,000	5.1%
5	Illinois	24,663,000	4.5%
6	New Jersey	24,472,000	4.5%
7	Massachusetts	20,635,000	3.8%
8	Pennsylvania	16,553,000	3.0%
9	Washington	15,125,000	2.8%
10	Michigan	14,757,000	2.7%
11	Virginia	14,010,000	2.6%
12	Ohio	13,693,000	2.5%
13	Georgia	12,902,000	2.4%
14	North Carolina	11,486,000	2.1%
15	Connecticut	10,521,000	1.9%
16	Maryland	10,009,000	1.8%
17	Arizona	9,869,000	1.8%
18	Colorado	9,845,000	1.8%
19	Oregon	9,409,000	1.7%
20	Wisconsin	9,085,000	1.7%
21	Missouri	8,144,000	1.5%
22	Minnesota	7,918,000	1.4%
23	Nevada	7,745,000	1.4%
24	Indiana	7,738,000	1.4%
25	Louisiana	6,159,000	1.1%
26	South Carolina	5,611,000	1.0%
27	Tennessee	5,290,000	1.0%
28	Idaho	5,142,000	0.9%
29	Alabama	4,934,000	0.9%
30	New Hampshire	4,373,000	0.8%
31	Kentucky	3,460,000	0.6%
32	Maine	3,179,000	0.6%
33	Rhode Island	3,033,000	0.6%
34	Hawaii	3,002,000	0.5%
35	New Mexico	2,771,000	0.5%
36	Oklahoma	2,672,000	0.5%
37	Kansas	2,516,000	0.5%
38	Delaware	2,382,000	0.4%
39	Iowa	2,353,000	0.4%
40	Arkansas	1,993,000	0.4%
41	Vermont	1,824,000	0.3%
42	Nebraska	1,791,000	0.3%
43	Montana	1,671,000	0.3%
44	Mississippi	1,657,000	0.3%
45	Utah	1,416,000	0.3%
46	Alaska	1,379,000	0.3%
47	West Virginia	1,135,000	0.2%
48	South Dakota	680,000	0.1%
49	North Dakota	591,000	0.1%
50	Wyoming	547,000	0.1%
	District of Columbia	2,597,000	0.5%

Source: U.S. Department of Health and Human Services, National Institute on Alcohol Abuse and Alcoholism
"Volume Beverage and Ethanol Consumption for States" (http://www.niaaa.nih.gov/databases/consum02.txt)
*This is apparent consumption and is based on several sources which together approximate sales but do not actually measure consumption. Reported state volumes reflect only in-state purchases. Accordingly, figures for some states may be skewed by purchases by nonresidents.

Adult Per Capita Wine Consumption in 2000

National Per Capita = 2.8 Gallons Consumed per Adult 21 Years and Older

ALPHA ORDER				RANK ORDER		
RANK	STATE	PER CAPITA		RANK	STATE	PER CAPITA
37	Alabama	1.6		1	Idaho	6.0
15	Alaska	3.4		2	Nevada	5.5
20	Arizona	2.8		3	New Hampshire	5.0
45	Arkansas	1.1		4	Massachusetts	4.5
5	California	4.3		5	California	4.3
17	Colorado	3.3		5	Connecticut	4.3
5	Connecticut	4.3		5	Delaware	4.3
5	Delaware	4.3		8	Vermont	4.2
13	Florida	3.5		9	New Jersey	4.1
25	Georgia	2.3		9	Rhode Island	4.1
13	Hawaii	3.5		11	Oregon	3.9
1	Idaho	6.0		12	Washington	3.7
19	Illinois	2.9		13	Florida	3.5
35	Indiana	1.8		13	Hawaii	3.5
45	Iowa	1.1		15	Alaska	3.4
40	Kansas	1.4		15	Maine	3.4
44	Kentucky	1.2		17	Colorado	3.3
30	Louisiana	2.0		17	New York	3.3
15	Maine	3.4		19	Illinois	2.9
22	Maryland	2.7		20	Arizona	2.8
4	Massachusetts	4.5		20	Virginia	2.8
28	Michigan	2.1		22	Maryland	2.7
25	Minnesota	2.3		23	Montana	2.6
49	Mississippi	0.9		24	Wisconsin	2.4
28	Missouri	2.1		25	Georgia	2.3
23	Montana	2.6		25	Minnesota	2.3
39	Nebraska	1.5		25	New Mexico	2.3
2	Nevada	5.5		28	Michigan	2.1
3	New Hampshire	5.0		28	Missouri	2.1
9	New Jersey	4.1		30	Louisiana	2.0
25	New Mexico	2.3		30	North Carolina	2.0
17	New York	3.3		30	South Carolina	2.0
30	North Carolina	2.0		30	Texas	2.0
41	North Dakota	1.3		34	Pennsylvania	1.9
36	Ohio	1.7		35	Indiana	1.8
45	Oklahoma	1.1		36	Ohio	1.7
11	Oregon	3.9		37	Alabama	1.6
34	Pennsylvania	1.9		37	Wyoming	1.6
9	Rhode Island	4.1		39	Nebraska	1.5
25	South Carolina	2.0		40	Kansas	1.4
41	South Dakota	1.3		41	North Dakota	1.3
41	Tennessee	1.3		41	South Dakota	1.3
30	Texas	2.0		41	Tennessee	1.3
48	Utah	1.0		44	Kentucky	1.2
8	Vermont	4.2		45	Arkansas	1.1
20	Virginia	2.8		45	Iowa	1.1
12	Washington	3.7		45	Oklahoma	1.1
49	West Virginia	0.9		48	Utah	1.0
24	Wisconsin	2.4		49	Mississippi	0.9
37	Wyoming	1.6		49	West Virginia	0.9
					District of Columbia	6.1

Source: Morgan Quitno Press using data from U.S. Dept. of HHS, National Institute on Alcohol Abuse and Alcoholism
"Volume Beverage and Ethanol Consumption for States" (http://www.niaaa.nih.gov/databases/consum02.txt)
*This is apparent consumption and is based on several sources which together approximate sales but do not
actually measure consumption. Reported state volumes reflect only in-state purchases. Accordingly, figures for
some states may be skewed by purchases by nonresidents.

Distilled Spirits Consumption in 2000

National Total = 354,548,000 Gallons of Distilled Spirits Consumed*

ALPHA ORDER

RANK	STATE	GALLONS	% of USA
27	Alabama	4,485,000	1.3%
46	Alaska	1,076,000	0.3%
20	Arizona	7,055,000	2.0%
34	Arkansas	2,796,000	0.8%
1	California	41,327,000	11.7%
17	Colorado	7,503,000	2.1%
25	Connecticut	4,959,000	1.4%
40	Delaware	1,622,000	0.5%
2	Florida	26,422,000	7.5%
11	Georgia	10,999,000	3.1%
42	Hawaii	1,434,000	0.4%
44	Idaho	1,253,000	0.4%
5	Illinois	15,281,000	4.3%
19	Indiana	7,261,000	2.0%
33	Iowa	2,863,000	0.8%
35	Kansas	2,692,000	0.8%
29	Kentucky	4,278,000	1.2%
22	Louisiana	6,043,000	1.7%
38	Maine	1,861,000	0.5%
15	Maryland	7,735,000	2.2%
10	Massachusetts	11,031,000	3.1%
6	Michigan	13,360,000	3.8%
13	Minnesota	8,359,000	2.4%
31	Mississippi	3,273,000	0.9%
18	Missouri	7,302,000	2.1%
45	Montana	1,213,000	0.3%
37	Nebraska	2,061,000	0.6%
26	Nevada	4,913,000	1.4%
30	New Hampshire	4,107,000	1.2%
7	New Jersey	12,681,000	3.6%
36	New Mexico	2,113,000	0.6%
3	New York	21,657,000	6.1%
14	North Carolina	8,204,000	2.3%
47	North Dakota	1,003,000	0.3%
9	Ohio	11,091,000	3.1%
32	Oklahoma	2,998,000	0.8%
28	Oregon	4,309,000	1.2%
8	Pennsylvania	11,576,000	3.3%
41	Rhode Island	1,461,000	0.4%
24	South Carolina	5,545,000	1.6%
48	South Dakota	996,000	0.3%
23	Tennessee	5,644,000	1.6%
4	Texas	19,897,000	5.6%
39	Utah	1,629,000	0.5%
50	Vermont	767,000	0.2%
21	Virginia	6,925,000	2.0%
16	Washington	7,599,000	2.1%
43	West Virginia	1,297,000	0.4%
12	Wisconsin	10,032,000	2.8%
49	Wyoming	837,000	0.2%

RANK ORDER

RANK	STATE	GALLONS	% of USA
1	California	41,327,000	11.7%
2	Florida	26,422,000	7.5%
3	New York	21,657,000	6.1%
4	Texas	19,897,000	5.6%
5	Illinois	15,281,000	4.3%
6	Michigan	13,360,000	3.8%
7	New Jersey	12,681,000	3.6%
8	Pennsylvania	11,576,000	3.3%
9	Ohio	11,091,000	3.1%
10	Massachusetts	11,031,000	3.1%
11	Georgia	10,999,000	3.1%
12	Wisconsin	10,032,000	2.8%
13	Minnesota	8,359,000	2.4%
14	North Carolina	8,204,000	2.3%
15	Maryland	7,735,000	2.2%
16	Washington	7,599,000	2.1%
17	Colorado	7,503,000	2.1%
18	Missouri	7,302,000	2.1%
19	Indiana	7,261,000	2.0%
20	Arizona	7,055,000	2.0%
21	Virginia	6,925,000	2.0%
22	Louisiana	6,043,000	1.7%
23	Tennessee	5,644,000	1.6%
24	South Carolina	5,545,000	1.6%
25	Connecticut	4,959,000	1.4%
26	Nevada	4,913,000	1.4%
27	Alabama	4,485,000	1.3%
28	Oregon	4,309,000	1.2%
29	Kentucky	4,278,000	1.2%
30	New Hampshire	4,107,000	1.2%
31	Mississippi	3,273,000	0.9%
32	Oklahoma	2,998,000	0.8%
33	Iowa	2,863,000	0.8%
34	Arkansas	2,796,000	0.8%
35	Kansas	2,692,000	0.8%
36	New Mexico	2,113,000	0.6%
37	Nebraska	2,061,000	0.6%
38	Maine	1,861,000	0.5%
39	Utah	1,629,000	0.5%
40	Delaware	1,622,000	0.5%
41	Rhode Island	1,461,000	0.4%
42	Hawaii	1,434,000	0.4%
43	West Virginia	1,297,000	0.4%
44	Idaho	1,253,000	0.4%
45	Montana	1,213,000	0.3%
46	Alaska	1,076,000	0.3%
47	North Dakota	1,003,000	0.3%
48	South Dakota	996,000	0.3%
49	Wyoming	837,000	0.2%
50	Vermont	767,000	0.2%
	District of Columbia	1,724,000	0.5%

Source: U.S. Department of Health and Human Services, National Institute on Alcohol Abuse and Alcoholism
"Volume Beverage and Ethanol Consumption for States" (http://www.niaaa.nih.gov/databases/consum02.txt)
*This is apparent consumption and is based on several sources which together approximate sales but do not actually measure consumption. Reported state volumes reflect only in-state purchases. Accordingly, figures for some states may be skewed by purchases by nonresidents.

Adult Per Capita Distilled Spirits Consumption in 2000

National Per Capita = 1.8 Gallons Consumed per Adult 21 Years and Older*

ALPHA ORDER

RANK	STATE	PER CAPITA
40	Alabama	1.4
5	Alaska	2.6
14	Arizona	2.0
36	Arkansas	1.5
25	California	1.8
6	Colorado	2.5
14	Connecticut	2.0
3	Delaware	2.9
10	Florida	2.3
20	Georgia	1.9
30	Hawaii	1.7
36	Idaho	1.5
25	Illinois	1.8
30	Indiana	1.7
40	Iowa	1.4
36	Kansas	1.5
36	Kentucky	1.5
14	Louisiana	2.0
14	Maine	2.0
12	Maryland	2.1
8	Massachusetts	2.4
20	Michigan	1.9
8	Minnesota	2.4
30	Mississippi	1.7
20	Missouri	1.9
20	Montana	1.9
30	Nebraska	1.7
2	Nevada	3.5
1	New Hampshire	4.7
12	New Jersey	2.1
30	New Mexico	1.7
35	New York	1.6
40	North Carolina	1.4
11	North Dakota	2.2
40	Ohio	1.4
47	Oklahoma	1.3
25	Oregon	1.8
47	Pennsylvania	1.3
14	Rhode Island	2.0
14	South Carolina	2.0
20	South Dakota	1.9
40	Tennessee	1.4
40	Texas	1.4
49	Utah	1.2
25	Vermont	1.8
40	Virginia	1.4
25	Washington	1.8
50	West Virginia	1.0
4	Wisconsin	2.7
6	Wyoming	2.5

RANK ORDER

RANK	STATE	PER CAPITA
1	New Hampshire	4.7
2	Nevada	3.5
3	Delaware	2.9
4	Wisconsin	2.7
5	Alaska	2.6
6	Colorado	2.5
6	Wyoming	2.5
8	Massachusetts	2.4
8	Minnesota	2.4
10	Florida	2.3
11	North Dakota	2.2
12	Maryland	2.1
12	New Jersey	2.1
14	Arizona	2.0
14	Connecticut	2.0
14	Louisiana	2.0
14	Maine	2.0
14	Rhode Island	2.0
14	South Carolina	2.0
20	Georgia	1.9
20	Michigan	1.9
20	Missouri	1.9
20	Montana	1.9
20	South Dakota	1.9
25	California	1.8
25	Illinois	1.8
25	Oregon	1.8
25	Vermont	1.8
25	Washington	1.8
30	Hawaii	1.7
30	Indiana	1.7
30	Mississippi	1.7
30	Nebraska	1.7
30	New Mexico	1.7
35	New York	1.6
36	Arkansas	1.5
36	Idaho	1.5
36	Kansas	1.5
36	Kentucky	1.5
40	Alabama	1.4
40	Iowa	1.4
40	North Carolina	1.4
40	Ohio	1.4
40	Tennessee	1.4
40	Texas	1.4
40	Virginia	1.4
47	Oklahoma	1.3
47	Pennsylvania	1.3
49	Utah	1.2
50	West Virginia	1.0

District of Columbia   4.1

Source: Morgan Quitno Press using data from U.S. Dept. of HHS, National Institute on Alcohol Abuse and Alcoholism "Volume Beverage and Ethanol Consumption for States" (http://www.niaaa.nih.gov/databases/consum02.txt)
*This is apparent consumption and is based on several sources which together approximate sales but do not actually measure consumption. Reported state volumes reflect only in-state purchases. Accordingly, figures for some states may be skewed by purchases by nonresidents.

Average Alcohol Consumption per Drinker in 1999

National Average = 4.21 Gallons*

ALPHA ORDER				RANK ORDER		
RANK	STATE	GALLONS		RANK	STATE	GALLONS
19	Alabama	4.74		1	Arizona	7.76
10	Alaska	5.06		2	Nevada	6.44
1	Arizona	7.76		3	Tennessee	6.41
17	Arkansas	4.75		4	New Hampshire	6.34
46	California	3.64		5	Oklahoma	6.01
33	Colorado	4.00		6	South Carolina	5.74
40	Connecticut	3.81		7	Mississippi	5.67
12	Delaware	4.94		8	Louisiana	5.51
14	Florida	4.82		9	West Virginia	5.08
16	Georgia	4.76		10	Alaska	5.06
17	Hawaii	4.75		11	Kentucky	5.03
13	Idaho	4.88		12	Delaware	4.94
32	Illinois	4.04		13	Idaho	4.88
47	Indiana	3.62		14	Florida	4.82
48	Iowa	3.59		15	North Carolina	4.79
35	Kansas	3.95		16	Georgia	4.76
11	Kentucky	5.03		17	Arkansas	4.75
8	Louisiana	5.51		17	Hawaii	4.75
41	Maine	3.79		19	Alabama	4.74
44	Maryland	3.65		20	Minnesota	4.72
34	Massachusetts	3.98		21	Ohio	4.58
49	Michigan	3.56		22	New Mexico	4.50
20	Minnesota	4.72		23	Montana	4.48
7	Mississippi	5.67		23	Utah	4.48
28	Missouri	4.24		25	North Dakota	4.43
23	Montana	4.48		25	Wyoming	4.43
27	Nebraska	4.29		27	Nebraska	4.29
2	Nevada	6.44		28	Missouri	4.24
4	New Hampshire	6.34		29	Texas	4.18
31	New Jersey	4.07		30	Rhode Island	4.14
22	New Mexico	4.50		31	New Jersey	4.07
44	New York	3.65		32	Illinois	4.04
15	North Carolina	4.79		33	Colorado	4.00
25	North Dakota	4.43		34	Massachusetts	3.98
21	Ohio	4.58		35	Kansas	3.95
5	Oklahoma	6.01		35	South Dakota	3.95
39	Oregon	3.82		37	Wisconsin	3.87
42	Pennsylvania	3.71		38	Vermont	3.86
30	Rhode Island	4.14		39	Oregon	3.82
6	South Carolina	5.74		40	Connecticut	3.81
35	South Dakota	3.95		41	Maine	3.79
3	Tennessee	6.41		42	Pennsylvania	3.71
29	Texas	4.18		43	Virginia	3.67
23	Utah	4.48		44	Maryland	3.65
38	Vermont	3.86		44	New York	3.65
43	Virginia	3.67		46	California	3.64
49	Washington	3.56		47	Indiana	3.62
9	West Virginia	5.08		48	Iowa	3.59
37	Wisconsin	3.87		49	Michigan	3.56
25	Wyoming	4.43		49	Washington	3.56

District of Columbia   7.43

Source: U.S. Department of Health and Human Services, National Institute on Alcohol Abuse and Alcoholism
"Per Capita and Per Drinker Ethanol Consumption for States" (http://www.niaaa.nih.gov/databases/consum04.txt)
*National percent calculated by the editors. This is consumption of actual alcohol, not entire volume of an alcoholic beverage (e.g. wine is roughly 11% absolute alcohol content).

Percent of Adults Who Do Not Drink Alcohol: 1999

National Percent = 47.5% of Population 18 Years and Older*

ALPHA ORDER

RANK	STATE	PERCENT
9	Alabama	60.4
32	Alaska	43.1
5	Arizona	65.5
7	Arkansas	61.7
42	California	39.6
48	Colorado	35.8
39	Connecticut	40.6
41	Delaware	40.0
29	Florida	44.8
16	Georgia	52.3
14	Hawaii	54.1
17	Idaho	51.1
34	Illinois	42.7
25	Indiana	45.7
28	Iowa	45.0
15	Kansas	53.2
6	Kentucky	65.1
13	Louisiana	54.6
40	Maine	40.2
35	Maryland	42.2
46	Massachusetts	38.5
38	Michigan	40.8
18	Minnesota	48.9
8	Mississippi	61.4
22	Missouri	46.6
32	Montana	43.1
20	Nebraska	47.8
47	Nevada	36.9
48	New Hampshire	35.8
23	New Jersey	46.0
24	New Mexico	45.9
21	New York	47.4
10	North Carolina	58.3
30	North Dakota	44.6
12	Ohio	56.2
1	Oklahoma	71.4
45	Oregon	39.1
19	Pennsylvania	48.5
36	Rhode Island	41.7
11	South Carolina	58.0
37	South Dakota	41.4
2	Tennessee	70.3
27	Texas	45.2
2	Utah	70.3
43	Vermont	39.5
25	Virginia	45.7
44	Washington	39.3
4	West Virginia	67.4
50	Wisconsin	28.9
31	Wyoming	43.9

RANK ORDER

RANK	STATE	PERCENT
1	Oklahoma	71.4
2	Tennessee	70.3
2	Utah	70.3
4	West Virginia	67.4
5	Arizona	65.5
6	Kentucky	65.1
7	Arkansas	61.7
8	Mississippi	61.4
9	Alabama	60.4
10	North Carolina	58.3
11	South Carolina	58.0
12	Ohio	56.2
13	Louisiana	54.6
14	Hawaii	54.1
15	Kansas	53.2
16	Georgia	52.3
17	Idaho	51.1
18	Minnesota	48.9
19	Pennsylvania	48.5
20	Nebraska	47.8
21	New York	47.4
22	Missouri	46.6
23	New Jersey	46.0
24	New Mexico	45.9
25	Indiana	45.7
25	Virginia	45.7
27	Texas	45.2
28	Iowa	45.0
29	Florida	44.8
30	North Dakota	44.6
31	Wyoming	43.9
32	Alaska	43.1
32	Montana	43.1
34	Illinois	42.7
35	Maryland	42.2
36	Rhode Island	41.7
37	South Dakota	41.4
38	Michigan	40.8
39	Connecticut	40.6
40	Maine	40.2
41	Delaware	40.0
42	California	39.6
43	Vermont	39.5
44	Washington	39.3
45	Oregon	39.1
46	Massachusetts	38.5
47	Nevada	36.9
48	Colorado	35.8
48	New Hampshire	35.8
50	Wisconsin	28.9

| | District of Columbia | 49.7 |

Source: U.S. Department of Health and Human Services, National Institute on Alcohol Abuse and Alcoholism
    "Per Capita and Per Drinker Ethanol Consumption for States" (http://www.niaaa.nih.gov/databases/consum04.txt)
National percent calculated by the editors.

Percent of Adults Who Are Binge Drinkers: 2002

National Median = 16.1% of Adults*

ALPHA ORDER				RANK ORDER		
RANK	STATE	PERCENT		RANK	STATE	PERCENT
34	Alabama	14.5		1	Wisconsin	24.9
11	Alaska	18.2		2	North Dakota	22.0
19	Arizona	16.9		3	Minnesota	21.1
42	Arkansas	12.7		4	Iowa	20.1
33	California	14.9		5	Montana	19.8
7	Colorado	18.6		5	Nevada	19.8
24	Connecticut	16.3		7	Colorado	18.6
9	Delaware	18.3		8	South Dakota	18.5
38	Florida	13.7		9	Delaware	18.3
41	Georgia	12.8		9	Massachusetts	18.3
45	Hawaii	11.9		11	Alaska	18.2
28	Idaho	15.8		12	Wyoming	18.1
14	Illinois	17.8		13	New York	17.9
26	Indiana	15.9		14	Illinois	17.8
4	Iowa	20.1		14	Texas	17.8
28	Kansas	15.8		16	Rhode Island	17.7
50	Kentucky	7.9		17	Nebraska	17.6
39	Louisiana	13.6		18	Missouri	17.2
31	Maine	15.4		19	Arizona	16.9
35	Maryland	14.4		19	Michigan	16.9
9	Massachusetts	18.3		19	Pennsylvania	16.9
19	Michigan	16.9		22	New Hampshire	16.6
3	Minnesota	21.1		23	Vermont	16.5
43	Mississippi	12.4		24	Connecticut	16.3
18	Missouri	17.2		24	Oregon	16.3
5	Montana	19.8		26	Indiana	15.9
17	Nebraska	17.6		26	Ohio	15.9
5	Nevada	19.8		28	Idaho	15.8
22	New Hampshire	16.6		28	Kansas	15.8
37	New Jersey	13.9		30	Virginia	15.6
35	New Mexico	14.4		31	Maine	15.4
13	New York	17.9		32	Washington	15.1
47	North Carolina	10.9		33	California	14.9
2	North Dakota	22.0		34	Alabama	14.5
26	Ohio	15.9		35	Maryland	14.4
40	Oklahoma	13.3		35	New Mexico	14.4
24	Oregon	16.3		37	New Jersey	13.9
19	Pennsylvania	16.9		38	Florida	13.7
16	Rhode Island	17.7		39	Louisiana	13.6
43	South Carolina	12.4		40	Oklahoma	13.3
8	South Dakota	18.5		41	Georgia	12.8
49	Tennessee	8.2		42	Arkansas	12.7
14	Texas	17.8		43	Mississippi	12.4
48	Utah	10.1		43	South Carolina	12.4
23	Vermont	16.5		45	Hawaii	11.9
30	Virginia	15.6		46	West Virginia	11.4
32	Washington	15.1		47	North Carolina	10.9
46	West Virginia	11.4		48	Utah	10.1
1	Wisconsin	24.9		49	Tennessee	8.2
12	Wyoming	18.1		50	Kentucky	7.9

District of Columbia   17.0

Source: U.S. Department of Health and Human Services, Centers for Disease Control and Prevention
"2002 Behavioral Risk Factor Surveillance Summary Prevalence Data" (http://apps.nccd.cdc.gov/brfss/)
*Persons 18 and older reporting consumption of five or more alcoholic drinks on one or more occasions during the previous month.

Percent of Adults Who Smoke: 2002

National Median = 23.1% of Adults*

RANK	STATE	PERCENT
17	Alabama	24.4
2	Alaska	29.4
22	Arizona	23.5
12	Arkansas	26.3
49	California	16.4
45	Colorado	20.4
46	Connecticut	19.5
14	Delaware	24.7
34	Florida	22.1
24	Georgia	23.3
43	Hawaii	21.1
44	Idaho	20.6
27	Illinois	22.9
5	Indiana	27.7
26	Iowa	23.1
34	Kansas	22.1
1	Kentucky	32.6
19	Louisiana	23.9
21	Maine	23.6
36	Maryland	22.0
48	Massachusetts	19.0
18	Michigan	24.2
37	Minnesota	21.7
6	Mississippi	27.4
8	Missouri	26.6
40	Montana	21.3
29	Nebraska	22.8
13	Nevada	26.0
25	New Hampshire	23.2
47	New Jersey	19.1
41	New Mexico	21.2
32	New York	22.4
11	North Carolina	26.4
38	North Dakota	21.5
8	Ohio	26.6
7	Oklahoma	26.7
32	Oregon	22.4
15	Pennsylvania	24.6
31	Rhode Island	22.5
8	South Carolina	26.6
30	South Dakota	22.6
4	Tennessee	27.8
27	Texas	22.9
50	Utah	12.7
41	Vermont	21.2
15	Virginia	24.6
38	Washington	21.5
3	West Virginia	28.4
23	Wisconsin	23.4
20	Wyoming	23.7

RANK	STATE	PERCENT
1	Kentucky	32.6
2	Alaska	29.4
3	West Virginia	28.4
4	Tennessee	27.8
5	Indiana	27.7
6	Mississippi	27.4
7	Oklahoma	26.7
8	Missouri	26.6
8	Ohio	26.6
8	South Carolina	26.6
11	North Carolina	26.4
12	Arkansas	26.3
13	Nevada	26.0
14	Delaware	24.7
15	Pennsylvania	24.6
15	Virginia	24.6
17	Alabama	24.4
18	Michigan	24.2
19	Louisiana	23.9
20	Wyoming	23.7
21	Maine	23.6
22	Arizona	23.5
23	Wisconsin	23.4
24	Georgia	23.3
25	New Hampshire	23.2
26	Iowa	23.1
27	Illinois	22.9
27	Texas	22.9
29	Nebraska	22.8
30	South Dakota	22.6
31	Rhode Island	22.5
32	New York	22.4
32	Oregon	22.4
34	Florida	22.1
34	Kansas	22.1
36	Maryland	22.0
37	Minnesota	21.7
38	North Dakota	21.5
38	Washington	21.5
40	Montana	21.3
41	New Mexico	21.2
41	Vermont	21.2
43	Hawaii	21.1
44	Idaho	20.6
45	Colorado	20.4
46	Connecticut	19.5
47	New Jersey	19.1
48	Massachusetts	19.0
49	California	16.4
50	Utah	12.7

	District of Columbia	20.4

Source: U.S. Department of Health and Human Services, Centers for Disease Control and Prevention
"2002 Behavioral Risk Factor Surveillance Summary Prevalence Data" (http://apps.nccd.cdc.gov/brfss/)
*Persons 18 and older who have smoked more than 100 cigarettes during their lifetime and who currently smoke everyday or some days.

Percent of Men Who Smoke: 2002

National Median = 25.9% of Men*

ALPHA ORDER

RANK	STATE	PERCENT
15	Alabama	27.5
3	Alaska	31.9
16	Arizona	27.0
11	Arkansas	28.7
49	California	19.7
44	Colorado	21.4
46	Connecticut	20.6
29	Delaware	25.4
37	Florida	23.6
17	Georgia	26.8
23	Hawaii	26.2
42	Idaho	21.6
24	Illinois	26.1
6	Indiana	29.8
21	Iowa	26.3
40	Kansas	23.2
1	Kentucky	34.8
19	Louisiana	26.6
20	Maine	26.4
27	Maryland	25.7
48	Massachusetts	20.2
32	Michigan	25.1
34	Minnesota	24.3
2	Mississippi	33.2
9	Missouri	29.6
45	Montana	21.3
21	Nebraska	26.3
12	Nevada	28.5
36	New Hampshire	23.9
47	New Jersey	20.4
39	New Mexico	23.3
26	New York	25.9
5	North Carolina	30.7
41	North Dakota	23.1
14	Ohio	28.4
8	Oklahoma	29.7
33	Oregon	24.6
24	Pennsylvania	26.1
34	Rhode Island	24.3
10	South Carolina	29.1
28	South Dakota	25.6
4	Tennessee	31.0
17	Texas	26.8
50	Utah	14.2
43	Vermont	21.5
12	Virginia	28.5
37	Washington	23.6
6	West Virginia	29.8
29	Wisconsin	25.4
31	Wyoming	25.3

RANK ORDER

RANK	STATE	PERCENT
1	Kentucky	34.8
2	Mississippi	33.2
3	Alaska	31.9
4	Tennessee	31.0
5	North Carolina	30.7
6	Indiana	29.8
6	West Virginia	29.8
8	Oklahoma	29.7
9	Missouri	29.6
10	South Carolina	29.1
11	Arkansas	28.7
12	Nevada	28.5
12	Virginia	28.5
14	Ohio	28.4
15	Alabama	27.5
16	Arizona	27.0
17	Georgia	26.8
17	Texas	26.8
19	Louisiana	26.6
20	Maine	26.4
21	Iowa	26.3
21	Nebraska	26.3
23	Hawaii	26.2
24	Illinois	26.1
24	Pennsylvania	26.1
26	New York	25.9
27	Maryland	25.7
28	South Dakota	25.6
29	Delaware	25.4
29	Wisconsin	25.4
31	Wyoming	25.3
32	Michigan	25.1
33	Oregon	24.6
34	Minnesota	24.3
34	Rhode Island	24.3
36	New Hampshire	23.9
37	Florida	23.6
37	Washington	23.6
39	New Mexico	23.3
40	Kansas	23.2
41	North Dakota	23.1
42	Idaho	21.6
43	Vermont	21.5
44	Colorado	21.4
45	Montana	21.3
46	Connecticut	20.6
47	New Jersey	20.4
48	Massachusetts	20.2
49	California	19.7
50	Utah	14.2

District of Columbia — 23.8

Source: U.S. Department of Health and Human Services, Centers for Disease Control and Prevention
    "2002 Behavioral Risk Factor Surveillance Summary Prevalence Data" (http://apps.nccd.cdc.gov/brfss/)
Men 18 and older who have smoked more than 100 cigarettes during their lifetime and who currently smoke everyday or some days.

Percent of Women Who Smoke: 2002

National Median = 20.9% of Women*

ALPHA ORDER

ALPHA ORDER

RANK	STATE	PERCENT
19	Alabama	21.6
3	Alaska	26.7
31	Arizona	20.1
8	Arkansas	24.1
49	California	13.3
37	Colorado	19.4
45	Connecticut	18.4
8	Delaware	24.1
28	Florida	20.7
32	Georgia	20.0
48	Hawaii	16.0
35	Idaho	19.7
34	Illinois	19.8
4	Indiana	25.8
29	Iowa	20.2
24	Kansas	20.9
1	Kentucky	30.5
20	Louisiana	21.5
23	Maine	21.1
44	Maryland	18.6
46	Massachusetts	18.0
12	Michigan	23.5
37	Minnesota	19.4
17	Mississippi	22.2
10	Missouri	23.9
21	Montana	21.4
37	Nebraska	19.4
12	Nevada	23.5
15	New Hampshire	22.6
47	New Jersey	17.9
41	New Mexico	19.3
41	New York	19.3
16	North Carolina	22.3
32	North Dakota	20.0
5	Ohio	25.0
11	Oklahoma	23.8
29	Oregon	20.2
14	Pennsylvania	23.2
24	Rhode Island	20.9
7	South Carolina	24.4
35	South Dakota	19.7
6	Tennessee	24.9
43	Texas	19.1
50	Utah	11.3
24	Vermont	20.9
24	Virginia	20.9
37	Washington	19.4
2	West Virginia	27.2
21	Wisconsin	21.4
18	Wyoming	22.0

RANK ORDER

RANK	STATE	PERCENT
1	Kentucky	30.5
2	West Virginia	27.2
3	Alaska	26.7
4	Indiana	25.8
5	Ohio	25.0
6	Tennessee	24.9
7	South Carolina	24.4
8	Arkansas	24.1
8	Delaware	24.1
10	Missouri	23.9
11	Oklahoma	23.8
12	Michigan	23.5
12	Nevada	23.5
14	Pennsylvania	23.2
15	New Hampshire	22.6
16	North Carolina	22.3
17	Mississippi	22.2
18	Wyoming	22.0
19	Alabama	21.6
20	Louisiana	21.5
21	Montana	21.4
21	Wisconsin	21.4
23	Maine	21.1
24	Kansas	20.9
24	Rhode Island	20.9
24	Vermont	20.9
24	Virginia	20.9
28	Florida	20.7
29	Iowa	20.2
29	Oregon	20.2
31	Arizona	20.1
32	Georgia	20.0
32	North Dakota	20.0
34	Illinois	19.8
35	Idaho	19.7
35	South Dakota	19.7
37	Colorado	19.4
37	Minnesota	19.4
37	Nebraska	19.4
37	Washington	19.4
41	New Mexico	19.3
41	New York	19.3
43	Texas	19.1
44	Maryland	18.6
45	Connecticut	18.4
46	Massachusetts	18.0
47	New Jersey	17.9
48	Hawaii	16.0
49	California	13.3
50	Utah	11.3
	District of Columbia	17.5

Source: U.S. Department of Health and Human Services, Centers for Disease Control and Prevention
    "2002 Behavioral Risk Factor Surveillance Summary Prevalence Data" (http://apps.nccd.cdc.gov/brfss/)
Women 18 and older who have smoked more than 100 cigarettes during their lifetime and who currently smoke everyday or some days.

Percent of Smokers Who Have Tried To Quit: 2002

National Median = 52.0% of Adults*

<table>
<tr><td colspan="3">ALPHA ORDER</td><td colspan="3">RANK ORDER</td></tr>
<tr><td>RANK</td><td>STATE</td><td>PERCENT</td><td>RANK</td><td>STATE</td><td>PERCENT</td></tr>
<tr><td>29</td><td>Alabama</td><td>50.9</td><td>1</td><td>Utah</td><td>66.2</td></tr>
<tr><td>36</td><td>Alaska</td><td>49.5</td><td>2</td><td>California</td><td>62.3</td></tr>
<tr><td>30</td><td>Arizona</td><td>50.5</td><td>3</td><td>Rhode Island</td><td>61.7</td></tr>
<tr><td>25</td><td>Arkansas</td><td>51.9</td><td>4</td><td>Connecticut</td><td>59.3</td></tr>
<tr><td>2</td><td>California</td><td>62.3</td><td>5</td><td>New York</td><td>58.0</td></tr>
<tr><td>28</td><td>Colorado</td><td>51.2</td><td>6</td><td>Maine</td><td>56.7</td></tr>
<tr><td>4</td><td>Connecticut</td><td>59.3</td><td>6</td><td>New Hampshire</td><td>56.7</td></tr>
<tr><td>32</td><td>Delaware</td><td>50.4</td><td>8</td><td>Michigan</td><td>56.1</td></tr>
<tr><td>40</td><td>Florida</td><td>48.0</td><td>9</td><td>Massachusetts</td><td>56.0</td></tr>
<tr><td>10</td><td>Georgia</td><td>55.4</td><td>10</td><td>Georgia</td><td>55.4</td></tr>
<tr><td>50</td><td>Hawaii</td><td>42.4</td><td>11</td><td>New Jersey</td><td>55.2</td></tr>
<tr><td>16</td><td>Idaho</td><td>53.2</td><td>12</td><td>Mississippi</td><td>53.9</td></tr>
<tr><td>33</td><td>Illinois</td><td>50.1</td><td>12</td><td>Wyoming</td><td>53.9</td></tr>
<tr><td>21</td><td>Indiana</td><td>52.4</td><td>14</td><td>South Carolina</td><td>53.6</td></tr>
<tr><td>44</td><td>Iowa</td><td>46.6</td><td>15</td><td>Louisiana</td><td>53.4</td></tr>
<tr><td>48</td><td>Kansas</td><td>44.2</td><td>16</td><td>Idaho</td><td>53.2</td></tr>
<tr><td>45</td><td>Kentucky</td><td>45.6</td><td>16</td><td>North Carolina</td><td>53.2</td></tr>
<tr><td>15</td><td>Louisiana</td><td>53.4</td><td>18</td><td>Minnesota</td><td>53.1</td></tr>
<tr><td>6</td><td>Maine</td><td>56.7</td><td>19</td><td>Washington</td><td>52.7</td></tr>
<tr><td>22</td><td>Maryland</td><td>52.3</td><td>20</td><td>Oregon</td><td>52.5</td></tr>
<tr><td>9</td><td>Massachusetts</td><td>56.0</td><td>21</td><td>Indiana</td><td>52.4</td></tr>
<tr><td>8</td><td>Michigan</td><td>56.1</td><td>22</td><td>Maryland</td><td>52.3</td></tr>
<tr><td>18</td><td>Minnesota</td><td>53.1</td><td>23</td><td>Nebraska</td><td>52.2</td></tr>
<tr><td>12</td><td>Mississippi</td><td>53.9</td><td>24</td><td>South Dakota</td><td>52.0</td></tr>
<tr><td>47</td><td>Missouri</td><td>44.5</td><td>25</td><td>Arkansas</td><td>51.9</td></tr>
<tr><td>46</td><td>Montana</td><td>45.0</td><td>26</td><td>Vermont</td><td>51.8</td></tr>
<tr><td>23</td><td>Nebraska</td><td>52.2</td><td>27</td><td>Wisconsin</td><td>51.7</td></tr>
<tr><td>36</td><td>Nevada</td><td>49.5</td><td>28</td><td>Colorado</td><td>51.2</td></tr>
<tr><td>6</td><td>New Hampshire</td><td>56.7</td><td>29</td><td>Alabama</td><td>50.9</td></tr>
<tr><td>11</td><td>New Jersey</td><td>55.2</td><td>30</td><td>Arizona</td><td>50.5</td></tr>
<tr><td>34</td><td>New Mexico</td><td>50.0</td><td>30</td><td>Virginia</td><td>50.5</td></tr>
<tr><td>5</td><td>New York</td><td>58.0</td><td>32</td><td>Delaware</td><td>50.4</td></tr>
<tr><td>16</td><td>North Carolina</td><td>53.2</td><td>33</td><td>Illinois</td><td>50.1</td></tr>
<tr><td>42</td><td>North Dakota</td><td>47.1</td><td>34</td><td>New Mexico</td><td>50.0</td></tr>
<tr><td>43</td><td>Ohio</td><td>46.7</td><td>35</td><td>Pennsylvania</td><td>49.8</td></tr>
<tr><td>38</td><td>Oklahoma</td><td>48.1</td><td>36</td><td>Alaska</td><td>49.5</td></tr>
<tr><td>20</td><td>Oregon</td><td>52.5</td><td>36</td><td>Nevada</td><td>49.5</td></tr>
<tr><td>35</td><td>Pennsylvania</td><td>49.8</td><td>38</td><td>Oklahoma</td><td>48.1</td></tr>
<tr><td>3</td><td>Rhode Island</td><td>61.7</td><td>38</td><td>Tennessee</td><td>48.1</td></tr>
<tr><td>14</td><td>South Carolina</td><td>53.6</td><td>40</td><td>Florida</td><td>48.0</td></tr>
<tr><td>24</td><td>South Dakota</td><td>52.0</td><td>41</td><td>Texas</td><td>47.5</td></tr>
<tr><td>38</td><td>Tennessee</td><td>48.1</td><td>42</td><td>North Dakota</td><td>47.1</td></tr>
<tr><td>41</td><td>Texas</td><td>47.5</td><td>43</td><td>Ohio</td><td>46.7</td></tr>
<tr><td>1</td><td>Utah</td><td>66.2</td><td>44</td><td>Iowa</td><td>46.6</td></tr>
<tr><td>26</td><td>Vermont</td><td>51.8</td><td>45</td><td>Kentucky</td><td>45.6</td></tr>
<tr><td>30</td><td>Virginia</td><td>50.5</td><td>46</td><td>Montana</td><td>45.0</td></tr>
<tr><td>19</td><td>Washington</td><td>52.7</td><td>47</td><td>Missouri</td><td>44.5</td></tr>
<tr><td>49</td><td>West Virginia</td><td>43.5</td><td>48</td><td>Kansas</td><td>44.2</td></tr>
<tr><td>27</td><td>Wisconsin</td><td>51.7</td><td>49</td><td>West Virginia</td><td>43.5</td></tr>
<tr><td>12</td><td>Wyoming</td><td>53.9</td><td>50</td><td>Hawaii</td><td>42.4</td></tr>
<tr><td></td><td></td><td></td><td></td><td>District of Columbia</td><td>58.9</td></tr>
</table>

Source: U.S. Department of Health and Human Services, Centers for Disease Control and Prevention
   "2002 Behavioral Risk Factor Surveillance Summary Prevalence Data" (http://apps.nccd.cdc.gov/brfss/)
*Of persons 18 and older who smoke everyday.

Percent of Population Who are Illicit Drug Users: 2001

National Percent = 6.7% of Population*

ALPHA ORDER				RANK ORDER		
RANK	STATE	PERCENT		RANK	STATE	PERCENT
34	Alabama	5.8		1	Massachusetts	10.7
3	Alaska	9.2		2	Vermont	10.5
20	Arizona	6.7		3	Alaska	9.2
20	Arkansas	6.7		3	Colorado	9.2
7	California	8.2		5	Oregon	8.7
3	Colorado	9.2		6	Maine	8.4
13	Connecticut	7.5		7	California	8.2
12	Delaware	7.6		7	Rhode Island	8.2
31	Florida	6.0		9	New Hampshire	8.0
29	Georgia	6.1		10	North Carolina	7.9
13	Hawaii	7.5		11	Washington	7.7
41	Idaho	5.4		12	Delaware	7.6
18	Illinois	7.2		13	Connecticut	7.5
44	Indiana	5.2		13	Hawaii	7.5
48	Iowa	4.5		13	Michigan	7.5
29	Kansas	6.1		13	New Mexico	7.5
20	Kentucky	6.7		17	Nevada	7.3
20	Louisiana	6.7		18	Illinois	7.2
6	Maine	8.4		19	New York	6.8
27	Maryland	6.2		20	Arizona	6.7
1	Massachusetts	10.7		20	Arkansas	6.7
13	Michigan	7.5		20	Kentucky	6.7
24	Minnesota	6.6		20	Louisiana	6.7
36	Mississippi	5.7		24	Minnesota	6.6
36	Missouri	5.7		25	Montana	6.3
25	Montana	6.3		25	Wisconsin	6.3
47	Nebraska	4.6		27	Maryland	6.2
17	Nevada	7.3		27	Tennessee	6.2
9	New Hampshire	8.0		29	Georgia	6.1
34	New Jersey	5.8		29	Kansas	6.1
13	New Mexico	7.5		31	Florida	6.0
19	New York	6.8		32	Ohio	5.9
10	North Carolina	7.9		32	Pennsylvania	5.9
50	North Dakota	4.1		34	Alabama	5.8
32	Ohio	5.9		34	New Jersey	5.8
41	Oklahoma	5.4		36	Mississippi	5.7
5	Oregon	8.7		36	Missouri	5.7
32	Pennsylvania	5.9		36	South Carolina	5.7
7	Rhode Island	8.2		36	Wyoming	5.7
36	South Carolina	5.7		40	Virginia	5.5
48	South Dakota	4.5		41	Idaho	5.4
27	Tennessee	6.2		41	Oklahoma	5.4
43	Texas	5.3		43	Texas	5.3
45	Utah	5.0		44	Indiana	5.2
2	Vermont	10.5		45	Utah	5.0
40	Virginia	5.5		45	West Virginia	5.0
11	Washington	7.7		47	Nebraska	4.6
45	West Virginia	5.0		48	Iowa	4.5
25	Wisconsin	6.3		48	South Dakota	4.5
36	Wyoming	5.7		50	North Dakota	4.1
					District of Columbia	8.1

Source: U.S. Department of Health and Human Services, Substance Abuse and Mental Health Services Administration
  "2001 National Household Survey on Drug Abuse" (September 2003)
*Population 12 years old and over who used any illicit drug at least once within month of survey.

Percent of Adults Obese: 2002

National Median = 22.2% of Adults*

ALPHA ORDER

RANK	STATE	PERCENT
4	Alabama	25.7
16	Alaska	23.4
36	Arizona	19.6
13	Arkansas	23.7
40	California	19.2
50	Colorado	16.5
46	Connecticut	18.0
24	Delaware	22.4
38	Florida	19.4
14	Georgia	23.5
49	Hawaii	17.1
34	Idaho	20.2
26	Illinois	21.9
10	Indiana	24.1
21	Iowa	22.9
23	Kansas	22.8
9	Kentucky	24.4
5	Louisiana	25.5
31	Maine	20.7
38	Maryland	19.4
45	Massachusetts	18.3
7	Michigan	25.4
24	Minnesota	22.4
2	Mississippi	26.8
18	Missouri	23.2
43	Montana	18.7
18	Nebraska	23.2
27	Nevada	21.6
47	New Hampshire	17.9
41	New Jersey	19.0
35	New Mexico	19.7
32	New York	20.6
14	North Carolina	23.5
16	North Dakota	23.4
20	Ohio	23.0
21	Oklahoma	22.9
33	Oregon	20.3
11	Pennsylvania	23.9
44	Rhode Island	18.5
3	South Carolina	25.8
30	South Dakota	21.2
8	Tennessee	24.5
5	Texas	25.5
48	Utah	17.5
42	Vermont	18.9
12	Virginia	23.8
29	Washington	21.3
1	West Virginia	27.6
27	Wisconsin	21.6
37	Wyoming	19.5

RANK ORDER

RANK	STATE	PERCENT
1	West Virginia	27.6
2	Mississippi	26.8
3	South Carolina	25.8
4	Alabama	25.7
5	Louisiana	25.5
5	Texas	25.5
7	Michigan	25.4
8	Tennessee	24.5
9	Kentucky	24.4
10	Indiana	24.1
11	Pennsylvania	23.9
12	Virginia	23.8
13	Arkansas	23.7
14	Georgia	23.5
14	North Carolina	23.5
16	Alaska	23.4
16	North Dakota	23.4
18	Missouri	23.2
18	Nebraska	23.2
20	Ohio	23.0
21	Iowa	22.9
21	Oklahoma	22.9
23	Kansas	22.8
24	Delaware	22.4
24	Minnesota	22.4
26	Illinois	21.9
27	Nevada	21.6
27	Wisconsin	21.6
29	Washington	21.3
30	South Dakota	21.2
31	Maine	20.7
32	New York	20.6
33	Oregon	20.3
34	Idaho	20.2
35	New Mexico	19.7
36	Arizona	19.6
37	Wyoming	19.5
38	Florida	19.4
38	Maryland	19.4
40	California	19.2
41	New Jersey	19.0
42	Vermont	18.9
43	Montana	18.7
44	Rhode Island	18.5
45	Massachusetts	18.3
46	Connecticut	18.0
47	New Hampshire	17.9
48	Utah	17.5
49	Hawaii	17.1
50	Colorado	16.5

| | District of Columbia | 20.7 |

Source: U.S. Department of Health and Human Services, Centers for Disease Control and Prevention
"2002 Behavioral Risk Factor Surveillance Summary Prevalence Data" (http://apps.nccd.cdc.gov/brfss/)
Persons 18 and older. Obese is defined as a Body Mass Index (BMI) of 30.0 or more regardless of sex. BMI is a ratio of height to weight. As an example, a person 5' 8" and weighing 197 pounds has a BMI of 30. See http://www.cdc.gov/nccdphp/dnpa/bmi/bmi-adult.htm.

Percent of Adults Overweight: 2002

National Median = 37.0% of Adults*

ALPHA ORDER

RANK	STATE	PERCENT
22	Alabama	37.0
9	Alaska	37.7
32	Arizona	36.6
19	Arkansas	37.2
13	California	37.5
22	Colorado	37.0
22	Connecticut	37.0
38	Delaware	36.2
11	Florida	37.6
49	Georgia	35.4
41	Hawaii	36.0
21	Idaho	37.1
15	Illinois	37.3
19	Indiana	37.2
4	Iowa	38.3
14	Kansas	37.4
6	Kentucky	38.1
44	Louisiana	35.6
7	Maine	38.0
2	Maryland	38.5
35	Massachusetts	36.3
27	Michigan	36.9
33	Minnesota	36.5
35	Mississippi	36.3
22	Missouri	37.0
8	Montana	37.9
22	Nebraska	37.0
15	Nevada	37.3
2	New Hampshire	38.5
15	New Jersey	37.3
30	New Mexico	36.7
30	New York	36.7
48	North Carolina	35.5
5	North Dakota	38.2
42	Ohio	35.8
42	Oklahoma	35.8
27	Oregon	36.9
44	Pennsylvania	35.6
11	Rhode Island	37.6
44	South Carolina	35.6
1	South Dakota	39.4
29	Tennessee	36.8
15	Texas	37.3
39	Utah	36.1
44	Vermont	35.6
50	Virginia	35.1
9	Washington	37.7
39	West Virginia	36.1
35	Wisconsin	36.3
34	Wyoming	36.4

RANK ORDER

RANK	STATE	PERCENT
1	South Dakota	39.4
2	Maryland	38.5
2	New Hampshire	38.5
4	Iowa	38.3
5	North Dakota	38.2
6	Kentucky	38.1
7	Maine	38.0
8	Montana	37.9
9	Alaska	37.7
9	Washington	37.7
11	Florida	37.6
11	Rhode Island	37.6
13	California	37.5
14	Kansas	37.4
15	Illinois	37.3
15	Nevada	37.3
15	New Jersey	37.3
15	Texas	37.3
19	Arkansas	37.2
19	Indiana	37.2
21	Idaho	37.1
22	Alabama	37.0
22	Colorado	37.0
22	Connecticut	37.0
22	Missouri	37.0
22	Nebraska	37.0
27	Michigan	36.9
27	Oregon	36.9
29	Tennessee	36.8
30	New Mexico	36.7
30	New York	36.7
32	Arizona	36.6
33	Minnesota	36.5
34	Wyoming	36.4
35	Massachusetts	36.3
35	Mississippi	36.3
35	Wisconsin	36.3
38	Delaware	36.2
39	Utah	36.1
39	West Virginia	36.1
41	Hawaii	36.0
42	Ohio	35.8
42	Oklahoma	35.8
44	Louisiana	35.6
44	Pennsylvania	35.6
44	South Carolina	35.6
44	Vermont	35.6
48	North Carolina	35.5
49	Georgia	35.4
50	Virginia	35.1

| | District of Columbia | 32.1 |

Source: U.S. Department of Health and Human Services, Centers for Disease Control and Prevention
"2002 Behavioral Risk Factor Surveillance Summary Prevalence Data" (http://apps.nccd.cdc.gov/brfss/)
*Persons 18 and older. Overweight is defined as a Body Mass Index (BMI) of 25.0 to 29.9 regardless of sex. BMI
is a ratio of height to weight. As an example, a person 5' 8" and weighing 171 pounds has a BMI of 26.
See http://www.cdc.gov/nccdphp/dnpa/bmi/bmi-adult.htm.

Percent of Adults at Risk for Health Problems
Because of Being Overweight: 2002
National Median = 58.9% of Adults*

ALPHA ORDER

RANK	STATE	PERCENT
4	Alabama	62.7
12	Alaska	61.1
42	Arizona	56.2
14	Arkansas	60.9
37	California	56.7
49	Colorado	53.5
45	Connecticut	55.0
29	Delaware	58.6
36	Florida	57.0
22	Georgia	58.9
50	Hawaii	53.1
33	Idaho	57.3
20	Illinois	59.3
9	Indiana	61.3
11	Iowa	61.2
16	Kansas	60.2
5	Kentucky	62.5
12	Louisiana	61.1
29	Maine	58.6
31	Maryland	57.9
46	Massachusetts	54.6
6	Michigan	62.2
22	Minnesota	58.9
2	Mississippi	63.1
16	Missouri	60.2
38	Montana	56.6
16	Nebraska	60.2
22	Nevada	58.9
40	New Hampshire	56.3
40	New Jersey	56.3
39	New Mexico	56.4
33	New York	57.3
21	North Carolina	59.0
7	North Dakota	61.6
27	Ohio	58.7
27	Oklahoma	58.7
35	Oregon	57.2
19	Pennsylvania	59.6
43	Rhode Island	56.1
8	South Carolina	61.4
15	South Dakota	60.6
9	Tennessee	61.3
3	Texas	62.8
48	Utah	53.6
47	Vermont	54.5
26	Virginia	58.8
22	Washington	58.9
1	West Virginia	63.7
31	Wisconsin	57.9
44	Wyoming	55.9

RANK ORDER

RANK	STATE	PERCENT
1	West Virginia	63.7
2	Mississippi	63.1
3	Texas	62.8
4	Alabama	62.7
5	Kentucky	62.5
6	Michigan	62.2
7	North Dakota	61.6
8	South Carolina	61.4
9	Indiana	61.3
9	Tennessee	61.3
11	Iowa	61.2
12	Alaska	61.1
12	Louisiana	61.1
14	Arkansas	60.9
15	South Dakota	60.6
16	Kansas	60.2
16	Missouri	60.2
16	Nebraska	60.2
19	Pennsylvania	59.6
20	Illinois	59.3
21	North Carolina	59.0
22	Georgia	58.9
22	Minnesota	58.9
22	Nevada	58.9
22	Washington	58.9
26	Virginia	58.8
27	Ohio	58.7
27	Oklahoma	58.7
29	Delaware	58.6
29	Maine	58.6
31	Maryland	57.9
31	Wisconsin	57.9
33	Idaho	57.3
33	New York	57.3
35	Oregon	57.2
36	Florida	57.0
37	California	56.7
38	Montana	56.6
39	New Mexico	56.4
40	New Hampshire	56.3
40	New Jersey	56.3
42	Arizona	56.2
43	Rhode Island	56.1
44	Wyoming	55.9
45	Connecticut	55.0
46	Massachusetts	54.6
47	Vermont	54.5
48	Utah	53.6
49	Colorado	53.5
50	Hawaii	53.1

	District of Columbia	52.7

Source: U.S. Department of Health and Human Services, Centers for Disease Control and Prevention
"2002 Behavioral Risk Factor Surveillance Summary Prevalence Data" (http://apps.nccd.cdc.gov/brfss/)
*Persons 18 and older. "At risk for health problems" is defined according to the NHANES II definition of a Body Mass Index (BMI) of 27.8 for men and 27.3 for women. BMI is a ratio of height to weight. As an example, a person 5' 8" and weighing 197 pounds has a BMI of 30. See http://www.cdc.gov/nccdphp/dnpa/bmi/bmi-adult.htm.

Percent of Adults Who Exercise Vigorously: 2001

National Median = 24.5% of Adults*

ALPHA ORDER

RANK	STATE	PERCENT
38	Alabama	21.3
1	Alaska	33.7
12	Arizona	28.1
31	Arkansas	23.7
18	California	26.1
8	Colorado	28.9
13	Connecticut	27.6
38	Delaware	21.3
36	Florida	22.6
34	Georgia	23.1
17	Hawaii	26.4
6	Idaho	29.7
20	Illinois	25.2
22	Indiana	24.9
45	Iowa	19.5
32	Kansas	23.5
50	Kentucky	10.9
48	Louisiana	17.9
16	Maine	26.6
22	Maryland	24.9
9	Massachusetts	28.7
28	Michigan	24.1
25	Minnesota	24.5
47	Mississippi	18.6
40	Missouri	20.8
28	Montana	24.1
49	Nebraska	16.4
15	Nevada	26.7
11	New Hampshire	28.3
35	New Jersey	22.7
19	New Mexico	25.8
37	New York	22.5
42	North Carolina	20.5
27	North Dakota	24.2
28	Ohio	24.1
46	Oklahoma	18.8
6	Oregon	29.7
25	Pennsylvania	24.5
24	Rhode Island	24.6
21	South Carolina	25.0
40	South Dakota	20.8
43	Tennessee	19.6
33	Texas	23.4
2	Utah	31.9
3	Vermont	30.6
14	Virginia	26.9
5	Washington	29.8
43	West Virginia	19.6
10	Wisconsin	28.4
4	Wyoming	30.5

RANK ORDER

RANK	STATE	PERCENT
1	Alaska	33.7
2	Utah	31.9
3	Vermont	30.6
4	Wyoming	30.5
5	Washington	29.8
6	Idaho	29.7
6	Oregon	29.7
8	Colorado	28.9
9	Massachusetts	28.7
10	Wisconsin	28.4
11	New Hampshire	28.3
12	Arizona	28.1
13	Connecticut	27.6
14	Virginia	26.9
15	Nevada	26.7
16	Maine	26.6
17	Hawaii	26.4
18	California	26.1
19	New Mexico	25.8
20	Illinois	25.2
21	South Carolina	25.0
22	Indiana	24.9
22	Maryland	24.9
24	Rhode Island	24.6
25	Minnesota	24.5
25	Pennsylvania	24.5
27	North Dakota	24.2
28	Michigan	24.1
28	Montana	24.1
28	Ohio	24.1
31	Arkansas	23.7
32	Kansas	23.5
33	Texas	23.4
34	Georgia	23.1
35	New Jersey	22.7
36	Florida	22.6
37	New York	22.5
38	Alabama	21.3
38	Delaware	21.3
40	Missouri	20.8
40	South Dakota	20.8
42	North Carolina	20.5
43	Tennessee	19.6
43	West Virginia	19.6
45	Iowa	19.5
46	Oklahoma	18.8
47	Mississippi	18.6
48	Louisiana	17.9
49	Nebraska	16.4
50	Kentucky	10.9

| | District of Columbia | 27.0 |

*Source: U.S. Department of Health and Human Services, Centers for Disease Control and Prevention
"2001 Behavioral Risk Factor Surveillance Summary Prevalence Report" (August 9, 2002)*
Persons 18 and older. Activity that caused large increases in breathing or heart rate at least 20 minutes three or more times per week (such as running, aerobics or heavy yardwork).

Percent of Adults With No Leisure Time Physical Activity: 2001

National Median = 25.8% of Adults*

RANK	STATE	PERCENT
9	Alabama	31.2
40	Alaska	21.1
37	Arizona	21.9
7	Arkansas	31.5
16	California	26.6
46	Colorado	19.2
30	Connecticut	24.0
25	Delaware	25.7
11	Florida	27.7
13	Georgia	27.3
47	Hawaii	18.9
41	Idaho	21.0
18	Illinois	26.5
21	Indiana	26.2
23	Iowa	25.9
15	Kansas	26.7
3	Kentucky	33.4
1	Louisiana	35.6
32	Maine	23.2
29	Maryland	24.2
35	Massachusetts	22.8
31	Michigan	23.4
48	Minnesota	17.1
3	Mississippi	33.4
12	Missouri	27.5
37	Montana	21.9
8	Nebraska	31.4
36	Nevada	22.6
45	New Hampshire	19.5
16	New Jersey	26.6
24	New Mexico	25.8
10	New York	28.7
19	North Carolina	26.4
32	North Dakota	23.2
21	Ohio	26.2
5	Oklahoma	32.8
42	Oregon	20.8
28	Pennsylvania	24.7
27	Rhode Island	24.9
19	South Carolina	26.4
26	South Dakota	25.4
2	Tennessee	35.1
14	Texas	27.1
50	Utah	16.5
44	Vermont	20.3
32	Virginia	23.2
48	Washington	17.1
6	West Virginia	31.7
43	Wisconsin	20.7
39	Wyoming	21.2

RANK	STATE	PERCENT
1	Louisiana	35.6
2	Tennessee	35.1
3	Kentucky	33.4
3	Mississippi	33.4
5	Oklahoma	32.8
6	West Virginia	31.7
7	Arkansas	31.5
8	Nebraska	31.4
9	Alabama	31.2
10	New York	28.7
11	Florida	27.7
12	Missouri	27.5
13	Georgia	27.3
14	Texas	27.1
15	Kansas	26.7
16	California	26.6
16	New Jersey	26.6
18	Illinois	26.5
19	North Carolina	26.4
19	South Carolina	26.4
21	Indiana	26.2
21	Ohio	26.2
23	Iowa	25.9
24	New Mexico	25.8
25	Delaware	25.7
26	South Dakota	25.4
27	Rhode Island	24.9
28	Pennsylvania	24.7
29	Maryland	24.2
30	Connecticut	24.0
31	Michigan	23.4
32	Maine	23.2
32	North Dakota	23.2
32	Virginia	23.2
35	Massachusetts	22.8
36	Nevada	22.6
37	Arizona	21.9
37	Montana	21.9
39	Wyoming	21.2
40	Alaska	21.1
41	Idaho	21.0
42	Oregon	20.8
43	Wisconsin	20.7
44	Vermont	20.3
45	New Hampshire	19.5
46	Colorado	19.2
47	Hawaii	18.9
48	Minnesota	17.1
48	Washington	17.1
50	Utah	16.5

District of Columbia   24.2

Source: U.S. Department of Health and Human Services, Centers for Disease Control and Prevention
   "2001 Behavioral Risk Factor Surveillance Summary Prevalence Report" (August 9, 2002)
Persons 18 and older reporting no leisure time physical activity in the past month.

Percent of Adults Who Have Visited a Dentist or Dental Clinic: 2002

National Median = 69.2%*

ALPHA ORDER

RANK	STATE	PERCENT
31	Alabama	67.8
40	Alaska	65.5
29	Arizona	68.2
46	Arkansas	60.9
28	California	68.4
36	Colorado	67.3
1	Connecticut	80.2
11	Delaware	74.5
27	Florida	69.0
41	Georgia	65.3
43	Hawaii	65.2
35	Idaho	67.5
13	Illinois	73.7
33	Indiana	67.6
8	Iowa	75.3
17	Kansas	72.7
36	Kentucky	67.3
38	Louisiana	66.6
21	Maine	71.0
9	Maryland	74.9
4	Massachusetts	77.3
7	Michigan	75.9
6	Minnesota	76.0
48	Mississippi	60.1
44	Missouri	64.7
39	Montana	66.4
14	Nebraska	73.3
45	Nevada	62.6
5	New Hampshire	76.8
12	New Jersey	74.3
41	New Mexico	65.3
18	New York	71.7
33	North Carolina	67.6
25	North Dakota	69.2
16	Ohio	73.1
47	Oklahoma	60.5
30	Oregon	68.0
20	Pennsylvania	71.4
3	Rhode Island	77.5
25	South Carolina	69.2
19	South Dakota	71.5
23	Tennessee	70.1
50	Texas	60.0
15	Utah	73.2
10	Vermont	74.6
24	Virginia	69.6
22	Washington	70.4
48	West Virginia	60.1
2	Wisconsin	77.7
31	Wyoming	67.8

RANK ORDER

RANK	STATE	PERCENT
1	Connecticut	80.2
2	Wisconsin	77.7
3	Rhode Island	77.5
4	Massachusetts	77.3
5	New Hampshire	76.8
6	Minnesota	76.0
7	Michigan	75.9
8	Iowa	75.3
9	Maryland	74.9
10	Vermont	74.6
11	Delaware	74.5
12	New Jersey	74.3
13	Illinois	73.7
14	Nebraska	73.3
15	Utah	73.2
16	Ohio	73.1
17	Kansas	72.7
18	New York	71.7
19	South Dakota	71.5
20	Pennsylvania	71.4
21	Maine	71.0
22	Washington	70.4
23	Tennessee	70.1
24	Virginia	69.6
25	North Dakota	69.2
25	South Carolina	69.2
27	Florida	69.0
28	California	68.4
29	Arizona	68.2
30	Oregon	68.0
31	Alabama	67.8
31	Wyoming	67.8
33	Indiana	67.6
33	North Carolina	67.6
35	Idaho	67.5
36	Colorado	67.3
36	Kentucky	67.3
38	Louisiana	66.6
39	Montana	66.4
40	Alaska	65.5
41	Georgia	65.3
41	New Mexico	65.3
43	Hawaii	65.2
44	Missouri	64.7
45	Nevada	62.6
46	Arkansas	60.9
47	Oklahoma	60.5
48	Mississippi	60.1
48	West Virginia	60.1
50	Texas	60.0

| | District of Columbia | 73.7 |

Source: U.S. Department of Health and Human Services, Centers for Disease Control and Prevention
"2002 Behavioral Risk Factor Surveillance Summary Prevalence Data" (http://apps.nccd.cdc.gov/brfss/)
*Persons 18 and older who have visited a dentist within the past year for any reason.

Percent of Adults Who Have Lost 6 or More Teeth Due to Decay: 2002

National Median = 17.6%*

ALPHA ORDER

RANK	STATE	PERCENT
6	Alabama	24.8
42	Alaska	15.3
37	Arizona	15.8
5	Arkansas	24.9
49	California	11.2
48	Colorado	11.4
43	Connecticut	14.9
17	Delaware	19.2
16	Florida	19.5
15	Georgia	20.3
46	Hawaii	12.9
39	Idaho	15.4
35	Illinois	16.5
14	Indiana	20.5
25	Iowa	17.6
38	Kansas	15.7
3	Kentucky	26.6
13	Louisiana	20.8
7	Maine	24.3
39	Maryland	15.4
24	Massachusetts	17.7
28	Michigan	17.3
47	Minnesota	12.1
2	Mississippi	26.9
9	Missouri	21.8
27	Montana	17.4
32	Nebraska	16.8
32	Nevada	16.8
28	New Hampshire	17.3
25	New Jersey	17.6
39	New Mexico	15.4
20	New York	18.3
10	North Carolina	21.7
20	North Dakota	18.3
18	Ohio	18.8
8	Oklahoma	22.2
34	Oregon	16.7
10	Pennsylvania	21.7
30	Rhode Island	17.0
12	South Carolina	21.3
19	South Dakota	18.7
4	Tennessee	25.6
44	Texas	14.2
50	Utah	10.4
22	Vermont	18.1
36	Virginia	16.4
45	Washington	13.8
1	West Virginia	33.8
23	Wisconsin	17.9
30	Wyoming	17.0

RANK ORDER

RANK	STATE	PERCENT
1	West Virginia	33.8
2	Mississippi	26.9
3	Kentucky	26.6
4	Tennessee	25.6
5	Arkansas	24.9
6	Alabama	24.8
7	Maine	24.3
8	Oklahoma	22.2
9	Missouri	21.8
10	North Carolina	21.7
10	Pennsylvania	21.7
12	South Carolina	21.3
13	Louisiana	20.8
14	Indiana	20.5
15	Georgia	20.3
16	Florida	19.5
17	Delaware	19.2
18	Ohio	18.8
19	South Dakota	18.7
20	New York	18.3
20	North Dakota	18.3
22	Vermont	18.1
23	Wisconsin	17.9
24	Massachusetts	17.7
25	Iowa	17.6
25	New Jersey	17.6
27	Montana	17.4
28	Michigan	17.3
28	New Hampshire	17.3
30	Rhode Island	17.0
30	Wyoming	17.0
32	Nebraska	16.8
32	Nevada	16.8
34	Oregon	16.7
35	Illinois	16.5
36	Virginia	16.4
37	Arizona	15.8
38	Kansas	15.7
39	Idaho	15.4
39	Maryland	15.4
39	New Mexico	15.4
42	Alaska	15.3
43	Connecticut	14.9
44	Texas	14.2
45	Washington	13.8
46	Hawaii	12.9
47	Minnesota	12.1
48	Colorado	11.4
49	California	11.2
50	Utah	10.4

District of Columbia	15.6

Source: U.S. Department of Health and Human Services, Centers for Disease Control and Prevention
"2002 Behavioral Risk Factor Surveillance Summary Prevalence Data" (http://apps.nccd.cdc.gov/brfss/)
*Persons 18 and older who have lost six or more teeth in their life due to decay or gum disease.

Percent of Adults 65 Years Old and Older
Who Have Lost All Their Natural Teeth: 2002
National Median = 22.8%*

ALPHA ORDER

RANK	STATE	PERCENT
11	Alabama	29.9
13	Alaska	26.3
37	Arizona	20.4
10	Arkansas	30.1
49	California	13.3
41	Colorado	19.2
46	Connecticut	16.0
14	Delaware	25.8
31	Florida	21.3
8	Georgia	32.6
50	Hawaii	13.1
27	Idaho	22.5
22	Illinois	24.0
19	Indiana	24.7
31	Iowa	21.3
26	Kansas	22.8
1	Kentucky	42.3
5	Louisiana	33.8
9	Maine	30.4
40	Maryland	19.3
25	Massachusetts	22.9
43	Michigan	18.8
47	Minnesota	14.8
4	Mississippi	35.1
12	Missouri	26.4
34	Montana	20.9
17	Nebraska	25.5
36	Nevada	20.5
29	New Hampshire	21.8
39	New Jersey	20.1
18	New Mexico	25.2
44	New York	18.7
6	North Carolina	33.3
24	North Dakota	23.2
23	Ohio	23.6
7	Oklahoma	33.2
42	Oregon	18.9
14	Pennsylvania	25.8
27	Rhode Island	22.5
21	South Carolina	24.4
19	South Dakota	24.7
3	Tennessee	36.0
37	Texas	20.4
48	Utah	14.7
30	Vermont	21.7
31	Virginia	21.3
45	Washington	16.8
2	West Virginia	41.9
35	Wisconsin	20.6
16	Wyoming	25.7

RANK ORDER

RANK	STATE	PERCENT
1	Kentucky	42.3
2	West Virginia	41.9
3	Tennessee	36.0
4	Mississippi	35.1
5	Louisiana	33.8
6	North Carolina	33.3
7	Oklahoma	33.2
8	Georgia	32.6
9	Maine	30.4
10	Arkansas	30.1
11	Alabama	29.9
12	Missouri	26.4
13	Alaska	26.3
14	Delaware	25.8
14	Pennsylvania	25.8
16	Wyoming	25.7
17	Nebraska	25.5
18	New Mexico	25.2
19	Indiana	24.7
19	South Dakota	24.7
21	South Carolina	24.4
22	Illinois	24.0
23	Ohio	23.6
24	North Dakota	23.2
25	Massachusetts	22.9
26	Kansas	22.8
27	Idaho	22.5
27	Rhode Island	22.5
29	New Hampshire	21.8
30	Vermont	21.7
31	Florida	21.3
31	Iowa	21.3
31	Virginia	21.3
34	Montana	20.9
35	Wisconsin	20.6
36	Nevada	20.5
37	Arizona	20.4
37	Texas	20.4
39	New Jersey	20.1
40	Maryland	19.3
41	Colorado	19.2
42	Oregon	18.9
43	Michigan	18.8
44	New York	18.7
45	Washington	16.8
46	Connecticut	16.0
47	Minnesota	14.8
48	Utah	14.7
49	California	13.3
50	Hawaii	13.1

| | District of Columbia | 16.7 |

*Source: U.S. Department of Health and Human Services, Centers for Disease Control and Prevention
"2002 Behavioral Risk Factor Surveillance Summary Prevalence Data" (http://apps.nccd.cdc.gov/brfss/)*
Age-adjusted percent of persons aged 65 years or more.

Percent of Adults Who Average Five or More Servings of Fruits and Vegetables Each Day: 2002
National Median = 22.6%*

ALPHA ORDER

RANK	STATE	PERCENT
34	Alabama	21.1
22	Alaska	22.8
25	Arizona	22.6
36	Arkansas	20.7
12	California	27.4
16	Colorado	23.9
1	Connecticut	30.3
44	Delaware	19.5
12	Florida	27.4
25	Georgia	22.6
40	Hawaii	20.4
32	Idaho	21.6
35	Illinois	20.9
31	Indiana	21.7
43	Iowa	19.8
47	Kansas	18.2
42	Kentucky	20.2
49	Louisiana	17.2
4	Maine	29.4
2	Maryland	29.7
2	Massachusetts	29.7
25	Michigan	22.6
23	Minnesota	22.7
45	Mississippi	19.2
45	Missouri	19.2
23	Montana	22.7
48	Nebraska	18.0
28	Nevada	22.3
7	New Hampshire	28.5
9	New Jersey	28.2
30	New Mexico	21.9
11	New York	27.7
20	North Carolina	23.6
40	North Dakota	20.4
39	Ohio	20.5
50	Oklahoma	14.4
14	Oregon	26.3
15	Pennsylvania	25.4
6	Rhode Island	28.6
16	South Carolina	23.9
36	South Dakota	20.7
8	Tennessee	28.4
16	Texas	23.9
38	Utah	20.6
5	Vermont	29.1
10	Virginia	27.9
19	Washington	23.8
33	West Virginia	21.3
21	Wisconsin	23.5
29	Wyoming	22.1

RANK ORDER

RANK	STATE	PERCENT
1	Connecticut	30.3
2	Maryland	29.7
2	Massachusetts	29.7
4	Maine	29.4
5	Vermont	29.1
6	Rhode Island	28.6
7	New Hampshire	28.5
8	Tennessee	28.4
9	New Jersey	28.2
10	Virginia	27.9
11	New York	27.7
12	California	27.4
12	Florida	27.4
14	Oregon	26.3
15	Pennsylvania	25.4
16	Colorado	23.9
16	South Carolina	23.9
16	Texas	23.9
19	Washington	23.8
20	North Carolina	23.6
21	Wisconsin	23.5
22	Alaska	22.8
23	Minnesota	22.7
23	Montana	22.7
25	Arizona	22.6
25	Georgia	22.6
25	Michigan	22.6
28	Nevada	22.3
29	Wyoming	22.1
30	New Mexico	21.9
31	Indiana	21.7
32	Idaho	21.6
33	West Virginia	21.3
34	Alabama	21.1
35	Illinois	20.9
36	Arkansas	20.7
36	South Dakota	20.7
38	Utah	20.6
39	Ohio	20.5
40	Hawaii	20.4
40	North Dakota	20.4
42	Kentucky	20.2
43	Iowa	19.8
44	Delaware	19.5
45	Mississippi	19.2
45	Missouri	19.2
47	Kansas	18.2
48	Nebraska	18.0
49	Louisiana	17.2
50	Oklahoma	14.4

District of Columbia 33.8

Source: U.S. Department of Health and Human Services, Centers for Disease Control and Prevention
   "2002 Behavioral Risk Factor Surveillance Summary Prevalence Data" (http://apps.nccd.cdc.gov/brfss/)
*Persons 18 and older.

Number of Days in Past Month When Physical Health was "Not Good": 2001

National Average = 3.5 Days*

ALPHA ORDER				RANK ORDER		
RANK	STATE	DAYS		RANK	STATE	DAYS
3	Alabama	4.2		1	West Virginia	5.3
18	Alaska	3.5		2	Arkansas	4.5
7	Arizona	3.9		3	Alabama	4.2
2	Arkansas	4.5		3	Mississippi	4.2
18	California	3.5		5	Oklahoma	4.1
27	Colorado	3.3		6	Kentucky	4.0
36	Connecticut	3.2		7	Arizona	3.9
22	Delaware	3.4		8	Rhode Island	3.8
18	Florida	3.5		8	South Carolina	3.8
27	Georgia	3.3		10	Maine	3.7
50	Hawaii	2.1		10	Michigan	3.7
27	Idaho	3.3		10	New Mexico	3.7
43	Illinois	3.0		10	New York	3.7
18	Indiana	3.5		10	Oregon	3.7
43	Iowa	3.0		15	Missouri	3.6
45	Kansas	2.9		15	Nevada	3.6
6	Kentucky	4.0		15	North Carolina	3.6
36	Louisiana	3.2		18	Alaska	3.5
10	Maine	3.7		18	California	3.5
40	Maryland	3.1		18	Florida	3.5
22	Massachusetts	3.4		18	Indiana	3.5
10	Michigan	3.7		22	Delaware	3.4
40	Minnesota	3.1		22	Massachusetts	3.4
3	Mississippi	4.2		22	Montana	3.4
15	Missouri	3.6		22	Pennsylvania	3.4
22	Montana	3.4		22	Washington	3.4
48	Nebraska	2.8		27	Colorado	3.3
15	Nevada	3.6		27	Georgia	3.3
45	New Hampshire	2.9		27	Idaho	3.3
27	New Jersey	3.3		27	New Jersey	3.3
10	New Mexico	3.7		27	Ohio	3.3
10	New York	3.7		27	Tennessee	3.3
15	North Carolina	3.6		27	Utah	3.3
49	North Dakota	2.7		27	Vermont	3.3
27	Ohio	3.3		27	Virginia	3.3
5	Oklahoma	4.1		36	Connecticut	3.2
10	Oregon	3.7		36	Louisiana	3.2
22	Pennsylvania	3.4		36	Texas	3.2
8	Rhode Island	3.8		36	Wisconsin	3.2
8	South Carolina	3.8		40	Maryland	3.1
45	South Dakota	2.9		40	Minnesota	3.1
27	Tennessee	3.3		40	Wyoming	3.1
36	Texas	3.2		43	Illinois	3.0
27	Utah	3.3		43	Iowa	3.0
27	Vermont	3.3		45	Kansas	2.9
27	Virginia	3.3		45	New Hampshire	2.9
22	Washington	3.4		45	South Dakota	2.9
1	West Virginia	5.3		48	Nebraska	2.8
36	Wisconsin	3.2		49	North Dakota	2.7
40	Wyoming	3.1		50	Hawaii	2.1
					District of Columbia**	NA

Source: U.S. Department of Health and Human Services, Centers for Disease Control and Prevention
"2001 Behavioral Risk Factor Surveillance Summary Prevalence Report" (August 9, 2002)
*Persons 18 and older.
**Not available.

Number of Days in Past Month When Mental Health was "Not Good": 2001

National Average = 3.4 Days*

ALPHA ORDER				RANK ORDER		
RANK	STATE	DAYS		RANK	STATE	DAYS
3	Alabama	4.3		1	Kentucky	4.7
29	Alaska	3.2		2	West Virginia	4.4
17	Arizona	3.4		3	Alabama	4.3
4	Arkansas	3.8		4	Arkansas	3.8
14	California	3.5		5	Georgia	3.7
8	Colorado	3.6		5	Michigan	3.7
29	Connecticut	3.2		5	Nevada	3.7
29	Delaware	3.2		8	Colorado	3.6
34	Florida	3.1		8	Indiana	3.6
5	Georgia	3.7		8	Pennsylvania	3.6
50	Hawaii	1.5		8	Rhode Island	3.6
14	Idaho	3.5		8	Utah	3.6
41	Illinois	2.9		8	Virginia	3.6
8	Indiana	3.6		14	California	3.5
44	Iowa	2.7		14	Idaho	3.5
41	Kansas	2.9		14	New York	3.5
1	Kentucky	4.7		17	Arizona	3.4
41	Louisiana	2.9		17	Massachusetts	3.4
26	Maine	3.3		17	Missouri	3.4
29	Maryland	3.2		17	New Jersey	3.4
17	Massachusetts	3.4		17	New Mexico	3.4
5	Michigan	3.7		17	Oklahoma	3.4
34	Minnesota	3.1		17	Oregon	3.4
34	Mississippi	3.1		17	South Carolina	3.4
17	Missouri	3.4		17	Texas	3.4
48	Montana	2.5		26	Maine	3.3
44	Nebraska	2.7		26	Ohio	3.3
5	Nevada	3.7		26	Washington	3.3
40	New Hampshire	3.0		29	Alaska	3.2
17	New Jersey	3.4		29	Connecticut	3.2
17	New Mexico	3.4		29	Delaware	3.2
14	New York	3.5		29	Maryland	3.2
44	North Carolina	2.7		29	Wisconsin	3.2
47	North Dakota	2.6		34	Florida	3.1
26	Ohio	3.3		34	Minnesota	3.1
17	Oklahoma	3.4		34	Mississippi	3.1
17	Oregon	3.4		34	Tennessee	3.1
8	Pennsylvania	3.6		34	Vermont	3.1
8	Rhode Island	3.6		34	Wyoming	3.1
17	South Carolina	3.4		40	New Hampshire	3.0
48	South Dakota	2.5		41	Illinois	2.9
34	Tennessee	3.1		41	Kansas	2.9
17	Texas	3.4		41	Louisiana	2.9
8	Utah	3.6		44	Iowa	2.7
34	Vermont	3.1		44	Nebraska	2.7
8	Virginia	3.6		44	North Carolina	2.7
26	Washington	3.3		47	North Dakota	2.6
2	West Virginia	4.4		48	Montana	2.5
29	Wisconsin	3.2		48	South Dakota	2.5
34	Wyoming	3.1		50	Hawaii	1.5
					District of Columbia**	NA

Source: U.S. Department of Health and Human Services, Centers for Disease Control and Prevention
"2001 Behavioral Risk Factor Surveillance Summary Prevalence Report" (August 9, 2002)
*Persons 18 and older.
**Not available.

Percent of Population Rating Their Health as Fair or Poor in 2002

National Median = 14.7% of Adults*

<table>
<tr><td colspan="3">ALPHA ORDER</td><td colspan="3">RANK ORDER</td></tr>
<tr><td>RANK</td><td>STATE</td><td>PERCENT</td><td>RANK</td><td>STATE</td><td>PERCENT</td></tr>
<tr><td>7</td><td>Alabama</td><td>19.7</td><td>1</td><td>Kentucky</td><td>23.8</td></tr>
<tr><td>35</td><td>Alaska</td><td>13.0</td><td>2</td><td>West Virginia</td><td>23.5</td></tr>
<tr><td>22</td><td>Arizona</td><td>15.1</td><td>3</td><td>Mississippi</td><td>23.0</td></tr>
<tr><td>8</td><td>Arkansas</td><td>19.0</td><td>4</td><td>North Carolina</td><td>21.0</td></tr>
<tr><td>19</td><td>California</td><td>15.6</td><td>5</td><td>Tennessee</td><td>20.7</td></tr>
<tr><td>39</td><td>Colorado</td><td>12.5</td><td>6</td><td>Texas</td><td>20.1</td></tr>
<tr><td>41</td><td>Connecticut</td><td>12.2</td><td>7</td><td>Alabama</td><td>19.7</td></tr>
<tr><td>24</td><td>Delaware</td><td>14.8</td><td>8</td><td>Arkansas</td><td>19.0</td></tr>
<tr><td>20</td><td>Florida</td><td>15.3</td><td>9</td><td>Louisiana</td><td>17.9</td></tr>
<tr><td>20</td><td>Georgia</td><td>15.3</td><td>10</td><td>Oklahoma</td><td>17.7</td></tr>
<tr><td>47</td><td>Hawaii</td><td>11.4</td><td>11</td><td>Nevada</td><td>17.2</td></tr>
<tr><td>31</td><td>Idaho</td><td>13.6</td><td>11</td><td>South Carolina</td><td>17.2</td></tr>
<tr><td>23</td><td>Illinois</td><td>14.9</td><td>13</td><td>Missouri</td><td>17.1</td></tr>
<tr><td>15</td><td>Indiana</td><td>16.4</td><td>14</td><td>New Mexico</td><td>17.0</td></tr>
<tr><td>46</td><td>Iowa</td><td>11.5</td><td>15</td><td>Indiana</td><td>16.4</td></tr>
<tr><td>40</td><td>Kansas</td><td>12.4</td><td>16</td><td>New York</td><td>16.1</td></tr>
<tr><td>1</td><td>Kentucky</td><td>23.8</td><td>16</td><td>Oregon</td><td>16.1</td></tr>
<tr><td>9</td><td>Louisiana</td><td>17.9</td><td>18</td><td>Pennsylvania</td><td>15.9</td></tr>
<tr><td>25</td><td>Maine</td><td>14.7</td><td>19</td><td>California</td><td>15.6</td></tr>
<tr><td>44</td><td>Maryland</td><td>11.7</td><td>20</td><td>Florida</td><td>15.3</td></tr>
<tr><td>34</td><td>Massachusetts</td><td>13.3</td><td>20</td><td>Georgia</td><td>15.3</td></tr>
<tr><td>33</td><td>Michigan</td><td>13.4</td><td>22</td><td>Arizona</td><td>15.1</td></tr>
<tr><td>48</td><td>Minnesota</td><td>10.9</td><td>23</td><td>Illinois</td><td>14.9</td></tr>
<tr><td>3</td><td>Mississippi</td><td>23.0</td><td>24</td><td>Delaware</td><td>14.8</td></tr>
<tr><td>13</td><td>Missouri</td><td>17.1</td><td>25</td><td>Maine</td><td>14.7</td></tr>
<tr><td>37</td><td>Montana</td><td>12.8</td><td>25</td><td>New Jersey</td><td>14.7</td></tr>
<tr><td>27</td><td>Nebraska</td><td>13.7</td><td>27</td><td>Nebraska</td><td>13.7</td></tr>
<tr><td>11</td><td>Nevada</td><td>17.2</td><td>27</td><td>Ohio</td><td>13.7</td></tr>
<tr><td>45</td><td>New Hampshire</td><td>11.6</td><td>27</td><td>Rhode Island</td><td>13.7</td></tr>
<tr><td>25</td><td>New Jersey</td><td>14.7</td><td>27</td><td>Virginia</td><td>13.7</td></tr>
<tr><td>14</td><td>New Mexico</td><td>17.0</td><td>31</td><td>Idaho</td><td>13.6</td></tr>
<tr><td>16</td><td>New York</td><td>16.1</td><td>31</td><td>North Dakota</td><td>13.6</td></tr>
<tr><td>4</td><td>North Carolina</td><td>21.0</td><td>33</td><td>Michigan</td><td>13.4</td></tr>
<tr><td>31</td><td>North Dakota</td><td>13.6</td><td>34</td><td>Massachusetts</td><td>13.3</td></tr>
<tr><td>27</td><td>Ohio</td><td>13.7</td><td>35</td><td>Alaska</td><td>13.0</td></tr>
<tr><td>10</td><td>Oklahoma</td><td>17.7</td><td>36</td><td>South Dakota</td><td>12.9</td></tr>
<tr><td>16</td><td>Oregon</td><td>16.1</td><td>37</td><td>Montana</td><td>12.8</td></tr>
<tr><td>18</td><td>Pennsylvania</td><td>15.9</td><td>38</td><td>Washington</td><td>12.6</td></tr>
<tr><td>27</td><td>Rhode Island</td><td>13.7</td><td>39</td><td>Colorado</td><td>12.5</td></tr>
<tr><td>11</td><td>South Carolina</td><td>17.2</td><td>40</td><td>Kansas</td><td>12.4</td></tr>
<tr><td>36</td><td>South Dakota</td><td>12.9</td><td>41</td><td>Connecticut</td><td>12.2</td></tr>
<tr><td>5</td><td>Tennessee</td><td>20.7</td><td>41</td><td>Wyoming</td><td>12.2</td></tr>
<tr><td>6</td><td>Texas</td><td>20.1</td><td>43</td><td>Wisconsin</td><td>12.0</td></tr>
<tr><td>50</td><td>Utah</td><td>10.4</td><td>44</td><td>Maryland</td><td>11.7</td></tr>
<tr><td>48</td><td>Vermont</td><td>10.9</td><td>45</td><td>New Hampshire</td><td>11.6</td></tr>
<tr><td>27</td><td>Virginia</td><td>13.7</td><td>46</td><td>Iowa</td><td>11.5</td></tr>
<tr><td>38</td><td>Washington</td><td>12.6</td><td>47</td><td>Hawaii</td><td>11.4</td></tr>
<tr><td>2</td><td>West Virginia</td><td>23.5</td><td>48</td><td>Minnesota</td><td>10.9</td></tr>
<tr><td>43</td><td>Wisconsin</td><td>12.0</td><td>48</td><td>Vermont</td><td>10.9</td></tr>
<tr><td>41</td><td>Wyoming</td><td>12.2</td><td>50</td><td>Utah</td><td>10.4</td></tr>
<tr><td></td><td></td><td></td><td></td><td>District of Columbia</td><td>10.8</td></tr>
</table>

Source: U.S. Department of Health and Human Services, Centers for Disease Control and Prevention
    "2002 Behavioral Risk Factor Surveillance Summary Prevalence Data" (http://apps.nccd.cdc.gov/brfss/)
*Persons 18 and older.

Safety Belt Usage Rate in 2002

National Rate = 75.0% Use Safety Belts*

ALPHA ORDER

RANK	STATE	PERCENT
16	Alabama	79
38	Alaska	66
23	Arizona	74
41	Arkansas	64
2	California	91
25	Colorado	73
17	Connecticut	78
28	Delaware	71
21	Florida	75
19	Georgia	77
3	Hawaii	90
43	Idaho	63
23	Illinois	74
26	Indiana	72
11	Iowa	82
47	Kansas	61
45	Kentucky	62
34	Louisiana	69
NA	Maine**	NA
6	Maryland	86
48	Massachusetts	51
9	Michigan	83
14	Minnesota	80
45	Mississippi	62
34	Missouri	69
17	Montana	78
30	Nebraska	70
21	Nevada	75
NA	New Hampshire**	NA
12	New Jersey	81
4	New Mexico	88
9	New York	83
8	North Carolina	84
43	North Dakota	63
30	Ohio	70
30	Oklahoma	70
4	Oregon	88
20	Pennsylvania	76
28	Rhode Island	71
38	South Carolina	66
41	South Dakota	64
36	Tennessee	67
12	Texas	81
14	Utah	80
7	Vermont	85
30	Virginia	70
1	Washington	93
26	West Virginia	72
38	Wisconsin	66
36	Wyoming	67

RANK ORDER

RANK	STATE	PERCENT
1	Washington	93
2	California	91
3	Hawaii	90
4	New Mexico	88
4	Oregon	88
6	Maryland	86
7	Vermont	85
8	North Carolina	84
9	Michigan	83
9	New York	83
11	Iowa	82
12	New Jersey	81
12	Texas	81
14	Minnesota	80
14	Utah	80
16	Alabama	79
17	Connecticut	78
17	Montana	78
19	Georgia	77
20	Pennsylvania	76
21	Florida	75
21	Nevada	75
23	Arizona	74
23	Illinois	74
25	Colorado	73
26	Indiana	72
26	West Virginia	72
28	Delaware	71
28	Rhode Island	71
30	Nebraska	70
30	Ohio	70
30	Oklahoma	70
30	Virginia	70
34	Louisiana	69
34	Missouri	69
36	Tennessee	67
36	Wyoming	67
38	Alaska	66
38	South Carolina	66
38	Wisconsin	66
41	Arkansas	64
41	South Dakota	64
43	Idaho	63
43	North Dakota	63
45	Kentucky	62
45	Mississippi	62
47	Kansas	61
48	Massachusetts	51
NA	Maine**	NA
NA	New Hampshire**	NA
	District of Columbia	85

Source: U.S. Department of Transportation, National Highway Traffic Safety Administration
    "Safety Belt Use in 2002" (http://www-nrd.nhtsa.dot.gov/pdf/nrd-30/NCSA/RNotes/2003/809-587.pdf)
*As of December 2002. National estimate is from the National Occupant Protection Use Survey (NOPUS) using a
different methodology.
**Not available.

VIII. APPENDIX

Population Charts

Population in 2003

National Total = 290,809,777*

ALPHA ORDER

RANK	STATE	POPULATION	% of USA
23	Alabama	4,500,752	1.5%
47	Alaska	648,818	0.2%
18	Arizona	5,580,811	1.9%
32	Arkansas	2,725,714	0.9%
1	California	35,484,453	12.2%
22	Colorado	4,550,688	1.6%
29	Connecticut	3,483,372	1.2%
45	Delaware	817,491	0.3%
4	Florida	17,019,068	5.9%
9	Georgia	8,684,715	3.0%
42	Hawaii	1,257,608	0.4%
39	Idaho	1,366,332	0.5%
5	Illinois	12,653,544	4.4%
14	Indiana	6,195,643	2.1%
30	Iowa	2,944,062	1.0%
33	Kansas	2,723,507	0.9%
26	Kentucky	4,117,827	1.4%
24	Louisiana	4,496,334	1.5%
40	Maine	1,305,728	0.4%
19	Maryland	5,508,909	1.9%
13	Massachusetts	6,433,422	2.2%
8	Michigan	10,079,985	3.5%
21	Minnesota	5,059,375	1.7%
31	Mississippi	2,881,281	1.0%
17	Missouri	5,704,484	2.0%
44	Montana	917,621	0.3%
38	Nebraska	1,739,291	0.6%
35	Nevada	2,241,154	0.8%
41	New Hampshire	1,287,687	0.4%
10	New Jersey	8,638,396	3.0%
36	New Mexico	1,874,614	0.6%
3	New York	19,190,115	6.6%
11	North Carolina	8,407,248	2.9%
48	North Dakota	633,837	0.2%
7	Ohio	11,435,798	3.9%
28	Oklahoma	3,511,532	1.2%
27	Oregon	3,559,596	1.2%
6	Pennsylvania	12,365,455	4.3%
43	Rhode Island	1,076,164	0.4%
25	South Carolina	4,147,152	1.4%
46	South Dakota	764,309	0.3%
16	Tennessee	5,841,748	2.0%
2	Texas	22,118,509	7.6%
34	Utah	2,351,467	0.8%
49	Vermont	619,107	0.2%
12	Virginia	7,386,330	2.5%
15	Washington	6,131,445	2.1%
37	West Virginia	1,810,354	0.6%
20	Wisconsin	5,472,299	1.9%
50	Wyoming	501,242	0.2%

RANK ORDER

RANK	STATE	POPULATION	% of USA
1	California	35,484,453	12.2%
2	Texas	22,118,509	7.6%
3	New York	19,190,115	6.6%
4	Florida	17,019,068	5.9%
5	Illinois	12,653,544	4.4%
6	Pennsylvania	12,365,455	4.3%
7	Ohio	11,435,798	3.9%
8	Michigan	10,079,985	3.5%
9	Georgia	8,684,715	3.0%
10	New Jersey	8,638,396	3.0%
11	North Carolina	8,407,248	2.9%
12	Virginia	7,386,330	2.5%
13	Massachusetts	6,433,422	2.2%
14	Indiana	6,195,643	2.1%
15	Washington	6,131,445	2.1%
16	Tennessee	5,841,748	2.0%
17	Missouri	5,704,484	2.0%
18	Arizona	5,580,811	1.9%
19	Maryland	5,508,909	1.9%
20	Wisconsin	5,472,299	1.9%
21	Minnesota	5,059,375	1.7%
22	Colorado	4,550,688	1.6%
23	Alabama	4,500,752	1.5%
24	Louisiana	4,496,334	1.5%
25	South Carolina	4,147,152	1.4%
26	Kentucky	4,117,827	1.4%
27	Oregon	3,559,596	1.2%
28	Oklahoma	3,511,532	1.2%
29	Connecticut	3,483,372	1.2%
30	Iowa	2,944,062	1.0%
31	Mississippi	2,881,281	1.0%
32	Arkansas	2,725,714	0.9%
33	Kansas	2,723,507	0.9%
34	Utah	2,351,467	0.8%
35	Nevada	2,241,154	0.8%
36	New Mexico	1,874,614	0.6%
37	West Virginia	1,810,354	0.6%
38	Nebraska	1,739,291	0.6%
39	Idaho	1,366,332	0.5%
40	Maine	1,305,728	0.4%
41	New Hampshire	1,287,687	0.4%
42	Hawaii	1,257,608	0.4%
43	Rhode Island	1,076,164	0.4%
44	Montana	917,621	0.3%
45	Delaware	817,491	0.3%
46	South Dakota	764,309	0.3%
47	Alaska	648,818	0.2%
48	North Dakota	633,837	0.2%
49	Vermont	619,107	0.2%
50	Wyoming	501,242	0.2%
	District of Columbia	563,384	0.2%

Source: U.S. Bureau of the Census
   "Population Estimates" (December 18, 2003, http://eire.census.gov/popest/estimates.php)
*Resident population.

Population in 2002

National Total = 287,973,924*

ALPHA ORDER

RANK	STATE	POPULATION	% of USA
23	Alabama	4,478,896	1.6%
47	Alaska	641,482	0.2%
19	Arizona	5,441,125	1.9%
33	Arkansas	2,706,268	0.9%
1	California	35,001,986	12.2%
22	Colorado	4,501,051	1.6%
29	Connecticut	3,458,587	1.2%
45	Delaware	805,945	0.3%
4	Florida	16,691,701	5.8%
10	Georgia	8,544,005	3.0%
42	Hawaii	1,240,663	0.4%
39	Idaho	1,343,124	0.5%
5	Illinois	12,586,447	4.4%
14	Indiana	6,156,913	2.1%
30	Iowa	2,935,840	1.0%
32	Kansas	2,711,769	0.9%
26	Kentucky	4,089,822	1.4%
24	Louisiana	4,476,192	1.6%
40	Maine	1,294,894	0.4%
18	Maryland	5,450,525	1.9%
13	Massachusetts	6,421,800	2.2%
8	Michigan	10,043,221	3.5%
21	Minnesota	5,024,791	1.7%
31	Mississippi	2,866,733	1.0%
17	Missouri	5,669,544	2.0%
44	Montana	910,372	0.3%
38	Nebraska	1,727,564	0.6%
35	Nevada	2,167,455	0.8%
41	New Hampshire	1,274,405	0.4%
9	New Jersey	8,575,252	3.0%
36	New Mexico	1,852,044	0.6%
3	New York	19,134,293	6.6%
11	North Carolina	8,305,820	2.9%
48	North Dakota	633,911	0.2%
7	Ohio	11,408,699	4.0%
28	Oklahoma	3,489,700	1.2%
27	Oregon	3,520,355	1.2%
6	Pennsylvania	12,328,827	4.3%
43	Rhode Island	1,068,326	0.4%
25	South Carolina	4,103,770	1.4%
46	South Dakota	760,437	0.3%
16	Tennessee	5,789,796	2.0%
2	Texas	21,736,925	7.5%
34	Utah	2,318,789	0.8%
49	Vermont	616,408	0.2%
12	Virginia	7,287,829	2.5%
15	Washington	6,067,060	2.1%
37	West Virginia	1,804,884	0.6%
20	Wisconsin	5,439,692	1.9%
50	Wyoming	498,830	0.2%

RANK ORDER

RANK	STATE	POPULATION	% of USA
1	California	35,001,986	12.2%
2	Texas	21,736,925	7.5%
3	New York	19,134,293	6.6%
4	Florida	16,691,701	5.8%
5	Illinois	12,586,447	4.4%
6	Pennsylvania	12,328,827	4.3%
7	Ohio	11,408,699	4.0%
8	Michigan	10,043,221	3.5%
9	New Jersey	8,575,252	3.0%
10	Georgia	8,544,005	3.0%
11	North Carolina	8,305,820	2.9%
12	Virginia	7,287,829	2.5%
13	Massachusetts	6,421,800	2.2%
14	Indiana	6,156,913	2.1%
15	Washington	6,067,060	2.1%
16	Tennessee	5,789,796	2.0%
17	Missouri	5,669,544	2.0%
18	Maryland	5,450,525	1.9%
19	Arizona	5,441,125	1.9%
20	Wisconsin	5,439,692	1.9%
21	Minnesota	5,024,791	1.7%
22	Colorado	4,501,051	1.6%
23	Alabama	4,478,896	1.6%
24	Louisiana	4,476,192	1.6%
25	South Carolina	4,103,770	1.4%
26	Kentucky	4,089,822	1.4%
27	Oregon	3,520,355	1.2%
28	Oklahoma	3,489,700	1.2%
29	Connecticut	3,458,587	1.2%
30	Iowa	2,935,840	1.0%
31	Mississippi	2,866,733	1.0%
32	Kansas	2,711,769	0.9%
33	Arkansas	2,706,268	0.9%
34	Utah	2,318,789	0.8%
35	Nevada	2,167,455	0.8%
36	New Mexico	1,852,044	0.6%
37	West Virginia	1,804,884	0.6%
38	Nebraska	1,727,564	0.6%
39	Idaho	1,343,124	0.5%
40	Maine	1,294,894	0.4%
41	New Hampshire	1,274,405	0.4%
42	Hawaii	1,240,663	0.4%
43	Rhode Island	1,068,326	0.4%
44	Montana	910,372	0.3%
45	Delaware	805,945	0.3%
46	South Dakota	760,437	0.3%
47	Alaska	641,482	0.2%
48	North Dakota	633,911	0.2%
49	Vermont	616,408	0.2%
50	Wyoming	498,830	0.2%
	District of Columbia	569,157	0.2%

Source: U.S. Bureau of the Census
"Population Estimates" (December 18, 2003, http://eire.census.gov/popest/estimates.php)
*Resident population. Revised estimates.

Male Population in 2002

National Total = 141,660,978 Males

ALPHA ORDER

RANK	STATE	MALES	% of USA
24	Alabama	2,169,135	1.5%
47	Alaska	333,121	0.2%
18	Arizona	2,725,856	1.9%
33	Arkansas	1,324,566	0.9%
1	California	17,516,452	12.4%
22	Colorado	2,270,151	1.6%
29	Connecticut	1,679,226	1.2%
45	Delaware	392,375	0.3%
4	Florida	8,171,203	5.8%
9	Georgia	4,217,976	3.0%
42	Hawaii	624,098	0.4%
39	Idaho	671,945	0.5%
5	Illinois	6,177,306	4.4%
14	Indiana	3,025,295	2.1%
30	Iowa	1,442,028	1.0%
32	Kansas	1,343,815	0.9%
25	Kentucky	2,001,568	1.4%
23	Louisiana	2,172,234	1.5%
40	Maine	630,137	0.4%
20	Maryland	2,639,040	1.9%
13	Massachusetts	3,102,377	2.2%
8	Michigan	4,934,223	3.5%
21	Minnesota	2,487,372	1.8%
31	Mississippi	1,388,879	1.0%
17	Missouri	2,761,830	1.9%
44	Montana	453,137	0.3%
38	Nebraska	853,495	0.6%
35	Nevada	1,107,082	0.8%
41	New Hampshire	627,621	0.4%
10	New Jersey	4,173,927	2.9%
36	New Mexico	912,159	0.6%
3	New York	9,251,295	6.5%
11	North Carolina	4,081,520	2.9%
48	North Dakota	316,578	0.2%
7	Ohio	5,553,185	3.9%
28	Oklahoma	1,719,873	1.2%
27	Oregon	1,747,855	1.2%
6	Pennsylvania	5,966,139	4.2%
43	Rhode Island	514,729	0.4%
26	South Carolina	1,995,285	1.4%
46	South Dakota	377,961	0.3%
16	Tennessee	2,826,216	2.0%
2	Texas	10,825,924	7.6%
34	Utah	1,161,454	0.8%
49	Vermont	302,244	0.2%
12	Virginia	3,580,749	2.5%
15	Washington	3,023,056	2.1%
37	West Virginia	877,003	0.6%
19	Wisconsin	2,689,757	1.9%
50	Wyoming	250,878	0.2%

RANK ORDER

RANK	STATE	MALES	% of USA
1	California	17,516,452	12.4%
2	Texas	10,825,924	7.6%
3	New York	9,251,295	6.5%
4	Florida	8,171,203	5.8%
5	Illinois	6,177,306	4.4%
6	Pennsylvania	5,966,139	4.2%
7	Ohio	5,553,185	3.9%
8	Michigan	4,934,223	3.5%
9	Georgia	4,217,976	3.0%
10	New Jersey	4,173,927	2.9%
11	North Carolina	4,081,520	2.9%
12	Virginia	3,580,749	2.5%
13	Massachusetts	3,102,377	2.2%
14	Indiana	3,025,295	2.1%
15	Washington	3,023,056	2.1%
16	Tennessee	2,826,216	2.0%
17	Missouri	2,761,830	1.9%
18	Arizona	2,725,856	1.9%
19	Wisconsin	2,689,757	1.9%
20	Maryland	2,639,040	1.9%
21	Minnesota	2,487,372	1.8%
22	Colorado	2,270,151	1.6%
23	Louisiana	2,172,234	1.5%
24	Alabama	2,169,135	1.5%
25	Kentucky	2,001,568	1.4%
26	South Carolina	1,995,285	1.4%
27	Oregon	1,747,855	1.2%
28	Oklahoma	1,719,873	1.2%
29	Connecticut	1,679,226	1.2%
30	Iowa	1,442,028	1.0%
31	Mississippi	1,388,879	1.0%
32	Kansas	1,343,815	0.9%
33	Arkansas	1,324,566	0.9%
34	Utah	1,161,454	0.8%
35	Nevada	1,107,082	0.8%
36	New Mexico	912,159	0.6%
37	West Virginia	877,003	0.6%
38	Nebraska	853,495	0.6%
39	Idaho	671,945	0.5%
40	Maine	630,137	0.4%
41	New Hampshire	627,621	0.4%
42	Hawaii	624,098	0.4%
43	Rhode Island	514,729	0.4%
44	Montana	453,137	0.3%
45	Delaware	392,375	0.3%
46	South Dakota	377,961	0.3%
47	Alaska	333,121	0.2%
48	North Dakota	316,578	0.2%
49	Vermont	302,244	0.2%
50	Wyoming	250,878	0.2%
	District of Columbia	269,648	0.2%

Source: U.S. Bureau of the Census
"Table ST-EST2002-ASRO-01 - State Characteristic Estimates" (September 18, 2003)

Female Population in 2002

National Total = 146,707,720 Females

ALPHA ORDER

RANK	STATE	FEMALES	% of USA
22	Alabama	2,317,373	1.6%
49	Alaska	310,665	0.2%
20	Arizona	2,730,597	1.9%
32	Arkansas	1,385,513	0.9%
1	California	17,599,581	12.0%
24	Colorado	2,236,391	1.5%
27	Connecticut	1,781,277	1.2%
45	Delaware	415,010	0.3%
4	Florida	8,541,946	5.8%
10	Georgia	4,342,334	3.0%
42	Hawaii	620,800	0.4%
39	Idaho	669,186	0.5%
5	Illinois	6,423,314	4.4%
14	Indiana	3,133,773	2.1%
30	Iowa	1,494,732	1.0%
33	Kansas	1,372,069	0.9%
26	Kentucky	2,091,323	1.4%
23	Louisiana	2,310,412	1.6%
40	Maine	664,327	0.5%
18	Maryland	2,819,097	1.9%
13	Massachusetts	3,325,424	2.3%
8	Michigan	5,116,223	3.5%
21	Minnesota	2,532,348	1.7%
31	Mississippi	1,482,903	1.0%
17	Missouri	2,910,749	2.0%
44	Montana	456,316	0.3%
38	Nebraska	875,685	0.6%
35	Nevada	1,066,409	0.7%
41	New Hampshire	647,435	0.4%
9	New Jersey	4,416,373	3.0%
36	New Mexico	942,900	0.6%
3	New York	9,906,237	6.8%
11	North Carolina	4,238,626	2.9%
47	North Dakota	317,532	0.2%
7	Ohio	5,868,082	4.0%
28	Oklahoma	1,773,841	1.2%
29	Oregon	1,773,660	1.2%
6	Pennsylvania	6,368,952	4.3%
43	Rhode Island	554,996	0.4%
25	South Carolina	2,111,898	1.4%
46	South Dakota	383,102	0.3%
16	Tennessee	2,971,073	2.0%
2	Texas	10,953,969	7.5%
34	Utah	1,154,802	0.8%
48	Vermont	314,348	0.2%
12	Virginia	3,712,793	2.5%
15	Washington	3,045,940	2.1%
37	West Virginia	924,870	0.6%
19	Wisconsin	2,751,439	1.9%
50	Wyoming	247,825	0.2%

RANK ORDER

RANK	STATE	FEMALES	% of USA
1	California	17,599,581	12.0%
2	Texas	10,953,969	7.5%
3	New York	9,906,237	6.8%
4	Florida	8,541,946	5.8%
5	Illinois	6,423,314	4.4%
6	Pennsylvania	6,368,952	4.3%
7	Ohio	5,868,082	4.0%
8	Michigan	5,116,223	3.5%
9	New Jersey	4,416,373	3.0%
10	Georgia	4,342,334	3.0%
11	North Carolina	4,238,626	2.9%
12	Virginia	3,712,793	2.5%
13	Massachusetts	3,325,424	2.3%
14	Indiana	3,133,773	2.1%
15	Washington	3,045,940	2.1%
16	Tennessee	2,971,073	2.0%
17	Missouri	2,910,749	2.0%
18	Maryland	2,819,097	1.9%
19	Wisconsin	2,751,439	1.9%
20	Arizona	2,730,597	1.9%
21	Minnesota	2,532,348	1.7%
22	Alabama	2,317,373	1.6%
23	Louisiana	2,310,412	1.6%
24	Colorado	2,236,391	1.5%
25	South Carolina	2,111,898	1.4%
26	Kentucky	2,091,323	1.4%
27	Connecticut	1,781,277	1.2%
28	Oklahoma	1,773,841	1.2%
29	Oregon	1,773,660	1.2%
30	Iowa	1,494,732	1.0%
31	Mississippi	1,482,903	1.0%
32	Arkansas	1,385,513	0.9%
33	Kansas	1,372,069	0.9%
34	Utah	1,154,802	0.8%
35	Nevada	1,066,409	0.7%
36	New Mexico	942,900	0.6%
37	West Virginia	924,870	0.6%
38	Nebraska	875,685	0.6%
39	Idaho	669,186	0.5%
40	Maine	664,327	0.5%
41	New Hampshire	647,435	0.4%
42	Hawaii	620,800	0.4%
43	Rhode Island	554,996	0.4%
44	Montana	456,316	0.3%
45	Delaware	415,010	0.3%
46	South Dakota	383,102	0.3%
47	North Dakota	317,532	0.2%
48	Vermont	314,348	0.2%
49	Alaska	310,665	0.2%
50	Wyoming	247,825	0.2%
	District of Columbia	301,250	0.2%

Source: U.S. Bureau of the Census
"Table ST-EST2002-ASRO-01 - State Characteristic Estimates" (September 18, 2003)

Population in 1998

National Total = 270,248,003*

ALPHA ORDER

RANK	STATE	POPULATION	% of USA
23	Alabama	4,351,037	1.6%
48	Alaska	615,205	0.2%
21	Arizona	4,667,277	1.7%
33	Arkansas	2,538,202	0.9%
1	California	32,682,794	12.1%
24	Colorado	3,968,967	1.5%
29	Connecticut	3,272,563	1.2%
45	Delaware	744,066	0.3%
4	Florida	14,908,230	5.5%
10	Georgia	7,636,522	2.8%
41	Hawaii	1,190,472	0.4%
40	Idaho	1,230,923	0.5%
5	Illinois	12,069,774	4.5%
14	Indiana	5,907,617	2.2%
30	Iowa	2,861,025	1.1%
32	Kansas	2,638,667	1.0%
25	Kentucky	3,934,310	1.5%
22	Louisiana	4,362,758	1.6%
39	Maine	1,247,554	0.5%
19	Maryland	5,130,072	1.9%
13	Massachusetts	6,144,407	2.3%
8	Michigan	9,820,231	3.6%
20	Minnesota	4,726,411	1.7%
31	Mississippi	2,751,335	1.0%
16	Missouri	5,437,562	2.0%
44	Montana	879,533	0.3%
38	Nebraska	1,660,772	0.6%
36	Nevada	1,743,772	0.6%
42	New Hampshire	1,185,823	0.4%
9	New Jersey	8,095,542	3.0%
37	New Mexico	1,733,535	0.6%
3	New York	18,159,175	6.7%
11	North Carolina	7,545,828	2.8%
47	North Dakota	637,808	0.2%
7	Ohio	11,237,752	4.2%
27	Oklahoma	3,339,478	1.2%
28	Oregon	3,282,055	1.2%
6	Pennsylvania	12,002,329	4.4%
43	Rhode Island	987,704	0.4%
26	South Carolina	3,839,578	1.4%
46	South Dakota	730,789	0.3%
17	Tennessee	5,432,679	2.0%
2	Texas	19,712,389	7.3%
34	Utah	2,100,562	0.8%
49	Vermont	590,579	0.2%
12	Virginia	6,789,225	2.5%
15	Washington	5,687,832	2.1%
35	West Virginia	1,811,688	0.7%
18	Wisconsin	5,222,124	1.9%
50	Wyoming	480,045	0.2%

RANK ORDER

RANK	STATE	POPULATION	% of USA
1	California	32,682,794	12.1%
2	Texas	19,712,389	7.3%
3	New York	18,159,175	6.7%
4	Florida	14,908,230	5.5%
5	Illinois	12,069,774	4.5%
6	Pennsylvania	12,002,329	4.4%
7	Ohio	11,237,752	4.2%
8	Michigan	9,820,231	3.6%
9	New Jersey	8,095,542	3.0%
10	Georgia	7,636,522	2.8%
11	North Carolina	7,545,828	2.8%
12	Virginia	6,789,225	2.5%
13	Massachusetts	6,144,407	2.3%
14	Indiana	5,907,617	2.2%
15	Washington	5,687,832	2.1%
16	Missouri	5,437,562	2.0%
17	Tennessee	5,432,679	2.0%
18	Wisconsin	5,222,124	1.9%
19	Maryland	5,130,072	1.9%
20	Minnesota	4,726,411	1.7%
21	Arizona	4,667,277	1.7%
22	Louisiana	4,362,758	1.6%
23	Alabama	4,351,037	1.6%
24	Colorado	3,968,967	1.5%
25	Kentucky	3,934,310	1.5%
26	South Carolina	3,839,578	1.4%
27	Oklahoma	3,339,478	1.2%
28	Oregon	3,282,055	1.2%
29	Connecticut	3,272,563	1.2%
30	Iowa	2,861,025	1.1%
31	Mississippi	2,751,335	1.0%
32	Kansas	2,638,667	1.0%
33	Arkansas	2,538,202	0.9%
34	Utah	2,100,562	0.8%
35	West Virginia	1,811,688	0.7%
36	Nevada	1,743,772	0.6%
37	New Mexico	1,733,535	0.6%
38	Nebraska	1,660,772	0.6%
39	Maine	1,247,554	0.5%
40	Idaho	1,230,923	0.5%
41	Hawaii	1,190,472	0.4%
42	New Hampshire	1,185,823	0.4%
43	Rhode Island	987,704	0.4%
44	Montana	879,533	0.3%
45	Delaware	744,066	0.3%
46	South Dakota	730,789	0.3%
47	North Dakota	637,808	0.2%
48	Alaska	615,205	0.2%
49	Vermont	590,579	0.2%
50	Wyoming	480,045	0.2%
	District of Columbia	521,426	0.2%

Source: U.S. Bureau of the Census
"State Population Estimates" (December 29, 1999, http://www.census.gov/population/estimates/state/st-99-3.txt)
*Includes armed forces residing in each state. This updates earlier 1998 population estimates.

IX. SOURCES

American Academy of Physicians Assistants
950 North Washington Street
Alexandria, VA 22314-1552
703-836-2272
www.aapa.org

American Cancer Society, Inc.
1599 Clifton Road, NE.
Atlanta, GA 30329-4251
800-227-2345
www.cancer.org

American Dental Association
211 E. Chicago Ave.
Chicago, IL 60611-2678
312-440-2500
www.ada.org

American Hospital Association
One North Franklin
Chicago, IL 60606-3421
312-422-3000
www.aha.org

American Medical Association
515 North State Street
Chicago, IL 60610
800-621-8335
www.ama-assn.org

American Osteopathic Association
142 East Ontario Street
Chicago, IL 60611
800-621-1773
www.aoa-net.org

American Podiatric Medical Association
9312 Old Georgetown Road
Bethesda, MD 20814
301-581-9200
www.apma.org

Bureau of Labor Statistics
Census of Fatal Occupational Injuries
OCWC/OSH Suite 3180
2 Massachusetts Ave., NE
Washington, DC 20212-0001
202-691-6175
www.bls.gov/iif/

Census Bureau
4700 Silver Hill Road
Suitland, MD 20746
301-457-2800
www.census.gov

Centers for Disease Control and Prevention
1600 Clifton Road, NE.
Atlanta, GA 30333
404-639-3311 (Public Affairs)
800-458-5231 (AIDS Clearinghouse)
www.cdc.gov

Centers for Medicare and Medicaid Services
(Formerly Health Care Financing Administration)
7500 Security Boulevard
Baltimore, MD 21244-1850
877-267-2323
www.cms.gov

Federation of Chiropractic Licensing Boards
901 54th Ave., Ste. 101
Greeley, CO 80634-4400
970-356-3500
www.fclb.org

Health Care Financing Administration
See **Centers for Medicare and Medicaid Services**

InterStudy
P.O. Box 4366
St. Paul, MN 55104
800-844-3351
www.hmodata.com

National Center for Health Statistics
U.S. Department of Health and Human Services
Division of Data Services
3311 Toledo Road
Hyattsville, MD 20782-2003
301-458-4636
www.cdc.gov/nchs/

**National Institute on Alcohol Abuse
and Alcoholism**
National Institutes of Health
5635 Fishers Lane, MSC 9304
Bethesda, MD 20892-9304
301-443-9970
www.niaaa.nih.gov/

National Highway Traffic Safety Admin.
400 Seventh Street, SW
Washington, DC 20590
202-366-9550
www.nhtsa.dot.gov

National Sporting Goods Association
1601 Feehanville Drive, Ste 300
Mt. Prospect, IL 60056
847-296-6742
www.nsga.org

Smoking and Health Office
Centers for Disease Control and Prevention
4770 Buford Hwy, NE., Mail Stop K-50
Atlanta, GA 30341-3724
770-488-5701
www.cdc.gov/tobacco/

X. INDEX

X. INDEX (continued)

X. INDEX (continued)

CHAPTER INDEX

Births and Reproductive Health

Deaths

Facilities

Finance

Incidence of Disease

Providers

Physical Fitness

HOW TO USE THIS INDEX

Place left thumb on the outer edge of this page. To locate the desired entry, fold back the remaining page edges and align the index edge mark with the appropriate page edge mark.

Other books by Morgan Quitno Press:

- *State Statistical Trends (monthly journal)*
- *State Rankings 2004 ($54.95)*
- *Crime State Rankings 2004 ($54.95)*
- *City Crime Rankings, 10th Edition ($42.95)*
- *Education State Rankings 2003-2004 ($49.95)*

Call toll free: 1-800-457-0742 or
visit us at www.statestats.com